NUMERICAL METHODS FOR ENGINEERS AND SCIENTISTS

NUMERICAL METHODS FOR ENGINEERS AND SCIENTISTS

Joe D. Hoffman

Professor of Mechanical Engineering
Purdue University

McGraw-Hill, Inc.

New York St. Louis San Francisco Auckland Bogotá
Caracas Lisbon London Madrid Mexico Milan Montreal
New Delhi Paris San Juan Singapore Sydney Tokyo Toronto

This book was set in Times Roman by Publication Services, Inc.
The editors were B.J. Clark and John M. Morriss;
the production supervisor was Kathryn Porzio.
The cover was designed by Rafael Hernandez.
Project supervision was done by Publication Services, Inc.
R. R. Donnelley & Sons Company was printer and binder.

NUMERICAL METHODS FOR ENGINEERS AND SCIENTISTS

2 3 4 5 6 7 8 9 0 DOC DOC 9 0 9 8 7 6 5 4 3 2

ISBN 0-07-029213-2

Library of Congress Cataloging-in-Publication Data

Hoffman, Joe D., (date).
Numerical methods for engineers and scientists / Joe D. Hoffman.
p. cm.
Includes bibliographical references.
ISBN 0-07-029213-2
1. Numerical analysis. I. Title.
QA297.H588 1992
519.4—dc20 91-33120

ABOUT THE AUTHOR

Joe D. Hoffman is a Professor of Mechanical Engineering at Purdue University. He is also the Director of the Thermal Sciences and Propulsion Center, which is a graduate research laboratory in the School of Mechanical Engineering. Dr. Hoffman has published two other books with Dr. Maurice J. Zucrow, the two volume set *Gas Dynamics, Vol. 1,* (1975) and *Gas Dynamics, Vol. II, Multidimensional Flow* (1976), John Wiley & Sons.

Dr. Hoffman was born in Memphis, Tennessee, on August 9, 1934. He attended Texas A&M University, graduating in 1958 with the Bachelor of Science in Mechanical Engineering degree and in 1959 with the Master of Science in Mechanical Engineering degree. He attended Purdue University from 1959 to 1962, graduating with the Doctor of Philosophy degree. He joined the Faculty of the School of Mechanical Engineering at Purdue University in January 1963, where he has remained since that time.

Dr. Hoffman worked as a Research Aerospace Engineer at the Propulsion Laboratory, U.S. Army Missile Command, Redstone Arsenal, Alabama, in 1966–1967. He was a Visiting Professor of Aerospace Engineering Sciences at the University of Colorado in 1973–1974. During 1980, he was a Research Physical Scientist at the U.S. Air Force Rocket Propulsion Laboratory, Edwards Air Force Base, California. Dr. Hoffman has consulted for approximately 40 days a year since 1963 for over 50 industries, government agencies, and universities. He has presented numerous short courses on numerical methods, computational fluid dynamics, and propulsion system design, both nationally and internationally.

Dr. Hoffman has authored over 40 papers in gas dynamics, nozzle performance prediction and design, numerical analysis, and computation fluid dynamics. He has acted as Thesis Advisor for more than 30 Ph.D. students. Dr. Hoffman is an Associate Fellow of the American Institute of Aeronautics and Astronautics. He is a member of Phi Kappa Phi, Phi Eta Sigma, Tau Beta Pi, Pi Tau Sigma, Sigma Xi, the American Society of Mechanical Engineers, and the American Society of Engineering Education.

TO MY WIFE CYNTHIA,
whose encouragement and support from the beginning
sustained me through the preparation of this work.

CONTENTS

PREFACE

The advances made in engineering, science, and technology during the past century have been, to a large extent, due to our increasing ability to describe physical processes accurately in mathematical terms and to solve these mathematical models, both exactly and numerically. The equations describing the physical world may be algebraic equations, ordinary differential equations, or partial differential equations. The objective of this book is to introduce the engineer and scientist to numerical methods that can be used to solve the equations that govern physical processes.

With the general accessibility of high-speed digital computers, it is now possible to obtain rapid and accurate solutions to many complex problems in engineering and science that were intractable only a few years ago. Numerical analysis is rapidly becoming the tool for solving the governing equations of engineering and science.

This book is written as an introductory text for engineers and scientists. It is suitable for use in a first or second course in numerical methods. It is assumed that the student has had courses in mathematics through calculus and ordinary differential equations and an introduction to partial differential equations. The material is appropriate for second-semester sophomores through beginning graduate students.

The approach taken in this book for solving differential equations is the finite difference approach. Other approaches, such as the finite element approach, the boundary element approach, and the spectral approach, are not considered at all. These methods have their place in the solution of problems in engineering and science. Their omission from this book is strictly a matter of personal choice and space.

The material presented in this book has been divided into three main parts:

I. Basic Tools of Numerical Analysis
II. Ordinary Differential Equations
III. Partial Differential Equations

At Purdue, this material is used in three separate courses. Parts I and II comprise the contents of an undergraduate course in the School of Mechanical Engineering. Parts I, II, and III comprise the contents of a first-year graduate course in the School of Mechanical Engineering. Part III comprises the first half of an advanced graduate-level course in computational fluid dynamics in the School of Mechanical Engineering. Although these courses are taught in the School of Mechanical Engineering, they are open to and taken by students from all the Schools of Engineering.

The philosophy of this book is to teach students how methods work, so that they can construct their own computer programs. The use of *canned* programs does not enhance one's ability to develop one's own programs. Consequently, canned programs are not considered in this book. However, the use of canned programs in practical problem solving, where appropriate, is encouraged.

Many people have encouraged me and assisted me during the writing of this book. I thank them all. Foremost among these is my loving wife, Cynthia Louise Hoffman, without whose constant support and encouragement over the eight years of writing, this work would not have been started or completed. My good friend and colleague, Professor H. Doyle Thompson of the School of Mechanical Engineering at Purdue University, was my major technical advisor, critic, and supporter. Thanks, Doyle. My graduate students provided much needed and appreciated help, criticism, and feedback. The assistance of Douglas Hofer in the derivation of the modified differential equations that appear throughout Part III is especially noted and appreciated. The bulk of the figures were prepared by Mark Bass; thanks, Mark. Lastly, without the assistance of a dedicated group of word processing specialists, this work would not have come to completion. In the early years, Linda Benefield and Karen Porter provided this assistance. Thanks to you both. In the final four years, my good friend Janice Napier devoted herself unsparingly to this work. Without her expertise, initiative, cheerful disposition, and willingness to find a way to put every character exactly where I wanted it, this work would have been a chore instead of a pleasure. Thank you, Janice.

McGraw-Hill and I would like to thank the following reviewers for their many helpful comments and suggestions: Shoeleh DiJulio, California State University, Northridge; Rakesh K. Kapania, Virginia Polytechnic Institute and State University; and Winston Lung, University of Virginia.

Joe D. Hoffman

INTRODUCTION

The objective of this book is to introduce the engineer and scientist to numerical methods that can be used to solve mathematical problems arising in engineering and science that cannot be solved by exact methods. With the general accessibility of high-speed digital computers, it is now possible to obtain rapid and accurate solutions to many complex problems that face the engineer and scientist.

The approach taken is as follows:

1. Introduce a type of problem.
2. Present sufficient background to understand the problem and possible methods of solution.
3. Develop one or more numerical methods for solving the problem.
4. Illustrate the numerical methods with examples.

In most cases, the numerical methods presented to solve a particular problem proceed from simple methods to complex methods, which in many cases parallel the chronological development of the methods. Some poor methods and some bad methods, as well as good methods, are presented for pedagogical reasons. Why one method does not work is almost as important as why another method does work.

The material in the book is divided into three main parts:

I. Basic Tools of Numerical Analysis
II. Ordinary Differential Equations
III. Partial Differential Equations

Part I considers many of the basic problems that arise in all branches of engineering and science. These problems include: solution of systems of linear algebraic equations, eigenproblems, solution of nonlinear equations, polynomial approximation and interpolation, numerical differentiation and difference formulas, and numerical integration. These topics are important both in their own right and as the foundation for Parts II and III.

Part II is devoted to the numerical solution of ordinary differential equations (ODEs). The general features of ODEs are discussed. The two classes of ODEs (i.e., initial-value ODEs and boundary-value ODEs) are introduced, and the two types of physical problems (i.e., propagation problems and equilibrium problems) are discussed. Numerous numerical methods for solving ODEs are presented.

Part III is devoted to the numerical solution of partial differential equations (PDEs). Some general features of PDEs are discussed. The three classes of PDEs (i.e., elliptic, parabolic, and hyperbolic PDEs) are introduced, and the two types of physical problems (i.e., equilibrium and propagation problems) are discussed. Several model equations are developed. Numerous numerical methods for solving the model PDEs are presented.

The material presented in this book is an introduction to numerical methods. Many practical problems can be solved by the methods presented here. Many other practical problems require other or more advanced numerical methods. Mastery of the material presented in this book will prepare the engineer and scientist to solve many of his or her everyday problems, give him or her the insight to recognize when other methods are required, and give him or her the background to study other methods in other books and journals.

NUMERICAL METHODS FOR ENGINEERS AND SCIENTISTS

PART 1

BASIC TOOLS OF NUMERICAL ANALYSIS

Section

I.1 INTRODUCTION

A variety of algebraic processes are required in all branches of engineering and science. These processes include the solution of systems of linear algebraic equations; eigenproblems; the solution of nonlinear equations; polynomial approximation and interpolation; numerical differentiation and difference formulas; and numerical integration. These topics are not only important in their own right, but they also lay the foundation for the solution of ordinary and partial differential equations, which are discussed in Parts II and III, respectively.

The objective of Part I is to introduce and discuss the general features of each of these algebraic processes, which are the basic tools of numerical analysis.

I.2 SYSTEMS OF LINEAR ALGEBRAIC EQUATIONS

Systems of equations arise in all branches of engineering and science. These equations may be algebraic, transcendental (i.e., involving trigonometric and exponential functions), ordinary differential equations, or partial differential equations. The equations may be linear or nonlinear. Chapter 1 is devoted to the solution of systems of linear algebraic equations of the form:

$$a_{11}x_1 + a_{12}x_2 + a_{13}x_3 + \cdots + a_{1n}x_n = b_1 \qquad \text{(I.1}a\text{)}$$

$$a_{21}x_1 + a_{22}x_2 + a_{23}x_3 + \cdots + a_{2n}x_n = b_2 \qquad \text{(I.1}b\text{)}$$

$$\vdots \qquad \vdots \qquad \vdots \qquad \vdots \qquad \vdots$$

$$a_{n1}x_1 + a_{n2}x_2 + a_{n3}x_3 + \cdots + a_{nn}x_n = b_n \qquad \text{(I.1}n\text{)}$$

where $x_j (j = 1, 2, \ldots, n)$ denotes the unknown variables, $a_{ij} (i, j = 1, 2, \ldots, n)$ denotes the coefficients of the unknown variables, and $b_i (i = 1, 2, \ldots, n)$ denotes the nonhomogeneous terms. For the coefficients a_{ij}, the first subscript, i, corresponds to equation i, and the second subscript, j, corresponds to variable x_j. The number of equations can range from two to hundreds, thousands, and even millions. Chapter 1 is devoted to the solution of systems of linear algebraic equations.

Systems of linear algebraic equations arise in many different problems, for example, network problems (e.g., electrical networks), fitting approximating functions (see Chapter 4), and systems of finite difference equations that arise in the numerical solution of differential equations (see Chapters 7 to 15). The list is endless.

Systems of linear algebraic equations can be expressed very conveniently, and solution methods can be developed very compactly, in terms of matrix notation. Consequently, the elementary properties of matrices and determinants are presented in Section 1.2.

Two fundamentally different approaches can be used to solve systems of linear algebraic equations;

1. Direct methods
2. Iterative methods

Direct methods are systematic procedures based on algebraic elimination. Several direct elimination methods are presented in Sections 1.3 to 1.5. Iterative methods obtain the solution asymptotically by an iterative procedure in which a trial solution is assumed, the trial solution is substituted into the system of equations to determine the mismatch or error, and an improved solution is obtained from the mismatch data. Several iterative methods are presented in Sections 1.6 and 1.8.

The notation, concepts, and procedures presented in Chapter 1 are used throughout the remainder of the book. A solid understanding of systems of linear algebraic equations is essential in numerical analysis.

I.3 EIGENPROBLEMS

Eigenproblems arise in the special case where a system of algebraic equations is homogeneous, that is, the b_i terms in Eq. (I.1) are all zero, and the coefficients contain an unspecified parameter λ. In general, when $b_i = 0$, the only solution to Eq. (I-1) is the trivial solution $\mathbf{x} = 0$. However, when the coefficients contain an unspecified parameter, the value of that parameter can be chosen so that the system of equations is redundant and an infinite number of solutions exist. For example,

$$(a_{11} - \lambda)x_1 + a_{12}x_2 = 0 \tag{I.2a}$$

$$a_{21}x_1 + (a_{22} - \lambda)x_2 = 0 \tag{I.2b}$$

is a linear 2×2 eigenproblem. The values of λ that make Eqs. (I.2a) and (I.2b) identical are the *eigenvalues* of Eq. (I.2). In that case, the two equations are redundant, so the only unique solution is $x_1 = x_2 = 0$. However, an infinite number of solutions can be obtained by specifying either x_1 or x_2, then calculating the other from either of the two redundant equations. The set of values of x_1 and x_2 corresponding to a particular value of λ is an *eigenvector* of Eq. (I.2). Chapter 2 is devoted to the solution of eigenproblems.

Eigenproblems can be encountered in the analysis of many physical systems. They arise in the analysis of the dynamic behavior of mechanical, electrical, fluid, thermal, and structural systems, as well as in the analysis of control systems. The objectives of Chapter 2 are to introduce the general features of eigenproblems and to present several methods for solving eigenproblems.

Eigenproblems are special problems of interest only in themselves. Consequently, an understanding of eigenproblems is not essential to the other concepts presented in this book.

I.4 NONLINEAR EQUATIONS

Nonlinear equations arise in many physical problems. The problem can be stated as follows:

> Given the continuous nonlinear function $f(x)$, find the value of x such that $f(x) = 0$.

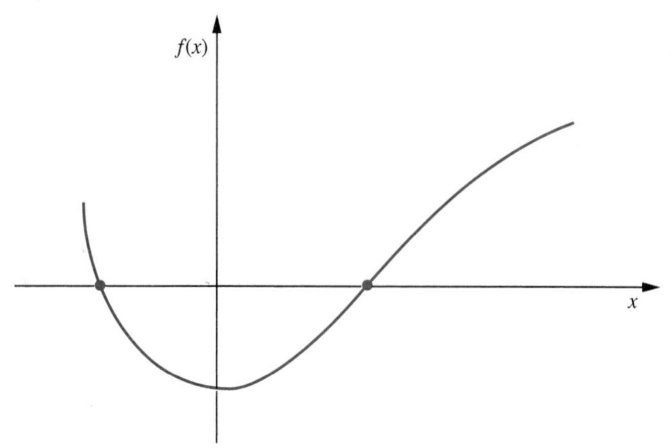

FIGURE I.1
Solution of a nonlinear function.

Figure I.1 illustrates the problem graphically. The function $f(x)$ may be an algebraic equation, a transcendental equation, the solution of a differential equation, or any nonlinear relationship between an input x and a response $f(x)$. Chapter 3 is devoted to the solution of nonlinear equations.

Nonlinear equations are solved by iterative methods. A trial solution is assumed, the trial solution is substituted into the nonlinear function to determine the error or mismatch, and the mismatch is used in some systematic manner to generate an improved estimate of the solution. The workhorse methods of choice for solving nonlinear equations are Newton's method and the secant method, which are presented in Sections 3.5 and 3.6, respectively. A detailed discussion of methods for solving polynomials is presented in Section 3.7. A brief introduction to the problems of solving systems of nonlinear equations is presented in Section 3.8.

Nonlinear equations occur throughout engineering and science. Nonlinear equations also arise in other areas of numerical analysis. For example, the shooting method for solving boundary-value ordinary differential equations, presented in Section 8.4, requires the solution of a nonlinear equation. Implicit methods for solving nonlinear differential equations yield nonlinear *difference equations*. The solution of such problems is discussed in Sections 7.11, 8.8, 9.9, 11.8, 12.14, 14.13, and 15.16. Consequently, a thorough understanding of methods for solving nonlinear equations is an essential requirement for the numerical analyst.

I.5 POLYNOMIAL APPROXIMATION

In many problems in engineering and science, the data under consideration are known only at discrete points, not as a continuous function. For example, the continuous function $f(x)$ may be known only at n discrete values of x:

$$y_i = y(x_i), \quad (i = 1, 2, \ldots, n) \tag{I.3}$$

Values of the function at points other than the known discrete points may be needed (i.e., interpolation). The derivative of the function may be needed (i.e., differentiation). The integral of the function may be required (i.e., integration). These processes, for discrete data, are performed by fitting an approximating function to the set of discrete data and performing the desired process on the approximating function. Many types of approximating functions can be used. Because of their simplicity, ease of evaluation, and ease of manipulation, polynomials are an excellent choice for an approximating function. The general nth-degree polynomial is specified by

$$P_n(x) = a_0 + a_1x + a_2x^2 + \cdots + a_nx^n \tag{I.4}$$

Polynomials can be fitted to a set of discrete data in two ways:

1. Exact fit
2. Approximate fit

An exact fit passes exactly through all the discrete data points. Procedures for determining exact polynomial fits are presented in Chapter 4. Direct fit polynomials and Lagrange polynomials are presented for fitting nonequally or equally spaced data. Newton difference polynomials are presented for fitting equally spaced data. The least squares procedure for determining approximate polynomial fits is presented in Section 4.11.

Polynomial approximation is essential for interpolation, differentiation, and integration of sets of discrete data. A good understanding of polynomial approximation is a necessary requirement for the numerical analyst.

I.6 NUMERICAL DIFFERENTIATION AND DIFFERENCE FORMULAS

The evaluation of derivatives, a process known as differentiation, is required in many problems in engineering and science. Differentiation of the function $f(x)$ is denoted by

$$\frac{d}{dx}\big(f(x)\big) = f'(x) \tag{I.5}$$

The function $f(x)$ may be a known function or a set of discrete data. In general, known functions can be differentiated exactly. Differentiation of discrete data requires an approximate numerical procedure. Numerical differentiation formulas can be developed by fitting approximating functions (e.g., polynomials) to a set of discrete data and differentiating the approximating function. For polynomial approximating functions, this yields

$$\frac{d}{dx}\big(f(x)\big) \approx \frac{d}{dx}\big(P_n(x)\big) \tag{I.6}$$

Numerical differentiation procedures are developed in Chapter 5.

The approximating polynomial may be fitted exactly to a set of discrete data by the methods presented in Sections 4.3 to 4.10, or fitted approximately by the least squares procedure described in Section 4.11. Several numerical differentiation formulas based on differentiation of polynomials are presented in Chapter 5.

Numerical differentiation formulas also can be developed using Taylor series. This approach is quite useful for developing difference formulas for approximating exact derivatives in the numerical solution of differential equations. Section 5.5 presents a table of difference formulas for use in the solution of differential equations.

Numerical differentiation of discrete data is not required very often. However, the numerical solution of differential equations, which is the subject of Parts II and III of this book, is one of the most important areas of numerical analysis. The use of difference formulas is essential in that application.

I.7 NUMERICAL INTEGRATION

The evaluation of integrals, a process known as *integration* or *quadrature*, is required in many problems in engineering and science. Integration of the function $f(x)$ is denoted by

$$I = \int_a^b f(x)\, dx \tag{I.7}$$

The function $f(x)$ may be a know function or a set of discrete data. Some known functions have an exact integral. Many known functions, however, do not have an exact integral, and an approximate numerical procedure is required to evaluate Eq. (I.7). When a known function is to be integrated numerically, it must first be discretized. Integration of discrete data always requires an approximate numerical procedure. Numerical integration (quadrature) formulas can be developed by fitting approximating functions (e.g., polynomials) to a set of discrete data and integrating the approximating function. For polynomial approximating functions, this gives

$$I = \int_a^b f(x)\, dx \approx \int_a^b P_n(x)\, dx \tag{I.8}$$

Numerical integration procedures are developed in Chapter 6.

The approximating function can be fitted exactly to a set of discrete data by the methods presented in Sections 4.3 to 4.10, or fitted approximately by the least squares procedure described in Section 4.11. For unequally spaced data, direct fit polynomials can be used. For equally spaced data, the Newton forward-difference polynomials of different degrees can be integrated to yield the Newton–Cotes formulas. The most prominent of these are the trapezoid rule and Simpson's $\frac{1}{3}$ rule. Section 6.3 presents these results. Romberg integration, which is a higher-order extrapolation of the trapezoid rule, is presented in Section 6.5. Adaptive integration procedures, in which the range of integration is subdivided automatically until a specified accuracy is obtained, are introduced in Section 6.6. Gaussian quadrature, which achieves higher-order accuracy for integrating known functions by specifying the locations of the discrete points, is presented in Section 6.7. The evaluation of multiple integrals is discussed in Section 6.8.

Numerical integration of both known functions and discrete data is a common problem. The concepts involved in numerical integration lead directly into numerical methods for solving differential equations.

SUMMARY

Part I of this book is devoted to the basic tools of numerical analysis. These topics are important in their own right. In addition, they provide the foundation for solving ordinary and partial differential equations, which are discussed in Parts II and III, respectively. The material presented in Part I comprises the basic language of numerical analysis. Familiarity and mastery of this material is essential for the understanding and use of more advanced numerical procedures.

CHAPTER 1

SYSTEMS OF LINEAR ALGEBRAIC EQUATIONS

Section

Example

1.1 INTRODUCTION

Systems of equations arise in all branches of engineering and science. These equations may be algebraic, transcendental (involving trigonometric and exponential functions), ordinary differential equations, or partial differential equations. The equations may be linear or nonlinear. Chapter 1 is devoted to the solution of systems of linear algebraic equations of the form

$$a_{11}x_1 + a_{12}x_2 + a_{13}x_3 + \cdots + a_{1n}x_n = b_1 \tag{1.1a}$$

$$a_{21}x_1 + a_{22}x_2 + a_{23}x_3 + \cdots + a_{2n}x_n = b_2 \tag{1.1b}$$

$$\vdots \qquad \vdots \qquad \vdots \qquad \vdots \qquad \vdots$$

$$a_{n1}x_1 + a_{n2}x_2 + a_{n3}x_3 + \cdots + a_{nn}x_n = b_n \tag{1.1n}$$

where $x_j (j = 1, 2, ..., n)$ denotes the unknown variables, $a_{ij} (i, j = 1, 2, ..., n)$ denotes the constant coefficients of the unknown variables, and $b_i (i = 1, 2, ..., n)$ denotes the nonhomogeneous terms. For the coefficients a_{ij}, the first subscript, i, corresponds to equation i, and the second subscript, j, corresponds to variable x_j. The number of equations can range from two to hundreds, thousands, and even millions.

In the most general case, the number of variables is not required to be the same as the number of equations. However, in most practical problems, they are the same. That is the case considered in this chapter. Even when they are the same, several solution possibilities exist, as illustrated in Fig. 1.1 for the system of two linear algebraic equations

$$a_{11}x_1 + a_{12}x_2 = b_1 \tag{1.2a}$$

$$a_{21}x_1 + a_{22}x_2 = b_2 \tag{1.2b}$$

The four solution possibilities are

1. A unique solution (a consistent set of equations), as illustrated in Fig. 1.1*a*.
2. No solution (an inconsistent set of equations), as illustrated in Fig. 1.1*b*.
3. An infinite number of solutions (a redundant set of equations), as illustrated in Fig. 1.1*c*.
4. The trivial solution $x_j = 0$ (a set of homogeneous equations), as illustrated in Fig. 1.1*d*.

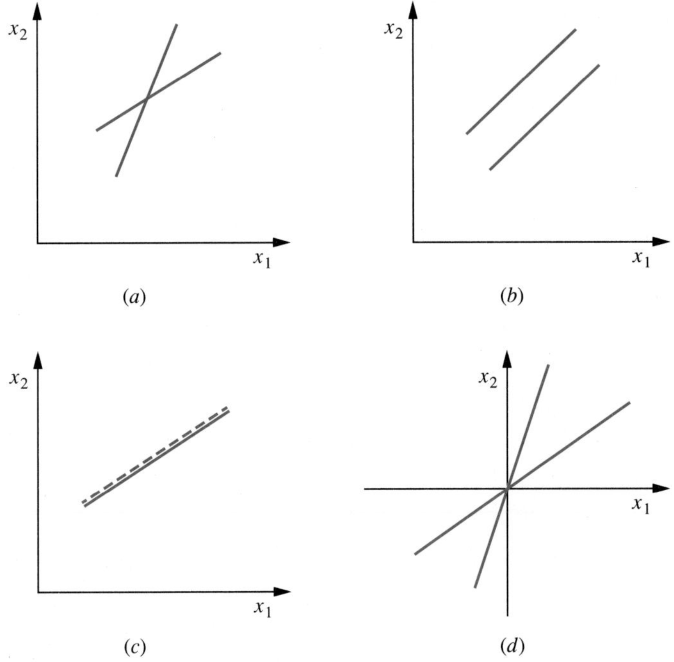

FIGURE 1-1
Solution of a system of two equations: (*a*) unique solution; (*b*) no solution; (*c*) an infinite number of solutions; (*d*) trivial solution.

In this chapter we shall be concerned with the first case, where a unique solution exists.

Systems of linear algebraic equations arise in many different types of problems, for example, network problems (e.g., electrical networks), fitting approximating functions (see Chapter 4), and systems of finite difference equations that arise in the numerical solution of differential equations (see Parts II and III). The list is endless.

There are two fundamentally different approaches for solving systems of linear algebraic equations:

1. Direct methods
2. Iterative methods

Direct methods are systematic procedures, based on algebraic elimination, that obtain the solution in a fixed number of operations. Examples of direct methods are Gauss elimination, Gauss–Jordan elimination, matrix inversion, and **LU** decomposition. Iterative methods, on the other hand, obtain the solution asymptotically by an iterative procedure. A trial solution is assumed, the trial solution is substituted into the system of equations to determine the *mismatch* in the trial solution, and an improved solution is obtained from the mismatch data. Examples of iterative methods are Jacobi iteration, Gauss–Seidel iteration, relaxation, and successive overrelaxation (SOR).

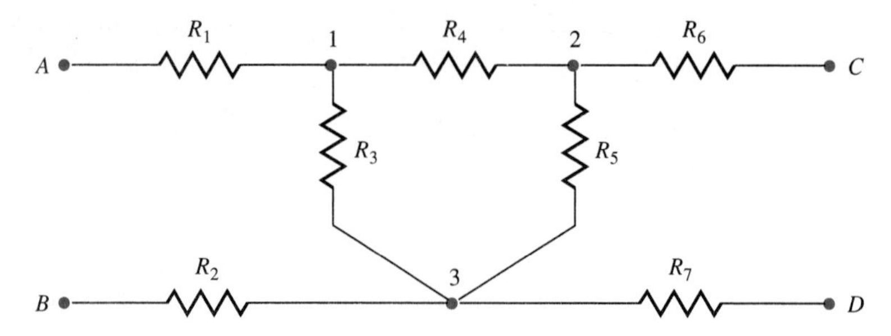

FIGURE 1-2
Electrical network.

Although no absolutely rigid rules apply, direct methods are generally used when one or more of the following conditions holds:

1. The number of equations is small (100 or less).
2. Most of the coefficients a_{ij} are nonzero.
3. The system of equations is not diagonally dominant (see "Matrix Definitions" in Section 1.2).
4. The system of equations is ill-conditioned (see Section 1.3).

Iterative methods are used when the number of equations is large and most of the coefficients are zero. Iterative methods generally diverge unless the system of equations is diagonally dominant.

As an example of a network problem, consider the electrical network illustrated in Fig. 1.2. Determine the voltages at nodes 1, 2, and 3. Apply Kirchhoff's law of currents which states that the sum of the currents flowing into a node is zero. That is, $\sum i = 0$, where $i = \Delta V/R$. Thus,

$$\text{Node 1}: \quad \frac{V_1 - V_A}{R_1} + \frac{V_1 - V_2}{R_4} + \frac{V_1 - V_3}{R_3} = 0 \tag{1.3a}$$

$$\text{Node 2}: \quad \frac{V_2 - V_1}{R_4} + \frac{V_2 - V_3}{R_5} + \frac{V_2 - V_C}{R_6} = 0 \tag{1.3b}$$

$$\text{Node 3}: \quad \frac{V_3 - V_B}{R_2} + \frac{V_3 - V_1}{R_3} + \frac{V_3 - V_2}{R_5} + \frac{V_3 - V_D}{R_7} = 0 \tag{1.3c}$$

Rearranging Eqs. (1.3) yields the following system of linear algebraic equations:

$$(R_3R_4 + R_1R_3 + R_1R_4)V_1 - (R_1R_3)V_2 - (R_1R_4)V_3 = (R_3R_4)V_A \tag{1.4a}$$

$$-(R_5R_6)V_1 + (R_5R_6 + R_4R_6 + R_4R_5)V_2 - (R_4R_6)V_3 = (R_4R_5)V_C \tag{1.4b}$$

$$-(R_2R_5R_7)V_1 - (R_2R_3R_7)V_2 + (R_3R_5R_7 + R_2R_5R_7 + R_2R_3R_7 + R_2R_3R_5)V_3$$
$$= (R_3R_5R_7)V_B + (R_2R_3R_5)V_D \tag{1.4c}$$

Methods for solving systems of linear algebraic equations are judged by their robustness, accuracy, efficiency, and simplicity. *Robustness* refers to how dependable the method is over a wide range of problems. *Accuracy* refers to the ability of the method to obtain the solution to the desired number of significant digits. Accuracy is limited by the number of digits in the computing device (such as hand calculation, pocket calculator, or electronic digital computer). *Efficiency* refers to the amount of computational effort required to achieve the solution to the desired accuracy. *Simplicity* refers to the ease of understanding and implementation of the method. Several methods, both direct and iterative, for solving systems of linear algebraic equations are presented in this chapter. Procedures are also presented for special problems, such as tridiagonal systems of equations. All these procedures are illustrated by example problems. Although the methods apply to large systems of equations, they are illustrated by applying them to small systems, usually three or four equations.

1.2 ELEMENTARY PROPERTIES OF MATRICES AND DETERMINANTS

Systems of linear algebraic equations can be expressed very conveniently, and solution methods for systems of linear algebraic equations can be developed very compactly, in terms of matrix notation. Consequently, the elementary properties of matrices are presented in this section. The elementary properties of determinants are also presented in order to complete the background material needed for the solution of systems of linear algebraic equations.

Matrix Definitions

A *matrix* is a rectangular array of elements (either numbers or symbolic expressions), which are arranged in orderly rows and columns. Each element of the matrix is distinct and separate. The location of an element in the matrix is important. Elements of a matrix are generally identified by a doubly subscripted lower-case letter, for example, a_{ij}, where the first subscript, i, identifies the row of the matrix and the second subscript, j, identifies the column of the matrix. The size of a matrix is specified by the number of rows times the number of columns. A matrix with n rows and m columns is said to be an n by m, or $n \times m$, matrix. Matrices are generally represented by either a boldface capital letter, for example, $\mathbf{A}$; the general element enclosed in brackets, for example, $[a_{ij}]$; or the full array of elements, as illustrated in Eq. (1.5).

$$\mathbf{A} = [a_{ij}] = \begin{bmatrix} a_{11} & a_{12} & \cdots & a_{1m} \\ a_{21} & a_{22} & \cdots & a_{2m} \\ \vdots & \vdots & \ddots & \vdots \\ a_{n1} & a_{n2} & \cdots & a_{nm} \end{bmatrix} \quad \begin{matrix} (i = 1, 2, \ldots, n) \\ (j = 1, 2, \ldots, m) \end{matrix} \tag{1.5}$$

Comparing Eqs. (1.1) and (1.5) shows that the coefficients of a system of linear algebraic equations form the elements of an $n \times n$ matrix.

A *vector* is a special type of matrix that has only one column or one row. Vectors are represented by either a boldface lower-case letter, for example, $\mathbf{x}$; the general element enclosed in brackets, for example, $[x_i]$ or $[x_j]$; or the full column or row of elements. A *column* vector is an $n \times 1$ matrix. Thus,

$$\mathbf{x} = [x_i] = \begin{bmatrix} x_1 \\ x_2 \\ \vdots \\ x_n \end{bmatrix} \tag{1.6a}$$

A *row* vector is a $1 \times n$ matrix. For example,

$$\mathbf{y} = [y_j] = [y_1 y_2 \cdots y_n] \tag{1.6b}$$

Unit vectors are special vectors that have a magnitude of unity (1). Thus,

$$|\mathbf{i}| = \left(i_1^2 + i_2^2 + \cdots + i_n^2\right)^{1/2} = 1 \tag{1.7}$$

Orthogonal systems of unit vectors, in which all the elements of each unit vector except one are zero, are used to define coordinate systems.

There are several special matrices of interest. A *square* matrix $\mathbf{S}$ is a matrix which has the same number of rows and columns, that is, $m = n$. For example,

$$\mathbf{S} = \begin{bmatrix} a_{11} & a_{12} & \cdots & a_{1n} \\ a_{21} & a_{22} & \cdots & a_{2n} \\ \vdots & \vdots & \ddots & \vdots \\ a_{n1} & a_{n2} & \cdots & a_{nn} \end{bmatrix} \tag{1.8}$$

is a square $n \times n$ matrix. Our interest will be devoted entirely to square matrices. The left-to-right downward-sloping line of elements from a_{11} to a_{nn} is called the *major* diagonal of the matrix. The left-to-right upward-sloping line of elements from a_{n1} to a_{1n} is called the *minor* diagonal of the matrix. A *diagonal* matrix $\mathbf{D}$ is a square matrix with all elements equal to zero except the elements on the major diagonal. For example,

$$\mathbf{D} = \begin{bmatrix} a_{11} & 0 & 0 & 0 \\ 0 & a_{22} & 0 & 0 \\ 0 & 0 & a_{33} & 0 \\ 0 & 0 & 0 & a_{44} \end{bmatrix} \tag{1.9}$$

is a 4×4 diagonal matrix. The *identity* matrix $\mathbf{I}$ is a diagonal matrix with unity diagonal elements. The identity matrix is the matrix equivalent of the scalar number unity. The matrix

$$\mathbf{I} = \begin{bmatrix} 1 & 0 & 0 & 0 \\ 0 & 1 & 0 & 0 \\ 0 & 0 & 1 & 0 \\ 0 & 0 & 0 & 1 \end{bmatrix} \tag{1.10}$$

is the 4×4 identity matrix.

A *triangular* matrix is a square matrix in which all the elements on one side of the major diagonal are zero. The remaining elements may be zero or nonzero. An *upper* triangular matrix $\mathbf{U}$ has all zero elements below the major diagonal. The matrix

$$\mathbf{U} = \begin{bmatrix} a_{11} & a_{12} & a_{13} & a_{14} \\ 0 & a_{22} & a_{23} & a_{24} \\ 0 & 0 & a_{33} & a_{34} \\ 0 & 0 & 0 & a_{44} \end{bmatrix} \tag{1.11}$$

is a 4×4 upper triangular matrix. A *lower* triangular matrix $\mathbf{L}$ has all zeros above the major diagonal. The matrix

$$\mathbf{L} = \begin{bmatrix} a_{11} & 0 & 0 & 0 \\ a_{21} & a_{22} & 0 & 0 \\ a_{31} & a_{32} & a_{33} & 0 \\ a_{41} & a_{42} & a_{43} & a_{44} \end{bmatrix} \tag{1.12}$$

is a 4×4 lower triangular matrix.

A *tridiagonal* matrix is a square matrix in which all the elements not on the major diagonal, or on the two diagonals surrounding the major diagonal, are zero. The elements on these three diagonals may or may not be zero. The matrix

$$\mathbf{T} = \begin{bmatrix} a_{11} & a_{12} & 0 & 0 & 0 \\ a_{21} & a_{22} & a_{23} & 0 & 0 \\ 0 & a_{32} & a_{33} & a_{34} & 0 \\ 0 & 0 & a_{43} & a_{44} & a_{45} \\ 0 & 0 & 0 & a_{54} & a_{55} \end{bmatrix} \tag{1.13}$$

is a 5×5 tridiagonal matrix.

Banded matrices have all zero elements except along particular diagonals. For example,

$$\mathbf{B} = \begin{bmatrix} a_{11} & a_{12} & 0 & a_{14} & 0 \\ a_{21} & a_{22} & a_{23} & 0 & a_{25} \\ 0 & a_{32} & a_{33} & a_{34} & 0 \\ a_{41} & 0 & a_{43} & a_{44} & a_{45} \\ 0 & a_{52} & 0 & a_{54} & a_{55} \end{bmatrix} \tag{1.14}$$

is a 5×5 banded matrix having five nonzero diagonals.

The *transpose* of an $n \times m$ matrix $\mathbf{A}$ is the matrix $\mathbf{A}^T$, which has elements $a_{ij}^T = a_{ji}$. The transpose of a column vector is a row vector and vice versa. *Symmetric* square matrices have identical corresponding elements on either side of the major diagonal. That is, $a_{ij} = a_{ji}$. In that case, $\mathbf{A} = \mathbf{A}^T$.

A *sparse* matrix is a matrix in which most of the elements are zero. Most large matrices arising in engineering and scientific applications are sparse matrices.

A matrix is *diagonally dominant* if the absolute value of each term on the major diagonal is equal to, or larger than, the sum of the absolute values of all the

other terms in that row, with the diagonal term being larger than the corresponding sum for at least one row. Thus, diagonal dominance is defined as

$$|a_{ii}| \geq \sum_{j=1, j \neq i}^{n} |a_{ij}| \qquad (i = 1, \ldots, n) \tag{1.15}$$

with > true for at least one row.

Elementary Matrix Algebra

Elementary matrix algebra consists of matrix addition, matrix subtraction, and matrix multiplication. Matrix division is not defined; an analogous operation is accomplished using the matrix inverse.

Matrix addition and subtraction consist of adding or subtracting the corresponding elements of two matrices of equal size. Let **A** and **B** be two matrices of equal size. Then

$$\mathbf{A} + \mathbf{B} = [a_{ij}] + [b_{ij}] = [a_{ij} + b_{ij}] = [c_{ij}] = \mathbf{C} \tag{1.16a}$$

$$\mathbf{A} - \mathbf{B} = [a_{ij}] - [b_{ij}] = [a_{ij} - b_{ij}] = [c_{ij}] = \mathbf{C} \tag{1.16b}$$

Unequal-sized matrices cannot be added or subtracted. Matrices of the same size are associative on addition. Thus,

$$\mathbf{A} + (\mathbf{B} + \mathbf{C}) = (\mathbf{A} + \mathbf{B}) + \mathbf{C} \tag{1.17}$$

Matrices of the same size are commutative on addition. Thus,

$$\mathbf{A} + \mathbf{B} = \mathbf{B} + \mathbf{A} \tag{1.18}$$

Example 1.1. Matrix addition. Add the two 3×3 matrices **A** and **B** to obtain the 3×3 matrix **C**, where

$$\mathbf{A} = \begin{bmatrix} 1 & 2 & 3 \\ 2 & 1 & 4 \\ 1 & 4 & 3 \end{bmatrix} \quad \text{and} \quad \mathbf{B} = \begin{bmatrix} 3 & 2 & 1 \\ -4 & 1 & 2 \\ 2 & 3 & -1 \end{bmatrix} \tag{1.19}$$

From Eq. (1.16*a*),

$$c_{ij} = a_{ij} + b_{ij} \tag{1.20}$$

Thus, $c_{11} = a_{11} + b_{11} = 1 + 3 = 4$, $c_{12} = a_{12} + b_{12} = 2 + 2 = 4$, and so on. The result is

$$\mathbf{A} + \mathbf{B} = \begin{bmatrix} (1+3) & (2+2) & (3+1) \\ (2-4) & (1+1) & (4+2) \\ (1+2) & (4+3) & (3-1) \end{bmatrix} = \begin{bmatrix} 4 & 4 & 4 \\ -2 & 2 & 6 \\ 3 & 7 & 2 \end{bmatrix} = \mathbf{C} \tag{1.21}$$

Matrix multiplication consists of row-element to column-element multiplication and summation of the resulting products. Multiplication of the two matrices **A** and **B** is defined only when the number of columns of matrix **A** is the same as the number of rows of matrix **B**. Matrices that satisfy this condition are called conformable in the order **A B**. Thus, if the size of matrix **A** is $n \times m$ and the size of matrix **B** is $m \times r$, then

$$\mathbf{AB} = [a_{ij}][b_{ij}] = [c_{ij}] = \mathbf{C}$$

$$c_{ij} = \sum_{k=1}^{m} a_{ik} b_{kj} \qquad (i = 1, 2, \ldots n; j = 1, 2, \ldots, r) \quad (1.22)$$

The size of matrix **C** is $n \times r$. Matrices that are not conformable cannot be multiplied.

It is easy to make errors when performing matrix multiplication by hand. It is helpful to trace across the rows of **A** with the left index finger while tracing down the columns of **B** with the right index finger, multiplying the corresponding elements, and summing the products. Matrix algebra is much better suited to computers than to humans.

Multiplication of the matrix **A** by the scalar α consists of multiplying each element of **A** by α. Thus,

$$\alpha \mathbf{A} = \alpha[a_{ij}] = [\alpha a_{ij}] = [b_{ij}] = \mathbf{B} \quad (1.23)$$

Example 1.2. Matrix multiplication. Multiply the 3×3 matrix **A** and the 3×2 matrix **B** to obtain the 3×2 matrix **C**, where

$$\mathbf{A} = \begin{bmatrix} 1 & 2 & 3 \\ 2 & 1 & 4 \\ 1 & 4 & 3 \end{bmatrix} \quad \text{and} \quad \mathbf{B} = \begin{bmatrix} 2 & 1 \\ 1 & 2 \\ 2 & 1 \end{bmatrix} \quad (1.24)$$

From Eq. (1.22),

$$c_{ij} = \sum_{k=1}^{3} a_{ik} b_{kj} \qquad (i = 1, 2, 3; j = 1, 2) \quad (1.25)$$

Evaluating Eq. (1.25) yields

$$c_{11} = a_{11}b_{11} + a_{12}b_{21} + a_{13}b_{31} = (1)(2) + (2)(1) + (3)(2) = 10 \quad (1.26a)$$

$$c_{12} = a_{11}b_{12} + a_{12}b_{22} + a_{13}b_{32} = (1)(1) + (2)(2) + (3)(1) = 8 \quad (1.26b)$$

$$c_{21} = a_{21}b_{11} + a_{22}b_{21} + a_{23}b_{31} = (2)(2) + (1)(1) + (4)(2) = 13 \quad (1.26c)$$

$$c_{22} = a_{21}b_{12} + a_{22}b_{22} + a_{23}b_{32} = (2)(1) + (1)(2) + (4)(1) = 8 \quad (1.26d)$$

$$c_{31} = a_{31}b_{11} + a_{32}b_{21} + a_{33}b_{31} = (1)(2) + (4)(1) + (3)(2) = 12 \quad (1.26e)$$

$$c_{32} = a_{31}b_{12} + a_{32}b_{22} + a_{33}b_{32} = (1)(1) + (4)(2) + (3)(1) = 12 \quad (1.26f)$$

Thus,

$$\mathbf{C} = [c_{ij}] = \begin{bmatrix} 10 & 8 \\ 13 & 8 \\ 12 & 12 \end{bmatrix} \quad (1.27)$$

Multiply the 3×2 matrix **C** by the scalar $\alpha = 2$ to obtain the 3×2 matrix **D**. From Eq. (1.23), $d_{11} = \alpha c_{11} = (2)(10) = 20$, $d_{12} = \alpha c_{12} = (2)(8) = 16$, and so on.

The result is

$$\alpha \mathbf{C} = \begin{bmatrix} (2)(10) & (2)(8) \\ (2)(13) & (2)(8) \\ (2)(12) & (2)(12) \end{bmatrix} = \begin{bmatrix} 20 & 16 \\ 26 & 16 \\ 24 & 24 \end{bmatrix} = \mathbf{D} \quad (1.28)$$

Matrices that are suitably conformable are associative on multiplication. Thus,

$$\mathbf{A}(\mathbf{BC}) = (\mathbf{AB})\mathbf{C} \tag{1.29}$$

Square matrices are conformable in either order. Thus, if **A** and **B** are $n \times n$ matrices,

$$\mathbf{AB} = \mathbf{C} \qquad \text{and} \qquad \mathbf{BA} = \mathbf{D} \tag{1.30}$$

where **C** and **D** are $n \times n$ matrices. However, square matrices, in general, are not commutative on multiplication. That is, in general

$$\mathbf{AB} \neq \mathbf{BA} \tag{1.31}$$

Matrices **A**, **B**, and **C** are distributive if **B** and **C** are the same size and **A** is conformable to **B** and **C**. Thus,

$$\mathbf{A}(\mathbf{B} + \mathbf{C}) = \mathbf{AB} + \mathbf{AC} \tag{1.32}$$

Consider the two square matrices **A** and **B**. Multiplying yields

$$\mathbf{AB} = \mathbf{C} \tag{1.33}$$

It might appear logical that the inverse operation of division would give

$$\mathbf{A} = \frac{\mathbf{C}}{\mathbf{B}} \tag{1.34}$$

Unfortunately, matrix division is not defined. However, for square matrices, an analogous concept is provided by the matrix *inverse*.

Consider the two square matrices **A** and **B**. If $\mathbf{AB} = \mathbf{I}$, then **B** is the inverse of **A**, which is denoted as $\mathbf{A}^{-1}$. Matrix inverses commute on multiplication. Thus,

$$\mathbf{AA}^{-1} = \mathbf{I} = \mathbf{A}^{-1}\mathbf{A} \tag{1.35}$$

The operation desired by Eq. (1.34), which is the inverse of the matrix multiplication specified by Eq. (1.33), is accomplished by matrix multiplication using the inverse matrix. Thus, the matrix equivalent of Eq. (1.34) is given by

$$\mathbf{A} = \mathbf{B}^{-1}\mathbf{C} \tag{1.36}$$

Procedures for evaluating the inverse of a square matrix are presented in Section 1.3 under "Gauss–Jordan elimination."

Matrix *decomposition* or *factorization* refers to the representation of a matrix as the product of two other matrices. For example, a known matrix **A** can be represented as the product of two unknown matrices **B** and **C**. Thus,

$$\mathbf{A} = \mathbf{BC} \tag{1.37}$$

Decomposition is not a unique process. There are, in general, an infinite number of matrices **B** and **C** whose product is **A**. A particularly useful decomposition for square matrices is

$$\mathbf{A} = \mathbf{LU} \tag{1.38}$$

where **L** and **U** are lower and upper triangular matrices, respectively. The **LU** decomposition method for solving systems of linear algebraic equations, which is presented in Section 1.4, is based on such a decomposition.

A matrix can be partitioned by grouping the elements of the matrix into *submatrices*. These submatrices can then be treated as elements of a smaller matrix. To ensure that the operations of matrix algebra can be applied to the submatrices of two partitioned matrices, the partitioning is generally into square submatrices of equal size. Matrix partitioning is especially convenient when solving sets of algebraic finite difference equations which arise in the numerical solution of differential equations. The block tridiagonal matrices considered in Section 1.5 are partitioned matrices.

Systems of Linear Algebraic Equations

Systems of linear algebraic equations, such as Eq. (1.1), can be expressed very compactly in matrix notation. Thus, Eq. (1.1) can be written as the matrix equation

$$\boxed{\mathbf{A}\mathbf{x} = \mathbf{b}}$$

where

$$\mathbf{A} = \begin{bmatrix} a_{11} & a_{12} & \cdots & a_{1n} \\ a_{21} & a_{22} & \cdots & a_{2n} \\ \vdots & \vdots & \ddots & \vdots \\ a_{n1} & a_{n2} & \cdots & a_{nn} \end{bmatrix}, \quad \mathbf{x} = \begin{bmatrix} x_1 \\ x_2 \\ \vdots \\ x_n \end{bmatrix}, \quad \text{and} \quad \mathbf{b} = \begin{bmatrix} b_1 \\ b_2 \\ \vdots \\ b_n \end{bmatrix} \tag{1.40}$$

Equation (1.1) can also be written as

$$\sum_{j=1}^{n} a_{ij} x_j = b_i \qquad (i = 1, \ldots, n) \tag{1.41}$$

or equivalently as

$$a_{ij} x_j = b_i \qquad (i, j = 1, \ldots, n) \tag{1.42}$$

where the summation convention holds, that is, the repeated index j is summed over its range. Equation (1.39) will be used throughout this book to represent a system of linear algebraic equations. $\mathbf{A}$ is called the *coefficient matrix*, and $\mathbf{b}$ is called *the right-hand-side vector*, the *nonhomogeneous vector*, or simply the $\mathbf{b}$ *vector*.

There are three so-called row operations that are useful for solving systems of linear algebraic equations.

1. Any equation (row) may be multiplied by a constant (a process known as scaling).
2. The order of the equations (rows) may be interchanged (a process known as pivoting).
3. Any equation (row) can be replaced by a weighted linear combination of that equation (row) with any other equation (row) (a process known as elimination).

In the context of the solution of a system of linear algebraic equations, these three row operations clearly do not change the solution. The appearance of the system of equations is obviously changed by any of these row operations, but the solution is unaffected. When one is solving systems of linear algebraic equations expressed in matrix notation, these row operations apply to the rows of the matrices representing the system of equations.

Determinants

The determinant of a square matrix **A** is a scalar associated with the matrix and can be represented by the collection of the elements of the square matrix, enclosed in vertical lines. Thus,

$$|\mathbf{A}| = \det(\mathbf{A}) = |a_{ij}| = \begin{vmatrix} a_{11} & a_{12} & \cdots & a_{1n} \\ a_{21} & a_{22} & \cdots & a_{2n} \\ \vdots & \vdots & \ddots & \vdots \\ a_{n1} & a_{n2} & \cdots & a_{nn} \end{vmatrix} \tag{1.43}$$

Only square matrices have determinants. In general, the value (*expansion*) of an $n \times n$ determinant is the sum of all possible products formed by choosing one and only one element from each row and each column of the determinant, with a plus or minus sign determined by the number of permutations of the row and column elements.

The value of the determinant of a 2×2 matrix can be found by taking the product of the elements on the major diagonal minus the product of the elements on the minor diagonal. Thus,

$$|\mathbf{A}| = \begin{vmatrix} a_{11} & a_{12} \\ a_{21} & a_{22} \end{vmatrix} = a_{11}a_{22} - a_{21}a_{12} \tag{1.44}$$

The scalar value of the determinant of a 3×3 matrix can be found by taking the sum of six triple product terms, which can be obtained from the *augmented* determinant:

$$\left| \begin{matrix} a_{11} & a_{12} & a_{13} \\ a_{21} & a_{22} & a_{23} \\ a_{31} & a_{32} & a_{33} \end{matrix} \right| \begin{matrix} a_{11} & a_{12} \\ a_{21} & a_{22} \\ a_{31} & a_{32} \end{matrix} \tag{1.45}$$

The 3×3 determinant is augmented by repeating the first two columns of the determinant on the right-hand side of the determinant. Three triple products are formed, starting with the elements of the first row multiplied by the two remaining elements on the left-to-right downward-sloping diagonals. Three more triple products are formed, starting with the elements of the third row multiplied by the two remaining elements on the left-to-right upward-sloping diagonals. The value of the determinant is the sum of the first three triple products minus the sum of the last three triple products. Thus

$$|\mathbf{A}| = a_{11}a_{22}a_{33} + a_{12}a_{23}a_{31} + a_{13}a_{21}a_{32} - a_{31}a_{22}a_{13} - a_{32}a_{23}a_{11} - a_{33}a_{21}a_{12} \tag{1.46}$$

Example 1.3. Evaluation of a 3 × 3 determinant by the diagonal method. Evaluate the determinant of the following matrix:

$$\mathbf{A} = \begin{bmatrix} 5 & 2 & 1 \\ 4 & 1 & -1 \\ -2 & 3 & -3 \end{bmatrix} \tag{1.47}$$

The augmented determinant is

$$\begin{vmatrix} 5 & 2 & 1 \\ 4 & 1 & -1 \\ -2 & 3 & -3 \end{vmatrix} \begin{matrix} 5 & 2 \\ 4 & 1 \\ -2 & 3 \end{matrix} \tag{1.48}$$

Applying Eq. (1.46) yields

$$|\mathbf{A}| = (5)(1)(-3) + (2)(-1)(-2) + (1)(4)(3) - (-2)(1)(1) - (3)(-1)(5) - (-3)(4)(2) = -15 + 4 + 12 + 2 + 15 + 24 = 42 \tag{1.49}$$

The diagonal method of evaluating determinants applies only to 2 × 2 and 3 × 3 determinants. It is incorrect for 4 × 4 or larger determinants.

One formal procedure for evaluating determinants is called *expansion by minors*, or the *method of cofactors*. In this procedure there are $n!$ products to be summed, where each product has n elements. Thus, the expansion of a 10 × 10 determinant requires the summation of 10! products (10! = 3, 628, 800), where each product involves 9 multiplications (the product of 10 elements). This is a total of 32,659,000 multiplications and 3,627,999 additions, not counting the work needed to keep track of the signs. Consequently, the evaluation of determinants by the method of cofactors is impractical, except for very small determinants.

Although the method of cofactors is not recommended for anything larger than a 4 × 4 determinant, it is useful to understand the concepts involved. The minor, M_{ij}, is the determinant of the $(n-1) \times (n-1)$ submatrix of the $n \times n$ matrix $\mathbf{A}$ obtained by deleting the ith row and the jth column. The cofactor A_{ij} associated with the minor M_{ij} is defined as

$$A_{ij} = (-1)^{i+j} M_{ij} \tag{1.50}$$

Using cofactors, the determinant of matrix $\mathbf{A}$ is the sum of the products of the elements of any row or column, multiplied by the corresponding cofactors. Thus, expanding along any fixed row i yields

$$\det(\mathbf{A}) = |\mathbf{A}| = \sum_{j=1}^{n} a_{ij} A_{ij} = \sum_{j=1}^{n} (-1)^{i+j} a_{ij} M_{ij} \tag{1.51}$$

Alternatively, expanding along any fixed column j yields

$$\det(\mathbf{A}) = |\mathbf{A}| = \sum_{i=1}^{n} a_{ij} A_{ij} = \sum_{i=1}^{n} (-1)^{i+j} a_{ij} M_{ij} \tag{1.52}$$

Each cofactor expansion reduces the order of the determinant by one, so there are n determinants of order $n-1$ to evaluate. By repeated application, the cofactors are eventually reduced to **3 × 3** determinants that can be evaluated by the diagonal method. The amount of work can be reduced by choosing the expansion rows and columns with as many zeros as possible.

If the value of the determinant of a matrix is zero, the matrix is said to be *singular*. A nonsingular matrix has a determinant that is nonzero. If any row or column of a matrix has all zero elements, that matrix is singular.

The determinant of a triangular matrix, either upper or lower triangular, is the product of the elements on the major diagonal. It is possible to transform any nonsingular matrix into a triangular matrix in such a way that the value of the determinant is either unchanged or changed in a well-defined way. This procedure is presented in Section 1.3 under "Determinants." The value of the determinant can then be evaluated quite easily as the product of the elements on the major diagonal.

Example 1.4. Evaluation of a 3×3 determinant by the cofactor method. Rework Example 1.3 using the cofactor method. Recall Eq. (1.47):

$$\mathbf{A} = \begin{bmatrix} 5 & 2 & 1 \\ 4 & 1 & -1 \\ -2 & 3 & -3 \end{bmatrix} \tag{1.53}$$

Evaluate $|\mathbf{A}|$ by expanding across the first row. Thus

$$|\mathbf{A}| = (5)\begin{vmatrix} 1 & -1 \\ 3 & -3 \end{vmatrix} - (2)\begin{vmatrix} 4 & -1 \\ -2 & -3 \end{vmatrix} + (1)\begin{vmatrix} 4 & 1 \\ -2 & 3 \end{vmatrix} \tag{1.54}$$

$$|\mathbf{A}| = 5(-3+3) - 2(-12-2) + (12+2) = 0 + 28 + 14 = 42 \tag{1.55}$$

1.3 DIRECT ELIMINATION METHODS

There are a number of methods for the direct solution of systems of linear algebraic equations. One of the more well known methods is Cramer's rule, which requires the evaluation of numerous determinants. Cramer's rule is highly inefficient and thus not recommended. More efficient methods, based on the elimination concept, are recommended. Both Cramer's rule and elimination methods are presented in this section. After presenting Cramer's rule, the elimination concept is applied to develop (a) Gauss elimination, (b) Gauss–Jordan elimination, (c) matrix inversion, and (d) determinant evaluation. These concepts are extended to **LU** decomposition and tridiagonal systems of equations in Sections 1.4 and 1.5, respectively.

Cramer's Rule

Consider the system of linear algebraic equations $\mathbf{Ax} = \mathbf{b}$, which represents n equations. Cramer's rule states that the solution for $x_j (j = 1, \ldots, n)$ is given by

$$x_j = \frac{\det(\mathbf{A}^j)}{\det(\mathbf{A})} \qquad (j = 1, \ldots, n) \tag{1.56}$$

where $\mathbf{A}^j$ is the $n \times n$ matrix obtained by replacing column j in matrix $\mathbf{A}$ by the column vector $\mathbf{b}$. For example, consider a system of two equations:

$$a_{11}x_1 + a_{12}x_2 = b_1 \tag{1.57a}$$

$$a_{21}x_1 + a_{22}x_2 = b_2 \tag{1.57b}$$

Cramer's rule yields

$$x_1 = \frac{\begin{vmatrix} b_1 & a_{12} \\ b_2 & a_{22} \end{vmatrix}}{\begin{vmatrix} a_{11} & a_{12} \\ a_{21} & a_{22} \end{vmatrix}} \quad \text{and} \quad x_2 = \frac{\begin{vmatrix} a_{11} & b_1 \\ a_{21} & b_2 \end{vmatrix}}{\begin{vmatrix} a_{11} & a_{12} \\ a_{21} & a_{22} \end{vmatrix}} \tag{1.58}$$

The determinants in Eqs. (1.58) can be evaluated by the diagonal method described in Section 1.2.

For systems containing more than three equations, the diagonal method does not work. In such cases, the method of cofactors, also presented in Section 1.2, could be used. The number of multiplications and divisions, N, required by the method of cofactors is

$$N = (n-1)(n+1)!$$

For a relatively small system of 10 equations (i.e., $n = 10$), $N = 360,000,000$, which is an enormous number of calculations. For $n = 100$, $N = 10^{157}$, which is obviously ridiculous. The preferred method for evaluating determinants is the elimination method presented in this section. The number of multiplications and divisions required by the elimination method is approximately $N = n^3 + n^2 - n$. Thus, for $n = 10$, $N = 1090$, and for $n = 100$, $N = 1,009,900$. Obviously, the elimination method is preferred.

Example 1.5. Cramer's rule. Solve the following system of linear algebraic equations by Cramer's rule.

$$5x_1 + 2x_2 + x_3 = 3 \tag{1.59a}$$

$$4x_1 + x_2 - x_3 = -3 \tag{1.59b}$$

$$-2x_1 + 3x_2 - 3x_3 = 5 \tag{1.59c}$$

First, calculate $\det(\mathbf{A})$. From Example 1.4,

$$\det(\mathbf{A}) = \begin{vmatrix} 5 & 2 & 1 \\ 4 & 1 & -1 \\ -2 & 3 & -3 \end{vmatrix} = 42 \tag{1.60}$$

Next, calculate $\det(\mathbf{A}^1)$, $\det(\mathbf{A}^2)$, and $\det(\mathbf{A}^3)$. For $\det(\mathbf{A}^1)$,

$$\det(\mathbf{A}^1) = \begin{vmatrix} 3 & 2 & 1 \\ -3 & 1 & -1 \\ 5 & 3 & -3 \end{vmatrix} = -42 \tag{1.61}$$

In a similar manner, $\det(\mathbf{A}^2) = 126$ and $\det(\mathbf{A}^3) = 84$. Thus,

$$x_1 = \frac{\det(\mathbf{A}^1)}{\det(\mathbf{A})} = \frac{-42}{42} = -1, \qquad x_2 = \frac{126}{42} = 3, \qquad x_3 = \frac{84}{42} = 2 \tag{1.62}$$

Elimination Methods

Elimination methods solve a system of linear algebraic equations by solving one equation for one of the unknowns, say x_1, in terms of the remaining unknowns,

x_2 to x_n, then substituting the expression for x_1 into the remaining $n-1$ equations to determine $n-1$ equations involving x_2 to x_n. This elimination procedure is repeated $n-1$ times until the last step yields an equation involving only x_n, from which the value of x_n can be calculated. This process is called *elimination*.

Once x_n has been calculated from the final step in the elimination process, x_{n-1} can be calculated from modified equation $n-1$, which contains only x_n and x_{n-1}. Then x_{n-2} can be calculated from modified equation n−2, which contains only x_n, x_{n-1}, and x_{n-2}. This procedure is repeated $n-1$ times to calculate x_{n-1} to x_1. This process is called *back substitution*.

ROW OPERATIONS. The elimination process employs the row operations presented in Section 1.2, which are repeated below:

1. Any equation may be multiplied by a constant.
2. The order of the equations may be interchanged.
3. Any equation can be replaced by a weighted linear combination of that equation with any other equation.

These row operations, which do change the appearance of the system of equations, do not change the solution to the system of equations.

The first row operation is used to scale the equations, if necessary. The second row operation is used to prevent divisions by zero and to reduce round-off errors. The third row operation is used to implement the systematic elimination process described in the preceding paragraphs.

ELIMINATION. We will consider the general problem of the solution of a set of linear algebraic equations and develop a systematic procedure that can be implemented easily. Consider a system of three equations:

$$a_{11}x_1 + a_{12}x_2 + a_{13}x_3 = b_1 \tag{1.63a}$$

$$a_{21}x_1 + a_{22}x_2 + a_{23}x_3 = b_2 \tag{1.63b}$$

$$a_{31}x_1 + a_{32}x_2 + a_{33}x_3 = b_3 \tag{1.63c}$$

Solve Eq. (1.63a) for x_1, assuming that $a_{11} \neq 0$. Thus,

$$x_1 = \frac{b_1 - a_{12}x_2 - a_{13}x_3}{a_{11}} \tag{1.64}$$

Substituting Eq. (1.64) into Eq. (1.63*b*) gives

$$a_{21}\frac{b_1 - a_{12}x_2 - a_{13}x_3}{a_{11}} + a_{22}x_2 + a_{23}x_3 = b_2 \tag{1.65}$$

which can be rearranged into the form

$$\left(a_{22} - \frac{a_{21}}{a_{11}}a_{12}\right)x_2 + \left(a_{23} - \frac{a_{21}}{a_{11}}a_{13}\right)x_3 = \left(b_2 - \frac{a_{21}}{a_{11}}b_1\right) \tag{1.66a}$$

In a similar manner, Eq. (1.63c) becomes

$$\left(a_{32} - \frac{a_{31}}{a_{11}}a_{12}\right)x_2 + \left(a_{33} - \frac{a_{31}}{a_{11}}a_{13}\right)x_3 = \left(b_3 - \frac{a_{31}}{a_{11}}b_1\right) \tag{1.66b}$$

Equations (1.66) can be written in the form

$$a_{22}^* x_2 + a_{23}^* x_3 = b_2^* \tag{1.67a}$$

$$a_{32}^* x_2 + a_{33}^* x_3 = b_3^* \tag{1.67b}$$

where the coefficients denoted by asterisks are given by

$$a_{22}^* = a_{22} - \frac{a_{21}}{a_{11}}a_{12}, \qquad a_{23}^* = a_{23} - \frac{a_{21}}{a_{11}}a_{13}, \qquad b_2^* = b_2 - \frac{a_{21}}{a_{11}}b_1 \tag{1.68a}$$

$$a_{32}^* = a_{32} - \frac{a_{31}}{a_{11}}a_{12}, \qquad a_{33}^* = a_{33} - \frac{a_{31}}{a_{11}}a_{13}, \qquad b_3^* = b_3 - \frac{a_{31}}{a_{11}}b_1 \tag{1.68b}$$

These coefficients have a regular pattern, which is given by

$$a_{ij}^* = a_{ij} - \frac{a_{i1}}{a_{11}}a_{1j} \tag{1.69a}$$

$$b_i^* = b_i - \frac{a_{i1}}{a_{11}}b_1 \tag{1.69b}$$

This pattern is independent of the number of equations being considered. Thus, for n equations, all coefficients a_{ij}^* can be computed using nested loops around Eqs. (1.69) for the indices ($i = 2, \ldots, n$) and ($j = 2, \ldots, n$). In a computer program, the new coefficients can be stored in place of the original coefficients, since the original coefficients are no longer needed.

Next solve Eq. (1.67*a*) for x_2, assuming that $a_{22}^* \neq 0$. Thus,

$$x_2 = \frac{b_2^* - a_{23}^* x_3}{a_{22}^*} \tag{1.70}$$

Substituting Eq. (1.70) into Eq. (1.67b) yields

$$a_{33}^{**} x_3 = b_3^{**} \tag{1.71}$$

where

$$a_{33}^{**} = a_{33}^* - \frac{a_{32}^*}{a_{22}^*}a_{23}^* \qquad \text{and} \qquad b_3^{**} = b_3^* - \frac{a_{32}^*}{a_{22}^*}b_2^* \tag{1.72}$$

Equations (1.72) can be written in general form as

$$a_{ij}^{**} = a_{ij}^* - \frac{a_{i2}^*}{a_{22}^*}a_{2j}^* \tag{1.73a}$$

$$b_i^{**} = b_i^* - \frac{a_{i2}^*}{a_{22}^*}b_2^* \tag{1.73b}$$

Once again, this pattern is independent of the number of equations being considered. Thus, for n equations, Eqs. (1.73) can be evaluated using nested loops for the indices ($i = 3, \ldots, n$) and ($j = 3, \ldots, n$). In a computer program, the new coefficients can be stored in place of the once modified coefficients, which are no longer needed.

For the problem of three equations under consideration, the original system of equations [Eqs. (1.63)] has been reduced to

$$a_{11}x_1 + a_{12}x_2 + a_{13}x_3 = b_1 \tag{1.74a}$$

$$a_{22}^*x_2 + a_{23}^*x_3 = b_2^* \tag{1.74b}$$

$$a_{33}^{**}x_3 = b_3^{**} \tag{1.74c}$$

which is equivalent to the original system. This completes the elimination process.

BACK SUBSTITUTION. The solution to Eqs. (1.74) is accomplished easily by back substitution. Starting with Eq. (1.74c) and working backwards yields

$$x_3 = \frac{b_3^{**}}{a_{33}^{**}} \tag{1.75a}$$

$$x_2 = \frac{b_2^* - a_{23}^*x_3}{a_{22}^*} \tag{1.75b}$$

$$x_1 = \frac{b_1 - a_{12}x_2 - a_{13}x_3}{a_{11}} \tag{1.75c}$$

SUMMARY. Example 1.6 illustrates the above procedure. The notation $R_i + kR_j$ next to the ith row indicates that the ith equation is replaced by the linear combination of the ith equation plus k times the jth equation. Thus, $R_2 - \left(\frac{4}{5}\right)R_1$ means replace Eq. (2) of the set (row 2) by the linear combination [Eq. (2) $-$ $\left(\frac{4}{5}\right)$ Eq. (1)]. The scalar k is chosen to eliminate the first coefficient in Eq. (i). The coefficient elimination proceeds in an orderly manner, so that once a coefficient has been eliminated, subsequent operations do not reintroduce nonzero values for that coefficient. Thus, all the coefficients below the major diagonal in the first column are eliminated by linear combinations with the first equation. Then the coefficients below the major diagonal in the second column are eliminated by linear combinations with the new second equation. This process, called elimination, is continued until all the coefficients below the major diagonal are eliminated. At this point, the last equation contains only one unknown, x_n, which can be solved for. Using that value, the $(n-1)$st equation is reduced to contain only one unknown, x_{n-1}, which can be solved for. This procedure, called back substitution, is repeated until the first equation has been solved for x_1.

The number of multiplications and divisions required by the elimination method is approximately $N = (n^3/3) + n^2 - (n/3)$. Thus, for $n = 10$, $N = 430$, and for $n = 100$, $N = 343,300$. This is a considerable improvement over the work required by Cramer's rule.

Example 1.6. Elimination. Solve the system of equations presented in Example 1.5 by elimination.

$$5x_1 + 2x_2 + x_3 = 3 \tag{1.76a}$$

$$4x_1 + x_2 - x_3 = -3 \tag{1.76b}$$

$$-2x_1 + 3x_2 - 3x_3 = 5 \tag{1.76c}$$

Systematically eliminate terms below the major diagonal, column by column, as indicated below:

$$\begin{bmatrix} 5x_1 & + & 2x_2 & + & x_3 & = & 3 \\ 4x_1 & + & x_2 & - & x_3 & = & -3 \\ -2x_1 & + & 3x_2 & - & 3x_3 & = & 5 \end{bmatrix} \begin{matrix} \\ R_2 - (\frac{4}{5})R_1 \\ R_3 - (-\frac{2}{5})R_1 \end{matrix} \tag{1.77}$$

$$\begin{bmatrix} 5x_1 & + & 2x_2 & + & x_3 & = & 3 \\ 0 & - & \frac{3}{5}x_2 & - & \frac{9}{5}x_3 & = & -\frac{27}{5} \\ 0 & + & \frac{19}{5}x_2 & - & \frac{13}{5}x_3 & = & \frac{31}{5} \end{bmatrix} \begin{matrix} \\ \\ R_3 - (-\frac{19}{3})R_2 \end{matrix} \tag{1.78}$$

$$\begin{bmatrix} 5x_1 & + & 2x_2 & + & x_3 & = & 3 \\ 0 & - & \frac{3}{5}x_2 & - & \frac{9}{5}x_3 & = & -\frac{27}{5} \\ 0 & + & 0 & - & 14x_3 & = & -28 \end{bmatrix} \tag{1.79}$$

Solve for x_3, x_2, and x_1 by back substitution, starting with the third equation:

$$x_3 = \frac{-28}{-14} = 2 \tag{1.80a}$$

$$x_2 = \frac{(-27/5) - (-9/5)(2)}{-3/5} = 3 \tag{1.80b}$$

$$x_1 = \frac{(3) - (2)(3) - (1)(2)}{5} = -1 \tag{1.80c}$$

The extension of the elimination procedure to n equations is straightforward.

SIMPLIFIED ELIMINATION. The elimination procedure illustrated in Example 1.6 involves manipulation of the coefficient matrix **A** and the nonhomogeneous vector **b**. The **x** vector is fixed. As long as the columns are not interchanged, column j corresponds to $\mathbf{x}_j$. Consequently, the **x** vector does not need to be carried throughout the operations. Only the elements of **A** and **b** need to be considered. Thus, the elimination procedure can be simplified by augmenting the **A** matrix with the **b** vector, performing the row operations on the elements of the augmented **A** matrix to accomplish the elimination process, and then performing the back substitution to determine the solution vector. This simplified elimination procedure is illustrated in Example 1.7.

Example 1.7. Simplified elimination. Rework Example 1.6 using the simplified elimination procedure. From Example 1.6, the **A** matrix augmented by the **b** vector is

$$[\mathbf{A} \mid \mathbf{b}] = \left[\begin{array}{ccc|c} 5 & 2 & 1 & 3 \\ 4 & 1 & -1 & -3 \\ -2 & 3 & -3 & 5 \end{array}\right] \tag{1.81}$$

Performing the row operations to accomplish the elimination process yields

$$\left[\begin{array}{rrr|r} 5 & 2 & 1 & 3 \\ 4 & 1 & -1 & -3 \\ -2 & 3 & -3 & 5 \end{array}\right] \begin{array}{l} \\ R_2 - (\frac{4}{5})R_1 \\ R_3 - (-\frac{2}{5})R_1 \end{array} \tag{1.82}$$

$$\left[\begin{array}{rrr|r} 5 & 2 & 1 & 3 \\ 0 & -\frac{3}{5} & -\frac{9}{5} & -\frac{27}{5} \\ 0 & \frac{19}{5} & -\frac{13}{5} & \frac{31}{5} \end{array}\right] \begin{array}{l} \\ \\ R_3 - (-\frac{19}{3})R_2 \end{array} \tag{1.83}$$

$$\left[\begin{array}{rrr|r} 5 & 2 & 1 & 3 \\ 0 & -\frac{3}{5} & -\frac{9}{5} & -\frac{27}{5} \\ 0 & 0 & -14 & -28 \end{array}\right] \begin{array}{l} x_1 = -1 \\ x_2 = 3 \\ x_3 = 2 \end{array} \tag{1.84}$$

The back substitution step is presented beside the triangularized augmented **A** matrix.

MULTIPLE B VECTORS. If more than one **b** vector is to be considered, the **A** matrix is simply augmented with all the **b** vectors simultaneously. The elimination process is then applied to the multiply augmented **A** matrix. Back substitution is then applied one column at a time to the modified **b** vectors.

Example 1.8. Elimination for multiple b vectors. Consider the system of equations presented in Example 1.7 with two **b** vectors, $\mathbf{b}_1$ and $\mathbf{b}_2$. The multiply augmented **A** matrix is

$$[\mathbf{A} \mid \mathbf{b}_1 \mathbf{b}_2] = \left[\begin{array}{rrr|rr} 5 & 2 & 1 & 3 & 2 \\ 4 & 1 & -1 & -3 & -2 \\ -2 & 3 & -3 & 5 & 8 \end{array}\right] \tag{1.85}$$

Performing the elimination process yields

$$\left[\begin{array}{rrr|rr} 5 & 2 & 1 & 3 & 2 \\ 0 & -\frac{3}{5} & -\frac{9}{5} & -\frac{27}{5} & -\frac{18}{5} \\ 0 & 0 & -14 & -28 & -14 \end{array}\right] \tag{1.86}$$

Performing the back substitution one column at a time yields

$$\mathbf{x}_1 = \begin{bmatrix} -1 \\ 3 \\ 2 \end{bmatrix} \quad \text{and} \quad \mathbf{x}_2 = \begin{bmatrix} -1 \\ 3 \\ 1 \end{bmatrix} \tag{1.87}$$

PIVOTING. The elimination procedure described so far fails immediately if a_{11} is zero. The procedure also fails if any subsequent element a_{ii} on the major diagonal is zero. Even though there may be no zeros on the major diagonal in the original matrix, the elimination process may create zeros on the major diagonal. The elimination procedure described so far must be modified to avoid zeros on the main diagonal. This result can be accomplished by rearranging the equations by interchanging equations (rows) or variables (columns)—before each elimination step to put the element of largest magnitude on the diagonal. Because the element on the major diagonal is called the *pivot* element, this process is called *pivoting*. Interchanging both rows and columns is called *full pivoting*. Full pivoting is quite complicated, and thus it is rarely used. Interchanging only rows is called *partial pivoting*. Only partial pivoting is considered in this book.

Pivoting eliminates zeros in the pivot elements during the elimination process. Pivoting also reduces round-off errors, since the pivot element becomes a divisor during the elimination process, and division by small numbers introduces larger round-off errors than division by large numbers. When the procedure is repeated, round-off errors can compound. This problem becomes more severe as the number of equations is increased.

Example 1.9. Pivoting. Use the elimination method with partial pivoting to solve the system of linear algebraic equations $\mathbf{Ax} = \mathbf{b}$:

$$\begin{bmatrix} 0 & 2 & 1 \\ 4 & 1 & -1 \\ -2 & 3 & -3 \end{bmatrix} \begin{bmatrix} x_1 \\ x_2 \\ x_3 \end{bmatrix} = \begin{bmatrix} 5 \\ -3 \\ 5 \end{bmatrix} \tag{1.88}$$

Apply the simplified elimination procedure by augmenting $\mathbf{A}$ with $\mathbf{b}$. The first pivot element is zero, so pivoting is required. The largest number (in magnitude) in the first column under the pivot element occurs in the second row. Thus, interchanging the first and second rows and performing the subsequent row operations gives

$$\left[\begin{array}{ccc:c} 4 & 1 & -1 & -3 \\ 0 & 2 & 1 & 5 \\ -2 & 3 & -3 & 5 \end{array}\right] \begin{array}{l} \\ \\ R_3 - (-\frac{2}{4})R_1 \end{array} \tag{1.89}$$

$$\left[\begin{array}{ccc:c} 4 & 1 & -1 & -3 \\ 0 & 2 & 1 & 5 \\ 0 & \frac{7}{2} & -\frac{7}{2} & \frac{7}{2} \end{array}\right] \tag{1.90}$$

Although the pivot element in the second row is not zero, it is not the largest element in the second column underneath the pivot element. Thus, pivoting is called for again. Note that pivoting is based only on the rows below the pivot element. The rows above the pivot element have already been through the elimination process. Using one of the rows above the pivot element would destroy the elimination already accomplished. Interchanging the second and third rows and performing the subsequent row operations yields

$$\left[\begin{array}{ccc:c} 4 & 1 & -1 & -3 \\ 0 & \frac{7}{2} & -\frac{7}{2} & \frac{7}{2} \\ 0 & 2 & 1 & 5 \end{array}\right] \begin{array}{l} \\ \\ R_3 - (\frac{4}{7})R_2 \end{array} \tag{1.91}$$

$$\left[\begin{array}{ccc:c} 4 & 1 & -1 & -3 \\ 0 & \frac{7}{2} & -\frac{7}{2} & \frac{7}{2} \\ 0 & 0 & 3 & 3 \end{array}\right] \begin{array}{l} x_1 = -1 \\ x_2 = 2 \\ x_3 = 1 \end{array} \tag{1.92}$$

The back substitution results are presented beside the triangularized augmented $\mathbf{A}$ matrix.

SCALING. The elimination process described so far may incur significant round-off errors when the magnitudes of the elements of one or more of the equations are greatly different from the magnitudes of the elements of the other equations. In such cases, *scaling* may be beneficial. Scaling is accomplished by dividing the elements of each row (including the $\mathbf{b}$ vector) by the largest element in the row (excluding the $\mathbf{b}$ vector). After scaling, pivoting is employed to reduce round-off error. Without scaling, pivoting may actually introduce round-off error in some cases. When all the elements of the coefficient matrix $\mathbf{A}$ are about the same order of magnitude, scaling should not be used, because (a) it requires more work and (b) it may actually increase the round-off error, since scaling itself introduces round-off errors.

Example 1.10. Scaling. We will investigate the advantage of scaling by solving the linear system

$$\begin{bmatrix} 3 & 2 & 105 \\ 2 & -3 & 103 \\ 1 & 1 & 3 \end{bmatrix} \mathbf{x} = \begin{bmatrix} 104 \\ 98 \\ 3 \end{bmatrix} \tag{1.93}$$

To accentuate the effects of round-off, carry only three significant figures in the calculations. For the first column, pivoting is not required. Thus, the augmented **A** matrix and the first set of row operations are given by

$$\left[\begin{array}{ccc:c} 3 & 2 & 105 & 104 \\ 2 & -3 & 103 & 98 \\ 1 & 1 & 3 & 3 \end{array}\right] \begin{array}{l} \\ R_2 - (0.667)\, R_1 \\ R_3 - (0.333)\, R_1 \end{array} \tag{1.94}$$

$$\left[\begin{array}{ccc:c} 3 & 2 & 105 & 104 \\ 0 & -4.33 & 33.0 & 28.6 \\ 0 & 0.334 & -32.0 & -31.6 \end{array}\right] \begin{array}{l} \\ \\ R_3 + (0.0771)\, R_2 \end{array} \tag{1.95}$$

Pivoting is not required for the second column. Performing the elimination indicated in Eq. (1.95) gives the triangularized matrix

$$\left[\begin{array}{ccc:c} 3 & 2 & 105 & 104 \\ 0 & -4.33 & 33.0 & 28.6 \\ 0 & 0 & -29.5 & -29.4 \end{array}\right] \tag{1.96}$$

Performing back substitution yields $x_3 = 0.997$, $x_2 = 0.924$, and $x_1 = -0.844$, which do not agree very well with the exact solution $x_3 = 1.0$, $x_2 = 1.0$, and $x_1 = -1.0$.

The effects of round-off can be reduced by scaling the equations before pivoting. Thus,

$$\left[\begin{array}{ccc:c} 0.0286 & 0.0190 & 1.000 & 0.991 \\ 0.0194 & -0.0291 & 1.000 & 0.952 \\ 0.333 & 0.333 & 1.000 & 1.000 \end{array}\right] \tag{1.97}$$

Pivoting is now called for in the first column. Pivoting, followed by the elimination steps, yields

$$\left[\begin{array}{ccc:c} 0.333 & 0.333 & 1.000 & 1.000 \\ 0.0194 & -0.0291 & 1.000 & 0.952 \\ 0.0286 & 0.0190 & 1.000 & 0.991 \end{array}\right] \begin{array}{l} \\ R_2 - (0.0583)\, R_1 \\ R_3 - (0.0859)\, R_1 \end{array} \tag{1.98}$$

$$\left[\begin{array}{ccc:c} 0.333 & 0.333 & 1.000 & 1.000 \\ 0 & -0.0485 & 0.942 & 0.894 \\ 0 & 0.00960 & 0.914 & 0.905 \end{array}\right] \begin{array}{l} \\ \\ R_3 - (0.198)\, R_2 \end{array} \tag{1.99}$$

$$\left[\begin{array}{ccc:c} 0.333 & 0.333 & 1.000 & 1.000 \\ 0 & -0.0485 & 0.942 & 0.894 \\ 0 & 0 & 0.727 & 0.728 \end{array}\right] \tag{1.100}$$

Performing back substitution yields $x_3 = 1.000$, $x_2 = 0.990$, and $x_1 = -0.990$. These results are quite close to the exact answer.

Gauss Elimination

The elimination procedure described in the preceding subsection, including scaling and pivoting, is commonly called Gauss elimination. It is the most important and most useful direct method for solving systems of linear algebraic equations. The Gauss–Jordan method, the matrix inverse method, **LU** decomposition, and the Thomas algorithm are all modifications or extensions of the Gauss elimination method. Scaling and pivoting are essential elements of Gauss elimination. In cases where all the elements of the coefficient matrix **A** are the same order of magnitude, scaling is not necessary. Pivoting to avoid zero pivot elements is always required. Pivoting to decrease round-off errors, while very desirable in general, can be omitted at some risk to the accuracy of the solution. When performing Gauss elimination by hand, decisions about scaling and pivoting can be made on a case-by-case basis. When writing a general-purpose computer program to apply Gauss elimination to arbitrary systems of equations, scaling and pivoting are an absolute necessity. Example 1.10 in Section 1.3 illustrates the complete Gauss elimination process.

When large systems of equations are solved on a computer, the pivoting step is generally implemented by simply keeping track of the order of the rows as they are interchanged, not by actually interchanging rows, a time-consuming and unnecessary operation. This is accomplished by using an order vector, **o**, whose elements denote the order in which the rows of the augmented coefficient matrix are to be processed. When a row interchange is required, instead of actually interchanging the two rows of elements, the corresponding elements of the order vector are interchanged. The rows of the augmented matrix are processed in the order indicated by the order vector during both the elimination step and the back substitution step.

As an example, consider the second part of Example 1.10. The order vector has the initial value $\mathbf{o}^T = (1\ 2\ 3)$. After scaling, rows 1 and 3 are to be interchanged. Instead of actually interchanging these rows as done in Example 1.10, the corresponding elements of the order vector are changed to yield $\mathbf{o}^T = (3\ 2\ 1)$. The first elimination step then uses the third row to eliminate x_1 from the second and first rows. Pivoting is not required for the second elimination step, so the order vector is unchanged, and the second row is used to eliminate x_2 from the first row. Back substitution is then performed in the row order 1, 2, 3. This procedure saves computer time for large systems of equations, but at the expense of a slightly more complicated program.

The number of multiplications and divisions for Gauss elimination for one **b** vector is approximately $N = (n^3/3) + n^2 - (n/3)$. For $n = 10$, $N = 430$, and for $n = 100$, $N = 343,300$. This is a considerable reduction compared to Cramer's rule.

The Gauss elimination procedure, in a format suitable for programming on a digital computer, is summarized as follows:

1. Augment the $n \times n$ **A** matrix with the right-hand-side vector **b** (or vectors, say, m in number) to obtain the $n \times (n + m)$ augmented matrix.
2. If appropriate, scale the rows of the augmented **A** matrix.

3. Search for the element of largest magnitude in the first column and pivot (interchange rows) to put that coefficient into the a_{11} pivot position. This step is actually accomplished by interchanging the corresponding elements of the order vector.
4. Apply the elimination procedure to rows 2 to n to create zeros in the first column below the pivot element. Do not actually calculate the zeros in column 1. The modified elements in each column from 2 to $n+m$ for rows 2 to n must be computed and stored in place of the original elements using the equation

$$a_{ij}^* = a_{ij} - \frac{a_{i1}}{a_{11}} a_{1j} \qquad (i = 2, \ldots, n; j = 2, \ldots, n + m) \tag{1.101}$$

5. Repeats steps 3 and 4 for rows 3 to n. At the conclusion of this step, the original **A** matrix, in pivoted form, is upper triangular.
6. Solve for **x** using back substitution. If more than one **b** vector is present, solve for the corresponding **x** vectors one at a time. Thus,

$$x_n = \frac{a_{n,n+1}^*}{a_{nn}^*} \tag{1.102a}$$

$$x_i = \frac{a_{i,n+1}^* - \sum_{j=i+1}^{n} a_{ij}^* x_j}{a_{ii}^*} \qquad (i = n-1, n-2, \ldots, 1) \tag{1.102b}$$

Gauss–Jordan Elimination

Gauss–Jordan elimination is a variation of Gauss elimination in which the elements above the major diagonal are eliminated (made zero) as well as the elements below the major diagonal. The **A** matrix is transformed to a diagonal matrix. The rows are usually scaled to yield unity diagonal elements, which transforms the **A** matrix to the identity matrix **I**. The transformed **b** vector is then the solution vector **x**. Gauss–Jordan elimination can be used for single or multiple **b** vectors.

The number of multiplications and divisions for Gauss–Jordan elimination is approximately $N = (n^3/2) + n^2 - (n/2)$, which is approximately 50 percent larger than for Gauss elimination. Consequently, Gauss elimination is preferred.

Example 1.11. Gauss–Jordan elimination. Rework Example 1.7, using Gauss–Jordan elimination. The augmented **A** matrix is [see Eq. (1.81)]

$$\left[\begin{array}{rrr|r} 5 & 2 & 1 & 3 \\ 4 & 1 & -1 & -3 \\ -2 & 3 & -3 & 5 \end{array}\right] \tag{1.103}$$

Scaling row 1 to give $a_{11} = 1$, then applying row reduction below row 1, gives

$$\left[\begin{array}{rrr|r} 1 & 0.4 & 0.2 & 0.6 \\ 4 & 1 & -1 & -3 \\ -2 & 3 & -3 & 5 \end{array}\right] \begin{array}{l} \\ R_2 - (4)R_1 \\ R_3 - (-2)R_1 \end{array} \tag{1.104}$$

$$\left[\begin{array}{ccc|c} 1 & 0.4 & 0.2 & 0.6 \\ 0 & -0.6 & -1.8 & -5.4 \\ 0 & 3.8 & -2.6 & 6.2 \end{array}\right] \tag{1.105}$$

Scaling row 2 to give $a_{22} = 1$, then applying row reduction both above and below row 2, yields

$$\left[\begin{array}{ccc|c} 1 & 0.4 & 0.2 & 0.6 \\ 0 & 1 & 3 & 9 \\ 0 & 3.8 & -2.6 & 6.2 \end{array}\right] \begin{matrix} R_1 - (0.4)R_2 \\ \\ R_3 - (3.8)R_2 \end{matrix} \tag{1.106}$$

$$\left[\begin{array}{ccc|c} 1 & 0 & -1 & -3 \\ 0 & 1 & 3 & 9 \\ 0 & 0 & -14 & -28 \end{array}\right] \tag{1.107}$$

Scaling row 3 to give $a_{33} = 1$, then applying row reduction above row 3, completes the process.

$$\left[\begin{array}{ccc|c} 1 & 0 & -1 & -3 \\ 0 & 1 & 3 & 9 \\ 0 & 0 & 1 & 2 \end{array}\right] \begin{matrix} R_1 - (-1)R_3 \\ R_2 - (3)R_3 \\ \\ \end{matrix} \tag{1.108}$$

The **A** matrix has been transformed to the identity matrix **I**, and the **b** vector has been transformed to the solution vector **x**. Thus,

$$\left[\begin{array}{ccc|c} 1 & 0 & 0 & -1 \\ 0 & 1 & 0 & 3 \\ 0 & 0 & 1 & 2 \end{array}\right] \begin{matrix} x_1 = -1 \\ x_2 = 3 \\ x_3 = 2 \end{matrix} \tag{1.109}$$

The primary use of Gauss–Jordan elimination is for obtaining the inverse of a matrix. The inverse of a square matrix **A** is the matrix $\mathbf{A}^{-1}$ such that $\mathbf{AA}^{-1} = \mathbf{I} = \mathbf{A}^{-1}\mathbf{A}$. Gauss–Jordan elimination can be used to evaluate the inverse of matrix **A** by augmenting **A** with the identity matrix **I** and applying the Gauss–Jordan procedure. The transformed **A** matrix is the identity matrix **I**, and the transformed identity matrix is the matrix inverse $\mathbf{A}^{-1}$. Thus, applying Gauss–Jordan elimination yields

$$\left[\mathbf{A} \;\vdots\; \mathbf{I}\right] \rightarrow \left[\mathbf{I} \;\vdots\; \mathbf{A}^{-1}\right] \tag{1.110}$$

The Gauss–Jordan elimination procedure, in a format suitable for programming on a digital computer, can be developed by modifying the Gauss elimination procedure presented in the preceding subsection. Step 1 is changed to augment the $n \times n$ **A** matrix with the $n \times n$ identity matrix **I**. Steps 2 and 3 of the procedure are the same. Before performing Step 4, the pivot element is scaled to unity by dividing all elements by the pivot element. Step 5 is expanded to perform elimination above the pivot element as well as below the pivot element. At the conclusion of step 5, the **A** matrix has been transformed to the identity matrix **I**, and the original identity matrix **I** has been transformed to the matrix inverse $\mathbf{A}^{-1}$.

Example 1.12. Matrix inverse by Gauss–Jordan elimination. Evaluate the inverse of the matrix **A** presented in Example 1.7. First, augment the matrix **A** with the identity matrix **I**. Thus,

$$[\mathbf{A} \,\vdots\, \mathbf{I}] = \left[\begin{array}{rrr|rrr} 5 & 2 & 1 & 1 & 0 & 0 \\ 4 & 1 & -1 & 0 & 1 & 0 \\ -2 & 3 & -3 & 0 & 0 & 1 \end{array}\right] \tag{1.111}$$

Performing Gauss–Jordan elimination transforms Eq. (1.111) to

$$\left[\begin{array}{rrr|rrr} 1 & 0 & 0 & 0 & \frac{9}{42} & -\frac{1}{14} \\ 0 & 1 & 0 & \frac{1}{3} & -\frac{13}{42} & \frac{3}{14} \\ 0 & 0 & 1 & \frac{1}{3} & -\frac{19}{42} & -\frac{1}{14} \end{array}\right] \tag{1.112}$$

from which

$$\mathbf{A}^{-1} = \frac{1}{42}\begin{bmatrix} 0 & 9 & -3 \\ 14 & -13 & 9 \\ 14 & -19 & -3 \end{bmatrix} \tag{1.113}$$

Multiplying **A** by $\mathbf{A}^{-1}$ yields the identity matrix **I**, thus verifying the computations.

The Matrix Inverse Method

Systems of linear algebraic equations can be solved using the inverse of the coefficient matrix. Consider the system of equations

$$\mathbf{Ax} = \mathbf{b} \tag{1.114}$$

Multiplying Eq. (1.114) by $\mathbf{A}^{-1}$ yields

$$\mathbf{A}^{-1}\mathbf{Ax} = \mathbf{Ix} = \mathbf{x} = \mathbf{A}^{-1}\mathbf{b} \tag{1.115}$$

from which

$$\boxed{\mathbf{x} = \mathbf{A}^{-1}\mathbf{b}} \tag{1.116}$$

Thus, when the matrix inverse $\mathbf{A}^{-1}$ of the coefficient matrix **A** is known, the solution vector **x** is simply the product of the matrix inverse $\mathbf{A}^{-1}$ and the right-hand-side vector **b**. Not all matrices have inverses. Singular matrices, that is, matrices whose determinant is zero, do not have inverses. The corresponding system of equations does not have a unique solution. The simplest method, and the recommended method for finding the inverse of a matrix is to perform Gauss–Jordan elimination on the matrix augmented with the identity matrix of the same size.

Example 1.13. The matrix inverse method. Solve the linear system considered in Example 1.7, using the matrix inverse method. The matrix inverse $\mathbf{A}^{-1}$ of the coefficient matrix **A** for that linear system is evaluated in Example 1.12. Multiplying $\mathbf{A}^{-1}$ by the nonhomogeneous vector **b** from Example 1.7 gives

$$\mathbf{A}^{-1}\mathbf{b} = \frac{1}{42}\begin{bmatrix} 0 & 9 & -3 \\ 14 & -13 & 9 \\ 14 & -19 & -3 \end{bmatrix}\begin{bmatrix} 3 \\ -3 \\ 5 \end{bmatrix} = \mathbf{x} \tag{1.117}$$

Performing the matrix multiplication yields

$$x_1 = \frac{1}{42}\Big((0)(3) + (9)(-3) + (-3)(5)\Big) = -1 \tag{1.118a}$$

$$x_2 = \frac{1}{42}\Big((14)(3) + (-13)(-3) + (9)(5)\Big) = 3 \tag{1.118b}$$

$$x_3 = \frac{1}{42}\Big((14)(3) + (-19)(-3) + (-3)(5)\Big) = 2 \tag{1.118c}$$

Determinants

The evaluation of determinants by the cofactor method is discussed in Section 1.2 and illustrated in Example 1.4. Approximately $N = (n-1)n!$ multiplications are required to evaluate the determinant of an $n \times n$ matrix by the cofactor method. For $n = 10$, $N = 32,659,000$. Evaluation of the determinants of large matrices by the cofactor method is prohibitively expensive, if not impossible. Fortunately, determinants can be evaluated much more efficiently by a variation of the elimination method.

First, consider the upper triangular matrix

$$\mathbf{A} = \begin{bmatrix} a_{11} & a_{12} & a_{13} & \cdots & a_{1n} \\ 0 & a_{22} & a_{23} & \cdots & a_{2n} \\ 0 & 0 & a_{33} & \cdots & a_{3n} \\ \vdots & \vdots & \vdots & \ddots & \vdots \\ 0 & 0 & 0 & \cdots & a_{nn} \end{bmatrix} \tag{1.119}$$

Expanding the determinant of **A** by cofactors down the first column gives a_{11} times the $(n-1) \times (n-1)$ determinant that has a_{22} as its first element in its first column and the remaining elements in its first column all zero. Expanding that determinant by cofactors down its first column yields a_{22} times the $(n-2)\times(n-2)$ determinant that has a_{33} as its first element in its first column and the remaining elements all zero. Continuing in this manner yields the result that the determinant of an upper triangular matrix (or a lower triangular matrix) is simply the product of the elements on the major diagonal. Thus,

$$|\mathbf{A}| = \prod_{i=1}^{n} a_{ii} \tag{1.120}$$

This result suggests the use of elimination to triangularize a general square matrix, then to evaluate its determinant using Eq. (1.120). This procedure works exactly as stated if no pivoting or scaling is used. When scaling and pivoting are used, the value of the determinant is changed, but in a predictable manner, so elimination can also be used with scaling and pivoting to evaluate determinants. The row operations presented in this section must be modified as follows to use elimination for the evaluation of determinants.

1. Multiplying a row by a constant multiplies the determinant by that constant.
2. Interchanging any two rows changes the sign of the determinant. Thus, an even number of row interchanges does not change the sign of the determinant, whereas an odd number of row interchanges changes the sign of the determinant.
3. Any row may be added to the multiple of any other row without changing the value of the determinant.

The modified elimination method based on the above row operations is an efficient way to evaluate the determinant of a matrix. The number of multiplications required is approximately $N = n^3 + n^2 - n$, which is orders and orders of magnitude less effort than the $N = (n-1)n!$ multiplications required by the cofactor method.

Example 1.14. Determinant evaluation by the elimination method. Rework Example 1.4 using the elimination method. Recall Eq. (1.53):

$$\mathbf{A} = \begin{bmatrix} 5 & 2 & 1 \\ 4 & 1 & -1 \\ -2 & 3 & -3 \end{bmatrix} \tag{1.121}$$

Scaling the matrix yields

$$(5)(4)(3)\begin{bmatrix} 1 & \frac{2}{5} & \frac{1}{5} \\ 1 & \frac{1}{4} & -\frac{1}{4} \\ -\frac{2}{3} & 1 & -1 \end{bmatrix} \begin{matrix} \\ R_2 - (1)R_1 \\ R_3 - \left(-\frac{2}{3}\right)R_1 \end{matrix} \tag{1.122}$$

Pivoting is not required. Performing the indicated row operations yields

$$60\begin{bmatrix} 1 & \frac{2}{5} & \frac{1}{5} \\ 0 & -\frac{3}{20} & -\frac{9}{20} \\ 0 & \frac{19}{15} & -\frac{13}{14} \end{bmatrix} \tag{1.123}$$

Pivoting is required. Interchanging the second and third rows gives

$$60\begin{bmatrix} 1 & \frac{2}{5} & \frac{1}{5} \\ 0 & \frac{19}{15} & -\frac{13}{15} \\ 0 & -\frac{3}{20} & -\frac{9}{20} \end{bmatrix} \begin{matrix} \\ \\ R_3 - \left(-\frac{9}{76}\right)R_2 \end{matrix} \tag{1.124}$$

Performing the indicated row operation yields

$$60\begin{bmatrix} 1 & \frac{2}{5} & \frac{1}{5} \\ 0 & \frac{19}{15} & -\frac{13}{15} \\ 0 & 0 & -\frac{42}{76} \end{bmatrix} \tag{1.125}$$

Multiplying the scaling factor 60 by the product of the elements on the major diagonal, and multiplying by $(-1)^1$ because of the single row interchange from Eq. (1.123) to (1.124), yields the value of $|\mathbf{A}|$:

$$|\mathbf{A}| = (-1)^1(60)(1)\left(\frac{19}{15}\right)\left(-\frac{42}{76}\right) = 42 \tag{1.126}$$

Ill-Conditioned Systems of Equations

No discussion of the solution of systems of linear algebraic equations would be complete without at least a brief introduction to the problem of *ill-conditioning*. Consider the system of two equations presented in Section 1.1 and illustrated in Fig. 1.1. The situations illustrated by Figs. 1.1*b* and 1.1*c*, two noncoincident straight lines and two coincident straight lines, respectively, correspond to the situation where the determinant of the coefficient matrix is zero. From Cramer's rule, it is obvious that no unique solution exists. When the determinant of the coefficient matrix is zero, the system of equations is said to be *singular*. This is the ultimate limit of ill-conditioning.

A less obvious, although equally serious, problem occurs when the determinant of the coefficient matrix is very small. In that case, round-off errors in the computing device can completely destroy the accuracy of the solution. Recall that any nonsingular square matrix can be triangularized. The determinant of the coefficient matrix is then simply the product of the diagonal elements, accounting for scaling and pivoting effects (see the subsection on "Determinants"). If any of the diagonal elements are small, the value of the determinant will be small. This situation is also an instance of ill-conditioning.

The effects of ill-conditioning can be minimized in several ways. Scaling and pivoting clearly reduce the effects of round-off and, thus, the effects of ill-conditioning. Row pivoting is quite straightforward. In some severe cases, both row and column pivoting may be required. Carrying more significant figures in the calculations obviously reduces the effects of ill-conditioning. Double-precision arithmetic on electronic digital computers is one way to increase the number of significant figures. Using computers that carry more significant figures in their basic arithmetic operations is another way to increase the number of significant figures.

There is no way to avoid the problems of ill-conditioning. Ill-conditioning is a property of the coefficient matrix. If a system of equations is ill-conditioned, it may require special handling to obtain an acceptable solution. In the limiting case of a singular matrix, no unique solution exists. One must always be aware of the possible occurrence of ill-conditioning when solving systems of linear algebraic equations.

1.4 LU DECOMPOSITION

Matrices (like scalars) can be decomposed, or factored, into the product of two other matrices (or scalars) in an infinite number of ways. Thus,

$$\mathbf{A} = \mathbf{BC} \tag{1.127}$$

When **B** and **C** are lower triangular and upper triangular, respectively, Eq. (1.127) becomes

$$\mathbf{A} = \mathbf{LU} \tag{1.128}$$

Specifying the diagonal elements of either **L** or **U** makes the factoring unique. Matrix factoring, or decomposition, can be used to reduce the work involved in Gauss elimination when multiple unknown **b** vectors are to be considered. The procedure based on unity elements on the major diagonal of **L** is called the *Doolittle* method. The procedure based on unity elements on the major diagonal of **U** is called the *Crout* method. A third method, called the *Cholesky* method, is based on the constraint that $\ell_{ii} = u_{ii}$.

Consider the linear system $\mathbf{Ax} = \mathbf{b}$. Let **A** be decomposed into the product of **L** and **U**, as illustrated in Eq. (1.128). The linear system became

$$\mathbf{LUx} = \mathbf{b} \tag{1.129}$$

Multiplying Eq. (1.129) by the inverse of **L**, $\mathbf{L}^{-1}$, gives

$$\mathbf{L}^{-1}\mathbf{LUx} = \mathbf{L}^{-1}\mathbf{b} \tag{1.130}$$

The left-hand side of Eq. (1.130) can be rearranged as

$$\mathbf{L}^{-1}\mathbf{LUx} = (\mathbf{L}^{-1}\mathbf{L})\mathbf{Ux} = \mathbf{IUx} = \mathbf{Ux} \tag{1.131}$$

The right-hand side of Eq. (1.130) defines the column vector $\mathbf{b}'$:

$$\mathbf{L}^{-1}\mathbf{b} = \mathbf{b}' \tag{1.132}$$

Substituting Eqs. (1.131) and (1.132) into Eq. (1.130) gives

$$\boxed{\mathbf{Ux} = \mathbf{b}'} \tag{1.133}$$

Multiplying Eq. (1.132) by **L** yields

$$\mathbf{LL}^{-1}\mathbf{b} = \mathbf{Ib} = \mathbf{b} = \mathbf{Lb}' \tag{1.134}$$

which yields

$$\boxed{\mathbf{Lb}' = \mathbf{b}} \tag{1.135}$$

Equation (1.135) is used to transform the **b** vector into the $\mathbf{b}'$ vector, and Eq. (1.133) is used to determine the solution vector **x**. Since Eq. (1.135) is lower triangular, forward substitution (analogous to back substitution, which is presented in Section 1.3) is used to solve for $\mathbf{b}'$. Since Eq. (1.133) is upper triangular, back substitution is used to solve for **x**.

The Doolittle Method

In the Doolittle method, the **U** matrix is the upper triangular matrix obtained by Gauss elimination, described in Section 1.3, and the **L** matrix is the lower triangular matrix containing the multipliers used in the Gauss elimination process as the elements below the diagonal with unity elements on the major diagonal. Equation (1.135) applies the steps performed in the triangularization of **A** to **U** to the **b** vector to transform **b** to **b**′. Equation (1.133) is simply the back substitution step of the Gauss elimination method. Consequently, once **L** and **U** have been determined, any **b** vector can be considered at any later time, and the corresponding solution vector **x** can be obtained simply by solving Eqs. (1.135) and (1.133), in that order.

Example 1.15. The Doolittle LU decomposition method. Solve Example 1.7 using the Doolittle method. The first step is to determine the **L** and **U** matrices. The **U** matrix is simply the upper triangular matrix determined by the Gauss elimination procedure in Example 1.7. The **L** matrix is simply the record of the elimination multipliers used to transform **A** to **U**. These multipliers are the numbers in parentheses in the row operations indicated in Eqs. (1.82) and (1.83) in Example 1.7. Thus, **L** and **U** are given by

$$\mathbf{L} = \begin{bmatrix} 1 & 0 & 0 \\ \frac{4}{5} & 1 & 0 \\ -\frac{2}{5} & -\frac{19}{3} & 1 \end{bmatrix} \quad \text{and} \quad \mathbf{U} = \begin{bmatrix} 5 & 2 & 1 \\ 0 & -\frac{3}{5} & -\frac{9}{5} \\ 0 & 0 & -14 \end{bmatrix} \tag{1.136}$$

Consider the first **b** vector from Example 1.8: $\mathbf{b}_1^T = (3 \ -3 \ 5)$. Equation (1.135) gives

$$\begin{bmatrix} 1 & 0 & 0 \\ \frac{4}{5} & 1 & 0 \\ -\frac{2}{5} & -\frac{19}{3} & 1 \end{bmatrix} \begin{bmatrix} b_1' \\ b_2' \\ b_3' \end{bmatrix} = \begin{bmatrix} 3 \\ -3 \\ 5 \end{bmatrix} \tag{1.137}$$

Performing forward substitution yields

$$b_1' = 3 \tag{1.138a}$$

$$b_2' = -3 - \left(\frac{4}{5}\right)(3) = -\frac{27}{5} \tag{1.138b}$$

$$b_3' = 5 - \left(-\frac{2}{5}\right)(3) - \left(-\frac{19}{3}\right)\left(-\frac{27}{5}\right) = -28 \tag{1.138c}$$

The **b**′ vector is simply the transformed **b** vector determined in Eq. (1.86). Equation (1.133) gives

$$\begin{bmatrix} 5 & 2 & 1 \\ 0 & -\frac{3}{5} & -\frac{9}{5} \\ 0 & 0 & -14 \end{bmatrix} \begin{bmatrix} x_1 \\ x_2 \\ x_3 \end{bmatrix} = \begin{bmatrix} 3 \\ -\frac{27}{5} \\ -28 \end{bmatrix} \tag{1.139}$$

Performing back substitution yields $\mathbf{x}_1^T = (-1 \ 3 \ 2)$. Repeating the process for $\mathbf{b}_2^T = (2 \ -2 \ 8)$ yields

$$\begin{bmatrix} 1 & 0 & 0 \\ \frac{4}{5} & 1 & 0 \\ -\frac{2}{5} & -\frac{19}{3} & 1 \end{bmatrix} \begin{bmatrix} b_1' \\ b_2' \\ b_3' \end{bmatrix} = \begin{bmatrix} 2 \\ -2 \\ 8 \end{bmatrix} \begin{matrix} b_1' = 2 \\ b_2' = -\frac{18}{5} \\ b_3' = -14 \end{matrix} \tag{1.140}$$

$$\begin{bmatrix} 5 & 2 & 1 \\ 0 & -\frac{3}{5} & -\frac{9}{5} \\ 0 & 0 & -14 \end{bmatrix} \begin{bmatrix} x_1 \\ x_2 \\ x_3 \end{bmatrix} = \begin{bmatrix} 2 \\ -\frac{18}{5} \\ -14 \end{bmatrix} \begin{matrix} x_1 = -1 \\ x_2 = 3 \\ x_3 = 1 \end{matrix} \tag{1.141}$$

When scaling and pivoting are used with **LU** decomposition methods, it is necessary to keep track of the scale factors in a scale vector **s** and the row order in an order vector **o**. When the rows in **A** are scaled during the elimination step, the scale factors are stored in the corresponding elements of the scale vector **s**. When the rows of **A** are interchanged during the elimination process, the corresponding elements of the order vector **o** are interchanged. When a new **b** vector is considered, it is first scaled by the elements of the scale vector **s**, then processed in the order corresponding to the elements of the order vector **o**.

The major advantage of **LU** decomposition methods is their efficiency when multiple unknown **b** vectors must be considered. The number of multiplications and divisions required by the complete Gauss elimination method is $N = (n^3/3) + n^2 - (n/3)$. The forward substitution step required to solve $\mathbf{Lb}' = \mathbf{b}$ requires $N = n^2 - (n/2)$ operations, and the back substitution step required to solve $\mathbf{Ux} = \mathbf{b}'$ requires $N = n^2 + n/2$ operations. Thus, the total number of multiplications and divisions required by **LU** decomposition, after **L** and **U** have been determined, is $2n^2$, which is much less work than required by Gauss elimination, especially for large systems.

The Doolittle method, in a format suitable for programming for a digital computer, is summarized as follows:

1. Define the scale vector $\mathbf{s}^{\mathrm{T}} = (1.0\ 1.0\ \ldots\ 1.0)$ and the order vector $\mathbf{o}^{\mathrm{T}} = (1\ 2\ \ldots\ n)$.
2. Perform steps 2 to 5 of the Gauss elimination procedure presented in Section 1.3. Store the scale factors in the scale vector **s** and the pivoting information in the order vector **o**. Store the row elimination multipliers in the locations of the eliminated elements. The results of this step are the **L** and **U** matrices.
3. If scaling is used, scale the **b** vector using the scale factors in the scale vector **s**.
4. Reorder the **b** vector (unscaled or scaled) into the order specified by the elements of the order vector **o**.
5. Compute the $\mathbf{b}'$ vector using forward substitution:

$$b_i' = b_i = \sum_{k=1}^{i-1} \ell_{ik} b_k' \qquad (i = 2, \ldots, n) \tag{1.142}$$

   where ℓ_{ik} are the elements of the **L** matrix.
6. Compute the **x** vector using back substitution:

$$x_i = \frac{b_i - \sum\limits_{k=i+1}^{n} u_{ik} x_k}{u_{ii}} \qquad (i = n-1, n-2, \ldots, 1) \tag{1.143}$$

   where u_{ii} are the elements of the **U** matrix.

The Crout Method

The Crout method, in which **U** has unity elements on the major diagonal, is similar to the Doolittle method in all other aspects. The **L** and **U** matrices are obtained by expanding the matrix equation **A** = **LU** term by term to determine the elements of the **L** and **U** matrices. The following results are obtained:

$$\ell_{i1} = a_{i1} \qquad (i = 1, 2, \ldots, n) \tag{1.144a}$$

$$u_{1j} = \frac{a_{1j}}{\ell_{11}} \qquad (j = 1, 2, \ldots, n) \tag{1.144b}$$

$$\ell_{ij} = a_{ij} - \sum_{k=1}^{j-1} \ell_{ik} u_{kj} \qquad (j \leq i, i = 2, 3, \ldots, n) \tag{1.144c}$$

$$u_{ij} = \frac{a_{ij} - \sum_{k=1}^{i-1} \ell_{ik} u_{kj}}{\ell_{ii}} \qquad (i < j, j = 3, 4, \ldots, n) \tag{1.144d}$$

The computations proceed by calculating a column of **L** followed by a row of **U**. In this manner the values of ℓ_{ij} needed to compute the next row of values of u_{ij} are computed before they are needed, and the values of u_{ij} needed to compute the next column of values of ℓ_{ij} are computed before they are needed. The elements of the **L** and **U** matrices can be stored in the places of the elements of the **A** matrix as they are computed. Scaling (if appropriate) and pivoting are implemented using the scale vector **s** and the order vector **o**, as described for the Doolittle method.

The Doolittle method is a straightforward adaptation of the Gauss elimination method. The Crout method, as specified by Eqs. (1.144), is somewhat more involved to understand and to program for digital computer implementation. Nevertheless, the majority of textbooks and the majority of programs in computer libraries are based on the Crout method. They are in every way equivalent. Due to the more straightforward logic of the Doolittle method, it is the method of choice in this book.

1.5 TRIDIAGONAL SYSTEMS OF EQUATIONS

When a large system of equations has a special pattern, such as a tridiagonal pattern, it is usually worthwhile to develop special methods for that unique pattern. There are a number of direct methods for solving systems of linear equations that have special patterns in the coefficient matrix. These methods are generally very efficient in computer time and storage. Such methods should be considered when the coefficient matrix fits the required pattern and when conserving computer storage or execution time is important. One algorithm that deserves special attention is the algorithm for tridiagonal matrices, often referred to as the Thomas (1949) algorithm. Large tridiagonal systems arise naturally in a number of problems, especially in the numerical solution of differential equations by implicit methods. Consequently, the Thomas algorithm has found a large number of applications.

The Thomas Algorithm

To derive the Thomas algorithm, we will apply the Gauss elimination procedure to a tridiagonal matrix, modifying the procedure to eliminate all unnecessary computations involving zeros. Consider the matrix equation

$$\mathbf{T}\mathbf{x} = \mathbf{b} \tag{1.145a}$$

where $\mathbf{T}$ is a tridiagonal matrix. Augmenting $\mathbf{T}$ with $\mathbf{b}$ and writing in expanded form gives

$$\left[\begin{array}{cccccccccc|c} a_{11} & a_{12} & 0 & 0 & 0 & \cdots & 0 & 0 & 0 & & b_1 \\ a_{21} & a_{22} & a_{23} & 0 & 0 & \cdots & 0 & 0 & 0 & & b_2 \\ 0 & a_{32} & a_{33} & a_{34} & 0 & \cdots & 0 & 0 & 0 & & b_3 \\ 0 & 0 & a_{43} & a_{44} & a_{45} & \cdots & 0 & 0 & 0 & & b_4 \\ \vdots & \vdots & \vdots & \vdots & \vdots & \ddots & \vdots & \vdots & \vdots & & \vdots \\ 0 & 0 & 0 & 0 & 0 & \cdots & a_{n-1,n-2} & a_{n-1,n-1} & a_{n-1,n} & & b_{n-1} \\ 0 & 0 & 0 & 0 & 0 & \cdots & 0 & a_{n,n-1} & a_{n,n} & & b_n \end{array}\right] \tag{1.145b}$$

Since all the elements of column 1 below row 2 are already zero, the only element to be eliminated in row 2 is a_{21}. Thus, replace row 2 by $R_2 - (a_{21}/a_{11})R_1$. Row 2 becomes

$$\left[0 \; \left(a_{22} - \frac{a_{21}}{a_{11}} a_{12}\right) \; a_{23} \; 0 \; 0 \; \cdots \; 0 \; 0 \; 0 \; \left(b_2 - \frac{a_{21}}{a_{11}} b_1\right)\right] \tag{1.145c}$$

Similarly, only a_{32} in column 2 must be eliminated from row 3, only a_{43} in column 3 must be eliminated from row 4, and so on. The eliminated element itself does not need to be calculated. In fact, storing the elimination multipliers in place of the eliminated elements allows this procedure to be used as an **LU** decomposition method. Only the diagonal element in each row and the corresponding component of the **b** vector are affected by the elimination. Thus, the elimination step involves only $2n$ multiplicative operations to place $\mathbf{T}$ in upper triangular form.

The $n \times n$ tridiagonal matrix $\mathbf{T}$ can be stored as an $n \times 3$ matrix, since there is no need to store the zeros. For simplicity, the tridiagonal matrix $\mathbf{T}$ will be stored as the three singly subscripted column vectors ℓ, $\mathbf{d}$, and $\mathbf{u}$. The elements $d_1, d_2, \ldots, d_n$ correspond to the major diagonal elements a_{ii} of the full matrix $\mathbf{T}$. The elements $\ell_2, \ell_3, \ldots, \ell_n$ correspond to the elements below the major diagonal of $\mathbf{T}$, that is, the $a_{i,i-1}$ elements of the full $\mathbf{T}$ matrix. The elements $u_1, u_2, \ldots, u_{n-1}$ correspond to the elements above the major diagonal of $\mathbf{T}$, that is, the $a_{i,i+1}$ elements in the full $\mathbf{T}$ matrix. The elements ℓ_1 and u_n do not exist.

Equation (1.145*a*), when expressed in terms of the ℓ, **d**, and **u** column vectors, becomes

$$\begin{bmatrix} d_1 & u_1 & 0 & 0 & 0 & \cdots & 0 & 0 & 0 \\ \ell_2 & d_2 & u_2 & 0 & 0 & \cdots & 0 & 0 & 0 \\ 0 & \ell_3 & d_3 & u_3 & 0 & \cdots & 0 & 0 & 0 \\ 0 & 0 & \ell_4 & d_4 & u_4 & \cdots & 0 & 0 & 0 \\ \vdots & \vdots & \vdots & \vdots & \vdots & \ddots & \vdots & \vdots & \vdots \\ 0 & 0 & 0 & 0 & 0 & \cdots & \ell_{n-1} & d_{n-1} & u_{n-1} \\ 0 & 0 & 0 & 0 & 0 & \cdots & 0 & \ell_n & d_n \end{bmatrix} \left[x_i\right] = \left[b_i\right] \tag{1.146}$$

Augmenting the **T** matrix by the **b** vector and performing the row reduction operations yields

$$\left[\begin{array}{ccccccccc|c} d_1 & u_1 & 0 & 0 & 0 & \cdots & 0 & 0 & 0 & b_1 \\ \ell_2 & d_2 & u_2 & 0 & 0 & \cdots & 0 & 0 & 0 & b_2 \\ 0 & \ell_3 & d_3 & u_3 & 0 & \cdots & 0 & 0 & 0 & b_3 \\ 0 & 0 & \ell_4 & d_4 & u_4 & \cdots & 0 & 0 & 0 & b_4 \\ \vdots & \vdots & \vdots & \vdots & \vdots & \ddots & \vdots & \vdots & \vdots & \vdots \\ 0 & 0 & 0 & 0 & 0 & \cdots & \ell_{n-1} & d_{n-1} & u_{n-1} & b_{n-1} \\ 0 & 0 & 0 & 0 & 0 & \cdots & 0 & \ell_n & d_n & b_n \end{array}\right] \begin{matrix} R_2 - \dfrac{\ell_2}{d_1} R_1 \\ \\ \\ \\ \\ \\ \\ \end{matrix} \tag{1.147a}$$

$$\left[\begin{array}{ccccccccc|c} d_1 & u_1 & 0 & 0 & 0 & \cdots & 0 & 0 & 0 & b_1 \\ (\ell_2/d_1) & d_2' & u_2 & 0 & 0 & \cdots & 0 & 0 & 0 & b_2' \\ 0 & \ell_3 & d_3 & u_3 & 0 & \cdots & 0 & 0 & 0 & b_3 \\ 0 & 0 & \ell_4 & d_4 & u_4 & \cdots & 0 & 0 & 0 & b_4 \\ \vdots & \vdots & \vdots & \vdots & \vdots & \ddots & \vdots & \vdots & \vdots & \vdots \\ 0 & 0 & 0 & 0 & 0 & \cdots & \ell_{n-1} & d_{n-1} & u_{n-1} & b_{n-1} \\ 0 & 0 & 0 & 0 & 0 & \cdots & 0 & \ell_n & d_n & b_n \end{array}\right] \begin{matrix} \\ \\ R_3 - \dfrac{\ell_3}{d_2'} R_2 \\ \\ \\ \\ \\ \end{matrix} \tag{1.147b}$$

$$\left[\begin{array}{ccccccccc|c} d_1 & u_1 & 0 & 0 & 0 & \cdots & 0 & 0 & 0 & b_1 \\ (\ell_2/d_1) & d_2' & u_2 & 0 & 0 & \cdots & 0 & 0 & 0 & b_2' \\ 0 & (\ell_3/d_2') & d_3' & u_3 & 0 & \cdots & 0 & 0 & 0 & b_3' \\ 0 & 0 & \ell_4 & d_4 & u_4 & \cdots & 0 & 0 & 0 & b_4 \\ \vdots & \vdots & \vdots & \vdots & \vdots & \ddots & \vdots & \vdots & \vdots & \vdots \\ 0 & 0 & 0 & 0 & 0 & \cdots & \ell_{n-1} & d_{n-1} & u_{n-1} & b_{n-1} \\ 0 & 0 & 0 & 0 & 0 & \cdots & 0 & \ell_n & d_n & b_n \end{array}\right] \begin{matrix} \\ \\ \\ R_4 - \left(\dfrac{\ell_4}{d_3'}\right) R_3 \\ \\ \\ \\ \end{matrix} \tag{1.147c}$$

This procedure is repeated until ℓ_n has been eliminated from row n.

The first row of **T** is unchanged. All the elements of ℓ are reduced to zero exactly, without calculation. The row elimination multipliers, (ℓ_i/d_{i-1}'), can be stored in place of the elements of ℓ for future use in an **LU** method. Since the elements above the elements of **u** are all zero, none of the elements of **u** are changed, so they are not recalculated. Consequently, the only terms that need to be recalculated in the **T** matrix are the elements of **d**. The elements of the **b** vector, of course, must be recalculated, corresponding to the row operations indicated in Eqs. (1.147). The upper triangularized **T** matrix and the transformed **b** vector become

$$\left[\begin{array}{cccccccccc|c} d_1 & u_1 & 0 & 0 & 0 & \cdots & 0 & 0 & 0 & b_1 \\ (\ell_2/d_1) & d_2' & u_2 & 0 & 0 & \cdots & 0 & 0 & 0 & b_2' \\ 0 & (\ell_3/d_2') & d_3' & u_3 & 0 & \cdots & 0 & 0 & 0 & b_3' \\ 0 & 0 & (\ell_4/d_3') & d_4' & u_4 & \cdots & 0 & 0 & 0 & b_4' \\ \vdots & \vdots & \vdots & \vdots & \vdots & \ddots & \vdots & \vdots & \vdots & \vdots \\ 0 & 0 & 0 & 0 & 0 & \cdots & (\ell_{n-1}/d_{n-2}') & d_{n-1}' & u_{n-1} & b_{n-1}' \\ 0 & 0 & 0 & 0 & 0 & \cdots & 0 & (\ell_n/d_{n-1}') & d_n' & b_n' \end{array}\right] \tag{1.148}$$

The row reduction equations are

$$d_i' = d_i - \frac{\ell_i}{d_{i-1}'} u_{i-1} \qquad (i = 2, 3, \ldots, n) \tag{1.149}$$

The elements of the transformed **b** vector are computed from

$$b_1' = b_1 \tag{1.150a}$$

$$b_i' = b_i - \frac{\ell_i}{d_{i-1}'} b_{i-1}' \qquad (i = 2, 3, \ldots, n) \tag{1.150b}$$

The computation of the transformed **b** vector can be done after the reduction of the **T** matrix by using the elimination multipliers stored in place of the ℓ vector. Consequently, this process is an **LU** decomposition method. The solution vector **x** is obtained by back substitution, which for Eq. (1.148) becomes

$$x_n = \frac{b_n'}{d_n'} \tag{1.151a}$$

$$x_i = \frac{b_i' - u_i x_{i+1}}{d_i'} \qquad (i = n-1, n-2, \ldots, 1) \tag{1.151b}$$

An alternate procedure stores the elements of **T** as the elements of the $n \times 3$ matrix $\mathbf{A}'$, where the first column of $\mathbf{A}'$ corresponds to ℓ, the second column of $\mathbf{A}'$ corresponds to **d**, and the third column of $\mathbf{A}'$ corresponds to **u**. In terms of this procedure, Eqs. (1.149) to (1.151) become:

$$a_{i,2}' = a_{i,2} - \frac{a_{i,1}}{a_{i-1,2}'} a_{i-1,3} \qquad (i = 2, 3, \ldots, n) \tag{1.149}$$

$$b_1' = b_1 \tag{1.150a}$$

$$b_i' = b_i - \frac{a_{i,1}}{a_{i-1,2}'} b_{i-1}' \qquad (i = 2, 3, \ldots, n) \tag{1.150b}$$

$$x_n = \frac{b'_n}{a'_{n,2}} \tag{1.151a}$$

$$x_i = \frac{b'_i - a'_{i,3}x_{i-1}}{a'_{i,2}} \qquad (i = n-1, n-2, \ldots, 1) \tag{1.151b}$$

Example 1.16. The Thomas algorithm. Solve the tridiagonal system of equations obtained in Example 8.3 corresponding to Table 8.8. In that example, the finite difference equation

$$T_{i-1} - (2 + \alpha^2 \Delta x^2)T_i + T_{i+1} = 0 \tag{1.152}$$

is solved for $\alpha = 2.0$ and $\Delta x = 0.125$, for which $(2 + \alpha^2 \Delta x^2) = 2.0625$, for $i = 2, \ldots, 8$, with $T_1 = 0$ and $T_9 = 100$. Writing Eq. (1.152) in the matrix form $\mathbf{Tx} = \mathbf{b}$ (where the temperatures T_i of Example 8.3 correspond to the elements of the $\mathbf{x}$ vector) yields

$$\mathbf{T} = \begin{bmatrix} & -2.0625 & 1 \\ 1 & -2.0625 & 1 \\ 1 & -2.0625 & 1 \\ 1 & -2.0625 & 1 \\ 1 & -2.0625 & 1 \\ 1 & -2.0625 & 1 \\ 1 & -2.0625 & \end{bmatrix} \quad \text{and} \quad \mathbf{b} = \begin{bmatrix} 0 \\ 0 \\ 0 \\ 0 \\ 0 \\ 0 \\ -100 \end{bmatrix} \tag{1.153}$$

where $\mathbf{T}$ is expressed as the three nonzero column vectors. The major diagonal terms (the center column of the $\mathbf{T}$ matrix) are transformed according to Eq. (1.149), and the $\mathbf{b}$ vector is transformed according to Eq. (1.150). The result is

$$\mathbf{T}' = \begin{bmatrix} & -2.062500 & 1.0 \\ (-0.484848) & -1.577652 & 1.0 \\ (-0.633854) & -1.428646 & 1.0 \\ (-0.699963) & -1.362537 & 1.0 \\ (-0.733925) & -1.328575 & 1.0 \\ (-0.752686) & -1.309814 & 1.0 \\ (-0.763467) & -1.299033 & \end{bmatrix} \quad \text{and} \quad \mathbf{b}' = \begin{bmatrix} 0 \\ 0 \\ 0 \\ 0 \\ 0 \\ 0 \\ -100 \end{bmatrix} \tag{1.154}$$

The solution vector is computed using Eq. (1.151). Thus,

$$\mathbf{x} = \begin{bmatrix} 6.984033 \\ 14.404569 \\ 22.725390 \\ 32.466548 \\ 44.236865 \\ 58.771987 \\ 76.980357 \end{bmatrix} \tag{1.155}$$

Equation (1.155) is the solution presented in Table 8.8 in Example 8.3.

Scaling can be used with the Thomas algorithm, if required. Pivoting destroys the tridiagonality of the system and cannot be used with the Thomas algorithm. Most large tridiagonal systems are diagonally dominant, so scaling and pivoting are not necessary.

The number of multiplications required by the elimination step is $N = 2n - 2$, and the number of multiplications and divisions required by the back substitution step is $N = 3n - 2$. Thus, the total number of operations is $N = 5n - 4$ for the complete Thomas algorithm. If the **T** matrix is constant and multiple **b** vectors are to be considered, only the back substitution step is required once the **T** matrix has been factored. In that case, $N = 3n - 2$ for subsequent **b** vectors. The advantages of the Thomas algorithm are quite apparent when compared to either the Gauss elimination method, for which $N = (n^3/3) + n^2 - (n/3)$, or the Doolittle **LU** decomposition method, for which $N = n^2 - (n/2)$ for each **b** vector after the first one. The Thomas algorithm, in a format suitable for programming for a digital computer, is summarized as follows:

1. Store the $n \times n$ tridiagonal matrix **T** in the three $n \times 1$ column vectors $\boldsymbol{\ell}$, **d**, and **u**. The right-hand-side vector **b** is also an $n \times 1$ column vector.
2. Compute the d'_i terms from the equation

$$d'_i = d_i - \frac{\ell_i}{d'_{i-1}} u_{i-1} \qquad (i = 2, 3, \ldots, n) \tag{1.156}$$

Store the row reduction multipliers (ℓ_i / d'_{i-1}) in place of ℓ_i.

3. Compute the b'_i terms from the equations

$$b'_1 = b_1 \tag{1.157a}$$

$$b'_i = b_i - \frac{\ell_i}{d'_{i-1}} b'_{i-1} \qquad (i = 2, 3, \ldots, n) \tag{1.157b}$$

4. Solve for x_i using back substitution from the equations

$$x_n = \frac{b'_n}{d'_n} \tag{1.158a}$$

$$x_i = \frac{b'_i - u_i x_{i+1}}{d'_i} \qquad (i = n-1, n-2, \ldots, 1) \tag{1.158b}$$

Block Tridiagonal Systems of Equations

The Thomas algorithm presented in the last subsection is an efficient method for solving the tridiagonal system of equations $\mathbf{Tx} = \mathbf{b}$. In that algorithm, all elements of the coefficient matrix $\mathbf{T}$ and the column vectors $\mathbf{x}$ and $\mathbf{b}$ are scalars. Another form of a tridiagonal system of equations arises in which the elements of $\mathbf{T}$ are partitioned into submatrices having similar patterns. Consider the following system of two coupled algebraic equations:

$$a_i x_{i-1} + b_i x_i + c_i x_{i+1} + d_i y_{i-1} + e_i y_i + f_i y_{i+1} = g_i \tag{1.159a}$$

$$A_i x_{i-1} + B_i x_i + C_i x_{i+1} + D_i y_{i-1} + E_i y_i + F_i y_{i+1} = G_i \tag{1.159b}$$

where both equations apply over the range $(i = 1, 2, \ldots, n)$, and x_0, y_0, x_{n+1}, and y_{n+1} are known. Equations (1.159) are typical of the finite difference equations that arise when solving systems of differential equations by numerical methods.

Applying Eqs. (1.159) over the range $(i = 1, \ldots, n)$ yields the result

$$\begin{bmatrix} b_1 & e_1 & c_1 & f_1 & 0 & 0 & 0 & 0 & \cdots & \cdots & 0 & 0 & 0 & 0 \\ B_1 & E_1 & C_1 & F_1 & 0 & 0 & 0 & 0 & \cdots & \cdots & 0 & 0 & 0 & 0 \\ a_2 & d_2 & b_2 & e_2 & c_2 & f_2 & 0 & 0 & \cdots & \cdots & 0 & 0 & 0 & 0 \\ A_2 & D_2 & B_2 & E_2 & C_2 & F_2 & 0 & 0 & \cdots & \cdots & 0 & 0 & 0 & 0 \\ 0 & 0 & a_3 & d_3 & b_3 & e_3 & c_3 & f_3 & \cdots & \cdots & 0 & 0 & 0 & 0 \\ 0 & 0 & A_3 & D_3 & B_3 & E_3 & C_3 & F_3 & \cdots & \cdots & 0 & 0 & 0 & 0 \\ \vdots & \vdots & \vdots & \vdots & \vdots & \vdots & \vdots & \vdots & \ddots & & \vdots & \vdots & \vdots & \vdots \\ \vdots & \vdots & \vdots & \vdots & \vdots & \vdots & \vdots & \vdots & & \ddots & \vdots & \vdots & \vdots & \vdots \\ 0 & 0 & 0 & 0 & 0 & 0 & 0 & 0 & \cdots & \cdots & a_n & d_n & b_n & e_n \\ 0 & 0 & 0 & 0 & 0 & 0 & 0 & 0 & \cdots & \cdots & A_n & D_n & B_n & E_n \end{bmatrix} \begin{bmatrix} x_1 \\ y_1 \\ x_2 \\ y_2 \\ x_3 \\ y_3 \\ \vdots \\ \vdots \\ x_n \\ y_n \end{bmatrix} = \begin{bmatrix} \overline{g}_1 \\ \overline{G}_1 \\ g_2 \\ G_2 \\ g_3 \\ G_3 \\ \vdots \\ \vdots \\ \overline{g}_n \\ \overline{G}_n \end{bmatrix} \tag{1.160}$$

where $\overline{g}_1 = g_1 - a_1 x_0 - d_1 y_0$, and so forth for $\overline{G}_1$, $\overline{g}_n$, and $\overline{G}_n$. The coefficient matrix and column vectors in Eq. (1.160) can be partitioned into 2×2 submatrices and 2×1 subvectors, respectively, as follows:

$$\left[\begin{array}{cc|cc|cc|cc|cc|cc|cc} b_1 & e_1 & c_1 & f_1 & 0 & 0 & 0 & 0 & \cdots & \cdots & 0 & 0 & 0 & 0 \\ B_1 & E_1 & C_1 & F_1 & 0 & 0 & 0 & 0 & \cdots & \cdots & 0 & 0 & 0 & 0 \\ \hline a_2 & d_2 & b_2 & e_2 & c_2 & f_2 & 0 & 0 & \cdots & \cdots & 0 & 0 & 0 & 0 \\ A_2 & D_2 & B_2 & E_2 & C_2 & F_2 & 0 & 0 & \cdots & \cdots & 0 & 0 & 0 & 0 \\ \hline 0 & 0 & a_3 & d_3 & b_3 & e_3 & c_3 & f_3 & \cdots & \cdots & 0 & 0 & 0 & 0 \\ 0 & 0 & A_3 & D_3 & B_3 & E_3 & C_3 & F_3 & \cdots & \cdots & 0 & 0 & 0 & 0 \\ \hline \vdots & \vdots & \vdots & \vdots & \vdots & \vdots & \vdots & \vdots & \ddots & & \vdots & \vdots & \vdots & \vdots \\ \vdots & \vdots & \vdots & \vdots & \vdots & \vdots & \vdots & \vdots & & \ddots & \vdots & \vdots & \vdots & \vdots \\ \hline 0 & 0 & 0 & 0 & 0 & 0 & 0 & 0 & \cdots & \cdots & a_n & d_n & b_n & e_n \\ 0 & 0 & 0 & 0 & 0 & 0 & 0 & 0 & \cdots & \cdots & A_n & D_n & B_n & E_n \end{array}\right] \left[\begin{array}{c} x_1 \\ y_1 \\ \hline x_2 \\ y_2 \\ \hline x_3 \\ y_3 \\ \hline \vdots \\ \vdots \\ \hline x_n \\ y_n \end{array}\right] = \left[\begin{array}{c} \overline{g}_1 \\ \overline{G}_1 \\ \hline g_2 \\ G_2 \\ \hline g_3 \\ G_3 \\ \hline \vdots \\ \vdots \\ \hline \overline{g}_n \\ \overline{G}_n \end{array}\right] \tag{1.161}$$

Equation (1.161) can be written as the block tridiagonal system of equations

$$\begin{bmatrix} \mathbf{D}_1 & \mathbf{C}_1 & \mathbf{0} & \mathbf{0} & \cdots & \mathbf{0} & \mathbf{0} \\ \mathbf{A}_2 & \mathbf{D}_2 & \mathbf{C}_2 & \mathbf{0} & \cdots & \mathbf{0} & \mathbf{0} \\ \mathbf{0} & \mathbf{A}_3 & \mathbf{D}_3 & \mathbf{C}_3 & \cdots & \mathbf{0} & \mathbf{0} \\ \vdots & \vdots & \vdots & \vdots & \ddots & \vdots & \vdots \\ \mathbf{0} & \mathbf{0} & \mathbf{0} & \mathbf{0} & \cdots & \mathbf{A}_n & \mathbf{D}_n \end{bmatrix} \begin{bmatrix} \mathbf{x}_1 \\ \mathbf{x}_2 \\ \mathbf{x}_3 \\ \vdots \\ \mathbf{x}_n \end{bmatrix} = \begin{bmatrix} \mathbf{b}_1 \\ \mathbf{b}_2 \\ \mathbf{b}_3 \\ \vdots \\ \mathbf{b}_n \end{bmatrix} \tag{1.162}$$

where $\mathbf{A}_i$, $\mathbf{D}_i$, and $\mathbf{C}_i$ are 2×2 submatrices defined by the corresponding positions in Eqs. (1.161) and (1.162), $\mathbf{x}_i$ and $\mathbf{b}_i$ are 2×1 column subvectors defined by the corresponding positions in Eqs. (1.161) and (1.162), and $\mathbf{0}$ denotes the 2×2 zero matrix.

Equation (1.162) is a 2×2 *block tridiagonal* system of equations. It can be solved very efficiently by a method similar to the Thomas algorithm, but using matrix addition, matrix subtraction, and matrix multiplication instead of the scalar processes used in the Thomas algorithm.

Consider the $m \times m$ block tridiagonal system

$$\mathbf{Tx} = \mathbf{b} \tag{1.163}$$

represented by Eq. (1.162), where $\mathbf{A}_i$, $\mathbf{D}_i$, and $\mathbf{C}_i$ are square $m \times m$ submatrices and $\mathbf{x}_i$ and $\mathbf{b}_i$ are $m \times 1$ column vectors:

$$\mathbf{A}_i = \begin{bmatrix} (a_i)_{11} & (a_i)_{12} & \cdots & (a_i)_{1m} \\ (a_i)_{21} & (a_i)_{22} & \cdots & (a_i)_{2m} \\ \vdots & \vdots & \ddots & \vdots \\ (a_i)_{m1} & (a_i)_{m2} & \cdots & (a_i)_{mm} \end{bmatrix}, \quad \mathbf{D}_i = \begin{bmatrix} (d_i)_{11} & (d_i)_{12} & \cdots & (d_i)_{1m} \\ (d_i)_{21} & (d_i)_{22} & \cdots & (d_i)_{2m} \\ \vdots & \vdots & \ddots & \vdots \\ (d_i)_{m1} & (d_i)_{m2} & \cdots & (d_i)_{mm} \end{bmatrix} \tag{1.164a}$$

$$\mathbf{C}_i = \begin{bmatrix} (c_i)_{11} & (c_i)_{12} & \cdots & (c_i)_{1m} \\ (c_i)_{21} & (c_i)_{22} & \cdots & (c_i)_{2m} \\ \vdots & \vdots & \ddots & \vdots \\ (c_i)_{m1} & (c_i)_{m2} & \cdots & (c_i)_{mm} \end{bmatrix}, \quad \mathbf{x}_i = \begin{bmatrix} (x_i)_1 \\ (x_i)_2 \\ \vdots \\ (x_i)_m \end{bmatrix}, \quad \text{and} \quad \mathbf{b}_i = \begin{bmatrix} (b_i)_1 \\ (b_i)_2 \\ \vdots \\ (b_i)_m \end{bmatrix} \tag{1.164b}$$

Equation (1.163) can be solved by **LU** decomposition as follows. Let $\mathbf{T} = \mathbf{LU}$. Then Eq. (1.163) becomes

$$\mathbf{LUx} = \mathbf{b} \tag{1.165}$$

Multiplying both sides of Eq. (1.165) by $\mathbf{L}^{-1}$ yields

$$(\mathbf{L}^{-1}\mathbf{L})\mathbf{Ux} = \mathbf{Ux} = \mathbf{L}^{-1}\mathbf{b} = \mathbf{y} \tag{1.166}$$

Equation (1.166) yields the two equations

$$\boxed{\begin{aligned} \mathbf{Ly} &= \mathbf{b} \qquad (1.167) \\ \mathbf{Ux} &= \mathbf{y} \qquad (1.168) \end{aligned}}$$

Once $\mathbf{L}$ and $\mathbf{U}$ have been specified, Eq. (1.167) can be solved by forward substitution for $\mathbf{y}$, and Eq. (1.168) can be solved by back substitution for $\mathbf{x}$.

An infinite number of $\mathbf{L}$ and $\mathbf{U}$ matrices can be defined such that $\mathbf{T} = \mathbf{LU}$. A convenient unique definition is obtained by specifying the major diagonal block submatrices of $\mathbf{U}$ to be $m \times m$ identity matrices $\mathbf{I}$. Thus,

$$\begin{bmatrix} \mathbf{D}_1 & \mathbf{C}_1 & \mathbf{0} & \mathbf{0} & \cdots & \mathbf{0} & \mathbf{0} \\ \mathbf{A}_2 & \mathbf{D}_2 & \mathbf{C}_2 & \mathbf{0} & \cdots & \mathbf{0} & \mathbf{0} \\ \mathbf{0} & \mathbf{A}_3 & \mathbf{D}_3 & \mathbf{C}_3 & \cdots & \mathbf{0} & \mathbf{0} \\ \vdots & \vdots & \vdots & \vdots & \ddots & \vdots & \vdots \\ \mathbf{0} & \mathbf{0} & \mathbf{0} & \mathbf{0} & \cdots & \mathbf{A}_n & \mathbf{D}_n \end{bmatrix} =$$

$$\begin{bmatrix} \mathbf{L}_1 & \mathbf{0} & \mathbf{0} & \mathbf{0} & \cdots & \mathbf{0} & \mathbf{0} \\ \mathbf{B}_2 & \mathbf{L}_2 & \mathbf{0} & \mathbf{0} & \cdots & \mathbf{0} & \mathbf{0} \\ \mathbf{0} & \mathbf{B}_3 & \mathbf{L}_3 & \mathbf{0} & \cdots & \mathbf{0} & \mathbf{0} \\ \vdots & \vdots & \vdots & \vdots & \ddots & \vdots & \vdots \\ \mathbf{0} & \mathbf{0} & \mathbf{0} & \mathbf{0} & \cdots & \mathbf{B}_n & \mathbf{L}_n \end{bmatrix} \begin{bmatrix} \mathbf{I} & \mathbf{U}_1 & \mathbf{0} & \mathbf{0} & \cdots & \mathbf{0} & \mathbf{0} \\ \mathbf{0} & \mathbf{I} & \mathbf{U}_2 & \mathbf{0} & \cdots & \mathbf{0} & \mathbf{0} \\ \mathbf{0} & \mathbf{0} & \mathbf{I} & \mathbf{U}_3 & \cdots & \mathbf{0} & \mathbf{0} \\ \vdots & \vdots & \vdots & \vdots & \ddots & \vdots & \vdots \\ \mathbf{0} & \mathbf{0} & \mathbf{0} & \mathbf{0} & \cdots & \mathbf{0} & \mathbf{I} \end{bmatrix} \tag{1.169}$$

From the rules of matrix multiplication, $\mathbf{D}_1$ is the summation of the matrix products of row 1 of $\mathbf{L}$ and column 1 of $\mathbf{U}$, and $\mathbf{C}_1$ is the summation of the matrix products of row 1 of $\mathbf{L}$ and column 2 of $\mathbf{U}$. Thus,

$$\mathbf{L}_1 = \mathbf{D}_1 \tag{1.170}$$

$$\mathbf{C}_1 = \mathbf{L}_1\mathbf{U}_1 \tag{1.171}$$

In general, $\mathbf{D}_i$ is the summation of the matrix products of row i of $\mathbf{L}$ and column i of $\mathbf{U}$. Thus

$$\mathbf{D}_i = \mathbf{B}_i\mathbf{U}_{i-1} + \mathbf{L}_i \qquad (i = 2, 3, \ldots, n) \tag{1.172}$$

In general, $\mathbf{C}_i$ is the summation of the matrix products of row i of $\mathbf{L}$ and column $i + 1$ of $\mathbf{U}$. Thus

$$\mathbf{C}_i = \mathbf{L}_i\mathbf{U}_i \qquad (i = 2, 3, \ldots, n) \tag{1.173}$$

Equations (1.170) to (1.173) can be solved as follows. Equation (1.170) gives $\mathbf{L}_1 = \mathbf{D}_1$. From Eq. (1.171), the columns of $\mathbf{U}_1$ can be determined, one at a time, from the corresponding columns of $\mathbf{C}_1$ using forward substitution. Then $\mathbf{L}_2$ can be computed directly from Eq. (1.172). Subsequent values of $\mathbf{U}_i$ can be computed, column by column, from Eq. (1.173), and subsequent values of $\mathbf{L}_i$ can be obtained from Eq. (1.172). This process yields the $\mathbf{L}_i$ and $\mathbf{U}_i$ matrices.

Next consider Eq. (1.167), $\mathbf{Ly} = \mathbf{b}$, written in expanded form:

$$\begin{bmatrix} \mathbf{L}_1 & \mathbf{0} & \mathbf{0} & \cdots & \mathbf{0} & \mathbf{0} \\ \mathbf{B}_2 & \mathbf{L}_2 & \mathbf{0} & \cdots & \mathbf{0} & \mathbf{0} \\ \mathbf{0} & \mathbf{B}_3 & \mathbf{L}_3 & \cdots & \mathbf{0} & \mathbf{0} \\ \vdots & \vdots & \vdots & \ddots & \vdots & \vdots \\ \mathbf{0} & \mathbf{0} & \mathbf{0} & \cdots & \mathbf{B}_n & \mathbf{L}_n \end{bmatrix} \begin{bmatrix} \mathbf{y}_1 \\ \mathbf{y}_2 \\ \mathbf{y}_3 \\ \vdots \\ \mathbf{y}_n \end{bmatrix} = \begin{bmatrix} \mathbf{b}_1 \\ \mathbf{b}_2 \\ \mathbf{b}_3 \\ \vdots \\ \mathbf{b}_n \end{bmatrix} \tag{1.174}$$

Multiplying row 1 of $\mathbf{L}$ by the column vector $\mathbf{y}$ gives

$$\mathbf{L}_1\mathbf{y}_1 = \mathbf{b}_1 \tag{1.175}$$

and multiplying row i of $\mathbf{L}$ by the column vector $\mathbf{y}$ gives

$$\mathbf{B}_i\mathbf{y}_{i-1} + \mathbf{L}_i\mathbf{y}_i = \mathbf{b}_i \qquad (i = 2, 3, \ldots, n) \tag{1.176}$$

Equations (1.175) and (1.176) can be solved for $\mathbf{y}_1$ and $\mathbf{y}_i$ $(i = 2, 3, \ldots, n)$, respectively, by forward substitution.

Finally, consider Eq. (1.168), $\mathbf{Ux} = \mathbf{y}$, written in expanded form:

$$\begin{bmatrix} \mathbf{I} & \mathbf{U}_1 & \mathbf{0} & \cdots & \mathbf{0} & \mathbf{0} \\ \mathbf{0} & \mathbf{I} & \mathbf{U}_2 & \cdots & \mathbf{0} & \mathbf{0} \\ \mathbf{0} & \mathbf{0} & \mathbf{I} & \cdots & \mathbf{0} & \mathbf{0} \\ \vdots & \vdots & \vdots & \ddots & \vdots & \vdots \\ \mathbf{0} & \mathbf{0} & \mathbf{0} & \cdots & \mathbf{0} & \mathbf{I} \end{bmatrix} \begin{bmatrix} \mathbf{x}_1 \\ \mathbf{x}_2 \\ \mathbf{x}_3 \\ \vdots \\ \mathbf{x}_n \end{bmatrix} = \begin{bmatrix} \mathbf{y}_1 \\ \mathbf{y}_2 \\ \mathbf{y}_3 \\ \vdots \\ \mathbf{y}_n \end{bmatrix} \tag{1.177}$$

Multiplying row n of $\mathbf{U}$ by the column vector $\mathbf{x}$ gives

$$\mathbf{x}_n = \mathbf{y}_n \tag{1.178a}$$

and multiplying row i of $\mathbf{U}$ by the column vector $\mathbf{x}$ gives

$$\mathbf{x}_i + \mathbf{U}_i\mathbf{x}_{i+1} = \mathbf{y}_i \qquad (i = n-1, n-2, \ldots, 1) \tag{1.178b}$$

Equation (1.178) can be solved for $\mathbf{x}_i$ by back substitution.

The block tridiagonal procedure, in a format suitable for programming on a digital computer, is summarized as follows:

1. Evaluate the $\mathbf{L}_i$ and $\mathbf{U}_i$ submatrices using Eqs. (1.170) to (1.173).
2. Compute the $\mathbf{y}_i$ subvectors from Eqs. (1.175) and (1.176) using forward substitution.
3. Compute the $\mathbf{x}_i$ solution subvectors from Eq. (1.178) using back substitution.

1.6 ITERATIVE METHODS

For many large systems of linear algebraic equations $\mathbf{Ax} = \mathbf{b}$, the coefficient matrix $\mathbf{A}$ is extremely sparse. That is, most of the elements of $\mathbf{A}$ are zero. It is generally more efficient to solve such systems of equations by iterative methods than by direct methods. Two iterative methods are presented in this section: Jacobi iteration and Gauss-Seidel iteration.

Iterative methods begin by assuming an initial solution vector $\mathbf{x}^{(0)}$. The initial solution vector is used to generate an improved solution vector, $\mathbf{x}^{(1)}$, based on some strategy for reducing the difference between $\mathbf{x}^{(0)}$ and the actual solution vector $\mathbf{x}$. This procedure is repeated (*iterated*) to convergence. The procedure is *convergent* if each iteration produces approximations to the solution vector that approach the exact solution vector as the number of iterations increases.

Iterative methods do not converge for all sets of equations, nor for all possible arrangements of a particular set of equations. Diagonal dominance is a sufficient condition for convergence of the Jacobi and the Gauss–Seidel methods for any initial solution vector. Diagonal dominance is defined by Eq. (1.15). Some systems that are not diagonally dominant can be rearranged by row interchanges to make them diagonally dominant. Some systems that are not diagonally dominant may converge for certain initial solution vectors, but convergence is not assured. Iterative methods should generally be avoided for systems of equations that cannot be made diagonally dominant.

When repeated application of an iterative algorithm produces insignificant changes in the solution vector, the procedure should be terminated. In other words, the algorithm is repeated (iterated) until some specified convergence criterion is achieved. Convergence is achieved when some measure of the relative or absolute change in the solution vector is less than a specified convergence criterion. The number of iterations required to achieve convergence depends on:

1. The dominance of the diagonal coefficients
2. The initial solution vector
3. The algorithm used
4. The convergence criterion specified

In general, the stronger the diagonal dominance, the fewer the number of iterations required to satisfy the convergence criterion.

Jacobi Iteration

Consider the general system of linear algebraic equations $\mathbf{Ax} = \mathbf{b}$, written in index notation:

$$\sum_{j=1}^{n} a_{ij} x_j = b_i \qquad (i = 1, 2, \ldots, n) \tag{1.179}$$

In Jacobi iteration, each equation of the system is solved for the component of the solution vector associated with the diagonal element, that is, x_i. Thus

$$x_i = \frac{1}{a_{ii}} \left(b_i - \sum_{j=1}^{i-1} a_{ij} x_j - \sum_{j=i+1}^{n} a_{ij} x_j \right) \qquad (i = 1, 2, \ldots, n) \tag{1.180}$$

An initial solution vector $\mathbf{x}^{(0)}$ is chosen. The superscript in parentheses denotes the iteration number, with zero denoting the initial solution vector. The initial solution vector $\mathbf{x}^{(0)}$ is substituted into Eq. (1.180) to yield the first improved solution vector $\mathbf{x}^{(1)}$. Thus,

$$x_i^{(1)} = \frac{1}{a_{ii}} \left(b_i - \sum_{j=1}^{i-1} a_{ij} x_j^{(0)} - \sum_{j=i+1}^{n} a_{ij} x_j^{(0)} \right) \qquad (i = 1, \ldots, n) \tag{1.181}$$

This procedure is repeated (iterated) until some convergence criterion is satisfied.

The Jacobi algorithm for the general iteration step $(k + 1)$ is:

$$x_i^{(k+1)} = \frac{1}{a_{ii}} \left(b_i - \sum_{j=1}^{i-1} a_{ij} x_j^{(k)} - \sum_{j=i+1}^{n} a_{ij} x_j^{(k)} \right) \qquad (i = 1, \ldots, n) \tag{1.182}$$

An equivalent, but more convenient, form of Eq. (1.182) can be obtained by adding and subtracting $x_i^{(k)}$ from Eq. (1.182) to yield

$$x_i^{(k+1)} = x_i^{(k)} + \frac{1}{a_{ii}}\left(b_i - \sum_{j=1}^{n} a_{ij}x_j^{(k)}\right) \qquad (i = 1, 2, \ldots, n) \tag{1.183}$$

Equation (1.183) is generally written as

$$x_i^{(k+1)} = x_i^{(k)} + \frac{R_i^{(k)}}{a_{ii}} \qquad (i = 1, 2, \ldots, n) \tag{1.184}$$

$$R_i^{(k)} = b_i - \sum_{j=1}^{n} a_{ij}x_j^{(k)} \qquad (i = 1, 2, \ldots, n) \tag{1.185}$$

where the term $R_i^{(k)}$ is called the *residual*. The residuals are simply the net values of the equations evaluated for the approximate solution vector $\mathbf{x}^{(k)}$.

The Jacobi method is sometimes called the method of *simultaneous* iteration, because all values of x_i are iterated simultaneously. That is, all values of $x_i^{(k+1)}$ depend only on the values of $x_i^{(k)}$. The order of processing the equations is immaterial.

Example 1.17. The Jacobi iteration method. To illustrate the Jacobi iteration method, we will solve the following system of linear algebraic equations:

$$\begin{bmatrix} 4 & -1 & 0 & 1 & 0 \\ -1 & 4 & -1 & 0 & 1 \\ 0 & -1 & 4 & -1 & 0 \\ 1 & 0 & -1 & 4 & -1 \\ 0 & 1 & 0 & -1 & 4 \end{bmatrix} \begin{bmatrix} x_1 \\ x_2 \\ x_3 \\ x_4 \\ x_5 \end{bmatrix} = \begin{bmatrix} 100 \\ 100 \\ 100 \\ 100 \\ 100 \end{bmatrix} \tag{1.186}$$

Equation (1.186), when expanded, becomes

$$4x_1 - x_2 + x_4 = 100 \tag{1.187.1}$$
$$-x_1 + 4x_2 - x_3 + x_5 = 100 \tag{1.187.2}$$
$$- x_2 + 4x_3 - x_4 = 100 \tag{1.187.3}$$
$$x_1 - x_3 + 4x_4 - x_5 = 100 \tag{1.187.4}$$
$$x_2 - x_4 + 4x_5 = 100 \tag{1.187.5}$$

Equation (1.187) can be rearranged to yield expressions for the residuals R_i. Thus,

$$R_1 = 100 - 4x_1 + x_2 - x_4 \tag{1.188.1}$$
$$R_2 = 100 + x_1 - 4x_2 + x_3 - x_5 \tag{1.188.2}$$
$$R_3 = 100 + x_2 - 4x_3 + x_4 \tag{1.188.3}$$
$$R_4 = 100 - x_1 + x_3 - 4x_4 + x_5 \tag{1.188.4}$$
$$R_5 = 100 - x_2 + x_4 - 4x_5 \tag{1.188.5}$$

To initiate the solution, let $\mathbf{x}^{(0)T} = (0.0\ 0.0\ 0.0\ 0.0\ 0.0)$. Substituting these values

TABLE 1.1
Solution by the Jacobi iteration method

k	x_1	x_2	x_3	x_4	x_5
0	0.000000	0.000000	0.000000	0.000000	0.000000
1	25.000000	25.000000	25.000000	25.000000	25.000000
2	25.000000	31.250000	37.500000	31.250000	25.000000
3	25.000000	34.375000	40.625000	34.375000	25.000000
4	25.000000	35.156250	42.187500	35.156250	25.000000
5	25.000000	35.546875	42.578125	35.546875	25.000000
⋮	⋮	⋮	⋮	⋮	⋮
16	25.000000	35.714284	42.857140	35.714284	25.000000
17	25.000000	35.714285	42.857142	35.714285	25.000000
18	25.000000	35.714285	42.857143	35.714285	25.000000

into Eq. (1.188) gives $R_i^{(0)} = 100.0$ ($i = 1, \ldots, 5$). Substituting these values into Eq. (1.184) gives $x_1^{(1)} = x_2^{(1)} = x_3^{(1)} = x_4^{(1)} = x_5^{(1)} = 25.0$. The procedure is then repeated with these values to obtain $\mathbf{x}^{(2)}$, etc.

The first and subsequent iterations are summarized in Table 1.1. Due to the symmetry of the coefficient matrix $\mathbf{A}$ and the symmetry of the $\mathbf{b}$ vector, $x_2 = x_4$. The calculations were carried out on a 13-decimal-digit computer and iterated until $|\Delta x_i|$ changed by less than 0.000001 between iterations, which required 18 iterations.

The Gauss–Seidel Method

In the Jacobi method, all values of $\mathbf{x}^{(k+1)}$ are based on $\mathbf{x}^{(k)}$. The Gauss–Seidel method is similar to the Jacobi method, except that the most recently computed values of all x_i are used in all computations. In brief, as better values of x_i are obtained, use them immediately. Like the Jacobi method, the Gauss–Seidel method requires diagonal dominance to ensure convergence. The Gauss–Seidel algorithm is obtained from the Jacobi algorithm, Eq. (1.182), by using $x_j^{(k+1)}$ values in the summation from $j = 1$ to $i - 1$ (assuming the sweeps through the equations proceed from $i = 1$ to n). Thus,

$$x_i^{(k+1)} = \frac{1}{a_{ii}}\left(b_i - \sum_{j=1}^{i-1} a_{ij}x_j^{(k+1)} - \sum_{j=i+1}^{n} a_{ij}x_j^{(k)}\right) \qquad (i = 1, \ldots, n) \quad (1.189)$$

Equation (1.189) can be written in terms of the residuals R_i by adding and subtracting $x_i^{(k)}$ and rearranging to yield

$$x_i^{(k+1)} = x_i^{(k)} + \frac{R_i^{(k)}}{a_{ii}} \qquad (i = 1, 2, \ldots, n) \quad (1.190)$$

$$R_i^{(k)} = b_i - \sum_{j=1}^{i-1} a_{ij}x_j^{(k+1)} - \sum_{j=i}^{n} a_{ij}x_j^{(k)} \qquad (i = 1, 2, \ldots, n) \quad (1.191)$$

TABLE 1.2
Solution by the Gauss–Seidel iteration method

k	x_1	x_2	x_3	x_4	x_5
0	0.000000	0.000000	0.000000	0.000000	0.000000
1	25.000000	31.250000	32.812500	26.953125	23.925781
2	26.074219	33.740234	40.173340	34.506226	25.191498
3	24.808502	34.947586	42.363453	35.686612	25.184757
4	24.815243	35.498485	42.796274	35.791447	25.073240
5	24.926760	35.662448	42.863474	35.752489	25.022510
⋮	⋮	⋮	⋮	⋮	⋮
13	25.000002	35.714287	42.857142	35.714285	24.999999
14	25.000001	35.714286	42.857143	35.714285	25.000000
15	25.000000	35.714286	42.857143	35.714286	25.000000

The Gauss–Seidel method is sometimes called the method of *successive* iteration, because the most recent values of all x_i are used in all the calculations. Gauss–Seidel iteration generally converges faster than Jacobi iteration.

Example 1.18. The Gauss–Seidel iteration method. Rework the problem presented in Example 1.17 using Gauss–Seidel iteration. The residuals are given by Eq. (1.188). Substituting the initial solution vector $\mathbf{x}^{(0)T} = (0.0\ 0.0\ 0.0\ 0.0\ 00)$ into Eq. (1.188.1) gives $R_1^{(0)} = 100.0$. Substituting that result into Eq. (1.190.1) gives $x_1^{(1)} = 25.0$. Substituting $\mathbf{x}^{\mathrm{T}} = (25.0\ 0.0\ 0.0\ 0.0\ 0.0)$ into Eq. (1.188.2) gives

$$R_2^{(1)} = (100.0 + 25.0) = 125.0 \tag{1.192}$$

Substituting this result into Eq. (1.190.2) yields

$$x_2^{(1)} = 0.0 + \frac{125.0}{4} = 31.25 \tag{1.193}$$

Continuing in this manner yields $R_3^{(1)} = 131.250$, $x_3^{(1)} = 32.81250$, $R_4^{(1)} = 107.81250$, $x_4^{(1)} = 26.953125$, $R_5^{(1)} = 95.703125$, and $x_5^{(1)} = 23.925781$.

The first and subsequent iterations are summarized in Table 1.2. The intermediate iteration are no longer symmetrical, as they were in Example 1.18. The calculations were carried out on a 13-decimal-digit computer and iterated until $|\Delta x_i|$ changed by less than 0.000001 between iterations. This required 15 iterations, which is three less than required by the Jacobi method in Example 1.17.

1.7 ACCURACY AND CONVERGENCE

All nonsingular systems of linear algebraic equations have an exact solution. In principle, when solved by direct methods, the exact solution can be obtained. However, all real calculations are performed with finite-word-length arithmetic, so round-off errors pollute the solution. Round-off errors can be minimized by scaling and pivoting, but even the most careful calculations are subject to the round-off characteristics of the computing device, whether hand computation, hand calculator, personal computer, or large mainframe computer.

When a system of linear algebraic equations is solved by iterative methods, the exact solution is approached asymptotically as the number of iterations increases. When the number of iterations increases without bound, the numerical solution yields the exact solution within the round-off limit of the computing device. Such solutions are said to be correct to *machine accuracy*. In most practical solutions, machine accuracy is not required. Thus, the iterative process should be terminated when some accuracy criterion (or criteria) has been satisfied. In iterative methods, the term *accuracy* refers to the number of significant figures obtained in the calculations, and the term *convergence* refers to the point in the iterative process when the desired accuracy is obtained.

ACCURACY. The accuracy of any approximate method is measured in terms of the error of the method. There are two ways to specify error: *absolute* error and *relative* error. Absolute error is defined as

$$\text{Absolute error} = \text{approximate value} - \text{exact value} \tag{1.194}$$

and relative error is defined as

$$\text{Relative error} = \frac{\text{Absolute error}}{\text{Exact value}} \tag{1.195}$$

Relative error can be stated directly or as a percentage.

Consider an iterative calculation for which the desired absolute error is $\pm$ 0.001. If the exact value is 100.000, then the approximate value is 100.000 $\pm$ 0.001, which has five significant digits. However, if the exact value is 0.0010000, then the approximate value is 0.0010000 $\pm$ 0.001, which has no significant digits. This example illustrates the danger of using absolute error as an accuracy criterion. When the magnitude of the exact answer is known, an absolute accuracy criterion can be specified to yield a specified number of significant digits in the approximate value. Otherwise, a relative accuracy criterion is preferable.

Consider an iterative calculation for which the desired relative error is $\pm$ 0.00001. If the exact value is 100.000, then the absolute error must be 100.000 ($\pm$ 0.00001) = $\pm$ 0.001 to satisfy the relative error criterion. This yields five significant digits in the approximate value. If the exact value is 0.0010000, then the absolute error must be 0.0010000 ($\pm$ 0.00001) = $\pm$ 0.00000001 to satisfy the relative error criterion. This yields five significant digits in the approximate value. A relative error criterion yields the same number of significant figures in the approximate value, regardless of the magnitude of the exact value.

CONVERGENCE. Convergence of an iterative process is achieved when the desired accuracy criterion (or criteria) is satisfied. Convergence criteria can be specified in terms of relative error or absolute error. Since the exact solution is unknown, the error at any step in the iterative process is based on the change in the quantity being calculated from one step to the next. Thus, for the iterative solution of a system of linear algebraic equations, the error $\Delta x_i = x_i^{(k+1)} - x_i^{\text{exact}}$ is approximated by $x_i^{(k+1)} - x_i^{(k)}$. The error can also be specified by the magnitudes of the residuals, R_i. When the exact answer (or the exact answer to machine accuracy) is obtained, the residuals are all zero. At each step in the iterative process, some of the residuals may be near zero while others are still quite large. Therefore, care is needed to ensure that the desired accuracy of the complete system of equations is achieved.

Let ϵ be the magnitude of the convergence tolerance. Several convergence criteria are possible. For an absolute error criterion, the following choices are possible:

$$\left|(\Delta x_i)_{\max}\right| \le \epsilon, \quad \sum_{i=1}^{n} \left|\Delta x_i\right| \le \epsilon, \quad \text{or} \quad \left(\sum_{i=1}^{n} (\Delta x_i)^2\right)^{1/2} \le \epsilon \tag{1.196}$$

For a relative error criterion, the following choices are possible:

$$\left|\frac{(\Delta x_i)_{\max}}{x_i}\right| \le \epsilon, \quad \sum_{i=1}^{n} \left|\frac{\Delta x_i}{x_i}\right| \le \epsilon, \quad \text{or} \quad \left(\sum_{i=1}^{n} \left(\frac{\Delta x_i}{x_i}\right)^2\right)^{1/2} \le \epsilon \tag{1.197}$$

The concepts of accuracy and convergence discussed in this section apply to all iterative procedures, not just the iterative solution of a system of linear algebraic equations. They are relevant in the solution of eigenvalue problems (Chapter 2), in the solution of nonlinear equations (Chapter 3), and in many other situations.

1.8 SUCCESSIVE OVERRELAXATION (SOR)

Iterative methods are frequently referred to as relaxation methods, since the iterative procedure can be viewed as relaxing $\mathbf{x}^{(0)}$ to the exact value $\mathbf{x}$. Historically, the term *relaxation* refers to a specific procedure attributed to Southwell (1940). Southwell's relaxation method embodied two procedures for accelerating the convergence of the basic iteration scheme. First, the relaxation order was determined by visually searching for the residual of greatest magnitude, $|R_i|_{\max}$, and then relaxing the corresponding equation by calculating a new value of x_i so that $(R_i)_{\max} = 0.0$. This changes the other residuals that depend on x_i. As the other residuals are relaxed, the value of R_i moves away from zero. The procedure is applied repetitively until all the residuals satisfy the convergence criterion (or criteria).

Southwell observed that in many cases the changes in x_i from iteration to iteration were always in the same directions. Consequently, overcorrecting (i.e., overrelaxing) the values of x_i by the right amount accelerates convergence. This procedure is illustrated in Fig. 1.3.

Southwell's method is quite efficient for hand calculations. However, the search for the largest residual is inefficient for computer application, since it can take as much computer time to search for the largest residual as it does to

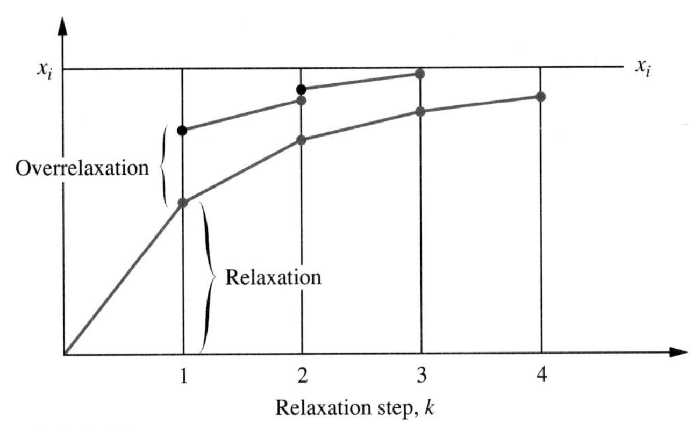

FIGURE 1-3
Overrelaxation.

make a complete pass through the iteration procedure. On the other hand, the overrelaxation concept is easy to implement on the computer and is very effective in accelerating the convergence rate of the Gauss–Seidel method.

The Gauss–Seidel method presented in Section 1.6 can be modified to include overrelaxation simply by multiplying the residual $R_i^{(k)}$ in Eq. (1.190) by the overrelaxation factor ω. Thus, the successive overrelaxation method is given by

$$x_i^{(k+1)} = x_i^{(k)} + \omega \frac{R_i^{(k)}}{a_{ii}} \qquad (i = 1, 2, \ldots, n) \tag{1.198}$$

$$R_i^{(k)} = b_i - \sum_{j=1}^{i-1} a_{ij} x_j^{(k+1)} - \sum_{j=i}^{n} a_{ij} x_j^{(k)} \qquad (i = 1, 2, \ldots, n) \tag{1.199}$$

When $\omega = 1$, Eq. (1.198) yields the Gauss–Seidel method. When $1 < \omega < 2$, the system of equations is *overrelaxed*. Overrelaxation is appropriate for systems of linear algebraic equations. When $\omega < 1$, the system of equations is *underrelaxed*. Underrelaxation is appropriate when the Gauss–Seidel algorithm causes the solution vector to overshoot, resulting in an oscillatory pattern. This behavior is generally associated with the iterative solution of systems of nonlinear algebraic equations. The iterative method diverges if $\omega \geq 2$. The relaxation factor does not change the final solution, since it multiplies the residual R_i, which is zero when the final solution is reached.

The major difficulty with the overrelaxation method is the determination of the best value for the overrelaxation factor ω. Unfortunately, there is not a good general method for determining the optimum value for the overrelaxation factor, ω_{opt}.

This optimum value depends on the size of the system of equations (the number of equations) and the nature of the equations (characteristics such as the strength of the diagonal dominance and the structure of the coefficient matrix). As a general rule, larger values of ω_{opt} are associated with larger systems of equations.

In Section 9.5, a method is described for estimating ω_{opt} for the system of equations obtained when solving the Laplace equation in a rectangular domain with Dirichlet boundary conditions. In the more general case, however, one must resort to numerical experimentation to determine ω_{opt}. In spite of this inconvenience, it is almost always worthwhile to search for a near-optimum value of ω if a system of equations is to be solved many times. In some problems, the computation time can be reduced by factors as large as 10 to 50. For serious calculations with a large number of equations, the potential is too great to ignore.

Example 1.19. The SOR method. To illustrate the SOR method, rework the problem presented in Example 1.18 using $\omega = 1.10$. The residuals are given by Eq. (1.188). Substituting the initial solution vector $\mathbf{x}^{(0)T} = (0.0\ 0.0\ 0.0\ 0.0\ 0.0)$ into Eq. (1.188.1) gives $R_1^{(0)} = 100.0$. Substituting that value into Eq. (1.198.1) with $\omega = 1.10$ gives $x_1^{(1)} = 27.50$. Substituting $\mathbf{x}^T = (27.50\ 0.0\ 0.0\ 0.0\ 0.0)$ into Eq. (1.188.2) gives

$$R_2^{(0)} = (100.0 + 27.50) = 127.50 \tag{1.200}$$

Substituting this result into Eq. (1.198.2) gives

$$x_2^{(1)} = 0.0 + 1.10\frac{127.50}{4} = 35.062500 \tag{1.201}$$

Continuing in this manner yields the results presented in Table 1.3.

The first and subsequent iterations are summarized in Table 1.3. The calculations were carried out on a 13-decimal-digit computer and iterated until $|\Delta x_i|$ changed by less than 0.000001 between iterations. This required 13 iterations, which is five less than required by the Jacobi method and two less than required by the Gauss–Seidel method.

TABLE 1.3
Solution by the SOR method

k	x_1	x_2	x_3	x_4	x_5
0	0.000000	0.000000	0.000000	0.000000	0.000000
1	27.500000	35.062500	37.142188	30.151602	26.149503
2	26.100497	34.194375	41.480925	35.905571	25.355629
3	24.419371	35.230346	42.914285	35.968342	25.167386
4	24.855114	35.692519	42.915308	35.790750	25.010375
5	24.987475	35.726188	42.875627	35.717992	24.996719
⋮	⋮	⋮	⋮	⋮	⋮
11	24.999996	35.714285	42.857145	35.714287	25.000000
12	25.000000	35.714286	42.857143	35.714286	25.000000
13	25.000000	35.714286	42.857143	35.714286	25.000000

TABLE 1.4
Number of iterations k as a function of ω

ω	k	ω	k
1.00	15	1.08	13
1.01	14	1.09	13
1.02	14	1.10	13
1.03	14	1.11	13
1.04	14	1.12	13
1.05	13	1.13	13
1.06	13	1.14	13
1.07	13	1.15	14

The value of overrelaxation is modest in this example. Its value becomes more significant as the number of equations increases.

The optimum value of ω can be determined by experimentation. If a problem is to be worked only once, that procedure would not be worthwhile. However, if a problem is to be worked many times with the same **A** matrix for different **b** vectors, then a search for ω_{opt} may be worthwhile. Table 1.4 presents the results of such a search for the problem considered in this example. For this problem, $1.05 \le \omega \le 1.14$ yields the most efficient solution. Much more dramatic results are obtained for large systems of equations.

SUMMARY

The basic methods for solving systems of linear algebraic equations are presented in this chapter. Since these methods use matrices and determinants, the elementary properties of matrices and determinants are presented.

Several direct solution methods are presented: Cramer's rule, Gauss elimination, Gauss–Jordan elimination, **LU** decomposition, and the Thomas algorithm for tridiagonal systems. Cramer's rule is impractical for solving systems with more than three or four equations. Gauss elimination is the workhorse method of choice. For systems of equations having a constant coefficient matrix but many right-hand-side vectors, **LU** decomposition is the method of choice. For tridiagonal systems, the Thomas algorithm is the method of choice. Direct methods are generally used when one or more of the following conditions holds: (1) the number of equations is small (100 or less), (2) most of the coefficients of the equations are nonzero, (3) the system of equations is not diagonally dominant, or (4) the system of equations is ill-conditioned.

Several iterative methods are presented: Jacobi iteration, Gauss–Seidel iteration, and successive overrelaxation (SOR). All iterative methods converge if the coefficient matrix is diagonally dominant. SOR is the workhorse method of choice. Although the determination of the optimum value of the overrelaxation factor ω is tedious, it is generally worthwhile if the system of equations is to be solved many times for many right-hand side vectors. Iterative methods are generally used when the number of equations is large, the coefficient matrix is sparse, and the coefficient matrix is diagonally dominant.

PROBLEMS

Section 1.2 Elementary Properties of Matrices and Determinants

Consider the following four matrices:

$$\mathbf{A} = \begin{bmatrix} 1 & 1 & 3 \\ 5 & 3 & 1 \\ 2 & 3 & 1 \end{bmatrix} \quad \mathbf{B} = \begin{bmatrix} 2 & 3 & 5 \\ 3 & 1 & -2 \\ 1 & 3 & 4 \end{bmatrix} \quad \mathbf{C} = \begin{bmatrix} 2 & 1 \\ 3 & 4 \\ 2 & 5 \end{bmatrix} \quad \mathbf{D} = \begin{bmatrix} 1 & 1 & 1 \\ 1 & 3 & 3 \\ 1 & 3 & 5 \end{bmatrix}$$

Determine the following quantities, if defined:

1. (*a*) $\mathbf{A}+\mathbf{B}$ (*b*) $\mathbf{B}+\mathbf{A}$ (*c*) $\mathbf{A}+\mathbf{D}$ (*d*) $\mathbf{A}+\mathbf{C}$ (*e*) $\mathbf{B}+\mathbf{C}$

2. (*a*) $\mathbf{A}-\mathbf{B}$ (*b*) $\mathbf{B}-\mathbf{A}$ (*c*) $\mathbf{A}-\mathbf{D}$ (*d*) $\mathbf{B}-\mathbf{D}$ (*e*) $\mathbf{A}-\mathbf{C}$
(*f*) $\mathbf{B}-\mathbf{C}$ (*g*) $\mathbf{C}-\mathbf{B}$ (*h*) $\mathbf{D}-\mathbf{C}$

***3.** *(*a*) $\mathbf{AC}$ (*b*) $\mathbf{BC}$ (*c*) $\mathbf{CA}$ (*d*) $\mathbf{CB}$ (*e*) $\mathbf{AD}$ (*f*) $\mathbf{BD}$
(*g*) $\mathbf{C}^T\mathbf{A}$ (*h*) $\mathbf{C}^T\mathbf{B}$ (*i*) $\mathbf{C}^T\mathbf{D}$ (*j*) $\mathbf{AA}^T$ (*k*) $\mathbf{BB}^T$ (*l*) $\mathbf{DD}^T$

4. (*a*) Compute **AB** and **BA** and show that $\mathbf{AB} \neq \mathbf{BA}$.
(*b*) Compute **AD** and **DA** and show that $\mathbf{AD} \neq \mathbf{DA}$.
(*c*) Compute **BD** and **DB** and show that $\mathbf{BD} \neq \mathbf{DB}$.

5. Show that: (*a*) $(\mathbf{AB})^T = \mathbf{B}^T\mathbf{A}^T$ and (*b*) $\mathbf{AB} = (\mathbf{Ab}_1\ \mathbf{Ab}_2\ \mathbf{Ab}_3)$, where $\mathbf{b}_1$, $\mathbf{b}_2$, and $\mathbf{b}_3$ are the columns of **B**.

6. Work Problem 5 for the general matrices **A** and **B**.

7. Verify that (*a*) $\mathbf{A}+(\mathbf{B}+\mathbf{D}) = (\mathbf{A}+\mathbf{B})+\mathbf{D}$ and (*b*) $\mathbf{A}(\mathbf{BD}) = (\mathbf{AB})\mathbf{D}$.

***8.** Calculate the following determinants by the diagonal method, if defined:
*(*a*) det(**A**) (*b*) det(**B**) *(*c*) det(**C**) *(*d*) det(**D**) (*e*) det(**AB**)
(*f*) det(**AD**) *(*g*) det(**BA**) (*h*) det(**DA**) (*i*) det(**CD**) (*j*) det($\mathbf{C}^T\mathbf{A}$)

9. Work Problem 8 using the cofactor method.

Section 1.3 Direct Elimination Methods

Solve the following systems of equations using Cramer's rule.

***10.**

$$\begin{aligned} -2x_1 + 3x_2 + x_3 &= 9 \\ 3x_1 + 4x_2 - 5x_3 &= 0 \\ x_1 - 2x_2 + x_3 &= -4 \end{aligned}$$

11.

$$\begin{bmatrix} 1 & 1 & 3 \\ 5 & 3 & 1 \\ 2 & 3 & 1 \end{bmatrix} \begin{bmatrix} x \\ y \\ z \end{bmatrix} = \begin{bmatrix} 2 \\ 3 \\ -1 \end{bmatrix}$$

***12.**

$$\begin{aligned} x_1 + 3x_2 + 2x_3 - x_4 &= 9 \\ 4x_1 + 2x_2 + 5x_3 + x_4 &= 27 \\ 3x_1 - 3x_2 + 2x_3 + 4x_4 &= 19 \\ -x_1 + 2x_2 - 3x_3 + 5x_4 &= 14 \end{aligned}$$

13. $$\begin{bmatrix} 3 & 1 & -1 & 3 \\ 2 & 1 & -2 & 0 \\ 0 & 3 & 2 & -2 \\ 1 & 1 & 1 & 5 \end{bmatrix} \begin{bmatrix} x_i \end{bmatrix} = \begin{bmatrix} 4 \\ -1 \\ 4 \\ -2 \end{bmatrix}$$

14. $$\begin{bmatrix} 1 & -2 & 1 \\ 2 & 1 & 2 \\ -1 & 1 & 3 \end{bmatrix} \begin{bmatrix} x_1 \\ x_2 \\ x_3 \end{bmatrix} = \begin{bmatrix} -1 \\ 3 \\ 8 \end{bmatrix}$$

15. $$\begin{bmatrix} 2 & 3 & 5 \\ 3 & 1 & -2 \\ 1 & 3 & 4 \end{bmatrix} \begin{bmatrix} x_1 \\ x_2 \\ x_3 \end{bmatrix} = \begin{bmatrix} 0 \\ -2 \\ -3 \end{bmatrix}$$

16. $$\begin{bmatrix} 2 & -2 & 2 & 1 \\ 2 & -4 & 1 & 3 \\ -1 & 3 & -4 & 2 \\ 2 & 4 & 3 & -2 \end{bmatrix} \begin{bmatrix} x_1 \\ x_2 \\ x_3 \\ x_4 \end{bmatrix} = \begin{bmatrix} 7 \\ 10 \\ -14 \\ 1 \end{bmatrix}$$

17. $$\begin{bmatrix} 1 & 1 & 1 \\ 1 & 2 & 1 \\ 3 & 3 & 4 \end{bmatrix} \begin{bmatrix} x_1 \\ x_2 \\ x_3 \end{bmatrix} = \begin{bmatrix} 0 \\ -4 \\ 1 \end{bmatrix}$$

***18.** Solve Problem 10 using Gauss elimination.
19. Solve Problem 11 using Gauss elimination.
***20.** Solve Problem 12 using Gauss elimination.
21. Solve Problem 13 using Gauss elimination.
22. Solve Problem 14 using Gauss elimination.
23. Solve Problem 15 using Gauss elimination.
24. Solve Problem 16 using Gauss elimination.
25. Solve Problem 17 using Gauss elimination.
***26.** Solve Problem 10 using Gauss–Jordan elimination.
27. Solve Problem 11 using Gauss–Jordan elimination.
***28.** Solve Problem 12 using Gauss–Jordan elimination.
29. Solve Problem 13 using Gauss–Jordan elimination.
30. Solve Problem 14 using Gauss–Jordan elimination.
31. Solve Problem 15 using Gauss–Jordan elimination.
32. Solve Problem 16 using Gauss–Jordan elimination.
33. Solve Problem 17 using Gauss–Jordan elimination.
***34.** Calculate the inverse of the coefficient matrix considered in Problem 10 using Gauss–Jordan elimination. Solve the system of equations using the matrix inverse method.
35. Solve Problem 11 by the procedure described in Problem 34.
***36.** Solve Problem 12 by the procedure described in Problem 34.
37. Solve Problem 13 by the procedure described in Problem 34.
38. Solve Problem 14 by the procedure described in Problem 34.
39. Solve Problem 15 by the procedure described in Problem 34.
40. Solve Problem 16 by the procedure described in Problem 34.
41. Solve Problem 17 by the procedure described in Problem 34.

Section 1.4 LU Decomposition

***42.** Solve Problem 10 by **LU** decomposition using the Doolittle method.
43. Solve Problem 11 by **LU** decomposition using the Doolittle method.
***44.** Solve Problem 12 by **LU** decomposition using the Doolittle method.
45. Solve Problem 13 by **LU** decomposition using the Doolittle method.
46. Solve Problem 14 by **LU** decomposition using the Doolittle method.
47. Solve Problem 15 by **LU** decomposition using the Doolittle method.
48. Solve Problem 16 by **LU** decomposition using the Doolittle method.
49. Solve Problem 17 by **LU** decomposition using the Doolittle method.
***50.** Solve Problem 10 by **LU** decomposition using the Crout method.
51. Solve Problem 11 by **LU** decomposition using the Crout method.
***52.** Solve Problem 12 by **LU** decomposition using the Crout method.
53. Solve Problem 13 by **LU** decomposition using the Crout method.
54. Solve Problem 14 by **LU** decomposition using the Crout method.
55. Solve Problem 15 by **LU** decomposition using the Crout method.
56. Solve Problem 16 by **LU** decomposition using the Crout method.
57. Solve Problem 17 by **LU** decomposition using the Crout method.

Section 1.5 Tridiagonal Systems of Equations

Solve the following systems of equations using the Thomas algorithm.

***58.**
$$\begin{bmatrix} 2 & 1 & 0 & 0 \\ 1 & 2 & 1 & 0 \\ 0 & 1 & 2 & 1 \\ 0 & 0 & 1 & 2 \end{bmatrix} \begin{bmatrix} x_1 \\ x_2 \\ x_3 \\ x_4 \end{bmatrix} = \begin{bmatrix} 4 \\ 8 \\ 12 \\ 11 \end{bmatrix}$$

59.
$$\begin{bmatrix} 3 & 2 & 0 & 0 \\ 2 & 3 & 2 & 0 \\ 0 & 2 & 3 & 2 \\ 0 & 0 & 2 & 3 \end{bmatrix} \begin{bmatrix} x_1 \\ x_2 \\ x_3 \\ x_4 \end{bmatrix} = \begin{bmatrix} 12 \\ 17 \\ 14 \\ 7 \end{bmatrix}$$

60.
$$\begin{bmatrix} -2 & 1 & 0 & 0 \\ 1 & -2 & 1 & 0 \\ 0 & 1 & -2 & 1 \\ 0 & 0 & 1 & -2 \end{bmatrix} \begin{bmatrix} x_1 \\ x_2 \\ x_3 \\ x_4 \end{bmatrix} = \begin{bmatrix} 1 \\ 2 \\ -7 \\ -1 \end{bmatrix}$$

61.
$$\begin{bmatrix} -2 & 1 & 0 & 0 \\ 1 & -2 & 1 & 0 \\ 0 & 1 & -2 & 1 \\ 0 & 0 & 1 & -2 \end{bmatrix} \begin{bmatrix} x_1 \\ x_2 \\ x_3 \\ x_4 \end{bmatrix} = \begin{bmatrix} 5 \\ 1 \\ 0 \\ 8 \end{bmatrix}$$

62.
$$\begin{bmatrix} 4 & -1 & 0 & 0 \\ -1 & 4 & -1 & 0 \\ 0 & -1 & 4 & -1 \\ 0 & 0 & -1 & 4 \end{bmatrix} [x_1] = \begin{bmatrix} 150 \\ 200 \\ 150 \\ 100 \end{bmatrix}$$

Section 1.6 Iterative Methods

Solve the following systems of equations by iterative methods. For the first guess, use $\mathbf{x}^{(0)T} = (0.0 \quad 0.0 \quad 0.0 \quad 0.0)$.

*63. Work Problem 58 using Jacobi iteration.
64. Work Problem 60 using Jacobi iteration.
65. Work Problem 61 using Jacobi iteration.
66. Work Problem 62 using Jacobi iteration.
*67. Work Problem 58 using Gauss-Seidel iteration.
68. Work Problem 60 using Gauss-Seidel iteration.
69. Work Problem 61 using Gauss-Seidel iteration.
70. Work Problem 62 using Gauss-Seidel iteration.

Section 1.7 Successive Overrelaxation (SOR)

*71. Work Problem 58 using the SOR method, with $\omega = 1.27$.
72. Work Problem 60 using the SOR method, with $\omega = 1.27$.
73. Work Problem 61 using the SOR method, with $\omega = 1.27$.
74. Work Problem 62 using the SOR method, with $\omega = 1.05$.
75. Work Problem 71 for $1.25 \le \omega \le 1.35$ with $\Delta\omega = 0.01$.
76. Work Problem 72 for $1.25 \le \omega \le 1.35$ with $\Delta\omega = 0.01$.
77. Work Problem 73 for $1.25 \le \omega \le 1.35$ with $\Delta\omega = 0.01$.
78. Work Problem 74 for $1.00 \le \omega \le 1.10$ with $\Delta\omega = 0.01$.

CHAPTER 2

EIGENPROBLEMS

Section

Example

2.1 INTRODUCTION

Chapter 1 is devoted to the solution of systems of linear algebraic equations:

$$\mathbf{Ax} = \mathbf{b} \tag{2.1}$$

As discussed in Section 1.1, Eq. (2.1) may have a unique solution (the case considered in Chapter 1); no solution; an infinite number of solutions; or the trivial solution $\mathbf{x} = \mathbf{0}$, if the system of equations is homogeneous:

$$\mathbf{Ax} = \mathbf{0} \tag{2.2}$$

The latter case is the subject of Chapter 2.

Consider a system of two homogeneous linear algebraic equations:

$$a_{11}x_1 + a_{12}x_2 = 0 \tag{2.3a}$$

$$a_{21}x_1 + a_{22}x_2 = 0 \tag{2.3b}$$

Equation (2.3) represents two straight lines in the x_1x_2 plane, both passing through the origin $x_1 = x_2 = 0$. Rearranging Eq. (2.3) gives

$$x_2 = -\frac{a_{11}}{a_{12}}x_1 = m_1x_1 \tag{2.4a}$$

$$x_2 = -\frac{a_{21}}{a_{22}}x_1 = m_2x_1 \tag{2.4b}$$

where m_1 and m_2 are the slopes of the two straight lines. Figure 2.1 illustrates Eq. (2.4) in the x_1x_2 plane. Both straight lines pass through the origin, where $x_1 = x_2 = 0$, which is the trivial solution. If the slopes m_1 and m_2 are different, there is no other solution, as illustrated in Fig. 2.1a. However, if $m_1 = m_2 = m$, as illustrated in Fig. 1.2b, then the two straight lines lie on top of each other and there are an infinite number of solutions. For any value of x_1, there is a corresponding value of x_2. The ratio of x_2 to x_1 is specified by value of the slope m.

If the coefficients a_{ij} in Eq. (2.4) are completely specified, then the slopes m_1 and m_2 are fixed, and one or the other of the two situations illustrated in Fig. 2.1 exists. However, if the coefficients a_{ij} in Eq. (2.4) contain an unspecified variable, say λ, then λ can be chosen so that $m_1 = m_2 = m$, and a solution other than the trivial solution exists. The variable λ is called an *eigenvalue*, and the solution vector $\mathbf{x}$ corresponding to λ is called an *eigenvector*. Problems involving eigenvalues and eigenvectors are called *eigenproblems*.

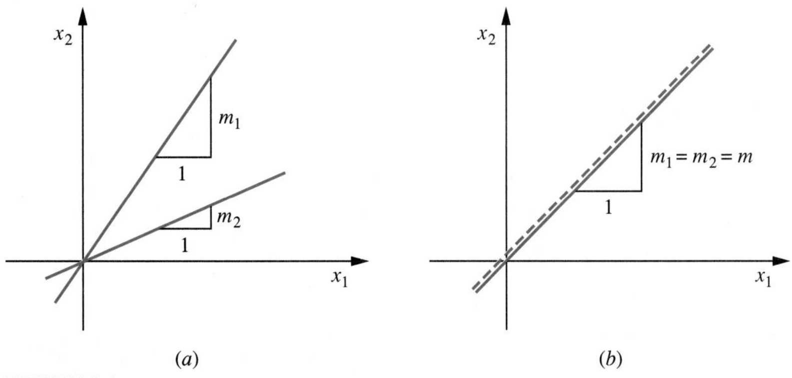

FIGURE 2.1
Graphical representation of Eq.(2.4). (a) $m_1 \neq m_2$. (b) $m_1 = m_2 = m$.

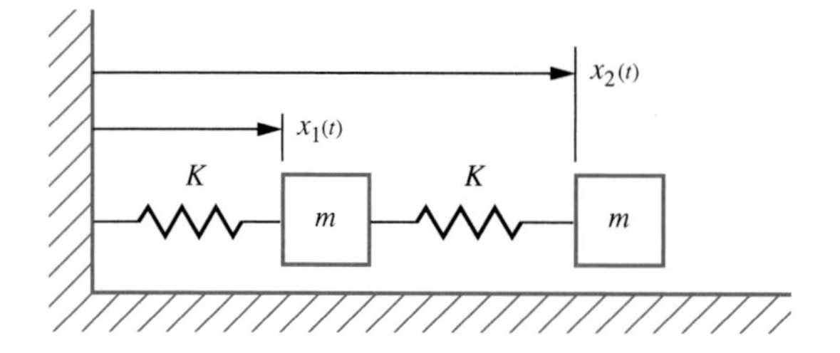

FIGURE 2.2
Undamped spring-mass system.

As an example, consider the steady periodic free vibration of the undamped spring–mass system illustrated in Fig. 2.2. Applying Newton's second law of motion gives

$$m\frac{d^2x_1}{dt^2} = K(x_2 - x_1) - Kx_1 = Kx_2 - 2Kx_1 \tag{2.5a}$$

$$m\frac{d^2x_2}{dt^2} = -K(x_2 - x_1) = Kx_1 - Kx_2 \tag{2.5b}$$

For steady periodic motion, $\mathbf{x} = \mathbf{X}\sin(\omega t + \phi)$, where $\mathbf{X}^T = (X_1\ X_2)$ is the amplitude of the oscillation, ω is the undamped natural frequency of oscillation, and ϕ is a phase angle. Substituting this expression into Eq. (2.5) and simplifying yields

$$(2 - \lambda)X_1 - X_2 = 0 \tag{2.6a}$$

$$-X_1 + (1 - \lambda)X_2 = 0 \tag{2.6b}$$

where λ is the eigenvalue given by

$$\boxed{\lambda = \frac{m\omega^2}{K}} \tag{2.7}$$

Equation (2.6) can be written in matrix form as

$$\boxed{\mathbf{Ax} = \lambda\mathbf{x}} \tag{2.8}$$

where $\mathbf{A}$ is the 2×2 coefficient matrix

$$\mathbf{A} = \begin{bmatrix} 2 & -1 \\ -1 & 1 \end{bmatrix} \tag{2.9}$$

$\mathbf{x}$ is the 2×1 column vector

$$\mathbf{x} = \begin{bmatrix} X_1 \\ X_2 \end{bmatrix} \tag{2.10}$$

and the eigenvalue λ is a scalar. The values of λ that satisfy Eq. (2.8) are the eigenvalues of Eq. (2.8). The corresponding values of $\mathbf{x}$ are the eigenvectors of Eq. (2.8). The eigenvalues determine the permissible frequencies of oscillation, that is, $\omega = \sqrt{\lambda K/m}$. The corresponding eigenvectors determine the mode shape (i.e., the relative value of X_1 and X_2). Equation (2.8) can be written as

$$\boxed{(\mathbf{A} - \lambda\mathbf{I})\mathbf{x} = \mathbf{0}} \tag{2.11}$$

Equation (2.11) represents a homogeneous system of linear equations. This is the classical eigenproblem.

Eigenproblems can be encountered in the analysis of many physical systems. They arise in the analysis of the dynamic behavior of mechanical, electrical, fluid, thermal, and structural systems, as well as in the analysis of control systems. The objectives of this chapter are to introduce the general features of eigenproblems, to present several methods for solving simple eigenproblems, and to illustrate those methods by examples.

2.2 BASIC CHARACTERISTICS OF EIGENPROBLEMS

The general concept of an eigenproblem is introduced in Section 2.1. The basic characteristics of eigenproblems are presented in this section.

Consider a nonhomogeneous system of linear algebraic equations:

$$\mathbf{Cx} = \mathbf{b} \tag{2.12}$$

Solving for $\mathbf{x}$ by Cramer's rule yields

$$x_j = \frac{\det(\mathbf{C}^j)}{\det(\mathbf{C})} \qquad (j = 1, \ldots, n) \tag{2.13}$$

where the matrix $\mathbf{C}^j$ is the matrix $\mathbf{C}$ with column j replaced by the vector $\mathbf{b}$. In general, $\det(\mathbf{C}) \neq 0$, and unique values are found for x_j.

Consider a homogeneous system of linear algebraic equations:

$$\mathbf{Cx} = \mathbf{0} \tag{2.14}$$

Solving for $\mathbf{x}$ by Cramer's rule yields

$$x_j = \frac{\det(\mathbf{C}^j)}{\det(\mathbf{C})} = \frac{0}{|\mathbf{C}|} \qquad (j = 1, \ldots, n) \tag{2.15}$$

Therefore, $\mathbf{x} = \mathbf{0}$ unless $\det(\mathbf{C}) = 0$. In general, $\det(\mathbf{C}) \neq 0$, and the only solution is the trivial solution $\mathbf{x} = \mathbf{0}$. For certain forms of $\mathbf{C}$ that involve an unspecified arbitrary scalar λ, the value of λ can be chosen to force $\det(\mathbf{C}) = 0$, so that a solution other than $\mathbf{x} = \mathbf{0}$ is possible. In that case $\mathbf{x}$ is not unique, but relative values of x_j can be found.

Consider the coefficient matrix $\mathbf{C}$ to be of the form

$$\mathbf{C} = \mathbf{A} - \lambda\mathbf{B} \tag{2.16}$$

where λ is an unspecified scalar. Then

$$\mathbf{Cx} = (\mathbf{A} - \lambda\mathbf{B})\mathbf{x} = \mathbf{0} \tag{2.17}$$

The values of λ are determined so that

$$\det(\mathbf{C}) = \det(\mathbf{A} - \lambda\mathbf{B}) = 0 \tag{2.18}$$

The corresponding values of λ are the eigenvalues.

The homogeneous system of equations is generally written in the form

$$\mathbf{Ax} = \lambda\mathbf{Bx} \tag{2.19}$$

In many problems $\mathbf{B} = \mathbf{I}$, and Eq. (2.19) becomes

$$\boxed{\mathbf{Ax} = \lambda\mathbf{x}} \tag{2.20}$$

In problems where $\mathbf{B} \neq \mathbf{I}$, define the matrix $\overline{\mathbf{A}} = (\mathbf{B}^{-1}\mathbf{A})$. Then Eq. (2.19) becomes

$$\boxed{\overline{\mathbf{A}}\mathbf{x} = \lambda\mathbf{x}} \tag{2.21}$$

which has the same form as Eq. (2.20). Equation (2.20) can be written in the alternate form

$$\boxed{(\mathbf{A} - \lambda\mathbf{I})\mathbf{x} = 0} \tag{2.22}$$

The eigenvalues can be found by expanding $\det(\mathbf{A} - \lambda\mathbf{I}) = 0$ and finding the roots of the resulting characteristic equation, which is an nth-order polynomial. For example, consider the eigenproblem specified by Eq. (2.6) in Section 2.1:

$$(2 - \lambda)X_1 - X_2 = 0 \tag{2.23a}$$

$$-X_1 + (1 - \lambda)X_2 = 0 \tag{2.23b}$$

Expanding $\det(\mathbf{A} - \lambda\mathbf{I}) = 0$ yields the characteristic equation

$$(2 - \lambda)(1 - \lambda) - 1 = 0 \tag{2.24}$$

which can be rearranged in the form

$$\lambda^2 - 3\lambda + 1 = 0 \tag{2.25}$$

Solving Eq. (2.25) by the quadratic formula yields the two eigenvalues

$$\lambda_1 = \frac{3 + \sqrt{5}}{2} = 2.6180\ldots \qquad \text{and} \qquad \lambda_2 = \frac{3 - \sqrt{5}}{2} = 0.3820\ldots \tag{2.26}$$

The two eigenvectors $\mathbf{x}_1$ and $\mathbf{x}_2$, corresponding to the two eigenvalues λ_1 and λ_2 respectively, are found by substituting the values of the eigenvalues into the system of equations and solving for the eigenvectors. Substituting $\lambda_1 = 2.6180$ into Eq. (2.23) gives

$$\begin{bmatrix} -0.6180 & -1 \\ -1 & -1.6180 \end{bmatrix} \begin{bmatrix} X_1 \\ X_2 \end{bmatrix} = \begin{bmatrix} 0 \\ 0 \end{bmatrix} \tag{2.27}$$

Augmenting the coefficient matrix by the right-hand-side zero vector and applying Gauss elimination yields

$$\left[\begin{array}{cc|c} -0.6180 & -1 & 0 \\ -1 & -1.6180 & 0 \end{array}\right] R_2 - \frac{1.0000}{0.6180} R_1 \tag{2.28a}$$

$$\left[\begin{array}{cc|c} -0.6180 & -1 & 0 \\ 0 & 0 & 0 \end{array}\right] \tag{2.28b}$$

Equation (2.28b) shows that the system of equations is dependent. Thus, a unique solution, other than the trivial solution $\mathbf{x}_1 = 0$, does not exist. Equation (2.28b) has an infinite number of solutions given by

$$X_2 = -0.6180 X_1 \qquad (\text{for } \lambda_1 = 2.6180) \tag{2.29}$$

Substituting $\lambda_2 = 0.3820$ into Eq. (2.23) gives

$$\begin{bmatrix} 1.6180 & -1 \\ -1 & 0.6180 \end{bmatrix} \begin{bmatrix} X_1 \\ X_2 \end{bmatrix} = \begin{bmatrix} 0 \\ 0 \end{bmatrix} \tag{2.30}$$

Solving Eq. (2.30) by Gauss elimination gives

$$\left[\begin{array}{cc|c} 1.6180 & -1 & 0 \\ 0 & 0 & 0 \end{array}\right] \tag{2.31}$$

which yields

$$X_2 = 1.6180 X_1 \qquad (\text{for } \lambda_2 = 0.3820) \tag{2.32}$$

These results can be interpreted as follows. The spring–mass system can vibrate freely at the two distinct frequencies specified by

$$\omega_1 = \sqrt{\frac{\lambda_1 K}{m}} \quad \text{and} \quad \omega_2 = \sqrt{\frac{\lambda_2 K}{m}} \tag{2.33}$$

At ω_1, when $X_1 = 1.0000$, $X_2 = -0.6180$. Thus, the two masses move in opposite directions, and the amplitude of oscillation of the second mass is 61.80 percent of that of the first mass. At ω_2, when $X_1 = 1.0000$, $X_2 = 1.6180$. The two masses move in the same direction, and the amplitude of oscillation of the second mass is 161.80 percent of that of the first mass.

Finally, we relate the result from Cramer's rule, Eq. (2.15), which requires $\det(\mathbf{A}) = 0$ to obtain any solution other than the trivial solution $\mathbf{x} = \mathbf{0}$, to the result from the graphical analysis presented in Section 2.1, which requires the slopes of the two lines to be the same to obtain any solution other than the trivial solution. From Eq. (2.24),

$$\det(\mathbf{A}) = (2 - \lambda)(1 - \lambda) - 1 = 0 \tag{2.34}$$

From Eq. (2.23),

$$X_2 = (2 - \lambda)X_1 = m_1 X_1 \tag{2.35a}$$

$$X_2 = \frac{1}{(1 - \lambda)} X_1 = m_2 X_1 \tag{2.35b}$$

Equating the slopes m_1 and m_2 gives

$$(2 - \lambda) = \frac{1}{(1 - \lambda)} \tag{2.36}$$

which can be rearranged as

$$(2 - \lambda)(1 - \lambda) - 1 = 0 \tag{2.37}$$

Equations (2.34) and (2.37) are identical. Thus, requiring the slopes of the two lines to be equal is equivalent to requiring that $\det(\mathbf{A}) = 0$, and vice versa.

In summary, eigenproblems arise from homogeneous systems of equations that contain an unspecified parameter in the coefficients. The characteristic equation is determined by expanding the determinant

$$\det(\mathbf{A} - \lambda \mathbf{I}) = 0 \tag{2.38}$$

which yields an nth-degree polynomial in λ, called the characteristic equation. Solving the characteristic equation yields n eigenvalues $\lambda_i (i = 1, 2, \ldots, n)$. The n eigenvectors $\mathbf{x}_i (i = 1, 2, \ldots, n)$, corresponding to the n eigenvalues $\lambda_i (i = 1, 2, \ldots, n)$, are found by substituting the individual eigenvalues into the homogeneous system of equations, which is then solved for the eigenvectors.

In principle, the solution of eigenproblems is straightforward. In practice, when the order of the system of equations is very large, expanding the characteristic determinant to obtain the characteristic equation is difficult. Solving high-order polynomials for the eigenvalues presents yet another difficult problem. Consequently, more straightforward procedures for solving eigenproblems are desired. An iterative numerical procedure, called the power method, and several variations are presented in the following sections to illustrate the numerical solution of eigenproblems.

2.3 THE POWER METHOD

Consider the eigenproblem

$$\boxed{\mathbf{A}\mathbf{x} = \lambda\mathbf{x}} \tag{2.39}$$

When the largest (in absolute value) eigenvalue of $\mathbf{A}$ is distinct, its value can be found using an iterative technique called the *power method*. The procedure is as follows:

1. Assume a trial value $\mathbf{x}^{(0)}$ for the eigenvector $\mathbf{x}$. Choose one component of $\mathbf{x}$ to be unity. That component will be referred to as the *unity component*.
2. Perform the matrix multiplication

$$\mathbf{A}\mathbf{x}^{(0)} = \mathbf{y}^{(1)} \tag{2.40}$$

3. Factor (scale) $\mathbf{y}^{(1)}$ so that the unity component remains unity.

$$\mathbf{y}^{(1)} = \lambda^{(1)}\mathbf{x}^{(1)} \tag{2.41}$$

4. Repeat Steps (2) and (3) with $\mathbf{x} = \mathbf{x}^{(1)}$. Iterate to convergence.

The general algorithm for the power method is

$$\boxed{\mathbf{A}\mathbf{x}^{(k)} = \mathbf{y}^{(k+1)} = \lambda^{(k+1)}\mathbf{x}^{(k+1)}} \tag{2.42}$$

At convergence, the value λ is the largest (in absolute value) eigenvalue of $\mathbf{A}$, and the vector $\mathbf{x}$ is the corresponding eigenvector (scaled to unity on the unity component). When the iterations indicate that the unity component could be zero, a different unity component must be chosen. The method is slow to converge when the magnitudes (in absolute value) of the largest eigenvalues are nearly the same. When the largest eigenvalues are of equal magnitude, the power method, as described, fails.

TABLE 2.1
The power method

k	λ	x_1	x_2	x_3
0		1.0000	1.0000	1.0000
1	4.0000	1.0000	1.5000	0.7500
2	4.0000	1.0000	1.4375	0.8125
3	4.0625	1.0000	1.4462	0.8000
4	4.0462	1.0000	1.4449	0.8023
⋮	⋮	⋮	⋮	⋮
8	4.0489	1.0000	1.4450	0.8019

Example 2.1. The power method. Find the largest eigenvalue and the corresponding eigenvector of the matrix

$$\mathbf{A} = \begin{bmatrix} 1 & 1 & 2 \\ 2 & 1 & 3 \\ 1 & 1 & 1 \end{bmatrix} \tag{2.43}$$

Assume $\mathbf{x}^{(0)\mathrm{T}} = (1 \;\; 1 \;\; 1)$. Scale the first component, x_1, to unity. Then apply Eq. (2.42).

$$\mathbf{Ax}^{(0)} = \begin{bmatrix} 1 & 1 & 2 \\ 2 & 1 & 3 \\ 1 & 1 & 1 \end{bmatrix}\begin{bmatrix} 1.0000 \\ 1.0000 \\ 1.0000 \end{bmatrix} = \begin{bmatrix} 4.0000 \\ 6.0000 \\ 3.0000 \end{bmatrix}; \; \lambda^{(1)} = 4.0000 \quad \text{and} \quad \mathbf{x}^{(1)} = \begin{bmatrix} 1.0000 \\ 1.5000 \\ 0.7500 \end{bmatrix} \tag{2.44}$$

$$\mathbf{Ax}^{(1)} = \begin{bmatrix} 1 & 1 & 2 \\ 2 & 1 & 3 \\ 1 & 1 & 1 \end{bmatrix}\begin{bmatrix} 1.0000 \\ 1.5000 \\ 0.7500 \end{bmatrix} = \begin{bmatrix} 4.0000 \\ 5.7500 \\ 3.2500 \end{bmatrix}; \; \lambda^{(2)} = 4.0000 \quad \text{and} \quad \mathbf{x}^{(2)} = \begin{bmatrix} 1.0000 \\ 1.4375 \\ 0.8125 \end{bmatrix} \tag{2.45}$$

The results of the first two iterations presented above and of subsequent iterations are presented in Table 2.1. These results were obtained on a 13-decimal-digit computer. The iterations were continued until both λ and all components of $\mathbf{x}$ changed by less than 0.0001 between iterations. The final solution for the largest eigenvalue, denoted as λ_1, and the corresponding eigenvector $\mathbf{x}_1$, is

$$\lambda_1 = 4.0489 \quad \text{and} \quad \mathbf{x}_1 = \begin{bmatrix} 1.0000 \\ 1.4450 \\ 0.8019 \end{bmatrix} \tag{2.46}$$

The basis of the power method is as follows. Assume that $\mathbf{A}$ is an $n \times n$ nonsingular matrix having n eigenvalues, $\lambda_1, \lambda_2, \ldots, \lambda_n$, with n corresponding linearly independent eigenvectors $\mathbf{x}_1, \mathbf{x}_2, \ldots, \mathbf{x}_n$. Assume further that $|\lambda_1| > |\lambda_2| > \ldots > |\lambda_n|$. Since the eigenvectors $\mathbf{x}_i (i = 1, 2, \ldots, n)$ are linearly independent (i.e., they span the n-dimensional space), any arbitrary vector $\mathbf{x}$ can be expressed as a linear combination of the eigenvectors. Thus,

$$\mathbf{x} = C_1\mathbf{x}_1 + C_2\mathbf{x}_2 + \cdots + C_n\mathbf{x}_n = \sum_{i=1}^{n} C_i\mathbf{x}_i \tag{2.47}$$

Multiplying both sides of Eq. (2.47) by $\mathbf{A}, \mathbf{A}^2, \ldots, \mathbf{A}^k$, and so on, where the superscript denotes repetitive matrix multiplication, and recalling that $\mathbf{A}\mathbf{x}_i = \lambda_i \mathbf{x}_i$, yields

$$\mathbf{A}\mathbf{x} = \mathbf{y}^{(1)} = \sum_{i=1}^{n} C_i \mathbf{A}\mathbf{x}_i = \sum_{i=1}^{n} C_i \lambda_i \mathbf{x}_i \tag{2.48a}$$

$$\mathbf{A}^2\mathbf{x} = \mathbf{y}^{(2)} = \sum_{i=1}^{n} C_i \lambda_i \mathbf{A}\mathbf{x}_i = \sum_{i=1}^{n} C_i \lambda_i^2 \mathbf{x}_i \tag{2.48b}$$

$$\vdots \quad \vdots \qquad \vdots \qquad \vdots$$

$$\mathbf{A}^k\mathbf{x} = \mathbf{y}^{(k)} = \sum_{i=1}^{n} C_i \lambda_i^{k-1} \mathbf{A}\mathbf{x}_i = \sum_{i=1}^{n} C_i \lambda_i^k \mathbf{x}_i \tag{2.49}$$

Factoring λ_1^k out of Eq. (2.49) yields

$$\mathbf{A}^k\mathbf{x} = \mathbf{y}^{(k)} = \lambda_1^k \sum_{i=1}^{n} C_i \left(\frac{\lambda_i}{\lambda_1}\right)^k \mathbf{x}_i \tag{2.50}$$

Since $|\lambda_1| > |\lambda_i|$ for $i = 2, 3, \ldots, n$, the ratios $(\lambda_i/\lambda_1)^k \to 0$ as $k \to \infty$, and Eq. (2.50) approaches the limit

$$\mathbf{A}^k\mathbf{x} = \mathbf{y}^{(k)} = \lambda_1^k C_1 \mathbf{x}_1 \tag{2.51}$$

Equation (2.51) approaches zero if $|\lambda_1| < 1$ and approaches infinity if $|\lambda_1| > 1$.

Equation (2.51) can be used to determine λ_1 if the products $\mathbf{A}^k\mathbf{x} = \mathbf{y}^{(k)}$ are scaled so that the limit of Eq. (2.51) is finite but nonzero. This can be accomplished by scaling any component of $\mathbf{y}^{(k)}$ to unity at each step in the process. Choose the first component of $\mathbf{y}^{(k)}$, $y_1^{(k)}$, to be that component. Thus, $x_1 = 1.0$, and the first component of Eq. (2.51) is

$$y_1^{(k)} = \lambda_1^k C_1 \tag{2.52}$$

Applying Eq. (2.51) one more time (i.e., from k to $k + 1$) yields

$$y_1^{(k+1)} = \lambda_1^{k+1} C_1 \tag{2.53}$$

Taking the ratio of Eq. (2.53) to Eq. (2.52) gives

$$\frac{\lambda_1^{k+1} C_1}{\lambda_1^k C_1} = \lambda_1 = \frac{y_1^{(k+1)}}{y_1^{(k)}} \tag{2.54}$$

Thus, if $y_1^{(k)} = 1$, then $y_1^{(k+1)} = \lambda_1$. If $y_1^{(k+1)}$ is scaled by λ_1 so that $y_1^{(k+1)} = 1$, then $y_1^{(k+2)} = \lambda_1$, and so on. Consequently, scaling a particular component of $\mathbf{y}$ each iteration essentially factors λ_1 out of $\mathbf{y}$, so that Eq. (2.51) converges to a finite value. In the limit as $k \to \infty$, the scaling factor approaches λ_1, and the scaled $\mathbf{y}$ vector approaches the eigenvector $\mathbf{x}_1$.

2.4 THE INVERSE POWER METHOD

When the smallest (in absolute value) eigenvalue of $\mathbf{A}$ is distinct, its value can be found using an iterative technique called the *inverse power method*. Essentially, this involves finding the eigenvalue of the inverse matrix $\mathbf{A}^{-1}$. Recall the original eigenproblem:

$$\mathbf{Ax} = \lambda\mathbf{x} \tag{2.55}$$

Multiplying Eq. (2.55) by $\mathbf{A}^{-1}$ gives

$$\mathbf{A}^{-1}\mathbf{Ax} = \mathbf{Ix} = \mathbf{x} = \lambda\mathbf{A}^{-1}\mathbf{x} \tag{2.56}$$

Rearranging Eq. (2.56) yields an eigenproblem for $\mathbf{A}^{-1}$. Thus,

$$\boxed{\mathbf{A}^{-1}\mathbf{x} = \left(\frac{1}{\lambda}\right)\mathbf{x} = \lambda_i\mathbf{x}} \tag{2.57}$$

The eigenvalues λ_i of $\mathbf{A}^{-1}$ are the reciprocals of the eigenvalues λ of $\mathbf{A}$. The eigenvectors of $\mathbf{A}^{-1}$ are the same as the eigenvectors of $\mathbf{A}$. The power method can be used to find the largest eigenvalue of $\mathbf{A}^{-1}$. The reciprocal of that eigenvalue is the smallest eigenvalue of $\mathbf{A}$.

In practice, the **LU** method is used to solve the inverse eigenproblem instead of calculating $\mathbf{A}^{-1}$. The problem to be solved is:

$$\mathbf{x}^{(n+1)} = \mathbf{A}^{-1}\mathbf{x}^{(n)} = \mathbf{y}^{n+1} \tag{2.58}$$

Multiplying Eq. (2.58) by $\mathbf{A}$ yields

$$\mathbf{AA}^{-1}\mathbf{x}^{(n)} = \mathbf{Ix}^{(n)} = \mathbf{x}^{(n)} = \mathbf{Ay}^{(n+1)} \tag{2.59}$$

which yields

$$\boxed{\mathbf{Ay}^{n+1} = \mathbf{x}^{n}} \tag{2.60}$$

Equation (2.60) is in the standard form $\mathbf{Ax} = \mathbf{b}$, where $\mathbf{x} = \mathbf{y}^{(n+1)}$ and $\mathbf{b} = \mathbf{x}^{(n)}$. Thus, for a given $\mathbf{x}^{(n)}$, $\mathbf{y}^{(n+1)}$ can be found by the Doolittle **LU** decomposition method. The procedure is as follows:

1. Solve for $\mathbf{L}$ and $\mathbf{U}$ such that $\mathbf{LU} = \mathbf{A}$ by the Doolittle method.
2. Assume $\mathbf{x}^{(0)}$. Designate a component of $\mathbf{x}$ to be unity.
3. Solve for $\mathbf{x}'$ by forward substitution using the equation

$$\mathbf{Lx}' = \mathbf{x}^{(0)} \tag{2.61}$$

4. Solve for $\mathbf{y}^{(1)}$ by back substitution using the equation

$$\mathbf{U}\mathbf{y}^{(1)} = \mathbf{x}' \tag{2.62}$$

5. Factor $\mathbf{y}^{(1)}$ so that the unity component is unity. Thus,

$$\mathbf{y}^{(1)} = \lambda_i^{(1)}\mathbf{x}^{(1)} \tag{2.63}$$

6. Repeat Steps (3) to (5) with $\mathbf{x}^{(1)}$. Iterate to convergence.

The general algorithm is

$$\mathbf{L}\mathbf{x}' = \mathbf{x}^{(k)} \tag{2.64}$$

$$\mathbf{U}\mathbf{y}^{(k+1)} = \mathbf{x}' \tag{2.65}$$

$$\mathbf{y}^{(k+1)} = \lambda_i^{(k+1)}\mathbf{x}^{(k+1)} \tag{2.66}$$

At convergence, $\lambda = 1/\lambda_i$, and $\mathbf{x}^{(k+1)}$ is the corresponding eigenvector.

Example 2.2. The inverse power method. Find the smallest eigenvalue and the corresponding eigenvector of the matrix

$$\mathbf{A} = \begin{bmatrix} 1 & 1 & 2 \\ 2 & 1 & 3 \\ 1 & 1 & 1 \end{bmatrix} \tag{2.67}$$

Assume $\mathbf{x}^{(0)\mathrm{T}} = (1\ \ 1\ \ 1)$. Scale the second component of $\mathbf{x}$ to unity. The first step is to solve for $\mathbf{L}$ and $\mathbf{U}$ by the Doolittle method. The results are

$$\mathbf{L} = \begin{bmatrix} 1 & 0 & 0 \\ 2 & 1 & 0 \\ 1 & 0 & 1 \end{bmatrix} \quad \text{and} \quad \mathbf{U} = \begin{bmatrix} 1 & 1 & 2 \\ 0 & -1 & -1 \\ 0 & 0 & -1 \end{bmatrix} \tag{2.68}$$

Solve for $\mathbf{x}'$ by forward substitution using $\mathbf{L}\mathbf{x}' = \mathbf{x}^{(0)}$.

$$\begin{bmatrix} 1 & 0 & 0 \\ 2 & 1 & 0 \\ 1 & 0 & 1 \end{bmatrix}\begin{bmatrix} x_1' \\ x_2' \\ x_3' \end{bmatrix} = \begin{bmatrix} 1.0 \\ 1.0 \\ 1.0 \end{bmatrix};$$

$$x_1' = 1.0$$

$$x_2' = 1.0 - 2.0(1.0) = -1.0 \tag{2.69}$$

$$x_3' = 1.0 - 1.0(1.0) - 0.0(-1.0) = 0.0$$

Solve for $\mathbf{y}^{(1)}$ by back substitution from $\mathbf{U}\mathbf{y}^{(1)} = \mathbf{x}'$.

$$\begin{bmatrix} 1 & 1 & 2 \\ 0 & -1 & -1 \\ 0 & 0 & -1 \end{bmatrix}\begin{bmatrix} y_1^{(1)} \\ y_2^{(1)} \\ y_3^{(1)} \end{bmatrix} = \begin{bmatrix} 1.0 \\ -1.0 \\ 0.0 \end{bmatrix};$$

TABLE 2.2
The inverse power method

k	λ_i	x_1	x_2	x_3
0		1.0000	1.0000	1.0000
1	1.0000	0.0000	1.0000	0.0000
2	−1.0000	−1.0000	1.0000	0.0000
3	−2.0000	−1.5000	1.0000	0.5000
4	−2.0000	−2.2500	1.0000	1.0000
5	−2.2500	−2.8889	1.0000	1.4444
⋮	⋮	⋮	⋮	⋮
21	−2.8019	−4.0489	1.0000	2.2470

$$y_1^{(1)} = \frac{1.0 - 1.0(1.0) - 2.0(0.0)}{1.0} = 0.0$$

$$y_2^{(1)} = \frac{-1.0 - (-1.0)(0.0)}{(-1.0)} = 1.0 \tag{2.70}$$

$$y_3^{(1)} = 0.0$$

Scale $\mathbf{y}^{(1)}$ so that the unity component (i.e., $y_2^{(1)}$) is unity.

$$\mathbf{y}^{(1)} = \begin{bmatrix} 0.0 \\ 1.0 \\ 0.0 \end{bmatrix}; \qquad \lambda_i^{(1)} = 1.0 \qquad \text{and} \qquad \mathbf{x}^{(1)} = \begin{bmatrix} 0.0 \\ 1.0 \\ 0.0 \end{bmatrix} \tag{2.71}$$

The results of the first iteration presented above, and of subsequent iterations, are presented in Table 2.2. These results were obtained on a 13-decimal-digit computer. The iterations were continued until both λ and all components of $\mathbf{x}$ changed by less than 0.0001 between iterations. The final solution for the smallest eigenvalue, denoted as λ_3, and the corresponding eigenvector $\mathbf{x}_3$, is

$$\lambda_3 = \frac{1}{\lambda_i} = \frac{1}{-2.8019} = -0.3569 \quad \text{and} \quad \mathbf{x}_3 = \begin{bmatrix} -4.0489 \\ 1.0000 \\ 2.2470 \end{bmatrix} \tag{2.72}$$

2.5 SHIFTING EIGENVALUES

The eigenvalues of a matrix $\mathbf{A}$ may be shifted by the scalar s by subtracting $s\mathbf{I}$ from both sides of the standard eigenproblem:

$$\mathbf{Ax} = \lambda\mathbf{x} \tag{2.73}$$

Subtracting $s\mathbf{Ix}$ from both sides of Eq. (2.73) gives

$$(\mathbf{A} - s\mathbf{I})\mathbf{x} = \mathbf{A}_s\mathbf{x} = (\lambda - s\mathbf{I})\mathbf{x} = (\lambda - s)\mathbf{x} = \lambda_s\mathbf{x} \tag{2.74}$$

which can be written as

$$\boxed{\mathbf{A}_s\mathbf{x} = \lambda_s\mathbf{x}} \tag{2.75}$$

Shifting the matrix **A** by the scalar s shifts the eigenvalues by s. Shifting the matrix by a scalar does not affect the eigenvectors. Shifting the eigenvalues of a matrix can be used (a) to find the largest eigenvalue of opposite sign to the largest eigenvalue in magnitude, and (b) to accelerate convergence for slowly converging eigenvalues.

Shifting Eigenvalues to Find the Largest Eigenvalue of Opposite Sign

When a matrix has both positive and negative eigenvalues, the largest (in magnitude) eigenvalue can be found by the power method. The largest (in magnitude) eigenvalue of opposite sign can then be found by shifting the eigenvalues by the largest (in magnitude) eigenvalue and finding the largest eigenvalue of the shifted matrix by the power method. The procedure is as follows:

1. Solve for the largest (in magnitude) eigenvalue λ_1.
2. Shift the eigenvalues of **A** by $s = \lambda_1$.
3. Solve for the eigenvalue λ_s of the shifted matrix $\mathbf{A}_s$ by the power method.
4. Calculate the largest eigenvalue of opposite sign by $\lambda = \lambda_s + s$.

Example 2.3. Shifting eigenvalues to find the largest eigenvalue of opposite sign. Find the largest (in magnitude) negative eigenvalue of matrix **A** by shifting the eigenvalues by $s = 4.0$ (recall that $\lambda_1 = 4.0489$). The original and shifted matrices are

$$\mathbf{A} = \begin{bmatrix} 1 & 1 & 2 \\ 2 & 1 & 3 \\ 1 & 1 & 1 \end{bmatrix} \quad \text{and} \quad \mathbf{A}_s = \begin{bmatrix} -3 & 1 & 2 \\ 2 & -3 & 3 \\ 1 & 1 & -3 \end{bmatrix} \tag{2.76}$$

Assume $\mathbf{x}^{(0)\mathrm{T}} = (1 \;\; 1 \;\; 1)$, and scale the third component of $\mathbf{x}$ to unity. Then apply the power method to $\mathbf{A}_s$. Thus,

$$\begin{bmatrix} -3 & 1 & 2 \\ 2 & -3 & 3 \\ 1 & 1 & -3 \end{bmatrix} \begin{bmatrix} 1.0000 \\ 1.0000 \\ 1.0000 \end{bmatrix} = \begin{bmatrix} 0.0000 \\ 2.0000 \\ -1.0000 \end{bmatrix};$$

$$\lambda_s^{(1)} = -1.0000 \quad \text{and} \quad \mathbf{x}^{(1)} = \begin{bmatrix} 0.0000 \\ -2.0000 \\ 1.0000 \end{bmatrix} \tag{2.77}$$

The results of the first iteration presented above and subsequent iterations are presented in Table 2.3. The largest eigenvalue of $\mathbf{A}_s$ is $\lambda_s = -4.6920$. Thus, the largest eigenvalue of opposite sign of **A** is

$$\lambda = \lambda_s + 4.0 = -0.6920 \tag{2.78}$$

Combining the results obtained in Examples 2.1 to 2.3 shows that the three eigenvalues of **A** are $\lambda = 4.0489, -0.3569$, and -0.6920. The two negative eigenvalues are close together, so the two largest eigenvalues of the shifted matrix $\mathbf{A}_s$ are close together. This is the reason the iterative process for λ_s in Example 2.3 converged slowly (i.e., 114 iterations).

TABLE 2.3
Shifting eigenvalues to find the largest eigenvalue of opposite sign

k	λ_s	x_1	x_2	x_3
0		1.0000	1.0000	1.0000
1	−1.0000	0.0000	−2.0000	1.0000
2	−5.0000	0.0000	−1.8000	1.0000
3	−4.8000	−0.0417	−1.7500	1.0000
4	−4.7917	−0.0783	−1.7043	1.0000
⋮	⋮	⋮	⋮	⋮
10	−4.7497	−0.2307	−1.5143	1.0000
⋮	⋮	⋮	⋮	⋮
114	−4.6920	−0.4450	−1.2471	1.0000

Shifting Eigenvalues to Accelerate Convergence

When an estimate of an eigenvalue of **A** is known, the eigenvalues can be shifted by this approximate value so that the shifted matrix has an eigenvalue near zero. That eigenvalue can be found by the inverse power method. The procedure is as follows:

1. Obtain an estimate λ_{est} of the eigenvalue λ, by several applications of the power method, for example.
2. Shift the eigenvalues by $s = \lambda_{\text{est}} : \lambda_s = \lambda - \lambda_{\text{est}}$.
3. Solve for λ_s by the inverse power method, where $\lambda_s = 1/\lambda_{s,i}$.
4. Calculate $\lambda = \lambda_s + s = 1/\lambda_{s,i} + s$.

Example 2.4. Shifting eigenvalues to accelerate convergence. Example 2.3 converged very slowly, because the two largest eigenvalues of the shifted matrix are close together. Convergence can be accelerated by using the results of an early iteration, say iteration 10, to shift the eigenvalues by the approximate eigenvalue, then using the inverse power method on the shifted matrix to accelerate convergence. From Example 2.3, after 10 iterations, $\lambda_s = -4.7497$. Shifting back to the original problem gives

$$\lambda = \lambda_s + s = -4.7497 + 4.0 = -0.7497 \tag{2.79}$$

Shifting the eigenvalues of the original matrix by $s = -0.7497$ yields the shifted matrix

$$\mathbf{A}_s = \begin{bmatrix} 1.7497 & 1 & 2 \\ 2 & 1.7497 & 3 \\ 1 & 1 & 1.7497 \end{bmatrix} \tag{2.80}$$

Assume $\mathbf{x}^{(0)\text{T}} = (-0.2307 \quad -1.5143 \quad 1.0000)$, continue scaling the third component of **x** to unity, and apply the inverse power method to $\mathbf{A}_s$. The **L** and **U** matrices corresponding to $\mathbf{A}_s$ are

$$\mathbf{L} = \begin{bmatrix} 1 & 0 & 0 \\ 1.1431 & 1 & 0 \\ 0.5715 & 0.7063 & 1 \end{bmatrix} \quad \text{and} \quad \mathbf{U} = \begin{bmatrix} 1.7497 & 1.0000 & 2.0000 \\ 0 & 0.6066 & 0.7139 \\ 0 & 0 & 0.1024 \end{bmatrix} \tag{2.81}$$

Solve for $\mathbf{x}'$ by substitution from $\mathbf{Lx}' = \mathbf{x}^{(10)}$.

$$\begin{bmatrix} 1 & 0 & 0 \\ 1.1431 & 1 & 0 \\ 0.5715 & 0.7063 & 1 \end{bmatrix} \begin{bmatrix} x_1' \\ x_2' \\ x_3' \end{bmatrix} = \begin{bmatrix} -0.2307 \\ -1.5143 \\ 1.0000 \end{bmatrix}; \qquad \begin{aligned} x_1' &= -0.2307 \\ x_2' &= -1.2506 \\ x_3' &= 2.0151 \end{aligned} \tag{2.82}$$

Solve for $\mathbf{y}^{(11)}$ by back substitution using $\mathbf{U}\,\mathbf{y}^{(11)} = \mathbf{x}'$.

$$\begin{bmatrix} 1.7497 & 1.0000 & 2.0000 \\ 0 & 0.6066 & 0.7139 \\ 0 & 0 & 0.1024 \end{bmatrix} \begin{bmatrix} y_1^{(11)} \\ y_2^{(11)} \\ y_3^{(11)} \end{bmatrix} = \begin{bmatrix} -0.2307 \\ -1.2506 \\ 2.0151 \end{bmatrix}; \qquad \begin{aligned} y_1^{(11)} &= -8.2102 \\ y_2^{(11)} &= -25.2140 \\ y_3^{(11)} &= 19.6743 \end{aligned} \tag{2.83}$$

Scale $\mathbf{y}^{(11)}$ so that the unity component (i.e., $y_3^{(11)}$) is unity.

$$\mathbf{y}^{(11)} = \begin{bmatrix} -8.2102 \\ -25.2140 \\ 19.6743 \end{bmatrix}; \qquad \lambda_{s,i}^{(11)} = 19.6743 \qquad \text{and} \qquad \mathbf{x}^{(11)} = \begin{bmatrix} -0.4173 \\ -1.2816 \\ 1.0000 \end{bmatrix} \tag{2.84}$$

After seven more iterations (a total of eight iterations), the solution converges to $\lambda_{s,i} = 17.3375$ and $\mathbf{x}^{\mathrm{T}} = (-0.4450 \quad -1.2470 \quad 1.0000)$. The results of the first iteration presented above and of subsequent iterations are presented in Table 2.4.

The eigenvalue λ_s of the shifted matrix is

$$\lambda_s = \frac{1}{\lambda_{s,i}} = \frac{1}{17.3375} = 0.0577 \tag{2.85}$$

Thus, the eigenvalue λ of the original matrix is

$$\lambda = \lambda_s + s = 0.0577 - 0.7497 = -0.6920 \tag{2.86}$$

This is the same result obtained in Example 2.3 with 114 iterations. The present solution required only 18 total iterations; ten for the initial solution and eight for the final solution.

TABLE 2.4
Shifting eigenvalues to accelerate convergence

k	$\lambda_{s,i}$	x_1	x_2	x_3
1	19.6743	−0.4173	−1.2816	1.0000
2	17.6398	−0.4410	−1.2520	1.0000
3	17.3811	−0.4445	−1.2477	1.0000
⋮	⋮	⋮	⋮	⋮
7	17.3375	−0.4450	−1.2470	1.0000
8	17.3375	−0.4450	−1.2470	1.0000

2.6 THE DIRECT METHOD

The power method and its variations presented in Sections 2.3 to 2.5 apply to eigenproblems of the form

$$\mathbf{A}\mathbf{x} = \lambda\mathbf{x} \tag{2.87}$$

Equation (2.87) is a linear eigenproblem. Nonlinear eigenproblems of the form

$$\boxed{\mathbf{A}\mathbf{x} = \mathbf{B}(\lambda)\mathbf{x}} \tag{2.88}$$

where $\mathbf{B}(\lambda)$ is a nonlinear function of λ, cannot be solved by the power method. Linear eigenproblems and nonlinear eigenproblems both can be solved by a direct approach, which involves finding the zeros of the characteristic equation directly.

For a linear eigenproblem, the characteristic equation is obtained from

$$\det(\mathbf{A} - \lambda\mathbf{I}) = 0 \tag{2.89}$$

Expanding Eq. (2.89), which can be time-consuming for a large system, yields an nth-degree polynomial in λ. The roots of the characteristic polynomial can be determined by the methods presented in Section 3.7 for finding the roots of polynomials.

For a nonlinear eigenproblem, the characteristic equation is obtained from

$$\det(\mathbf{A} - \mathbf{B}(\lambda)) = 0 \tag{2.90}$$

Expanding Eq. (2.90) yields a nonlinear function of λ, which can be solved by the methods presented in Chapter 3.

An alternate approach to solving for the roots of the characteristic equation directly is to solve Eqs. (2.89) and (2.90) directly. This can be accomplished by applying the secant method, presented in Section 3.6, to Eqs. (2.89) and (2.90) directly. Two initial approximations of λ are assumed, λ_0 and λ_1, the corresponding values of the characteristic determinant are computed, and these results are used to construct a linear relationship between λ and the value of the characteristic determinant. The solution of that linear relationship is taken as the next approximation to λ, and the procedure is repeated iteratively to convergence. Reasonable initial approximations are required, especially for nonlinear eigenproblems.

The direct method determines only the eigenvalues. The corresponding eigenvectors must be determined by substituting the eigenvalues into the system of equations and solving for the corresponding eigenvectors.

Example 2.5. The direct method. Consider the nonlinear eigenproblem

$$2x_1 + x_2 = \sin(\lambda)x_1 \tag{2.91a}$$

$$x_1 + x_2 = \cos(\lambda)x_2 \tag{2.91b}$$

The characteristic determinant corresponding to Eq. (2.91) is

$$f(\lambda) = \det(\mathbf{A} - \mathbf{B}(\lambda)) = \begin{vmatrix} (2 - \sin(\lambda)) & 1 \\ 1 & (1 - \cos(\lambda)) \end{vmatrix} = 0 \tag{2.92}$$

TABLE 2.5
The direct method

k	λ_i	$f(\lambda_i)$	Slope
0	70.0	−0.302339	
1	80.0	−0.161094	0.0141245
2	91.405286	0.024833	0.0163018
3	89.881984	−0.002058	0.0176526
4	89.998548	−0.000025	0.0174352
5	90.000001	0.00000002	0.0174511
6	90.000000		

We can solve Eq. (2.92) by the secant method. Let $\lambda_0 = 70$ deg and $\lambda_1 = 80$ deg. Thus,

$$f_1 = f(\lambda_1) = \begin{vmatrix} (2 - \sin(70)) & 1 \\ 1 & (1 - \cos(70)) \end{vmatrix}$$

$$= \begin{vmatrix} 1.0603 & 1.0 \\ 1.0 & 0.6580 \end{vmatrix} = -0.3023 \qquad (2.93a)$$

$$f_2 = f(\lambda_2) = \begin{vmatrix} (2 - \sin(80)) & 1 \\ 1 & (1 - \cos(80)) \end{vmatrix}$$

$$= \begin{vmatrix} 1.0152 & 1.0 \\ 1.0 & 0.8264 \end{vmatrix} = -0.1610 \qquad (2.93b)$$

Writing the linear relationship between λ and $f(\lambda)$ yields

$$\frac{f(\lambda_2) - f(\lambda_1)}{\lambda_2 - \lambda_1} = \text{Slope} = \frac{f(\lambda) - f(\lambda_2)}{\lambda - \lambda_2} \qquad (2.94)$$

where $f(\lambda) = 0$ is the desired solution. Thus,

$$\text{Slope} = \frac{-0.1610 - (-0.3023)}{[80.0 - 70.0](\pi/180)} = 0.01413 \qquad (2.95)$$

Solving Eq. (2.94) for λ to give $f(\lambda) = 0$ yields

$$\lambda = \lambda_2 - \frac{f(\lambda_2)}{\text{Slope}} = 80.0 - \frac{-0.1610}{0.01413} = 91.3942 \qquad (2.96)$$

The results of the first iteration presented above and of subsequent iterations are presented in Table 2.5. The result is $\lambda = 90.000$ deg. This result can be verified quite simply by visual inspection of Eq. (2.91). These results were obtained on a 13-decimal-digit computer and terminated when the change in λ between iterations was less than 0.000001.

2.7 OTHER METHODS

The power method for solving eigenproblems is presented in the preceding sections. The power method can be used to solve eigenproblems for small matrices. However, for large matrices, more powerful methods are required. Such methods are beyond the scope of the present elementary presentation. This section presents a brief discussion of other methods for solving eigenproblems.

Most of the more powerful methods apply to special types of matrices. Many of them apply to symmetric matrices. Generally speaking, the original matrix is transformed into a simpler form (e.g., diagonal or tridiagonal) that has the same eigenvalues. Iterative methods are then employed. More information on the subject can be found in Fadeev and Fadeeva (1963); Householder (1964); Wilkinson (1965); Stewart (1973); Ralston and Rabinowitz (1978); and Press, Flannery, Teukolsky, and Vetterling (1986). Numerous computer programs for solving eigenproblems can be found in the IMSL (International Mathematical and Statistics Library) and in the EISPACK program written at Argonne National Laboratories. See Rice (1983) and Smith et al. (1976) for a discussion of these programs.

The *Jacobi method* transforms a symmetric matrix into a diagonal matrix. The off-diagonal elements are eliminated in a systematic manner. However, elimination of subsequent off-diagonal elements creates nonzero values in previously eliminated elements. Consequently, the transformation approaches a diagonal matrix iteratively. The Given method and the Householder method reduce a symmetric matrix to a tridiagonal matrix in a direct rather than an iterative manner. Consequently, they are more efficient than the Jacobi method. The resulting tridiagonal matrix can be expanded, and the corresponding characteristic equation can be solved for the eigenvalues by iterative techniques.

For more general matrices, the *LR method* and the *QR method* can be employed. Due to its robustness, the QR method is generally the method of choice. See Wilkinson (1965) for a discussion of the QR method. The Householder method can be applied to nonsymmetrical matrices to reduce them to *Hessenberg matrices,* whose eigenvalues can then be found by the QR method.

Finally, *deflation* techniques can be employed for symmetric matrices. After the largest eigenvalue λ_1 of matrix $\mathbf{A}$ is found, by the power method for example, a new matrix $\mathbf{B}$ is formed whose eigenvalues are the same as the eigenvalues of $\mathbf{A}$, except that the largest eigenvalue λ_1 is replaced by zero in $\mathbf{B}$. The power method can then be applied to $\mathbf{B}$ to determine its largest eigenvalue, which is the second largest eigenvalue λ_2 of $\mathbf{A}$. In principle, deflation can be applied repetitively to find all the eigenvalues of $\mathbf{A}$. However, round-off errors generally pollute the results after a few deflations. The results obtained by deflation can be used to shift the $\mathbf{A}$ matrix by the approximate eigenvalues; the resulting problem is then solved by the inverse power method presented in Section 2.5 to find more accurate values.

SUMMARY

The general features of eigenproblems are presented in this chapter. The present treatment is introductory and rather elementary. However, it does highlight the general features of eigenproblems. The power method can be used to find the largest (in magnitude) eigenvalue of a general matrix and the corresponding eigenvector. The inverse power method can be used to find the smallest (in magnitude) eigenvalue and the corresponding eigenvector. Intermediate eigenvalues can be found by shifting the eigenvalues by the value of suspected eigenvalues and using the inverse power method. Shifting eigenvalues and applying the inverse power method can be used to accelerate the convergence rate for slowly converging eigenvalues. One advantage of the power method and its variations is that the corresponding eigenvector is found as a byproduct of finding the eigenvalues. A brief discussion of more advanced methods for solving eigenproblems is presented as an introduction for further study.

PROBLEMS

Consider the linear eigenproblem $\mathbf{Ax} = \lambda\mathbf{x}$ for the matrices given below. Solve the problems presented below for the specified matrices. Carry at least six figures after the decimal place. Iterate until the solutions (both λ and $\mathbf{x}$) are constant to three digits after the decimal place. Begin all problems with $\mathbf{x}^{(0)T} = (1.0 \quad 1.0 \quad \cdots \quad 1.0)$ unless otherwise specified. Show all the results for the first three iterations. Tabulate the results of subsequent iterations. Several of these problems require a large number of iterations.

$$\mathbf{A} = \begin{bmatrix} 2 & 1 \\ 3 & 4 \end{bmatrix} \qquad \mathbf{B} = \begin{bmatrix} 3 & 2 \\ 3 & 4 \end{bmatrix} \qquad \mathbf{C} = \begin{bmatrix} 2 & 3 \\ 1 & 4 \end{bmatrix}$$

$$\mathbf{D} = \begin{bmatrix} 1 & 1 & 2 \\ 2 & 1 & 1 \\ 1 & 1 & 3 \end{bmatrix} \qquad \mathbf{E} = \begin{bmatrix} 1 & 1 & 2 \\ 2 & 1 & 3 \\ 1 & 1 & 1 \end{bmatrix} \qquad \mathbf{F} = \begin{bmatrix} 2 & 1 & 2 \\ 1 & 1 & 3 \\ 1 & 1 & 1 \end{bmatrix}$$

$$\mathbf{G} = \begin{bmatrix} 1 & 1 & 1 & 2 \\ 2 & 1 & 1 & 1 \\ 3 & 2 & 1 & 2 \\ 2 & 1 & 1 & 4 \end{bmatrix} \qquad \mathbf{H} = \begin{bmatrix} 1 & 2 & 1 & 2 \\ 2 & 1 & 1 & 1 \\ 3 & 2 & 1 & 2 \\ 2 & 1 & 1 & 4 \end{bmatrix}$$

Section 2.2 Basic Characteristics of Eigenproblems

1. Solve for the eigenvalues of matrices **A**, **B**, and **C** by expanding the determinant of $(\mathbf{A} - \lambda\mathbf{I})$ and solving the characteristic equation by the quadratic formula. Solve for the corresponding eigenvectors by substituting the eigenvalues into the equation $(\mathbf{A} - \lambda\mathbf{I})\mathbf{x} = 0$ and solving for $\mathbf{x}$. Let the first component of $\mathbf{x}$ be unity.
2. Solve for the eigenvalues of matrices **D**, **E**, and **F** by expanding the determinant of $(\mathbf{A} - \lambda\mathbf{I})$ and solving the characteristic equation by Newton's method. Solve for the corresponding eigenvectors by substituting the eigenvalues into the equation $(\mathbf{A} - \lambda\mathbf{I})\mathbf{x} = 0$ and solving for $\mathbf{x}$. Let the first component of $\mathbf{x}$ be unity.

Section 2.3 The Power Method

3. Solve for the largest (in magnitude) eigenvalue of the matrix **A** and the corresponding eigenvector $\mathbf{x}$ by the power method.
   (a) Let the first component of $\mathbf{x}$ be the unity component.

(*b*) Let the second component of **x** be the unity component.
(*c*) Show that the eigenvectors obtained in Parts (*a*) and (*b*) are equivalent.

4. Solve Problem 3 with $\mathbf{x}^{(0)T} = (1.0 \quad 0.0)$ and $(0.0 \quad 1.0)$ in Parts (*a*) and (*b*), respectively.

5. Solve Problem 3 for the matrix **B**.

6. Solve Problem 4 for the matrix **B**.

7. Solve Problem 3 for the matrix **C**.

8. Solve Problem 4 for the matrix **C**.

***9.** Solve for the largest (in magnitude) eigenvalue of the matrix **D** and the corresponding eigenvector **x** by the power method.
(*a*) Let the first component of **x** be the unity component.
(*b*) Let the second component of **x** be the unity component.
(*c*) Let the third component of **x** be the unity component.
(*d*) Show that the eigenvectors obtained in Parts (*a*), (*b*), and (*c*) are equivalent.

10. Solve Problem 9 with $\mathbf{x}^{(0)T} = (1.0 \quad 0.0 \quad 0.0)$, $(0.0 \quad 1.0 \quad 0.0)$, and $(0.0 \quad 0.0 \quad 1.0)$ in Parts (*a*), (*b*), and (*c*), respectively.

11. Solve Problem 9 for the matrix **E**.

12. Solve Problem 10 for the matrix **E**.

13. Solve Problem 9 for the matrix **F**.

14. Solve Problem 10 for the matrix **F**.

***15.** Solve for the largest (in magnitude) eigenvalue of the matrix **G** and the corresponding eigenvector **x** by the power method.
(*a*) Let the first component of **x** be the unity component.
(*b*) Let the second component of **x** be the unity component.
(*c*) Let the third component of **x** be the unity component.
(*d*) Let the fourth component of **x** be the unity component.
(*e*) Show that the eigenvectors obtained in Parts (*a*) to (*d*) are equivalent.

16. Solve Problem 15 with $\mathbf{x}^{(0)T} = (1.0 \quad 0.0 \quad 0.0 \quad 0.0)$, $(0.0 \quad 1.0 \quad 0.0 \quad 0.0)$, $(0.0 \quad 0.0 \quad 1.0 \quad 0$ and $(0.0 \quad 0.0 \quad 0.0 \quad 1.0)$ in Parts (*a*) to (*d*), respectively.

17. Solve Problem 15 for the matrix **H**.

18. Solve Problem 16 for the matrix **H**.

Section 2.4 The Inverse Power Method

19. Solve for the smallest (in magnitude) eigenvalue of the matrix **A** and the corresponding eigenvector **x** by the inverse power method using the matrix inverse. Use Gauss–Jordan elimination to find the matrix inverse.
(*a*) Let the first component of **x** be the unity component.
(*b*) Let the second component of **x** be the unity component.
(*c*) Show that the eigenvectors obtained in Parts (*a*) and (*b*) are equivalent.

20. Solve Problem 19 with $\mathbf{x}^{(0)T} = (1.0\ 0.0)$ and $(0.0\ 1.0)$ in Parts (*a*) and (*b*), respectively.

21. Solve Problem 19 for the matrix **B**.

22. Solve Problem 20 for the matrix **B**.

23. Solve Problem 19 for the matrix **C**.

24. Solve Problem 20 for the matrix **C**.

*25. Solve for the smallest (in magnitude) eigenvalue of the matrix **D** and the corresponding eigenvector **x** by the inverse power method using the matrix inverse. Use Gauss-Jordan elimination to find the matrix inverse.
   (*a*) Let the first component of **x** be the unity component.
   (*b*) Let the second component of **x** be the unity component.
   (*c*) Let the third component of **x** be the unity component.
   (*d*) Show that the eigenvectors obtained in Parts (*a*), (*b*), and (*c*) are equivalent.

26. Solve Problem 25 with $\mathbf{x}^{(0)T} = (1.0 \quad 0.0 \quad 0.0)$, $(0.0 \quad 1.0 \quad 0.0)$, and $(0.0 \quad 0.0 \quad 1.0)$ in Parts (*a*), (*b*), and (*c*), respectively.
27. Solve Problem 25 for the matrix **E**.
28. Solve Problem 26 for the matrix **E**.
29. Solve Problem 25 for the matrix **F**.
30. Solve Problem 26 for the matrix **F**.

*31. Solve for the smallest (in magnitude) eigenvalue of the matrix **G** and the corresponding eigenvector **x** by the inverse power method using the matrix inverse. Use Gauss-Jordan elimination to find the matrix inverse.
   (*a*) Let the first component of **x** be the unity component.
   (*b*) Let the second component of **x** be the unity component.
   (*c*) Let the third component of **x** be the unity component.
   (*d*) Let the fourth component of **x** be the unity component.
   (*e*) Show that the eigenvectors obtained in Parts (*a*) to (*d*) are equivalent.

32. Solve Problem 31 with $\mathbf{x}^{(0)T} = (1.0 \quad 0.0 \quad 0.0 \quad 0.0)$, $(0.0 \quad 1.0 \quad 0.0 \quad 0.0)$, $(0.0 \quad 0.0 \quad 1.0 \quad 0.0)$, and $(0.0 \quad 0.0 \quad 0.0 \quad 1.0)$ in Parts (*a*) to (*d*), respectively.
33. Solve Problem 31 for the matrix **H**.
34. Solve Problem 32 for the matrix **H**.
35. Solve Problem 19 using **LU** decomposition.
36. Solve Problem 21 using **LU** decomposition.
37. Solve Problem 23 using **LU** decomposition.
38. Solve Problem 25 using **LU** decomposition.
39. Solve Problem 27 using **LU** decomposition.
40. Solve Problem 29 using **LU** decomposition.
41. Solve Problem 31 using **LU** decomposition.
42. Solve Problem 33 using **LU** decomposition.

Section 2.5 Shifting Eigenvalues

43. Solve for the smallest eigenvalue of the matrix **A** and the corresponding eigenvector **x** by shifting the eigenvalues by $s = 5.0$ and applying the power method. Let the first component of **x** be the unity component.
44. Solve Problem 43 for the matrix **B** by shifting by $s = 6.0$.
45. Solve Problem 43 for the matrix **C** by shifting by $s = 5.0$.
46. Solve Problem 43 for the matrix **D** by shifting by $s = 4.5$.
47. Solve Problem 43 for the matrix **E** by shifting by $s = 4.0$.
48. Solve Problem 43 for the matrix **F** by shifting by $s = 4.0$.
49. Solve Problem 43 for the matrix **G** by shifting by $s = 6.6$.
50. Solve Problem 43 for the matrix **H** by shifting by $s = 6.8$.

*51. The third eigenvalue of the matrix **D** and the corresponding eigenvector **x** can be found in a trial-and-error manner by assuming a value for λ between the smallest (in absolute value) and largest (in absolute value) eigenvalues, shifting the matrix by that value, and applying the inverse power method to the shifted matrix. Solve for the third eigenvalue of **D** by shifting by $s = 0.8$ and applying the inverse power method using **LU** decomposition. Let the first component of **x** be the unity component.

52. Solve Problem 51 for the matrix **E** by shifting by $s = -0.4$.

53. Solve Problem 51 for the matrix **F** by shifting by $s = 0.6$.

*54. The third and fourth eigenvalues of the matrix **G** and the corresponding eigenvectors can be found in a trial and error manner by assuming a value for λ between the smallest (in absolute value) and largest (in absolute value) eigenvalues, shifting the matrix by that value, and applying the inverse power method to the shifted matrix. This procedure can be quite time consuming for large matrices. Solve for these two eigenvalues by shifting **G** by $s = 1.5$ and -0.5 and applying the inverse power method using **LU** decomposition. Let the first component of **x** be the unity component.

55. Solve Problem 54 for the matrix **H** by shifting by $s = 1.7$ and -0.5.

*56. The convergence rate of Problem 46 can be accelerated by stopping the iterative procedure after a few iterations, shifting the approximate result back to determine an improved approximation of λ, shifting the original matrix by this improved approximation of λ, and continuing with the inverse power method. The results for Problem 46 after 10 iterations are $\lambda_s^{(10)} = -4.722050$ and $\mathbf{x}^{(10)T} = (1.0 \quad -1.330367 \quad 0.047476)$. Apply this concept to complete the solution.

57. Apply the procedure described in Problem 56 to accelerate the convergence of Problem 47. After 20 iterations in that problem, $\lambda_s^{(20)} = -4.683851$ and $\mathbf{x}^{(20)T} = (0.256981 \quad 1.0 \quad -0.732794)$.

58. Apply the procedure described in Problem 56 to accelerate the convergence of Problem 48. After 10 iterations in that problem, $\lambda_s^{(10)} = -4.397633$ and $\mathbf{x}^{(10)T} = (1.0 \quad 9.439458 \quad -5.961342)$.

59. Apply the procedure described in Problem 56 to accelerate the convergence of Problem 49. After 20 iterations in that problem, $\lambda_s^{(20)} = -7.388013$ and $\mathbf{x}^{(20)T} = (1.0 \quad -0.250521 \quad -1.385861 \quad -0.074527)$.

60. Apply the procedure described in Problem 56 to accelerate the convergence of Problem 50. After 20 iterations in that problem, $\lambda_s^{(20)} = -8.304477$ and $\mathbf{x}^{(20)} = (1.0 \quad -1.249896 \quad 0.587978 \quad -0.270088)$.

Section 2.6 The Direct Method

*61. Solve for the largest eigenvalue of matrix **D** by the direct method using the secant method. Let $\lambda^{(0)} = 5.0$ and $\lambda^{(1)} = 4.0$.

62. Solve for the largest eigenvalue of matrix **E** by the direct method using the secant method. Let $\lambda^{(0)} = 5.0$ and $\lambda^{(1)} = 4.0$.

63. Solve for the largest eigenvalue of matrix **F** by the direct method using the secant method. Let $\lambda^{(0)} = 5.0$ and $\lambda^{(1)} = 4.0$.

64. Solve for the largest eigenvalue of matrix **G** by the direct method using the secant method. Let $\lambda^{(0)} = 7.0$ and $\lambda^{(1)} = 6.0$.

65. Solve for the largest eigenvalue of matrix **H** by the direct method using the secant method. Let $\lambda^{(0)} = 7.0$ and $\lambda^{(1)} = 6.0$.

*66. Solve for the smallest eigenvalue of matrix **D** by the direct method using the secant method. Let $\lambda^{(0)} = 0.0$ and $\lambda^{(1)} = -0.5$.

67. Solve for the smallest eigenvalue of matrix **E** by the direct method using the secant method. Let $\lambda^{(0)} = -0.5$ and $\lambda^{(1)} = -1.0$.

68. Solve for the smallest eigenvalue of matrix **F** by the direct method using the secant method. Let $\lambda^{(0)} = -0.5$ and $\lambda^{(1)} = -1.0$.

69. Solve for the smallest eigenvalue of matrix **G** by the direct method using the secant method. Let $\lambda^{(0)} = -0.8$ and $\lambda^{(1)} = -1.0$.

70. Solve for the smallest eigenvalue of matrix **H** by the direct method using the secant method. Let $\lambda^{(0)} = -1.1$ and $\lambda^{(1)} = -1.5$.

CHAPTER 3

NONLINEAR EQUATIONS

Section

Example

3.1 INTRODUCTION

Many problems in engineering and science require the solution of a nonlinear equation or function. The problem can be stated as follows:

> Given the continuous nonlinear function $f(x)$, find the value $x = \alpha$ such that $f(\alpha) = 0$ or $f(\alpha) = \beta$.

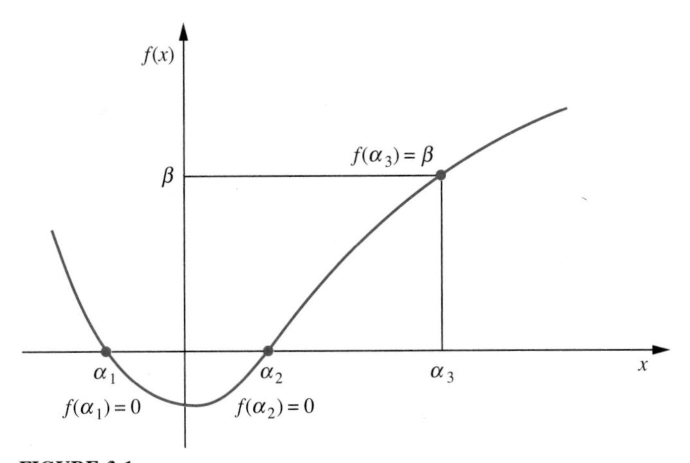

FIGURE 3.1
Solution of a nonlinear function.

Figure 3.1 illustrates the problem graphically. The function $f(x)$ may be an algebraic equation, a transcendental equation (i.e., an equation involving trigonometric or exponential functions), the solution of a differential equation, or any nonlinear relationship between an input x and a response $f(x)$.

As an example of a nonlinear function, consider the four-bar linkage illustrated in Fig. 3.2. The angle α is the input to this mechanism, and the angle ϕ is the output. A relationship between α and ϕ can be obtained by writing the vector loop equation:

$$\mathbf{r}_2 + \mathbf{r}_3 + \mathbf{r}_4 - \mathbf{r}_1 = 0 \tag{3.1}$$

Let $\mathbf{r}_1$ lie along the x-axis. Equation (3.1) can be written as two scalar equations,

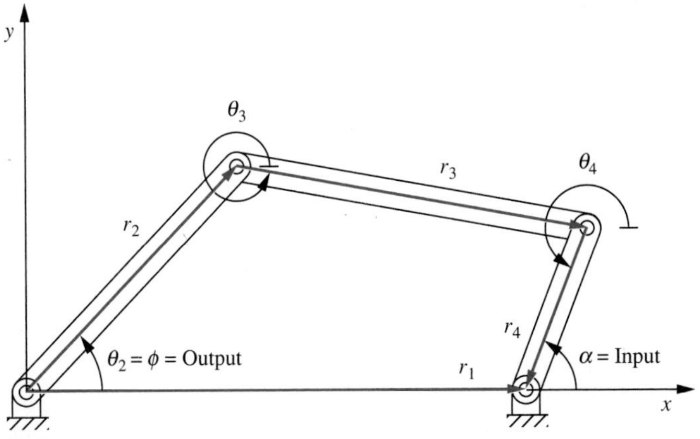

FIGURE 3.2
Four-bar linkage.

corresponding to the x and y components of the $\mathbf{r}$ vectors. Thus,

$$r_2 \cos(\theta_2) + r_3 \cos(\theta_3) + r_4 \cos(\theta_4) - r_1 = 0 \tag{3.2a}$$

$$r_2 \sin(\theta_2) + r_3 \sin(\theta_3) + r_4 \sin(\theta_4) = 0 \tag{3.2b}$$

Combining Eqs. (3.2), letting $\theta_2 = \phi$ and $\theta_4 = \alpha + \pi$, and simplifying yields Freudenstein's (1955) equation:

$$R_1 \cos(\alpha) - R_2 \cos(\phi) + R_3 - \cos(\alpha - \phi) = 0 \tag{3.3}$$

where

$$R_1 = \frac{r_1}{r_2}, \quad R_2 = \frac{r_1}{r_4}, \quad \text{and} \quad R_3 = \frac{r_1^2 + r_2^2 - r_3^2 + r_4^2}{2r_2r_4} \tag{3.4}$$

Consider the four-bar linkage specified by $r_1 = 10$, $r_2 = 6$, $r_3 = 8$, and $r_4 = 4$. Thus, $R_1 = \frac{5}{3}$, $R_2 = \frac{5}{2}$, $R_3 = \frac{11}{6}$, and Eq. (3.3) becomes

$$\frac{5}{3}\cos(\alpha) - \frac{5}{2}\cos(\phi) + \frac{11}{6} - \cos(\alpha - \phi) = 0 \tag{3.5}$$

The solution to Eq. (3.5) is tabulated in Table 3.1 and illustrated in Fig. 3.3. This problem will be used throughout Chapter 3 to illustrate methods of solving nonlinear equations.

TABLE 3.1
Solution of the four-bar linkage problem

α, deg	ϕ, deg	α, deg	ϕ, deg
10.0	8.069345	100.0	75.270873
20.0	16.113229	110.0	81.069445
30.0	24.104946	120.0	86.101495
40.0	32.015180	130.0	90.124080
50.0	39.810401	140.0	92.823533
60.0	47.450827	150.0	93.822497
70.0	54.887763	160.0	92.734963
80.0	62.059980	170.0	89.306031
90.0	68.888734	180.0	83.620630

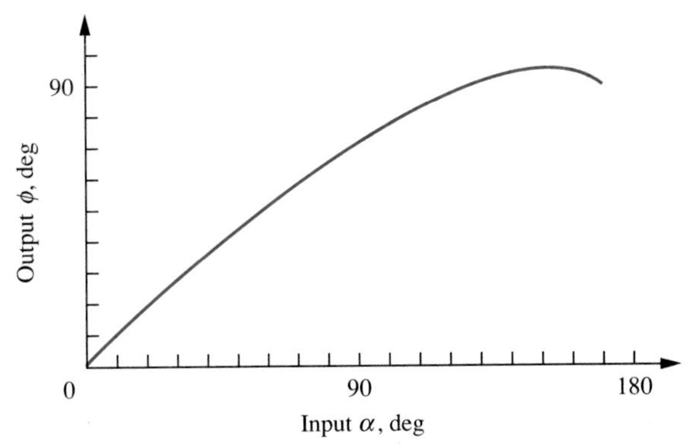

FIGURE 3.3
Solution of the four-bar linkage problem.

3.2 BOUNDING AND REFINING THE SOLUTION

There are two distinct phases in finding the solution of a nonlinear equation:

1. Bounding the solution
2. Refining the solution

These two phases are discussed in this section.

Bounding the Solution

Bounding the solution involves finding a rough estimate of the solution, which can be used as the starting point in a systematic procedure that refines the solution to a specified tolerance in an efficient manner. Several possible procedures are

1. Systematic search (see the following paragraph)
2. Past experience with the problem or a similar problem
3. Solution of a simplified approximate model
4. Previous solution in a sequence of solutions

One systematic search procedure is as follows: Compute $f(x)$ for $-1 < x < 1$, at intervals of small Δx. Compute $f(1/x)$ for $-1 < (1/x) < 1$, at intervals of small $\Delta(1/x)$. The solution lies between sign changes in $f(x)$.

Whatever procedure is used to bound the solution, the initial approximate solution must be sufficiently close to the exact solution to ensure that (a) the systematic refinement procedure converges and (b) the solution converges to the desired root of the equation.

Refining the Solution

Refining the solution involves determining the solution to a specified tolerance, by an efficient systematic procedure. Four methods for refining the solution are presented in this chapter:

1. Interval halving
2. Fixed-point iteration
3. Newton's method
4. The secant method

All four methods are illustrated by applying them to solve the four-bar linkage problem presented in Section 3.1.

3.3 INTERVAL HALVING

One of the simplest methods of finding the solution of a nonlinear equation is interval halving (also known as *bisection)*. In this method, two estimates of the solution that bracket the solution must first be obtained, as illustrated in Fig. 3.4. In this case, $f(a_1) < 0$ and $f(b_1) > 0$. The solution, $x = \alpha$, obviously lies between a_1 and b_1, that is, in the interval $a_1 < x < b_1$. The interval between a_1 and b_1 can be halved by averaging a_1 and b_1. Thus, $c_1 = (a_1 + b_1)/2$. We now have two intervals: $a_1 < x < c_1$ and $c_1 < x < b_1$. The interval containing the solution $x = \alpha$ is determined by evaluating $f(c_1)$. If $f(c_1) > 0$, the solution $x = \alpha$ must be to the left of c_1, that is, in the interval $a_1 < x < c_1$. If $f(c_1) < 0$, the solution $x = \alpha$ must be to the right of c_1, that is, in the interval $c_1 < x < b_1$. Thus, if $f(c_1) > 0$, let $a_2 = a_1$ and $b_2 = c_1$ and repeat the process. If $f(c_1) < 0$, let $a_2 = c_1$ and $b_2 = b_1$ and repeat the process. The algorithm is as follows:

$$c_i = \frac{a_i + b_i}{2} \tag{3.6}$$

$$\textit{If}\ \ f(c_i) > 0: \quad a_{i+1} = a_i \quad \text{and} \quad b_{i+1} = c_i \tag{3.7a}$$

$$\textit{If}\ \ f(c_i) < 0: \quad a_{i+1} = c_i \quad \text{and} \quad b_{i+1} = b_i \tag{3.7b}$$

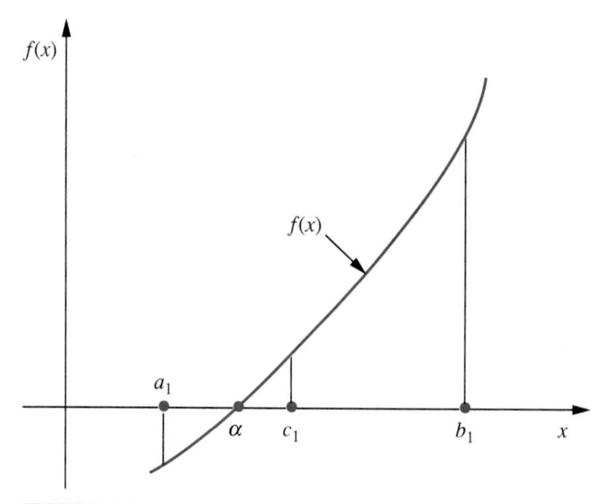

FIGURE 3.4
Interval halving.

Interval halving is an iterative procedure. The solution is not obtained directly by a single calculation. Each application of Eqs. (3.6) and (3.7) is called an *iteration*. The iterations are continued until the size of the interval decreases below a prespecified tolerance ϵ, that is, $|a_i - b_i| \leq \epsilon$, or the value of $f(x)$ decreases below a prespecified tolerance δ, that is, $|f(c_i) - f(c_{i-1})| \leq \delta$.

Example 3.1. Interval halving. Solve the four-bar linkage problem presented in Section 3.1 for an input of $\alpha = 40$ deg by interval halving. In problems involving trigonometric functions, the angles must be expressed in radians. However, degrees are a more common unit of angular measure. Consequently, in all the examples in this chapter, the calculations are performed in radians, but the angles are expressed in degrees in the equations and in the tabular results. Recall Eq. (3.5):

$$f(\phi) = \frac{5}{3}\cos(40) - \frac{5}{2}\cos(\phi) + \frac{11}{6} - \cos(40 - \phi) = 0 \tag{3.8}$$

Let $\phi_a = 30$ deg and $\phi_b = 40$ deg. From Eq. (3.8),

$$f(\phi_a) = f(30) = \frac{5}{3}\cos(40) - \frac{5}{2}\cos(30) + \frac{11}{6} - \cos(40 - 30) = -0.039797 \tag{3.9a}$$

$$f(\phi_b) = f(40) = \frac{5}{3}\cos(40) - \frac{5}{2}\cos(40) + \frac{11}{6} - \cos(40 - 40) = 0.194963 \tag{3.9b}$$

Thus, $\phi_a = 30$ deg and $\phi_b = 40$ deg bracket the solution. From Eq. (3.6),

$$\phi_c = \frac{\phi_a + \phi_b}{2} = \frac{30 + 40}{2} = 35 \tag{3.10}$$

Substituting $\phi_c = 35$ deg into Eq. (3.8) yields

$$f(\phi_c) = f(35) = \frac{5}{3}\cos(40) - \frac{5}{2}\cos(35) + \frac{11}{6} - \cos(40 - 35) = 0.065999 \tag{3.11}$$

Since $f(\phi_c) > 0$, $\phi_b = \phi_c$ for the next iteration.

The solution is presented in Table 3.2. The convergence criterion is $|\phi_a - \phi_b| \leq 0.000001$ deg, which requires 24 iterations. Clearly, convergence is rather slow. The

TABLE 3.2
Solution by interval halving

i	ϕ_a	$f(\phi_a)$	ϕ_b	$f(\phi_b)$	ϕ_c
1	30.000000	−0.03979719	40.000000	0.19496296	35.000000
2	30.000000	−0.03979719	35.000000	0.06599926	32.500000
3	30.000000	−0.03979719	32.500000	0.01015060	31.250000
4	31.250000	−0.01556712	32.500000	0.01015060	31.875000
5	31.875000	−0.00289347	32.500000	0.01015060	32.187500
6	31.875000	−0.00289347	32.187500	0.00358236	32.031250
7	31.875000	−0.00289347	32.031250	0.00033288	31.953125
⋮	⋮	⋮	⋮	⋮	⋮
22	32.015176	−0.00000009	32.015181	0.00000000	32.015178
23	32.015178	−0.00000004	32.015181	0.00000000	32.015179
24	32.015179	−0.00000002	32.015181	0.00000000	32.015180
	32.015180				

results presented in Table 3.2 were obtained on a 13-decimal-digit computer. The results in the table are rounded in the sixth digit after the decimal place. The final solution agrees with the exact solution presented in Table 3.1 to eight significant figures.

The major advantage of interval halving is that the error in the solution is bounded. Since $a_i < \alpha < b_i$, the maximum error in α is $|a_i - b_i|$. The major disadvantage is that the solution converges slowly. That is, it can take a large number of iterations to reach the convergence criterion.

3.4 FIXED-POINT ITERATION

The interval halving method presented in Section 3.3 converges very slowly. More efficient methods for finding the solution of a nonlinear equation are desirable. The procedure known as *fixed-point iteration* involves solving the problem $f(x) = 0$ by rearranging $f(x)$ into the form $x = g(x)$, then finding $x = \alpha$ such that $\alpha = g(\alpha)$, which is equivalent to $f(\alpha) = 0$. The value of x such that $x = g(x)$ is called a *fixed point* of $g(x)$. Fixed-point iteration essentially solves two functions simultaneously: $x(x)$ and $g(x)$. The point of intersection of these two functions is the solution to $x = g(x)$, and thus to $f(x) = 0$. This process is illustrated in Fig. 3.5.

Since $g(x)$ is also a nonlinear function, the solution must be obtained iteratively. An initial approximation to the solution, x_1, must be determined. This value is substituted into the function $g(x)$ to determine the next approximation. The algorithm is as follows:

$$\boxed{x_{i+1} = g(x_i)} \tag{3.12}$$

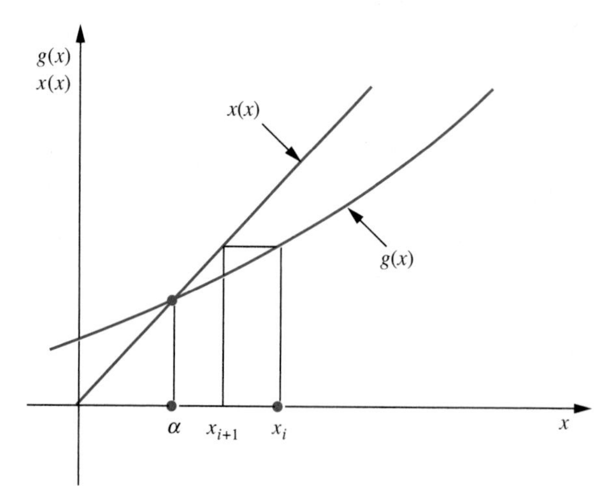

FIGURE 3.5
Fixed-point iteration.

The procedure is repeated (iterated) until a convergence criterion is satisfied. For example,

$$|x_{i+1} - x_i| \le \epsilon \tag{3.13}$$

Example 3.2. Fixed-point iteration. Solve the four-bar linkage problem presented in Section 3.1 by fixed-point iteration. Recall Eq. (3.3):

$$f(\phi) = R_1 \cos(\alpha) - R_2 \cos(\phi) + R_3 - \cos(\alpha - \phi) = 0 \tag{3.14}$$

Equation (3.14) can be rearranged into the form $\phi = g(\phi)$ by separating the term $R_2 \cos(\phi)$ and solving for ϕ. Thus,

$$\phi = \cos^{-1}\left(\frac{1}{R_2}\Big(R_1 \cos(\alpha) + R_3 - \cos(\alpha - \phi)\Big)\right) = \cos^{-1}\big(u(\phi)\big) = g(\phi) \tag{3.15}$$

where

$$u(\phi) = \frac{1}{R_2}\Big(R_1 \cos(\alpha) + R_3 - \cos(\alpha - \phi)\Big) \tag{3.16}$$

The derivative of $g(\phi)$, that is, $g'(\phi)$, is of interest in the analysis of convergence, which is discussed immediately following this example. Recall that

$$d\left(\cos^{-1}(u)\right) = -\frac{1}{\sqrt{1-u^2}}\,du \tag{3.17}$$

Solving for $g'(\phi)$ gives

$$g'(\phi) = -\frac{1}{\sqrt{1-u^2}}\frac{du}{d\phi} \tag{3.18}$$

which yields

$$g'(\phi) = \frac{\sin(\alpha - \phi)}{R_2\sqrt{1-u^2}} \tag{3.19}$$

For the four-bar linkage problem presented in Section 3.1, $R_1 = \frac{5}{3}$, $R_2 = \frac{5}{2}$, and $R_3 = \frac{11}{6}$. Find the output ϕ for the input $\alpha = 40$ deg. Equations (3.16), (3.15), and (3.19) become

$$u(\phi) = \frac{2}{5}\left(\frac{5}{3}\cos(40) + \frac{11}{6} - \cos(40 - \phi)\right) \tag{3.20}$$

$$\phi_{i+1} = g(\phi_i) = \cos^{-1}\big(u(\phi_i)\big) \tag{3.21}$$

$$g'(\phi) = \frac{2}{5}\frac{\sin(40 - \phi)}{\sqrt{1 - [u(\phi)]^2}} \tag{3.22}$$

Let $\phi_1 = 30$ deg. Equations (3.20) to (3.22) give

$$u(30) = \frac{2}{5}\left(\frac{5}{3}\cos(40) + \frac{11}{6} - \cos(40 - 30)\right) = 0.850107 \tag{3.23}$$

$$\phi_2 = g(\phi_1) = g(30) = \cos^{-1}\big(u(30)\big) = \cos^{-1}(0.850107) = 31.776742 \tag{3.24}$$

$$g'(30) = \frac{2}{5}\frac{\sin(40 - 30)}{\sqrt{1 - (0.850107)^2}} = 0.131899 \tag{3.25}$$

TABLE 3.3
Solution by fixed-point iteration

i	ϕ_i	$u(\phi_i)$	ϕ_{i+1}	$f(\phi_{i+1})$	$g'(\phi_i)$
1	30.000000	0.850107	31.776742	−0.03979719	0.131899
2	31.776742	0.848142	31.989810	−0.00491050	0.107995
3	31.989810	0.847932	32.012517	−0.00052505	0.105148
4	32.012517	0.847910	32.014901	−0.00005515	0.104845
5	32.014901	0.847908	32.015151	−0.00000578	0.104814
6	32.015151	0.847908	32.015177	−0.00000061	0.104810
7	32.015177	0.847908	32.015180	−0.00000006	0.104810
8	32.015180	0.847908	32.015180	−0.00000001	0.104810
	32.015180				

Substituting $\phi_2 = 31.776742$ into Eq. (3.14) gives $f(\phi_2) = -0.039797$. The entire procedure is now repeated with $\phi_2 = 31.776742$ deg.

These results and the results of the subsequent iterations are presented in Table 3.3. The convergence criterion is $|\phi_{i+1} - \phi_i| \le 0.000001$ deg, which requires eight iterations. This is a considerable improvement over the interval halving method presented in Example 3.1, which requires 24 iterations.

The convergence rate of the fixed-point iteration method can be analyzed as follows. The general procedure is given by Eq. (3.12):

$$x_{i+1} = g(x_i) \tag{3.26}$$

Let $x = \alpha$ denote the solution and $e = x - \alpha$ denote the error. Subtracting $\alpha = g(\alpha)$ from Eq. (3.26) gives

$$x_{i+1} - \alpha = e_{i+1} = g(x_i) - g(\alpha) \tag{3.27}$$

Expressing $g(\alpha)$ in a Taylor series about x_i gives:

$$g(\alpha) = g(x_i) + g'(\xi)(\alpha - x_i), \quad x_i \le \xi \le \alpha \tag{3.28}$$

Solving Eq. (3.28) for $[g(x_i) - g(\alpha)]$ and substituting into Eq. (3.27) yields

$$\boxed{e_{i+1} = g'(\xi)e_i} \tag{3.29}$$

where $e_i = (x_i - \alpha)$. For convergence,

$$\left|\frac{e_{i+1}}{e_i}\right| = |g'(\xi)| < 1 \tag{3.30}$$

Consequently, the fixed-point iteration method converges only if $|g'(\xi)| < 1$. Convergence is linear since e_{i+1} is linearly dependent on e_i. If $|g'(\xi)| > 1$, the procedure diverges. If $|g'(\xi)| < 1$ but close to 1.0, convergence is quite slow. For the example presented in Table 3.3, $|g'(\xi)| \approx 0.1$, which means that the error decreases by a factor of approximately 10 at each iteration. Such rapid convergence does not occur when $|g'(\xi)|$ is close to 1.0. For example, for $|g'(\xi)| = 0.9$, approximately nine times as many iterations would be required to reach the same convergence criterion.

If the nonlinear equation $f(\phi) = 0$ is rearranged into the form

$$\phi = \phi + f(\phi) = g(\phi) \tag{3.31}$$

the fixed-point iteration formula becomes

$$\phi_{i+1} = \phi_i + f(\phi_i) = g(\phi_i) \tag{3.32}$$

and $g'(\phi)$ is given by Eq. (3.33)

$$g'(\phi) = 1 + R_2 \sin(\phi) - \sin(\alpha - \phi) \tag{3.34}$$

Substituting the final solution value $\phi = 32.015180$ deg into Eq. (3.34) gives $g'(\phi) = 2.186449$, which is larger than 1.0. The iteration method would not converge to the desired solution for this rearrangement of $f(\phi) = 0$ into $\phi = g(\phi)$. In fact, the solution converges to $\phi = -9.747105$ deg, for which $g'(\phi) = -0.186449$. This is also a solution to the four-bar linkage problem, but not the desired solution.

Methods that sometimes work and sometimes fail are undesirable. Consequently, the fixed-point iteration method for solving nonlinear equations is not recommended.

3.5 NEWTON'S METHOD

Newton's method for solving nonlinear equations is one of the most well-known and powerful procedures in all of numerical analysis. It always converges if the initial approximation is sufficiently close to the solution, and it converges quadratically. Its only disadvantage is that the derivative $f'(x)$ of the nonlinear function $f(x)$ must be evaluated.

Newton's method is illustrated graphically in Fig. 3.6. The function $f(x)$ is nonlinear. We locally approximate $f(x)$ by the linear function $g(x)$, which is tangent to $f(x)$, and find the solution for $g(x) = 0$. Newton's method is sometimes called the *tangent method*. That solution is then taken as the next approximation to the solution $x = \alpha$ of $f(x) = 0$. The procedure is applied iteratively to convergence. Thus,

$$f'(x_i) = \text{Slope of } f(x) = \frac{f(\alpha) - f(x_i)}{x_{i+1} - x_i} \tag{3.35}$$

Solving Eq. (3.35) for x_{i+1} yields

$$\boxed{x_{i+1} = x_i + \frac{f(\alpha) - f(x_i)}{f'(x_i)}} \tag{3.36}$$

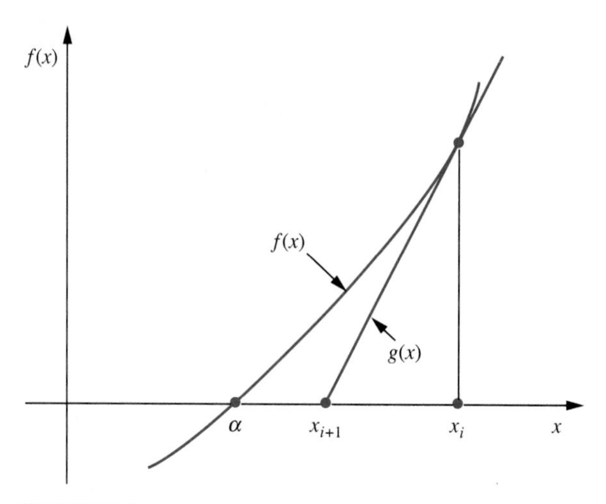

FIGURE 3.6
Newton's method.

Equation (3.36) is applied repetitively until either one or both of the following convergence criteria are satisfied:

$$|x_{i+1} - x_i| \le \epsilon \quad \text{and} \quad |f(x_{i+1}) - f(x_i)| \le \delta \tag{3.37}$$

Newton's method also can be obtained from the Taylor series. Thus,

$$f(x_{i+1}) = f(x_i) + f'(x_i)(x_{i+1} - x_i) + \ldots \tag{3.38}$$

Truncating Eq. (3.38) after the first derivative term and solving for x_{i+1} as the next approximation to α yields

$$x_{i+1} = x_i + \frac{f(\alpha) - f(x_i)}{f'(x_i)} \tag{3.39}$$

Equation (3.39) is the same as Eq. (3.36).

Example 3.3. Newton's method. To illustrate Newton's method, we solve the four-bar linkage problem presented in Section 3.1. Recall Eq. (3.3):

$$f(\phi) = R_1 \cos(\alpha) - R_2 \cos(\phi) + R_3 - \cos(\alpha - \phi) = 0 \tag{3.40}$$

The derivative $f'(\phi)$ is

$$f'(\phi) = R_2 \sin(\phi) - \sin(\alpha - \phi) \tag{3.41}$$

For this problem, $f(\phi) = 0$. Thus, Eq. (3.36) yields

$$\phi_{i+1} = \phi_i + \frac{0.0 - f(\phi_i)}{f'(\phi_i)} \tag{3.42}$$

TABLE 3.4
Solution by Newton's method

i	ϕ_i	$f(\phi_i)$	$f'(\phi_i)$	ϕ_{i+1}
1	30.000000	−0.03979719	0.018786	32.118463
2	32.118463	0.00214376	0.020805	32.015423
3	32.015423	0.00000503	0.020708	32.015180
4	32.015180	0.00000000	0.020707	32.015180
	32.015180			

For $R_1 = \frac{5}{3}$, $R_2 = \frac{5}{2}$, $R_3 = \frac{11}{6}$, and $\alpha = 40$ deg, Eqs. (3.40) and (3.41) become

$$f(\phi) = \frac{5}{3}\cos(40) - \frac{5}{2}\cos(\phi) + \frac{11}{6} - \cos(40 - \phi) \tag{3.43}$$

$$f'(\phi) = \frac{5}{2}\sin(\phi) - \sin(40 - \phi) \tag{3.44}$$

For the first iteration let $\phi_1 = 30$ deg. Equations (3.43) and (3.44) give

$$f(\phi_1) = \frac{5}{3}\cos(40) - \frac{5}{2}\cos(30) + \frac{11}{6} - \cos(40 - 30) = -0.039797 \tag{3.45}$$

$$f'(\phi_1) = \left(\frac{5}{2}\sin(30) - \sin(40 - 30)\right)\frac{\pi}{180} = 0.018786 \tag{3.46}$$

where $\pi/180$ converts radians to degrees. Substituting these results into Eq. (3.42) yields

$$\phi_2 = 30 + \frac{[0.0 - (-0.039797)]}{0.018786} = 32.118463 \tag{3.47}$$

These results and the results of subsequent iterations are presented in Table 3.4. The convergence criterion $|\phi_{i+1} - \phi_i| \le 0.000001$ deg is satisfied on the fourth iteration. This is a considerable improvement over both the interval halving method and the fixed-point iteration method.

The convergence rate of Newton's method is determined as follows. Consider Eq. (3.36) for the case where $f(x) = 0$:

$$x_{i+1} = x_i - \frac{f(x_i)}{f'(x_i)} \tag{3.48}$$

Let $x = \alpha$ denote the solution and $e = (x - \alpha)$ denote the error. Subtracting α from both sides of Eq. (3.48) gives

$$x_{i+1} - \alpha = e_{i+1} = x_i - \alpha - \frac{f(x_i)}{f'(x_i)} = e_i - \frac{f(x_i)}{f'(x_i)} \tag{3.49}$$

Expressing $f(x)$ in a truncated Taylor series about x_i and evaluating at $x = \alpha$ yields

$$f(\alpha) = f(x_i) + f'(x_i)(\alpha - x_i) + \frac{1}{2}f''(\xi)(\alpha - x_i)^2 = 0, \; x_i \le \xi \le \alpha \quad (3.50)$$

Letting $e_i = (x_i - \alpha)$ and solving Eq. (3.50) for $f(x_i)$ gives

$$f(x_i) = f'(x_i)e_i - \frac{1}{2}f''(\xi)e_i^2 \quad (3.51)$$

Substituting Eq. (3.51) into Eq. (3.49) gives

$$e_{i+1} = e_i - \frac{f'(x_i)e_i - 1/2 f''(\xi)e_i^2}{f'(x_i)} = \frac{1}{2}\frac{f''(\xi)}{f'(x_i)}e_i^2 \quad (3.52)$$

In the limit as $i \to \infty$, $x_i \to \alpha$, $f'(x_i) \to f'(\alpha)$, $f''(\xi) \to f''(\alpha)$, and Eq. (3.52) becomes

$$\boxed{e_{i+1} = \frac{1}{2}\frac{f''(\alpha)}{f'(\alpha)}e_i^2} \quad (3.53)$$

Convergence is quadratic, or second order. The number of significant figures essentially doubles each iteration.

For convergence,

$$\left|\frac{e_{i+1}}{e_i}\right| = \frac{1}{2}\left|\frac{f''(\xi)}{f'(x_i)}e_i\right| < 1 \quad (3.54)$$

From Eq. (3.51), neglecting e_i^2 compared to e_i yields

$$e_i = (x_i - \alpha) = \frac{f(x_i)}{f'(x_i)} \quad (3.55)$$

Substituting Eq. (3.55) into Eq. (3.54) gives

$$\left|\frac{e_{i+1}}{e_i}\right| = \frac{1}{2}\left|\frac{f(x_i)f''(\xi)}{\left(f'(x_i)\right)^2}\right| < 1 \quad (3.56)$$

As the solution is approached, $f(x_i) \to 0$, and Eq. (3.56) is always satisfied. For a poor initial estimate, however, Eq. (3.56) may not be satisfied. In that case, the procedure may converge to an alternate solution, or the solution may jump around wildly for a while and then converge to the desired solution or an alternate solution. The procedure will not diverge disastrously like the fixed-point iteration method when $|g'(x)| > 1$.

Newton's method requires the value of $f'(x)$ in addition to the value of $f(x)$. When $f(x)$ is an algebraic equation or a transcendental equation, $f'(x)$ can be determined analytically. However, when $f(x)$ is a general nonlinear relationship between an input x and an output $f(x)$, $f'(x)$ cannot be determined analytically. In that case, $f'(x)$ must be estimated numerically by evaluating $f(x)$ at x_i and $x_i + \epsilon$, and approximating $f'(x_i)$ as

$$f'(x_i) = \frac{f(x_i + \epsilon) - f(x_i)}{\epsilon} \tag{3.57}$$

This procedure doubles the number of function evaluations at each iteration. In such cases, the secant method, which is presented in Section 3.6, is preferred. If ϵ is small, round-off errors are introduced, and if ϵ is too large, the convergence rate is decreased.

In some cases, the efficiency of Newton's method can be increased by using the same value of $f'(x)$ for several iterations. As long as the sign of $f'(x)$ does not change, the iterates x_i move toward the solution $x = \alpha$. However, the second-order convergence is lost, so the overall procedure converges more slowly. However, in problems where evaluation of $f'(x)$ is more costly than evaluation of $f(x)$, this approximate procedure may be less costly. This is especially true in the solution of systems of nonlinear equations, which is discussed in Section 3.8.

A higher-order version of Newton's method can be obtained by retaining the second derivative term in the Taylor series presented in Eq. (3.38). This procedure requires the evaluation of $f''(x)$ and the solution of a quadratic equation for $\Delta x = x_{i+1} - x_i$. This procedure is not used very often.

Newton's method can be used to determine complex roots of real functions or complex roots of complex functions. A complex initial estimate is required, and complex arithmetic must be employed.

Newton's method has several problems. Some functions are difficult to differentiate analytically, and some functions cannot be differentiated analytically at all. In such cases, the secant method presented in Section 3.6 is recommended. When multiple roots occur, convergence drops to first order. The presence of local minima in $f(x)$ in the neighborhood of a root may cause oscillations in the solution. The presence of inflection points in $f(x)$ in the neighborhood of a root can cause problems.

3.6 THE SECANT METHOD

When the derivative function $f'(x)$ is unavailable or prohibitively costly to evaluate, an alternative to Newton's method is required. The preferred alternative is the *secant method*.

The secant method is illustrated graphically in Fig. 3.7. The function $f(x)$ is nonlinear. The nonlinear function $f(x)$ is approximated locally by the linear function $g(x)$, which is the secant to $f(x)$, and the solution for $g(x) = 0$ is found. (A *secant* to a curve is the straight line that passes through two points on the curve.) The solution of $g(x) = 0$ is then taken as the next approximation to the solution $x = \alpha$ of $f(x) = 0$. The procedure is applied repetitively to convergence. Two initial approximations, x_0 and x_1, are required to initiate the secant method. The slope of the secant passing through

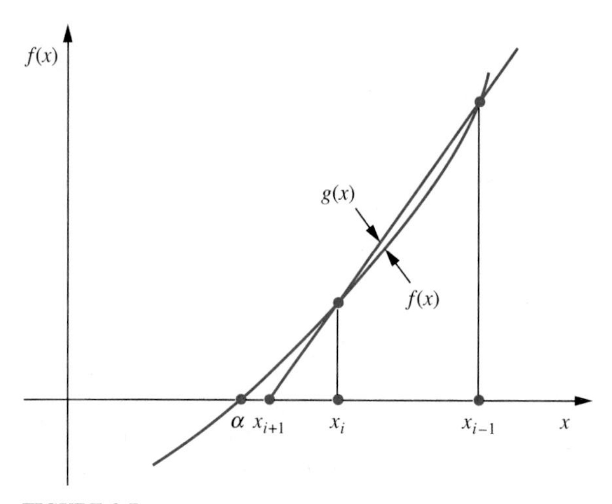

FIGURE 3.7
The secant method.

these two points is

$$g'(x_i) = \frac{f(x_i) - f(x_{i-1})}{x_i - x_{i-1}} \tag{3.58}$$

The equation of the secant line is given by

$$\frac{f(\alpha) - f(x_i)}{x_{i+1} - x_i} = g'(x_i) \tag{3.59}$$

Solving Eq. (3.59) for x_{i+1} yields

$$\boxed{x_{i+1} = x_i + \frac{f(\alpha) - f(x_i)}{g'(x_i)}} \tag{3.60}$$

Equation (3.60) is applied repetitively until either one or both of the following convergence criteria are satisfied:

$$|x_{i+1} - x_i| \le \epsilon \qquad \text{and} \qquad |f(x_{i+1}) - f(x_i)| \le \delta \tag{3.61}$$

Example 3.4. The secant method. Solve the four-bar linkage problem presented in Section 3.1 by the secant method. Recall Eq. (3.3):

$$f(\phi) = R_1 \cos(\alpha) - R_2 \cos(\phi) + R_3 - \cos(\alpha - \phi) = 0 \tag{3.62}$$

For this problem, $f(\phi) = 0$. Thus, Eq. (3.60) yields

$$\boxed{\phi_{i+1} = \phi_i + \frac{0.0 - f(\phi_i)}{g'(\phi_i)}} \tag{3.63}$$

TABLE 3.5
Solution by the secant method

i	ϕ_i	$f(\phi_i)$	$g'(\phi_i)$	ϕ_{i+1}
0	30.000000	−0.03979719		
1	40.000000	0.19496296	0.023476	31.695228
2	31.695228	−0.00657688	0.024268	31.966238
3	31.966238	−0.00101233	0.020533	32.015542
4	32.015542	0.00000749	0.020684	32.015180
5	32.015180	−0.00000001	0.020708	32.015180
	32.015180			

where $g'(\phi_i)$ is given by

$$g'(\phi_i) = \frac{f(\phi_i) - f(\phi_{i-1})}{\phi_i - \phi_{i-1}} \tag{3.64}$$

For $R_1 = \frac{5}{3}$, $R_2 = \frac{5}{2}$, $R_3 = \frac{11}{6}$, and $\alpha = 40$ deg, Eq. (3.62) becomes

$$\boxed{f(\phi) = \frac{5}{3}\cos(40) - \frac{5}{2}\cos(\phi) + \frac{11}{6} - \cos(40 - \phi)} \tag{3.65}$$

For the first iteration, let $\phi_0 = 30$ deg and $\phi_1 = 40$ deg. Equation (3.65) gives

$$f(\phi_0) = \frac{5}{3}\cos(40) - \frac{5}{2}\cos(30) + \frac{11}{6} - \cos(40 - 30) = -0.03979719 \tag{3.66a}$$

$$f(\phi_1) = \frac{5}{3}\cos(40) - \frac{5}{2}\cos(40) + \frac{11}{6} - \cos(40 - 40) = 0.19496296 \tag{3.66b}$$

Substituting these results into Eq. (3.64) gives

$$g'(\phi_1) = \frac{(0.19496296) - (-0.03979719)}{40 - 30} = 0.023476 \tag{3.67}$$

Substituting into Eq. (3.63) yields

$$\phi_2 = 40 + \frac{0.0 - (0.19496296)}{0.023476} = 31.695228 \tag{3.68}$$

These results and the results of subsequent iterations are presented in Table 3.5. The convergence criterion $|\phi_{i+1} - \phi_i| \leq 0.000001$ deg is satisfied on the fifth iteration.

The convergence rate of the secant method was analyzed by Jeeves (1958), who showed that

$$\boxed{e_{i+1} = \left(\frac{1}{2}\frac{f''(\alpha)}{f'(\alpha)}\right)^{0.62...} e_i^{1.62...}} \tag{3.69}$$

Convergence occurs at the rate 1.62..., which is considerably faster than the linear convergence rate of the fixed-point iteration method but somewhat slower than the quadratic convergence rate of Newton's method.

The question of which method is more efficient, Newton's method or the secant method, was also answered by Jeeves. He showed that if the effort required to evaluate $f'(x)$ is less than 43 percent of the effort required to evaluate $f(x)$, then Newton's method is more efficient. Otherwise, the secant method is more efficient.

Two methods that bear a similarity to the secant method are the *false position (regula falsi) method* and *Muller's* (1956) *method*. The false position method is similar to the interval halving method in that the two approximations to the zero always bracket the zero, and it is similar to the secant method in that the zero of the straight line passing through the two points is taken as the next approximation to the zero. This procedure generally approaches the zero from one side, so the interval containing the zero does not approach zero. The convergence rate is faster than for the interval halving method, but slower than for the secant method. The secant method is preferred.

In Muller's method, three approximations to the zero are required, and the next approximation is the zero of the parabola that passes through the three points. The convergence rate of Muller's method is approximately 1.84 in the vicinity of a zero, compared to 2.0 for Newton's method and 1.62 for the secant method. Like the secant method, it does not require the evaluation of the derivative of $f(x)$, the three approximations are not required to bracket the zero, and both real zeros and complex zeros can be found. Generally speaking, the secant method is preferred, because it is simpler.

Except for the problem of evaluating derivatives, the problems with Newton's method discussed at the end of Section 3.5 also apply to the secant method.

3.7 POLYNOMIALS

The methods of solving nonlinear equations presented in Sections 3.3 to 3.6 apply to any form of nonlinear equation. One very common form of nonlinear equation is a *polynomial*. Several special features of solving polynomials are discussed in this section.

The basic properties of polynomials are discussed in Section 4.2. The general form of an nth-degree polynomial is

$$P_n(x) = a_0 + a_1 x + a_2 x^2 + \cdots + a_n x^n \tag{3.70}$$

where n denotes the degree of the polynomial and a_0 to a_n are constant coefficients. The coefficients a_0 to a_n may be real or complex. The evaluation of a polynomial with real coefficients and its derivatives is straightforward, using nested multiplication and synthetic division, as discussed in Section 4.2.

The *fundamental theorem of algebra* states that an nth-degree polynomial has exactly n roots, or zeros. The zeros may be real or complex. If the coefficients are all real, the complex zeros always occur in conjugate pairs. The zeros may be distinct or repeated. The single zero of a linear polynomial can be determined directly. The two zeros of a second-degree polynomial can be determined from the quadratic formula. Exact formulas also exist for the zeros of third- and fourth-degree polynomials, but they are quite complicated and rarely used. Iterative methods must be used for higher-degree polynomials. Descartes' rule of signs, which applies to polynomials having real coefficients, states that the number of positive zeros of $P_n(x)$ is equal to the number of sign changes in the nonzero coefficients of $P_n(x)$, or is smaller by an even integer. The number of negative zeros is found in a similar manner by considering $P_n(-x)$. For example, the fourth-degree polynomial

$$P_4(x) = -4 + 2x + 3x^2 - 2x^3 + x^4 \tag{3.71}$$

has three sign changes in the coefficients of $P_n(x)$ and one sign change in the coefficients of $P_n(-x) = -4 - 2x + 3x^2 + 2x^3 + x^4$. Thus, the polynomial must have either three positive real zeros and one negative real zero, or one positive real zero, one negative real zero, and two complex conjugate zeros. The actual zeros are -1, 1, $1 + \sqrt{-1}$, and $1 - \sqrt{-1}$.

The two methods presented in Sections 3.5 and 3.6, Newton's method and the secant method, can both be used to find the zeros of polynomials. In view of the possibility of complex zeros, complex arithmetic must be used in the computations. The initial estimates must be complex to find complex zeros. The examples presented in the next paragraph were computed with Newton's method using complex arithmetic.

The zeros of high-degree polynomials are quite sensitive to the values of the coefficients. Consider the factored fifth-degree polynomial

$$P_5(x) = (x - 1)(x - 2)(x - 3)(x - 4)(x - 5) \tag{3.72}$$

which has the five positive real zeros 1, 2, 3, 4, and 5. Expanding Eq. (3.72) yields the usual polynomial form:

$$P_5(x) = -120 + 274x - 225x^2 + 85x^3 - 15x^4 + x^5 \tag{3.73}$$

Descartes' rule of signs shows that there are either five positive real zeros; three positive real zeros and two complex conjugate zeros; or one positive real zero and two pairs of complex conjugate zeros. Solving Eq. (3.73) with Newton's method, starting with the five initial guesses 0.9, 1.9, 2.9, 3.9, and 4.9, yields the five positive real zeros. To illustrate the sensitivity of the zeros to the values of the coefficients, we change the coefficient of x^2, which is 225, to 226, which is a change of only 0.44 percent. Starting with the same five initial guesses yields the five zeros 1.0514, 1.6191, 1.0514, 1.0514, and 5.5075. Only three distinct zeros are found. Changing the third and fourth initial guesses to $2.9 + \sqrt{-1.0}$ and $2.9 - \sqrt{-1.0}$ yields the five zeros 1.0514, 1.6191,

$3.4110 + \sqrt{-1.0793}$, $3.4110 - \sqrt{-1.0793}$, and 5.5075. Thus, a change of only 0.44 percent in one coefficient has made a major change in the zeros, including the introduction of a complex conjugate pair of zeros. This simple example illustrates the dangers associated with finding the zeros of high-degree polynomials.

One procedure for finding the zeros of high-degree polynomials is to find one zero by any method, then deflating the polynomial one degree by factoring out the known zero using synthetic division, as discussed in Section 4.2. The deflated $(n-1)$st-degree polynomial is then solved for the next zero. This procedure can be repeated until all the zeros are determined. The major limitation of this approach is that the coefficients of the deflated polynomial are not exact, so the zeros of the deflated polynomial are not the precise zeros of the original polynomial. Further deflations propagate the errors more and more, so the subsequent zeros become less and less accurate. This problem is less serious if the zeros are found in order from the smallest to the largest. In general, the zeros of the deflated polynomials should be used as first estimates for those zeros, which are then refined by solving the original polynomial.

Newton's method and the secant method work well for finding the complex zeros of polynomials, provided that complex arithmetic is used and reasonable complex initial guesses are specified. Complex arithmetic is straightforward on digital computers. However, complex arithmetic is tedious when performed by hand calculation. Several methods that do not require complex arithmetic exist for extracting complex roots of polynomials that have real coefficients. Among these are Bairstow's method, the QD (quotient-difference) method [see Henrici (1964)], and Graeffe's method [see Hildebrand (1956)]. The QD method and Graeff's method can find all the roots of a polynomial, whereas Bairstow's method extracts quadratic factors, which can then be solved by the quadratic formula. These three methods use only real arithmetic. The QD method, which does not require initial guesses, can be used to obtain estimates for all the zeros of a polynomial, which can then be refined using Newton's method.

When a polynomial has complex coefficients, Newton's method or the secant method is the method of choice, using complex arithmetic and complex initial guesses.

3.8 SYSTEMS OF NONLINEAR EQUATIONS

Many problems in engineering and science require the solution of a system of nonlinear equations. Consider the system of two nonlinear equations

$$f(x, y) = 0 \tag{3.74a}$$

$$g(x, y) = 0 \tag{3.74b}$$

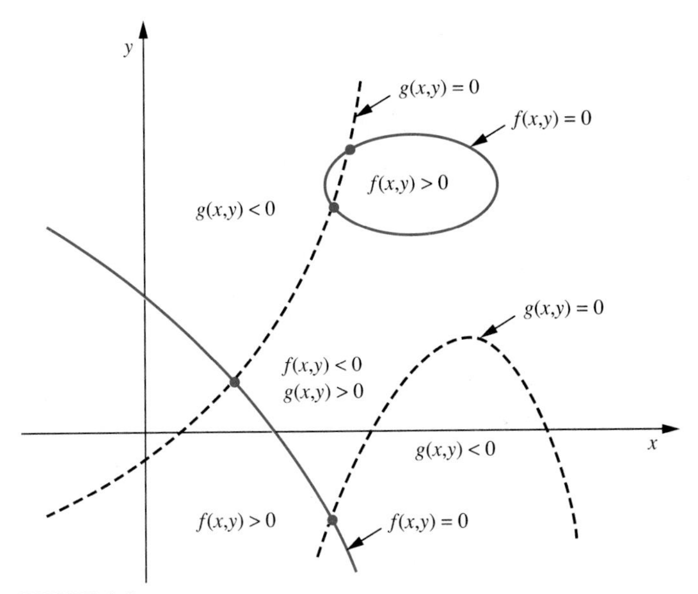

FIGURE 3.8
Solution of two nonlinear equations.

The problem can be stated as follows:

> Given the continuous functions $f(x, y)$ and $g(x, y)$, find the values $x = x^*$ and $y = y^*$ such that $f(x^*, y^*) = 0$ and $g(x^*, y^*) = 0$.

The problem is illustrated graphically in Fig. 3.8. The functions $f(x, y)$ and $g(x, y)$ may be algebraic equations, transcendental equations, solutions of differential equations, or any nonlinear relationships between the inputs x and y and the outputs $f(x, y)$ and $g(x, y)$. The $f(x, y) = 0$ and $g(x, y) = 0$ contours divide the xy plane into regions where $f(x, y)$ and $g(x, y)$ are positive or negative. The solutions to Eq. (3.74) are the intersections of the $f(x, y) = g(x, y) = 0$ contours, if any. The number of solutions is not known a priori. Four such intersections are illustrated in Fig. 3.8. This problem is considerably more complicated than the solution of a single nonlinear equation.

Interval halving and fixed-point iteration are not readily extendible to systems of nonlinear equations. Newton's method, however, can be extended to solve systems of nonlinear equations. In this section, Newton's method is extended to solve the system of two nonlinear equations specified by Eq. (3.74).

Assume that an approximate solution to Eq. (3.74) is known: (x_i, y_i). Express $f(x, y)$ and $g(x, y)$ in two-variable Taylor series (see the Appendix) about

(x_i, y_i), and evaluate the Taylor series at (x^*, y^*). Thus,

$$f(x^*, y^*) = f_i + f_x|_i (x^* - x_i) + f_y|_i (y^* - y_i) + \cdots = 0 \qquad (3.75a)$$

$$g(x^*, y^*) = g_i + g_x|_i (x^* - x_i) + g_y|_i (y^* - y_i) + \cdots = 0 \qquad (3.75b)$$

Truncating Eq. (3.75) after the first derivative terms and rearranging yields

$$f_x|_i \, \Delta x_i + f_y|_i \Delta y_i = -f_i \qquad (3.76b)$$

$$g_x|_i \, \Delta x_i + g_y|_i \Delta y_i = -g_i \qquad (3.76a)$$

where Δx_i and Δy_i are approximations to $(x^* - x_i)$ and $(y^* - y_i)$, respectively. Thus,

$$x_{i+1} = x_i + \Delta x_i \qquad (3.77a)$$

$$y_{i+1} = y_i + \Delta y_i \qquad (3.77b)$$

Equations (3.76) and (3.77) are applied repetitively until either one or both of the following convergence criteria are satisfied:

$$|\Delta x_i| \le \epsilon_x \quad \text{and} \quad |\Delta y_i| \le \epsilon_y \qquad (3.78a)$$

$$|f_{i+1} - f_i| \le \delta_f \quad \text{and} \quad |g_{i+1} - g_i| \le \delta_g \qquad (3.78b)$$

Example 3.5. Solution of two equations by Newton's method. As an example of Newton's method for solving two nonlinear equations, we will solve the four-bar linkage problem presented in Section 3.1. Recall the two scalar components of the vector loop equation, Eq. (3.2):

$$f(\theta_2, \theta_3) = r_2 \cos(\theta_2) + r_3 \cos(\theta_3) + r_4 \cos(\theta_4) - r_1 = 0 \qquad (3.79a)$$

$$g(\theta_2, \theta_3) = r_2 \sin(\theta_2) + r_3 \sin(\theta_3) + r_4 \sin(\theta_4) = 0 \qquad (3.79b)$$

where r_1 to r_4 are specified, θ_4 is the input angle, and θ_2 and θ_3 are the two output angles.

Let θ_2^* and θ_3^* be the solution to Eq. (3.79), and θ_2 and θ_3 be an approximation to the solution. Writing Taylor series for $f(\theta_2, \theta_3)$ and $g(\theta_2, \theta_3)$ about (θ_2, θ_3) and evaluating at (θ_2^*, θ_3^*) gives

$$f(\theta_2^*, \theta_3^*) = f|_{\theta_2,\theta_3} + f_{\theta_2}|_{\theta_2,\theta_3} \Delta\theta_2 + f_{\theta_3}|_{\theta_2,\theta_3} \Delta\theta_3 + \cdots = 0 \qquad (3.80a)$$

$$g(\theta_2^*, \theta_3^*) = g|_{\theta_2,\theta_3} + g_{\theta_2}|_{\theta_2,\theta_3} \Delta\theta_2 + g_{\theta_3}|_{\theta_2,\theta_3} \Delta\theta_3 + \cdots = 0 \qquad (3.80b)$$

TABLE 3.6
Solution of two equations by Newton's method

i	θ_2, deg	θ_3, deg	$f(\theta_2, \theta_3)$	$g(\theta_2, \theta_3)$	$\Delta\theta_2$, deg	$\Delta\theta_3$, deg
1	30.000000	0.000000	0.131975E+00	0.428850E+00	2.520530	−4.708541
2	32.520530	−4.708541	−0.319833E−01	−0.223639E−02	−0.500219	0.333480
3	32.020311	−4.375061	−0.328234E−03	−0.111507E−03	−0.005130	0.004073
4	32.015181	−4.370988	−0.405454E−07	−0.112109E−07	−0.000001	0.000000
	32.015180	−4.370987				

where $\Delta\theta_2 = (\theta_2^* - \theta_2)$ and $\Delta\theta_3 = (\theta_3^* - \theta_3)$. From Eq. (3.79),

$$f_{\theta_2} = -r_2 \sin(\theta_2) \quad \text{and} \quad f_{\theta_3} = -r_3 \sin(\theta_3) \tag{3.81a}$$

$$g_{\theta_2} = r_2 \cos(\theta_2) \quad \text{and} \quad g_{\theta_3} = r_3 \cos(\theta_3) \tag{3.81b}$$

Solving Eqs. (3.80) for $\Delta\theta_2$ and $\Delta\theta_3$ yields the following equations:

$$(f_{\theta_2}|_{\theta_2,\theta_3})\,\Delta\theta_2 + (f_{\theta_3}|_{\theta_2,\theta_3})\,\Delta\theta_3 = -f(\theta_2, \theta_3) \tag{3.82a}$$

$$(g_{\theta_2}|_{\theta_2,\theta_3})\Delta\theta_2 + (g_{\theta_3}|_{\theta_2,\theta_3})\Delta\theta_3 = -g(\theta_2, \theta_3) \tag{3.82b}$$

For the problem presented in Section 3.1, $r_1 = 10$, $r_2 = 6$, $r_3 = 8$, and $r_4 = 4$. Consider the case where $\theta_4 = 220$ deg. Let $\theta_2^{(1)} = 30$ deg and $\theta_3^{(1)} = 0$ deg. From Eq. (3.80)

$$f(30.0, 0.0) = 6\cos(30) + 8\cos(0) + 4\cos(220) - 10 = 0.131975 \tag{3.83a}$$

$$g(30.0, 0.0) = 6\sin(30) + 8\sin(0) + 4\sin(220) = 0.428850 \tag{3.83b}$$

Equations (3.81*a*) and (3.81*b*) give

$$f_{\theta_2} = (-6\sin(30))\tfrac{\pi}{180} = -0.052360 \quad \text{and} \quad f_{\theta_3} = (-8\sin(0))\tfrac{\pi}{180} = 0.0 \tag{3.84a}$$

$$g_{\theta_2} = (6\cos(30))\tfrac{\pi}{180} = 0.090690 \quad \text{and} \quad g_{\theta_3} = (8\cos(0))\tfrac{\pi}{180} = 0.139626 \tag{3.84b}$$

where $\pi/180$ converts radians to degrees. Substituting these results into Eq. (3.82) gives

$$-0.052360\Delta\theta_2 + 0.0\Delta\theta_3 = -0.131975 \tag{3.85a}$$

$$0.090690\Delta\theta_2 + 0.139626\Delta\theta_3 = -0.428850 \tag{3.85b}$$

Solving Eqs. (3.85) gives

$$\Delta\theta_2 = 2.520530 \text{ deg} \tag{3.86a}$$

$$\Delta\theta_3 = -4.708541 \text{ deg} \tag{3.86b}$$

Thus,

$$\theta_2 = 32.520530 \text{ deg} \quad \text{and} \quad \theta_3 = -4.708541 \text{ deg} \tag{3.87}$$

These results and the results of subsequent iterations are presented in Table 3.6. These results were obtained on a 13-decimal-digit computer. As illustrated in Fig. 3.2, $\theta_2 = \phi$. From Table 3.1, $\phi = 32.015180$, which is the same as θ_2.

In the general case,

$$\boxed{\mathbf{f}(\mathbf{x}) = \mathbf{0}} \tag{3.88}$$

where $\mathbf{f}(\mathbf{x}) = (f_1(\mathbf{x}), f_2(\mathbf{x}), \ldots, f_n(\mathbf{x}))$ and $\mathbf{x} = (x_1, x_2, \ldots, x_n)$. In this case, Eqs. (3.76) and (3.77) become

$$\boxed{\mathbf{A}\boldsymbol{\Delta} = \mathbf{f}_i} \tag{3.89}$$

where $\mathbf{A}$ is the $n \times n$ matrix of partial derivatives

$$\mathbf{A} = \begin{bmatrix} (f_1)_{x_1} & (f_1)_{x_2} & \cdots & (f_1)_{x_n} \\ (f_2)_{x_1} & (f_2)_{x_2} & \cdots & (f_2)_{x_n} \\ \vdots & \vdots & \ddots & \vdots \\ (f_n)_{x_1} & (f_n)_{x_2} & \cdots & (f_n)_{x_n} \end{bmatrix} \tag{3.90}$$

$\boldsymbol{\Delta}$ is the column vector of corrections,

$$\boldsymbol{\Delta}^{\mathrm{T}} = (\Delta x_1 \quad \Delta x_2 \quad \ldots \quad \Delta x_n) \tag{3.91}$$

and $\mathbf{f}_i$ is the column vector of function values

$$\mathbf{f}_i^{\mathrm{T}} = (f_1 \ f_2 \ \ldots \ f_n)_i \tag{3.92}$$

The most costly part of solving systems of nonlinear equations is the evaluation of the matrix $\mathbf{A}$ of partial derivatives. Letting $\mathbf{A}$ be constant may yield a much less costly solution. However, $\mathbf{A}$ must be reasonably accurate for this procedure to work. A strategy based on making several corrections using constant $\mathbf{A}$, then reevaluating $\mathbf{A}$, may yield the most economical solution.

In situations where the partial derivatives of $\mathbf{f}(\mathbf{x})$ cannot be evaluated analytically, the above procedure cannot be applied. One alternate approach is to estimate the partial derivatives in Eq. (3.90) numerically. Thus,

$$\frac{\partial f_i}{\partial x_j} = \frac{f_i(\mathbf{x} + \Delta x_j) - f_i(\mathbf{x})}{\Delta x_j} \qquad (i, j = 1, 2, \ldots, n) \tag{3.93}$$

This procedure has two disadvantages. First, the number of calculations is increased. Second, if Δx_j is too small, round-off errors pollute the solution, and if Δx_j is too large, the convergence rate can decrease to first order. Nevertheless, this is one procedure for solving systems of nonlinear equations where the partial derivatives of $\mathbf{f}(\mathbf{x})$ cannot be determined analytically.

An alternate approach involves constructing a single nonlinear function $F(\mathbf{x})$ by adding together the sums of the squares of the individual functions $f_i(\mathbf{x})$. The function $F(\mathbf{x})$ has a global minimum of zero when all of the individual functions are zero. Multidimensional minimization techniques can be applied to minimize $F(\mathbf{x})$, which yields the solution to the system of nonlinear equations, $\mathbf{f}(\mathbf{x}) = 0$. The book by Dennis and Schnadel (1983) introduces such procedures.

3.9 SUMMARY

Several methods for solving nonlinear equations are presented in this chapter. The nonlinear equation may be an algebraic equation, a transcendental equation, the solution of a differential equation, or any nonlinear relationship between an input x and a response $f(x)$.

Interval halving converges very slowly, but is certain to converge, because the zero lies in the interval being halved. This method is not recommended unless the nonlinear function is so poorly behaved that all other methods fail.

Fixed-point iteration converges only if the derivative of the nonlinear function is less than unity in magnitude. Consequently, it is not recommended.

Newton's method and the secant method are both effective methods for solving nonlinear equations. Both methods generally require reasonable initial estimates. Newton's method converges faster than the secant method (i.e., second order compared to 1.62 order), but Newton's method requires the evaluation of the derivative of the nonlinear function. If the effort required to evaluate the derivative is less than 43 percent of the effort required to evaluate the function itself, Newton's method requires less total effort than the secant method. Otherwise, the secant method requires less total effort. For functions whose derivative cannot be evaluated, the secant method is recommended. Both methods can find complex zeros if complex arithmetic is used. The secant method is recommended as the best general-purpose method.

The higher-order variations of Newton's method and the secant method, that is, the second-order Taylor series method and Muller's method, respectively, while quite effective, are not used frequently. This is probably because Newton's method and the secant method are so efficient that the slightly more complicated logic of the higher-order methods is not justified.

Solving systems of nonlinear equations is a difficult task. For systems of nonlinear equations that have analytical partial derivatives, Newton's method can be used. Otherwise, multidimensional minimization techniques should be used. No single approach has proven to be the most effective. Solving systems of nonlinear equations remains a difficult problem.

PROBLEMS

In all the problems in this chapter, carry at least six significant figures in all calculations, unless otherwise noted. Continue all iterative procedures until four significant figures have converged.

Section 3.2 Interval Halving

***1.** Use interval halving to determine the roots of the following functions in the interval given by the two indicated values.

(a) $f(x) = x - \cos x = 0$ (0.5 and 1.0)
(b) $f(x) = e^x - \sin(\pi x/3) = 0$ (−3.5 and − 2.5)
(c) $f(x) = e^x - 2x - 2 = 0$ (1.0 and 2.0)
(d) $f(x) = x^3 - 2x^2 - 2x + 1 = 0$ (0.0 and 1.0)

2. Find the two points of intersection of the two curves $y = e^x$ and $y = 3x + 2$ using interval halving. Use (−1.0 and 0.0) and (2.0 and 3.0) as starting values.

***3.** Find the two points of intersection of the two curves $y = e^x$ and $y = x^4$ using interval halving. Use (−1.0 and 0.0) and (1.0 and 2.0) as starting values.

4. Problems 1 to 3 can be solved using any two initial values of x that bracket the root. Choose other sets of initial values of x to gain additional exercise with interval halving.

Section 3.4 Fixed-Point Iteration

***5.** Work Problem 1 by fixed-point iteration with x_0 equal to the smaller starting value.

6. Work Problem 1 by fixed-point iteration with x_0 equal to the larger starting value.

7. Problem 2 considers the function $f(x) = e^x - (3x + 2) = 0$, which can be rearranged into the following three forms: (a) $x = e^x - (2x + 2)$, (b) $x = (e^x - 2)/3$, and (c) $x = \ln(3x + 2)$. Solve for the positive root by fixed-point iteration for all three forms, with $x_0 = 1.0$.

***8.** Work Problem 3 by fixed-point iteration, with $x_0 = -1.0$ and 1.0.

9. The function $f(x) = (x + 2)(x - 4) = x^2 - 2x - 8 = 0$ has the two roots $x = -2$ and 4. Rearrange $f(x)$ into the form $x = g(x)$ to obtain the root (a) $x = -2$ and (b) $x = 4$, starting with $x_0 = -1$ and 3, respectively. The function $f(x)$ can be rearranged in several ways, for example: (a) $x = 8/(x - 2)$, (b) $x = (2x + 8)^{1/2}$, and (c) $x = (x^2 - 8)/2$. One form always converges to $x = -2$, one form always converges to $x = 4$, and one form always diverges. Determine the behavior of the three forms.

10. For what starting values of x might the expression $x = 1/(x + 1)$ not converge?

11. The function $f(x) = e^x - 3x^2 = 0$ has three roots. The function can be rearranged into the form $x = \pm(\exp(x)/3)^{1/2}$. Starting with $x_0 = 0$, find the roots corresponding to: (a) the + sign (near $x = 1.0$) and (b) the − sign (near −0.5). (c) The third root is near $x = 4.0$. Show that the above form will not converge to this root, even with an initial guess close to the exact root. Develop a form of $x = g(x)$ that will converge to this root, and solve for the third root.

12. The cubic polynomial $f(x) = x^3 + 3x^2 - 2x - 4 = 0$ has a root near $x = 1.0$. Find two forms of $x = g(x)$ that will converge to this root. Solve these two forms for the root, starting with $x_0 = 1.0$.

Section 3.5 Newton's Method

***13.** Solve Problem 1 by Newton's method. Use the larger initial value as the starting value.

***14.** Find the positive root of $f(x) = x^{15} - 1 = 0$ by Newton's method, starting with $x_0 = 1.1$.

15. Solve Problem 14 using $x = 0.5$ as the initial guess. You may want to solve this problem on a computer, since a large number of iterations may be required.

16. The nth root of the number N can be found by solving the equation $x^n - N = 0$.

(a) For this equation, show that Newton's method gives

$$x_{i+1} = \frac{1}{n}\left((n - 1)x_i + \frac{N}{x_i^{n+1}}\right)$$

(*b*) Use the above result to solve the following problems: (*i*) $(161)^{1/3}$, (*ii*) $(21.75)^{1/4}$, (*iii*) $(238.56)^{1/5}$. Use $x = 6.0$, 2.0, and 3.0, respectively, as starting values.

17. Consider the function $f(x) = e^x - 2x^2 = 0$.
(*a*) Find the two positive roots using Newton's method.
(*b*) Find the negative root using Newton's method.

Section 3.6 The Secant Method

***18.** Solve Problem 1 by the secant method. Use the interval bounds as starting values.

***19.** Find the positive root of $f(x) = x^{15} - 1 = 0$ by the secant method using $x = 1.2$ and 1.1 as starting values.

20. Work Problem 19 by the secant method with $x = 0.5$ and 0.6 as starting values.

21. Solve Problem 16*b* by the secant method. Use the starting values given there for x_0, and let $x_1 = 1.1x_0$.

22. Solve Problem 17 using the secant method.

Section 3.7 Polynomials

***23.** Use Newton's method to find the real roots of the following polynomials:

*(*a*) $x^3 - 5x^2 + 7x - 3 = 0$ (*b*) $x^4 - 9x^3 + 24x^2 - 36x + 80 = 0$
(*c*) $x^3 - 2x^2 - 2x + 1 = 0$ (*d*) $3x^3 + 4x^2 - 8x - 2 = 0$

***24.** Use Newton's method to find the complex roots of the following polynomials:

(*a*) $x^4 - 9x^3 + 24x^2 - 36x + 80 = 0$
*(*b*) $x^3 + 2x^2 + x + 2 = 0$
(*c*) $x^5 - 15x^4 + 85x^3 - 226x^2 + 274x - 120 = 0$

Section 3.8 Systems of Nonlinear Equations

Solve the following systems of nonlinear equations using Newton's method.

***25.** $(x - 1)^2 + (y - 2)^2 = 3$ and $x^2/4 + y^2/3 = 1$. Solve for all roots.

26. $y = \cosh x$ and $x^2 + y^2 = 2$. Solve for both roots.

27. $x^2 + y^2 = 2x + y$ and $x^2/4 + y^2 = 1$.

28. $y^2(1 - x) = x^3$ and $x^2 + y^2 = 1$.

29. $x^3 + y^3 - 3xy = 0$ and $x^2 + y^2 = 1$.

30. $(x^2 + y^2)^2 = 2xy$ and $y = x^3$.

31. $(2x)^{2/3} + y^{2/3} = (9)^{1/3}$ and $x^2/4 + y^2 = 1$.

Applied Problems

Several applied problems from various disciplines are presented in this section. All of these problems can be solved by any of the methods presented in this chapter. An infinite variety of exercises can be constructed by changing the numerical values of the parameters of the problem, changing the starting values, or both.

32. Consider the four-bar linkage problem presented in Section 3.1. Solve for any (or all) of the results presented in Table 3.1.
33. Consider the four-bar linkage problem described in Section 3.1. Rearrange this problem to solve for the value of r_1 such that $\phi = 60$ deg when $\alpha = 75$ deg. Numerous variations of this problem can be obtained by specifying combinations of ϕ and α.
34. Write a computer program to solve Freudenstein's equation, Eq. (3.3), by the secant method. Calculate ϕ for $\alpha = 40$ deg to 90 deg in increments $\Delta\alpha = 10$ deg. For $\alpha = 40$ deg, let $\phi_0 = 25$ deg and $\phi_1 = 30$ deg. For subsequent values of α, let ϕ_0 be the solution value for the previous value of α, and $\phi_1 = \phi_0 + 1.0$. Continue the calculations until ϕ changes by less than 0.00001 deg. Design the program output as illustrated in Example 3.4.
35. Solve the four-bar linkage problem for $\theta_4 = 210$ deg by solving the two scalar components of the vector loop equation, Eq. (3.2), by Newton's method. Let the initial guesses be $\theta_2 = 20$ deg and $\theta_3 = 0$ deg. Continue the calculations until θ_2 and θ_3 change by less than 0.00001 deg. Show all calculations for the first iteration. Summarize the first iteration and subsequent iterations in a table, as illustrated in Example 3.6.
36. The van der Waals equation of state for a vapor is

$$\left(P + \frac{a}{v^2}\right)(v - b) = RT \tag{P3.36.1}$$

where P is the pressure (Pa $= \text{N/m}^2$), v is the specific volume (m^3/kg), T is the temperature (K), R is the gas constant (J/kg-K), and a and b are empirical constants. Consider water vapor, for which $R = 461.495$ J/kg-K, $a = 1703.28$ Pa-(m^3/kg)^3, and $b = 0.00169099$ (m^3/kg). Equation (P3.36.1) can be rearranged into the form

$$Pv^3 - (Pb + RT)v^2 + av - ab = 0 \tag{P3.36.2}$$

Calculate the specific volume v for $P = 10{,}000$ kPa and $T = 800$ K. Use the ideal gas law, $Pv = RT$, to obtain the initial guess (or guesses). Present the results in the format illustrated in the examples.
37. Write a computer program to solve the van der Waals equation of state by the secant method. Follow the procedure described in Problem 3.36 to initiate the calculations. Design the program output as illustrated in Example 3.4. For $P = 10{,}000$ kPa, calculate v corresponding to $T = 700$, 800, 900, 1000, 1100, 1200, 1300, 1400, 1500, and 1600 K. Write the program so that all the cases can be calculated in one run by stacking input data decks.
38. When an incompressible fluid flows steadily through a round pipe, the pressure drop due to the effects of wall friction is given by the empirical formula:

$$\Delta P = -0.5 f \rho V^2 (L/D) \tag{P3.38.1}$$

where ΔP is the pressure drop, ρ is the density, V is the velocity, L is the pipe length, D is the pipe diameter, and f is the D'Arcy friction coefficient. Several empirical formulas exist for the friction coefficient f as a function of the dimensionless Reynolds number $\text{Re} = DV\rho/\mu$, where μ is the viscosity. For flow in the turbulent regime between completely smooth pipe surfaces and wholly rough pipe surfaces, Colebrook (1939) developed the following empirical equation for the friction coefficient f:

$$\frac{1}{f^{1/2}} = -2\log_{10}\left(\frac{\epsilon/D}{3.7} + \frac{2.51}{\text{Re} f^{1/2}}\right) \tag{P3.38.2}$$

where ϵ is the pipe surface roughness. Develop a procedure to determine f for specified values of ϵ/D and Re. Use the approximation proposed by Genereaux (1939) to determine the initial approximation(s):

$$f = 0.16\ \mathrm{Re}^{-0.16} \tag{P3.38.3}$$

Solve for f for a pipe having $\epsilon/D = 0.001$ for Re $= 10^n$, for $n = 4, 5, 6$, and 7.

39. Write a computer program to solve the Colebrook equation, Eq. (P3.37.2), by the secant method for the friction coefficient f for specified values of the roughness ratio ϵ/D and the Reynolds number Re. Use the approximation proposed by Genereaux (1939) and 90 percent of that value as the initial approximations. Solve Problem 3.38 using the program.

40. Consider quasi-one-dimensional isentropic flow of a perfect gas through the variable-area channel illustrated in the figure. The relationship between the Mach number M and the flow area A, derived by Zucrow and Hoffman (1976) [Eq. (4.29) in that book], is given by

$$\epsilon = \frac{A}{A^*} = \frac{1}{M}\left(\frac{2}{\gamma+1}\left(1 + \frac{\gamma-1}{2}M^2\right)\right)^{(\gamma+1)/2(\gamma-1)} \tag{P3.40}$$

where A^* is the choking area (in other words, the area where $M = 1$) and γ is the specific heat ratio of the flowing gas. For each value of ϵ, two values of M exist, one less than unity (subsonic flow) and one greater than unity (supersonic flow). Calculate both values of M for $\epsilon = 10.0$ and $\gamma = 1.4$ by Newton's method. For the subsonic root, let $M_0 = 0.2$. For the supersonic root, let $M_0 = 5.0$.

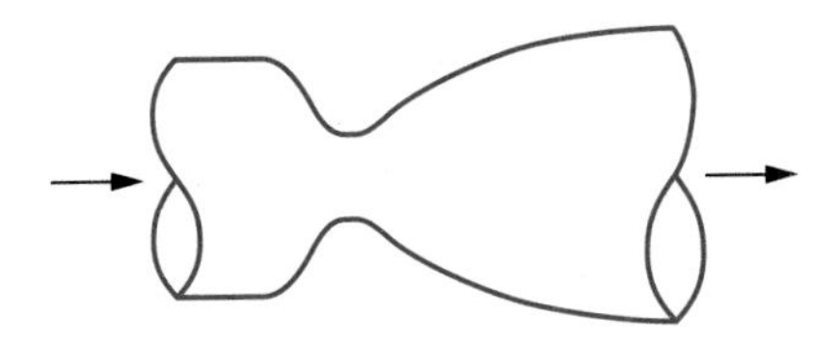

41. Solve Problem 3.40 by the secant method. For the subsonic root, let $M_0 = 0.4$ and $M_1 = 0.6$. For the supersonic root, let $M_0 = 3.0$ and $M_1 = 4.0$.

42. Write a computer program to solve the $M - \epsilon$ equation presented in Problem 3.40 by Newton's method for specified values of γ and ϵ. (*a*) Solve Problem 3.40 using the program. (*b*) Construct a table of M vs. ϵ for $1.0 \le \epsilon \le 10$, for subsonic flow, in increments $\Delta\epsilon = 0.1$. For $\epsilon = 1.1$, let $M_0 = 0.8$. For subsequent values of ϵ, let M_0 be the previous solution value.

43. Write a computer program to solve the $M - \epsilon$ equation presented in Problem 3.40 by the secant method for specified values of γ and ϵ. (*a*) Solve Problem 3.41 using the program. (*b*) Construct a table of M vs. ϵ for $1.0 \le \epsilon \le 10$, for supersonic flow, in increments $\Delta\epsilon = 0.1$. For $\epsilon = 1.1$, let $M_0 = 1.2$ and $M_1 = 1.3$. For subsequent values of ϵ, let M_0 be the previous solution value and $M_1 = 1.1\ M_0$.

44. Consider isentropic supersonic flow around the sharp expansion corner illustrated in the figure. The relationship between the Mach number before the corner (M_1) and after the corner (M_2), derived by Zucrow and Hoffman (1976) [Eq. (8.11) in that book], is given by

$$\delta = b^{1/2}\left(\tan^{-1}\left(\frac{M_2^2-1}{b}\right)^{1/2} - \tan^{-1}\left(\frac{M_1^2-1}{b}\right)^{1/2}\right) - \left(\tan^{-1}\left((M_2^2-1)^{1/2}\right) - \tan^{-1}\left((M_1^2-1)^{1/2}\right)\right) \tag{P3.44}$$

where $b = (\gamma + 1)/(\gamma - 1)$ and γ is the specific heat ratio of the gas. Develop a procedure to solve for M_2 for specified values of γ, δ, and M_1. For $\gamma = 1.4$, solve for M_2 for the following combinations of M_1 and δ: (*a*) 1.0 and 10.0 deg, (*b*) 1.0 and 20.0 deg, (*c*) 1.5 and 10.0 deg, and (*d*) 1.5 and 20.0 deg. Use $M_2^{(0)} = 2.0$ and $M_2^{(1)} = 1.5$.

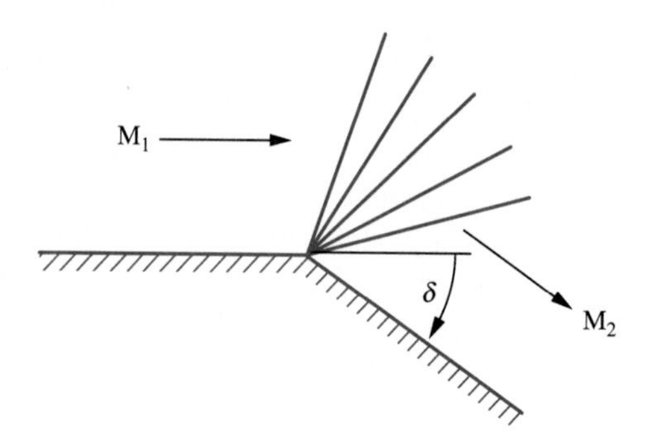

45. Write a computer program to solve Eq. (P3.44) by the secant method for specified values of γ, δ, and M_1. (*a*) Solve Problem 3.44 using the program. (*b*) Construct a table of M vs. δ for $\gamma = 1.4$ and $M_1 = 1.0$, for $0 < \delta < 40$ deg, in increments $\Delta\delta = 1.0$ deg. For $\delta = 1.0$ deg, let $M_0 = 1.06$ and $M_1 = 1.08$. For subsequent values of δ, let M_0 be the previous solution value and $M_1 = 1.01\ M_0$.

CHAPTER 4

POLYNOMIAL APPROXIMATION AND INTERPOLATION

Section

Example

4.1 INTRODUCTION

In many problems in engineering and science, the data being considered are known only at a set of discrete points, not as a continuous function. For example, the continuous function

$$y = f(x) \tag{4.1}$$

may be known only at n discrete values of x:

$$y_i = y(x_i), \qquad (i = 1, 2, \ldots, n) \tag{4.2}$$

Discrete data, or tabular data, may consist of small sets of smooth data, large sets of smooth data, small sets of rough data, or large sets of rough data.

In many applications, the values of the discrete data are not all that is needed. Values of the function at points other than the known discrete points may be needed (i.e., interpolation). The derivative of the function may be required (i.e., differentiation). The integral of the function may be of interest (i.e., integration). Thus, the processes of *interpolation, differentiation*, and *integration* of a set of discrete data are of interest. These processes are illustrated in Fig. 4.1. These processes are performed by fitting an *approximating function* to the set of discrete data and performing the desired process on the approximating function.

Many types of approximating functions exist. In fact, any analytical function can be used as an approximating function. Three of the more common approximating functions are

1. Polynomials
2. Trigonometric functions
3. Exponential functions

Approximating functions should have the following properties:

1. The approximating function should be easy to determine.
2. It should be easy to evaluate.
3. It should be easy to differentiate.
4. It should be easy to integrate.

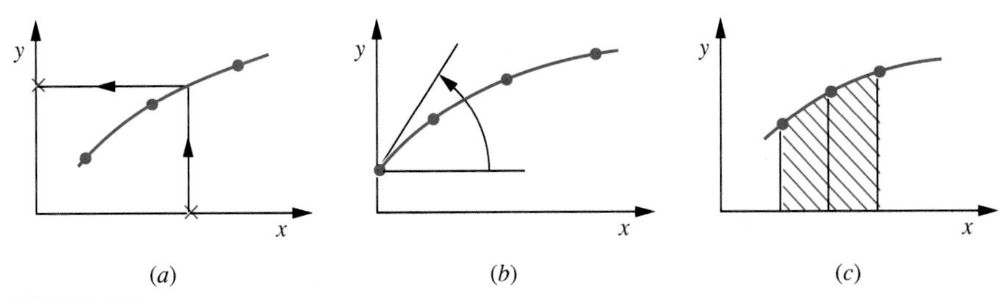

FIGURE 4.1
Applications of approximating functions: (*a*) interpolation; (*b*) differentiation; (*c*) integration.

Polynomials satisfy all four of these properties. Consequently, polynomial approximating functions are used in this book to fit sets of discrete data for interpolation, differentiation, and integration.

There are two fundamentally different ways of fitting a polynomial to a set of discrete data:

1. Exact fits
2. Approximate fits

An *exact fit* yields a polynomial that passes exactly through all of the discrete points, as illustrated in Fig. 4.2*a*. This type of fit is useful for small sets of smooth data. Exact polynomial fits are discussed in Sections 4.3 to 4.10. An *approximate fit* yields a polynomial that passes through the set of data in the *best manner possible*, without being required to pass exactly through any of the data points, as illustrated in Figure 4.2*b*. Several definitions of "best manner possible" exist. Approximate fits are useful for large sets of smooth data or rough sets of data. In this book, the least squares procedure is used for approximate fits.

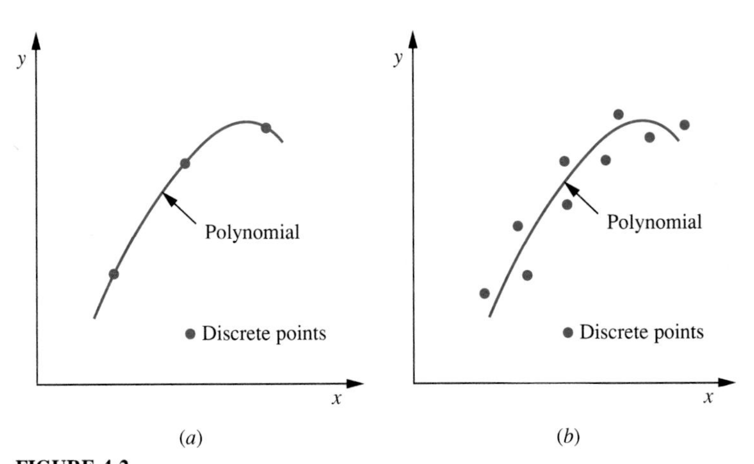

FIGURE 4.2
Polynomial approximation: (*a*) exact fit; (*b*) approximate fit.

A set of discrete data may be equally spaced or unequally spaced in the independent variable x. In the general case where the data are unequally spaced, several procedures can be used to fit approximating polynomials, for example direct fit polynomials, Lagrange polynomials, and divided-difference polynomials. Methods such as these require a considerable amount of effort. When the data are equally spaced, procedures based on *differences* can be used, including the Newton forward-difference polynomial, the Newton backward-difference polynomial, and many others. These methods are quite easy to apply. Both types of methods are considered in this chapter.

Several procedures for polynomial approximation are developed in this chapter. Application of these results for interpolation is illustrated by examples. Numerical differentiation and numerical integration are discussed in Chapters 5 and 6, respectively.

4.2 PROPERTIES OF POLYNOMIALS

The general form of an nth-degree polynomial is

$$P_n(x) = a_0 + a_1 x + a_2 x^2 + \cdots + a_n x^n \tag{4.3}$$

where n denotes the degree of the polynomial, and a_0 to a_n are constant coefficients. There are $n + 1$ coefficients, so $n + 1$ discrete data points are required to obtain unique values for the coefficients.

The property of polynomials that makes them suitable as approximating functions is stated by the *Weierstrass approximation theorem*:

> If $f(x)$ is a continuous function in the closed interval $a \le x \le b$, then for every $\epsilon > 0$ there exists a polynomial $P_n(x)$, where the value of n depends on the value of ϵ, such that for all x in the closed interval $a \le x \le b$,
>
> $$|f(x) - P_n(x)| < \epsilon.$$

Consequently, any continuous function can be approximated to any accuracy by a polynomial of high enough degree. In practice, low-degree polynomials are employed, so care must be taken to achieve the desired accuracy.

Polynomials satisfy a *uniqueness theorem*:

> A polynomial of degree n passing exactly through $n + 1$ discrete points is *unique*.

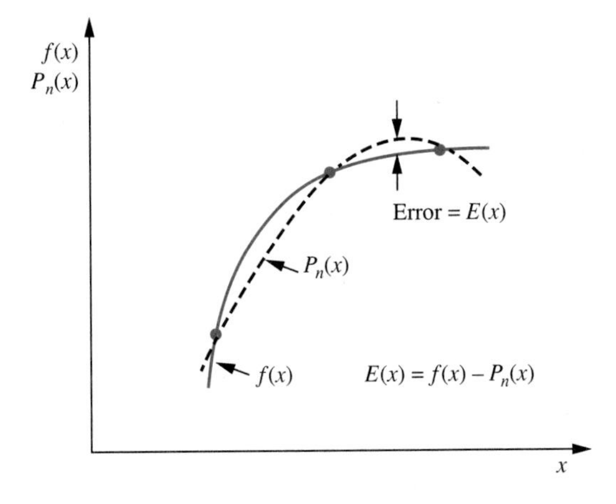

FIGURE 4.3
Error in polynomial approximation.

The polynomial through a specific set of points may take many different forms, but all forms are equivalent. Any form can be manipulated into any other form by simple algebraic rearrangement.

The Taylor series (see the Appendix) is a polynomial of infinite order. Thus,

$$f(x) = f(x_0) + f'(x_0)(x - x_0) + \frac{1}{2!}f''(x_0)(x - x_0)^2 + \cdots \tag{4.4}$$

It is, of course, impossible to evaluate an infinite number of terms. The Taylor polynomial of degree n is defined by

$$f(x) = P_n(x) + R_{n+1}(x) \tag{4.5}$$

where the Taylor polynomial $P_n(x)$ and the remainder term $R_{n+1}(x)$ are given by

$$P_n(x) = f(x_0) + f'(x_0)(x - x_0) + \cdots + \frac{1}{n!}f^{(n)}(x_0)(x - x_0)^n \tag{4.6}$$

$$R_{n+1}(x) = \frac{1}{(n+1)!}f^{(n+1)}(\xi)(x - x_0)^{n+1}, \; x_0 \le \xi \le x \tag{4.7}$$

The Taylor polynomial is a truncated Taylor series, with an explicit remainder, or error, term. The Taylor polynomial cannot be used as an approximating function for discrete data, because the derivatives required in the coefficients cannot be determined. It does have great significance, however, for polynomial approximation, because it has an explicit error term.

When a polynomial of degree n, $P_n(x)$, is fitted exactly to a set of $n + 1$ discrete data points, $(x_0, f_0), (x_1, f_1), \ldots, (x_n, f_n)$, as illustrated in Fig. 4.3, the polynomial has no error at the data points themselves. However, at the locations between the data points, there is an error, which is defined by

$$E(x) = f(x) - P_n(x) \tag{4.8}$$

It can be shown that the error term $E(x)$ has the form

$$E(x) = \frac{1}{(n+1)!}(x - x_0)(x - x_1)\cdots(x - x_n)f^{(n+1)}(\xi) \tag{4.9}$$

where $x_0 \le \xi \le x_n$. This form of the error term is used extensively in error analysis of procedures based on approximating polynomials.

The evaluation of a polynomial $P_n(x)$ for a particular value of x is straightforward. For example, the fourth-degree polynomial $P_4(x)$

$$P_4(x) = a_0 + a_1 x + a_2 x^2 + a_3 x^3 + a_4 x^4 \tag{4.10}$$

requires $(0 + 1 + 2 + 3 + 4) = 10$ multiplications and four additions. Equation (4.10) can be written in the nested form

$$P_4(x) = a_0 + x\Big(a_1 + x\big(a_2 + x(a_3 + a_4 x)\big)\Big) \tag{4.11}$$

which requires four multiplications and four additions. For a polynomial of degree n, $P_n(x)$, *nested multiplication* is given by

$$P_n(x) = a_0 + x\bigg(a_1 + x\Big(a_2 + x\big(a_3 + \cdots x(a_{n-1} + a_n x)\big)\Big)\bigg) \tag{4.12}$$

which requires n multiplications and n additions. Equation (4.12) can be evaluated by constructing the sequence

$$\begin{aligned} b_n &= a_n \\ b_i &= a_i + x b_{i+1} \qquad (i = n-1, n-2, \ldots, 0) \end{aligned} \tag{4.13}$$

where $P_n(x) = b_0$.

Differentiation of polynomials is also straightforward. For the general term $a_i x^i$,

$$\frac{d}{dx}\left(a_i x^i\right) = i a_i x^{i-1} \tag{4.14}$$

The derivatives of the nth-degree polynomial $P_n(x)$ are

$$\frac{dP_n(x)}{dx} = P_n'(x) = a_1 + 2a_2x + \cdots + na_nx^{n-1} = P_{n-1}(x) \quad (4.15a)$$

$$\frac{d^2P_n(x)}{dx^2} = P_n''(x) = 2a_2 + 6a_3x + \cdots + n(n-1)a_nx^{n-2} = P_{n-2}(x) \quad (4.15b)$$

$$\vdots$$

$$P_n^{(n)} = n!a_n \quad (4.15n)$$

$$P_n^{(n+1)} = 0 \quad (4.16)$$

Integration of polynomials is equally straightforward. For the general term a_ix^i,

$$\int a_ix^i\,dx = \frac{a_i}{i+1}x^{i+1} + \text{Constant} \quad (4.17)$$

The integral of the nth-degree polynomial $P_n(x)$ is

$$I = \int P_n(x)\,dx = \int (a_0 + a_1x + \cdots + a_nx^n)\,dx \quad (4.18)$$

$$I = a_0x + \frac{a_1}{2}x^2 + \cdots + \frac{a_n}{n+1}x^{n+1} + \text{Constant} = P_{n+1}(x) \quad (4.19)$$

Several other properties of polynomials are quite useful. The *division algorithm* states that

$$P_n(x) = (x - r)Q_{n-1}(x) + R \quad (4.20)$$

where r is any number, $Q_{n-1}(x)$ is a polynomial of degree $n-1$, and R is a constant remainder. The *remainder theorem* states that

$$P_n(r) = R \quad (4.21)$$

The *factor theorem* states that if $P_n(r) = 0$, then $(x - r)$ is a factor of $P_n(x)$, which means that r is a root, or zero, of $P_n(x)$. The derivative of $P_n(x)$, $P_n'(x)$, can be obtained from Eq. (4.20). Thus,

$$P_n'(x) = Q_{n-1}(x) + (x - r)Q_{n-1}'(x) \quad (4.22)$$

At $x = r$,

$$P_n'(r) = Q_{n-1}(r) \quad (4.23)$$

Consequently, first derivatives of an nth-degree polynomial can be evaluated from the $(n-1)$st-degree polynomial $Q_{n-1}(x)$. Higher-order derivatives can be determined by applying the procedure to $Q_{n-1}(x)$, and so forth.

The $(n-1)$st-degree polynomial $Q_{n-1}(x)$, which can be used to evaluate the derivative $P_n'(x)$, and the remainder R, which yields $P_n(r) = R$, can be evaluated by the *synthetic division algorithm*. Consider $P_n(x)$ in the form given by Eq. (4.3) and $Q_{n-1}(x)$ in the form

$$Q_{n-1}(x) = b_1 + b_2x + b_3x^2 + \cdots + b_{n-1}x^{n-2} + b_nx^{n-1} \quad (4.24)$$

Substituting Eqs. (4.3) and (4.24) into Eq. (4.20) and equating coefficients of like powers of x yields

$$b_n = a_n \tag{4.25.n}$$
$$b_{n-1} = a_{n-1} + r b_n \tag{4.25.n − 1}$$
$$\vdots \quad \vdots \quad \vdots$$
$$b_1 = a_1 + r b_2 \tag{4.25.1}$$
$$b_0 = a_0 + r b_1 = R \tag{4.25.0}$$

Equation (4.25) can be written as

$$\boxed{\begin{aligned} b_n &= a_n \\ b_i &= a_i + r b_{i+1} \qquad (i = n-1, n-2, \ldots, 0) \end{aligned}} \tag{4.26}$$

Equation (4.26) is identical to the nested multiplication algorithm presented in Eq. (4.13), for $x = r$.

If a root, or zero, of $P_n(x)$ is known, $P_n(x)$ can be *deflated* by removing the factor $(x - r)$ to yield the $(n - 1)$st-degree polynomial $Q_{n-1}(x)$. From Eq. (4.20), if r is a zero of $P_n(x)$, then $P_n(r) = 0$ and $R = 0$, and Eq. (4.20) yields

$$Q_{n-1}(x) = 0 \tag{4.27)}$$

The deflated polynomial $Q_{n-1}(x)$ has $n - 1$ roots, or zeros, which are the remaining zeros of $P_n(x)$.

The properties of polynomials presented in this section make them extremely useful as approximating functions.

Example 4.1. Polynomial evaluation. We illustrate nested multiplication and synthetic division by considering the fifth-degree polynomial considered in Section 3.7, Eq. (3.73) (see p. 105):

$$P_5(x) = -120 + 274x - 225x^2 + 85x^3 - 15x^4 + x^5 \tag{4.28}$$

Recall that the zeros of Eq. (4.28) are $x = 1, 2, 3, 4$, and 5. Evaluate $P_5(2.5)$ and $P_5'(2.5)$, and determine the deflated polynomial $P_4(x)$ obtained by factoring out the factor $(x - 2)$.

Evaluating $P_5(2.5)$ by nested multiplication by applying Eq. (4.13) yields

$$b_5 = 1 \tag{4.29.5}$$
$$b_4 = -15 + 2.5(1) = -12.5 \tag{4.29.4}$$
$$b_3 = 85 + 2.5(-12.5) = 53.75 \tag{4.29.3}$$
$$b_2 = -225 + 2.5(53.75) = -90.625 \tag{4.29.2}$$
$$b_1 = 274 + 2.5(-90.625) = 47.4375 \tag{4.29.1}$$
$$b_0 = -120 + 2.5(47.4375) = -1.40625 \tag{4.29.0}$$

Thus, $P_5(2.5) = b_0 = -1.40625$. From Eq. (4.23), $P_5'(2.5) = Q_4(2.5)$, where $Q_4(x)$ is given by

$$Q_4(x) = 47.4375 - 90.625x + 53.75x^2 - 12.5x^3 + x^4 \tag{4.30}$$

Evaluating $Q_4(2.5)$ by nested multiplication, Eq. (4.13), gives

$$c_4 = 1 \tag{4.31.4}$$

$$c_3 = -12.5 + 2.5(1) = -10.0 \tag{4.31.3}$$

$$c_2 = 53.75 + 2.5(-10.0) = 28.75 \tag{4.31.2}$$

$$c_1 = -90.625 + 2.5(28.75) = -18.75 \tag{4.31.1}$$

$$c_0 = 47.4375 + 2.5(-18.75) = 0.5625 \tag{4.31.0}$$

Thus, $P_5'(2.5) = Q_4(2.5) = 0.5625$. These results can be verified by direct evaluation of Eq. (4.28) at $x = 2.5$.

To illustrate deflation, we deflate $P_5(x)$ by factoring out the factor $(x - 2)$. Applying the synthetic division algorithm, Eq. (4.26), which is the same as the nested multiplication algorithm, Eq. (4.13), for $r = 2$ yields

$$b_5 = 1 \tag{4.32.5}$$

$$b_4 = -15 + 2(1) = -13 \tag{4.32.4}$$

$$b_3 = 85 + 2(-13) = 59 \tag{4.32.3}$$

$$b_2 = -225 + 2(59) = -107 \tag{4.32.2}$$

$$b_1 = 274 + 2(-107) = 60 \tag{4.32.1}$$

$$b_0 = -120 + 2(60) = 0 \tag{4.32.0}$$

Thus, the deflated fourth-degree polynomial is

$$Q_4(x) = 60 - 107x + 59x^2 - 13x^3 + x^4 \tag{4.33}$$

This result can be verified directly by expanding the product of the four linear factors $(x - 1)(x - 3)(x - 4)(x - 5)$.

4.3 DIRECT FIT POLYNOMIALS

First, we will consider a completely general procedure for fitting a polynomial to a set of equally spaced or unequally spaced data. Given $n + 1$ sets of data $[x_0, f(x_0)], [x_1, f(x_1)], \ldots, [x_n, f(x_n)]$, which will be written as $(x_0, f_0), (x_1, f_1), \ldots, (x_n, f_n)$, determine the unique nth-degree polynomial $P_n(x)$ that passes exactly through the $n + 1$ points:

$$\boxed{P_n(x) = a_0 + a_1 x + a_2 x^2 + \cdots + a_n x^n} \tag{4.34}$$

For simplicity of notation, let $f(x_i) = f_i$. Substituting each data point into

Eq. (4.34) yields the $n + 1$ equations

$$f_0 = a_0 + a_1 x_0 + a_2 x_0^2 + \cdots + a_n x_0^n \quad (4.35.0)$$

$$f_1 = a_0 + a_1 x_1 + a_2 x_1^2 + \cdots + a_n x_1^n \quad (4.35.1)$$

$$\vdots \quad \vdots \quad \vdots \quad \vdots \quad \vdots$$

$$f_n = a_0 + a_1 x_n + a_2 x_n^2 + \cdots + a_n x_n^n \quad (4.35.n)$$

There are $n + 1$ linear equations containing the $n + 1$ coefficients a_0 to a_n. Equation (4.35) can be solved for a_0 to a_n by Gauss elimination. The resulting polynomial is the unique nth-degree polynomial that passes exactly through the $n + 1$ data points. The direct fit polynomial procedure works for both equally spaced and unequally spaced data.

Example 4.2. Interpolation by a direct fit polynomial. To illustrate interpolation by a direct fit polynomial, consider the simple function $y = f(x) = 1/x$ and construct the following set of six-significant-figure data:

x	$f(x)$
3.4	0.294118
3.5	0.285714
3.6	0.277778

Interpolate for y at $x = 3.44$. The exact value is

$$y(3.44) = f(3.44) = \frac{1}{3.44} = 0.290698\ldots \quad (4.36)$$

Fit a second-degree polynomial to the three data points:

$$P_2(x) = a + bx + cx^2 \quad (4.37)$$

$$0.294118 = a + b(3.4) + c(3.4)^2 \quad (4.38.1)$$

$$0.285714 = a + b(3.5) + c(3.5)^2 \quad (4.38.2)$$

$$0.277778 = a + b(3.6) + c(3.6)^2 \quad (4.38.3)$$

Solving for a, b, and c by Gauss elimination without scaling or pivoting yields

$$P_2(x) = 0.858314 - 0.245500x + 0.023400x^2 \quad (4.39)$$

Substituting $x = 3.44$ into Eq. (4.39) gives

$$P_2(3.44) = 0.858314 - 0.245500(3.44) + 0.023400(3.44)^2 = 0.290700 \quad (4.40)$$

The error is $P_2(3.44) - f(3.44) = 0.290770 - 0.290698 = 0.000002$.

4.4 LAGRANGE POLYNOMIALS

The direct fit polynomial presented in Section 4.3, while quite straightforward in principle, has several drawbacks. It requires a considerable amount of effort to solve the system of equations for the coefficients. For a high-degree polynomial

(n greater than about four), the system of equations can be ill-conditioned, which causes large errors in the values of the coefficients. A simpler, more direct procedure is desired. One such procedure is the Lagrange polynomial, which can be fitted to unequally spaced data or equally spaced data.

Consider the two data points $[a, f(a)]$ and $[b, f(b)]$. The linear Lagrange polynomial $P_1(x)$ that passes through these two points is given by

$$P_1(x) = \frac{(x-b)}{(a-b)}f(a) + \frac{(x-a)}{(b-a)}f(b) \tag{4.41}$$

Substituting $x = a$ and $x = b$ into Eq. (4.41) yields

$$P_1(a) = \frac{(a-b)}{(a-b)}f(a) + \frac{(a-a)}{(b-a)}f(b) = f(a) \tag{4.42a}$$

$$P_1(b) = \frac{(b-b)}{(a-b)}f(a) + \frac{(b-a)}{(b-a)}f(b) = f(b) \tag{4.42b}$$

which demonstrates that Eq. (4.41) passes through the two data points. Given the three data points $[a, f(a)]$, $[b, f(b)]$, and $[c, f(c)]$, the quadratic Lagrange polynomial $P_2(x)$ that passes through the three data points is given by

$$P_2(x) = \frac{(x-b)(x-c)}{(a-b)(a-c)}f(a) + \frac{(x-a)(x-c)}{(b-a)(b-c)}f(b) + \frac{(x-a)(x-b)}{(c-a)(c-b)}f(c) \tag{4.43}$$

Substitution of the values of x substantiates that Eq. (4.43) passes through the three data points.

This procedure can be applied to any set of $n + 1$ points to determine the nth-degree polynomial $P_n(x)$ that passes exactly through the data points. Given the $n + 1$ data points $[a, f(a)]$, $[b, f(b)]$, $\ldots$, $[k, f(k)]$,

$$P_n(x) = \frac{(x-b)(x-c)\ldots(x-k)}{(a-b)(a-c)\ldots(a-k)}f(a) + \frac{(x-a)(x-c)\ldots(x-k)}{(b-a)(b-c)\ldots(b-k)}f(b) + \cdots + \frac{(x-a)(x-b)\ldots(x-j)}{(k-a)(k-b)\ldots(k-j)}f(k) \tag{4.44}$$

The Lagrange polynomial can be used for both unequally spaced data and equally spaced data. No system of equations must be solved to evaluate the polynomial. However, a considerable amount of computational effort is involved, especially for higher-degree polynomials.

The form of the Lagrange polynomial is quite different in appearance from the form of the direct fit polynomial, Eq. (4.34). However, by the uniqueness theorem, the two forms both represent the unique polynomial that passes exactly through a set of data points.

Example 4.3. Interpolation by Lagrange polynomials. Consider the following four data points, which satisfy the simple function $y = f(x) = 1/x$:

x	$f(x)$
3.40	0.294118
3.50	0.285714
3.55	0.281690
3.65	0.273973

Interpolate for $y = f(3.44)$, using linear, quadratic, and cubic Lagrange interpolating polynomials. The exact value is $y = 1/3.44 = 0.290698\ldots$

Linear interpolation yields

$$P_1(3.44) = \frac{(3.44 - 3.50)}{(3.40 - 3.50)}(0.294118) + \frac{(3.44 - 3.40)}{(3.50 - 3.40)}(0.285714) = 0.290756 \quad (4.45)$$

Quadratic interpolation gives

$$\begin{aligned} P_2(3.44) = {} & \frac{(3.44 - 3.50)(3.44 - 3.55)}{(3.40 - 3.50)(3.40 - 3.55)}(0.294118) \\ & + \frac{(3.44 - 3.40)(3.44 - 3.55)}{(3.50 - 3.40)(3.50 - 3.55)}(0.285714) \\ & + \frac{(3.44 - 3.40)(3.44 - 3.50)}{(3.55 - 3.40)(3.55 - 3.50)}(0.281690) = 0.290699 \end{aligned} \quad (4.46)$$

Cubic interpolation yields

$$\begin{aligned} P_3(3.44) = {} & \frac{(3.44 - 3.50)(3.44 - 3.55)(3.44 - 3.65)}{(3.40 - 3.50)(3.40 - 3.55)(3.40 - 3.65)}(0.294118) \\ & + \frac{(3.44 - 3.40)(3.44 - 3.55)(3.44 - 3.65)}{(3.50 - 3.40)(3.50 - 3.55)(3.50 - 3.65)}(0.285714) \\ & + \frac{(3.44 - 3.40)(3.44 - 3.50)(3.44 - 3.65)}{(3.55 - 3.40)(3.55 - 3.50)(3.55 - 3.65)}(0.281690) \\ & + \frac{(3.44 - 3.40)(3.44 - 3.50)(3.44 - 3.55)}{(3.65 - 3.40)(3.65 - 3.50)(3.65 - 3.55)}(0.273973) = 0.290698 \end{aligned} \quad (4.47)$$

The results are summarized below, where the initial value at $x = 3.40$, the results of linear, quadratic, and cubic interpolation, and the error, $P(3.44) - 0.290698$, are tabulated. The advantages of higher-order interpolation are obvious.

P(3.44) = 0.294118	Initial value	Error:	0.003420
= 0.290756	Linear interpolation		0.000058
= 0.290699	Quadratic interpolation		0.000001
= 0.290698	Cubic interpolation		0.000000

4.5 DIFFERENCE TABLES AND POLYNOMIAL FITTING

Fitting approximating polynomials to tabular data is considerably simpler when the values of the independent variable are equally spaced. Implementation of polynomial fitting for equally spaced data is best accomplished in terms of differences. Consequently, the concepts of *differences* and *difference tables* are introduced in this section for use in Sections 4.6, 4.7, and 4.8.

A difference table is an arrangement of a set of data $[x, f(x)]$ in a table where the x values are given in ascending order, with additional columns composed of the differences of the numbers in the preceding column. A triangular array is obtained, as illustrated in Table 4.1.

The numbers appearing in a difference table are unique. However, three different interpretations can be assigned to these numbers, each with its unique notation. The forward difference relative to point i is $(f_{i+1} - f_i)$, the backward difference relative to point $i+1$ is $(f_{i+1} - f_i)$, and the centered difference relative to point $i + \frac{1}{2}$ is $(f_{i+1} - f_i)$. The forward-difference operator Δ is defined as:

$$\Delta f(x_i) = \Delta f_i = (f_{i+1} - f_i) \tag{4.48}$$

The backward-difference operator ∇ is defined as:

$$\nabla f(x_{i+1}) = \nabla f_{i+1} = (f_{i+1} - f_i) \tag{4.49}$$

The centered-difference operator δ is defined as

$$\delta f(x_{i+1/2}) = \delta f_{i+1/2} = (f_{i+1} - f_i) \tag{4.50}$$

TABLE 4.1.
Difference table

x	$f(x)$			
x_0	f_0			
		$(f_1 - f_0)$		
x_1	f_1		$(f_2 - 2f_1 + f_0)$	
		$(f_2 - f_1)$		$(f_3 - 3f_2 + 3f_1 - f_0)$
x_2	f_2		$(f_3 - 2f_2 + f_1)$	
		$(f_3 - f_2)$		
x_3	f_3			

TABLE 4.2
Forward-difference table

x	$f(x)$	Δf	$\Delta^2 f$	$\Delta^3 f$
x_0	f_0			
		Δf_0		
x_1	f_1		$\Delta^2 f_0$	
		Δf_1		$\Delta^3 f_0$
x_2	f_2		$\Delta^2 f_1$	
		Δf_2		
x_3	f_3			

TABLE 4.3.
Backward-difference table

x	$f(x)$	∇f	$\nabla^2 f$	$\nabla^3 f$
x_{-3}	f_{-3}			
		∇f_{-2}		
x_{-2}	f_{-2}		$\nabla^2 f_{-1}$	
		∇f_{-1}		$\nabla^3 f_0$
x_{-1}	f_{-1}		$\nabla^2 f_0$	
		∇f_0		
x_0	f_0			

A difference table, such as Table 4.1, can be interpreted as a forward-difference table, a backward-difference table, or a centered-difference table, as illustrated in Tables 4.2 to 4.4. The numbers in the tables are identical. Only the notation is different. The three different types of interpretation and notation simplify the use of difference tables in the construction of approximating polynomials, which is discussed in Sections 4.6, 4.7, and 4.8.

Example 4.4. Difference table for $f(x) = 1/x$. Construct a six-place difference table for the function $f(x) = 1/x$ for $3.0 \le x \le 4.0$ with $\Delta x = 0.1$. The results are presented in Table 4.5, which uses the forward-difference notation to denote the columns of differences.

Several observations can be made from Table 4.5. The first and second differences are quite smooth. The third differences, while monotonic, are not very smooth. The fourth differences are not monotonic, and the fifth differences are extremely ragged. The magnitudes of the higher-order differences decrease rapidly. If the differences are not smooth and decreasing, several possible explanations exist.

TABLE 4.4.
Centered-difference table

x	f	δf	$\delta^2 f$	$\delta^3 f$	$\delta^4 f$
x_{-2}	f_{-2}				
		$\delta f_{-3/2}$			
x_{-1}	f_{-1}		$\delta^2 f_{-1}$		
		$\delta f_{-1/2}$		$\delta^3 f_{-1/2}$	
x_0	f_0		$\delta^2 f_0$		$\delta^4 f_0$
		$\delta f_{1/2}$		$\delta^3 f_{1/2}$	
x_1	f_1		$\delta^2 f_1$		
		$\delta f_{3/2}$			
x_2	f_2				

1. The original data set has errors.
2. The increment Δx may be too large.
3. There may be a singularity in $f(x)$ or its derivatives in the range of the table.

Difference tables are useful for evaluating the quality of a set of tabular data.

Tabular data have a finite number of digits. The last digit is typically rounded off. Round-off has an effect on the accuracy of the higher-order differences. To illustrate this effect, consider a difference table showing only the round-off error in the last significant digit. The worst possible round-off situation occurs when every other number is rounded off by one-half in opposing directions, as illustrated in Table 4.6.

Table 4.6 shows that the errors due to round-off in the original data oscillate and double in magnitude for each higher-order difference. The maximum error in the differences is given by

$$\text{Maximum round-off error in } \Delta^n f = \pm 2^{n-1} \tag{4.51}$$

TABLE 4.5
Difference table for $f(x) = 1/x$

x	$f(x)$	$\Delta f(x)$	$\Delta^2 f(x)$	$\Delta^3 f(x)$	$\Delta^4 f(x)$	$\Delta^5 f(x)$
3.0	0.333333					
		−0.010752				
3.1	0.322581		0.000671			
		−0.010081		−0.000060		
3.2	0.312500		0.000611		0.000007	
		−0.009470		−0.000053		−0.000004
3.3	0.303030		0.000558		0.000003	
		−0.008912		−0.000050		0.000007
3.4	0.294118		0.000508		0.000010	
		−0.008404		−0.000040		−0.000010
3.5	0.285714		0.000468		0.000000	
		−0.007936		−0.000040		0.000008
3.6	0.277778		0.000428		0.000008	
		−0.007508		−0.000032		−0.000008
3.7	0.270270		0.000396		0.000000	
		−0.007112		−0.000032		0.000006
3.8	0.263158		0.000364		0.000006	
		−0.006748		−0.000026		
3.9	0.256410		0.000338			
		−0.006410				
4.0	0.250000					

TABLE 4.6
Difference table for round-off errors

x	f	Δf	$\Delta^2 f$	$\Delta^3 f$	$\Delta^4 f$
–	$+\frac{1}{2}$				
		-1			
–	$-\frac{1}{2}$		2		
		1		-4	
–	$+\frac{1}{2}$		-2		8
		-1		4	
–	$-\frac{1}{2}$		2		-8
		1		-4	
–	$+\frac{1}{2}$		-2		
		-1			
–	$-\frac{1}{2}$				

For the results presented in Table 4.5, $\Delta^5 f$ oscillates between -10 and $+8$. From Eq. (4.51), the maximum round-off error in $\Delta^5 f$ is $\pm 2^{5-1} = \pm 16$. Consequently, the $\Delta^5 f$ values are completely masked by the accumulated round-off error.

The preceding discussion applies to equally spaced data. A similar procedure, called *divided differences*, can be applied to unequally spaced data. A divided difference is defined as the difference in the function values at two points, divided by the difference in the values of the corresponding independent variable. Thus, the first divided difference at point i is defined as

$$f[x_i, x_{i+1}] = \frac{f_{i+1} - f_i}{x_{i+1} - x_i} \tag{4.52}$$

The second divided difference is defined as

$$f[x_i, x_{i+1}, x_{i+2}] = \frac{f[x_{i+2}, x_{i+1}] - f[x_{i+1}, x_i]}{x_{i+2} - x_i} \tag{4.53}$$

Similar expressions can be obtained for divided differences of any order. Approximating polynomials for unequally spaced data can be constructed using divided differences. That procedure is not presented in this book.

Polynomial fitting can be accomplished using the values in a difference table. The degree of polynomial needed to give a satisfactory fit to a set of tabular data can be estimated by considering the properties of polynomials. The nth-degree polynomial $P_n(x)$ is given by

$$P_n(x) = a_n x^n + (\text{lower degree terms}) = a_n x^n + (\text{LDTs}) \tag{4.54}$$

In Section 4.2, it is shown [see Eqs. (4.15n) and (4.16)] that

$$P_n^{(n)}(x) = n!a_n = \text{constant} \tag{4.55}$$

$$P_n^{(n+1)}(x) = 0 \tag{4.56}$$

Evaluate the first forward difference of $P_n(x)$.

$$\Delta[P_n(x)] = \Delta(a_n x^n) + \Delta(\text{LDTs}) \tag{4.57}$$

$$\Delta[P_n(x)] = a_n(x+h)^n - a_n x^n + (\text{LDTs}) \tag{4.58}$$

Expanding $(x+h)^n$ in a binomial expansion gives

$$\Delta[P_n(x)] = [a_n x^n + a_n n x^{n-1} h + \cdots + a_n h^n] - a_n x^n + (\text{LDTs}) \tag{4.59}$$

which yields

$$\Delta[P_n(x)] = (a_n n h)x^{n-1} + (\text{LDTs}) = P_{n-1}(x) \tag{4.60}$$

Evaluating the second forward difference of P_n(x) gives

$$\Delta^2[P_n(x)] = \Delta[(a_n n h)x^{n-1}] + \Delta(\text{LDTs}) \tag{4.61}$$

which yields

$$\Delta^2[P_n(x)] = a_n n(n-1)h^2 x^{n-2} + (\text{LDTs}) \tag{4.62}$$

In a similar manner it can be shown that

$$\Delta^n P_n(x) = a_n n! h^n = \text{constant} \qquad \text{and} \qquad \Delta^{n+1} P_n(x) = 0 \tag{4.63}$$

Note the similarity between $P_n^{(n)}(x)$ and $\Delta^n P_n(x)$. In fact, $P_n^{(n)}(x) = \Delta^n P_n(x)/h^n$. Thus, if $f(x) = P_n(x)$, then $\Delta^n f(x) = \text{constant}$. Consequently, if $\Delta^n f(x) \approx \text{constant}$, $f(x)$ can be approximated by $P_n(x)$.

4.6 THE NEWTON FORWARD-DIFFERENCE POLYNOMIAL

Given $n+1$ data points $[x, f(x)]$, one form of the unique nth-degree polynomial that passes through the $n+1$ points is given by

$$\begin{aligned} P_n(x) &= f_0 + s\Delta f_0 + \frac{s(s-1)}{2!}\Delta^2 f_0 + \frac{s(s-1)(s-2)}{3!}\Delta^3 f_0 \\ &\quad + \cdots + \frac{s(s-1)(s-2)\cdots[s-(n-1)]}{n!}\Delta^n f_0 \end{aligned} \tag{4.64}$$

where s is the interpolating variable

$$s = \frac{x - x_0}{\Delta x} = \frac{x - x_0}{h} \quad \text{and} \quad x = x_0 + sh \tag{4.65}$$

Equation (4.64) does not look anything like the direct fit polynomial [see Eq. (4.34)] or the Lagrange polynomial [see Eq. (4.44)]. However, if Eq. (4.64) is a polynomial of degree n and it passes exactly through the $n + 1$ data points, it must be one form of the unique polynomial that passes through this set of data.

The interpolating variable $s = (x - x_0)/h$ is linear in x. Consequently, the last term in Eq. (4.64) is order n, and Eq. (4.64) is an nth-degree polynomial. Let $s = 0$. Then $x = x_0$, $f = f_0$, and $P_n(x_0) = f_0$. Let $s = 1$. Then $x = x_0 + h = x_1$, $f = f_1$, and $P_n(x_1) = f_0 + \Delta f_0 = f_0 + (f_1 - f_0) = f_1$. In a similar manner, it can be shown that $P_n(x) = f(x)$ for the $n + 1$ discrete points. Therefore, $P_n(x)$ is the desired unique nth-degree polynomial. Equation (4.64) is called the *Newton forward-difference polynomial*.

The Newton forward-difference polynomial can be expressed in a more compact form by introducing the definition of the binomial coefficient. Thus,

$$\binom{s}{i} = \left(\frac{s(s-1)(s-2)\cdots[s-(i-1)]}{i!}\right) \tag{4.66}$$

In terms of binomial coefficients, the Newton forward-difference polynomial is

$$P_n(x) = f_0 + \binom{s}{1}\Delta f_0 + \binom{s}{2}\Delta^2 f_0 + \binom{s}{3}\Delta^3 f_0 + \cdots \tag{4.67}$$

A major advantage of the Newton forward-difference polynomial, in addition to its simplicity, is that each higher-degree polynomial is obtained from the previous lower-degree polynomial simply by adding the next term. The work already performed for the lower-degree polynomial does not have to be repeated. This feature is in sharp contrast to the direct fit polynomial and the Lagrange polynomial, where all of the work must be repeated each time the degree of the polynomial is changed. This feature makes it simple to determine when the desired accuracy has been obtained. When the next term in the polynomial is less than some prespecified value, the desired accuracy has been obtained.

Example 4.5. Interpolation by the Newton forward-difference polynomial. From the six-place difference table for $f(x) = 1/x$, Table 4.5, calculate P(3.44) by the Newton forward-difference polynomial. The exact solution is $f(3.44) = 1/3.44 = 0.290698\ldots$

In Table 4.5, $h = 0.1$. Choose $x_0 = 3.40$. Then,

$$s = \frac{x - x_0}{h} = \frac{3.44 - 3.40}{0.1} = 0.4 \tag{4.68}$$

Equation (4.64) gives

$$P(3.44) = f(3.4) + s\Delta f(3.4) + \frac{s(s-1)}{2!}\Delta^2 f(3.4) + \frac{s(s-1)(s-2)}{3!}\Delta^3 f(3.4) + \cdots \tag{4.69}$$

Substituting $s = 0.4$ and the values of the differences into Eq. (4.69) gives

$$P(3.44) = 0.294118 + (0.4)(-0.008404) + \frac{(0.4)(0.4-1)}{2}(0.000468) + \frac{(0.4)(0.4-1)(0.4-2)}{6}(-0.000040) + \cdots \tag{4.70}$$

Evaluating Eq. (4.70) term by term yields the following results and errors:

$P(3.44) = 0.294118$	initial value	Error:	0.003420
$= 0.290756$	linear interpolation		0.000058
$= 0.290700$	quadratic interpolation		0.000002
$= 0.290698$	cubic interpolation		0.000000

The advantage of higher-order interpolation is obvious.

In this example, the base point $x_0 = 3.4$ was selected so that the point of interpolation, $x = 3.44$, falls within the range of data used to determine the polynomial, that is, interpolation occurs. If x_0 is chosen so that x does not fall within the range of fit, extrapolation occurs, and the results are less accurate. For example, let $x_0 = 3.2$, for which $s = 2.4$. The following results and errors are obtained:

$P(3.44) = 0.312500$	initial value	Error:	0.021802
$= 0.289772$	linear interpolation		−0.000926
$= 0.290709$	quadratic interpolation		0.000011
$= 0.290698$	cubic interpolation		0.000000

The increase in error is significant for linear and quadratic extrapolation. For $x_0 = 3.2$, the cubic yields an interpolating polynomial.

The error term for the Newton forward-difference polynomial can be obtained from the general error term [see Eq. (4.9)]:

$$E(x) = \frac{1}{(n+1)!}(x - x_0)(x - x_1)\cdots(x - x_n)f^{(n+1)}(\xi) \tag{4.71}$$

From Eq. (4.65),

$$(x - x_0) = (x_0 + sh) - x_0 = sh \tag{4.72a}$$

$$(x - x_1) = (x_0 + sh) - x_1 = sh - (x_1 - x_0) = (s-1)h \tag{4.72b}$$

$$\vdots$$

$$(x - x_n) = (x_0 + sh) - x_n = sh - (x_n - x_0) = (s-n)h \tag{4.72n}$$

Substituting Eq. (4.72) into Eq. (4.71) gives

$$E(x) = \frac{1}{(n+1)!} s(s-1)(s-2)\cdots(s-n)h^{n+1}f^{(n+1)}(\xi) \tag{4.73}$$

which can be written as

$$E(x) = \binom{s}{n+1} h^{n+1}f^{(n+1)}(\xi) \tag{4.74}$$

From Eq. (4.67), for $P_n(x)$, the term after the nth-term is

$$\binom{s}{n+1} \Delta^{n+1} f_0 \tag{4.75}$$

The error term, Eq. (4.74), can be obtained from Eq. (4.75) by the replacement

$$\Delta^{n+1} f_0 \rightarrow h^{n+1}f^{(n+1)}(\xi) \tag{4.76}$$

This procedure can be used to obtain the error term for all polynomials based on a set of equally spaced discrete data points.

4.7 THE NEWTON BACKWARD-DIFFERENCE POLYNOMIAL

The Newton forward-difference polynomial, Eq. (4.64), can be applied at the top or in the middle of a set of tabular data, where the downward-sloping forward differences illustrated in Table 4.2 exist. However, at the bottom of a set of tabular data, the required forward differences do not exist, and the Newton forward-difference polynomial cannot be used. In that case, an approach that uses the upward-sloping backward differences illustrated in Table 4.3 is required. One such polynomial is developed in this section.

Given $n+1$ data points $[x, f(x)]$, one form of the unique nth-degree polynomial that passes through the $n+1$ points is given by:

$$\begin{aligned} P_n(x) &= f_0 + s\nabla f_0 + \frac{(s+1)s}{2!}\nabla^2 f_0 + \frac{(s+2)(s+1)s}{3!}\nabla^3 f_0 \\ &\quad + \cdots + \frac{[s+(n-1)]\cdots(s+1)s}{n!}\nabla^n f_0 \end{aligned} \tag{4.77}$$

where s is the interpolating variable

$$s = \frac{x - x_0}{\Delta x} = \frac{x - x_0}{h} \qquad \text{and} \qquad x = x_0 + sh \tag{4.78}$$

The interpolating variable $s = (x - x_0)/h$ is linear in x. Consequently, the last term in Eq. (4.77) is order n, and Eq. (4.77) is an nth-degree polynomial. Let $s = 0$. Then $x = x_0$, $f = f_0$, and $P_n(x_0) = f_0$. Let $s = -1$. Then $x = x_0 - h = x_{-1}$, $f = f_{-1}$, and $P_n(x_{-1}) = f_0 - \nabla f_0 = f_0 - (f_0 - f_{-1}) = f_{-1}$. In a similar manner, it can be shown that $P_n(x) = f(x)$ for the $n + 1$ discrete points. Therefore, $P_n(x)$ is the desired unique nth-degree polynomial. Equation (4.77) is called the *Newton backward-difference polynomial.*

The Newton backward-difference polynomial can be expressed in a more compact form by introducing the definition of the binomial coefficient. Thus,

$$\binom{s+j}{i} = \frac{(s+j)[(s+j)-1]\cdots s \cdots [(s+j)-(i-1)]}{i!} \tag{4.79}$$

In terms of binomial coefficients, the Newton backward-difference polynomial is

$$\boxed{P_n(x) = f_0 + \binom{s}{1}\nabla f_0 + \binom{s+1}{2}\nabla^2 f_0 + \binom{s+2}{3}\nabla^3 f_0 + \cdots} \tag{4.80}$$

Example 4.6. Interpolation by the Newton backward-difference polynomial. From the six-place difference table for $f(x) = 1/x$, Table 4.5, calculate P(3.44) by the Newton backward-difference polynomial. The exact solution is $f(3.44) = 0.290698\ldots$ In Table 4.5, $h = 0.1$. Choose $x_0 = 3.50$. Then,

$$s = \frac{x - x_0}{h} = \frac{3.44 - 3.50}{0.1} = -0.6 \tag{4.81}$$

Equation (4.77) gives

$$P(3.44) = f(3.5) + s\nabla f(3.5) + \frac{(s+1)s}{2!}\nabla^2 f(3.5) + \frac{(s+2)(s+1)s}{3!}\nabla^3 f(3.5) + \cdots \tag{4.82}$$

Substituting $s = -0.6$ and the values of the differences gives

$$P(3.44) = 0.285714 + (-0.6)(-0.008404) + \frac{(-0.6+1)(-0.6)}{2}(0.000508)$$
$$+ \frac{(-0.6+2)(-0.6+1)(-0.6)}{6}(-0.000050) + \cdots \tag{4.83}$$

Evaluating Eq. (4.83) term by term yields the following results and errors:

			Error:
$P(3.44)$	$= 0.285714$	initial value	0.004984
	$= 0.290756$	linear interpolation	0.000058
	$= 0.290695$	quadratic interpolation	−0.000003
	$= 0.290698$	cubic interpolation	0.000000

The advantages of higher-order interpolation are obvious.

The error term for the Newton backward-difference polynomial can be obtained from the general error term, Eq. (4.9), by making the substitutions

$$(x - x_0) = sh \tag{4.84a}$$

$$(x - x_1) = (x_0 + sh) - x_1 = sh + (x_0 - x_1) = (s + 1)h \tag{4.84b}$$

$$\cdots\cdots\cdots\cdots\cdots\cdots\cdots\cdots\cdots\cdots$$

$$(x - x_n) = (x_0 + sh) - x_n = sh + (x_0 - x_n) = (s + n)h \tag{4.84n}$$

Substituting Eq. (4.84) into Eq. (4.9) yields

$$E(x) = \frac{1}{(n+1)!}(s + n)(s + n - 1)\cdots(s + 1)sh^{n+1}f^{(n+1)}(\xi) \tag{4.85}$$

which can be written as

$$\boxed{E(x) = \binom{s + n}{(n + 1)!} h^{n+1} f^{(n+1)}(\xi)} \tag{4.86}$$

Equation (4.86) can be obtained from Eq. (4.80) by the following replacement in the $(n + 1)$st term:

$$\nabla^{n+1} f_0 \rightarrow h^{n+1} f^{(n+1)}(\xi) \tag{4.87}$$

4.8 OTHER APPROXIMATING POLYNOMIALS

The Newton forward- and backward-difference polynomials, presented in Sections 4.6 and 4.7, respectively, are examples of approximating polynomials based on differences. The Newton forward-difference polynomial uses forward differences, which follow a downward-sloping path in the forward-difference table illustrated in Table 4.2. The Newton backward-difference polynomial uses backward differences, which follow an upward-sloping path in the backward-difference table illustrated in Table 4.3. Numerous other polynomials based on other paths through a difference table can be constructed. Two of the more important are presented in this section.

The Newton forward- and backward-difference polynomials are essential for fitting an approximating polynomial at the beginning and end, respectively, of a set of tabular data. However, other forms of approximating polynomials can be developed in the middle of a set of tabular data by using the centered-difference table presented in Table 4.4. The base point for the *Stirling centered-difference polynomial* is point x_0. This polynomial is based on the values of the centered differences with respect to x_0. That is, the polynomial follows a horizontal path through the difference table that is centered on point x_0. As illustrated in Table 4.4, even centered differences with respect to x_0 exist, but odd centered differences do not. Odd centered differences are based on the averages of the centered differences at the half points $x_{-1/2}$ and $x_{1/2}$. The Stirling centered-difference polynomial is

$$P_n(x) = f_0 + \binom{s}{1}\frac{1}{2}\left(\delta f_{1/2} + \delta f_{-1/2}\right) + \frac{1}{2}\left(\binom{s+1}{2} + \binom{s}{2}\right)\delta^2 f_0 + \binom{s+1}{3}\frac{1}{2}\left(\delta^3 f_{1/2} + \delta^3 f_{-1/2}\right) + \frac{1}{2}\left(\binom{s+2}{4} + \binom{s+1}{4}\right)\delta^4 f_0 + \cdots \tag{4.88}$$

It can be shown by direct substitution that the Stirling centered-difference polynomials of even degree are order n and pass exactly through the data points used to construct the differences appearing in the polynomial. The odd-degree polynomials use data from one additional point.

The base point for the *Bessel centered-difference polynomial* is point $x_{1/2}$. This polynomial is based on the values of the centered differences with respect to $x_{1/2}$. That is, the polynomial follows a horizontal path through the difference table which is centered on point $x_{1/2}$. As illustrated in Table 4.4, odd centered differences with respect to $x_{1/2}$ exist, but even centered differences do not. Even centered differences are based on the averages of the centered differences at points x_0 and x_1. The Bessel centered-difference polynomial is:

$$P_n(x) = \frac{1}{2}\left(f_0 + f_1\right) + \frac{1}{2}\left(\binom{s}{1} + \binom{s-1}{1}\right)\delta f_{1/2} + \binom{s}{2}\frac{1}{2}\left(\delta^2 f_0 + \delta^2 f_1\right) + \frac{1}{2}\left(\binom{s+1}{3} + \binom{s}{3}\right)\delta^3 f_{1/2} + \binom{s+1}{4}\frac{1}{2}\left(\delta^4 f_0 + \delta^4 f_1\right) + \cdots \tag{4.89}$$

It can be shown by direct substitution that the Bessel centered-difference polynomials of odd degree are order n and pass exactly through the data points used to construct the centered differences appearing in the polynomial. The even-degree polynomials use data from one additional point.

Centered-difference polynomials are useful in the middle of a set of tabular data where the centered differences exist to the full extent of the table. However, from the uniqueness theorem for polynomials (see Section 4.2), the polynomial of degree n that passes through a specific set of $n + 1$ points is unique. Thus, the

TABLE 4.7
Bivariate tabular data

	x_1	x_2	x_3	x_4
y_1	z_{11}	z_{12}	z_{13}	z_{14}
y_2	z_{21}	z_{22}	z_{23}	z_{24}
y_3	z_{31}	z_{32}	z_{33}	z_{34}
y_4	z_{41}	z_{42}	z_{43}	z_{44}

Newton polynomials and the centered-difference polynomials are all equivalent when fitted to the same data points. The Newton polynomials are somewhat simpler to evaluate. Consequently, when the data points to be fitted by a polynomial are prespecified, the Newton polynomials are recommended.

4.9 MULTIVARIATE APPROXIMATION

All of the approximating polynomials discussed so far are single-variable, or univariate, polynomials. That is, the dependent variable is a function of a single independent variable: $y = f(x)$. Many problems arise in engineering and science where the dependent variable is a function of two or more independent variables; for example, $z = f(x, y)$ is a two-variable, or bivariate, function. Such functions in general are called multivariate functions. When multivariate functions are given by tabular data, multivariate approximation is required for interpolation, differentiation, and integration. Two exact fit procedures for multivariate approximation are presented in this section.

1. Successive univariate approximation
2. Direct multivariate approximation

Approximate fit procedures for multivariate approximation are discussed in Section 4.11.

Successive Univariate Polynomial Aproximation

Consider the bivariate function $z = f(x, y)$. A set of tabular data is illustrated in Table 4.7.

Simply stated, *successive univariate approximation* first fits a set of univariate approximating functions, polynomials for example, at each value of one of the independent variables. Interpolation, differentiation, or integration is then performed on each of these univariate approximating functions to yield values of the desired operation at the specified value of the other independent variable. A univariate approximating function is then fitted to those results as a function of the first independent variable. The final process of interpolation, differentiation, or integration is then performed on that univariate approximating function. The approximating functions employed for successive univariate approximation can be of any functional form. Successive univariate polynomial approximation is generally used.

TABLE 4.8
Enthalpy of steam

	T, F		
P, psia	800	1000	1200
1150	1380.4	1500.2	1614.5
1200	1377.7	1499.0	1613.6
1250	1375.2	1497.1	1612.6

Example 4.7. Successive univariate polynomial interpolation. Table 4.8 shows values of enthalpy, $h(P, T)$, from a table of properties of steam. Use successive quadratic univariate polynomial interpolation to calculate the enthalpy h at $P = 1225$ psia and $T = 1100$ F (the value from the steam tables is 1556.0 Btu/lbm).

First fit the quadratic polynomial

$$h(P_i, T) = a + bT + cT^2 \tag{4.90}$$

at each pressure level P_i, and interpolate for the values of h at $T = 1100$ F. At $P = 1150$ psia,

$$a + 800b + (800)^2c = 1380.4 \tag{4.91a}$$

$$a + 1000b + (1000)^2c = 1500.2 \tag{4.91b}$$

$$a + 1200b + (1200)^2c = 1614.5 \tag{4.91c}$$

Solving for a, b, and c by Gauss elimination yields

$$h(1150, T) = 846.2 + 0.7228T - 0.00006875T^2 \tag{4.92}$$

Evaluating Eq. (4.92) at $T = 1100$ gives $h(1150,1100) = 1558.1$ Btu/lbm. At $P = 1200$ psia, $h(1200,T) = 825.5 + 0.7573\ T - 0.00008375T^2$, and $h(1200,1100) = 1557.2$ Btu/lbm. At $P = 1250$ psia, $h(1250,T) = 823.6 + 0.7535\ T - 0.00008000\ T^2$, and $h(1250,1100) = 1555.7$ Btu/lbm.

Next fit the quadratic polynomial

$$h(P,1100) = a + bP + cP^2 \tag{4.93}$$

at $T = 1100$ F, and interpolate for the value of h at $P = 1225$ psia.

$$a + 1150\ b + (1150)^2c = 1558.1 \tag{4.94a}$$

$$a + 1200\ b + (1200)^2c = 1557.2 \tag{4.94b}$$

$$a + 1250\ b + (1250)^2c = 1555.7 \tag{4.94c}$$

Solving for a, b, and c by Gauss elimination gives

$$h(P,1100) = 1413.2 + 0.2640P - 0.00012000P^2 \tag{4.95}$$

Evaluating Eq. (4.95) at $P = 1225$ yields $h(1225,1100) = 1556.5$ Btu/lbm. The error in this result is $\Delta h = 1556.5 - 1556.0 = 0.5$ Btu/lbm.

Direct Multivariate Polynomial Approximation

Consider the bivariate function $z = f(x, y)$ and the set of tabular data illustrated in Table 4.7. The tabular data can be fitted by a multivariate polynomial of the form

$$z = f(x, y) = a + bx + cy + dxy + ex^2 + fy^2 + gx^2y + hxy^2 + ix^3 + jy^3 + \cdots \quad (4.96)$$

The number of data points must equal the number of terms in the polynomial. A linear bivariate polynomial in x and y is obtained by including the first four terms in Eq. (4.94). The resulting polynomial is exactly equivalent to successive univariate polynomial approximation if the same four data points are used. A quadratic bivariate polynomial in x and y is obtained by including the first eight terms in Eq. (4.94). The number of terms in the approximating polynomial increases rapidly as the order of approximation increases. This leads to ill-conditioned systems of linear equations for determining the coefficients. Consequently, multivariate high-order approximation must be used with caution.

Example 4.8. Direct multivariate polynomial interpolation. Solve the interpolation problem presented in Example 4.7 by direct multivariate linear interpolation. The form of the approximating polynomial is

$$h = a + bT + cP + dPT \quad (4.97)$$

Substituting the four data points that bracket $P = 1225$ psia and $T = 1100$ F into Eq. (4.97) gives

$$1499.0 = a + (1000)b + (1200)c + (1000)(1200)d \quad (4.98a)$$

$$1497.1 = a + (1000)b + (1250)c + (1000)(1250)d \quad (4.98b)$$

$$1613.6 = a + (1200)b + (1200)c + (1200)(1200)d \quad (4.98c)$$

$$1612.6 = a + (1200)b + (1250)c + (1200)(1250)d \quad (4.98d)$$

Solving for a, b, c, and d by Gauss elimination yields

$$h = 1079.60 + 0.4650T - 0.1280P + 0.0900 \times 10^{-3}PT \quad (4.99)$$

Substituting $P = 1225$ and $T = 1100$ into Eq. (4.99) gives $h(1225,1100) = 1555.6$ Btu/lbm. The error in this result is $\Delta h = 1555.6 - 1556.0 = -0.4$ Btu/lbm.

4.10 INVERSE INTERPOLATION AND PIECEWISE INTERPOLATION

Inverse Interpolation

Interpolation is the process of determining the value of the dependent variable f corresponding to a particular value of the independent variable x, when the function $f(x)$ is described by a set of tabular data. Inverse interpolation is the process of determining the value of the independent variable x corresponding to a particular value of the dependent variable f. In other words, inverse interpolation is evaluation of the inverse function $x(f)$. Inverse interpolation can be accomplished by

1. Fitting a polynomial to the inverse function $x(f)$
2. Solving a direct fit polynomial $f(x)$ iteratively for $x(f)$

Fitting a polynomial to the inverse function $x(f)$ appears to be the obvious approach. However, some problems may occur. The inverse function $x(f)$ may not resemble a polynomial. The values of f most certainly are not equally spaced. In such cases, a direct fit polynomial $f(x)$ may be preferred, even though it must be solved iteratively for $x(f)$, by Newton's method for example.

Example 4.9. Inverse interpolation. To illustrate inverse interpolation, we find the value of x for which $f(x) = 0.30$ in Table 4.1, using the three closest data points. Thus,

x	$f(x)$	$\Delta f(x)$	$\Delta^2 f(x)$
3.3	0.303030		
		−0.008912	
3.4	0.294118		0.000508
		−0.008404	
3.5	0.285714		

The exact solution is $x = 1/f(x) = 1/0.3 = 3.333333\ldots$

First, let's evaluate the quadratic Lagrange polynomial $x = x(f)$. Thus,

$$x = \frac{(0.30 - 0.294118)(0.30 - 0.285714)}{(0.303030 - 0.294118)(0.303030 - 0.285714)}(3.3)$$

$$+ \frac{(0.30 - 0.303030)(0.30 - 0.285714)}{(0.294118 - 0.303030)(0.294118 - 0.285714)}(3.4)$$

$$+ \frac{(0.30 - 0.303030)(0.30 - 0.294118)}{(0.285714 - 0.303030)(0.285714 - 0.294118)}(3.5) \tag{4.100}$$

which yields $x = 3.333301$. The error is $\Delta x = 3.333301 - 3.333333 = -0.000032$.

Next, evaluate the quadratic Newton forward-difference polynomial for $f = f(x)$. Thus,

$$f(x) = f_0 + s\Delta f_0 + \frac{s(s-1)}{2}\Delta^2 f_0 \tag{4.101}$$

Substituting the known values into Eq. (4.101) yields

$$0.30 = 0.303030 - 0.008912\,s + \frac{s(s-1)}{2}(0.000508) \tag{4.102}$$

Simplifying Eq. (4.102) gives

$$0.000508s^2 - 0.018332\,s + 0.006060 = 0 \tag{4.103}$$

Solving Eq. (4.103) by the quadratic formula yields the two solutions $s = 0.333654$ and 35.752960. The second root is obviously extraneous. Solving for x yields

$$x = x_0 + sh = 3.3 + (0.333654)(0.1) = 3.333365 \tag{4.104}$$

The error is $\Delta x = 3.3333665 - 3.333333 = 0.000032$.

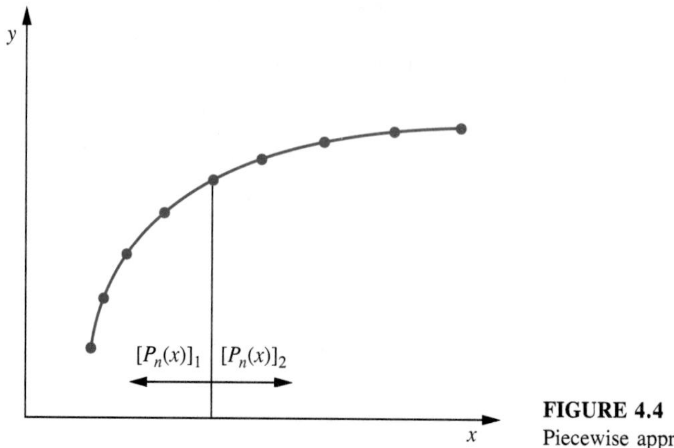

FIGURE 4.4
Piecewise approximation.

Piecewise Interpolation

So far, our discussions have been devoted to fitting a single polynomial to a set of tabular data. When the number of data points is large, an exact fit requires a high-degree polynomial, which is undesirable. A least squares fit using a low-degree polynomial avoids this problem, but may yield an inaccurate fit. This situation can be avoided by fitting a series of two or more low-degree polynomials to the set of tabular data, where each individual low-degree polynomial is fitted for a subinterval of the total interval, as illustrated in Figure 4.4. Piecewise approximation can be performed using the exact polynomial fits discussed in Sections 4.3 to 4.8 or the approximate polynomial fits discussed in Section 4.11.

4.11 LEAST SQUARES APPROXIMATION

Section 4.1 discusses the need for approximating functions for sets of discrete data (i.e., for interpolation, differentiation, and integration), the desirable properties of approximating functions, and the benefits of using polynomials for approximating functions. For small sets of smooth data, exact fits such as presented in Sections 4.3 to 4.9 are desirable. However, for large sets of data and sets of rough data, approximate fits are desirable. Approximate polynomial fits are the subject of this section.

Introduction

An approximate fit yields a polynomial that passes through the set of points in the *best possible manner* without being required to pass exactly through any of the points. Several definitions of "best possible manner" exist. Consider the set of discrete points $[x_i, Y(x_i)] = (x_i, Y_i)$ and the approximate polynomial $y(x)$ chosen to represent the set of discrete points, as illustrated in Figure 4.5. The discrete points do not fall on the approximating polynomial. The deviations (i.e.,

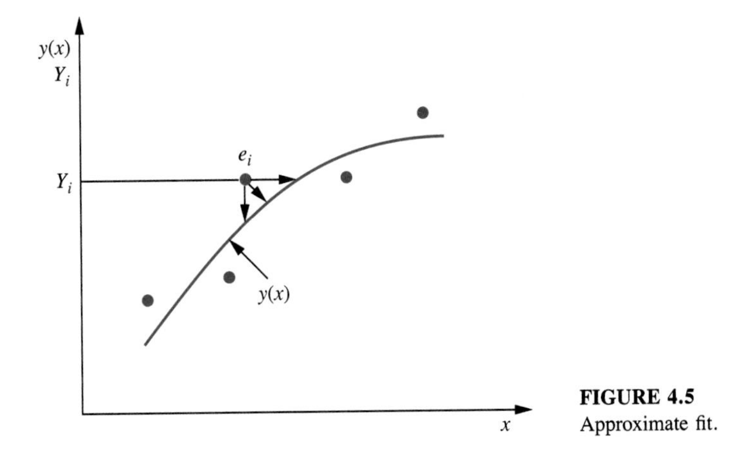

FIGURE 4.5
Approximate fit.

distances) of the points from the approximating function must be minimized in some manner. Some ambiguity is possible in the definition of the deviation. For example, if the values of the independent variable x_i are considered exact, then all the deviation is assigned to the dependent variable Y_i, and the deviation e_i is the vertical distance between Y_i and $y_i = f(x_i)$. Thus,

$$\boxed{e_i = Y_i - y_i} \tag{4.105}$$

It is certainly possible that the values of Y_i are quite accurate, but the corresponding values of x_i are in error. In that case, the deviation would be measured by the horizontal distance illustrated in Figure 4.5. If x_i and y_i both have uncertainties in their values, then the perpendicular distance between a point and the approximating function would be the deviation. The usual approach in approximate fitting of tabular data is to assume that the deviation is the vertical distance between a point and the approximating function, as specified by Eq. (4.105).

Several best-fit criteria exist, as illustrated in Figure 4.6 for a straight-line approximation. Figure 4.6*a* illustrates the situation where the sum of the deviations at two points is minimized. Any straight line that passes through the midpoint of the line segment connecting the two points yields the sum of the deviations equal to zero. Minimizing the sum of the absolute values of the deviations would yield the unique line that passes exactly through the two points. That procedure also has deficiencies, however, as illustrated in Figure 4.6*b*, where two points having the same value of the independent variable have different values of the dependent variable. The best straight line obviously passes midway between these two points, but any line passing between these two points yields the same value for the sum of the absolute values of the deviations. The *minimax* criterion is illustrated in Figure 4.6*c*, where the maximum deviation is minimized. This procedure gives poor

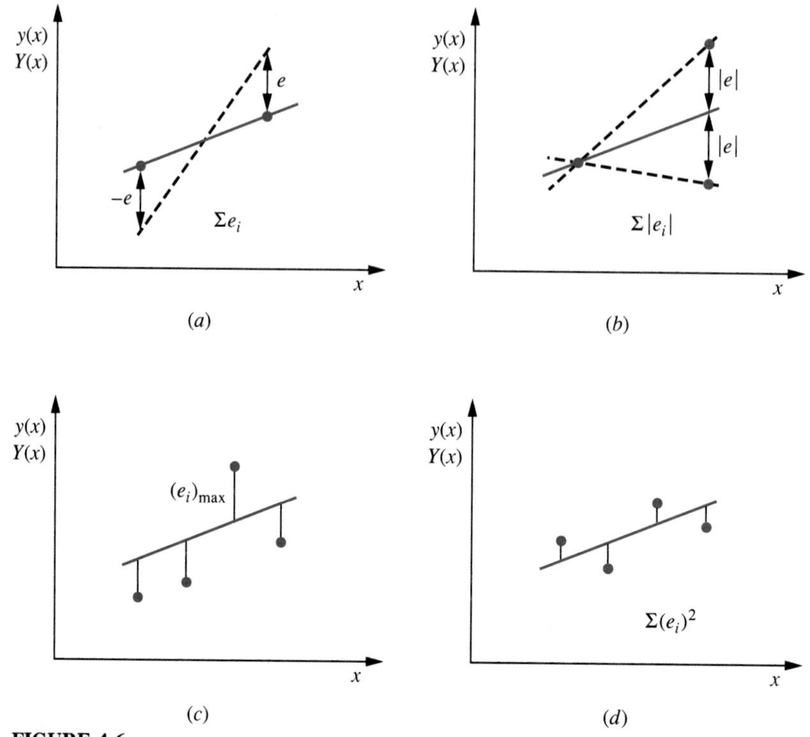

FIGURE 4.6
Best fit criteria: (*a*) minimize $\sum e_i$; (*b*) minimize $\sum |e_i|$; (*c*) minimax; (*d*) least squares.

results when one point is far removed from the other points. Figure 4.6*d* illustrates the least squares criteria, in which the sum of the squares of the deviations is minimized. The least squares procedure yields a good compromise criterion for the best-fit approximation.

The least squares procedure is defined as follows. Given N data points $[x_i, Y(x_i)] = (x_i, Y_i)$, choose the functional form of the approximating function to be fit, $y = y(x)$, and minimize the sum of the squares of the deviations, $e_i = (Y_i - y_i)$.

The Straight-Line Approximation

The simplest polynomial is a linear polynomial, the straight line. Least squares straight-line approximations are an extremely useful and common approximate fit. The least squares straight-line fit is determined as follows. Given N data points (x_i, Y_i), fit the best straight line through the set of data. The approximating function is

$$\boxed{y = b + mx} \tag{4.106}$$

At each value of x_i, Eq. (4.106) gives

$$y_i = (b + mx_i) \qquad (i = 1, \ldots, N) \tag{4.107}$$

The deviation e_i at each value of x_i is

$$e_i = (Y_i - y_i) \qquad (i = 1, \ldots, N) \tag{4.108}$$

The sum of the squares of the deviations defines the function $S(b, m)$:

$$S(b, m) = \sum_{i=1}^{N} (e_i)^2 = \sum_{i=1}^{N} (Y_i - b - mx_i)^2 \tag{4.109}$$

The function $S(b, m)$ is a minimum when $\partial S/\partial b = \partial S/\partial m = 0$. Thus,

$$\frac{\partial S}{\partial b} = \sum_{i=1}^{N} 2(Y_i - b - mx_i)(-1) = 0 \tag{4.110a}$$

$$\frac{\partial S}{\partial m} = \sum_{i=1}^{N} 2(Y_i - b - mx_i)(-x_i) = 0 \tag{4.110b}$$

Dividing by 2 and rearranging yields

$$bN + m\sum_{i=1}^{N} x_i = \sum_{i=1}^{N} Y_i \tag{4.111a}$$

$$b\sum_{i=1}^{N} x_i + m\sum_{i=1}^{N} x_i^2 = \sum_{i=1}^{N} x_i Y_i \tag{4.111b}$$

Equations (4.111) are called the *normal equations* of the least squares fit. They can be solved for b and m by Gauss elimination.

Example 4.10. Least squares straight-line approximation. Consider the constant-pressure specific heat for air at low temperatures presented in Table 4.9, where T is the temperature (K) and C_p is the specific heat (J/gm-K). The exact values, approximate values from the least squares straight-line approximation, and percent error are also presented in the table. Determine a least squares straight-line approximation for the set of data:

$$C_p = b + mT \tag{4.112}$$

For this problem, Eq. (4.111) becomes

$$b8 + m\sum_{i=1}^{8} T_i = \sum_{i=1}^{8} (C_p)_i \tag{4.113}$$

$$b\sum_{i=1}^{8} T_i + m\sum_{i=1}^{8} T_i^2 = \sum_{i=1}^{8} T_i (C_p)_i \tag{4.114}$$

TABLE 4.9
Specific heat of air at low temperatures

T	C_p, exact	C_p, approx	Error, %
300	1.0045	0.9948	−0.97
400	1.0134	1.0153	0.19
500	1.0296	1.0358	0.61
600	1.0507	1.0564	0.54
700	1.0743	1.0769	0.24
800	1.0984	1.0974	−0.09
900	1.1212	1.1180	−0.29
1000	1.1410	1.1385	−0.22

Evaluating the summations and substituting into Eq. (4.114) gives

$$8b + 5200m = 8.5331 \tag{4.115a}$$

$$5200b + 3{,}800{,}000m = 5632.74 \tag{4.115b}$$

Solving for b and m by Gauss elimination without scaling or pivoting yields

$$\boxed{C_p = 0.933194 + 0.205298 \times 10^{-3}T} \tag{4.116}$$

Substituting the initial values of T into Eq. (4.116) gives the results presented in Table 4.9. Figure 4.7 presents the exact data and the least squares straight-line approximation. The straight line is a reasonable approximation, except possibly at the low values of temperature.

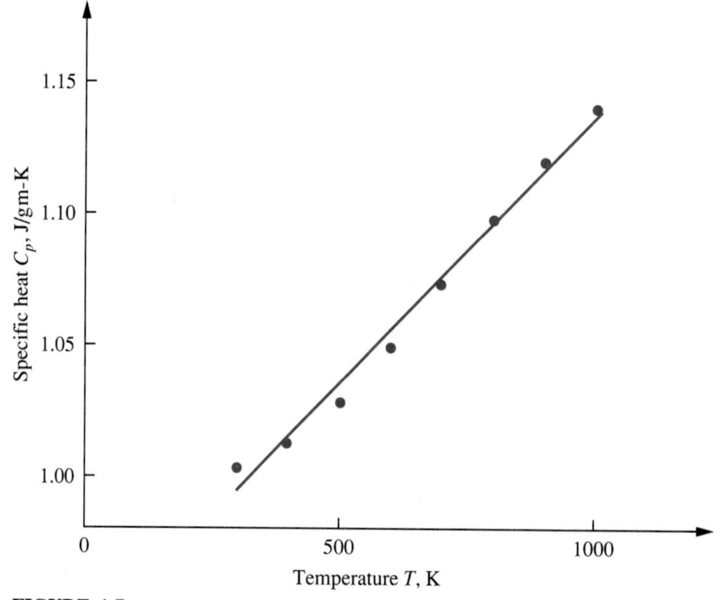

FIGURE 4.7
Least squares straight-line approximation.

Higher-Degree Polynomial Approximation

The least squares procedure developed in the preceding subsection can be applied to higher-degree polynomials. Given the N data points (x_i, Y_i), fit the best nth-degree polynomial through the set of data. Consider the nth-degree polynomial:

$$y = a_0 + a_1 x + a_2 x^2 + \cdots + a_n x^n \tag{4.117}$$

The sum of the squares of the deviations is given by

$$S(a_0, a_1, \ldots, a_n) = \sum_{i=1}^{N} (e_i)^2 = \sum_{i=1}^{N} (Y_i - a_0 - a_1 x_i - \cdots - a_n x_i^n)^2 \tag{4.118}$$

The function $S(a_0, a_1, \ldots, a_n)$ is a minimum when

$$\frac{\partial S}{\partial a_0} = \sum_{i=1}^{N} 2(Y_i - a_0 - a_1 x_i - \cdots - a_n x_i^n)(-1) = 0 \tag{4.119a}$$

$$\vdots$$

$$\frac{\partial S}{\partial a_n} = \sum_{i=1}^{N} 2(Y_i - a_0 - a_1 x_i - \cdots - a_n x_i^n)(-x_i^n) = 0 \tag{4.119b}$$

Dividing by 2 and rearranging yields the normal equations:

$$a_0 N + a_1 \sum_{i=1}^{N} x_i + \cdots + a_n \sum_{i=1}^{N} x_i^n = \sum_{i=1}^{N} Y_i \tag{4.120a}$$

$$\vdots$$

$$a_0 \sum_{i=1}^{N} x_i^n + a_1 \sum_{i=1}^{N} x_i^{n+1} + \cdots + a_n \sum_{i=1}^{N} x_i^{2n} = \sum_{i=1}^{N} x_i^n Y_i \tag{4.120b}$$

Equations (4.120) can be solved for a_0 to a_n by Gauss elimination.

A problem arises for high-degree polynomials. The coefficients N to $\sum x_i^{2n}$ in Eq. (4.120) vary over a range of several orders of magnitude, which gives rise to ill-conditioned systems. Normalizing each equation helps the situation. Double-precision calculations are frequently required. Values of n up to 5 or 6 generally yield good results, values of n between 6 and 10 may or may not yield good results, and values of n greater than 10 generally yield poor results.

Example 4.11. Least squares quadratic polynomial approximation. Consider the constant-pressure specific heat of air at high temperatures presented in Table 4.10, where T is the temperature (K) and C_p is the specific heat (J/gm-K). The exact values, approximate values from the least squares quadratic polynomial approximation, and percent error are

TABLE 4.10
Specific heat of air at high tamperatures

T_g	C_p, exact	C_p, approx	Error, %
1000	1.1410	1.1427	0.15
1500	1.2095	1.2059	−0.29
2000	1.2520	1.2522	0.02
2500	1.2782	1.2815	0.26
3000	1.2955	1.2938	−0.13

also presented in the table. Determine a least squares quadratic polynomial approximation for this set of data:

$$C_p = a + bT + cT^2 \tag{4.121}$$

For this problem, Eq. (4.120) becomes

$$5a + b\sum T_i + c\sum T_i^2 = \sum (C_p)_i \tag{4.122a}$$

$$a\sum T_i + b\sum T_i^2 + c\sum T_i^3 = \sum T_i(C_p)_i \tag{4.122b}$$

$$a\sum T_i^2 + b\sum T_i^3 + c\sum T_i^4 = \sum T_i^2(C_p)_i \tag{4.122c}$$

Evaluating the summations and substituting into Eq. (4.122) gives

$$5a + 10 \times 10^3 b + 22.5 \times 10^6 c = 6.1762 \tag{4.123a}$$

$$10 \times 10^3 a + 22.5 \times 10^6 b + 55 \times 10^9 c = 12.5413 \times 10^3 \tag{4.123b}$$

$$22.5 \times 10^6 a + 55 \times 10^9 b + 142.125 \times 10^{12} c = 288.5186 \times 10^6 \tag{4.123c}$$

Solving for a, b, and c by Gauss elimination yields

$$\boxed{C_p = 0.965460 + 0.211197 \times 10^{-3}T - 0.0339143 \times 10^{-6}T^2} \tag{4.124}$$

Substituting the initial values of T into Eq. (4.124) gives the results presented in Table 4.10. Figure 4.8 presents the exact data and the least squares quadratic polynomial approximation. The quadratic polynomial is a reasonable approximation of the discrete data.

Multivariate Polynomial Approximation

Many problems arise in engineering and science where the dependent variable is a function of two or more independent variables. For example, $z = f(x, y)$ is a two-variable, or bivariate, function. Two exact fit procedures for multivariate approximation are presented in Section 4.9. Least squares multivariate approximation is considered in this section.

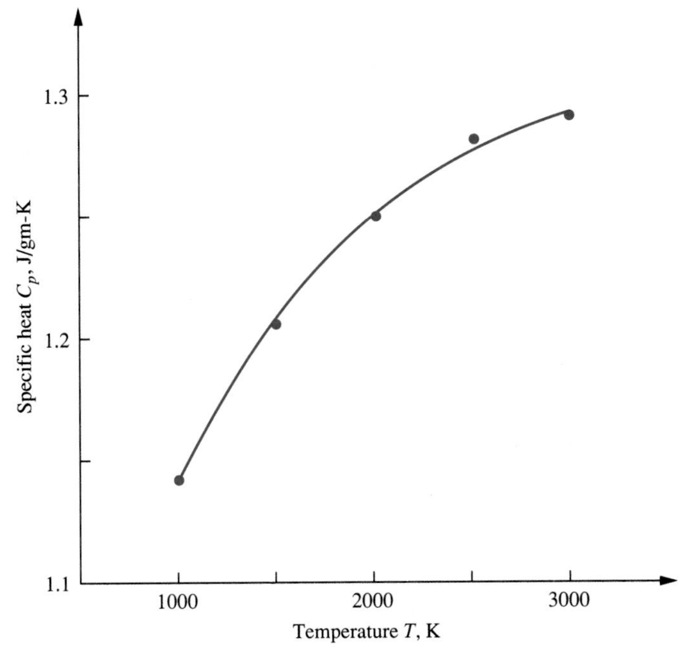

FIGURE 4.8
Least squares quadratic approximation.

Given the N data points (x_i, y_i, Z_i), fit the best linear bivariate polynomial through the set of data. Consider the linear polynomial:

$$\boxed{z = a + bx + cy} \tag{4.125}$$

The sum of the squares of the deviations is given by

$$S(a, b, c) = \sum (e_i)^2 = \sum (Z_i - a - bx_i - cy_i)^2 \tag{4.126}$$

The function $S(a, b, c)$ is a minimum when

$$\frac{\partial S}{\partial a} = \sum 2(Z_i - a - bx_i - cy_i)(-1) = 0 \tag{4.127a}$$

$$\frac{\partial S}{\partial b} = \sum 2(Z_i - a - bx_i - cy_i)(-x_i) = 0 \tag{4.127b}$$

$$\frac{\partial S}{\partial c} = \sum 2(Z_i - a - bx_i - cy_i)(-y_i) = 0 \tag{4.127c}$$

Dividing by 2 and rearranging yields the normal equations:

$$aN + b\sum x_i + c\sum y_i = \sum Z_i \tag{4.128a}$$

$$a\sum x_i + b\sum x_i^2 + c\sum x_i y_i = \sum x_i Z_i \tag{4.128b}$$

$$a\sum y_i + b\sum x_i y_i + c\sum y_i^2 = \sum y_i Z_i \tag{4.128c}$$

Equation (4.128) can be solved for a, b, and c by Gauss elimination.

A linear fit to a set of bivariate data may be inadequate. Consider the quadratic bivariate polynomial

$$z = a + bx + cy + dx^2 + ey^2 + fxy \tag{4.129}$$

The sum of the squares of the deviations is given by

$$S(a, \ldots, f) = \sum (Z_i - a - bx_i - cy_i - dx_i^2 - ey_i^2 - fx_i y_i)^2 \tag{4.130}$$

The function $S(a, \ldots, f)$ is a minimum when

$$\frac{\partial S}{\partial a} = \sum 2(Z_i - a - bx_i - cy_i - dx_i^2 - ey_i^2 - fx_i y_i)(-1) = 0 \tag{4.131a}$$

$$\frac{\partial S}{\partial f} = \sum 2(Z_i - a - bx_i - cy_i - dx_i^2 - ey_i^2 - fx_i y_i)(-x_i y_i) = 0 \tag{4.131f}$$

Dividing by 2 and rearranging yields the normal equations:

$$aN + b\sum x_i + c\sum y_i + d\sum x_i^2 + e\sum y_i^2 + f\sum x_i y_i = \sum Z_i \tag{4.132a}$$

$$a\sum x_i + b\sum x_i^2 + c\sum x_i y_i + d\sum x_i^3 + e\sum x_i y_i^2 + f\sum x_i^2 y_i = \sum x_i Z_i \tag{4.132b}$$

$$a\sum y_i + b\sum x_i y_i + c\sum y_i^2 + d\sum x_i^2 y_i + e\sum y_i^3 + f\sum x_i y_i^2 = \sum y_i Z_i \tag{4.132c}$$

$$a\sum x_i^2 + b\sum x_i^3 + c\sum x_i^2 y_i + d\sum x_i^4 + e\sum x_i^2 y_i^2 + f\sum x_i^3 y_i = \sum x_i^2 Z_i \tag{4.132d}$$

$$a\sum y_i^2+b\sum x_iy_i^2+c\sum y_i^3+d\sum x_i^2y_i^2+e\sum y_i^4+f\sum x_iy_i^3 = \sum y_i^2Z_i \quad (4.132e)$$

$$a\sum x_iy_i + b\sum x_i^2y_i + c\sum x_iy_i^2 + d\sum x_i^3y_i + e\sum x_iy_i^3 + f\sum x_i^2y_i^2 = \sum x_iy_iZ_i \quad (4.132f)$$

Equations (4.132) can be solved for a to f by Gauss elimination.

Example 4.12. Least squares quadratic bivariate polynomial approximation. Rework Example 4.7 to calculate the enthalpy of steam at $P = 1225$ psia and $T = 1100$ F, based on the data in Table 4.8, using a least squares quadratic bivariate polynomial. Let the variables x, y, and Z in Eq. (4.132) correspond to P, T, and h, respectively. Evaluating the summations and substituting into Eq. (4.132) gives

$$\begin{bmatrix} 9\text{ E0} & 10.800\text{ E3} & 9.000\text{ E3} & 12.975\text{ E6} & 9.240\text{ E6} & 10.800\text{ E6} \\ 10.800\text{ E3} & 12.975\text{ E6} & 10.800\text{ E6} & 15.606\text{ E9} & 11.088\text{ E9} & 12.975\text{ E9} \\ 9.000\text{ E3} & 10.800\text{ E6} & 9.240\text{ E6} & 12.975\text{ E9} & 9.720\text{ E9} & 11.088\text{ E9} \\ 12.975\text{ E6} & 15.606\text{ E9} & 12.975\text{ E9} & 18.792\text{ E12} & 13.321\text{ E12} & 15.606\text{ E12} \\ 9.240\text{ E6} & 11.088\text{ E9} & 9.720\text{ E9} & 13.321\text{ E12} & 10.450\text{ E12} & 11.664\text{ E12} \\ 10.800\text{ E6} & 12.975\text{ E9} & 11.088\text{ E9} & 15.606\text{ E12} & 11.664\text{ E12} & 13.321\text{ E12} \end{bmatrix} \begin{bmatrix} a \\ b \\ c \\ d \\ e \\ f \end{bmatrix} = \begin{bmatrix} 13.470\text{ E3} \\ 16.164\text{ E6} \\ 13.612\text{ E6} \\ 19.418\text{ E9} \\ 14.112\text{ E9} \\ 16.334\text{ E9} \end{bmatrix} \quad (4.133)$$

Due to the large magnitudes of the coefficients, they are expressed in exponential format (i.e., $x.xxx$ En = $x.xxx \times 10^n$). Each row in Eq. (4.133) should be normalized by the exponential term in the first coefficient of each row. Solving Eq. (4.133) by Gauss elimination yields

$$h(P, T) = 914.03 - 0.020500P + 0.64550T - 0.000040000P^2 - 0.000077500T^2 + 0.000082500PT \quad (4.134)$$

Evaluating Eq. (4.134) yields $h(1225.0, 1100.0) = 1556.3$ Btu/lbm. The error is $\Delta h = 1556.3 - 1556.0 = 0.3$ Btu/lbm, which is smaller than the error incurred in Example 4.7 obtained by successive exact univariate quadratic interpolation.

Equation (4.132) can be written as the matrix equation

$$\mathbf{Ax} = \mathbf{b} \quad (4.135)$$

where $\mathbf{A}$ is the 6×6 coefficient matrix, $\mathbf{x}$ is the column vector of coefficients (i.e., a to f), and $\mathbf{b}$ is the column vector of nonhomogeneous terms. The solution to Eq. (4.135) is

$$\mathbf{x} = \mathbf{A}^{-1}\mathbf{b} \quad (4.136)$$

where $\mathbf{A}^{-1}$ is the inverse of $\mathbf{A}$. In general, solving Eq. (4.135) by Gauss elimination is more efficient than calculating $\mathbf{A}^{-1}$. However, for equally-spaced (i.e., Δx = constant and Δy = constant) data, a considerable simplification can be achieved. This is accomplished by locally transforming the independent variables so that $x = y = 0$ at the center point of the table. In this case, $\mathbf{A}$ is constant for the entire table, so $\mathbf{A}^{-1}$ can be determined once for the entire table, and Eq. (4.136) can be used to calculate the coefficients a to f very efficiently. Only the nonhomogeneous vector $\mathbf{b}$ changes from point to point and must be recalculated.

Nonlinear Functions

One advantage of using polynomials for least squares approximation is that the normal equations are linear, so it is straightforward to solve for the coefficients of the polynomials. In some engineering and scientific problems, however, the underlying physics suggests forms of approximating functions other than polynomials. Examples of several such functions are presented in this section.

Many physical processes are governed by a nonlinear equation of the form

$$y = ax^b \tag{4.137}$$

Taking the natural logarithm of Eq. (4.137) gives

$$\ln(y) = \ln(a) + b\ln(x) \tag{4.138}$$

Let $y' = \ln(y)$, $a' = \ln(a)$, and $x' = \ln(x)$. Equation (4.138) becomes

$$y' = a' + bx' \tag{4.139}$$

which is a linear polynomial. Equation (4.139) can be used as a least squares approximation by applying the results developed in this Section under "The Straight-Line Approximation."

Another functional form that occurs frequently in physical processes is

$$y = ae^{bx} \tag{4.140}$$

Taking the natural logarithm of Eq. (4.140) gives

$$\ln(y) = \ln(a) + bx \tag{4.141}$$

which can be written as the linear polynomial

$$y' = a' + bx \tag{4.142}$$

Equations (4.137) and (4.140) are examples of nonlinear functions that can be manipulated into a linear form. Some nonlinear functions cannot be so manipulated. For example, consider the nonlinear function

$$y = \frac{a}{1 + bx} \tag{4.143}$$

For a given set of data (x_i, Y_i), $i = 1, \ldots, N$, the sum of the squares of the deviations is

$$S(a, b) = \sum \left(Y_i - \frac{a}{1 + bx_i} \right)^2 \tag{4.144}$$

The function $S(a, b)$ is a minimum when

$$\frac{\partial S}{\partial a} = \sum 2 \left(Y_i - \frac{a}{1 + bx_i} \right) \left(-\frac{1}{1 + bx_i} \right) = 0 \tag{4.145a}$$

$$\frac{\partial S}{\partial b} = \sum 2 \left(Y_i - \frac{a}{1 + bx_i} \right) \left(\frac{x_i}{(1 + bx_i)^2} \right) = 0 \tag{4.145b}$$

Equation (4.145) comprises a pair of nonlinear equations for determining the coefficients a and b. They can be solved by methods for solving systems of nonlinear equations—by Newton's method, as discussed in Section 3.8, for example.

SUMMARY

Procedures for developing approximating polynomials for discrete data are presented in this chapter. For small sets of smooth data, exact fits are desirable. The direct fit polynomial and the Lagrange polynomial work well for unequally spaced data. For equally spaced data, polynomials based on differences are recommended. The Newton forward- and backward-difference polynomials are simple to fit and evaluate. These two polynomials are used extensively in Chapters 5 and 6 to develop procedures for numerical differentiation and integration, respectively. Procedures are discussed for multivariate approximation, inverse interpolation, and piecewise approximation.

Procedures for developing least squares approximations for discrete data are also presented in this chapter. Least squares approximations are useful for large sets of data and sets of rough data. Least squares polynomial approximation is straightforward, both for one independent variable and for more than one independent variable. The least squares normal equations corresponding to polynomial approximating functions are linear, which leads to very efficient solution procedures. For nonlinear approximating functions, the least squares normal equations are nonlinear, which leads to complicated solution procedures. Least squares polynomial approximation is a straightforward, simple, and accurate procedure for obtaining approximating functions for large sets of data or sets of rough data.

PROBLEMS

Section 4.2 Properties of Polynomials

*1. For the polynomial $P_3(x) = x^3 - 9x^2 + 26x - 24$, calculate the following:
   (a) $P_3(1.5)$ by nested multiplication,
   (b) $P_3'(1.5)$ by constructing $Q_2(x)$, and evaluating $Q_2(1.5)$ by nested multiplication, and
   (c) the deflated polynomial $Q_2(x)$ obtained by removing the factor $(x - 2)$.

2. Work Problem 1 for $x = 2.5$ and remove the factor $(x - 3)$.
3. Work Problem 1 for $x = 3.5$ and remove the factor $(x - 4)$.
4. For the polynomial $P_4(x) = x^4 - 10x^3 + 35x^2 - 50x + 24$, calculate the following:
   (a) $P_4(1.5)$ by nested multiplication,
   (b) $P_4'(1.5)$ by constructing $Q_3(x)$ and evaluating $Q_3(1.5)$ by nested multiplication, and
   (c) the deflated polynomial $Q_3(x)$ obtained by removing the factor $(x - 1)$.
5. Work Problem 4 for $x = 2.5$ and remove the factor $(x - 2)$.
6. Work Problem 4 for $x = 3.5$ and remove the factor $(x - 3)$.
7. Work Problem 4 for $x = 4.5$ and remove the factor $(x - 4)$.
8. For the polynomial $P_5(x) = x^5 - 20x^4 + 155x^3 - 580x^2 + 1044x - 720$, calculate the following:
   (a) $P_5(1.5)$ by nested multiplication,
   (b) $P_5'(1.5)$ by constructing $Q_4(x)$ evaluating $Q_4(1.5)$ by nested multiplication, and
   (c) the deflated polynomial $Q_4(x)$ obtained by removing the factor $(x - 2)$.
9. Work Problem 8 for $x = 2.5$ and remove the factor $(x - 3)$.
10. Work Problem 8 for $x = 3.5$ and remove the factor $(x - 4)$.
11. Work Problem 8 for $x = 4.5$ and remove the factor $(x - 5)$.
12. Work Problem 8 for $x = 5.5$ and remove the factor $(x - 6)$.

Section 4.3 Direct Fit Polynomials

The set of data in Table P4.1 is considered in several of the problems that follow.

TABLE P4.1
Tabular data

x	$f(x)$	x	$f(x)$	x	$f(x)$
0.4	5.1600	1.4	3.3886	2.2	5.7491
0.6	3.6933	1.6	3.8100	2.4	6.5933
0.8	3.1400	1.8	4.3511	2.6	7.5292
1.0	3.0000	2.0	5.0000	2.8	8.5543
1.2	3.1067				

*13. The order of an approximating polynomial specifies the rate at which the error of the polynomial approximation approaches zero as the increment in the tabular data approaches zero, that is, Error $= 0(\Delta x^n)$. Estimate the order of a linear direct fit polynomial by calculating $f(2.0)$ for the data in Table P4.1, using $x = 1.6$ and 2.4, and $x = 1.8$ and 2.2, calculating the errors, and calculating the ratio of the errors. Repeat the calculations for $x = 1.6$ and 2.8, and $x = 1.8$ and 2.4. Compare the results and discuss.

14. Consider the set of generic data in Table P4.2:

TABLE P4.2
Generic data.

x	$f(x)$
$x_{i-1} = -\Delta x_-$	f_{i-1}
$x_1 = 0$	f_i
$x_{i+1} = +\Delta x_+$	f_{i+1}

Determine the direct fit quadratic polynomials for the tabular set of generic data for (*a*) $\Delta x_- = \Delta x_+ = \Delta x$, and (*b*) $\Delta x_- \neq \Delta x_+$.

15. The formal order of a direct fit polynomial $P_n(x)$ can be determined by expressing all function values (f_{i-1}, f_{i+1}, and so on) in the polynomial in terms of a Taylor series at the base point and comparing that result to the Taylor series for $f(x)$ at the base point. For the direct fit polynomials developed in Problem 14, show that the order is $O(\Delta x^3)$ for Part (*a*) and $O(\Delta x_-^2) + O(\Delta x_+^2)$ for Part (*b*).

***16.** Consider the data in the range $0.4 \leq x \leq 1.2$ in Table P4.1. Using direct fit polynomials, calculate: (*a*) $P_2(0.9)$ using the first three points, (*b*) $P_2(0.9)$ using the last three points, (*c*) $P_3(0.9)$ using the first four points, (*d*) $P_3(0.9)$ using the last four points, and (*e*) $P_4(0.9)$ using all five data points.

17. Work Problem 16 for $x = 1.5$ and $1.2 \leq x \leq 2.0$.

18. Work Problem 16 for $x = 2.5$ and $2.0 \leq x \leq 2.8$.

19. The constant-pressure specific heat and enthalpy of air are tabulated in Table P4.3.

TABLE P4.3
Properties of air

T, K	C_p, kJ/kg-K	h, kJ/kg	T, K	C_p, kJ/kg-K	h, kJ/kg
1000	1.1410	1047.248	1400	1.1982	1515.792
1100	1.1573	1162.174	1500	1.2095	1636.188
1200	1.1722	1278.663	1600	1.2197	1757.657
1300	1.1858	1396.578			

Using direct fit polynomials with the base point as close to the specified value of T as possible, calculate (*a*) $C_p(1120)$ using two points, (*b*) $C_p(1120)$ using three points, (*c*) $C_p(1480)$ using two points, and (*d*) $C_p(1480)$ using three points.

20. Work Problem 19 for $h(T)$ instead of $C_p(T)$.

Section 4.4 Lagrange Polynomials

***21.** Work Problem 16 using Lagrange polynomials.

22. Work Problem 17 using Lagrange polynomials.

23. Work Problem 18 using Lagrange polynomials.

24. Work Problem 19 using Lagrange polynomials.

25. Work Problem 20 using Lagrange polynomials.

Section 4.5 Difference Tables and Polynomial Fitting

26. Construct a six-place difference table for the function $f(x) = x^3 - 9x^2 + 26x - 24$ in the range $1.0 \leq x \leq 2.0$ for $\Delta x = 0.1$. Discuss the results. Analyze the effects of roundoff.

27. Construct a difference table for the data in Table P4.1. Discuss the results. Analyze the effects of roundoff. Comment on the degree of polynomial required to approximate these data at the beginning, middle, and end of the table.

28. Construct a difference table for $C_p(T)$ for the data presented in Table P4.3. Discuss the results. Analyze the effects of roundoff. What degree of polynomial is required to approximate this set of data?

29. Work Problem 28 for $h(T)$.

Section 4.6 The Newton Forward-Difference Polynomial

***30.** Work Problem 16 using Newton forward-difference polynomials.
31. Work Problem 17 using Newton forward-difference polynomials.
32. Work Problem 18 using Newton forward-difference polynomials.
33. Work Problem 19 using Newton forward-difference polynomials.
34. Work Problem 20 using Newton forward-difference polynomials.

Section 4.7 The Newton Backward-Difference Polynomial

***35.** Work Problem 16 using Newton backward-difference polynomials.
36. Work Problem 17 using Newton backward-difference polynomials.
37. Work Problem 18 using Newton backward-difference polynomials.
38. Work Problem 19 using Newton backward-difference polynomials.
39. Work Problem 20 using Newton backward-difference polynomials.
40. For the data in Table 3 in the temperature range $1200 \leq T \leq 1400$, construct a direct fit polynomial, a Newton forward-difference polynomial, and a Newton backward-difference polynomial for $C_p(T)$. Rewrite both Newton polynomials in the form $C_p(T) = a + bT + CT^2$, and show that the three polynomials are identical.
41. Work Problem 40 including a second-order Lagrange polynomial.

Section 4.8 Other Approximating Functions

42. Work Problem 16 using Stirling centered-difference polynomials.
43. Work Problem 17 using Stirling centered-difference polynomials.
44. Work Problem 18 using Stirling centered-difference polynomials.
45. Work Problem 19 using Stirling centered-difference polynomials.
46. Work Problem 20 using Stirling centered-difference polynomials.
47. Work Problem 16 using Bessel centered-difference polynomials.
48. Work Problem 17 using Bessel centered-difference polynomials.
49. Work Problem 18 using Bessel centered-difference polynomials.
50. Work Problem 19 using Bessel centered-difference polynomials.
51. Work Problem 20 using Bessel centered-difference polynomials.

Section 4.9 Multivariate Interpolation

***52.** The specific volume v (m^3/kg) of steam, corresponding to the van der Waals equation of state (see Problem 3.36), as a function of pressure P (kN/m^2) and temperature T (K), in the neighborhood of $P = 10,000$ kN/m^2 and $T = 800$ K, is tabulated in Table P4.4.

TABLE P4.4
Specific volume of steam

	T, K		
P, kN/m^2	700	800	900
9,000	0.031980	0.037948	0.043675
10,000	0.028345	0.033827	0.039053
11,000	0.025360	0.030452	0.035270

Use successive quadratic univariate interpolation to calculate $v(9500, 750)$. The exact value is 0.032965.

53. Work Problem 52 for $v(9{,}500, 850)$. The exact value is 0.038534.
54. Work Problem 52 for $v(10{,}500, 750)$. The exact value is 0.029466.
55. Work Problem 52 for $v(10{,}500, 850)$. The exact value is 0.034590.
***56.** Solve Problem 52 by direct linear bivariate interpolation for $v(9500, 750)$:

$$v = a + bT + cP + dPT$$

57. Work Problem 56 for $v(9{,}500, 850)$.
58. Work Problem 56 for $v(10{,}500, 750)$.
59. Work Problem 56 for $v(10{,}500, 850)$.
60. Solve Problem 52 by direct quadratic bivariate interpolation for $v(9500, 750)$:

$$v = a + bT + cP + dPT + eT^2 + fP^2$$

61. Work Problem 60 for $v(9{,}500, 850)$.
62. Work Problem 60 for $v(10{,}500, 750)$.
63. Work Problem 60 for $v(10{,}500, 850)$.

Section 4.10 Inverse Interpolation and Piecewise Interpolation

***64.** For the data in Table P4.1, calculate the value of x for which $f(x) = 4.0$ in the range $1.6 \leq x \leq 2.0$ by *(a)* a direct fit quadratic polynomial, *(b)* a Lagrange quadratic polynomial, and *(c)* a Newton forward-difference quadratic polynomial. Compare the results.
65. Work Problem 64 for $f(x) = 6.0$ in the range $2.0 \leq x \leq 2.4$.
66. Work Problem 64 for $f(x) = 7.0$ in the range $2.4 \leq x \leq 2.8$.
67. For the data in Table P4.3, calculate the value of T for which $C_p(T) = 1.1500$ by *(a)* a direct fit quadratic polynomial, *(b)* a Lagrange quadratic polynomial, and *(c)* a Newton forward-difference quadratic polynomial. Compare the results.
68. Work Problem 67 for $C_p(T) = 1.1800$.
69. Work Problem 67 for $C_p(T) = 1.2000$.
70. Consider the C_p data in Table P4.3 for the range $1000 \leq T \leq 1400$. Calculate $C_p(1150)$ by quadratic interpolation with *(a)* $\Delta T = 200$ and *(b)* $\Delta T = 100$. The exact value is 1.1649. Compute the errors and the ratios of the errors and discuss.
71. Work Problem 70 for $C_p(1450)$ for the range $1200 \leq T \leq 1600$. The exact value is 1.2040.
72. Work Problem 70 for $h(1150)$. The exact value is 1220.232.
73. Work Problem 70 for $h(1450)$. The exact value is 1159.659.

4.11 Least Squares Approximation

*74. Consider the C_p data in Table P4.3 for the range $1000 \le T \le 1400$. Find the best straight-line approximation to this set of data. Compute the deviations at each data point.

75. Work Problem 74 using every other data point. Compare the results with the results of Problem 74.

76. Work Problem 74 for a quadratic polynomial. Compare the results with the results of Problem 74.

77. Work Problem 74 for the inverse function $T(C_p)$. Compare the results with the results of Problem 74.

78. Work Problem 74 for the inverse function $T(C_p)$ for a quadratic polynomial. Compare the results with the results of Problem 76.

79. Consider the data for the specific volume of steam, $v = v(P, T)$, given in Table P4.4. Develop a least squares linear bivariate polynomial for the set of data in the form

$$v = a + bT + cP + dPT$$

Compute the derivation at each data point. Calculate $v(9500, 750)$ and compare with the result from Problem 60.

80. Work Problem 79 for the least squares quadratic bivariate polynomial

$$v = a + bT + cP + dPT + eT^2 + fP^2$$

*81. Fit the $C_p(T)$ data in Table P4.3 to the fourth-degree polynomial

$$C_p(T) = a + bT + cT^2 + dT^3 + eT^4$$

Compute the deviations.

*82. When an incompressible fluids flows steadily through a round pipe, the pressure drop ΔP due to friction is given by

$$\Delta P = -0.5 f \rho V^2 (L/D)$$

where ρ is the fluid density, V is the velocity, L/D is the pipe length-to-diameter ratio, and f is the D'Arcy friction coefficients. For laminar flow, the friction coefficient f can be related to the Reynolds number Re by a relationship of the form

$$f = a Re^b$$

Use the measured data in Table P4.5 to determine a and b by a least squares fit. Compute the deviation at each data point.

TABLE P4.5
Friction coefficient.

Re	500	1000	1500	2000
f	0.0320	0.0160	0.0107	0.0080

83. Reaction rates for chemical reactions are usually expressed in the form

$$K = BT^{\alpha} \exp(-E/RT)$$

For a particular reaction, measured values of the backward and forward reaction rates, K_b and K_f, respectively, are given by Table P4.6.

TABLE P4.6
Reaction rates.

T,K	K_b	K_f
1000	7.5 E+15	4.6 E−07
2000	3.8 E+15	5.9 E+04
3000	2.5 E+15	2.5 E+08
4000	1.9 E+15	1.4 E+10
5000	1.5 E+15	1.5 E+11

(*a*) Determine B and α for the backward reaction rate K_b, for which $E/R = 0$. (*b*) Determine B, α, and E/R for the forward reaction rate K_f.

84. The data in Table P4.1 can be fitted by the expression

$$f = \frac{a}{x} + bx^2$$

Develop a least squares procedure to determine a and b. Solve for a and b for the entire set of data in Table 1. Compute the deviations.

CHAPTER 5

NUMERICAL DIFFERENTIATION AND DIFFERENCE FORMULAS

Section

Example

5.1 INTRODUCTION

The evaluation of derivatives, a process known as *differentiation*, is required in many problems in engineering and science:

$$\frac{d}{dx}\big(f(x)\big) = f'(x) = f_x(x) \tag{5.1}$$

where the alternate notations $f'(x)$ and $f_x(x)$ are used for simplicity. The function $f(x)$ that is to be differentiated may be a known function or a set of discrete data. In general, known functions can be differentiated exactly. Differentiation of discrete data, however, requires an approximate numerical procedure.

Numerical differentiation formulas can be developed by fitting an approximating function (e.g., a polynomial) to a set of discrete data and differentiating the approximating function:

$$\frac{d}{dx}\big(f(x)\big) \approx \frac{d}{dx}\big(P_n(x)\big) \tag{5.2}$$

This process is illustrated in Fig. 5.1, which shows that even though the approximating polynomial $P_n(x)$ passes through the discrete data points exactly, the derivative of the polynomial may not be a very accurate approximation of the derivative of the exact function $f(x)$. In general, numerical differentiation is an inherently inaccurate process.

To perform numerical differentiation, an approximating polynomial is fitted to the discrete data or to a subset of the discrete data, and the approximating polynomial is differentiated. The polynomial may be fitted exactly to a set of discrete data by the methods presented in Sections 4.3 to 4.8, or approximately by a least squares fit, as described in Section 4.11. In both cases, the degree of the approximating polynomial chosen to represent the discrete data is the only parameter under our control.

Several numerical differentiation procedures are presented in this chapter. Direct polynomial fit is applied to both equally spaced and unequally spaced data. Differentiation formulas based on both Newton forward-difference and backward-difference polynomials are developed for equally spaced data.

Numerical differentiation formulas can also be developed using Taylor series. This approach is quite useful for developing difference formulas for approximating exact derivatives in the numerical solution of differential equations.

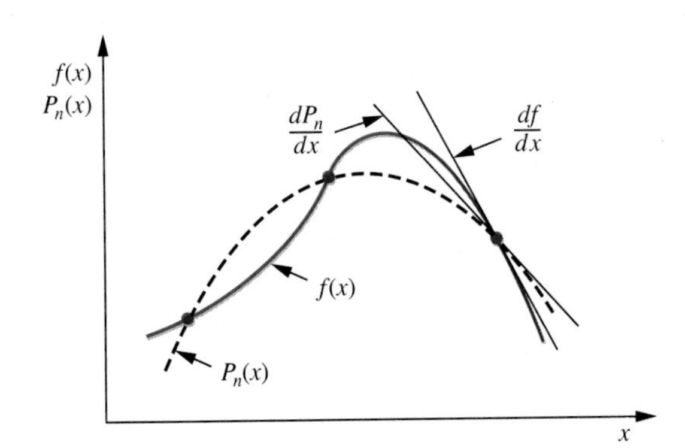

FIGURE 5.1
Numerical differentiation.

The simple function

$$f(x) = \frac{1}{x} \tag{5.3}$$

which has the exact derivatives

$$\frac{d}{dx}\left(\frac{1}{x}\right) = f'(x) = -\frac{1}{x^2} \tag{5.4a}$$

$$\frac{d^2}{dx^2}\left(\frac{1}{x}\right) = f''(x) = \frac{2}{x^3} \tag{5.4b}$$

is considered in this chapter to illustrate numerical differentiation procedures. In particular, at $x = 3.5$,

$$f'(3.5) = -\frac{1}{(3.5)^2} = -0.081633\ldots \tag{5.5a}$$

$$f''(3.5) = \frac{2}{(3.5)^3} = 0.046647\ldots \tag{5.5b}$$

5.2 DIRECT FIT POLYNOMIAL

A straightforward numerical differentiation procedure that can be used for both equally spaced data and unequally spaced data is based on fitting the data directly by a polynomial and differentiating that polynomial. Thus,

$$f(x) = P_n(x) = a_0 + a_1x + a_2x^2 + \cdots \tag{5.6}$$

where $P_n(x)$ is determined by one of the following methods:

1. Given $N = n+1$ points $[x_i, f(x_i)]$, determine the exact nth-degree polynomial that passes through the data points, as discussed in Section 4.3.
2. Given $N > n+1$ data points $[x_i, f(x_i)]$, determine the least squares nth-degree polynomial that best fits the data points, as discussed in Section 4.11.

After the approximating polynomial has been fitted, the derivatives are determined by

$$f'(x) = \frac{d}{dx}\big(P_n(x)\big) \tag{5.7}$$

Substituting Eq. (5.6) into Eq. (5.7) and differentiating yields

$$f'(x) = P_n'(x) = a_1 + 2a_2x + \cdots \tag{5.8}$$

$$f''(x) = P_n''(x) = 2a_2 + 6a_3x + \cdots \tag{5.9}$$

Example 5.1. Direct fit polynomial. Solve the example problem presented in Section 5.1 by a direct fit polynomial:

$$f'(x) = \frac{d}{dx}\left(\frac{1}{x}\right) = \frac{d}{dx}\left(P_n(x)\right) \tag{5.10}$$

Consider the following three data points:

x	$f(x)$
3.4	0.294118
3.5	0.285714
3.6	0.277778

Fit the quadratic polynomial $P_2(x) = a + bx + cx^2$ to the three data points:

$$0.294118 = a + b(3.4) + c(3.4)^2 \tag{5.11a}$$

$$0.285714 = a + b(3.5) + c(3.5)^2 \tag{5.11b}$$

$$0.277778 = a + b(3.6) + c(3.6)^2 \tag{5.11c}$$

Solving for a, b, and c by Gauss elimination gives:

$$P_2(x) = 0.858314 - 0.245500x + 0.023400x^2 \tag{5.12}$$

Substituting Eq. (5.12) into Eqs. (5.8) and (5.9) yields

$$P_2'(x) = -0.245500 + 0.046800x \tag{5.13a}$$

$$P_2'(3.5) = -0.245500 + (0.04680)(3.5) = -0.081700 \tag{5.13b}$$

$$P_2''(x) = 0.046800 \tag{5.14}$$

The error in $f'(3.5)$ is $P_2'(3.5) - f'(3.5) = -0.081700 - (-0.081633) = -0.000067$, and the error in $f''(3.5)$ is $P_2''(3.5) - f''(3.5) = 0.046800 - 0.046647 = 0.000153$.

5.3 NEWTON POLYNOMIALS

The direct fit polynomial presented in Section 5.2 requires a significant amount of effort in the evaluation of the polynomial coefficients. When the function to be differentiated is known at equally spaced points, the Newton forward-difference and backward-difference polynomials, presented in Sections 4.6 and 4.7 respectively, can be fitted to the discrete data with much less effort, thus significantly decreasing the amount of effort required to evaluate the derivatives. Thus,

$$\boxed{f'(x) = \frac{d}{dx}\big(P_n(x)\big)} \tag{5.15}$$

where $P_n(x)$ is either the Newton forward-difference or backward-difference polynomial.

The Newton Forward-Difference Polynomial

Recall the Newton forward-difference polynomial [Eq. (4.64)]:

$$P_n(x_0 + sh) = f_0 + s\Delta f_0 + \frac{s(s-1)}{2}\Delta^2 f_0 + \frac{s(s-1)(s-2)}{6}\Delta^3 f_0 + \cdots$$
$$+ \frac{s(s-1)(s-2)\cdots[s-(n-1)]}{n!}\Delta^n f_0 + \text{Error} \tag{5.16}$$

$$\text{Error} = \binom{s}{n+1} h^{n+1} f^{(n+1)}(\xi), \qquad x_0 \le \xi \le x_n \tag{5.17}$$

where the interpolating parameter s is given by

$$s = \frac{x - x_0}{h} \rightarrow x = x_0 + sh \tag{5.18}$$

Equation (5.15) requires that the approximating polynomial be an explicit function of x, whereas Eq. (5.16) is implicit in x. Either Eq. (5.16) must be made explicit in x by introducing Eq. (5.18) into Eq. (5.16), or the differentiation formula in Eq. (5.15) must be transformed into an explicit function of s, so that Eq. (5.16) can be used directly. The first approach leads to a complicated result, so the second approach is taken. Thus,

$$f'(x) = \frac{d}{dx}\big(P_n(x)\big) = P_n'(x) = \frac{d}{ds}\big(P_n(s)\big)\frac{ds}{dx} \tag{5.19}$$

From Eq. (5.18),

$$\frac{ds}{dx} = \frac{1}{h} \tag{5.20}$$

Thus, Eq. (5.15) becomes

$$\boxed{P_n'(x) = \frac{1}{h}\frac{d}{ds}\big(P_n(s)\big)} \tag{5.21}$$

Substituting Eq. (5.16) into Eq. (5.21) gives

$$P_n'(x) = \frac{1}{h}\bigg(\Delta f_0 + \frac{1}{2}\big((s-1)+s\big)\Delta^2 f_0 + \frac{1}{6}\big((s-1)(s-2)+s(s-2)+s(s-1)\big)\Delta^3 f_0 + \cdots\bigg) \tag{5.22}$$

Simplifying Eq. (5.22) yields

$$P_n'(x) = \frac{1}{h}\left(\Delta f_0 + \frac{2s-1}{2}\Delta^2 f_0 + \frac{3s^2-6s+2}{6}\Delta^3 f_0 + \cdots\right) \tag{5.23}$$

The second derivative is obtained as follows:

$$P_n''(x) = \frac{d}{dx}\big(f'(x)\big) = \frac{d}{ds}\big(f'(s)\big)\frac{ds}{dx} = \frac{1}{h}\frac{d}{ds}\big(f'(s)\big) \tag{5.24}$$

Substituting Eq. (5.23) into Eq. (5.24) yields

$$P_n''(x) = \frac{1}{h}\frac{d}{ds}\big(P_n'(x)\big) = \frac{1}{h^2}\left(\Delta^2 f_0 + (s-1)\Delta^3 f_0 + \cdots\right) \tag{5.25}$$

Higher-order derivatives are obtained in a similar manner. Recall that $\Delta^n f$ becomes less and less accurate as n increases. Consequently, higher-order derivatives become increasingly less accurate.

At $x = x_0$, $s = 0$, and Eqs. (5.23) and (5.25) become

$$P_n'(x_0) = \frac{1}{h}\left(\Delta f_0 - \frac{1}{2}\Delta^2 f_0 + \frac{1}{3}\Delta^3 f_0 - \frac{1}{4}\Delta^4 f_0 + \cdots\right) \tag{5.26}$$

$$P_n''(x_0) = \frac{1}{h^2}\left(\Delta^2 f_0 - \Delta^3 f_0 + \cdots\right) \tag{5.27}$$

Equations (5.26) and (5.27) are one-sided forward-difference formulas.

The error associated with numerical differentiation can be determined by differentiating the error term, Eq. (5.17). Thus,

$$\frac{d}{dx}\big(\text{Error}\big) = \frac{d}{ds}\left(\binom{s}{n+1} h^{n+1} f^{(n+1)}(\xi)\right)\frac{1}{h} \tag{5.28}$$

Recall the definition of the binomial coefficient:

$$\binom{s}{n+1} = \frac{s(s-1)(s-2)\cdots(s-n)}{(n+1)!} \tag{5.29}$$

Substituting Eq. (5.29) into (5.28) yields

$$\frac{d}{dx}\big(\text{Error}\big) = h^n f^{(n+1)}(\xi) \times \left(\frac{(s-1)(s-2)\cdots(s-n) + \cdots + s(s-1)\cdots(s-n+1)}{(n+1)!}\right) \tag{5.30}$$

At $x = x_0$, $s = 0$, and

$$\frac{d}{dx}\big(\text{Error}(x_0)\big) = \frac{(-1)^n}{(n+1)} h^n f^{(n+1)}(\xi) \neq 0 \tag{5.31}$$

Even though there is no error in $P_n(x_0)$, there is error in $P_n'(x_0)$.

The order of the error is the rate at which the error approaches zero as the interval h approaches zero. Equation (5.31) shows that the one-sided first derivative approximation $P_n'(x_0)$ is order n, which is written as $O(h^n)$, when the nth-forward difference is accounted for. Each differentiation introduces another h into the denominator of the error term, so the order of the results drop by one for each differentiation. Thus, $P_n'(x_0)$ is $O(h^n)$, $P_n''(x_0)$ is $O(h^{n-1})$, etc.

A more direct way to determine the order of a derivative approximation is to recall that the error term in any of the difference polynomials is given by the first neglected term in the polynomial, with $\Delta^{(n+1)}f$ replaced by $h^{n+1}f^{(n+1)}(\xi)$. Each differentiation introduces an h into the denominator of the error term. For example, from Eqs. (5.26) and (5.27), if terms through $\Delta^2 f_0$ are accounted for, the error is $O(h^3)/h = O(h^2)$ for $P_2'(\text{x})$ and $O(h^3)/h^2 = O(h)$ for $P_2''(x_0)$. To achieve $O(h^2)$ for $P''(x_0)$, $P_3(x)$ must be used.

Example 5.2. Newton forward-difference polynomial, one-sided. Solve the example problem presented in Section 5.1, using the Newton forward-difference polynomial with the base point at $x_0 = 3.5$, so that $x = x_0 = 3.5$ in Eqs. (5.26) and (5.27). Equation (5.26) gives

$$P_n'(3.5) = \frac{1}{0.1}\left((-0.007936) - \frac{1}{2}(0.000428) + \frac{1}{3}(-0.000032) + \cdots\right) \tag{5.32}$$

Evaluating Eq. (5.32) term by term yields

$P_n'(3.5) = -0.07936\_$	first order	Error:	$0.00227\_$
$-0.08150\_$	second order		$0.00013\_$
$-0.08161\_$	third order		$0.00002\_$

The first-order result is quite inaccurate. The second- and third-order results are quite good. In all cases, only five significant digits after the decimal place are obtained.

Equation (5.27) gives

$$P_n''(3.5) = \frac{1}{(0.1)^2}\big(0.000428 - (-0.000032) + \cdots\big) \tag{5.33}$$

Evaluating Eq. (5.33) term by term yields

$f''(3.5) = 0.0428\_\_$	first order	Error	$-0.0038\_\_$
$0.0460\_\_$	second order		$-0.0006\_\_$

The first-order result is very poor. The second-order result, although much more accurate, has only four significant digits after the decimal place.

The results presented in this section illustrate the inherent inaccuracy associated with numerical differentiation. Equations (5.26) and (5.27) are both one-sided formulas. More accurate results can be obtained with centered differentiation formulas.

Centered differentiation formulas can be obtained by evaluating the Newton forward-difference polynomial at points within the range of fit. For example, at $x = x_1$, $s = 1$, and Eqs. (5.23) and (5.25) give

$$P_n'(x_1) = \frac{1}{h}\left(\Delta f_0 + \frac{1}{2}\Delta^2 f_0 - \frac{1}{6}\Delta^3 f_0 + \cdots\right) \tag{5.34}$$

$$P_n''(x_1) = \frac{1}{h^2}\left(\Delta^2 f_0 + \frac{1}{12}\Delta^4 f_0 + \cdots\right) \tag{5.35}$$

From Eq. (5.34), $P_2'(x_1)$ is $O(h^2)$, as is the one-sided approximation, Eq. (5.26). However, $P_2''(x_1)$ is $O(h^2)$, whereas the one-sided approximation, Eq. (5.27), is $O(h)$. The increased order of the approximation of $P_2''(x_1)$ is due to centering the polynomial fit at point x_1.

Example 5.3. Newton forward-difference polynomial, centered. To illustrate a centered differentiation formula, we will work the example problem presented in Section 5.1, using $x_0 = 3.4$ as the base point, so that $x_1 = 3.5$ is in the middle of the range of fit. Thus, Eq. (5.34) gives

$$P_n'(3.5) = \frac{1}{0.1}\left(-0.008404 + \frac{1}{2}(0.000468) - \frac{1}{6}(-0.000040) + \cdots\right) \tag{5.36}$$

$P_n'(3.5) = -0.08404_-$	first order	Error	-0.00241_-
-0.08170_-	second order		-0.00007_-
-0.08163_-	third order		-0.00000_-

Equation (5.35) gives

$$P_n''(3.5) = \frac{1}{(0.1)^2}(0.000468 + \cdots) \tag{5.37}$$

$P_n''(3.5) = 0.0468_{--}$ second order Error $= 0.0002_{--}$

These centered results are considerably more accurate than the one-sided results obtained in Example 5.2.

The Newton Backward-Difference Polynomial

Recall the Newton backward-difference polynomial [Eq. (4.77)]:

$$P_n(x_0 + sh) = f_0 + s\nabla f_0 + \frac{(s+1)s}{2!}\nabla^2 f_0 + \frac{(s+2)(s+1)s}{3!}\nabla^3 f_0 + \cdots \tag{5.38}$$

The derivative $f'(x)$ is obtained from $P_n(s)$ as follows:

$$f'(x) = P_n'(x) = \frac{1}{h}\frac{d}{ds}\big(P_n(s)\big) \tag{5.39}$$

Substituting Eq. (5.38) into Eq. (5.39) and simplifying gives

$$P_n'(x) = \frac{1}{h}\left(\nabla f_0 + \frac{2s+1}{2}\nabla^2 f_0 + \frac{3s^2+6s+2}{6}\nabla^3 f_0 + \cdots\right) \tag{5.40}$$

The derivative $P_n''(x)$ is given by

$$P_n''(x) = \frac{1}{h^2}\left(\nabla^2 f_0 + (s+1)\nabla^3 f_0 + \cdots\right) \tag{5.41}$$

Higher-order derivatives are obtained in a similar manner. Recall that $\nabla^n f$ becomes less and less accurate as n increases. Consequently, higher-order derivatives become increasingly less accurate.

At $x = x_0$, $s = 0$, and Eqs. (5.40) and (5.41) become

$$P_n'(x_0) = \frac{1}{h}\left(\nabla f_0 + \frac{1}{2}\nabla^2 f_0 + \frac{1}{3}\nabla^3 f_0 + \cdots\right) \tag{5.42}$$

$$P_n''(x_0) = \frac{1}{h^2}\left(\nabla^2 f_0 + \nabla^3 f_0 + \cdots\right) \tag{5.43}$$

Equations (5.42) and (5.43) are one-sided backward-difference formulas.

Centered-difference formulas are obtained by evaluating the Newton backward-difference polynomial at points within the range of fit. For example, at $x = x_{-1}$, $s = -1$, and Eqs. (5.40) and (5.41) gives

$$P_n'(x_{-1}) = \frac{1}{h}\left(\nabla f_0 - \frac{1}{2}\nabla^2 f_0 - \frac{1}{6}\nabla^3 f_0 + \cdots\right) \tag{5.44}$$

$$P_n''(x_{-1}) = \left(\nabla^2 f_0 - \frac{1}{12}\nabla^4 f_0 + \cdots\right) \tag{5.45}$$

The order of the derivative approximations are obtained by dividing the order of the first neglected term in each formula by the appropriate power of h, as discussed in the preceding subsection for derivative approximations based on Newton forward-difference polynomials.

Difference Formulas

The formulas for derivatives developed in the previous subsections are expressed in terms of differences. Those formulas can be expressed directly in terms of function values if the order of the approximation is specified. The resulting formulas are called *difference formulas*. Several difference formulas are developed in this subsection to illustrate the procedure.

Consider the one-sided forward-difference formula for the first derivative, Eq. (5.26):

$$P_n'(x_0) = \frac{1}{h}\left(\Delta f_0 - \frac{1}{2}\Delta^2 f_0 + \frac{1}{3}\Delta^3 f_0 - \cdots\right) \tag{5.46}$$

Recall that the error term associated with truncating the Newton forward-difference polynomial is obtained from the leading truncated term by replacing $\Delta^n f_0$ by $f^{(n)}(\xi)h^n$. Truncating Eq. (5.46) after Δf_0 gives

$$P_n'(x_0) = \frac{1}{h}(\Delta f_0 + O(h^2)) \tag{5.47}$$

where $O(h^2)$, read as "order h-squared," denotes the error term and indicates the dependence of the error on the step size h. Substituting $\Delta f_0 = (f_1 - f_0)$ into Eq. (5.47) yields

$$P_n'(x_0) = \frac{f_1 - f_0}{h} + O(h) \tag{5.48}$$

Equation (5.48) is a one-sided first-order forward-difference formula for $f'(x_0)$. Truncating Eq. (5.46) after the $\Delta^2 f_0$ term gives

$$P_n'(x_0) = \frac{1}{h}\left(\Delta f_0 - \frac{1}{2}\Delta^2 f_0 + O(h^3)\right) \tag{5.49}$$

Substituting for Δf_0 and $\Delta^2 f_0$ and simplifying yields

$$P_n'(x_0) = \frac{-3f_0 + 4f_1 - f_2}{2h} + O(h^2) \tag{5.50}$$

Higher-order difference formulas can be obtained in a similar manner.

Consider the one-sided forward-difference formula for the second derivative, Eq. (5.27). The following difference formulas can be obtained in the same manner as Eqs. (5.48) and (5.50) were developed.

$$P_n''(x_0) = \frac{f_0 - 2f_1 + f_2}{h^2} + O(h) \tag{5.51}$$

$$P_n''(x_0) = \frac{2f_0 - 5f_1 + 4f_2 - f_3}{h^2} + O(h^2) \tag{5.52}$$

Centered-difference formulas for $P_n'(x_1)$ and $P_n''(x_1)$ can be derived from Eqs. (5.34) and (5.35). Thus,

$$P_n'(x_1) = \frac{f_2 - f_0}{2h} + O(h^2) \tag{5.53}$$

$$P_n''(x_1) = \frac{f_0 - 2f_1 + f_2}{h^2} + O(h^2) \tag{5.54}$$

Difference formulas of any order can be developed in a similar manner for derivatives of any order, based on one-sided, centered, or nonsymmetrical differences. A selection of difference formulas is presented in Table 5.1 in Section 5.5.

Example 5.4. Difference formulas. We will illustrate the use of difference formulas by solving the example problem presented in Section 5.1 using difference formulas. Calculate the second-order centered-difference approximation of $f'(3.5)$ and $f''(3.5)$ using Eqs. (5.53) and (5.54). Thus,

$$P_n'(3.5) = \frac{f(3.6) - f(3.4)}{2(0.1)} = \frac{0.277778 - 0.294118}{2(0.1)} = -0.081700 \tag{5.55}$$

$$P_n''(3.5) = \frac{f(3.6) - 2f(3.5) + f(3.4)}{(0.1)^2} \tag{5.56a}$$

$$P_n''(3.5) = \frac{0.277778 - 2(0.285714) + 0.294118}{(0.1)^2} = 0.046800 \tag{5.56b}$$

These results are identical to the second-order results obtained in Example 5.3.

5.4 TAYLOR SERIES APPROACH

Difference formulas can also be developed using Taylor series. This approach is especially useful for deriving finite difference approximations of exact derivatives (both total derivatives and partial derivatives) that appear in differential equations.

Difference formulas for functions of a single variable, for example $f(x)$, can be developed from the Taylor series for a function of a single variable (see the Appendix):

$$f(x) = f_0 + f'|_0\,\Delta x + \frac{1}{2}f''|_0\,\Delta x^2 + \cdots + \frac{1}{n!}f^{(n)}|_0\,\Delta x^n + \cdots \tag{5.57}$$

where $f_0 = f(x_0)$, $f'|_0 = f'(x_0)$, and so on. The continuous spatial domain $D(x)$ must be discretized into an equally spaced grid of discrete points, as illustrated in Fig. 5.2. For the discrete grid,

$$f(x_i) = f_i \tag{5.58}$$

where the subscript i denotes a particular spatial location. The Taylor series for

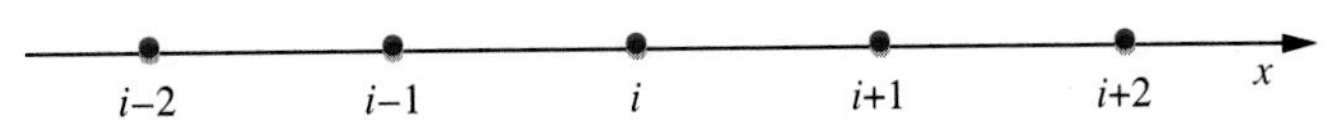

FIGURE 5.2
Discretized x space.

$f(x)$ at grid points surrounding point i can be combined to obtain difference formulas for $f'(x_i)$, $f''(x_i)$, etc.

Difference formulas for functions of several variables, for example $f(x, t)$, can be developed from the Taylor series for a function of several variables (see the Appendix). For the two-variable function $f(x, t)$, the Taylor series is given by

$$\begin{aligned} f(x, t) &= f_0 + \left(f_x|_0\,\Delta x + f_t|_0\,\Delta t\right) \\ &\quad + \frac{1}{2}\left(f_{xx}|_0\,\Delta x^2 + 2f_{xt}|_0\,\Delta x\,\Delta t + f_{tt}|_0\,\Delta t^2\right) + \cdots \\ &\quad + \frac{1}{n!}\left(f_{(n)x}|_0\,\Delta x^n + \cdots + f_{(n)t}|_0\,\Delta t^n\right) + \cdots \end{aligned} \tag{5.59}$$

where $f_0 = f(x_0, t_0)$, $f_{(n)x}$ denotes $\partial^n f/\partial x^n$, and so on. The continuous domain $D(x, t)$ must be discretized into an orthogonal equally spaced grid of discrete points, as illustrated in Fig. 5.3. For the discrete grid,

$$f(x_i, t^n) = f_i^n \tag{5.60}$$

where the subscript i denotes a particular spatial location and the superscript n denotes a particular time. The Taylor series for $f(x, t)$ at grid points surrounding point (i,n) can be combined to obtain difference formulas for f_x, f_t, etc.

For partial derivatives of $f(x, t)$ with respect to x, $t = t_0 =$ constant, $\Delta t = 0$, and Eq. (5.59) becomes

$$f(x, t_0) = f_0 + f_x|_0\,\Delta x + \frac{1}{2}f_{xx}|_0\,\Delta x^2 + \cdots + \frac{1}{n!}f_{(n)x}|_0\,\Delta x^n + \cdots \tag{5.61}$$

Equation (5.61) is identical in form to Eq. (5.57), where $f'|_0$ corresponds to $f_x|_0$,

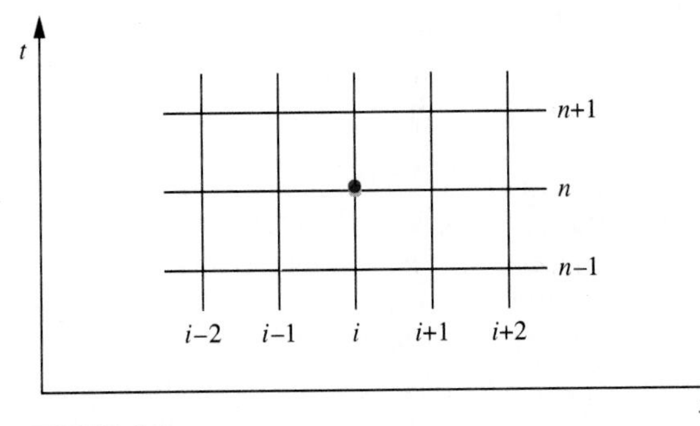

FIGURE 5.3
Discretized xt space.

etc. The partial derivative $f_x|_0$ of the function $f(x, t)$ can be obtained from Eq. (5.61) in exactly the same manner as the total derivative $f'|_0$ of the function $f(x)$ is obtained from Eq. (5.57). Since Eqs. (5.57) and (5.61) are identical in form, the difference formulas for $f'|_0$ and $f_x|_0$ are identical if the same discrete grid points are used to develop the difference formulas. Consequently, difference formulas for partial derivatives of a function of several variables can be derived from the Taylor series for a function of a single variable. To emphasize this concept, the following common notation for derivatives will be used in the development of difference formulas for total derivatives and partial derivatives:

$$\frac{d}{dx}(f(x)) = f_x \tag{5.62}$$

$$\frac{\partial}{\partial x}(f(x, t)) = f_x \tag{5.63}$$

In a similar manner, partial derivatives of $f(x, t)$ with respect to t can be obtained from the expression

$$f(x_0, t) = f_0 + f_t|_0\,\Delta t + \frac{1}{2} f_{tt}|_0\,\Delta t^2 + \cdots + \frac{1}{n!} f_{(n)t}|_0\,\Delta t^n + \cdots \tag{5.64}$$

Partial derivatives of $f(x, t)$ with respect to t are identical in form to total derivatives of $f(t)$ with respect to t.

This approach does not work for mixed partial derivatives, such as f_{xt}. Difference formulas for mixed partial derivatives must be determined directly from the Taylor series for several variables.

The Taylor series for the function $f(x)$, Eq. (5.57), can be written as

$$f(x) = f_0 + f_x|_0\,\Delta x + \frac{1}{2} f_{xx}|_0\,\Delta x^2 + \cdots + \frac{1}{n!} f_{(n)x}|_0\,\Delta x^n + \cdots \tag{5.65}$$

The Taylor formula with remainder (see the Appendix) is

$$f(x) = f_0 + f_x|_0\,\Delta x + \frac{1}{2} f_{xx}|_0\,\Delta x^2 + \cdots + \frac{1}{n!} f_{(n)x}|_0\,\Delta x^n + R_{n+1} \tag{5.66}$$

where the remainder term R_{n+1} is given by

$$R_{n+1} = \frac{1}{(n+1)!} f_{(n+1)x}(\xi)\,\Delta x^{n+1} \tag{5.67}$$

where $x_0 \le \xi \le x_0 + \Delta x$.

The infinite Taylor series [Eq. (5.65)] and the Taylor formula with remainder [Eq. (5.66)] are equivalent. The error incurred by truncating the infinite Taylor series after the nth derivative is exactly the remainder term of the nth-order Taylor formula. Truncating the Taylor series is equivalent to dropping the remainder term of the Taylor formula. Finite difference approximations of exact derivatives can be obtained by solving for the exact derivative from either the infinite Taylor series or the Taylor formula, and then either truncating the Taylor series or dropping the remainder term of the Taylor formula. These two procedures are identical. The terms that are truncated from the infinite Taylor series, which are identical to the remainder term of the Taylor formula, are called the *truncation error* of the finite difference approximation of the exact derivative. In most cases, our main concern is the order of the truncation error, which is the rate at which the truncation error approaches zero as $\Delta x \rightarrow 0$. The order of the truncation error, which is the order of the remainder term, is denoted by the notation $O(\Delta x^n)$.

Consider the equally spaced discrete finite difference grid illustrated in Fig. 5.2. Choose point i as the base point and write the Taylor series for f_{i+1} and f_{i-1}:

$$f_{i+1} = f_i + f_x|_i \Delta x + \tfrac{1}{2} f_{xx}|_i \Delta x^2 + \tfrac{1}{6} f_{xxx}|_i \Delta x^3 + \tfrac{1}{24} f_{xxxx}|_i \Delta x^4 + \cdots \quad (5.68)$$

$$f_{i-1} = f_i - f_x|_i \Delta x + \tfrac{1}{2} f_{xx}|_i \Delta x^2 - \tfrac{1}{6} f_{xxx}|_i \Delta x^3 + \tfrac{1}{24} f_{xxxx}|_i \Delta x^4 - \cdots \quad (5.69)$$

Subtracting f_{i-1} from f_{i+1} gives

$$f_{i+1} - f_{i-1} = 2 f_x|_i \Delta x + \frac{1}{3} f_{xxx}|_i \Delta x^3 + \cdots \quad (5.70)$$

Letting the f_{xxx} term be the remainder term and solving for $f_x|_i$ yields

$$f_x|_i = \frac{f_{i+1} - f_{i-1}}{2\Delta x} - \frac{1}{6} f_{xxx}(\bar{\xi}) \Delta x^2 \quad (5.71)$$

where $x_{i-1} \le \bar{\xi} \le x_{i+1}$. Equation (5.71) is an exact expression for $f_x|_i$. If the remainder term is dropped, which is equivalent to truncating the infinite Taylor series, Eqs. (5.68) and (5.69), Eq. (5.71) yields a finite difference approximation of $f_x|_i$. The truncated result is identical to the result obtained from the Newton forward-difference polynomial, Eq. (5.53).

Adding f_{i+1} and f_{i-1} gives

$$f_{i+1} + f_{i-1} = 2 f_i + f_{xx}|_i \Delta x^2 + \frac{1}{12} f_{xxxx}|_i \Delta x^4 + \cdots \quad (5.72)$$

Letting the f_{xxxx} term be the remainder term and solving for $f_{xx}|_i$ yields

$$f_{xx}|_i = \frac{f_{i+1} - 2f_i + f_{i-1}}{\Delta x^2} - \frac{1}{12} f_{xxxx}(\xi) \Delta x^2 \quad (5.73)$$

The truncated result is identical to the result obtained from the Newton forward-difference polynomial, Eq. (5.54).

Equations (5.71) and (5.73) are centered-difference formulas. They are inherently more accurate than one-sided difference formulas.

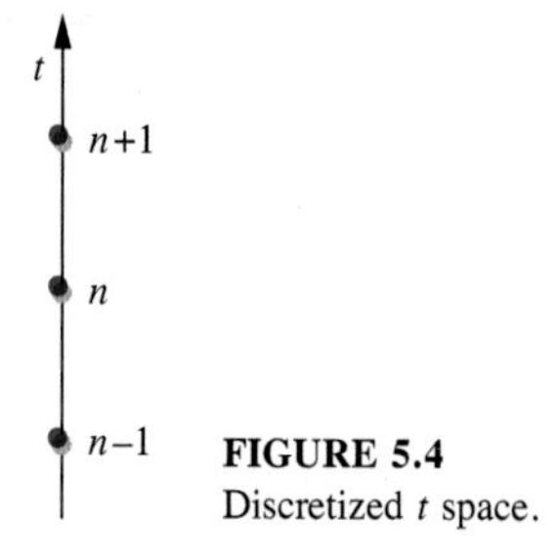

FIGURE 5.4
Discretized t space.

Equations (5.71) and (5.73) are difference formulas for spatial derivatives. Difference formulas for *time* derivatives can be developed in a similar manner. The time dimension can be discretized into a discrete temporal grid, as illustrated in Figure 5.4, where the superscript n denotes a specific value of time. Thus,

$$f(t^n) = f^n \tag{5.74}$$

Choose point n as the base point, and write the Taylor series for f^{n+1} and f^{n-1}:

$$f^{n+1} = f^n + f_t|^n \, \Delta t + \frac{1}{2} f_{tt}|^n \, \Delta t^2 + \cdots \tag{5.75}$$

$$f^{n-1} = f^n - f_t|^n \, \Delta t + \frac{1}{2} f_{tt}|^n \, \Delta t^2 - \cdots \tag{5.76}$$

Letting the f_{tt} term be the remainder term and solving Eq. (5.75) for $f_t|^n$ yields

$$\boxed{f_t|^n = \frac{f^{n+1} - f^n}{\Delta t} - \frac{1}{2} f_{tt}(\tau) \, \Delta t} \tag{5.77}$$

where $t^n \le \tau \le t^{n+1}$. Equation (5.77) is a first-order forward-difference formula for $f_t|^n$.

Subtracting f^{n-1} from f^{n+1} gives

$$f^{n+1} - f^{n-1} = 2 f_t|^n \, \Delta t + \frac{1}{3} f_{ttt}|^n \, \Delta t^3 + \cdots \tag{5.78}$$

Letting the f_{ttt} term be the remainder term and solving for $f_t|^n$ yields

$$\boxed{f_t|^n = \frac{f^{n+1} - f^{n-1}}{2\Delta t} - \frac{1}{6} f_{ttt}(\bar{\tau}) \, \Delta t^2} \tag{5.79}$$

where $t^{n-1} \le \bar{\tau} \le t^{n+1}$. Equation (5.79) is a second-order centered-difference formula for $f_t|^n$. Centered-difference formulas are inherently more accurate than one-sided difference formulas, such as Eq. (5.77).

Difference formulas of any order, based on one-sided forward differences, one-sided backward differences, centered differences, nonsymmetrical differences, etc., can be obtained by different combinations of the Taylor series for $f(x)$ or $f(t)$ at various grid points. Higher-order difference formulas require more grid points, as do formulas for higher-order derivatives.

Example 5.5. Third-order nonsymmetrical difference formula for f_x. Develop a third-order, nonsymmetrical, backward-biased difference formula for f_x. The Taylor series for $f(x)$ is:

$$f(x) = f_i + f_x|_i \Delta x + \frac{1}{2} f_{xx}|_i \Delta x^2 + \frac{1}{6} f_{xxx}|_i \Delta x^3 + \frac{1}{24} f_{xxxx}|_i \Delta x^4 + \cdots \tag{5.80}$$

Two questions must be answered before the difference formula can be developed:

1. What is the order of the remainder term?
2. How many grid points are required?

The coefficient of f_x is Δx. If the remainder term in the difference formula is to be $O(\Delta x^3)$, then the remainder term in the Taylor series must be $O(\Delta x^4)$. Consequently, three grid points, in addition to the base point i, are required, so that f_{xx} and f_{xxx} can be eliminated from the Taylor series expansions, thus giving a third-order difference formula for f_x. For a backward-biased difference formula, choose grid points $i+1$, $i-1$, and $i-2$.

The fourth-order Taylor series for f_{i+1}, f_{i-1}, and f_{i-2} are

$$f_{i+1} = f_i + f_x|_i \Delta x + \frac{1}{2} f_{xx}|_i \Delta x^2 + \frac{1}{6} f_{xxx}|_i \Delta x^3 + \frac{1}{24} f_{xxxx}(\xi_1) \Delta x^4 + \cdots \tag{5.81}$$

$$f_{i-1} = f_i - f_x|_i \Delta x + \frac{1}{2} f_{xx}|_i \Delta x^2 - \frac{1}{6} f_{xxx}|_i \Delta x^3 + \frac{1}{24} f_{xxxx}(\xi_{-1}) \Delta x^4 - \cdots \tag{5.82}$$

$$f_{i-2} = f_i - 2f_x|_i \Delta x + \frac{4}{2} f_{xx}|_i \Delta x^2 - \frac{8}{6} f_{xxx}|_i \Delta x^3 + \frac{16}{24} f_{xxxx}(\xi_{-2}) \Delta x^4 - \cdots \tag{5.83}$$

Forming the combination $f_{i+1} - f_{i-1}$ gives

$$\left(f_{i+1} - f_{i-1}\right) = 2f_x|_i \Delta x + \frac{2}{6} f_{xxx}|_i \Delta x^3 + O(\Delta x^5) \tag{5.84}$$

Forming the combination $4f_{i+1} - f_{i-2}$ gives

$$\left(4f_{i+1} - f_{i-2}\right) = 3f_i + 6f_x|_i \Delta x + \frac{12}{6} f_{xxx}|_i \Delta x^3 - \frac{12}{24} f_{xxxx}(\bar{\xi}) \Delta x^4 \tag{5.85}$$

where $x_{i-2} \le \bar{\xi} \le x_{i+1}$. Multiplying Eq. (5.84) by 6 and subtracting Eq. (5.85) gives

$$6\left(f_{i+1} - f_{i-1}\right) - \left(4f_{i+1} - f_{i-2}\right) = -3f_i + 6f_x|_i \Delta x + \frac{12}{24} f_{xxxx}(\bar{\xi}) \Delta x^4 \tag{5.86}$$

Solving Eq. (5.86) for $f_x|_i$ yields

$$\boxed{f_x|_i = \frac{f_{i-2} - 6f_{i-1} + 3f_i + 2f_{i+1}}{6\Delta x} - \frac{1}{12} f_{xxxx}(\bar{\xi}) \Delta x^3} \tag{5.87}$$

TABLE 5.1
Difference formulas

$$f_t|^n = \frac{f^{n+1} - f^n}{\Delta t} - \frac{1}{2} f_{tt}(\tau)\Delta t \tag{5.88}$$

$$f_t|^n = \frac{f^n - f^{n-1}}{\Delta t} + \frac{1}{2} f_{tt}(\tau)\Delta t \tag{5.89}$$

$$f_t|^{n+(\frac{1}{2})} = \frac{f^{n+1} - f^n}{\Delta t} - \frac{1}{24} f_{ttt}(\tau)\Delta t^2 \tag{5.90}$$

$$f_t|^n = \frac{f^{n+1} - f^{n-1}}{2\Delta t} - \frac{1}{6} f_{ttt}(\tau)\Delta t^2 \tag{5.91}$$

$$f_x|_i = \frac{f_{i+1} - f_i}{\Delta x} - \frac{1}{2} f_{xx}(\xi)\Delta x \tag{5.92}$$

$$f_x|_i = \frac{f_i - f_{i-1}}{\Delta x} + \frac{1}{2} f_{xx}(\xi)\Delta x \tag{5.93}$$

$$f_x|_i = \frac{f_{i+1} - f_{i-1}}{2\Delta x} - \frac{1}{6} f_{xxx}(\xi)\Delta x^2 \tag{5.94}$$

$$f_x|_i = \frac{-3f_i + 4f_{i+1} - f_{i+2}}{2\Delta x} - \frac{1}{3} f_{xxx}(\xi)\Delta x^2 \tag{5.95}$$

$$f_x|_i = \frac{f_{i-2} - 4f_{i-1} + 3f_i}{2\Delta x} + \frac{1}{3} f_{xxx}(\xi)\Delta x^2 \tag{5.96}$$

$$f_x|_i = \frac{-11f_i + 18f_{i+1} - 9f_{i+2} + 2f_{i+3}}{6\Delta x} - \frac{1}{4} f_{xxxx}(\xi)\Delta x^3 \tag{5.97}$$

In summary, the procedure for developing difference formulas by the Taylor series approach is as follows:

1. Specify the order n of the derivative, $f_{(n)x}$, for which the difference formula is to be developed.
2. Choose the order m of the remainder term in the difference formula, Δx^m.
3. Determine the order of the remainder term in the Taylor series, Δx^{m+n}.
4. Specify the type of difference formula desired: centered, one-sided, or nonsymmetrical.
5. Determine the number of Taylor series required, which is at most $(m + n - 1)$.
6. Write the Taylor series of order $(m + n)$ at the $(m + n - 1)$ grid points.
7. Combine the Taylor series to eliminate the undesired derivatives, and solve for the desired derivative.

TABLE 5.1 (Continued)
Difference formulas

$$f_x|_i = \frac{-2f_{i-3} + 9f_{i-2} - 18f_{i-1} + 11f_i}{6\Delta x} + \frac{1}{4}f_{xxxx}(\xi)\Delta x^3 \tag{5.98}$$

$$f_x|_i = \frac{f_{i-2} - 6f_{i-1} + 3f_i + 2f_{i+1}}{6\Delta x} - \frac{1}{12}f_{xxxx}(\xi)\Delta x^3 \tag{5.99}$$

$$f_x|_i = \frac{-2f_{i-1} - 3f_i + 6f_{i+1} - f_{i+2}}{6\Delta x} + \frac{1}{12}f_{xxxx}(\xi)\Delta x^3 \tag{5.100}$$

$$f_x|_i = \frac{f_{i-2} - 8f_i + 8f_{i+1} - f_{i+2}}{12\Delta x} + \frac{1}{30}f_{xxxx}(\xi)\Delta x^4 \tag{5.101}$$

$$f_{xx}|_i = \frac{f_i - 2f_{i+1} + f_{i+2}}{\Delta x^2} - f_{xxx}(\xi)\Delta x \tag{5.102}$$

$$f_{xx}|_i = \frac{f_{i-2} - 2f_{i-1} + f_i}{\Delta x^2} + f_{xxx}(\xi)\Delta x \tag{5.103}$$

$$f_{xx}|_i = \frac{f_{i+1} - 2f_i + f_{i-1}}{\Delta x^2} - \frac{1}{12}f_{xxxx}(\xi)\Delta x^2 \tag{5.104}$$

$$f_{xx}|_i = \frac{2f_i - 5f_{i+1} + 4f_{i+2} - f_{i+3}}{\Delta x^2} + \frac{11}{12}f_{xxxx}(\xi)\Delta x^2 \tag{5.105}$$

$$f_{xx}|_i = \frac{-f_{i-3} + 4f_{i-2} - 5f_{i-1} + 2f_i}{\Delta x^2} + \frac{11}{12}f_{xxxx}(\xi)\Delta x^2 \tag{5.106}$$

$$f_{xx}|_i = \frac{-f_{i-2} + 16f_{i-1} - 30f_i + 16f_{i+1} - f_{i+2}}{12\Delta x^2} + \frac{1}{90}f_{xxxxxx}(\xi)\Delta x^4 \tag{5.107}$$

5.5 DIFFERENCE FORMULAS

Table 5.1 presents several difference formulas for both time derivatives and space derivatives. These difference formulas are used extensively in Chapters 7 and 8 in the numerical solution of ordinary differential equations, and in Chapters 9 to 15 in the numerical solution of partial differential equations.

SUMMARY

Procedures for numerical differentiation of discrete data and for developing difference formulas are presented in this chapter. The numerical differentiation formulas are based on approximating polynomials. The direct fit polynomial works well for both equally spaced and nonequally spaced data. The Newton polynomials yield simple differentiation formulas for equally spaced data. Least squares fit polynomials can be used for large sets of data or sets of rough data.

Difference formulas, which approximate derivatives in terms of function values in the neighborhood of a particular point, are derived by both the Newton polynomial approach and the Taylor series approach. Difference formulas are used extensively in the numerical solution of differential equations.

PROBLEMS

The following table, Table P5.1, is for $f(x) = \exp(x)$. This table is used in several of the problems in this chapter.

TABLE P5.1
Values of $f(x)$

x	$f(x)$	x	$f(x)$	x	$f(x)$
0.94	2.559981	0.99	2.691234	1.03	2.801066
0.95	2.585710	1.00	2.718282	1.04	2.829217
0.96	2.611696	1.01	2.745601	1.05	2.857651
0.97	2.637944	1.02	2.773195	1.06	2.886371
0.98	2.664456				

Section 5.2 Direct Fit Polynomials

* **1.** For the data in Table P5.1, evaluate $f'(1.0)$ and $f''(1.0)$ using direct fit polynomials with the following data points: (*a*) 1.00 and 1.01, (*b*) 1.00, 1.01, and 1.02, and (*c*) 1.00, 1.01, 1.02, and 1.03. Compute and compare the errors.

2. Work Problem 1 with the following data points: (*a*) 0.99 and 1.00, (*b*) 0.98, 0.99, and 1.00, and (*c*) 0.97, 0.98, 0.99, and 1.00. Compute and compare the errors.

3. Work Problem 1 with the following data points: (*a*) 0.99 and 1.01, and (*b*) 0.99, 1.00, and 1.01. Compute and compare the errors.

4. Compare the errors in Problems 1 to 3 and discuss.

5. Work Problem 1 with the following data points: (*a*) 0.98 and 1.02, (*b*) 0.98, 1.00, and 1.02, (*c*) 0.96 and 1.04, and (*d*) 0.96, 1.00, and 1.04. Compute the errors and compare the ratios of the errors for Parts (*a*) and (*c*) and Parts (*b*) and (*d*). Compare the results with the results of Problem 3.

Difference formulas can be derived from direct fit polynomials by fitting a polynomial to a set of symbolic data and differentiating the resulting polynomial. The truncation errors of such difference formulas can be obtained by substituting Taylor series into the difference formulas to recover the derivative being approximated accompanied by all the neglected terms in the approximation. Use the symbolic table below, where Δx is considered constant, to work the following problems. Note that the algebra is simplified considerably by letting the base point value of x be zero and the other values of x be multiples of the constant increment size Δx.

TABLE P5.2
Symbolic values of $f(x)$

x	$f(x)$	x	$f(x)$
x_{i-2}	f_{i-2}	x_{i+1}	f_{i+1}
x_{i-1}	f_{i-1}	x_{i+2}	f_{i+2}
x_i	f_i		

6. Derive difference formulas for $f'(x)$ by direct polynomial fit using the following data points: (*a*) i and $i+1$, (*b*) $i-1$ and i, (*c*) $i-1$ and $i+1$, (*d*) $i-1$, i, and $i+1$, (*e*) i, $i+1$, and $i+2$, and (*f*) $i-2$, $i-1$, i, $i+1$, and $i+2$. For each result, determine the leading truncation error term. Compare with the results presented in Table 5.1.

7. Derive difference formulas for $f''(x)$ by direct polynomial fit using the following data points: (*a*) $i-1$, i, and $i+1$, (*b*) i, $i+1$, and $i+2$, (*c*) $i-2$, $i-1$, i, $i+1$, and $i+2$, and (*d*) i, $i+1$, $i+2$, and $i+3$. For each result, determine the leading truncation error term. Compare with the results presented in Table 5.1.

Section 5.3 Newton Polynomials

The data presented in Table P5.1 are used in the following problems. Construct a difference table for that set of data through third differences for use in these problems.

*** 8.** For the data in Table P5.1, evaluate $f'(1.0)$ and $f''(1.0)$ using Newton forward-difference polynomials of orders one, two, and three with the following points: (*a*) 1.00 to 1.03 and (*b*) 1.00 to 1.06. Compare the errors and ratios of the errors for the two increment sizes.

9. For the data in Table P5.1, evaluate $f'(1.0)$ and $f''(1.0)$ using Newton backward-difference polynomials of orders one, two, and three with the following points: (*a*) 0.97 to 1.00, and (*b*) 0.94 to 1.00. Compare the errors and the ratios of the errors for the two increment sizes.

10. For the data in Table P5.1, evaluate $f'(1.0)$ and $f''(1.0)$ using Newton forward-difference polynomials of orders one and two with the following points: (*a*) 0.99 to 1.01, and (*b*) 0.98 to 1.02. Compare the errors and the ratios of the errors for these two increment sizes. Compare with the results of Problems 8 and 9.

Difference formulas can be derived from Newton polynomials by fitting a polynomial to a set of symbolic data and differentiating the resulting polynomial. The truncation error can be determined from the error term of the Newton polynomial. The symbolic data in Table P5.2 are used in the following problems. Construct a difference table for that set of data.

11. Work Problem 6 using Newton forward-difference polynomials.

12. Work Problem 7 using Newton forward-difference polynomials.

Section 5.4 Taylor Series Approach

13. Derive Eqs. (5.88) to (5.91).

14. Derive Eqs. (5.92) to (5.101).

15. Derive Eqs. (5.102) to (5.107).

16. Verify Eq. (5.87) by substituting Taylor series for the function values to recover the first derivative and the leading truncation error term.

Applied Problems

***17.** When a fluid flows over a surface, the shear stress τ (N/m^2) at the surface is given by the expression

$$\tau = \mu \left.\frac{du}{dy}\right|_{\text{surface}} \tag{1}$$

where μ is the viscosity (N-s/m^2), u is the velocity parallel to the surface (m/s), and y is the distance normal to the surface (cm). Measurements of the velocity of an air stream flowing above a surface are made with an LDV (laser Doppler velocimeter). The following values were obtained:

TABLE P5.3
Velocity

y	u	y	u
0.0	0.00	2.0	88.89
1.0	55.56	3.0	100.00

At the local temperature, $\mu = 0.00024$ N-s/m^2. Calculate (*a*) the difference table for $u(y)$, (*b*) du/dy at the surface based on first-, second-, and third-order polynomials, (*c*) the corresponding values of the shear stress at the surface, and (*d*) the shear force acting on a flat plate 10 cm long and 5 cm wide.

18. When a fluid flows over a surface, the heat transfer rate $\dot{q}$ (J/s) to the surface is given by the expression

$$\dot{q} = -kA \left.\frac{dT}{dy}\right|_{\text{surface}} \tag{2}$$

where k is the thermal conductivity (J/s-m-K), T is the temperature (K), and y is the distance normal to the surface (cm). Measurements of the temperature of an air stream flowing above a surface are made with a thermocouple. The following values were obtained:

TABLE P5.4
Temperature

y	T	y	T
0.0	1000.00	2.0	355.56
1.0	533.33	3.0	300.00

At the average temperature, $k = 0.030$ J/s-m-K. Calculate (*a*) the difference table for $T(y)$, (*b*) dT/dy at the surface based on first-, second-, and third-order polynomials, (*c*) the corresponding values of the heat flux $\dot{q}/A$ at the surface, and (*d*) the heat transfer to a flat plate 10 cm long and 5 cm wide.

CHAPTER

6

NUMERICAL INTEGRATION

Section

Example

6.1 INTRODUCTION

The evaluation of integrals, a process known as *integration* or *quadrature*, is required in many problems in engineering and science.

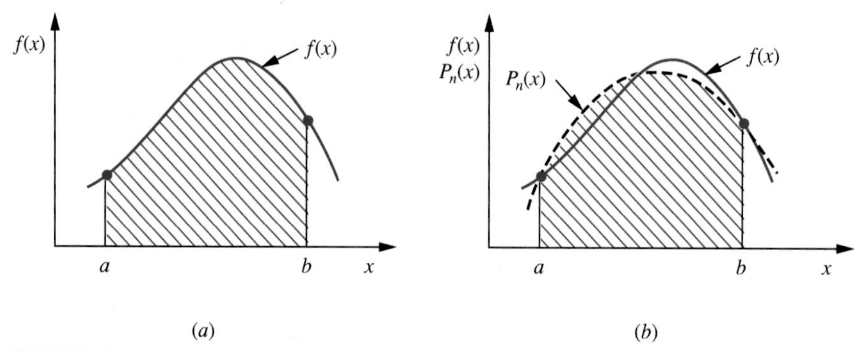

FIGURE 6.1
Numerical integration: (*a*) exact integral; (*b*) approximate integral.

$$I = \int_a^b f(x)\,dx \tag{6.1}$$

The function $f(x)$ that is to be integrated may be a known function or a set of discrete data. Some known functions have an exact integral, in which case Eq. (6.1) can be evaluated exactly in closed form. Many known functions, however, do not have an exact integral, and an approximate numerical procedure is required to evaluate Eq. (6.1). In many cases, the function $f(x)$ is known only at a set of discrete points, in which case an approximate numerical procedure is again required to evaluate Eq. (6.1). The evaluation of integrals by approximate numerical procedures is the subject of this chapter.

Numerical integration (quadrature) formulas can be developed by fitting approximating functions (e.g., polynomials) to discrete data and integrating the approximating function.

$$I = \int_a^b f(x)\,dx \approx \int_a^b P_n(x)\,dx \tag{6.2}$$

This process is illustrated in Figure 6.1.

Several types of problems arise. The function to be integrated may be known only at a set of discrete points. In that case, an approximating polynomial is fitted to the discrete points, or several subsets of the discrete points, and the resulting polynomial, or polynomials, is integrated. The polynomial may be fitted to a set of points exactly, by the methods presented in Sections 4.3 to 4.8, or approximately, by a least squares fit, as described in Section 4.11. In either case, the degree of the approximating polynomial chosen to represent the discrete data is the only parameter under our control.

When a known function is to be integrated, several parameters are under our control. The total number of discrete points can be chosen arbitrarily. The degree of the approximating polynomial chosen to represent the discrete data can be chosen. The locations of the points at which the known function is discretized can also be chosen to enhance the accuracy of the procedure.

Procedures are presented in this chapter for all of the situations discussed above. Direct fit polynomials are applied to prespecified unequally spaced data. Integration formulas based on Newton forward-difference polynomials are developed for equally spaced data. An important method, Romberg integration, based on extrapolation of solutions for successively halved increments, is presented. Adaptive integration, a procedure for minimizing the number of function evaluations required to integrate a known function, is discussed. Lastly, Gaussian quadrature, which specifies the locations of the points at which known functions are discretized, is discussed.

The simple function

$$\boxed{f(x) = \frac{1}{x}} \tag{6.3}$$

is considered in this chapter to illustrate numerical integration methods. In particular,

$$I = \int_{3.1}^{3.9} \frac{1}{x}\,dx = \ln(x)\Big|_{3.1}^{3.9} = \ln\left(\frac{3.9}{3.1}\right) = 0.22957444\ldots \tag{6.4}$$

The procedures presented in this chapter for evaluating integrals lead directly into integration of ordinary differential equations, which is discussed in Chapters 7 and 8.

6.2 DIRECT FIT POLYNOMIALS

A straightforward numerical integration procedure which can be used for both equally spaced data and unequally spaced data is based on fitting the data directly by a polynomial and integrating that polynomial. Thus,

$$\boxed{f(x) = P_n(x) = a_0 + a_1 x + a_2 x^2 + \cdots} \tag{6.5}$$

where $P_n(x)$ is determined by one of the following methods:

1. Given $N = n + 1$ sets of discrete data $[x_i, f(x_i)]$, determine the exact nth-degree polynomial that passes through the data points, as discussed in Section 4.3.
2. Given $N > n + 1$ sets of discrete data $[x_i, f(x_i)]$, determine the least squares nth-degree polynomial that best fits the data points, as discussed in Section 4.11.

3. Given a known function $f(x)$, evaluate $f(x)$ at N discrete points and fit a polynomial by an exact fit or a least squares fit.

After the approximating polynomial has been fitted, the integral becomes

$$I = \int_a^b f(x)\,dx \approx \int_a^b P_n(x)\,dx \tag{6.6}$$

Substituting Eq. (6.5) into Eq. (6.6) and integrating yields

$$I = \left(a_0 x + a_1 \frac{x^2}{2} + a_2 \frac{x^3}{3} + \cdots \right)\Big|_a^b \tag{6.7}$$

Introducing the limits of integration and evaluating Eq. (6.7) gives the value of the integral.

Example 6.1. Direct fit polynomial. Solve the example problem presented in Section 6.1 by a direct fit polynomial.

$$I = \int_{3.1}^{3.9} \frac{1}{x}\,dx = \int_{3.1}^{3.9} P_n(x)\,dx \tag{6.8}$$

Consider the following three data points:

x	$f(x)$
3.1	0.32258065
3.5	0.28571429
3.9	0.25641026

Fit the quadratic polynomial $P_2(x) = a + bx + cx^2$ to the three data points:

$$0.32258065 = a + b(3.1) + c(3.1)^2 \tag{6.9a}$$

$$0.28571429 = a + b(3.5) + c(3.5)^2 \tag{6.9b}$$

$$0.25641026 = a + b(3.9) + c(3.9)^2 \tag{6.9c}$$

Solving for a, b, and c by Gauss elimination gives

$$P_2(x) = 0.86470519 - 0.24813896x + 0.02363228x^2 \tag{6.10}$$

Substituting Eq. (6.10) into Eq. (6.8) and integrating yields

$$I = \left((0.86470519)x + \frac{1}{2}(-0.24813896)x^2 + \frac{1}{3}(0.02363228)x^3 \right)\Big|_{3.1}^{3.9} \tag{6.11}$$

$$\boxed{I = 0.22957974} \tag{6.12}$$

The error is $0.22957974 - 0.22957444 = 0.00000530$.

6.3 NEWTON FORWARD-DIFFERENCE POLYNOMIALS

The direct fit polynomial procedure presented in Section 6.2 requires a significant amount of effort in the evaluation of the polynomial coefficients. When the function to be integrated is known at equally spaced points, the Newton forward-difference polynomial presented in Section 4.6 can be fitted to the discrete data with much less effort, thus significantly decreasing the amount of effort required. Thus,

$$\boxed{I = \int_a^b f(x)\,dx \approx \int_a^b P_n(x)\,dx} \tag{6.13}$$

where $P_n(x)$ is the Newton forward-difference polynomial [see Eq. (4.64)]:

$$P_n(x_0 + sh) = f_0 + s\Delta f_0 + \frac{s(s-1)}{2}\Delta^2 f_0 + \frac{s(s-1)(s-2)}{6}\Delta^3 f_0 + \cdots$$
$$+ \frac{s(s-1)(s-2)\cdots[s-(n-1)]}{n!}\Delta^n f_0 + \text{Error} \tag{6.14}$$

$$\text{Error} = \binom{s}{n+1} h^{n+1} f^{(n+1)}(\xi), \qquad x_0 \le x \le x_n \tag{6.15}$$

where the interpolating parameter s is given by

$$s = \frac{x - x_0}{h} \rightarrow x = x_0 + sh \tag{6.16}$$

Equation (6.13) requires that the approximating polynomial be an explicit function of x, whereas Eq. (6.14) is implicit in x. Either Eq. (6.14) must be made explicit in x by introducing Eq. (6.16) into Eq. (6.14), or the second integral in Eq. (6.13) must be transformed into an explicit function of s, so that Eq. (6.14) can be used directly. The first approach leads to a complicated result, so the second approach is taken. Thus,

$$I = \int_a^b f(x)\,dx \approx \int_a^b P_n(x)\,dx = h\int_{s(a)}^{s(b)} P_n(s)\,ds \tag{6.17}$$

where, from Eq. (6.16)

$$dx = h\ ds \tag{6.18}$$

The limits of integration, $x = a$ and $x = b$, are expressed in terms of the interpolating parameter s by choosing $x = a$ as the base point of the polynomial, so that $x = a$ corresponds to $s = 0$ and $x = b$ corresponds to $s = s$. Introducing these results into Eq. (6.17) yields

$$I = h \int_0^s P_n(x_0 + sh)\,ds \tag{6.19}$$

Each choice of the order n of the interpolating polynomial yields a different numerical integration formula. Table 6.1 lists the more common formulas. Higher-order formulas have been developed [see Abramowitz and Stegun (1964)], but those presented in Table 6.1 are sufficient for most problems in engineering and science. The rectangle rule has poor accuracy, so it is not considered further. The other three rules are developed in this section.

The Trapezoid Rule

The *trapezoid rule* is obtained by fitting a first-order polynomial to two discrete points, as illustrated in Figure 6.2. The upper limit of integration x_1 corresponds to $s = 1$. Thus, Eq. (6.19) gives

$$\Delta I = h \int_0^1 (f_0 + s\Delta f_0)\,ds = h\left(sf_0 + \frac{s^2}{2}\Delta f_0\right)\Bigg|_0^1 \tag{6.20}$$

where ΔI denotes the integral for a single interval. Evaluating Eq. (6.20) and introducing $\Delta f_0 = (f_1 - f_0)$ yields

$$\Delta I = h\left(f_0 + \frac{1}{2}\Delta f_0\right) = h\left(f_0 + \frac{1}{2}(f_1 - f_0)\right) \tag{6.21}$$

Simplifying yields the trapezoid rule for a single interval:

$$\Delta I = \frac{1}{2}h(f_0 + f_1) \tag{6.22}$$

TABLE 6.1
Numerical integration formulas

n	Formula
0	Rectangle rule
1	Trapezoid rule
2	Simpson's $\frac{1}{3}$ rule
3	Simpson's $\frac{3}{8}$ rule

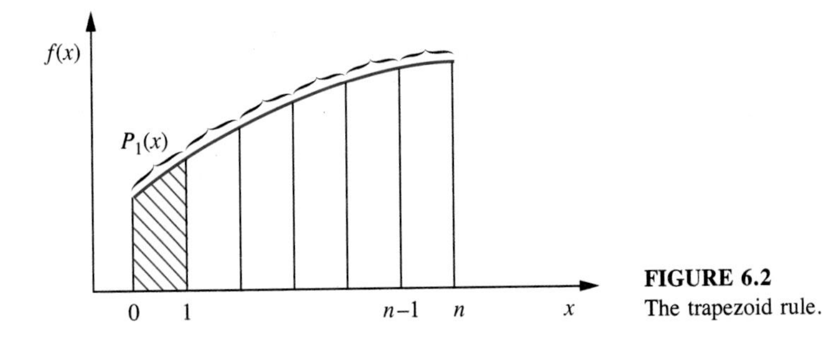

FIGURE 6.2
The trapezoid rule.

The composite trapezoid rule is obtained by applying Eq. (6.22) over all the intervals of interest. Thus,

$$I = \sum_{i=0}^{n-1} \Delta I_i = \sum_{i=0}^{n-1} \frac{1}{2} h_i (f_i + f_{i+1}) \tag{6.23}$$

where $h_i = (x_{i+1} - x_i)$. Equation (6.23) does not require equally spaced data. When the data are equally spaced, Eq. (6.23) simplifies to

$$I = \frac{1}{2} h (f_0 + 2f_1 + 2f_2 + \cdots + 2f_{n-1} + f_n) \tag{6.24}$$

The error of the trapezoid rule for a single interval is obtained by integrating the error term given by Eq. (6.15). Thus,

$$\text{Error} = h \int_0^1 \frac{s(s-1)}{2} h^2 f''(\xi)\, ds = -\frac{1}{12} h^3 f''(\xi) = O(h^3) \tag{6.25}$$

Thus, the local error is $O(h^3)$. The total error for equally spaced data is given by

$$\sum_{i=0}^{n-1} \text{Error} = \sum_{i=0}^{n-1} -\frac{1}{12} h^3 f''(\xi) = n\left(-\frac{1}{12} h^3 f''(\bar{\xi})\right) \tag{6.26}$$

where $x_0 \le \bar{\xi} \le x_n$. The number of steps $n = (x_n - x_0)/h$. Therefore,

$$\text{Total Error} = -\frac{1}{12}(x_n - x_0) h^2 f''(\bar{\xi}) = O(h^2) \tag{6.27}$$

Thus, the global (i.e., total) error is $O(h^2)$.

Example 6.2. The trapezoid rule. Solve the example problem presented in Section 6.1 by the trapezoid rule. Recall that $f(x) = 1/x$. Solving the problem for one interval of $h = 0.8$ gives

$$I(h = 0.8) = \frac{0.8}{2}\Big(0.32258065 + 0.25641026\Big) = 0.23159636 \tag{6.28}$$

Break the total interval into two subintervals of $h = 0.4$ and apply the composite rule. Thus,

$$I(h = 0.4) = \frac{0.4}{2}\Big(0.32258065 + 2(0.28571429) + 0.25641026\Big) = 0.23008389 \tag{6.29}$$

For four intervals of $h = 0.2$, the composite rule yields

$$I(h = 0.2) = \frac{0.2}{2}\Big(0.32258065 + 2(0.30303030 + 0.28571429 + 0.27027027) + 0.25641026\Big) = 0.22970206 \tag{6.30}$$

Finally, for eight intervals of $h = 0.1$,

$$I(h = 0.1) = \frac{0.1}{2}\Big(0.32258065 + 2(0.31250000 + \cdots + 0.26315789) + 0.25641026\Big) = 0.22960636 \tag{6.31}$$

Recall that the exact answer is $I = 0.22957444$.

The results are tabulated in Table 6.2, which also presents the errors and the ratios of the errors between successive interval sizes. The global error of the trapezoid rule is $O(h^2)$. Thus, for successive interval halvings,

$$\text{Ratio} = \frac{E(h)}{E(h/2)} = \frac{O(h^2)}{O(h/2)^2} = 2^2 = 4 \tag{6.32}$$

The results presented in Table 6.2 illustrate the second-order behavior of the trapezoid rule.

TABLE 6.2
Results for the trapezoid rule

h	I	Error	Ratio
0.8	0.23159636	0.00202192	
			3.97
0.4	0.23008389	0.00050945	
			3.99
0.2	0.22970206	0.00012762	
			4.00
0.1	0.22960636	0.00003192	

Simpson's $\frac{1}{3}$ Rule

Simpson's $\frac{1}{3}$ rule is obtained by fitting a second-order polynomial to three equally spaced discrete points, as illustrated in Fig. 6.3. The upper limit of integration x_2 corresponds to $s = 2$. Thus, Eq. (6.19) gives

$$\Delta I = h \int_0^2 \left(f_0 + s\Delta f_0 + \frac{s(s-1)}{2} \Delta^2 f_0 \right) ds \tag{6.33}$$

Performing the integration, evaluating the result, and introducing the expressions for Δf_0 and $\Delta^2 f_0$, yield Simpson's $\frac{1}{3}$ rule for a single set of two intervals:

$$\boxed{\Delta I = \frac{1}{3} h(f_0 + 4f_1 + f_2)} \tag{6.34}$$

The composite Simpson's $\frac{1}{3}$ rule for equally spaced data is obtained by applying Eq. (6.34) over the entire range of integration. Note that the total number of intervals must be even. Thus,

$$\boxed{I = \frac{1}{3} h(f_0 + 4f_1 + 2f_2 + 4f_3 + \cdots + 4f_{n-1} + f_n)} \tag{6.35}$$

The error of Simpson's $\frac{1}{3}$ rule for a single set of two intervals is obtained by evaluating the error term given by Eq. (6.15). Thus,

$$\text{Error} = h \int_0^2 \frac{s(s-1)(s-2)}{6} h^3 f'''(\xi)\, ds = 0 \tag{6.36}$$

This surprising result does not mean that the error is zero. It simply means that the cubic term is identically zero, and the error is obtained from the next term in

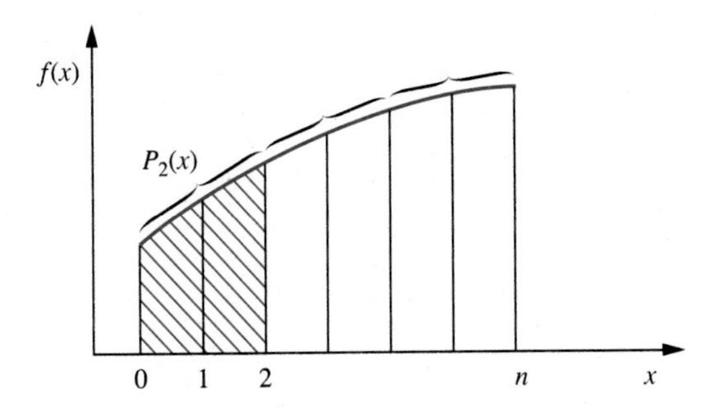

FIGURE 6.3
Simpson's $\frac{1}{3}$ rule

the Newton forward-difference polynomial. Thus,

$$\text{Error} = h\int_0^2 \frac{s(s-1)(s-2)(s-3)}{24} h^4 f^{(4)}(\xi)\, ds = -\frac{1}{90} h^5 f^{(4)}(\xi) \tag{6.37}$$

Thus, the local error is $O(h^5)$. By an analysis similar to that performed for the trapezoid rule, it can be shown that the global error is $O(h^4)$.

Example 6.3. Simpson's $\frac{1}{3}$ rule. Solve the example problem presented in Section 6.1 using Simpson's $\frac{1}{3}$ rule. Recall that $f(x) = 1/x$. Solving the problem for $h = 0.4$, which gives two intervals, the minimum permissible number of intervals for Simpson's $\frac{1}{3}$ rule, yields

$$I(h = 0.4) = \frac{0.4}{3}\Big(0.32258065 + 4(0.28571429) + 0.25641026\Big)$$

$$= 0.22957974 \tag{6.38}$$

Breaking the total range of integration into four intervals of $h = 0.2$ and applying the composite rule yields:

$$I(h = 0.2) = \frac{0.2}{3}\Big(0.32258065 + 4(0.30303030) + 2(0.28571429)$$

$$+4(0.27027027) + 0.25641026\Big) = 0.22957478 \tag{6.39}$$

Finally, for eight intervals of $h = 0.1$,

$$I(h = 0.1) = \frac{0.1}{3}\Big(0.32258015 + 4(0.31250000) + 2(0.30303030)$$

$$+ 4(0.29411765) + 2(0.28571429) + 4(0.27777778) + 2(0.27027027)$$

$$+ 4(0.26315789) + 0.25641026\Big) = 0.22957446 \tag{6.40}$$

Recall that the exact answer is $I = 0.22957444$.

The results are tabulated in Table 6.3, which also presents the errors and the ratios of the errors between successive interval sizes. The global error of Simpson's $\frac{1}{3}$ rule is

TABLE 6.3
Results for Simpson's $\frac{1}{3}$ rule

h	I	Error	Ratio
0.4	0.22957974	0.00000530	
			15.59
0.2	0.22957478	0.00000034	
			15.45
0.1	0.22957446	0.00000002	

$O(h^4)$. Thus, for successive interval halvings,

$$\text{Ratio} = \frac{E(h)}{E(h/2)} = \frac{O(h)^4}{O(h/2)^4} = 2^4 = 16 \tag{6.41}$$

The results presented in Table 6.3 illustrate the fourth-order behavior of Simpson's $\frac{1}{3}$ rule.

Simpson's $\frac{3}{8}$ Rule

Simpson's $\frac{3}{8}$ rule is obtained by fitting a third-order polynomial to four equally spaced discrete points, as illustrated in Fig. 6.4. The upper limit of integration x_3 corresponds to $s = 3$. Thus, Eq. (6.19) gives

$$\Delta I = h \int_0^3 \left(f_0 + s\Delta f_0 + \frac{s(s-1)}{2}\Delta^2 f_0 + \frac{s(s-1)(s-2)}{6}\Delta^3 f_0 \right) ds \tag{6.42}$$

Performing the integration, evaluating the result, and introducing expressions for Δf_0, $\Delta^2 f_0$, and $\Delta^3 f_0$, yields Simpson's $\frac{3}{8}$ rule for a single set of three intervals:

$$\boxed{\Delta I = \frac{3}{8}h(f_0 + 3f_1 + 3f_2 + f_3)} \tag{6.43}$$

The composite Simpson's $\frac{3}{8}$ rule is obtained by applying Eq. (6.43) over the entire range of integration. Note that the total number of intervals must be a multiple of three. Thus,

$$\boxed{I = \frac{3}{8}h(f_0 + 3f_1 + 3f_2 + 2f_3 + 3f_4 + \cdots + 3f_{n-1} + f_n)} \tag{6.44}$$

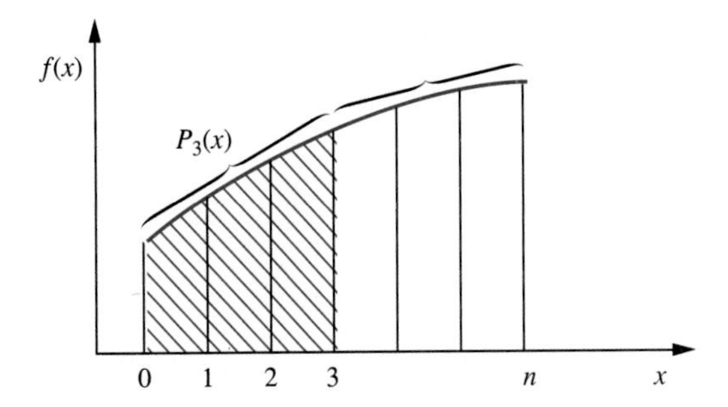

FIGURE 6.4
Simpson's $\frac{3}{8}$ rule.

The error of Simpson's $\frac{3}{8}$ rule for a single set of three intervals is obtained by evaluating the error term given by Eq. (6.15). Thus,

$$\text{Error} = h \int_0^3 \frac{s(s-1)(s-2)(s-3)}{24} h^4 f^{(4)}(\xi)\, ds = -\frac{3}{80} h^5 f^{(4)}(\xi) \tag{6.45}$$

The local error is $O(h^5)$ and the global error is $O(h^4)$.

Simpson's $\frac{1}{3}$ rule and Simpson's $\frac{3}{8}$ rule have the same order, as shown by Eqs. (6.37) and (6.45). The coefficient in the local error of Simpson's $\frac{1}{3}$ rule is $-\frac{1}{90}$, whereas the corresponding coefficient for Simpson's $\frac{3}{8}$ rule is $-\frac{3}{80}$. Consequently, Simpson's $\frac{1}{3}$ rule should be more accurate than Simpson's $\frac{3}{8}$ rule. In view of this result, what use, if any, is Simpson's $\frac{3}{8}$ rule? Simpson's $\frac{3}{8}$ rule is useful when the total number of intervals is odd. Three intervals can be evaluated by the $\frac{3}{8}$ rule, and the remaining even number of intervals can be evaluated by the $\frac{1}{3}$ rule.

Newton–Cotes Formulas

Numerical integration formulas based on equally spaced intervals are frequently called Newton–Cotes formulas. The trapezoid rule and Simpson's $\frac{1}{3}$ and $\frac{3}{8}$ rules are the first three Newton-Cotes formulas. The first 10 Newton-Cotes formulas are presented in Abramowitz and Stegun (1964). Newton–Cotes formulas can be expressed in the general form:

$$I = \int_a^b f(x)\, dx = n\beta h(\alpha_0 f_0 + \alpha_1 f_1 + \cdots) + \text{Error} \tag{6.46}$$

where n denotes both the number of intervals and the degree of the polynomial, β and α_i are coefficients, and Error denotes the local error term. Table 6.4 presents n, β, α_i, and Error for the first seven Newton-Cotes formulas.

TABLE 6.4
Newton–Cotes formulas

n	B	α_0	α_1	α_2	α_3	α_4	α_5	α_6	α_7	Error
1	1/2	1	1							$-1/12 f^{(2)} h^3$
2	1/6	1	4	1						$-1/90 f^{(4)} h^5$
3	1/8	1	3	3	1					$-3/80 f^{(4)} h^5$
4	1/90	7	32	12	32	7				$-8/945 f^{(6)} h^7$
5	1/288	19	75	50	50	75	19			$-275/12096 f^{(6)} h^7$
6	1/840	41	216	27	272	27	216	41		$-9/1400 f^{(8)} h^9$
7	1/17280	751	3577	1323	2989	2989	1323	3577	751	$-8123/518400 f^{(8)} h^9$

6.4 ERROR ESTIMATION, CONTROL, AND EXTRAPOLATION

Many numerical algorithms approximate an exact calculation by an approximate calculation having an error that depends on an increment h. Examples include numerical differentiation, numerical integration, numerical solution of ordinary differential equations, and numerical solution of partial differential equations. If the functional form of the error is known, it is possible to estimate the error by evaluating the algorithm for two different increment sizes. The error estimate can be used for both error control and extrapolation (also known as the deferred approach to the limit). The general concepts of error estimation, control, and extrapolation are presented in this section.

Consider a numerical algorithm that approximates an exact calculation with an error that depends on an interval h. Thus,

$$\boxed{f_{\text{exact}} = f(h) + Ah^n + Bh^{n+m} + \cdots} \tag{6.47}$$

Apply the algorithm at two interval sizes, h_1 and h_2, where $h_1 = h$ and $h_2 = h/R$. Thus,

$$f_{\text{exact}} = f(h) + Ah^n + O(h^{n+m}) \tag{6.48}$$

$$f_{\text{exact}} = f\left(\frac{h}{R}\right) + A\left(\frac{h}{R}\right)^n + O(h^{n+m}) \tag{6.49}$$

Subtracting Eq. (6.48) from Eq. (6.49) gives

$$0 = f\left(\frac{h}{R}\right) - f(h) + A\left(\frac{h}{R}\right)^n - Ah^n + O(h^{n+m}) \tag{6.50}$$

Solving Eq. (6.50) for the error term Ah^n yields

$$\boxed{\text{Error} = Ah^n = \frac{R^n}{R^{n-1}}\left(f\left(\frac{h}{R}\right) - f(h)\right) + O(h^{n+m})} \tag{6.51}$$

Equation (6.51) can be used to estimate the error of the calculation with increment h. If the error estimate is larger than a prespecified upper error limit, the increment can be reduced and the calculation repeated. If the error estimate is smaller than a prespecified lower error limit, the subsequent increment size can be increased.

After the prespecified error limit has been satisfied, the final value of the calculation can be improved by adding the estimated error term to the final calculated value for the smaller step size. This process is known as *extrapolation*, or the *deferred approach to the limit*. The error for the calculation with the smaller step size is given by

$$\text{Error} = A(h/R)^n = \frac{1}{R^{n-1}}\left(f\left(\frac{h}{R}\right) - f(h)\right) + O(h^{n+m}) \tag{6.52}$$

Adding Eq. (6.52) to Eq. (6.49) yields the extrapolation formula

$$\text{Improved value} = \text{More accurate value} + \frac{1}{R^{n-1}}\left(\text{More accurate value} - \text{Less accurate value}\right) \tag{6.53}$$

where the more accurate value is obviously the value obtained with the smaller increment.

6.5 ROMBERG INTEGRATION

When extrapolation is applied to numerical integration by the trapezoid rule, the result is called *Romberg integration*. Recall the composite trapezoid rule:

$$I = \sum_{i=0}^{n-1} \Delta I_i = \frac{1}{2}h(f_0 + 2f_1 + 2f_2 + \cdots + 2f_{n-1} + f_n) \tag{6.54}$$

It can be shown that the error of the composite trapezoid rule has the form

$$\text{Error} = C_1h^2 + C_2h^4 + C_3h^6 + \cdots \tag{6.55}$$

Applying the error estimation formula, Eq. (6.53), with $n = 2$, $m = 2$, and $R = 2$, gives

$$\text{Error} = \frac{1}{3}\left(I\left(\frac{h}{2}\right) - I(h)\right) \tag{6.56}$$

Equation (6.56) can be used for error estimation and control. Adding the error estimate to the more accurate result yields the extrapolation formula:

$$I(\text{Extrapolated}) = I(h/2) + \frac{1}{3}\left(I\left(\frac{h}{2}\right) - I(h)\right) \tag{6.57}$$

The extrapolated result in Eq. (6.57) is $O(h^4)$. If two extrapolated $O(h^4)$ results are available, those two results can be extrapolated to obtain an $O(h^6)$ result.

TABLE 6.5
Results for Romberg integration

h	I, $O(h^2)$	Error	$O(h^4)$	Error	$O(h^6)$
0.8	0.23159636				
		−0.00050416	0.22957973		
0.4	0.23008389			−0.00000033	0.22957445
		−0.00012728	0.22957478		
0.2	0.22970206			−0.00000002	0.22957444
		−0.00003190	0.22957446		
0.1	0.22960636				

In that procedure, $n = 4$ in Eq. (6.53). Successively higher-order extrapolations can be performed until roundoff error reduces any further improvement.

Example 6.4. Romberg integration. Apply extrapolation to the results obtained in Example 6.2, in which the trapezoid rule was used to solve the example problem presented in Section 6.1. The results presented in Table 6.2 and the results obtained by extrapolation are presented in Table 6.5.

The $O(h^4)$ results are identical to the results for the $O(h^4)$ Simpson's $\frac{1}{3}$ rule presented in Table 6.3. The second $O(h^6)$ result agrees with the exact answer to eight significant digits.

6.6 ADAPTIVE INTEGRATION

Any desired accuracy (within roundoff limits) can be obtained by the numerical integration formulas presented in Section 6.3 by taking smaller and smaller increments. This approach is generally undesirable, since evaluation of the integrand function $f(x)$ is the most time-consuming portion of the calculation.

When the function to be integrated is known so that it can be evaluated at any location, the step size h can be chosen arbitrarily, so the increment can be reduced as far as desired. However, it is not obvious how to choose h to achieve a desired accuracy. Error estimation, as described in Section 6.4, can be used to choose h to satisfy a prespecified error criterion. Successive extrapolation, that is, Romberg integration, can be used to increase the accuracy further. This procedure requires the step size h to be a constant over the entire region of integration. However, the behavior of the integrand function $f(x)$ may not require a uniform step size to achieve the desired overall accuracy. In regions where the integrand function is slowly varying, only a few points should be required to achieve the desired accuracy. In regions when the integrand function is rapidly varying, a large number of points may be required to achieve the desired accuracy.

Consider the integrand function illustrated in Fig. 6.5. In region de, $f(x)$ is essentially constant, and the increment h may be very large. However, in region ad, $f(x)$ varies rapidly, and the increment h must be very small. In fact, region

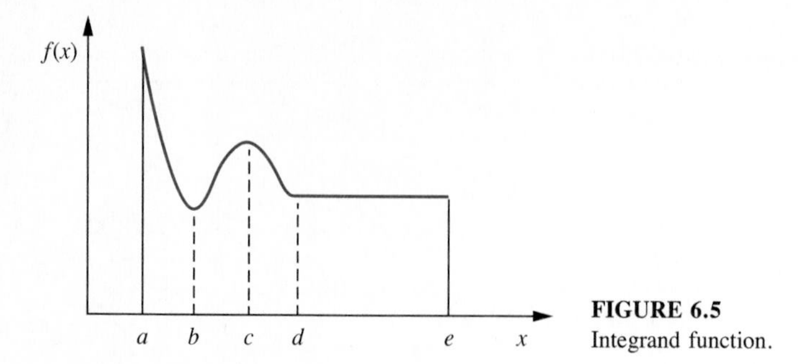

FIGURE 6.5
Integrand function.

ad should be broken into three regions, as illustrated. Visual inspection of the integrand function can identify regions where h can be large or small. However, constructing a plot of the integrand function is time-consuming and undesirable. A more straightforward automatic numerical procedure is required to break the overall region of integration into subregions in which the values of h may differ greatly.

Adaptive integration is a generic name denoting a strategy to achieve the desired accuracy with the minimum number of integrand function evaluations. A basic integration formula must be chosen, for example the trapezoid rule or Simpson's $\frac{1}{3}$ rule. The overall interval of integration is broken into several subintervals, and each subinterval is evaluated to the desired accuracy by subdividing each individual subinterval as required until the desired accuracy is obtained. Extrapolation may or may not be used in each subinterval.

Adaptive integration is motivated by the same concerns that motivate piecewise approximation, which is discussed in Section 4.10.

Example 6.5. Adaptive integration using the trapezoid rule. We will illustrate adaptive integration by evaluating the following integral using the trapezoid rule:

$$I = \int_{0.1}^{0.9} \frac{1}{x}\, dx \tag{6.58}$$

The exact solution is

$$I = \ln(x)\Big|_{0.1}^{0.9} = \ln\left(\frac{0.9}{0.1}\right) = 2.197225 \tag{6.59}$$

First, we evaluate Eq. (6.58) with a uniform increment h over the entire interval of integration, starting with $h = (0.9 - 0.1) = 0.8$, and successively halving h until the error estimate given by Eq. (6.53) is less than 0.001. For the second-order trapezoid rule with step size halving (i.e., $R = 2$), Eq. (6.53) yields

$$\text{Error} = \frac{1}{3}\left(I\left(\frac{h}{2}\right) - I(h)\right) \tag{6.60}$$

The results are presented in Table 6.6. To satisfy the error criterion $|\text{Error}| \leq 0.001$, 129 integrand function evaluations with $h = 0.00625$ are required. Extrapolating the final result yields

$$I = 2.197546 + (-0.000321) = 2.197225 \tag{6.61}$$

which agrees with the exact answer to six digits after the decimal place.

TABLE 6.6
Integration using the trapezoid rule

h	n	I	Error
0.80000	2	4.444444	
0.40000	3	3.022222	−0.474074
0.20000	5	2.463492	−0.186243
0.10000	9	2.273413	−0.063360
0.05000	17	2.217330	−0.018694
0.02500	33	2.202337	−0.004998
0.01250	65	2.198509	−0.001276
0.00625	129	2.197546	−0.000321

Next, we break the total interval of integration into two subintervals, $0.1 \le x \le 0.5$ and $0.5 \le x \le 0.9$. The error criterion for the two subintervals is $0.001/2 = 0.0005$. The results for the two subintervals are presented in Table 6.7. To satisfy the error criterion requires 65 and 17 function evaluations, respectively, in the two subintervals, for a total of 82 function evaluations. This is 47 less than before, which is a reduction of 36 percent. Extrapolating the two final results yields

$$I_1 = 1.609750 + (-0.000312) = 1.609438 \tag{6.62}$$

$$I_2 = 0.587931 + (-0.000144) = 0.587787 \tag{6.63}$$

which yields

$$I = I_1 + I_2 = 2.197225 \tag{6.64}$$

which agrees with the exact answer to six digits after the decimal place.

Example 6.5 presents a simple example of adaptive integration. The extrapolation step increases the accuracy significantly. This suggests that using Romberg integration as the basic integration method may yield a significant decrease in the number of function evaluations. Further increases in accuracy can be obtained by

TABLE 6.7
Adaptive integration using the trapezoid rule

h	n	I	Error
0.40000	2	2.400000	
0.20000	3	1.866667	−0.177778
0.10000	5	1.683333	−0.061111
0.05000	9	1.628968	−0.018122
0.02500	17	1.614406	−0.004854
0.01250	33	1.610686	−0.001240
0.00625	65	1.609750	−0.000312
0.40000	2	0.622222	
0.20000	3	0.596825	−0.008466
0.10000	5	0.590079	−0.002249
0.05000	9	0.588362	−0.000572
0.02500	17	0.587931	−0.000144

subdividing the total interval of integration into more than two subintervals. More sophisticated strategies can be employed to increase the efficiency of adaptive integration even further. The strategy employed in Example 6.5 is the simplest possible strategy.

6.7 GAUSSIAN QUADRATURE

The numerical integration methods presented in Section 6.3 are all based on equally spaced data. Consequently, if n points are considered, an $(n+1)$st-degree polynomial can be fitted to the data points and integrated. The resulting formulas have the form:

$$I = \int_a^b f(x)\,dx = \sum_{i=1}^{n} C_i f(x_i) \tag{6.65}$$

where x_i are the locations at which the function $f(x)$ is known and C_i are weighting factors. When the locations x_i are prespecified, this approach yields the best possible result. However, when a known function is to be integrated, an additional degree of freedom exists: the locations x_i at which the function $f(x)$ is evaluated. Thus, if n points are used, $2n$ parameters are available: x_i and C_i $(i = 1, 2, \ldots, n)$. With $2n$ parameters, it is possible to fit a polynomial of degree $2n-1$. Consequently, it should be possible to obtain numerical integration methods of much greater accuracy by choosing the values of x_i appropriately. *Gaussian quadrature* is one such method.

Gaussian quadrature formulas are obtained by choosing the values of x_i and C_i in Eq. (6.65) so that the integral of a polynomial of degree $2n-1$ is exact. To simplify the development of the formulas, consider the integral of a function $f(t)$ between the limits of -1 and $+1$:

$$I = \int_{-1}^{1} F(t)\,dt = \sum_{i=1}^{n} C_i F(t_i) \tag{6.66}$$

First, consider two points (i.e., $n = 2$), as illustrated in Fig. 6.6. Choose t_1, t_2, C_1, and C_2 so that I is exact for the four polynomials $F(t) = 1$, t, t^2, and t^3. Thus,

$$I[F(t) = 1] = \int_{-1}^{1} (1)\,dt = t|_{-1}^{1} = 2 = C_1(1) + C_2(1) = C_1 + C_2 \tag{6.67a}$$

$$I[F(t) = t] = \int_{-1}^{1} t\,dt = \frac{1}{2}t^2|_{-1}^{1} = 0 = C_1 t_1 + C_2 t_2 \tag{6.67b}$$

$$I[F(t) = t^2] = \int_{-1}^{1} t^2\,dt = \frac{1}{3}t^3|_{-1}^{1} = \frac{2}{3} = C_1 t_1^2 + C_2 t_2^2 \tag{6.67c}$$

$$I[F(t) = t^3] = \int_{-1}^{1} t^3\,dt = \frac{1}{4}t^4|_{-1}^{1} = 0 = C_1 t_1^3 + C_2 t_2^3 \tag{6.67d}$$

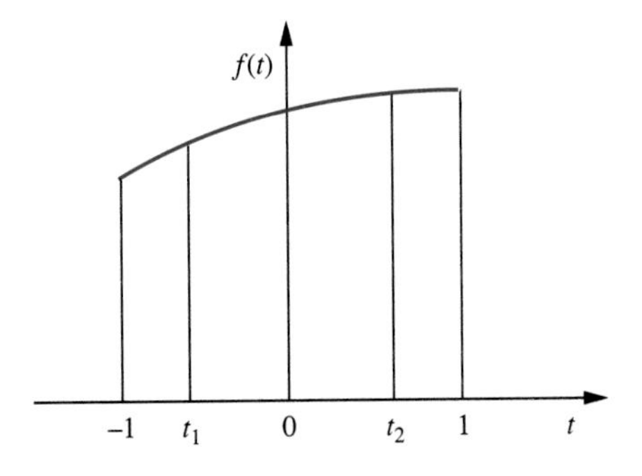

FIGURE 6.6
Gaussian quadrature.

Solving Eqs. (6.67) yields

$$C_1 = C_2 = 1, \qquad t_1 = -\frac{1}{\sqrt{3}}, \qquad \text{and} \qquad t_2 = \frac{1}{\sqrt{3}} \tag{6.68}$$

Thus, Eq. (6.66) yields

$$I = \int_{-1}^{1} F(t)\,dt = F\left(-\frac{1}{\sqrt{3}}\right) + F\left(\frac{1}{\sqrt{3}}\right) \tag{6.69}$$

The actual problem of interest is

$$I = \int_{a}^{b} f(x)\,dx \tag{6.70}$$

The problem presented in Eq. (6.70) can be transformed from x-space to t-space by the transformation

$$x = mt + c \tag{6.71}$$

where $x = a \rightarrow t = -1$, $x = b \rightarrow t = 1$, and $dx = m dt$. Thus,

$$a = m(-1) + c \qquad \text{and} \qquad b = m(1) + c \tag{6.72}$$

which gives

$$m = \frac{b-a}{2} \qquad \text{and} \qquad c = \frac{b+a}{2} \tag{6.73}$$

Thus, Eq. (6.71) becomes

$$x = \left(\frac{b-a}{2}\right)t + \left(\frac{b+a}{2}\right) \tag{6.74}$$

TABLE 6.8
Gaussian quadrature parameters

n	t_i	C_i	Order
2	$-1/\sqrt{3}$	1	3
	$1/\sqrt{3}$	1	
3	$-\sqrt{0.6}$	5/9	5
	0	8/9	
	$\sqrt{0.6}$	5/9	
4	−0.8611363116	0.3478548451	7
	−0.3399810436	0.6521451549	
	0.3399810436	0.6521451549	
	0.8611363116	0.3478548451	

and Eq. (6.70) becomes

$$I = \int_a^b f(x)\,dx = \int_{-1}^{1} f\big(x(t)\big)\ m\ dt = \int_{-1}^{1} f(mt + c)m\,dt \tag{6.75}$$

Define the function $F(t)$:

$$F(t) = f\big(x(t)\big) = f(mt + c) \tag{6.76}$$

Substituting Eqs. (6.73) and (6.76) into Eq. (6.75) yields

$$\boxed{I = \left(\frac{b-a}{2}\right)\int_{-1}^{1} F(t)\,dt} \tag{6.77}$$

Higher-order formulas can be developed in a similar manner. Thus,

$$\boxed{\int_a^a f(x)\,dx = \left(\frac{b-a}{2}\right)\sum_{i=1}^{n} C_i F(t_i)} \tag{6.78}$$

Table 6.8 presents t_i and C_i for $n = 2$, 3, and 4. Higher-order results are presented by Abramowitz and Stegun (1964).

Example 6.6. Gaussian quadrature. To illustrate Gaussian quadrature, we will solve the example problem presented in Section 6.1, where $f(x) = 1/x$, $a = 3.1$, and $b = 3.9$. Consider the two point formula applied to the entire range of integration as a single interval. From Eq. (6.73),

$$m = \frac{b-a}{2} = 0.4 \qquad \text{and} \qquad c = \frac{b+a}{2} = 3.5 \tag{6.79}$$

Equations (6.74) and (6.76) become

$$x = 0.4t + 3.5 \qquad \text{and} \qquad F(t) = \frac{1}{0.4t + 3.5} \tag{6.80}$$

Substituting these results into Eq. (6.78) with $n = 2$ gives

$$I = 0.4\int_{-1}^{1} F(t)\,dt = 0.4\left((1)F\left(-\frac{1}{\sqrt{3}}\right) + (1)F\left(\frac{1}{\sqrt{3}}\right)\right) \tag{6.81}$$

Evaluating F(t) gives

$$F\left(-\frac{1}{\sqrt{3}}\right) = \frac{1}{0.4\left(-1/\sqrt{3}\right) + 3.5} = 0.30589834 \tag{6.82a}$$

$$F\left(\frac{1}{\sqrt{3}}\right) = \frac{1}{0.4\left(1/\sqrt{3}\right) + 3.5} = 0.26802896 \tag{6.82b}$$

Substituting Eq. (6.82) into Eq. (6.81) yields

$$I = 0.4\big((1)(0.30589834) + (1)(0.26802896)\big) = 0.22957092 \tag{6.83}$$

Recall that the exact value is $I = 0.22957444$. This result is comparable to Simpson's $\frac{1}{3}$ rule applied over the entire range of integration in a single step, that is, $h = 0.4$.

Next, we will apply the two point formula over two intervals, each one-half of the total range of integration. Thus,

$$I = \int_{3.1}^{3.9} \frac{1}{x}\,dx = \int_{3.1}^{3.5} \frac{1}{x}\,dx + \int_{3.5}^{3.9} \frac{1}{x}\,dx = I_1 + I_2 \tag{6.84}$$

For I_1, $a = 3.1$, $b = 3.5$, $(b - a)/2 = 0.2$, and $(b + a)/2 = 3.3$. Thus,

$$x = 0.2t + 3.3, \qquad F(t) = \frac{1}{0.2t + 3.3} \tag{6.85}$$

$$I_1 = 0.2\int_{-1}^{1} F(t)\,dt = 0.2\left((1)F\left(-\frac{1}{\sqrt{3}}\right) + (1)F\left(\frac{1}{\sqrt{3}}\right)\right) \tag{6.86}$$

$$I_1 = 0.2\left(\frac{1}{0.2\left(-1/\sqrt{3}\right) + 3.3} + \frac{1}{0.2\left(1/\sqrt{3}\right) + 3.3}\right) = 0.12136071 \tag{6.87}$$

For I_2, $a = 3.5$, $b = 3.9$, $(b - a)/2 = 0.2$, and $(b + a)/2 = 3.7$. Thus,

$$x = 0.2t + 3.7, \qquad F(t) = \frac{1}{0.2t + 3.7} \tag{6.88}$$

$$I_2 = 0.2\int_{-1}^{1} F(t)\,dt = 0.2\left((1)F\left(-\frac{1}{\sqrt{3}}\right) + (1)F\left(\frac{1}{\sqrt{3}}\right)\right) \tag{6.89}$$

$$I_2 = 0.2\left(\frac{1}{0.2\left(-1/\sqrt{3}\right)+3.7} + \frac{1}{0.2\left(1/\sqrt{3}\right)+3.7}\right) = 0.10821350 \tag{6.90}$$

Summing the results yields the value of the total integral:

$$I = I_1 + I_2 = 0.12136071 + 0.10821350 = 0.22957421 \tag{6.91}$$

The error is -0.00000023. This result is comparable to Simpson's $\frac{1}{3}$ rule with $h = 0.2$.

Next we will apply the three-point formula over the entire range of integration as a single interval. Thus,

$$a = 3.1, b = 3.9, (b-a)/2 = 0.4, \text{ and } (b+a)/2 = 3.5.$$

$$x = 0.4t + 3.5, f(t) = \frac{1}{0.4t + 3.5} \tag{6.92}$$

$$I = 0.4\left(\frac{5}{9}F\left(-\sqrt{0.6}\right) + \frac{8}{9}F(0) + \frac{5}{9}F\left(\sqrt{0.6}\right)\right) \tag{6.93}$$

$$I = 0.4\left(\frac{5}{9}\frac{1}{0.4\left(-\sqrt{0.6}\right)+3.5} + \frac{8}{9}\frac{1}{0.4(0)+3.5} + \frac{5}{9}\frac{1}{0.4\left(\sqrt{0.6}\right)+3.5}\right)$$
$$= 0.22957443 \tag{6.94}$$

The error is $0.22957443 - 0.22957444 = -0.00000001$. This result is comparable to Simpson's $\frac{1}{3}$ rule with $h = 0.1$.

As a final result, evaluate the integral using the sixth-order formula based on the fifth-order Newton forward-difference polynomial. That formula is (see Table 6.4)

$$I = \frac{5h}{288}(19f_0 + 75f_1 + 50f_2 + 50f_3 + 75f_4 + 19f_5) + O(h^7) \tag{6.95}$$

For five equally spaced intervals, $h = (3.9 - 3.1)/5 = 0.16$. Thus

$$I = \frac{5(0.16)}{288}\left(19\left(\frac{1}{3.10}\right) + 75\left(\frac{1}{3.26}\right) + 50\left(\frac{1}{3.42}\right) + 50\left(\frac{1}{3.58}\right)\right.$$
$$\left. + 75\left(\frac{1}{3.74}\right) + 19\left(\frac{1}{3.90}\right)\right) = 0.22957445 \tag{6.96}$$

The error is $0.22957445 - 0.22957444 = 0.00000001$. This result is comparable to Gaussian quadrature with three points.

6.8 MULTIPLE INTEGRALS

The numerical integration formulas developed in the preceding sections for evaluating single integrals can be used to evaluate multiple integrals. Consider the double integral

$$\boxed{I = \int_c^d \int_a^b f(x, y)\, dx\, dy} \tag{6.97}$$

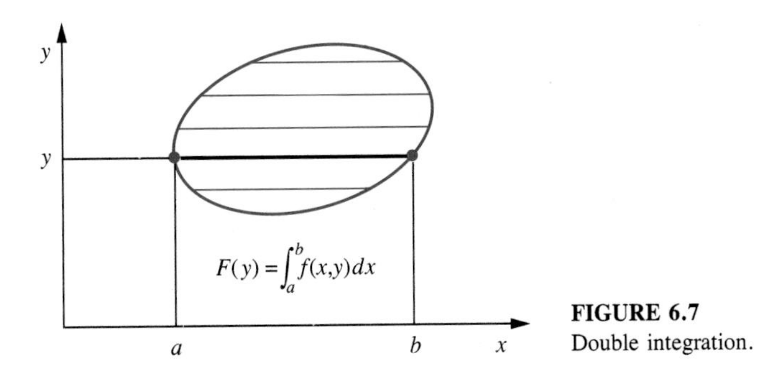

FIGURE 6.7
Double integration.

Equation (6.97) can be written in the form:

$$I = \int_c^d \left(\int_a^b f(x, y)\, dx \right) dy = \int_c^d F(y)\, dy \tag{6.98}$$

where

$$F(y) = \int_a^b f(x, y)\, dx, \qquad y = \text{Constant} \tag{6.99}$$

The double integral I is evaluated in two steps:

1. Evaluate $F(y)$ at selected values of y by a numerical integration formula.
2. Evaluate $I = \int F(y)\, dy$ by a numerical integration formula.

If the limits of integration are variable, as illustrated in Fig. 6.7, that must be accounted for.

Example 6.7. Double integration. To illustrate multiple integration with constant limits of integration, we will calculate the volume of the square body illustrated in Fig. 6.8*a*. The base of the body is a $2L$ by $2L$ square L units tall. The top of the body is a pointed figure obtained by removing the volume enclosed with four cylinders of radius L, as illustrated in Fig. 6.8*b*. As illustrated in Fig. 6.8*c*, the volume is the same in all four xy quadrants. The height of the body is denoted by $h(x, y)$. Thus, the volume of the body is given by

$$\text{Volume} = 4 \int_0^L \int_0^L h(x, y)\, dx\, dy \tag{6.100}$$

The height $h(x, y)$ along a line of y = Constant, the dashed line illustrated in Fig. 6.8*c*, can be determined by referring to Fig. 6.8*d*, where the dashed line in Fig. 6.8*d* corresponds to $h(x, y)$ along the dashed line of Fig. 6.8*c*. For $0 \le x \le y$,

$$h(x, y) = 2L - y = \text{Constant} \tag{6.101}$$

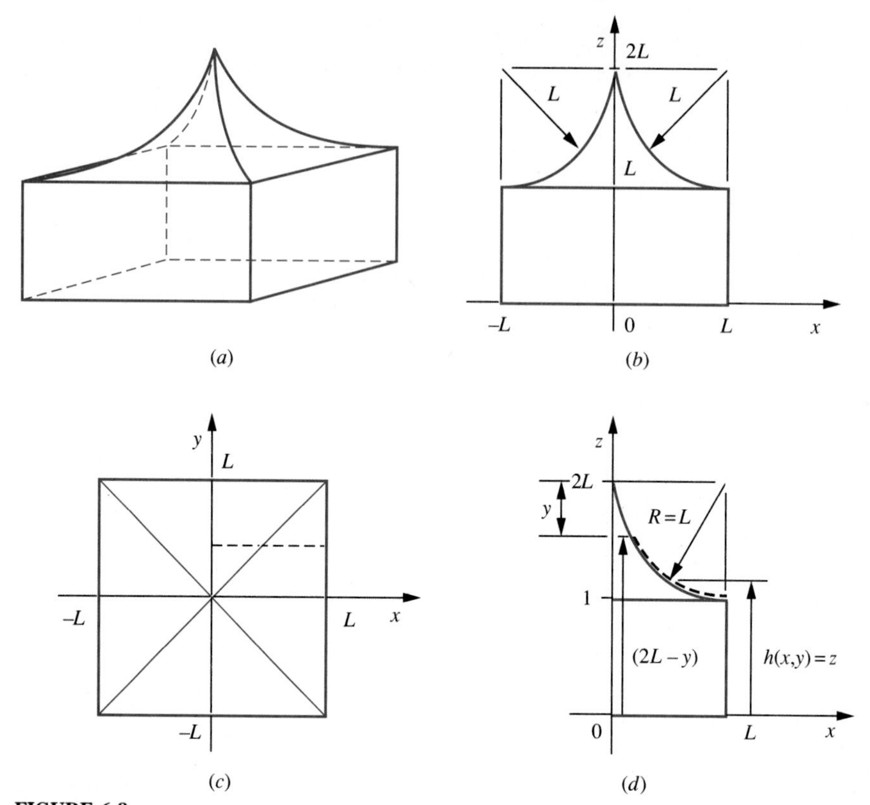

FIGURE 6.8
Square body: (*a*) isometric view; (*b*) front view; (*c*) top view; (*d*) $h(x, y)$.

For $y \leq x \leq 2L$,

$$h(x, y) = z = 2L - \left(L^2 - (x - L)^2\right)^{1/2} \tag{6.102}$$

The exact solution of Eq. (6.100) is

$$\text{Volume} = (4.383482\ldots)L^3 \tag{6.103}$$

where L is the generic length scale. For $L = 1$, Volume $= 4.383482\ldots$

Equation (6.100) can be written as

$$\text{Volume} = 4\int_0^1 F(y)\,dy \tag{6.104}$$

where the function $F(y)$ is given by

$$F(y) = \int_0^1 h(x, y)\,dx, \qquad y = \text{Constant} \tag{6.105}$$

Table 6.9 presents $h(x, y)$ for a 6×6 discrete grid (i.e., $ix = iy = 6$), so that $\Delta x = \Delta y = 0.2$. Using the trapezoid rule to integrate Eq. (6.105) for the six values of y gives

TABLE 6.9
Height of the square body

	x					
y	0.0	0.2	0.4	0.6	0.8	1.0
0.0	2.0000	1.4000	1.2000	1.0835	1.0202	1.0000
0.2	1.4000	1.4000	1.2000	1.0835	1.0202	1.0000
0.4	1.2000	1.2000	1.2000	1.0835	1.0202	1.0000
0.6	1.0835	1.0835	1.0835	1.0835	1.0202	1.0000
0.8	1.0202	1.0202	1.0202	1.0202	1.0202	1.0000
1.0	1.0000	1.0000	1.0000	1.0000	1.0000	1.0000

the results presented in Table 6.10. For example, for $y = 0.0$,

$$F(y) = \frac{0.2}{2}\Big(2.0000 + 2(1.4000 + 1.2000 + 1.0835 + 1.0202) + 1.0000\Big) = 1.240738 \quad (6.106)$$

Using the trapezoid rule to integrate Eq. (6.104) yields

$$\text{Volume} = \frac{0.2}{2}\Big(1.240738 + 2(1.180738 + 1.120738 + 1.062480 + 1.018184) + 1.000000\Big) = 4.402007 \quad (6.107)$$

Table 6.11 presents the solution for seven grid densities, each double the preceding density in both ix and iy.

The numerical calculations presented in Example 6.7 are relatively straightforward because the limits of integration in Eq. (6.100) are constant. When the limits of integration are variable, the same approach is applicable, but the numerical calculations are considerably more tedious.

Example 6.7 uses the trapezoid rule. The results presented in Tables 6.10 and 6.11 can be improved by extrapolation. Simpson's $\frac{1}{3}$ rule could be used instead of the trapezoid rule. When the integrand is a known function, adaptive integration techniques can be employed, as can Gaussian quadrature. The extension to triple and higher integrals, while tedious, is straightforward.

TABLE 6.10
The function $F(y)$ for the square body

i	y	$F(y)$
1	0.000000	1.240738
2	0.200000	1.180738
3	0.400000	1.120738
4	0.600000	1.062480
5	0.800000	1.018184
6	1.000000	1.000000

TABLE 6.11
Volume of the square body

$ix = iy$	Volume	Error
6	4.402007	0.018525
11	4.387731	0.004249
21	4.384476	0.000999
41	4.383718	0.000236
81	4.383538	0.000056
161	4.383495	0.000013
321	4.383485	0.000003

SUMMARY

Procedures for the numerical integration of both discrete data and known functions are presented in this chapter. These procedures are based on fitting approximating polynomials to the data and integrating the approximating polynomials. The direct fit polynomial method works well for both equally spaced data and nonequally spaced data. Least squares fit polynomials can be used for large sets of data or sets of rough data. The Newton–Cotes formulas, which are based on Newton forward-difference polynomials, give simple integration formulas for equally spaced data.

Methods of error estimation and control are presented. Extrapolation, or the deferred approach to the limit, is discussed. Romberg integration, which is extrapolation of the trapezoid rule, is developed. Adaptive integration procedures are suggested to reduce the effort required to integrate rapidly varying functions. Gaussian quadrature, which increases the accuracy of integrating known functions where the sampling locations can be chosen arbitrarily, is presented. An example of multiple integration is presented to illustrate the extension of the one-dimensional integration formulas to multiple dimensions.

PROBLEMS

The integrals presented in Problems 1 and 2 are used throughout this chapter to illustrate numerical integration methods.

1. Evaluate the following integrals analytically:

$(a)\ \int_0^5 (3x^2 + 2)\,dx, \quad (b)\ \int_{1.0}^{2.0} (x^3 + 3x^2 + 2x + 1)\,dx,$

$(c)\ \int_0^{10} (5x^4 + 4x^3 + 2x + 3)\,dx$

2. Evaluate the following integrals analytically:

$(a)\ \int_0^{\pi} (5 + \sin x)\,dx, \quad (b)\ \int_{\pi}^{\pi/4} (e^{2x} + \cos x)\,dx, \quad (c)\ \int_{1.5}^{2.5} \ln x\,dx$

$(d)\ \int_{0.1}^{1.0} e^x\,dx, \quad (e)\ \int_{0.2}^{1.2} \tan x\,dx$

In the numerical integration problems, the word *interval* denotes the total range of integration, the word *subinterval* denotes subdivisions of the total range of integration, and the word *increment* denotes a single increment Δx.

Section 6.2 Direct Fit Polynomials

3. Evaluate the integrals in Problem 2 by direct fit polynomials of order 2 and order 3 over the total interval. Repeat the calculations, breaking the total interval into two equal subintervals. Compute the errors and the ratios of the errors for the two interval sizes.

Section 6.3 Newton Forward-Difference Polynomials

4. Solve Problem 1 using the trapezoid rule for $n = 1, 2, 4$, and 8 subintervals. Compute the errors and the ratios of the errors.

* **5.** Solve Problem 2 using the trapezoid rule for $n = 1, 2, 4$, and 8 subintervals. Compute the errors and the ratios of the errors.

* **6.** Consider the function $f(x)$ tabulated below:

x	$f(x)$	x	$f(x)$	x	$f(x)$
0.4	5.1600	1.4	3.3886	2.2	5.7491
0.6	3.6933	1.6	3.8100	2.4	6.5933
0.8	3.1400	1.8	4.3511	2.6	7.5292
1.0	3.0000	2.0	5.0000	2.8	8.5543
1.2	3.1067				

Evaluate the integral $\int_{0.4}^{2.0} f(x)\,dx$ using the trapezoid rule with $n = 1, 2, 4$, and 8 subintervals. The exact value is 5.86420916. Compute the errors and the ratios of the errors.

7. Consider the function $f(x)$ tabulated below:

x	$f(x)$	x	$f(x)$	x	$f(x)$
0.4	6.0900	1.4	6.9686	2.2	4.4782
0.6	7.1400	1.6	6.5025	2.4	3.6150
0.8	7.4850	1.8	5.9267	2.6	2.6631
1.0	7.5000	2.0	5.2500	2.8	1.6243
1.2	7.3100				

Evaluate the integral $\int_{0.4}^{2.0} f(x)\,dx$ using the trapezoid rule with $n = 1, 2, 4$, and 8 subintervals. The exact value is 10.92130980. Compute the errors and the ratios of the errors.

8. Evaluate the integrals in Problem 1 using Simpson's $\frac{1}{3}$ rule for $n = 1, 2, 4$, and 8 subintervals. Compute the errors and the ratio of the errors.

* **9.** Work Problem 8 for the integrals in Problem 2.

10. Work Problem 6 using Simpson's $\frac{1}{3}$ rule with $n = 1, 2, 4$, and 8 subintervals.

11. Work Problem 7 using Simpson's $\frac{1}{3}$ rule with $n = 1, 2, 4$, and 8 subintervals.

12. Evaluate the integrals in Problem 1 by Simpson's $\frac{3}{8}$ rule using $n = 1, 2, 4$, and 8 subintervals. Compute the errors and the ratios of the errors.

***13.** Work Problem 12 for the integrals in Problem 2.

14. Evaluate $I = \int_{0.4}^{2.8} f(x)\,dx$ for the function $f(x)$ tabulated in Problem 6 using Simpson's $\frac{3}{8}$ rule with $n = 1, 2$, and 4 subintervals.

15. Evaluate $I = \int_{0.4}^{2.8} f(x)\,dx$ for the function $f(x)$ tabulated in Problem 7 using Simpson's $\frac{3}{8}$ rule with $n = 1$, 2, and 4 subintervals.

16. Evaluate the integrals in Problem 1 using Simpson's rules with $n = 5$ and 7 increments.

17. Evaluate the integrals in Problem 2 using Simpson's rules with $n = 5$ and 7 increments.

18. Derive the Newton–Cotes formulas for polynomials of degree $n = 4$, 5, 6, and 7.

19. Evaluate the integrals in Problem 2 using the Newton–Cotes fourth-order formula with 1, 2, and 4 subintervals.

***20.** Evaluate the integrals in Problem 2 using the Newton–Cotes fifth-order formula with 1, 2, and 4 subintervals.

21. Evaluate the integrals in Problem 2 using the Newton–Cotes sixth-order formula with 1, 2, and 4 subintervals.

22. Evaluate the integrals in Problem 2 using the Newton–Cotes seventh-order formula with 1, 2, and 4 subintervals.

Section 6.5 Romberg Integration

23. Evaluate the following integrals using Romberg integration with four subintervals. Let the first subinterval be the total interval.

$$(a)\ \int_0^{\pi/4} \tan x\,dx, \quad (b)\ \int_0^{0.5} e^{-x}\,dx, \quad (c)\ \int_0^{3/4} e^{-x^2}\,dx, \quad (d)\ \int_1^{2.5} (x^5 - x^2)\,dx$$

24. Evaluate the integrals in Problem 1 using Romberg integration with four subintervals. Let the first subinterval be the total interval.

***25.** Evaluate the integrals in Problem 2 using Romberg integration with four subintervals. Let the first subinterval be the total interval.

26. Work Problem 6 using Romberg integration with three subintervals. Let the first subinterval be the total interval.

27. Work Problem 7 using Romberg integration with three subintervals. Let the first subinterval be the total interval.

28. Which row of a Romberg table yields $\int_a^b f(x)\,dx$ exactly if $f(x)$ is a polynomial of degree k, where (*a*) $k = 3$, (*b*) $k = 5$, and (*c*) $k = 7$? Verify your conclusion for $\int_0^2 x^k\,dx$. Start with one interval.

Section 6.6 Adaptive Integration

29. Evaluate $I = \int_{-2.0}^{0.4} e^{-x}\,dx$ using Romberg integration. (*a*) Start with the total interval. Let the first subinterval be the total interval. (*b*) Divide the total interval into two equal subintervals and use Romberg integration in each subinterval. Let the first sub-subinterval in each subinterval be the total subinterval. (*c*) Divide the total interval into the two subintervals $-2.0 \le x \le -0.4$ and $-0.4 \le x \le 0.4$ and repeat Part (*b*). (*d*) Compare the errors incurred for the three cases.

30. Evaluate $I = \int_1^3 \ln x\,dx$ using Romberg integration. (*a*) Start with the total interval. Let the first subinterval be the total interval. (*b*) Divide the total interval into two equal subintervals and use Romberg integration in each subinterval. Let the first sub-subinterval in each subinterval be the total subinterval.

Section 6.7 Gaussian Quadrature

***31.** Evaluate the integrals in Problem 2 using two-point Gaussian quadrature with $n = 1$, 2, 4, and 8 subintervals.

***32.** Evaluate the integrals in Problem 2 using three-point Gaussian quadrature with $n = 1, 2, 4$, and 8 subintervals.

***33.** Evaluate the integrals in Problem 2 using four-point Gaussian quadrature with $n = 1, 2$, and 4 subintervals.

34. Evaluate the following integrals using k-point Gaussian quadrature for $k = 2, 3$, and 4, with $n = 1, 2, 4$, and 8 subintervals. Compare the results with the analytical solution.

$$(a)\ \int_1^{2.6} x e^{-x^2}\,dx, \quad (b)\ \int_1^3 \cosh x\,dx, \quad (c)\ \int_0^4 \sinh x\,dx, \quad (d)\ \int_{-1}^2 e^{-x}\sin x\,dx.$$

35. (*a*) What is the smallest k for which k-point Gaussian quadrature is exact for a polynomial of degree 7? (*b*) Verify the answer to Part (*a*) by evaluating $\int_0^2 x^7 dx$.

Section 6.8 Multiple Integrals

36. Evaluate the multiple integral $\int_{-1}^1 \int_0^2 (4x^3 - 2x^2y + 3xy^2)\,dx\,dy$ (*a*) analytically, (*b*) using the trapezoid rule, and (*c*) using Simpson's $\frac{1}{3}$ rule.

37. Evaluate the multiple integral $\int_0^1 \int_0^2 \sin(x^2 + y^2)\,dx\,dy$ (*a*) analytically, (*b*) using the trapezoid rule, and (*c*) using Simpson's $\frac{1}{3}$ rule.

38. Evaluate the multiple integral $\int_0^1 \int_0^{e^x} \left(x^2 + \frac{1}{y}\right) dy\,dx$ (*a*) analytically, (*b*) using the trapezoid rule for both integrals, (*c*) using three-point Gaussian quadrature for both integrals, (*d*) using the trapezoid rule for the y integral and three-point Gaussian quadrature for the x integral, (*e*) using three-point Gaussian quadrature for the y integral and the trapezoid rule for the x integral.

39. Evaluate the multiple integral $\int_{-1}^1 \int_0^{x^2} xy\,dy\,dx$ by the procedures described in Problem 38.

40. Evaluate the integral $\int\int_R \exp\left(\sqrt{x + y^2}\right) dy\,dx$, where R is the area enclosed by the circle $x^2 + y^2 = 1$. Use Cartesian coordinates.

41. Find the volume of a circular pyramid with height and base radius equal to 1. Use Cartesian coordinates.

PART II

ORDINARY DIFFERENTIAL EQUATIONS

Section

II.1 INTRODUCTION

Differential equations arise in all fields of engineering and science. Most real physical processes are governed by differential equations. In general, most real physical processes involve more than one independent variable, and the corresponding differential equations are *partial* differential equations (PDEs). In many cases, however, simplifying assumptions are made that reduce the PDEs to *ordinary* differential equations (ODEs). Part II of this book is devoted to the solution of ordinary differential equations.

Some general features of ordinary differential equations are discussed in Part II. The two classes of ODEs (i.e., *initial-value* and *boundary-value* ODEs) are introduced. The two corresponding types of physical problems (i.e., *propagation* and *equilibrium* problems) are discussed.

The objectives of Part II are (a) to present the general features of ordinary differential equations; (b) to discuss the relationship between the type of physical problem being solved, the class of the corresponding governing ODE, and the type of numerical method required; and (c) to present examples to illustrate these concepts.

II.2 GENERAL FEATURES OF ORDINARY DIFFERENTIAL EQUATIONS

An ordinary differential equation (ODE) is an equation stating a relationship between a function of a single independent variable and the total derivatives of this function with respect to this independent variable. The symbol y is used generically for the dependent variable throughout Part II. In most problems in engineering and science, the independent variable is either time (t) or space (x). The dependent variable depends on the physical problem being modeled. Ordinary differential equations are the subject of Part II of this book. If more than one independent variable exists, then partial derivatives occur and partial differential equations (PDEs) are obtained. Partial differential equations are the subject of Part III of this book.

The *order* of an ODE is the order of the highest derivative in the differential equation. The general first-order ODE is

$$\frac{dy}{dt} = f(t, y) \tag{II.1}$$

where $f(t, y)$ is called the *derivative function*. For simplicity of notation, differentiation usually will be denoted by the superscript notation

$$y' = \frac{dy}{dt} \tag{II.2}$$

Thus, Eq. (II.1) can be written as

$$y' = f(t, y) \tag{II.3}$$

The general nth-order ODE for $y(t)$ has the form

$$a_n y^{(n)} + a_{n-1} y^{(n-1)} + \cdots + a_1 y' + a_0 y = F(t) \tag{II.4}$$

where the notation $y^{(n)}$ denotes the nth-order derivative $d^n y/dt^n$, and so on.

The solution of an ordinary differential equation is that particular function $y(t)$ or $y(x)$ that identically satisfies the ODE in the domain of interest $D(t)$ or $D(x)$, respectively, and satisfies the auxiliary conditions specified on the boundaries of the domain of interest. In a few special cases, the solution of an ODE can be expressed in closed form. In the majority of problems in engineering and science, the solution must be obtained by numerical methods. Such problems are the subject of Part II of this book.

Equations (II.3) and (II.4) are *linear* ordinary differential equations. A linear ODE is one in which all the derivatives appear in linear form and none of the coefficients depends on the dependent variable. The coefficients may be functions of the independent variable, in which case the ODE is a *variable-coefficient* linear ODE. For example,

$$y' + \alpha y = F(t) \tag{II.5}$$

is a linear, constant-coefficient, first-order ODE, whereas

$$y' + \alpha x y = F(t) \tag{II.6}$$

is a linear, variable-coefficient, first-order ODE. If the coefficients depend on the dependent variable, or the derivatives appear in a nonlinear form, then the ODE is nonlinear. For example,

$$yy' + \alpha y = 0 \tag{II.7}$$

$$(y')^2 + \alpha y = 0 \tag{II.8}$$

are nonlinear first-order ODEs.

A *homogeneous* differential equation is one in which each term involves the dependent variable or one of its derivatives. A *nonhomogeneous* differential equation contains additional terms, known as *nonhomogeneous terms*, *source terms*, or *forcing functions*. For example,

$$y' + \alpha y = 0 \tag{II.9}$$

is a linear, first-order, homogeneous ODE, and

$$y' + \alpha y = F(t) \tag{II.10}$$

is a linear, first-order, nonhomogeneous ODE, where $F(t)$ is the known nonhomogeneous term.

Many practical problems involve several dependent variables, each of which is a function of the same single independent variable, and each of which is governed by an ordinary differential equation. Such coupled sets of ordinary differential equations are called *systems* of ordinary differential equations. Thus, the two coupled ODEs

$$y' = f(t, y, z) \tag{II.11a}$$

$$z' = g(t, y, z) \tag{II.11b}$$

form a system of ordinary differential equations.

The general solution of a differential equation contains one or more constants of integration. Thus, a *family* of solutions is obtained. The number of constants of integration is equal to the order of the differential equation. The particular member of this family of solutions that is of interest is determined by auxiliary conditions. Obviously, the number of auxiliary conditions must equal the number of constants of integration, which is the same as the order of the differential equation.

As illustrated in the preceding discussion, a wide variety of ordinary differential equations exists. Each problem has its own special governing equation or equations and its own peculiarities, which must be considered individually. However, useful insights into the general features of ODEs can be obtained by studying two special cases. The first special case is the general nonlinear first-order ODE

$$\boxed{y' = f(t, y)} \tag{II.12}$$

The second special case is the general nonlinear second-order ODE

$$\boxed{y'' + P(x, y)y' + Q(x, y)y = F(x)} \tag{II.13}$$

These two special cases are studied in the following sections.

II.3 CLASSIFICATION OF ORDINARY DIFFERENTIAL EQUATIONS

Physical problems are governed by many different ordinary differential equations. There are two different types, or *classes*, of ordinary differential equations, depending on the type of auxiliary conditions specified. If the auxiliary conditions are specified at the same value of the independent variable and the solution is to be *marched* forward from that initial location, the differential equation is an *initial-value* ODE. If the auxiliary conditions are specified at two values of the independent variable (the end points or boundaries of the domain of interest), the differential equation is a *boundary-value* ODE.

Figure II.1 illustrates the solution of an initial-value ODE. The initial value of the dependent variable is specified at some value of the independent variable, and the solution domain $D(t)$ is open. Initial-value ODEs are solved by *marching* numerical methods.

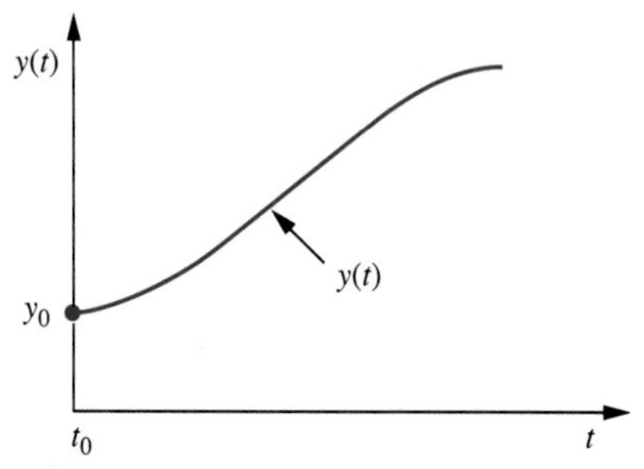

FIGURE II.1
Solution of an initial-value ODE.

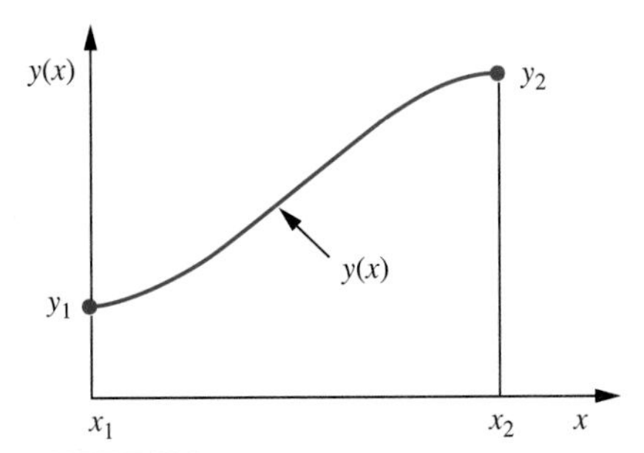

FIGURE II.2
Solution of a boundary-value ODE.

Figure II.2 illustrates the solution of a boundary-value ODE. The boundary values of the dependent variable are specified at two values of the independent variable, and the solution domain $D(x)$ is closed. Boundary-value ODEs are solved by both marching numerical methods and *equilibrium* numerical methods.

II.4 CLASSIFICATION OF PHYSICAL PROBLEMS

Physical problems fall into one of the following three general classifications:

1. Propagation problems
2. Equilibrium problems
3. Eigenproblems

Each of these three types of physical problems has its own special features, its own particular type of ordinary differential equation, and its own numerical solution methods. A clear understanding of these concepts is essential if meaningful numerical solutions are to be obtained.

Propagation problems are initial-value problems in *open* domains, in which the known information (initial values) is marched forward in time or space from the initial state. The known information, that is, the initial values, is specified at one value of the independent variable. Propagation problems are governed by initial-value ordinary differential equations. The order of the governing ordinary differential equation may be 1 or greater. The number of initial values must be equal to the order of the differential equation.

Propagation problems may be unsteady, time (t)-marching problems or steady, space (x)-marching problems. The marching direction in a steady, space-marching problem is sometimes called the *time-like* direction, and the corresponding coordinate is called the *time-like* coordinate. Figure II.3 illustrates the open solution domains $D(t)$ and $D(x)$ associated with time-marching and space-marching propagation problems, respectively.

Equilibrium problems are boundary-value problems in *closed* domains, in which the known information (boundary values) is specified at two different values

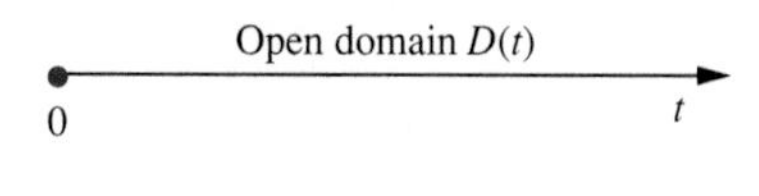

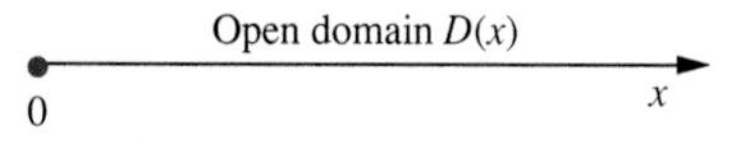

FIGURE II.3
Solution domain for propagation problems.

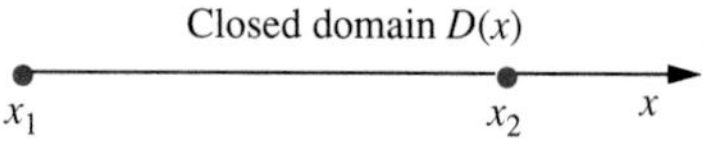

FIGURE II.4
Solution domain for equilibrium problems.

of the independent variable: the end points (boundaries) of the solution domain. Equilibrium problems are governed by boundary-value ordinary differential equations. The order of the governing differential equation must be at least 2 and may be greater. The number of boundary values must be equal to the order of the differential equation. Equilibrium problems are steady state problems in closed domains. Figure II.4 illustrates the closed solution domain $D(x)$ associated with equilibrium problems.

Eigenproblems are a special type of equilibrium problem in which the solution exists only for special values (i.e., *eigenvalues*) of a parameter of the problem. The eigenvalues are to be determined in addition to the corresponding equilibrium configuration of the system.

II.5 INITIAL-VALUE ORDINARY DIFFERENTIAL EQUATIONS

A classical example of an initial-value ODE is the general first-order ODE

$$\boxed{y' = f(t, y), \qquad y(t_0) = y_0} \tag{II.14}$$

Equation (II.14) applies to many problems in engineering and science. In the following discussion, the general features of Eq. (II.14) are illustrated for the problem of transient heat transfer by radiation from a lumped mass to its surroundings and that of transient motion of a mass–damper–spring system.

Consider the lumped mass m illustrated in Fig. II.5. Heat transfer from the lumped mass m to its surroundings by radiation is governed by the Stefan–Boltzmann law of radiation:

$$\dot{q}_r = A\epsilon\sigma(T^4 - T_a^4) \tag{II.15}$$

where $\dot{q}_r$ is the heat transfer rate (J/s), A is the surface area of the lumped mass (m^2), ϵ is the Stefan–Boltzmann constant (5.67×10^{-8} J/m^2-K^4-s), σ is the emissivity of the body (dimensionless), which is the ratio of the actual radiation to the radiation from a blackbody, T is the internal temperature of the lumped mass

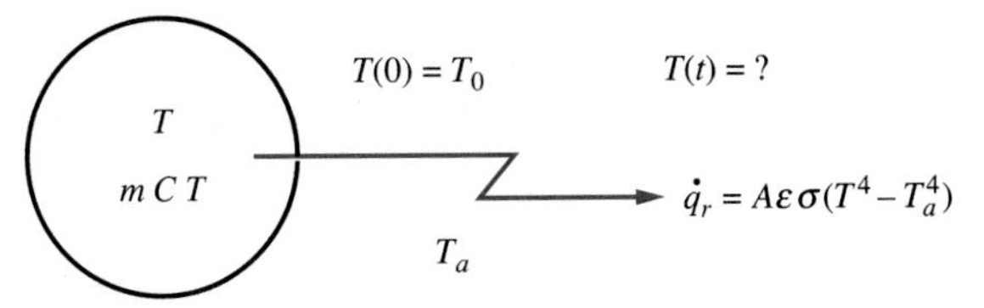

FIGURE II.5
Heat transfer by radiation from a lumped mass.

(K), and T_a is the ambient temperature [i.e., the temperature of the surroundings (K)]. The energy E stored in the lumped mass is given by

$$E = mCT \tag{II.16}$$

where m is the mass of the lumped mass (kg) and C is the specific heat of the material (J/kg-K). An energy balance states that the rate at which the energy stored in the lumped mass changes is equal to the rate at which heat is transferred to the surroundings. Thus,

$$\frac{d(mCT)}{dt} = -\dot{q}_r = -A\epsilon\sigma(T^4 - T_a^4) \tag{II.17}$$

The minus sign in Eq. (II.17) is required so that the rate of change of stored energy is negative when T is greater than T_a. For constant m and C, Eq. (II.17) can be written as

$$\frac{dT}{dt} = T' = -\alpha(T^4 - T_a^4) \tag{II.18}$$

where

$$\alpha = \frac{A\epsilon\sigma}{mC} \tag{II.19}$$

Consider the case where the temperature of the surroundings is constant and the initial temperature of the lumped mass is $T(0) = T_0$. The initial-value problem is stated as follows:

$$\boxed{T' = -\alpha\left(T^4 - T_a^4\right) = f(t, T), \qquad T(0) = T_0} \tag{II.20}$$

Equation (II.20) is in the general form expressed in Eq. (II.14). Equation (II.20) is a nonlinear first-order initial-value ODE. The solution of Eq. (II.20) is the function $T(t)$, which describes the temperature of the lumped mass corresponding to the initial condition $T(0) = T_0$. Equation (II.20) is an example of a nonlinear first-order initial-value ODE.

Another classical example of an initial-value ODE is the second-order ODE governing the transient motion of a mass–damper–spring system. Consider the physical arrangement illustrated in Fig. II.6. Motion of the mass is governed by Newton's second law of motion:

$$\sum F = ma = m\frac{dV}{dt} = m\frac{d^2x}{dt^2} \tag{II.21}$$

where F denotes an external force acting on the mass (N), m denotes the mass of the mass (kg), a denotes the acceleration (m/s^2), V denotes the velocity (m/s), and x denotes the displacement (m). The spring applies a retarding force to the mass, given by the empirical equation

$$F_{\text{spring}} = K(x)x \tag{II.22}$$

where $K(x)$ is the *spring constant*—which may depend on the displacement of the spring. The damper applies a retarding force to the mass given by the empirical equation

$$F_{\text{damper}} = C(V)\frac{dx}{dt} \tag{II.23}$$

where $C(V)$ is the *damping coefficient*—which may depend on the velocity V. The force $F(t)$ is an externally applied forcing function. Substituting Eqs. (II.22) and (II.23) into Eq. (II.21) yields

$$F(t) - C(V)\frac{dx}{dt} - K(x)x = m\frac{d^2x}{dt^2} \tag{II.24}$$

where the minus signs are required so that the retarding forces act in the negative direction for positive displacement and velocity, and vice versa. Equation (II.24) can be written as

$$\boxed{m\frac{d^2x}{dt^2} + C(V)\frac{dx}{dt} + K(x)x = F(t)} \tag{II.25}$$

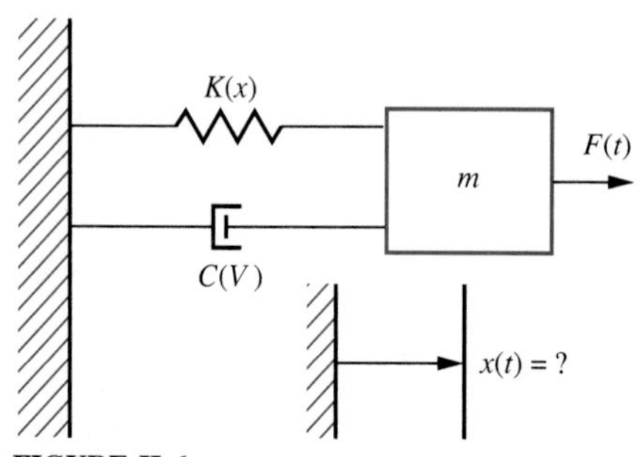

FIGURE II.6
Motion of a mass–damper–spring system.

Equation (II.25) is a nonlinear second-order initial-value ODE. Two initial conditions are required:

$$x(t_0) = x_0 \qquad \text{and} \qquad \frac{dx}{dt}(t_0) = V(t_0) = V_0 \tag{II.26}$$

The solution of Eq. (II.25) is the function $x(t)$, which describes the motion of the mass corresponding to the specified initial conditions $x(t_0) = x_0$ and $V(t_0) = V_0$. Equation (II.25) is a classical example of a second-order initial-value ODE.

In summary, two classical examples of initial-value ODEs are represented by Eqs. (II.20) and (II.25). Many more complicated examples of initial-value ODEs appear in the fields of engineering and science. Higher-order ODEs and systems of ODEs occur frequently. Numerical procedures for solving initial-value ODEs are presented in Chapter 7.

II.6 BOUNDARY-VALUE ORDINARY DIFFERENTIAL EQUATIONS

A classical example of a boundary-value ODE is the general second-order ODE

$$\boxed{y'' + P(x,y)y' + Q(x,y)y = F(x), \qquad y(x_1) = y_1 \quad \text{and} \quad y(x_2) = y_2} \tag{II.27}$$

Equation (II.27) applies to many problems in engineering and science. In the following discussion, the general features of Eq. (II.27) are illustrated for the problem of steady one-dimensional heat conduction in a rod.

Consider the rod of constant cross-sectional area illustrated in Fig. II.7. Heat conduction transfers energy along the rod, and energy is transferred from the rod to the surroundings by convection. An energy balance on the differential control volume yields:

$$\dot{q}(x) = \dot{q}(x + dx) + \dot{q}_c \tag{II.28}$$

which can be written as

$$\dot{q}(x) = \dot{q}(x) + \frac{d}{dx}\big(\dot{q}(x)\big)\,dx + \dot{q}_c \tag{II.29}$$

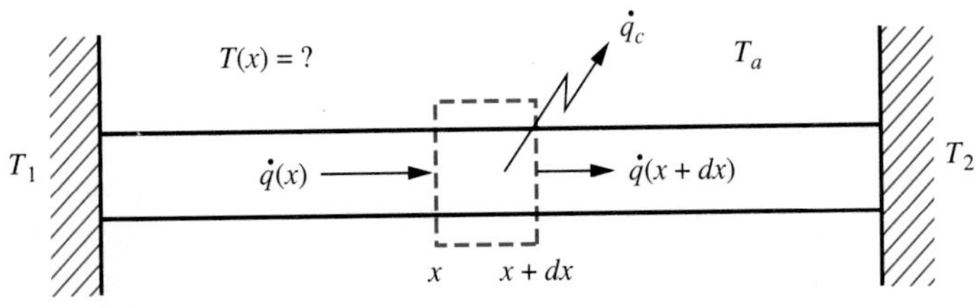

FIGURE II.7
Steady heat conduction in a rod.

$$\frac{d}{dx}\left(\dot{q}(x)\right) dx + \dot{q}_c = 0 \tag{II.30}$$

Heat conduction is governed by Fourier's law of conduction, which states that

$$\dot{q} = -kA\frac{dT}{dx} \tag{II.31}$$

where $\dot{q}$ is the energy transfer rate (J/s), k is the thermal conductivity of the solid (J/s-m-K), A is the cross-sectional area of the rod (m^2), and dT/dx is the temperature gradient (K/m). Heat transfer by convection is governed by Newton's law of cooling:

$$\dot{q}_c = hA(T - T_a) \tag{II.32}$$

where h is an empirical heat transfer coefficient (J/s-m^2-K), A is the surface area of the rod ($A = P\,dx$, m^2), P is the perimeter of the rod (m), and T_a is the ambient temperature [i.e., the temperature of the surroundings, (K)]. Substituting Eqs. (II.31) and (II.32) into Eq. (II.30) gives

$$\frac{d}{dx}\left(-kA\frac{dT}{dx}\right)dx + h(P\,dx)(T - T_a) = 0 \tag{II.33}$$

For constant k and A, Eq. (II.33) yields

$$\frac{d^2T}{dx^2} - \frac{hP}{kA}(T - T_a) = 0 \tag{II.34}$$

which can be written as

$$\boxed{T'' - \alpha^2 T = -\alpha^2 T_a} \tag{II.35}$$

where $\alpha^2 = hP/kA$.

Equation (II.35) is in the general form expressed in Eq. (II.27). Equation (II.35) is a linear second-order boundary-value ODE. The solution of Eq. (II.35) is the function $T(x)$, which describes the temperature distribution in the rod corresponding to the boundary conditions

$$T(x_1) = T_1 \qquad \text{and} \qquad T(x_2) = T_2 \tag{II.36}$$

Equation (II.35) is a classical example of a second-order boundary-value problem.

In summary, a classical example of a boundary-value problem is given by Eq. (II.35). Numerous other examples of boundary-value ODEs occur in engineering and science, including higher-order ODEs and systems of ODEs. Numerical procedures for solving boundary-value ODEs are presented in Chapter 8.

SUMMARY

The general features of ordinary differential equations are presented in Part II. Ordinary differential equations are classified as initial-value or boundary-value differential equations, according to whether the auxiliary conditions are specified at a single initial time (or location) or at two locations, respectively. Examples of several ordinary differential equations that arise in engineering and science have been presented.

The classical example of a first-order initial-value ODE is

$$y' = f(t, y), \qquad y(t_0) = y_0 \tag{II.37}$$

Chapter 7 presents several numerical methods for solving Eq. (II.37) and illustrates those methods with numerical examples.

The classical example of a second-order boundary-value ODE is

$$y'' + P(x, y)y' + Q(x, y)y = F(x), \qquad y(x_1) = y_1 \quad \text{and} \quad y(x_2) = y_2 \tag{II.38}$$

Chapter 8 presents several numerical methods for solving Eq. (II.38) and illustrates those methods with numerical examples.

CHAPTER 7

ONE-DIMENSIONAL INITIAL-VALUE PROBLEMS

Section

Example

7.1 INTRODUCTION

The general features of *initial-value* ordinary differential equations (ODEs) are discussed in Section II.5. In that section it is shown that initial-value ODEs govern *propagation* problems, which are initial-value problems in *open* domains. Consequently, initial-value ODEs are solved numerically by *marching* methods. This chapter is devoted to presenting the basic properties of finite difference methods for solving initial-value (i.e., propagation) problems and to developing several specific finite difference methods.

The objective of a finite difference method for solving an ordinary differential equation (ODE) is to transform a calculus problem into an algebra problem by

1. *Discretizing* the continuous physical domain
2. *Approximating* the exact derivatives in the ODE by algebraic finite difference approximations (FDAs)
3. *Substituting* the FDAs into the ODE to obtain an algebraic finite difference equation (FDE)

Numerous initial-value ordinary differential equations arise in engineering and science. Single ODEs, which govern a single dependent variable, arise frequently, as do coupled systems of ODEs, which govern several dependent variables. Initial-value ODEs may be linear or nonlinear, first- or higher-order, and homogeneous or nonhomogeneous. In this chapter, the majority of attention is devoted to the general first-order ODE

$$\boxed{y' = \frac{dy}{dt} = f(t, y), \qquad y(t_0) = y_0} \tag{7.1}$$

where y' denotes the first derivative and $f(t, y)$ is called the derivative function. The solution to Eq. (7.1) is the function $y(t)$. This function must satisfy an initial condition at $t = t_0$, $y(t_0) = y_0$. The solution domain is open, that is, the independent variable t has an unspecified (i.e., open) final value. Several finite difference methods for solving Eq. (7.1) are developed in this chapter. Procedures for solving systems of ODEs and higher-order ODEs, based on the methods for solving Eq. (7.1), are discussed.

Equation (7.1) applies to many problems in engineering and science. Most people have some physical understanding of heat transfer, due to its presence in many aspects of our daily life. Consequently, the first-order ODE governing unsteady heat transfer from a lumped mass, presented in Section II.5, is considered in this chapter to illustrate finite difference methods for solving first-order initial-value ODEs. That equation, Eq. (II.20), is

$$T' = -\alpha(T^4 - T_a^4) = f(t, T), \qquad T(0) = T_0 = 2500 \quad \text{and} \quad T_a = 250 \tag{7.2}$$

The exact solution to Eq. (7.2) can be obtained by separating variables, simplifying $1/(T^4 - T_a^4)$ by a partial-fraction expansion, and integrating. The result is

$$\tan^{-1}\left(\frac{T}{T_a}\right) - \tan^{-1}\left(\frac{T_0}{T_a}\right) + \frac{1}{2}\ln\left(\frac{(T_0 - T_a)(T + T_a)}{(T - T_a)(T_0 + T_a)}\right) = 2\alpha T_a^3 t \tag{7.3}$$

For $T_0 = 2500$, $T_a = 250$, and $\alpha = 2.0 \times 10^{-12}$, Eq. (7.3) becomes

$$\tan^{-1}\left(\frac{T}{250}\right) - \tan^{-1}\left(\frac{2500}{250}\right) + \frac{1}{2}\ln\left(\frac{(2500 - 250)(T + 250)}{(T - 250)(2500 + 250)}\right) = 2(2.0 \times 10^{-12})250^3 t \tag{7.4}$$

The exact solution at selected values of time, obtained by solving Eq. (7.4) by the secant method, is tabulated in Table 7.1 and illustrated in Fig. 7.1.

TABLE 7.1
Exact solution of the radiation problem

t, s	T, K	t, s	T, K
0.00	2500.00000000	6.00	2154.47079576
1.00	2426.43487359	7.00	2113.03386111
2.00	2360.82998846	8.00	2074.61189788
3.00	2301.79075068	9.00	2038.84084646
4.00	2248.24731405	10.00	2005.41636581
5.00	2199.36266993		

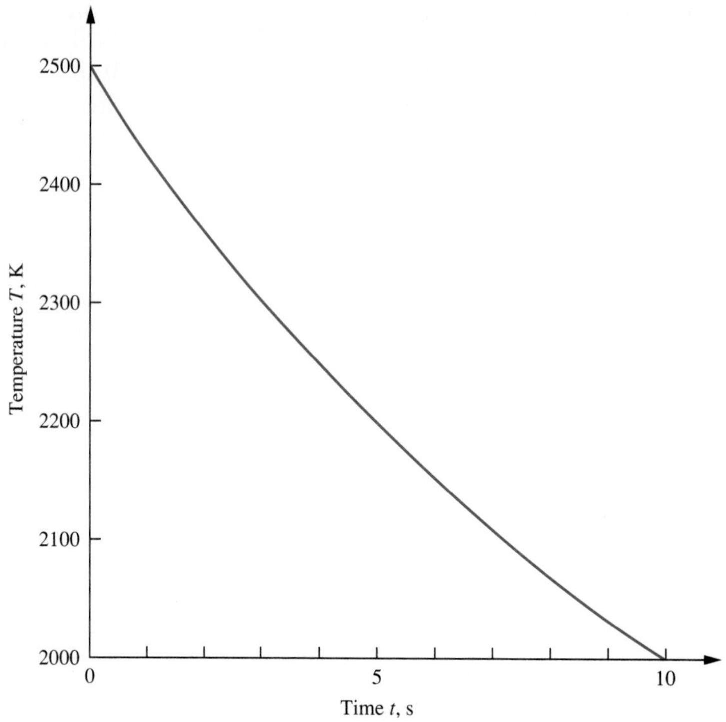

FIGURE 7.1
Exact solution of the radiation problem.

7.2 GENERAL FEATURES OF INITIAL-VALUE ORDINARY DIFFERENTIAL EQUATIONS

Several general features of initial-value ordinary differential equations are discussed in this section. The properties of the linear first-order ODE are presented in some detail. The properties of nonlinear first-order ODEs, systems of first-order ODEs, and higher-order ODEs are discussed briefly.

The Linear First-Order ODE

The general first-order ODE is given by Eq. (7.1). The linear first-order ODE is given by

$$\boxed{y' + \alpha y = F(t), \qquad y(t_0) = y_0} \tag{7.5}$$

where α is a real constant, which can be positive or negative.

The exact solution of Eq. (7.5) is the sum of the *complementary solution* $y_c(t)$ and the particular solution $y_p(t)$:

$$y(t) = y_c(t) + y_p(t) \tag{7.6}$$

The complementary solution is the solution of the homogeneous ODE

$$y_c' + \alpha y_c = 0 \tag{7.7}$$

The particular solution is the function that satisfies the nonhomogeneous ODE

$$y_p' + \alpha y_p = F(t) \tag{7.8}$$

The complementary solution, which depends only on the homogeneous ODE, describes the inherent properties of the ODE and the early transient behavior. The particular solution, which depends on the nonhomogeneous term, describes the asymptotic response of the ODE to the nonhomogeneous term at large values of the independent variable.

The complementary solution $y_c(t)$ is given by

$$y_c(t) = Ae^{-\alpha t} \tag{7.9}$$

which can be shown to satisfy Eq. (7.7) by direct substitution. The coefficient A can be determined by the initial condition, $y(t_0) = y_0$, after the complete solution $y(t)$ to the ODE has been obtained. The particular solution $y_p(t)$ is given by

$$y_p(t) = B_0F(t) + B_1F'(t) + B_2F''(t) + \cdots \tag{7.10}$$

where the terms $F^{(i)}(t)$ are the derivatives of the nonhomogeneous term. These terms, $B_iF^{(i)}(t)$, continue until $F^{(i)}(t)$ repeats its functional form or becomes zero. The coefficients B_0, B_1, and so on, can be determined by substituting Eq. (7.10) into Eq. (7.8), grouping similar functional forms, and requiring that the coefficient of each functional form be zero, so that Eq. (7.8) is satisfied for all values of the independent variable.

The total solution of Eq. (7.5) is determined by substituting Eqs. (7.9) and (7.10) into Eq. (7.6). Thus,

$$\boxed{y(t) = Ae^{-\alpha t} + B_0F(t) + B_1F'(t) + \cdots} \tag{7.11}$$

The constant of integration, A, can be determined by requiring Eq. (7.11) to satisfy the initial condition, $y(t_0) = y_0$.

The homogeneous ODE $y' + \alpha y = 0$ has two completely different types of solutions, depending on whether α is positive or negative. Consider the pair of ODEs:

$$y' + \alpha y = 0 \tag{7.12}$$

$$y' - \alpha y = 0 \tag{7.13}$$

where α is a positive real constant. The solutions to Eqs. (7.12) and (7.13) are

$$y(t) = Ae^{-\alpha t} \tag{7.14}$$

$$y(t) = Ae^{\alpha t} \tag{7.15}$$

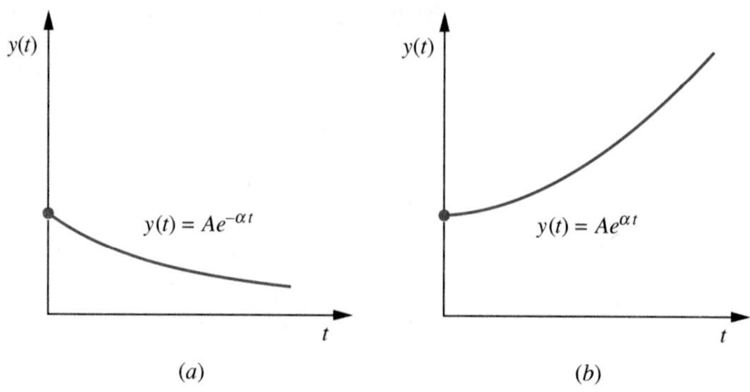

FIGURE 7.2
Solution of the first-order homogeneous ODE: (a) $y' + \alpha y = 0$; (b) $y' - \alpha y = 0$.

Equations (7.14) and (7.15) are illustrated in Fig. 7.2. For $y(t) = Ae^{-\alpha t}$ (i.e., $y' + \alpha y = 0$), the solution decays exponentially with time. For $y(t) = Ae^{\alpha t}$ (i.e., $y' - \alpha y = 0$), the solution grows exponentially without bound. Any numerical method for solving the ODEs must behave in a similar manner.

The Nonlinear First-Order ODE

The nonlinear first-order ODE is given by

$$\boxed{y' = f(t, y), \qquad y(t_0) = y_0} \tag{7.16}$$

where $f(t, y)$ is a nonlinear function of y. The general features of the solution of a nonlinear ODE in a small neighborhood of the initial point are similar to the general features of the solution of a linear ODE.

The nonlinear ODE can be linearized by expressing $f(t, y)$ in a Taylor series about the initial point and dropping all terms higher than first order. Thus,

$$f(t, y) = f_0 + f_t|_0 (t - t_0) + f_y|_0 (y - y_0) + \cdots \tag{7.17}$$

$$= (f_0 - f_t|_0 t_0 - f_y|_0 y_0) + f_t|_0 t + f_y|_0 y + \cdots \tag{7.18}$$

$$= -\alpha y + F(t) + \text{Higher-order terms} \tag{7.19}$$

where $\alpha = -f_y|_0$ and

$$F(t) = \left(f_0 - f_t|_0 t_0 - f_y|_0 y_0\right) + f_t|_0 t \tag{7.20}$$

Dropping the higher-order terms and substituting Eq. (7.19) into the nonlinear ODE, Eq. (7.16), gives

$$\boxed{y' + \alpha y = F(t), \qquad y(t_0) = y_0} \tag{7.21}$$

Most of the general features of the finite difference solution of a nonlinear ODE can be determined by analyzing the linearized form of the nonlinear ODE. Consequently, Eq. (7.21) will be used extensively as a model ODE to investigate the general behavior of the finite difference solution of first-order ODEs.

Systems of First-Order ODEs

Systems of coupled first-order ODEs can be solved by solving all the differential equations simultaneously, using methods developed for solving single first-order ODEs. Consequently, Chapter 7 is devoted mainly to solving single first-order ODEs. A discussion of the solution of systems of first-order ODEs is presented in Section 7.12.

Higher-Order ODEs

Higher-order ODEs generally can be replaced by a system of first-order ODEs. Each higher-order ODE in a system of higher-order ODEs can be replaced by a system of first-order ODEs, thus yielding coupled systems of first-order ODEs. Consequently, Chapter 7 is devoted mainly to solving first-order ODEs. A discussion of the solution of higher-order ODEs is presented in Section 7.13.

Summary

Four types of initial-value ODEs have been considered

1. The linear first-order ODE
2. The nonlinear first-order ODE
3. Systems of first-order ODEs
4. Higher-order ODEs

The general features of ODE Types (2), (3), and (4) are similar to the general features of the linear first-order ODE. Consequently, Chapter 7 is devoted mainly to analyzing the behavior of numerical integration methods applied to the linear first-order ODE.

The foregoing discussion considers unsteady, time-marching (i.e., t) initial-value (propagation) problems. Steady, space-marching (i.e., x) initial-value problems are also propagation problems. Occasionally the space coordinate in a steady, space-marching problem is referred to as a time-like coordinate. Throughout Chapter 7, time-marching initial-value problems are used to illustrate the general features, behavior, and solution of initial-value ODEs. All the results presented in Chapter 7 can be applied directly to steady, space-marching initial-value problems by simply changing t to x in all the discussions, equations, and results.

7.3 THE TAYLOR SERIES METHOD

In theory, the infinite Taylor series can be used to evaluate a function, given its derivative function and its value at some point. Consider the nonlinear first-order ODE:

$$\boxed{y' = f(t, y), \qquad y(t_0) = y_0} \tag{7.22}$$

The Taylor series for $y(t)$ at $t = t_0$ is (see the Appendix):

$$y(t) = y(t_0) + y'(t_0)(t - t_0) + \frac{1}{2}y''(t_0)(t - t_0)^2 + \frac{1}{6}y'''(t_0)(t - t_0)^3$$

$$+ \cdots + \frac{1}{n!}y^{(n)}(t_0)(t - t_0)^n + \cdots \tag{7.23}$$

Equation (7.23) can be written in the simpler-appearing form

$$y(t) = y_0 + y'|_0\,\Delta t + \frac{1}{2}y''|_0\,\Delta t^2 + \frac{1}{6}y'''|_0\,\Delta t^3 + \cdots \tag{7.24}$$

where $y'(t_0) = y'|_0$, and so on, and $\Delta t = (t - t_0)$.

Equation (7.24) can be employed to evaluate $y(t)$ if y_0 and the values of the derivatives at t_0 can be determined. The value of y_0 is the initial condition specified in Eq. (7.22). The first derivative $y'|_0$ can be determined by evaluating the derivative function $f(t, y)$ at t_0: $y'|_0 = f(t_0, y_0)$. The higher-order derivatives in Eq. (7.24) can be determined by successively differentiating the lower-order derivatives, starting with y'. Thus,

$$y'' = (y')' = \frac{d(y')}{dt} \tag{7.25a}$$

$$d(y') = \frac{\partial y'}{\partial t}dt + \frac{\partial y'}{\partial y}dy \tag{7.25b}$$

$$\frac{d(y')}{dt} = \frac{\partial y'}{\partial t} + \frac{\partial y'}{\partial y}\frac{dy}{dt} \tag{7.25c}$$

$$y'' = y'_t + y'_y y' \tag{7.25d}$$

$$y''' = (y'')' = \frac{d(y'')}{dt} = \frac{\partial}{\partial t}(y'_t + y'_y y') + \frac{\partial}{\partial y}(y'_t + y'_y y')\,\frac{dy}{dt} \tag{7.26a}$$

$$y''' = y'_{tt} + 2y'_{ty}y' + y'_t y'_y + (y'_y)^2 y' + y'_{yy}(y')^2 \tag{7.26b}$$

Higher-order derivatives become progressively more complicated. It is not practical to evaluate a large number of the higher-order derivatives. Consequently, the Taylor series must be truncated. The remainder term in a finite Taylor series (see the Appendix) is

$$\text{Remainder} = \frac{1}{(n+1)!} y^{(n+1)}(\tau)\, \Delta t^{n+1} \tag{7.27}$$

where $t_0 \leq \tau \leq t$. Dropping the remainder term yields a finite truncated Taylor series. Error estimation is difficult, since τ is unknown.

Example 7.1. Solution by the Taylor series method. Solve the radiation problem presented in Section 7.1 by the Taylor series method. The ODE is

$$T' = f(t, T) = -\alpha(T^4 - T_a^4), \qquad T(0) = 2500 \quad \text{and} \quad T_a = 250 \tag{7.28}$$

The Taylor series for $T(t)$ is given by

$$\boxed{T(t) = T_0 + T'|_0\, t + \frac{1}{2} T''|_0\, t^2 + \frac{1}{6} T'''|_0\, t^3 + \frac{1}{24} T^{(4)}|_0\, t^4 + \cdots} \tag{7.29}$$

where $\Delta t = t - t_0 = t$. From Eq. (7.28),

$$T_0 = 2500 \tag{7.30}$$

$$T'|_0 = -\alpha(T^4 - T_a^4)|_0 = -(2 \times 10^{-12})(2500^4 - 250^4) = -77.117188 \tag{7.31}$$

Solving for the higher-order derivatives yields:

$$T'' = (T')' = \frac{\partial T'}{\partial t} + \frac{\partial T'}{\partial T} T' = 0 - 4\alpha T^3 T' = 4\alpha^2 T^3 (T^4 - T_a^4) \tag{7.32a}$$

$$T_0'' = -4(2.0 \times 10^{-12}) 2500^3 (-77.117188) = 9.764648 \tag{7.32b}$$

$$T''' = (T'')' = \frac{\partial T''}{\partial t} + \frac{\partial T''}{\partial T} T' = 0 + 28\alpha^2 T^6 T' = -28\alpha^3 T^6 (T^4 - T_a^4) \tag{7.33a}$$

$$T_0''' = 28(2 \times 10^{-12})^2 2500^6 (-77.117188) = -2.136017 \tag{7.33b}$$

$$T^{(4)} = (T''')' = \frac{\partial T'''}{\partial t} + \frac{\partial T'''}{\partial T} T' = 0 - 280\alpha^3 T^9 T' = 280\alpha^4 T^9 (T^4 - T_a^4) \tag{7.34a}$$

$$T_0^{(4)} = -280(2.0 \times 10^{-12})^3 2500^9 (-77.117188) = 0.667505 \tag{7.34b}$$

The solution obtained from Eq. (7.29) is tabulated in Table 7.2, where each T_i denotes the Taylor series through the ith derivative term. These solutions are also presented in Fig. 7.3.

From Fig. 7.3, it is obvious that the accuracy of the solution improves as the number of terms in the Taylor series increases. However, even with four terms, the solution is not very accurate for $t > 3.0$. The Taylor series method is not an efficient method for solving initial-value ODEs.

TABLE 7.2
Solution by the Taylor series method

t	T_1	T_2	T_3	T_4	T_{exact}
0.0	2500.00	2500.00	2500.00	2500.00	2500.00
1.0	2421.88	2426.77	2426.41	2426.44	2426.43
2.0	2343.77	2363.29	2360.45	2360.89	2360.83
3.0	2265.65	2309.59	2299.98	2302.23	2301.79
4.0	2187.53	2265.65	2242.86	2249.98	2247.25
5.0	2109.41	2231.47	2186.97	2204.35	2199.36
6.0	2031.30	2207.06	2130.16	2166.21	2154.47
7.0	1953.18	2192.41	2070.30	2137.08	2113.03
7.0	1875.06	2187.53	2005.26	2119.18	2074.61
9.0	1796.95	2192.41	1932.89	2115.37	2037.84
10.0	1717.83	2207.06	1851.06	2129.18	2005.42

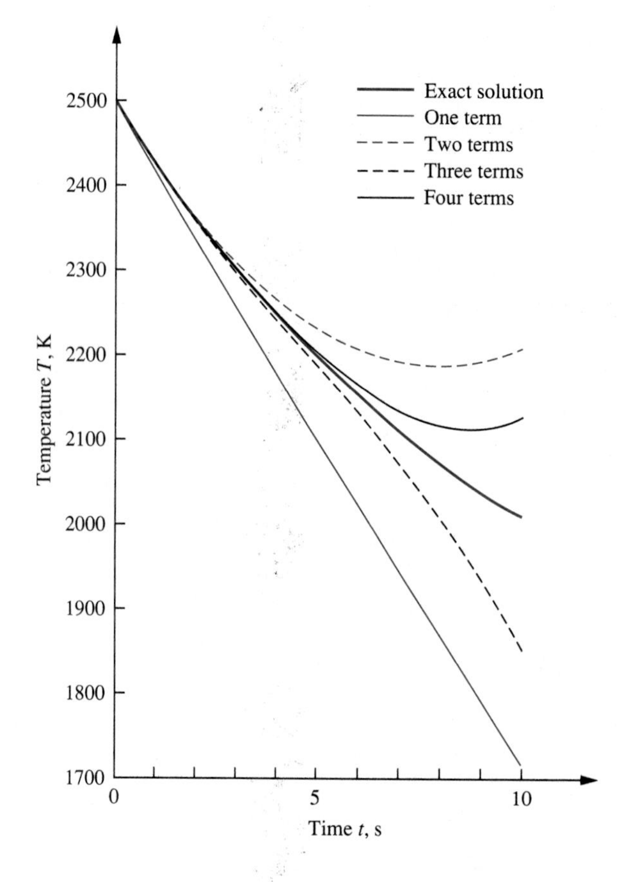

FIGURE 7.3
Solution by the Taylor series method.

Even though the Taylor series method is not an efficient method for solving initial-value ODEs, it is the basis of many excellent numerical methods. As illustrated in Fig. 7.3, the solution by the Taylor series method is quite accurate for small values of t. Therein lies the basis for more accurate methods of solving ODEs. Simply put, use the Taylor series method for a small step in the neighborhood of the initial point. Then reevaluate the coefficients (i.e., the derivatives) at the new point. Successive reevaluation of the coefficients as the solution progresses yields a much more accurate solution. This concept is the basis of most numerical methods for solving initial-value ODEs.

7.4 FINITE DIFFERENCE GRIDS AND FINITE DIFFERENCE APPROXIMATIONS

As stated in Section 7.1, the objective of a finite difference method for solving an ordinary differential equation (ODE) is to transform a calculus problem into an algebra problem by

1. Discretizing the continuous physical domain
2. Approximating the exact derivatives in the ODE by algebraic finite difference approximations (FDAs)
3. Substituting the FDAs into the ODE to obtain an algebraic finite difference equation (FDE)

Discretizing the continuous physical domain and approximating the exact derivatives by finite difference approximations are discussed in this section. The development of finite difference equations is discussed in the next section.

The solution domains $D(t)$ and $D(x)$ in t-space and x-space, respectively, are illustrated in Fig. 7.4. The solution domain must be discretized by a one-dimensional set of discrete grid points, which yields the finite difference grid. The finite difference solution of the ODE will be obtained at these grid points. For the present, let these grid points be equally spaced, having uniform spacing Δt (or Δx). The resulting finite difference grid is illustrated in Fig. 7.4. Nonuniform grids, in which Δt (or Δx) is variable, are discussed in Chapter 13. The subscript n is used to denote the physical grid points, that is, t_n (or x_n). Thus, grid point n corresponds to location t_n (or x_n) in the solution domain $D(t)$ [or $D(x)$]. The total number of grid points is denoted by $nmax$. For the remainder of this chapter, time, t, will be chosen as the independent variable. Similar results hold for steady, space-marching problems in which space,

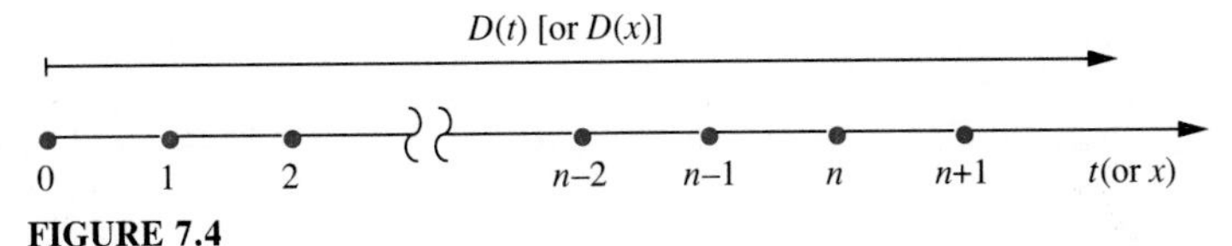

FIGURE 7.4
Solution domain and finite difference grid.

x, is the independent variable. All the results in terms of time, t, can be applied directly to space, x, simply by changing t to x.

The dependent variable at a grid point is denoted by the same subscript notation that is used to denote the grid points themselves. Thus, the function $y(t)$ at grid point n is denoted by

$$y(t_n) = y_n \tag{7.35}$$

In a similar manner, derivatives are denoted by

$$\frac{dy}{dt}(t_n) = y'(t_n) = y'|_n \tag{7.36}$$

Now that the finite difference grid has been specified, finite difference approximations of the exact derivatives in the ODE must be obtained. This is accomplished by using Taylor series expansions of the dependent variable about a particular grid point. This has been done in Section 5.4, where approximations of various types (i.e., forward, backward, and centered) of various orders (first order, second order, and so on) are developed for various derivatives (first derivative, second derivative, and so on). Selected portions of those results are presented in Table 5.1.

In the development of finite difference approximations, a distinction must be made between the exact solution of the differential equation and the solution of the finite difference equation, which is an approximation of the exact differential equation. For the remainder of this chapter, the exact solution of the ODE is denoted by an overbar on the symbol for the dependent variable [i.e., $\bar{y}(t)$], and the approximate solution is denoted by the symbol for the dependent variable without an overbar [i.e., $y(t)$]. Thus,

$$\bar{y}(t) = \text{exact solution}$$
$$y(t) = \text{approximate solution}$$

This very precise distinction between the exact solution of a differential equation and the approximate solution of a differential equation is required for studies of consistency, order, stability, and convergence, which are defined in Section 7.6.

Exact derivatives, such as $\bar{y}'$, can be approximated at a grid point, in terms of the values of $\bar{y}$ at that grid point and adjacent grid points, in several ways. For example, consider the partial derivative $\bar{y}'$. Writing the Taylor series for $\bar{y}_{n+1}$, using grid point n as the base point, gives

$$\bar{y}_{n+1} = \bar{y}_n + \bar{y}'|_n \, \Delta t + \frac{1}{2}\bar{y}''|_n \, \Delta t^2 + \cdots \tag{7.37}$$

where the convention $(\Delta t)^m \rightarrow \Delta t^m$ is employed for compactness. Equation (7.37) can be expressed as the Taylor polynomial with remainder (see the Appendix):

$$\bar{y}_{n+1} = \bar{y}_n + \bar{y}'|_n \, \Delta t + \frac{1}{2}\bar{y}''|_n \, \Delta t^2 + \cdots + \frac{1}{m!}\bar{y}^{(m)}|_n \, \Delta t^m + R_{m+1} \tag{7.38}$$

where the remainder term R_{m+1} is given by

$$R_{m+1} = \frac{1}{(m+1)!}\bar{y}^{(m+1)}(\tau) \, \Delta t^{m+1} \tag{7.39}$$

where $t \leq \tau \leq t + \Delta t$. If the infinite Taylor series is truncated after the mth derivative term to obtain an approximation of $\bar{y}_{n+1}$, then the remainder term R_{m+1} is the error associated with the truncated Taylor series. In most cases, our main concern is the order of the error, which is the rate at which the error goes to zero as $\Delta t \to 0$.

Solving Eq. (7.37) for $\bar{y}'|_n$ yields

$$\bar{y}'|_n = \frac{\bar{y}_{n+1} - \bar{y}_n}{\Delta t} - \frac{1}{2}\bar{y}''|_n \, \Delta t - \cdots \tag{7.40}$$

Equivalently, from Eq. (7.38),

$$\bar{y}'|_n = \frac{\bar{y}_{n+1} - \bar{y}_n}{\Delta t} - \frac{1}{2}\bar{y}''|_n \, \Delta t - \cdots - \frac{R_{m+1}}{\Delta t} \tag{7.41}$$

which can be written as

$$\bar{y}'|_n = \frac{\bar{y}_{n+1} - \bar{y}_n}{\Delta t} - \cdots - O(\Delta t^m) \tag{7.42}$$

where

$$\frac{R_{m+1}}{\Delta t} = \frac{1}{(m+1)!}\bar{y}^{(m+1)}(\tau)\frac{\Delta t^{m+1}}{\Delta t} = O(\Delta t^m) \tag{7.43}$$

and the term $O(\Delta t^m)$ denotes that the remainder term is order m. If the Taylor series is terminated after the $\bar{y}'|_n$ term, then Eqs. (7.41) and (7.43) give

$$\bar{y}'|_n = \frac{\bar{y}_{n+1} - \bar{y}_n}{\Delta t} - \frac{1}{2}\bar{y}''(\tau) \, \Delta t \tag{7.44}$$

which can be written as

$$\boxed{\bar{y}'|_n = \frac{\bar{y}_{n+1} - \bar{y}_n}{\Delta t} + E(\bar{y}'_t|_n) = \frac{\bar{y}_{n+1} - \bar{y}_n}{\Delta t} + O(\Delta t)} \tag{7.45}$$

where the remainder term $E(\bar{y}'|_n)$ is

$$E(\bar{y}'|_n) = -\frac{1}{2}\bar{y}''(\tau) \, \Delta t = O(\Delta t) \tag{7.46}$$

A finite difference approximation of $\bar{y}'|_n$, which will be denoted by $y'|_n$, can be obtained from Eq. (7.45) by neglecting the remainder term. Thus,

$$y'|_n = \frac{y_{n+1} - y_n}{\Delta t}, \qquad O(\Delta t) \tag{7.47}$$

where the $O(\Delta t)$ term is shown to remind us of the order of the approximation. The remainder term, which has been neglected in Eq. (7.47), is called the *truncation error* of the finite difference approximation of $\bar{y}'|_n$. Equation (7.47) is a first-order forward-difference approximation of $\bar{y}'$ at grid point n.

A first-order backward-difference approximation of $\bar{y}'$ at grid point $n + 1$ can be obtained by writing the Taylor series for $\bar{y}_n$ using grid point $n + 1$ as the base point. Thus,

$$y'|_{n+1} = \frac{y_{n+1} - y_n}{\Delta t}, \qquad O(\Delta t) \tag{7.48}$$

A second-order centered-difference approximation of $\bar{y}'$ at grid point $n + \frac{1}{2}$ can be obtained by writing Taylor series for $\bar{y}_{n+1}$ and $\bar{y}_n$ about grid point $n + \frac{1}{2}$, subtracting them, and solving for $\bar{y}'|_{n+1/2}$. Thus,

$$y'|_{n+1/2} = \frac{y_{n+1} - y_n}{\Delta t}, \qquad O(\Delta t^2) \tag{7.49}$$

A second-order centered-difference approximation of $\bar{y}'$ at grid point n can be obtained by writing Taylor series for $\bar{y}_{n+1}$ and $\bar{y}_{n-1}$ about grid point n, subtracting them, and solving for $\bar{y}'|_n$. Thus,

$$y'|_n = \frac{y_{n+1} - y_{n-1}}{2\Delta t}, \qquad O(\Delta t^2) \tag{7.50}$$

Equations (7.47), (7.48), and (7.49) involve the function $y(t)$ at two adjacent grid points, n and $n + 1$. Equation (7.50) also involves $y(t)$ at two grid points, $n - 1$ and $n + 1$. However, *three* grid points are involved, because $n - 1$ and $n + 1$ are separated by $2\Delta t$. Finite difference approximations involving $y(t)$ at two adjacent grid points are called *single-point* methods, because only one known point is involved (i.e., point n). Finite difference approximations involving

$y(t)$ at three grid points are called *two-point* methods, because two known points are involved (i.e., points $n-1$ and n). The number of grid points employed in a finite difference approximation can have a significant impact on the amount of computer storage required to solve the resulting finite difference equation in a computer program and on the complexity of the program logic. Consequently, the number of grid points is an important property of a finite difference method.

Equations (7.47) to (7.50) can be applied to steady, space-marching problems simply by changing t to x in all of the equations.

Occasionally a finite difference approximation of an exact derivative is presented without its development. In such cases, the truncation error and order can be determined by a Taylor series analysis. For example, consider the following finite difference approximation:

$$\text{FDA} = \frac{y_{n+1} - y_n}{\Delta t} \tag{7.51}$$

The Taylor series for the approximate solution $y(t)$ with base point n is

$$y_{n+1} = y_n + y'|_n \, \Delta t + \frac{1}{2} y''|_n \, \Delta t^2 + \cdots \tag{7.52}$$

Substituting the Taylor series for y_{n+1} into the FDA gives

$$\text{FDA} = \frac{y_n + y'|_n \, \Delta t + (1/2) y''|_n \, \Delta t^2 + \cdots - y_n}{\Delta t} = y'|_n + \frac{1}{2} y''|_n \, \Delta t + \cdots \tag{7.53}$$

As $\Delta t \to 0$, the FDA $\to y'|_n$ which shows that the FDA is an approximation of the exact derivative $\bar{y}'$ at grid point n. The order of the FDA is $O(\Delta t)$. The exact form of the truncation error relative to grid point n is determined. Choosing other base points for the Taylor series yields the truncation errors relative to those base points.

An FDA of an exact derivative is *consistent* with the exact derivative if the FDA approaches the exact derivative as $\Delta t \to 0$. Consistency is an important property of the finite difference approximation of differential equations (both ordinary and partial).

7.5 FINITE DIFFERENCE EQUATIONS

Finite difference solutions of ordinary differential equations are obtained by discretizing the continuous solution domain and replacing the exact derivatives in the ordinary differential equations by finite difference approximations, such as Eqs. (7.47) to (7.50), to obtain a finite difference approximation of the differential equation. Such approximations are called *finite difference equations* (FDEs).

Several finite difference methods for solving ODEs are presented in this section. The explicit Euler method and the implicit Euler method are developed and compared, and the modified Euler predictor–corrector method is developed. These three methods are illustrated by applying them to solve the radiation problem presented in Section 7.1.

More accurate methods are presented in subsequent sections of this chapter. Those methods are presented without derivation in this section, where they are illustrated by using them to solve the radiation problem: the fourth-order Runge–Kutta method; the fourth-order Adams–Bashforth method; the fourth-order Adams–Bashforth–Moulton predictor–corrector method; and the fourth-order Adams–Bashforth–Moulton method with mop-up. The derivations of these methods are presented in Sections 7.9 and 7.10.

The Explicit Euler Method

Consider the general nonlinear first-order ODE:

$$\boxed{\bar{y}' = \bar{f}(t, \bar{y}), \qquad \bar{y}(t_0) = \bar{y}_0} \tag{7.54}$$

Choose point n as the base point and develop a finite difference approximation of Eq. (7.54) at that point. The finite difference grid is illustrated in Fig. 7.5, where the cross (i.e., $\times$) denotes the base point for the finite difference approximation of Eq. (7.54). The first-order forward-difference finite difference approximation of $\bar{y}'$ is given by Eq. (7.44):

$$\bar{y}'|_n = \frac{\bar{y}_{n+1} - \bar{y}_n}{\Delta t} - \frac{1}{2}\bar{y}''(\tau_n)\,\Delta t \tag{7.55}$$

Substituting Eq. (7.55) into Eq. (7.54) and evaluating $\bar{f}(t, \bar{y})$ at point n yields

$$\frac{\bar{y}_{n+1} - \bar{y}_n}{\Delta t} - \frac{1}{2}\bar{y}''(\tau_n)\,\Delta t = \bar{f}(t_n, \bar{y}_n) = \bar{f}_n \tag{7.56}$$

Solving Eq. (7.56) for $\bar{y}_{n+1}$ gives

$$\bar{y}_{n+1} = \bar{y}_n + \Delta t \bar{f}_n + \frac{1}{2}\bar{y}''(\tau_n)\,\Delta t^2 = \bar{y}_n + \Delta t \bar{f}_n + O(\Delta t^2) \tag{7.57}$$

Equation (7.57) is an exact expression for $\bar{y}_{n+1}$. However, the remainder term cannot be evaluated. An approximation of $\bar{y}_{n+1}$ can be obtained by dropping the remainder term, which is equivalent to truncating the Taylor series expansion for $\bar{y}_{n+1}$. Consequently, the remainder term is called the truncation error, and Eq. (7.57) becomes

$$\boxed{y_{n+1} = y_n + \Delta t\, f_n, \qquad O(\Delta t^2)} \tag{7.58}$$

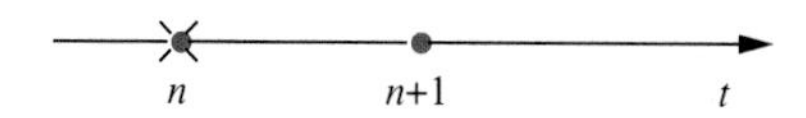

FIGURE 7.5
Finite difference grid for the explicit Euler method.

where the $O(\Delta t^2)$ term is included as a reminder of the order of the truncation error. Equation (7.58) is the explicit Euler approximation of the general first-order ODE.

Several features of Eq. (7.58) are summarized below.

1. The method is explicit, since f_n does not depend on y_{n+1}.
2. The method requires only one known point. Hence, it is a single-point method.
3. A single finite difference equation is required to advance the solution from n to $n + 1$. Thus, the method is a single-step method.
4. The method requires only one derivative function evaluation [i.e., $f(t, y)$] per step.
5. The error in calculating y_{n+1} for a single step, the local truncation error, is $O(\Delta t^2)$.
6. The global (i.e., total) error accumulated after N steps is $O(\Delta t)$. This result is derived in the following discussion.

Equation (7.58) is applied repetitively to march from the initial point t_0 to the final point t_N, as illustrated in Fig. 7.6. The solution at t_N is

$$y_N = y_0 + \sum_{n=0}^{N-1} (y_{n+1} - y_n) = y_0 + \sum_{n=0}^{N-1} \Delta y_{n+1} \tag{7.59}$$

The total truncation error is given by

$$\text{Error} = \sum_{n=0}^{N-1} \frac{1}{2} y''(\tau_n)\,\Delta t^2 = N \frac{1}{2} y''(\tau) \Delta t^2 \tag{7.60}$$

where $t_0 \le \tau \le t_N$. The number of steps N is related to the step size Δt as follows:

$$N = \frac{t_N - t_0}{\Delta t} \tag{7.61}$$

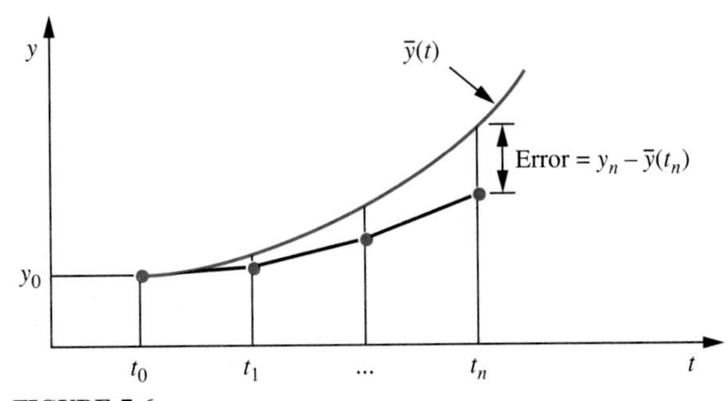

FIGURE 7.6
Repetitive application of the explicit Euler method.

Substituting Eq. (7.61) into Eq. (7.60) yields

$$\text{Error} = \frac{1}{2}(t_N - t_0)y''(\tau)\,\Delta t = O(\Delta t) \tag{7.62}$$

Consequently, the global (i.e., total) error of the explicit Euler method is $O(\Delta t)$, which is the same as the order of the finite difference approximation of the exact derivative $\bar{y}'$, which is shown in Eq. (7.55).

The result developed in the preceding paragraph applies to all finite difference approximations of first-order ordinary differential equations. The order of the global error is always one less than the order of the single-step truncation error, and the order of the global error is always equal to the order of the finite difference approximation of the exact derivative $\bar{y}'$.

Example 7.2. Solution by the explicit Euler method. Solve the radiation problem presented in Section 7.1, using Eq. (7.58). The derivative function is $f(t, T) = -\alpha(T^4 - T_a^4)$. The FDE is

$$T_{n+1} = T_n + \Delta t\, f_n \tag{7.63}$$

Let $\Delta t = 2.0$ s. For the first time step

$$f_0 = -(2.0 \times 10^{-12})(2500^4 - 250^4) = -78.117188 \tag{7.64a}$$

$$T_1 = 2500 + 2.0(-78.117188) = 2343.765625 \tag{7.64b}$$

These results and the results of subsequent time steps for t from 0.0 s to 10.0 s are summarized in Table 7.3. The results for $\Delta t = 1.0$ s are also presented in Table 7.3.

Several important concepts are illustrated in Table 7.3. First, the solutions for both step sizes are following the general trend of the exact solution correctly. The solution for the smaller step size is more accurate than the solution for the larger step size. In fact, the order of the method can be estimated by comparing the errors at $t = 10.0$ s. From Eq. (7.62),

$$E(\Delta t = 2.0) = \frac{1}{2}(t_N - t_0)T''(\tau)(2.0) \tag{7.65a}$$

$$E(\Delta t = 1.0) = \frac{1}{2}(t_N - t_0)T''(\tau)(1.0) \tag{7.65b}$$

Assuming that $T''(\tau)$ in Eqs. (7.65*a*) and (7.65*b*) are approximately equal, the ratio of the theoretical errors is

$$\text{Ratio} = \frac{E(\Delta t = 2.0)}{E(\Delta t = 1.0)} = \frac{2.0}{1.0} = 2 \tag{7.66a}$$

From Table 7.3, at $t = 10.0$ s, the ratio of the numerical errors is

$$\text{Ratio} = \frac{E(\Delta t = 2.0)}{E(\Delta t = 1.0)} = \frac{-31.403718}{-14.936553} = 2.10 \tag{7.66b}$$

TABLE 7.3
Solution by the explicit Euler method

t_n t_{n+1}	T_n T_{n+1}	f_n	T_{exact}	Error
0.00	2500.000000	−78.117188		
2.00	2343.765625	−60.343500	2360.829988	−17.064363
4.00	2223.078626	−48.840469	2248.247314	−25.168688
6.00	2125.397688	−40.804463	2154.470796	−29.073108
8.00	2043.788762	−34.888057	2074.611898	−30.823136
10.00	1974.012648		2005.416366	−31.403718
0.00	2500.000000	−78.117188		
1.00	2421.882813	−68.800752	2426.434874	−4.552061
2.00	2353.082061	−61.308819	2360.829988	−7.747928
3.00	2291.773242	−55.163914	2301.790751	−10.017509
4.00	2236.609328	−50.040625	2248.247314	−11.637986
5.00	2186.568703	−45.709691	2199.362670	−12.793967
6.00	2140.859012	−42.005049	2154.470796	−13.611784
7.00	2098.853963	−38.803549	2113.033861	−14.179898
8.00	2060.050413	−36.011995	2074.611898	−14.561484
9.00	2024.038418	−33.558606	2038.840846	−14.802428
10.00	1990.479813		2005.416366	−14.936553

Equation (7.66) shows that the method is first-order. The value of 2.10 is not exactly equal to the theoretical value of 2, due to the finite step size. The theoretical value of 2 is achieved only in the limit as $\Delta t \to 0$. Order is discussed in more detail in Section 7.6.

Another feature illustrated in Table 7.3 is that the errors are relatively large. This is due to the large $O(\Delta t)$ truncation error. The errors are all negative, indicating that the numerical solution leads the exact solution. This occurs because the derivative function $f(t, T)$ decreases with t, as illustrated in Table 7.3. The derivative function in the FDE is evaluated at point n, the beginning of the interval of integration, where it has its largest value for the interval. Consequently, the numerical solution leads the exact solution.

The final feature of the explicit Euler method that is illustrated in Table 7.3 is that the numerical solution approaches the exact solution as the step size decreases. This property of a finite difference method is called *convergence*. Convergence is necessary for a finite difference method to be of any use in solving an ordinary differential equation. Convergence is discussed in more detail in Section 7.6.

When the base point for the finite difference approximation of an ODE is point n, the unknown value y_{n+1} appears in the finite difference approximation of $\bar{y}'$, but not in the derivative function $\bar{f}(t, \bar{y})$. Such FDEs are called *explicit* FDEs. The explicit Euler method is the simplest example of an explicit FDE.

When the base point for the finite difference approximation of an ODE is point $n+1$, the unknown value y_{n+1} appears in the finite difference approximation of $\bar{y}'$ and also in the derivative function $\bar{f}(t, \bar{y})$. Such FDEs are called *implicit* FDEs. An example of an implicit FDE is presented in the next subsection.

The Implicit Euler Method

Consider the general nonlinear first-order ODE:

$$\boxed{\bar{y}' = \bar{f}(t, \bar{y}), \qquad \bar{y}(t_0) = \bar{y}_0} \tag{7.67}$$

Choose point $n+1$ as the base point, and develop a finite difference approximation of Eq. (7.67). The finite difference grid is illustrated in Fig. 7.7. The first-order backward-difference finite difference approximation of $\bar{y}'$ is given by Eq. (7.48). Substituting Eq. (7.48) into Eq. (7.67) and evaluating $\bar{f}(t, \bar{y})$ at point $n+1$ yields

$$\frac{\bar{y}_{n+1} - \bar{y}_n}{\Delta t} + O(\Delta t) = \bar{f}(t_{n+1}, \bar{y}_{n+1}) = \bar{f}_{n+1} \tag{7.68}$$

Solving Eq. (7.68) for $\bar{y}_{n+1}$ gives

$$\bar{y}_{n+1} = \bar{y}_n + \Delta t\, \bar{f}_{n+1} + O(\Delta t^2) \tag{7.69}$$

Dropping the $O(\Delta t^2)$ remainder term gives the implicit Euler FDE:

$$\boxed{y_{n+1} = y_n + \Delta t\, f_{n+1}, \qquad O(\Delta t^2)} \tag{7.70}$$

Several features of Eq. (7.70) are summarized below.

1. The method is implicit, since f_{n+1} depends on y_{n+1}. If $f(t, y)$ is linear in y, then f_{n+1} is linear in y_{n+1}, and Eq. (7.70) is a linear FDE. If $f(t, y)$ is nonlinear in y, Eq. (7.70) is a nonlinear FDE.
2. The method is a single-point, single-step method.
3. The method requires only one derivative function evaluation per step if $f(t, y)$ is linear in y. If $f(t, y)$ is nonlinear in y, Eq. (7.70) is nonlinear in y_{n+1}, and several evaluations of the derivative function may be required to solve the nonlinear FDE.
4. The single step truncation error is $O(\Delta t^2)$, and the global error is $O(\Delta t)$.

Example 7.3. Solution by the implicit Euler method. Solve the radiation problem presented in Section 7.1 using Eq. (7.70). The derivative function is $f(t, T) = -\alpha(T^4 - T_a^4)$. Substituting the derivative function f_{n+1} into Eq. (7.70) gives

$$T_{n+1} = T_n - \Delta t\, \alpha \left(T_{n+1}^4 - T_a^4\right) \tag{7.71}$$

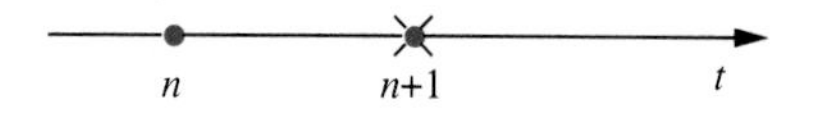

FIGURE 7.7
Finite difference grid for the implicit Euler method.

TABLE 7.4
Solution by the implicit Euler method

t_n t_{n+1}	T_n T_{n+1}	T_{exact}	Error
0.00	2500.000000		
2.00	2373.145960	2360.829988	12.315972
4.00	2267.431887	2248.247314	19.184573
6.00	2177.517153	2154.470796	23.046357
8.00	2099.773878	2074.611898	25.161980
10.00	2031.642170	2005.416366	26.225804
0.00	2500.000000		
1.00	2430.244100	2426.434874	3.809226
2.00	2367.426413	2360.829988	6.596424
⋮	⋮	⋮	⋮
9.00	2052.303498	2038.840846	13.462651
10.00	2019.073062	2005.416366	13.656696

Equation (7.71) is a nonlinear FDE. Procedures for solving nonlinear FDEs are presented in Section 7.11. Let $\Delta t = 2.0$ s. For the first time step,

$$T_1 = 2500 - 2.0(2.0 \times 10^{-12})(T_1^4 - 250^4) \tag{7.72}$$

Equation (7.72) is solved by Newton's method in Example 7.14. The result is $T_1 = 2373.145960$. This result and the results of subsequent time steps are presented in Table 7.4.

The results presented in Table 7.4 behave generally the same as the results presented in Table 7.3 and discussed in Example 7.2. An error analysis at $t = 10.0$ s gives

$$\text{Ratio} = \frac{E(\Delta t = 2.0)}{E(\Delta t = 1.0)} = \frac{26.225804}{13.656696} = 1.92 \tag{7.73}$$

which shows that the method is first-order. The errors are all positive, indicating that the numerical solution lags the exact solution. This result is in direct contrast to the error behavior of the explicit Euler method, where a leading error was observed. In the present case, the derivative function in the FDE is evaluated at point $n + 1$, the end of the interval of integration, where it has its smallest value. Consequently, the numerical solution lags the exact solution.

Comparison of the Explicit and Implicit Euler Methods

The explicit and implicit Euler methods are both first-order [i.e., $O(\Delta t)$] methods. As illustrated in Examples 7.2 and 7.3, the errors in these two methods are comparable for the same step size. For nonlinear ODEs, the explicit Euler method is straightforward, but the implicit Euler method yields a nonlinear FDE, which is more difficult to solve. So what is the advantage, if any, of the implicit Euler method?

The implicit Euler method is unconditionally stable, whereas the explicit Euler method is conditionally stable. This difference can be illustrated by solving the linear first-order homogeneous ODE

$$\bar{y}' + \bar{y} = 0, \qquad \bar{y}(0) = 1 \tag{7.74}$$

The exact solution of Eq. (7.74) is

$$\bar{y}(t) = e^{-t} \tag{7.75}$$

Solving Eq. (7.74) by the explicit Euler method gives the FDE

$$y_{n+1} = y_n + \Delta t\, f_n = y_n + \Delta t(-y_n) \tag{7.76}$$

$$\boxed{y_{n+1} = (1 - \Delta t) y_n} \tag{7.77}$$

The solutions for several values of Δt are presented in Fig. 7.8. The numerical solutions behave in a physically correct manner (i.e., remain bounded) for $\Delta t \le 2.0$. For $\Delta t \le 1.0$, the numerical solution monotonically approaches the exact asymptotic solution $\bar{y}(\infty) = 0$. For $1.0 \le \Delta t < 2.0$, the numerical solution oscillates about the exact asymptotic solution in a damped manner and approaches the exact asymptotic solution as $t \to \infty$. For $\Delta t = 2.0$, the numerical solution oscillates about the exact solution in a stable manner but never approaches the exact asymptotic solution. For $\Delta t > 2.0$, the numerical solution oscillates about the exact asymptotic solution in an unstable manner and grows exponentially without bound. This is *numerical instability*. The explicit Euler method is *conditionally stable* for this ODE, that is, it is stable if $\Delta t \le 2.0$. The oscillatory behavior for $1.0 < \Delta t < 2.0$ is called *overshoot*. It is not instability, but it does not model physical reality; thus, it is unacceptable.

Solving the ODE by the implicit Euler method gives the FDE

$$y_{n+1} = y_n + \Delta t\, f_{n+1} = y_n + \Delta t(-y_{n+1}) \tag{7.78}$$

which is implicit. Since Eq. (7.78) is linear in y_{n+1}, it can be solved explicitly for y_{n+1} to yield

$$\boxed{y_{n+1} = \frac{y_n}{1 + \Delta t}} \tag{7.79}$$

The solutions for several values of Δt are presented in Fig. 7.9. The numerical solutions behave in a physically correct manner for all values of Δt. This is *unconditional stability*, which is the main advantage of implicit methods. The error increases as Δt increases, but this is an accuracy problem, not a stability problem.

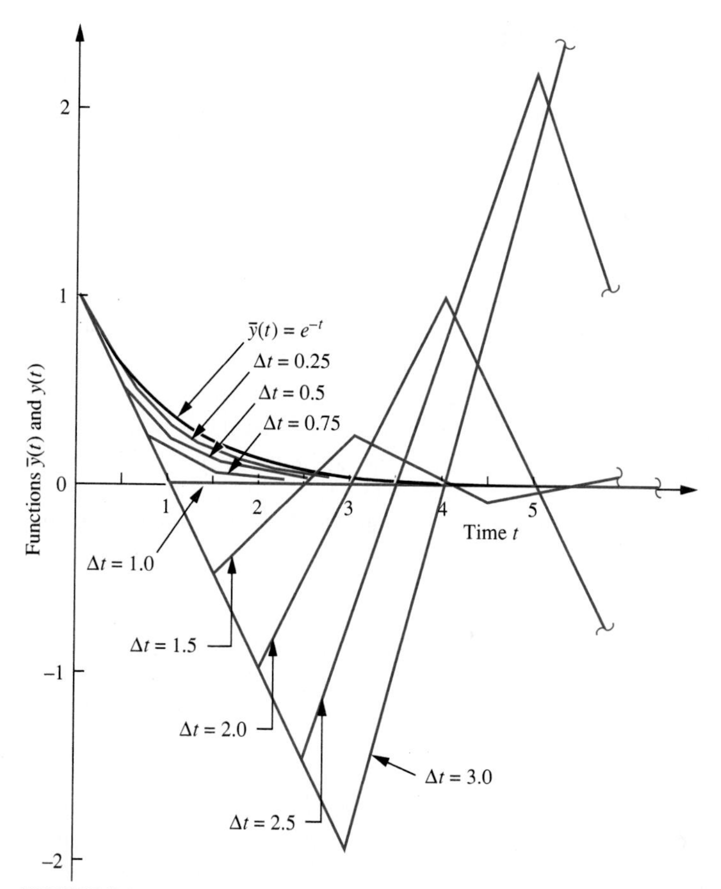

FIGURE 7.8
Behavior of the explicit Euler method.

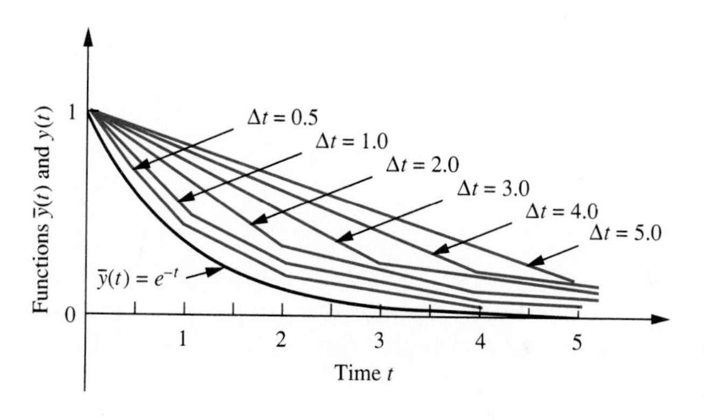

FIGURE 7.9
Behavior of the implicit Euler method.

The Modified Euler Predictor–Corrector Method

The explicit and implicit Euler methods are single-step methods, that is, the solution is obtained in one step by applying a single finite difference equation. Both of these methods are first-order methods, since the finite difference approximation of $\bar{y}'$ is first order in both cases. Higher-order methods can be obtained by using higher-order finite difference approximations of $\bar{y}'$. Such methods require either more than one step or more than one known point.

Explicit methods, such as the first-order explicit Euler method, lead to simple linear finite difference equations. However, as illustrated in the last section, the FDEs are conditionally stable. Implicit methods, such as the first-order implicit Euler method, lead to nonlinear FDEs when the derivative function is nonlinear. However, as illustrated in the last section for the implicit Euler method, the FDEs are unconditionally stable. The contrasting features of these two methods suggest a compromise that seeks to maintain the advantages of both methods (i.e., linear FDEs and unconditional stability) while removing the disadvantages of both methods (i.e., conditional stability and nonlinear FDEs). *Predictor–corrector* methods yield such a compromise. An explicit method is used to predict the solution, and an implicit method is used to correct the solution. Predictor–corrector methods are numerically explicit. They generally have the accuracy (i.e., order) of the corrector (i.e., implicit) method. Predictor–corrector methods are generally conditionally stable, however, and the stable step size may not be much larger than that of the explicit predictor method. The motivation for developing predictor–corrector methods is the increased accuracy obtainable with higher-order implicit methods without the problems associated with nonlinear FDEs.

The modified Euler predictor–corrector method is presented in this section to illustrate these concepts. More accurate predictor–corrector methods are presented in Section 7.10.

Consider the general nonlinear first-order ODE $\bar{y}' = \bar{f}(t, \bar{y})$, $\bar{y}(t_0) = \bar{y}_0$. Construct a finite difference approximation of this ODE at point $(n + \frac{1}{2})$ by using the second-order centered-difference approximation of $\bar{y}'$, Eq. (7.49), and evaluating $\bar{f}(t, \bar{y})$ at the midpoint of the interval. The finite difference grid is illustrated in Fig. 7.10. Thus,

$$\bar{y}'|_{n+1/2} = \frac{\bar{y}_{n+1} - \bar{y}_n}{\Delta t} + O(\Delta t^2) = \bar{f}(t_n + \Delta t/2, \bar{y}_{n+1/2}) = \bar{f}_{n+1/2} \tag{7.80}$$

Solving Eq. (7.80) for $\bar{y}_{n+1}$ yields

$$\bar{y}_{n+1} = \bar{y}_n + \Delta t\, \bar{f}_{n+1/2} + O(\Delta t^3) \tag{7.81}$$

Equation (7.81) is implicit, since $\bar{f}_{n+1/2}$ depends on $\bar{y}_{n+1/2}$. Equation (7.81) has a third-order remainder term, whereas Eq. (7.57) for the explicit Euler method and Eq. (7.69) for the implicit Euler method both have second-order remainder

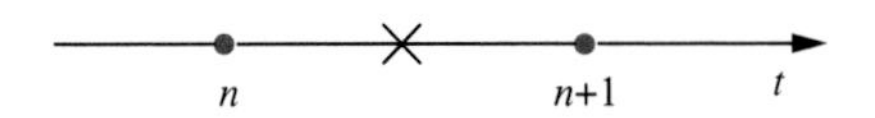

FIGURE 7.10
Finite difference grid for the modified Euler method.

terms. Dropping the $O(\Delta t^3)$ remainder term gives

$$y_{n+1} = y_n + \Delta t\, f_{n+1/2}, \qquad O(\Delta t^3) \tag{7.82}$$

Equation (7.82) is the implicit midpoint finite difference equation.

Equation (7.82) is implicit, since $f_{n+1/2}$ depends on $y_{n+1/2}$. A more serious problem exists, because Eq. (7.82) contains two unknowns, $y_{n+1/2}$ and y_{n+1}, in a single equation. The second problem can be eliminated by expressing $f_{n+1/2}$ in terms of f_n and f_{n+1} by writing Taylor series for $\bar{f}_n$ and $\bar{f}_{n+1}$ at grid point $(n + 1/2)$. Thus,

$$\bar{f}_n = \bar{f}_{n+1/2} + \bar{f}'|_{n+1/2}(-\Delta t/2) + O(\Delta t^2) \tag{7.83a}$$

$$\bar{f}_{n+1} = \bar{f}_{n+1/2} + \bar{f}'|_{n+1/2}(\Delta t/2) + O(\Delta t^2) \tag{7.83b}$$

Adding Eqs. (7.83*a*) and (7.83*b*) and solving for $\bar{f}_{n+1/2}$ gives

$$\bar{f}_{n+1/2} = \frac{1}{2}(\bar{f}_n + \bar{f}_{n+1}) + O(\Delta t^2) \tag{7.84}$$

Substituting Eq. (7.84) into Eq. (7.81) gives

$$\bar{y}_{n+1} = \bar{y}_n + \frac{1}{2}\Delta t\left(\bar{f}_n + \bar{f}_{n+1} + O(\Delta t^2)\right) + O(\Delta t^3) \tag{7.85}$$

Dropping the remainder terms yields the trapezoid rule finite difference equation:

$$y_{n+1} = y_n + \frac{1}{2}\Delta t(f_n + f_{n+1}), \qquad O(\Delta t^3) \tag{7.86}$$

The local truncation error is $O(\Delta t^3)$, giving an $O(\Delta t^2)$ global truncation error.

Equation (7.86) is still implicit, since f_{n+1} depends on y_{n+1}. For a linear ODE, Eq. (7.86) can be solved directly for y_{n+1}. However, for a nonlinear ODE, Eq. (7.86) yields a nonlinear finite difference equation. One method for circumventing this complication is to predict y_{n+1} using the explicit Euler method, Eq. (7.58); to use this predicted value of y_{n+1} to evaluate f_{n+1}; and then to correct y_{n+1} using the trapezoid rule, Eq. (7.86). Thus, a two-step predictor–corrector method is obtained:

$$y^P_{n+1} = y_n + \Delta t f_n \tag{7.87a}$$

$$y^C_{n+1} = y_n + \frac{1}{2}\Delta t(f_n + f^P_{n+1}) \tag{7.87b}$$

where the superscripts P and C denote the results of the predictor and corrector steps, respectively, and

$$f_{n+1}^P = f(t_{n+1}, y_{n+1}^P) \tag{7.88}$$

This two-step method is known as the *modified Euler predictor–corrector* method.

The truncation error of Eq. (7.87*b*) is $O(\Delta t^3)$, while the truncation error of Eq. (7.87*a*) is $O(\Delta t^2)$. What is the truncation error of the combined two-step method? For the linear first-order homogeneous ODE $\bar{y}' + \alpha\bar{y} = 0$, Eq. (7.57) gives

$$\bar{y}_{n+1}^P = \bar{y}_n + h(-\alpha\bar{y}_n) + O(\Delta t^2) = (1 - \alpha h)\bar{y}_n + O(\Delta t^2) \tag{7.89}$$

where $h = \Delta t$. Substituting Eq. (7.89) into Eq. (7.87*b*) yields

$$\bar{y}_{n+1}^C = \bar{y}_n + \frac{1}{2}h\big(-\alpha\bar{y}_n - \alpha(1 - \alpha h)\bar{y}_n + O(\Delta t^2)\big) + O(\Delta t^3) \tag{7.90}$$

$$\bar{y}_{n+1}^C = \left(1 - \alpha h + \frac{(\alpha h)^2}{2}\right)\bar{y}_n + O(\Delta t^3) \tag{7.91}$$

Equation (7.91) shows that the combined two-step method has an $O(\Delta t^3)$ local truncation error. Thus, the combined method has the order of the corrector FDE.

The general features of Eq. (7.87) are presented below.

1. The FDE is explicit.
2. The method is a single-point, two-step, predictor–corrector method.
3. The method requires two derivative function evaluations per step.
4. The single step truncation error is $O(\Delta t^3)$, and the global error is $O(\Delta t^2)$.

Example 7.4. Solution by the modified Euler method. To illustrate the modified Euler method, let's solve the radiation problem presented in Section 7.1 using Eq. (7.87). The derivative function is $f(t, T) = -\alpha(T^4 - T_a^4)$. Equation (7.87) yields

$$T_{n+1}^P = T_n + \Delta t\, f_n \tag{7.92a}$$

$$f_{n+1}^P = f(t_{n+1}, T_{n+1}^P) \tag{7.92b}$$

$$T_{n+1}^C = T_n + \frac{1}{2}\Delta t(f_n + f_{n+1}^P) \tag{7.92c}$$

Let $\Delta t = 2.0$ s. For the first time step, the predictor FDE gives

$$f_0 = -(2.0 \times 10^{-12})(2500^4 - 250^4) = -78.117188 \tag{7.93a}$$

$$T_1^P = 2500 + 2.0(-78.117188) = 2343.765625 \tag{7.93b}$$

The corrector FDE yields

$$f_1^P = -(2.0 \times 10^{-12})(2343.765625^4 - 250^4) = -60.343500 \tag{7.93c}$$

$$T_1^C = 2500 + \frac{1}{2}(2.0)(-78.117188 - 60.343500) = 2361.539313 \tag{7.93d}$$

These results and the results of subsequent time steps are summarized in Table 7.5. The exact solution and the errors are presented for comparison.

TABLE 7.5
Solution by the modified Euler method

t_n t_{n+1}	T_n T^P_{n+1} T^C_{n+1}	f_n f^P_{n+1}	T_{exact}	Error
0.00	2500.000000	−78.117188		
	2343.765625	−60.343500		
2.00	2361.539313	−62.195099	2360.829988	0.709324
	2237.149114	−50.088957		
4.00	2249.255256	−51.182169	2248.247314	1.007942
⋮	⋮	⋮	⋮	⋮
8.00	2075.759555	−37.123319	2074.611898	1.147657
	2001.512918	−32.089124		
10.00	2006.547112		2005.416366	1.130746
0.00	2500.000000	−78.117188		
	2421.882813	−68.800752		
1.00	2426.541030	−69.331663	2426.434874	0.106157
	2357.209367	−61.740150		
2.00	2361.005124	−62.138836	2360.829988	0.175136
⋮	⋮	⋮	⋮	⋮
9.00	2039.122290	−34.570443	2038.840846	0.281444
	2004.551847	−32.284502		
10.00	2005.694818		2005.416366	0.278452

The errors presented in Table 7.5 for the second-order modified Euler method for $\Delta t = 1.0$ s are approximately 50 times smaller than the errors presented in Table 7.3 for the first-order explicit Euler method. This illustrates the advantage of the higher-order method. To achieve a factor-of-50 decrease in the error for a first-order method requires a reduction of 50 in the step size, which increases the number of derivative function evaluations by a factor of 50. The same reduction in error was achieved with the second-order method, at the expense of twice as many derivative function evaluations. An error analysis at $t = 10.0$ s gives

$$\text{Ratio} = \frac{E(\Delta t = 2.0)}{E(\Delta t = 1.0)} = \frac{1.130746}{0.278452} = 4.06 \tag{7.94}$$

which demonstrates that the method is second-order, since the theoretical error ratio for an $O(\Delta t^2)$ method is 4.

The corrector step of the modified Euler method, Eq. (7.87), may be iterated, if desired, by reevaluating f_{n+1} based on y^C_{n+1}. Thus, $f^C_{n+1} = f(t_{n+1}, y^C_{n+1})$. Iteration is generally not as worthwhile as taking a smaller step size.

The modified Euler method is one of the simplest multistep methods. A more accurate class of multistep methods, called Runge–Kutta methods, is developed in Section 7.9. The fourth-order Runge–Kutta method is illustrated in the next subsection.

The Fourth-Order Runge–Kutta Method

The modified Euler predictor–corrector method is a second-order multistep (i.e., two-step) method. More accurate multistep methods are desirable. One approach for obtaining higher-order multistep methods is presented in Section 7.9. Those methods, which are called Runge–Kutta methods, obtain higher-order accuracy by introducing intermediate points between points n and $n+1$. There are many Runge–Kutta methods. A very popular fourth-order Runge–Kutta method is presented in this section. A complete derivation of the family of second-order Runge-Kutta methods is presented in Section 7.9 to illustrate the process.

The basic idea of Runge–Kutta methods is to assume that $\Delta y_n = (y_{n+1} - y_n)$ is the weighted summation of several Δy_i ($i = 1, 2, \ldots$), where each Δy_i is based on a different value of the derivative function $f(t, y)$. Thus,

$$y_{n+1} - y_n = C_1\,\Delta y_1 + C_2\,\Delta y_2 + C_3\,\Delta y_3 + \cdots \tag{7.95}$$

$$\Delta y_1 = \Delta t\, f(t_n, y_n) \tag{7.96a}$$

$$\Delta y_2 = \Delta t\, f(t_n + \alpha_2, y_n + \beta_2) \tag{7.96b}$$

$$\Delta y_3 = \Delta t\, f(t_n + \alpha_3, y_n + \beta_3) \tag{7.96c}$$

and so on. The first Δy, Δy_1, is the explicit Euler Δy. The subsequent Δy_i are evaluated at various locations within the interval, $t_n \le t \le t_{n+1}$, as defined by $t_i = t_n + \alpha_i$, with the corresponding values of $y_i = y_n + \beta_i$, where β_i is some combination of the earlier Δy_j values ($j = 1, 2, \ldots, i-1$). Substituting Eq. (7.96) into Eq. (7.95) yields

$$y_{n+1} - y_n = C_1\,\Delta t\, f(t_n, y_n) + C_2\,\Delta t\, f(t_n + \alpha_2, y_n + \beta_2) + C_3\,\Delta t\, f(t_n + \alpha_3, y_n + \beta_3) + \cdots \tag{7.97}$$

The free parameters in Eq. (7.97), that is, C_1, $C_2, \ldots, \alpha_2$, $\alpha_3, \ldots,$ and β_2, $\beta_3, \ldots,$ are chosen by requiring Eq. (7.97) to match the Taylor series for $\overline{y}(t)$ through terms of a specified order. This procedure is illustrated in Section 7.9 for the second-order Runge–Kutta method.

The most popular Runge-Kutta method is the following fourth-order-method:

$$\boxed{y_{n+1} = y_n + \frac{1}{6}(\Delta y_1 + 2\Delta y_2 + 2\Delta y_3 + \Delta y_4)} \tag{7.98}$$

$$\Delta y_1 = \Delta t\, f(t_n, y_n) \tag{7.99a}$$

$$\Delta y_2 = \Delta t\, f\left(t_n + \frac{\Delta t}{2}, y_n + \frac{\Delta y_1}{2}\right) \tag{7.99b}$$

$$\Delta y_3 = \Delta t\, f\left(t_n + \frac{\Delta t}{2}, y_n + \frac{\Delta y_2}{2}\right) \tag{7.99c}$$

$$\Delta y_4 = \Delta t\, f(t_n + \Delta t, y_n + \Delta y_3) \tag{7.99d}$$

Equation (7.99*a*) is the explicit Euler method Δy, Eq. (7.99*b*) is the midpoint method Δy based on the Euler method as a predictor, Eq. (7.99*c*) is the midpoint method Δy based on the first midpoint method as a predictor, and Eq. (7.99*d*) is the implicit Euler method Δy based on the second midpoint method as a predictor.

The fourth-order Runge–Kutta method has the following features:

1. The FDEs are explicit.
2. The method is a single-point, four-step method.
3. The method requires four derivative function evaluations per step.
4. The single-step truncation error is $O(\Delta t^5)$, and the global error is $O(\Delta t^4)$.

Example 7.5. Solution by the fourth-order Runge–Kutta method. Solve the radiation problem presented in Section 7.1 using the fourth-order Runge–Kutta method. The derivative function is $f(t, T) = -\alpha(T^4 - T_a^4)$. This particular derivative function does not depend explicitly on t, which simplifies the calculations somewhat. Thus, $f(t, T) = f(T)$. Let $\Delta t = 1.0$ s. For the first time step,

$$\Delta y_1 = 1.0(-2.0 \times 10^{-12})(2500^4 - 250^4) = -78.11718750 \tag{7.100a}$$

$$\Delta y_2 = 1.0(-2.0 \times 10^{-12})\left(\left(2500 + \frac{-78.11718750}{2}\right)^4 - 250^4\right) = -73.34809423 \tag{7.100b}$$

$$\Delta y_3 = 1.0(-2.0 \times 10^{-12})\left(\left(2500 + \frac{-73.34809423}{2}\right)^4 - 250^4\right) = -73.63282264 \tag{7.100c}$$

$$\Delta y_4 = 1.0(-2.0 \times 10^{-12})\left((2500 + 73.63282264)^4 - 250^4\right) = -69.31179347 \tag{7.100d}$$

$$T_1 = 2500 + \frac{1}{6}\Big(-78.11718750 + 2(-73.34809423) + 2(-73.63282264) - 69.31179347\Big) = 2426.43486422 \tag{7.101}$$

These results and the results of subsequent time steps are summarized in Table 7.6.

The results presented in Table 7.6 are presented to eight digits after the decimal place. The error at $t = 10.0$ s is $-$ 0.00001394, which compares with $-$ 14.936553 for the first-order explicit Euler method and 0.278452 for the second-order modified Euler method. The advantage of the fourth-order method is apparent. However, the fourth-order Runge–Kutta method requires four derivative function evaluations per step as compared to one for the first-order explicit Euler method and two for the second-order modified Euler method. The ratio of the errors of the modified Euler method and the Runge–Kutta method at $t = 10.0$ s is $= 0.278452/0.00001394 \approx 20{,}000$. To reduce the error of the second-order modified Euler method by this ratio requires a step size reduction of

$$\text{Ratio} = \left(\frac{\Delta t_1}{\Delta t_2}\right)^2 = 20{,}000 \tag{7.102}$$

TABLE 7.6
Solution by the fourth-order Runge–Kutta method

t_n t_{n+1}	T_n T_{n+1}	Δy_1 Δy_3	Δy_2 Δy_4	Error
0.00	2500.00000000	−78.11718750	−73.34809423	
		−73.63282264	−69.31179347	
1.00	2426.43486422	−69.31952885	−65.44244456	−0.00000937
		−65.65489333	−62.11513358	
2.00	2360.82997451	−62.12039705	−58.91480392	−0.00001394
3.00	2301.79073466	−56.13489412	−53.44621530	−0.00001602
⋮	⋮	⋮	⋮	⋮
9.00	2038.84083184	−34.55135611	−33.39484092	−0.00001462
10.00	2005.41635186	−33.43307590	−32.33969012	−0.00001394

which gives $\Delta t_1/\Delta t_2 \approx 140$. Even accounting for the fact that the Runge–Kutta method requires twice as much effort per step as the second-order modified Euler method (i.e., four derivative function evaluations compared to two), the modified Euler method would require approximately 70 times as much effort to achieve the same accuracy as the Runge–Kutta method.

The Fourth-Order Adams–Bashforth Method

All of the methods presented so far are single-point methods, that is, the solution at point $n + 1$ is based on a single-known point, point n. The simplest single-point methods, the explicit and implicit Euler methods, are first-order methods. The modified Euler method is a second-order single-point method. However, it requires two derivative function evaluations for each step. Higher-order methods with fewer derivative function evaluations can be developed by using more than one known point. Such methods are called *multipoint methods*.

One approach for deriving multipoint methods is presented in Section 7.10. Multipoint methods are generally predictor–corrector methods, which are somewhat similar in concept to the modified Euler predictor–corrector method. An explicit multipoint method is used as a predictor, and an implicit multipoint method is used as a corrector. The explicit fourth-order Adams–Bashforth method is presented in this subsection. The derivation of this method is presented in Section 7.10.

There are several ways to derive multipoint methods, all of which are equivalent. We shall derive them by fitting Newton backward-difference polynomials to selected points and integrating over a specified interval. Consider the general first-order ODE:

$$\boxed{\bar{y}' = \bar{f}(t, \bar{y}), \qquad \bar{y}(t_0) = \bar{y}_0} \tag{7.103}$$

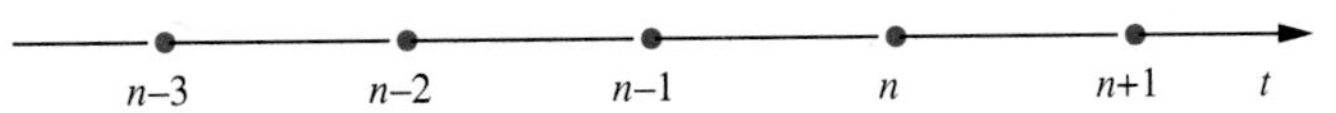

FIGURE 7.11
Finite difference grid for multipoint methods.

Recalling that $\bar{y}' = d\bar{y}/dt$, Eq. (7.103) can be written as

$$d\bar{y} = \bar{f}(t, \bar{y})\, dt = F[t, \bar{y}(t)]\, dt = F(t)\, dt \tag{7.104}$$

Integrating Eq. (7.104) from some initial point (e.g., n, $n-1$, etc.) to the unknown point $n+1$ yields

$$\int_{?}^{\bar{y}_{n+1}} d\bar{y} = \int_{?}^{t_{n+1}} F(t)\, dt \tag{7.105}$$

Consider the finite difference grid illustrated in Fig. 7.11. The function $F(t)$ can be approximated by fitting a kth-degree Newton backward-difference polynomial, $P_k(t)$, with base point n, to two or more points in the finite difference grid. Equation (7.105) becomes

$$\boxed{\int_{?}^{\bar{y}_{n+1}} d\bar{y} = \int_{?}^{t_{n+1}} P_k(t)dt} \tag{7.106}$$

Families of methods can be devised by choosing different degrees of interpolating polynomials and different initial points of integration.

Explicit multipoint methods are obtained when the polynomial is fitted at base point n. Implicit multipoint methods are obtained when the polynomial is fitted at base point $n+1$. Predictor–corrector multipoint methods are constructed using an explicit method for the predictor and an implicit method for the corrector.

The fourth-order explicit Adams–Bashforth method is obtained by fitting a third-order Newton backward-difference polynomial to point n and integrating Eq. (7.106) from n to $n+1$. That procedure is presented in Section 7.10. The result is:

$$\bar{y}_{n+1} = \bar{y}_n + \frac{\Delta t}{24}(55\bar{f}_n - 59\bar{f}_{n-1} + 37\bar{f}_{n-2} - 9\bar{f}_{n-3}) + \frac{251}{720}\Delta t^5\, \bar{y}^{(5)}(\tau) \tag{7.107}$$

The fourth-order Adams–Bashforth FDE is obtained by dropping the remainder term in Eq. (7.107). Thus,

$$\boxed{y_{n+1} = y_n + \frac{\Delta t}{24}\big(55f_n - 59f_{n-1} + 37f_{n-2} - 9f_{n-3}\big), \qquad O(\Delta t^5)} \tag{7.108}$$

The general features of the fourth-order Adams–Bashforth method are summarized below.

1. The FDE is explicit.
2. The method is a four-point, single-step method. Thus, in addition to the initial value, three starting values are required. These can be obtained by a single-point method, such as the fourth-order Runge–Kutta method.
3. The FDE requires one derivative function evaluation per step.
4. The single step truncation error is $O(\Delta t^5)$, and the global error is $O(\Delta t^4)$.

Example 7.6. Solution by the fourth-order Adams–Bashforth method. To illustrate the fourth-order Adams–Bashforth method, we will solve the radiation problem presented in Section 7.1 using Eq. (7.108). The derivative function is $f(t, T) = -\alpha(T^4 - T_a^4)$. Let $\Delta t = 1.0$ s. For starting values, use the exact solution presented in Table 7.1. For $t_4 = 4.0$ s,

$$T_4 = 2301.79075068 + \frac{1.0}{24}\Big(55(-56.13489568) - 59(-62.12039852) + 37(-69.31952992) - 9(-78.11718750)\Big) = 2248.28726445 \quad (7.109)$$

These results and the results of subsequent time steps are summarized in Table 7.7.

The results presented in Table 7.7 are presented to eight digits after the decimal place. The error at $t = 10.0$ s is 0.08304739, which compares with − 0.00001394 for the fourth-order Runge–Kutta method presented in Example 7.5. The ratio of the errors is (0.08304739/0.00001394) = 5957. However, the fourth-order Runge–Kutta method requires four derivative function evaluations per step, as compared to one for the fourth-order Adams–Bashforth method. If the step size of the fourth-order Adams–Bashforth method is decreased by four, thus increasing the number of grid points and derivative function evaluations by four, the error should decrease by $4^4 = 256$. This decrease in error is approximately 23 times less than the value of 5957 for the ratio of errors of the two methods for the same step size. Consequently, the fourth-order Runge–Kutta method,

TABLE 7.7
Solution by the fourth-order Adams–Bashforth method

t_n t_{n+1}	T_n T_{n+1}	f_n	T_{exact}	Error
0.00	2500.00000000	−78.11718750		
1.00	2426.43487359	−69.31952992	exact	
2.00	2360.82998846	−62.12039852	solution	
3.00	2301.79075068	−56.13489658		
4.00	2248.28726445	−51.09410509	2248.24731405	0.03995039
5.00	2199.42076817	−46.79406570	2199.36266993	0.05809824
6.00	2154.54456123	−43.08967167	2154.47079576	0.07376546
7.00	2113.11331570	−39.86906485	2113.03386111	0.07945458
8.00	2074.69492306	−37.04720071	2074.61189788	0.08302518
9.00	2038.92440333	−34.55702274	2038.84084646	0.08355687
10.00	2005.49941320		2005.41636581	0.08304739

for comparable computing effort, equals or exceeds the fourth-order Adams–Bashforth method in accuracy in this problem. Repeating the calculations with the fourth-order Adams–Bashforth method for $\Delta t = 0.25$ s gives T(10.0) = 2005.41679503, for which the error is 0.00042922. This error is approximately 31 times larger than the error of the fourth-order Runge–Kutta method (i.e., − 0.00001394), which substantiates the above conclusions. The ratio of the errors for the fourth-order Adams–Bashforth method is

$$\text{Ratio} = \frac{E(\Delta t = 1.0)}{E(\Delta t = 0.25)} = \frac{0.08304739}{0.00042922} = 193.4 \tag{7.110}$$

The theoretical value is $(1.0/0.25)^4 = 256$, which demonstrates that the method is $O(h^4)$.

The Fourth-Order Adams–Bashforth–Moulton Method

The fourth-order Adams–Bashforth FDE presented in the preceding subsection is an explicit FDE. Implicit multipoint methods can be obtained by fitting a Newton backward-difference polynomial to point $n+1$ and integrating Eq. (7.106) from n to $n+1$. The resulting FDEs are called Adams–Moulton FDEs. The fourth-order Adams–Moulton FDE is derived in Section 7.10. The result is

$$\bar{y}_{n+1} = \bar{y}_n + \frac{\Delta t}{24}(9\bar{f}_{n+1} + 19\bar{f}_n - 5\bar{f}_{n-1} + \bar{f}_{n-2}) - \frac{19}{720}\Delta t^5\, \bar{y}^{(5)}(\tau) \tag{7.111}$$

The fourth-order Adams–Moulton FDE is obtained by dropping the remainder term in Eq. (7.111). Equation (7.111) is implicit, since f_{n+1} depends on y_{n+1}. Equation (7.111) can be used as a corrector FDE with the explicit fourth-order Adams–Bashforth FDE, Eq. (7.108), as a predictor. The combined predictor–corrector method is called the fourth-order Adams–Bashforth–Moulton method. Thus,

$$y_{n+1}^P = y_n + \frac{\Delta t}{24}(55f_n - 59f_{n-1} + 37f_{n-2} - 9f_{n-3}) \tag{7.112}$$

$$y_{n+1}^C = y_n + \frac{\Delta t}{24}(9f_{n+1}^P + 19f_n - 5f_{n-1} + f_{n-2}) \tag{7.113}$$

where $f_{n+1}^P = f(t_{n+1}, y_{n+1}^P)$.

The general features of the fourth-order Adams–Bashforth–Moulton method are summarized below.

1. The FDEs are explicit.
2. The method is a four-point, two-step method. Thus, in addition to the initial value, three starting values are required.
3. The two FDEs require a total of two derivative function evaluations per step.

4. The single-step truncation error is $O(\Delta t^5)$, and the global error is $O(\Delta t^4)$.
5. The local truncation errors of the predictor and corrector FDEs can be combined for error estimation, error control, and extrapolation. These procedures are presented later in this section.

Example 7.7. Solution by the fourth-order Adams–Bashforth–Moulton method. Solve the radiation problem by the fourth-order Adams–Bashforth–Moulton method. The derivative function is $f(t, T) = -\alpha(T^4 - T_a^4)$. For starting values, use the exact solution from Table 7.1. For $t_4 = 4.0$ s,

$$T_4^P = 2248.28726445 \qquad \text{from Example 7.6} \tag{7.114a}$$

$$f_4^P = -(2.0 \times 10^{-12})(2248.28726445^4 - 250^4) = -51.09410509 \tag{7.114b}$$

$$T_4^C = 2301.79075068 + \frac{1.0}{24}\Big(9(-51.09410509) + 19(-56.13489568) - 5(-62.12039852) + (-69.31952992)\Big) = 2248.24377147 \tag{7.114c}$$

These results and the results of subsequent time steps are presented in Table 7.8.

The error at $t = 10.0$ s is -0.00747128, which compares with 0.08304739 for the fourth-order Adams–Bashforth method presented in Table 7.7. The ratio of the errors is $(0.08304739)/(-0.00747128) = -11.1$. Comparing the coefficients of the truncation errors of the two FDEs, Eqs. (7.107) and (7.111), yields the ratio $[(251/720)/(-19/720)] = -13.2$. Evidently the application of the corrector reduces the error by a factor of approximately 10. However, one additional derivative function evaluation is required. Using the additional derivative function evaluation with the fourth-order Adams–Bashforth method with the grid size halved would yield an error ratio of $[1/(1/2)]^4 = 16$, which is somewhat better than -13.2. So what, if any, are the ad-

TABLE 7.8
Solution by the fourth-order Adams–Bashforth–Moulton method

t_n t_{n+1}	T_n T_{n+1}^P T_{n+1}^C	f_n f_{n+1}^P	T_{exact}	Error
0.00	2500.00000000	−78.11718750		
1.00	2426.43487359	−69.31952992	exact	
2.00	2360.82998846	−62.12039852	solution	
3.00	2301.79075068	−56.13489658		
	2248.28726445	−51.09410509		
4.00	2248.24377147	−51.09015095	2248.24731405	−0.00354259
	2199.38633676	−46.79113508		
5.00	2199.35714631	−46.78865065	2199.36266993	−0.00552362
	2154.48362826	−43.08479649		
6.00	2154.46415999	−43.08323895	2154.47079576	−0.00663578
⋮	⋮	⋮	⋮	⋮
9.00	2038.83330713	−34.55084593	2038.84084646	−0.00753933
	2005.41425154	−32.34010922		
10.00	2005.40889453		2005.41636581	−0.00747128

vantages of the fourth-order Adams–Bashforth–Moulton method over the fourth-order Adams–Bashforth method? There are two advantages: the stability limit of the fourth-order Adams–Bashforth–Moulton method is approximately ten times larger than that of the fourth-order Adams–Bashforth method, and the error terms of the predictor and corrector can be used for error estimation, error control, and extrapolation, as discussed in the next two subsections.

Error Estimation, Error Control, and Extrapolation

The concepts of error estimation, error control, and extrapolation are presented in Section 6.4 for numerical quadrature. A similar procedure can be used for error estimation, error control, and extrapolation when solving ODEs numerically. Consider a FDE of $O(\Delta t^n)$. For a single step,

$$\overline{y}_{n+1} = y_{n+1}(\Delta t) + C\,\Delta t^{n+1} \tag{7.115}$$

where $y_{n+1}(\Delta t)$ denotes the value of y_{n+1} computed with step size Δt. The local error $C\,\Delta t^{n+1}$ can be estimated by repeating the calculation using step size $\Delta t/2$, as illustrated in Fig. 7.12. Thus,

$$\overline{y}_{n+1} = y_{n+1}\left(\frac{\Delta t}{2}\right) + 2\left(C\left(\frac{\Delta t}{2}\right)^{n+1}\right) \tag{7.116}$$

Subtracting Eq. (7.116) from Eq. (7.115) and solving for $C\,\Delta t^{n+1}$ yields

$$\boxed{C\,\Delta t^{n+1} = \left(y_{n+1}\left(\frac{\Delta t}{2}\right) - y_{n+1}(\Delta t)\right)\left(\frac{2^n}{2^n - 1}\right)} \tag{7.117}$$

If $|C\,\Delta t^{n+1}| <$ (lower error limit), increase (double) the step size. If $|C\,\Delta t^{n+1}| >$ (upper error limit), decrease (halve) the step size. This method of error estimation requires 200 percent more work at each step. Consequently, it should be used only occasionally. The error estimate can be added to the numerical solution, a process known as extrapolation.

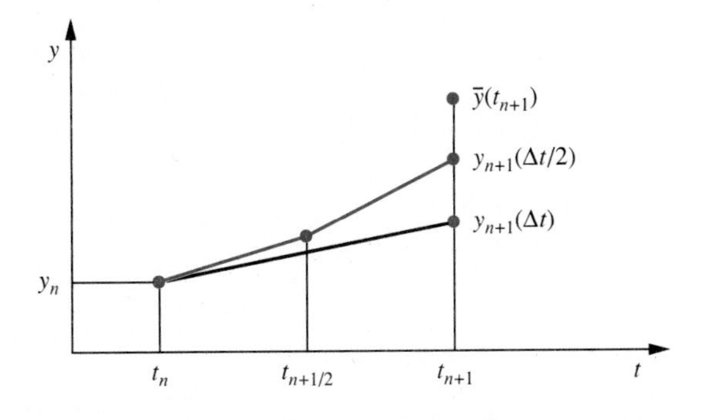

FIGURE 7.12
Step size halving for error estimation.

A more efficient error estimation procedure can be obtained for predictor–corrector methods. The truncation error terms of the two FDEs can be combined to obtain an estimate for the single-step truncation error without additional derivative function evaluations. This error estimate can be used for step size control. The error estimate can also be used to extrapolate the two solutions, a process commonly called *mop-up*.

Error Estimation and Extrapolation for the Adams–Bashforth–Moulton Method

The fourth-order Adams–Bashforth predictor FDE and the fourth-order Adams–Moulton corrector FDE are given by Eqs. (7.107) and (7.111), respectively. These equations can be expressed as

$$\bar{y}_{n+1} = y_{n+1}^P + \frac{251}{720}\Delta t^5\, y^{(5)}(\tau^P) \tag{7.118}$$

$$\bar{y}_{n+1} = y_{n+1}^C - \frac{19}{720}\Delta t^5\, y^{(5)}(\tau^C) \tag{7.119}$$

where $t_{n-3} \le \tau^P \le t_n$ and $t_{n-2} \le \tau^C \le t_{n+1}$. Assuming that $y^{(5)}(\tau^P) = y^{(5)}(\tau^C) = y^{(5)}(\tau)$, which is a reasonable approximation, Eqs. (7.118) and (7.119) can be combined to give

$$y_{n+1}^C - y_{n+1}^P = \Delta t^5\, y^{(5)}(\tau)\left(\frac{19}{720} + \frac{251}{720}\right) \tag{7.120}$$

from which

$$\Delta t^5\, y^{(5)}(\tau) = \frac{720}{19 + 251}(y_{n+1}^C - y_{n+1}^P) \tag{7.121}$$

The corrector error is given by

$$\text{Corrector Error} = -\frac{19}{720}\Delta t^5\, y^{(5)}(\tau) = -\frac{19}{19 + 251}(y_{n+1}^C - y_{n+1}^P) \tag{7.122}$$

If |Corrector Error| is less than a prescribed lower error limit, increase (double) the step size. If |Corrector Error| is greater than a prescribed upper error limit, decrease (halve) the step size. This method of error estimation requires no additional derivative function evaluations. When the step size is doubled, every other previous solution point is used to determine the four known points. When the step size is halved, the solution at the two additional points at $n + \frac{1}{2}$ and $n + \frac{3}{2}$ can be obtained by fourth-order interpolation.

Once an estimate of the error has been obtained, it can be used to extrapolate the solution. For the predictor, the truncation error is given by

$$\text{Predictor Error} = \frac{251}{720}\Delta t^5\, y^{(5)}(\tau) = \frac{251}{19 + 251}(y_{n+1}^C - y_{n+1}^P) \tag{7.123}$$

Unfortunately, y_{n+1}^C is not known until the corrector FDE is evaluated. An estimate of the predictor error can be obtained by lagging the term $(y_{n+1}^C - y_{n+1}^P)$. Thus, assume that $(y_{n+1}^C - y_{n+1}^P) \approx (y_n^C - y_n^P)$. The mop-up correction (i.e., extrapolation) for the fourth-order Adams–Bashforth predictor FDE is

$$\Delta y_{n+1}^{P,M} = \frac{251}{19 + 251}(y_n^C - y_n^P) \tag{7.124}$$

The mopped-up (i.e., extrapolated) predictor solution is

$$y_{n+1}^{P,M} = y_{n+1}^P + \Delta y_{n+1}^{P,M} \tag{7.125}$$

On the first step, Eq. (7.125) cannot be applied, since the values on the right-hand side are lagged one step. Two choices are possible. First, the predictor mop-up can be skipped on the first step. Alternatively, the corrector can be applied to give y_{n+1}^C, then Eq. (7.124) can be evaluated, and the predictor mop-up can be evaluated. The corrector FDE is then reevaluated at point $n + 1$. This procedure, which involves one additional derivative function evaluation on the first step only, is recommended.

The value of $y_{n+1}^{P,M}$ is used to evaluate $f_{n+1}^{P,M}$ for use in the fourth-order Adams–Moulton corrector FDE, Eq. (7.113). Thus,

$$f_{n+1}^P = f_{n+1}^{P,M} = f(t_{n+1}, y_{n+1}^{P,M}) \tag{7.126}$$

$$y_{n+1}^C = y_n + \frac{h}{24}(9f_{n+1}^{P,M} + 19f_n - 5f_{n-1} + f_{n-2}) \tag{7.127}$$

The mop-up correction (i.e., extrapolation) for the fourth-order Adams–Moulton corrector FDE is then

$$\Delta y_{n+1}^{C,M} = -\frac{19}{19 + 251}(y_{n+1}^C - y_{n+1}^P) \tag{7.128}$$

Note that y_{n+1}^P, not $y_{n+1}^{P,M}$, is used in Eq. (7.128). The mopped-up (i., extrapolated) corrector solution is

$$y_{n+1}^{C,M} = y_{n+1}^C + \Delta y_{n+1}^{C,M} \tag{7.129}$$

Errors

Five types of errors can occur in the numerical solution of differential equations:

1. Errors in the initial data (assumed nonexistent)
2. Algebraic errors (assumed nonexistent)
3. Truncation errors
4. Round-off errors
5. Inherited error

These errors, their interactions, and their effects on the numerical solution are discussed in this subsection. This discussion is equally relevant to the numerical solution of ODEs, which is the subject of Part II, and the numerical solution of PDEs, which is the subject of Part III.

A differential equation has an infinite number of solutions, depending on the initial conditions. Thus, a family of solutions exists, as illustrated in Fig. 7.13. Figure 7.13*a* illustrates a family of converging solutions, and Figure 7.13*b* illustrates a family of diverging solutions. An error in the initial condition simply moves the solution to a different member of the solution family. Such errors are assumed to be nonexistent, as are algebraic errors in the computations.

An important concept is illustrated in Fig. 7.13. Any error in the numerical solution essentially moves the numerical solution to a different member of the solution family. Consider the converging family of solutions illustrated in Figure 7.13*a*. Since the members of the solution family converge as t increases, errors in the numerical solution of any type tend to diminish as t increases. By contrast, for the diverging family of solutions illustrated in Fig. 7.13*b*, errors in the numerical solution of any type tend to grow as t increases. This contrasting behavior can be explained as follows. For the converging solution family illustrated in Fig. 7.13*a*, at each value of t, the slopes $\bar{y}' = \bar{f}(t, \bar{y})$ of the solution

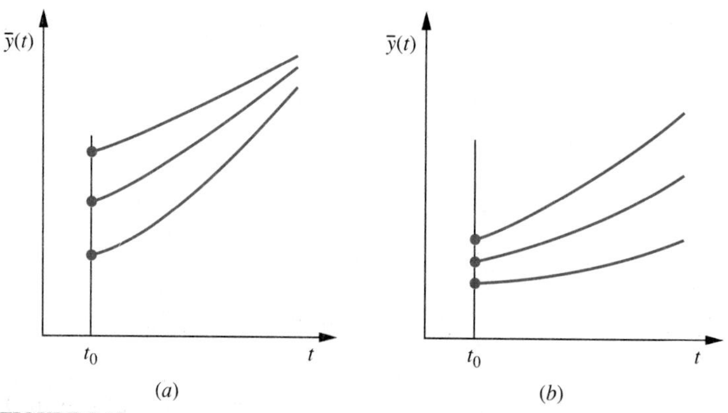

FIGURE 7.13
Families of solutions of a differential equation: (*a*) Converging solutions; (*b*) diverging solutions.

curves decrease as $\bar{y}$ increases; that is, $\partial \bar{f}(t, \bar{y})/\partial \bar{y} < 0$. For the diverging solution family illustrated in Fig. 7.13*b*, at each value of t, the slopes $\bar{y}' = \bar{f}(t, \bar{y})$ of the solution curves increase as $\bar{y}$ increases; that is, $\partial \bar{f}(t, \bar{y})/\partial \bar{y} > 0$. Thus, when $\partial \bar{f}/\partial \bar{y} < 0$, errors tend to diminish as the numerical solution progresses, whereas, when $\partial \bar{f}/\partial \bar{y} > 0$, errors tend to grow as the numerical solution progresses.

Truncation error is the error incurred in a single step caused by truncating the Taylor series expressions for the exact derivatives. Truncation error depends on the step size and is $O(\Delta t^n)$. Truncation error decreases as the step size Δt decreases. Truncation errors propagate from step to step and accumulate as the number of steps increases.

Round-off errors are caused by the finite word length employed in the calculations. Round-off errors are more significant when small differences in large numbers are calculated. Consequently, round-off error increases as the step size Δt decreases. Most electronic digital computers have either 32-bit or 64-bit word length, corresponding to approximately 7 or 13 significant decimal digits, respectively. Care must be exercised to ensure that enough significant digits are maintained in numerical calculations so that round-off is not significant. Round-off errors propagate from step to step and tend to accumulate as the number of calculations (i.e., steps) increases.

If round-off errors are negligible, the total truncation error is the sum of the local truncation errors, which decrease as Δt decreases and vice versa. If the truncation errors are negligible, the total round-off error is the sum of the local round-off errors, which increase as Δt decreases and vice versa. The total error at a particular point is roughly equal to the sum of the total truncation error and the total round-off error. The optimum step size is the step size at which the total error is a minimum. In practice, enough significant digits should be carried in the calculation so that round-off errors are negligible, and the step size is chosen based on a compromise between minimizing total truncation error and minimizing cost (i.e., computer time).

Inherited error is the sum of all accumulated errors from all previous steps. The presence of inherited error means that the initial condition for the next step is incorrect. Essentially, each step places the numerical solution on a different member of the solution family. Assuming that algebraic errors are nonexistent and that round-off errors are negligible, inherited error is the sum of all previous truncation errors, as illustrated in Fig. 7.14. On the first step, the total error is the local truncation error. The initial point for the second step is on a different member of the solution family. Another truncation error is made on the second step. This truncation error is relative to the exact solution passing through Point 1. The total error at Point 2 is due both to the inherited error at Point 1, which places the solution on a different member of the solution family, and the local truncation error of the second step. This dual error source, inherited error and local truncation error, affects the solution at each step. For a converging solution family (i.e., $\partial \bar{f}/\partial \bar{y} < 0$), inherited error tends to decrease as the solution progresses. For a diverging solution family (i.e., $\partial \bar{f}/\partial \bar{y} > 0$), inherited error tends to grow as the solution progresses. The practical consequence of these

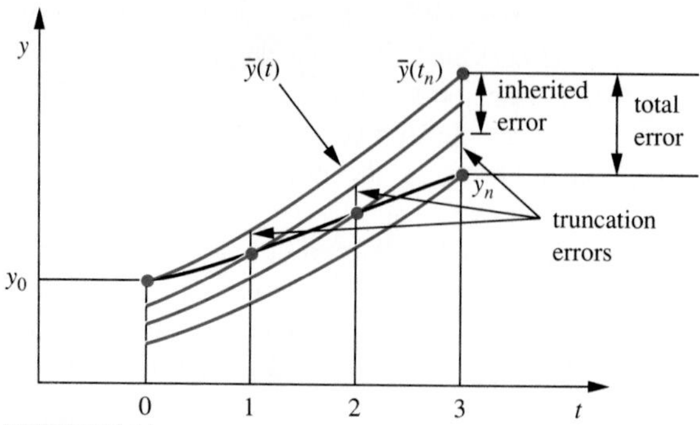

FIGURE 7.14
Truncation error, inherited error, and total error.

TABLE 7.9
Summary of selected finite difference methods

The Explicit Euler Method

$$y_{n+1} = y_n + \Delta t\, f_n \tag{7.130}$$

The Implicit Euler Method

$$y_{n+1} = y_n + \Delta t\, f_{n+1} \tag{7.131}$$

The Modified Euler Method

$$y_{n+1}^P = y_n + \Delta t\, f_n \qquad y_{n+1}^C = y_n + \tfrac{1}{2}\Delta t(f_n + f_{n+1}^P) \tag{7.132}$$

The Fourth-Order Runge–Kutta Method

$$y_{n+1} = y_n + \tfrac{1}{6}(k_1 + 2k_2 + 2k_3 + k_4) \tag{7.133}$$

$$k_1 = \Delta y_1 = \Delta t\, f(t_n, y_n) \qquad k_2 = \Delta y_2 = \Delta t\, f(t_n + \Delta t/2, y_n + \Delta y_1/2)$$
$$k_3 = \Delta y_3 = \Delta t\, f(t_n + \Delta t/2, y_n + \Delta y_2/2) \quad k_4 = \Delta y_4 = \Delta t\, f(t_n + \Delta t, y_n + \Delta y_3) \tag{7.134}$$

The Adams–Bashforth–Moulton Method

$$y_{n+1}^P = y_n + \frac{\Delta t}{24}(55f_n - 59f_{n-1} + 37f_{n-2} - 9f_{n-3}) \tag{7.135}$$

$$y_{n+1}^C = y_n + \frac{\Delta t}{24}(9f_{n+1}^P + 19f_n - 5f_{n-1} + f_{n-2}) \tag{7.136}$$

The Adams–Bashforth–Moulton Method with Mop-Up

$$\Delta y_{n+1}^{P,M} = \frac{251}{270}(y_n^C - y_n^P) \qquad y_{n+1}^{P,M} = y_{n+1}^P + \Delta y_{n+1}^{P,M} \tag{7.137}$$

$$\Delta y_{n+1}^{C,M} = -\frac{19}{270}(y_{n+1}^C - y_n^P) \qquad y_{n+1}^{C,M} = y_{n+1}^C + \Delta y_{n+1}^{C,M} \tag{7.138}$$

effects is that smaller step sizes may be required when solving ODEs that govern diverging solution families than when solving ODEs that govern converging solution families.

Summary of Results

Several finite difference methods for solving first-order initial-value ordinary differential equations are presented in this section. Five of the more prominent methods are summarized in Table 7.9.

The radiation problem presented in Section 7.1 was solved by these five methods. The errors for a step size of $\Delta t = 1.0$ s are presented in Fig. 7.15. The first-order Euler method and the second-order modified Euler method are clearly inferior to the fourth-order methods. The Runge–Kutta method is an excellent method. However, it requires four derivative function evaluations per step, compared to one for the Adams–Bashforth method and two for the Adams–Bashforth–Moulton method. The Runge-Kutta method and the Adams–Bashforth method both suffer from the lack of an efficient error control procedure. The Adams–Bashforth–Moulton method, which has a simple error control procedure, is the best compromise between accuracy and error control efficiency. Consequently, the Adams–Bashforth–Moulton method with a Runge–Kutta starting procedure is recommended for solving most first-order initial-value ODEs.

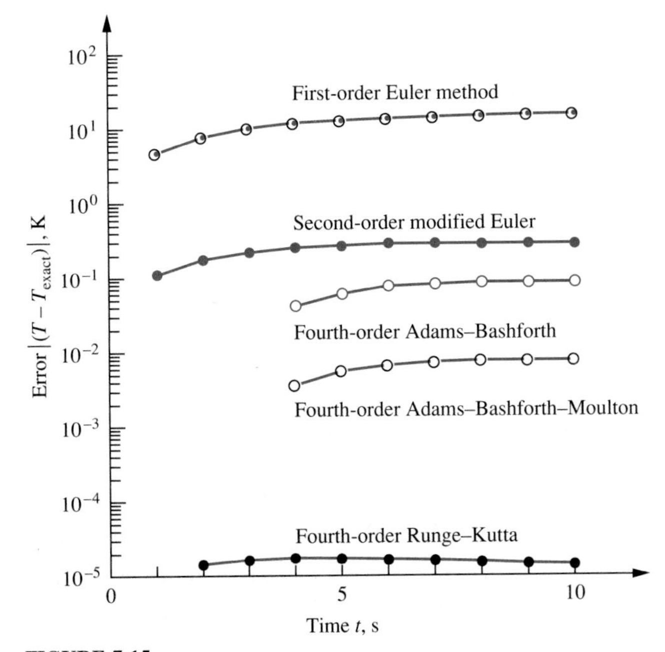

FIGURE 7.15
Errors in the solution of the radiation problem.

Summary

This section has introduced several basic features of finite difference methods for solving differential equations (both ODEs and PDEs). Examples were presented to illustrate these concepts:

1. Whether the FDE is explicit or implicit
2. The number of known points required in the FDE
3. The number of steps required to advance the solution one grid point
4. The number of derivative function evaluations required per step
5. The order of the single-step truncation error of the FDE
6. The order of the global error of the method

Four basic properties of FDEs for solving ODEs were identified:

1. Consistency
2. Order
3. Stability
4. Convergence

These properties must be considered before a finite difference method is employed. These properties are discussed in more detail in the next three sections.

The concepts presented in this section also apply to the numerical solution of propagation problems having more than one independent variable, that is, partial differential equations.

7.6 CONSISTENCY, ORDER, STABILITY, AND CONVERGENCE

There are several important properties of finite difference equations for initial-value ODEs that must be considered before numerical computations are performed:

1. Consistency
2. Order
3. Stability
4. Convergence

These concepts are defined and discussed in this section.

First consider the concept of *consistency*.

> *An FDE is consistent with an ODE if the difference between the FDE and the ODE (i.e., the truncation error) vanishes as the size of the grid spacing* Δt *goes to zero.*

When the truncation errors of the finite difference approximations of the individual exact derivatives are known, proof of consistency is straightforward. When the truncation errors of the individual finite difference approximations are not known, the complete finite difference equation must be analyzed for consistency. That is accomplished by expressing each term in the finite difference equation by a Taylor series expansion about a particular grid point. The resulting equation, which is called the *modified differential equation* (MDE), can then be simplified to yield the exact form of the truncation error of the complete finite difference equation. Consistency can then be investigated by letting the grid spacing go to zero. Examples of this approach are presented in Section 7.7.

Next consider the concept of order, which is introduced in Section 7.5.

> *The order of a finite difference solution of an ODE is the rate at which the global error approaches zero as the size of the grid spacing Δt goes to zero. The order of a finite difference equation is the same as the order of the FDAs of the exact derivatives (i.e., the truncation error).*

As shown in Section 7.5 [see Eq. (7.62)], the order of a finite difference equation is the same as the order of the truncation error terms in the finite difference approximations of the individual exact derivatives in the ODE.

Next consider the concept of *stability*. First, the general behavior of the exact solution of the ODE must be considered. If the exact solution of the ODE is unbounded, as illustrated in Figure 7.16*a*, then the numerical solution must also be unbounded. The concept of stability does not apply in that case. However, if the exact solution of the ODE is bounded, as illustrated in Figure 7.16*b*, then the numerical solution also must be bounded. The concept of stability applies in

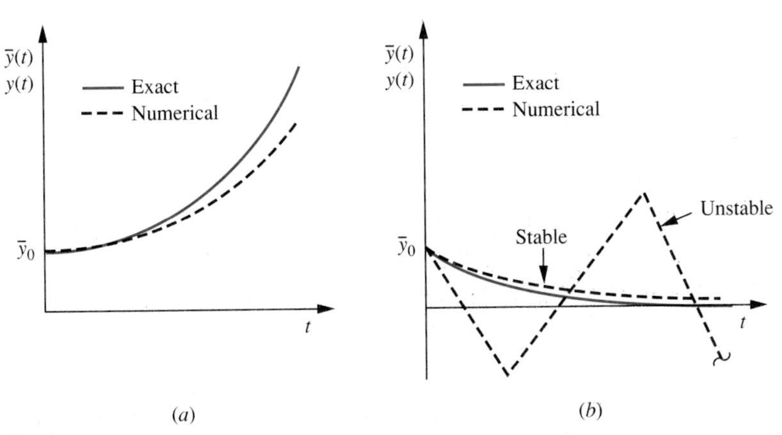

FIGURE 7.16
General behavior of initial-value ODEs: (*a*) Unbounded; (*b*) bounded.

this latter case. Several definitions of stability are in common use. In this book, stability is defined as follows:

> *An FDE is stable if it produces a bounded solution when the exact solution is bounded, and it is unstable if it produces an unbounded solution when the exact solution is bounded.*

Finally, consider the concept of *convergence*:

> *A finite difference method is convergent if the solution of the FDE approaches the exact solution of the ODE as the size of the grid spacing Δt goes to zero.*

Let $\bar{y}$ denote the exact solution of the ordinary differential equation, y denote the solution of the finite difference equation, and E denote the difference between them (i.e., the global error). The statement of convergence is:

$$y - \bar{y} = E \to 0 \qquad \text{as} \qquad \Delta t \to 0 \tag{7.139}$$

The proof of convergence of a finite difference method is in the domain of the mathematician. We shall not attempt to prove convergence directly. However, the convergence of a finite difference method is related to the consistency and stability of the finite difference equation. The following equivalence theorem will be used in this book to ensure convergence:

> *Given a well-posed linear initial-value problem and a finite difference approximation to it that is consistent, stability is the necessary and sufficient condition for convergence.*

Thus, the question of convergence of a finite difference method is answered by a study of the consistency and stability of the finite difference equation. If the finite difference equation is consistent and stable, then the finite difference method is convergent.

The equivalence theorem applies to well-posed, linear, initial-value problems. A well-posed problem is one that has a complete set of consistent initial conditions. All real problems should be well-posed. Many problems in engineering and science, however, are not linear. There is no equivalence theorem for such problems. Experience has shown, however, that finite difference equations that are consistent and whose linearized equivalent is stable generally converge, even for nonlinear initial-value problems.

In summary, the concepts of consistency, order, stability, and convergence must always be considered when solving a differential equation by finite difference methods. Consistency and order can be determined from the modified differential equation, as illustrated in Section 7.7. Stability can be determined by a stability analysis, as presented in Section 7.8. Convergence can be ensured through the equivalence theorem by demonstrating consistency and stability.

7.7 THE MODIFIED DIFFERENTIAL EQUATION

Several important properties of finite difference equations that approximate ordinary differential equations are introduced in the preceding sections, in particular, consistency, order, stability, and convergence. These properties are also important in the finite difference solution of partial differential equations. Warming and Hyett (1974) developed a convenient technique for investigating these properties for PDEs. That same technique can be used to investigate consistency and order of finite difference approximations of ODEs.

The technique involves determining the actual ODE that is solved by the finite difference equation. This actual ODE is called the *modified differential equation* (MDE). Following Warming and Hyett, the MDE is determined by expressing each term in the FDE in a Taylor series at some base point. Effectively, the process changes the FDE back into an ODE, which is the MDE. Terms appearing in the MDE that do not appear in the original differential equation are truncation error terms. Analysis of the truncation error terms leads directly to the determination of consistency and order.

Consider the general first-order ordinary differential equation:

$$\boxed{\bar{y}' = \bar{f}(t, \bar{y})} \tag{7.140}$$

The finite difference equation that approximates the exact ordinary differential equation is obtained by replacing the exact derivative $\bar{y}'$ by the finite difference approximation y' and the exact derivative function $\bar{f}$ by the approximation f. Thus, the finite difference equation is

$$\boxed{y' = f} \tag{7.141}$$

The modified differential equation (MDE) is the actual ODE that is solved by the FDE. Let $y(t)$ be the exact solution of the FDE, Eq. (7.141). Each term in Eq. (7.141) can be expressed in a Taylor series at some base point. Substituting those expressions into Eq. (7.141) yields

$$y' = f(t, y) + \sum_{m}^{\infty} A_m \frac{d^m y}{dt^m} \tag{7.142}$$

Equation (7.142) is the actual ODE that is solved by the FDE, that is, it is the modified differential equation. The MDE must contain all the terms appearing in the exact ODE (i.e., $\bar{y}' = \bar{f}$). It also contains an infinite number of higher-order derivatives. If all the terms involving these higher-order derivatives vanish as $\Delta t \to 0$, then the MDE becomes identical to the exact ODE in the limit as $\Delta t \to 0$. In that case, the MDE is a consistent approximation of the exact ODE. If one or more of the terms involving these higher-order derivatives does not vanish as $\Delta t \to 0$, then the FDE is not a consistent approximation of the exact ODE. At finite-size grid spacing, the MDE always differs from the exact ODE.

Example 7.8. The MDE for the explicit Euler method. As an example, consider the linear first-order ODE

$$\bar{y}' + \alpha \bar{y} = F(t) \tag{7.143}$$

The explicit Euler FDE is [see Eq. (7.58)]

$$y_{n+1} = y_n + \Delta t\, f_n \tag{7.144}$$

Applying Eq. (7.144) to Eq. (7.143) gives

$$y_{n+1} = y_n - \alpha h y_n + h F_n \tag{7.145}$$

where $h = \Delta t$. Let grid point n be the base point, and write the Taylor series for y_{n+1}. Thus,

$$y_{n+1} = y_n + hy'|_n + \frac{1}{2}h^2 y''|_n + \frac{1}{6}h^3 y'''|_n + \cdots \tag{7.146}$$

Substituting Eq. (7.146) into Eq. (7.145) gives

$$y_n + hy'|_n + \frac{1}{2}h^2 y''|_n + \frac{1}{6}h^3 y'''|_n + \cdots = y_n - \alpha h y_n + hF_n \tag{7.147}$$

Cancelling zero-order terms, dividing through by h, and rearranging terms yields the *first* form of the MDE:

$$y'|_n + \alpha y_n = F_n - \frac{1}{2}hy''|_n - \frac{1}{6}h^2 y'''|_n - \cdots \tag{7.148}$$

Equation (7.148) is in the form of Eq. (7.142). Equation (7.148) is the MDE corresponding to the explicit Euler approximation of the linear first-order ODE, Eq. (7.143).

Let $h = \Delta t \to 0$ in the MDE to obtain the ODE with which the MDE is consistent. Thus, Eq. (7.148) becomes

$$y'|_n + \alpha y_n = F_n - \frac{1}{2}(0)y''|_n - \frac{1}{6}(0)^2 y'''|_n - \cdots \tag{7.149}$$

$$\boxed{y'|_n + \alpha y_n = F_n} \tag{7.150}$$

Equation (7.150) is identical to the linear first-order ODE $\bar{y}' + \alpha\bar{y} = F(t)$. Consequently, Eq. (7.144) is consistent with $\bar{y}' + \alpha\bar{y} = F(t)$.

The order of the FDE is the order of the lowest-order term in the MDE. From Eq. (7.148),

$$y'|_n + \alpha y_n = F_n + O(h) \tag{7.151}$$

Thus, Eq. (7.144) is an $O(\Delta t)$ approximation of $\bar{y}' + \alpha\bar{y} = F(t)$.

A second form of the MDE can be obtained by eliminating the leading truncation error term, the term involving y'' in Eq. (7.148), from the first form of the MDE by differentiating the MDE itself. An illustration of this procedure is presented in the next example.

Example 7.9. The MDE for the modified Euler method. Recall the FDEs for the modified Euler method [Eq. (7.87)]:

$$y_{n+1}^P = y_n + \Delta t f_n \tag{7.152a}$$

$$y_{n+1}^C = y_n + \frac{1}{2}\Delta t(f_n + f_{n+1}^P) \tag{7.152b}$$

Consider the linear first-order ODE:

$$\bar{y}' = -\alpha\bar{y} + F(t) = \bar{f}(t, \bar{y}) \tag{7.153}$$

Substituting Eq. (7.153) into Eq. (7.152*a*) gives

$$y_{n+1}^P = y_n - \alpha h y_n + hF_n \tag{7.154}$$

where $h = \Delta t$. Substituting Eqs. (7.153) and (7.154) into Eq. (7.152*b*) yields the single-step FDE:

$$y_{n+1} = \left(1 - \alpha h + \frac{1}{2}(\alpha h)^2\right)y_n - \frac{1}{2}\alpha h^2 F_n + \frac{1}{2}h(F_n + F_{n+1}) \tag{7.155}$$

Substituting Taylor series for $y(t)$ and $F(t)$ at base point n into Eq. (7.155) and dropping the subscript n for clarity gives

$$y + hy' + \frac{1}{2}h^2 y'' + \frac{1}{6}h^3 y''' + \cdots = \left(1 - \alpha h + \frac{1}{2}(\alpha h)^2\right)y - \frac{1}{2}\alpha h^2 F$$
$$+ \frac{1}{2}h\left(F + \left(F + hF' + \frac{1}{2}h^2 F'' + \frac{1}{6}h^3 F''' + \cdots\right)\right) \tag{7.156}$$

Cancelling zero-order terms, dividing through by h, dropping all third- and higher-order terms, and rearranging the remaining terms yields the first form of the MDE:

$$y' = -\alpha y + F + \frac{1}{2}\alpha^2 h y - \frac{1}{2} h y'' - \frac{1}{6} h^2 y''' + \cdots$$
$$- \frac{1}{2}\alpha h F + \frac{1}{2} h F' + \frac{1}{4} h^2 F'' + \cdots \tag{7.157}$$

As $h = \Delta t \to 0$, Eq. (7.157) approaches $y' = -\alpha y + F$. Consequently, Eq. (7.155) is consistent with Eq. (7.153). It appears that the truncation error is $O(\Delta t)$. However, there are four $O(\Delta t)$ terms in Eq. (7.157). Further analysis shows that Eq. (7.157) is actually $O(\Delta t^2)$. This is demonstrated by evaluating y'' by differentiating Eq. (7.157). Thus,

$$y'' = (y')' = -\alpha y' + F' + \frac{1}{2}\alpha^2 h y' - \frac{1}{2} h y''' - \frac{1}{6} h^2 y^{(4)} + \cdots$$
$$- \frac{1}{2}\alpha h F' + \frac{1}{2} h F'' + \frac{1}{4} h^2 F''' + \cdots \tag{7.158}$$

Introducing y' from Eq. (7.157) into Eq. (7.158) gives

$$y'' = \left(\alpha^2 y - \alpha F - \frac{1}{2}\alpha^3 h y + \frac{1}{2}\alpha h y'' + \frac{1}{6}\alpha h^2 y''' + \cdots \right.$$
$$\left. + \frac{1}{2}\alpha^2 h F - \frac{1}{2}\alpha h F' - \frac{1}{4}\alpha h^2 F'' + \cdots \right) + F'$$
$$+ \left(\frac{1}{2}\alpha^3 h y - \frac{1}{2}\alpha^2 h F - \frac{1}{4}\alpha^4 h^2 y + \frac{1}{4}\alpha^2 h^2 y'' + \frac{1}{12}\alpha^2 h^2 y''' \right.$$
$$\left. + \frac{1}{4}\alpha^3 h^2 F - \frac{1}{4}\alpha^2 h^2 F' - \frac{1}{8}\alpha^2 h^3 F''' \right)$$
$$- \frac{1}{2} h y''' - \frac{1}{6} h^2 y^{(4)} + \cdots - \frac{1}{2}\alpha h F' + \frac{1}{2} h F'' + \frac{1}{4} h^2 F''' + \cdots \tag{7.159}$$

Retaining only terms of $O(h)$ and $O(h^2)$ in Eq. (7.157) and substituting terms of $O(h)$ from Eq. (7.159) [since y'' is multiplied by h in Eq. (7.157)] into Eq. (7.157) gives

$$y' = -\alpha y + F + \frac{1}{2}\alpha^2 h y - \frac{1}{2} h \left(\alpha^2 y - \alpha F - \frac{1}{2}\alpha^3 h y + \frac{1}{2}\alpha h y'' \right.$$
$$\left. + \frac{1}{2}\alpha^2 h F - \frac{1}{2}\alpha h F' + F' - \frac{1}{2}\alpha^3 h y + \frac{1}{2}\alpha^2 h F - \frac{1}{2} h y''' - \frac{1}{2}\alpha h F' + \frac{1}{2} h F'' \right)$$
$$- \frac{1}{6} h^2 y''' - \frac{1}{2}\alpha h F + \frac{1}{2} h F' + \frac{1}{4} h^2 F'' + \cdots \tag{7.160}$$

Simplifying Eq. (7.160) and retaining only the second-order terms yields

$$y' = -\alpha y + F + \frac{1}{2}\alpha^3 h^2 y - \frac{1}{4}\alpha h^2 y'' + \frac{1}{12}h^2 y''' - \frac{1}{2}\alpha^2 h^2 F + \frac{1}{2}\alpha h^2 F' + \cdots \tag{7.161}$$

Equation (7.161) is the second form of the MDE.

The lowest-order terms in Eq. (7.161) are $O(\Delta t^2)$. Consequently, Eq. (7.155) is an $O(\Delta t^2)$ approximation of Eq. (7.153). The first form of the MDE did not identify the correct order of Eq. (7.155). Any time the first form of the MDE does not identify the expected order of the finite difference approximation of an ODE, it may be necessary to evaluate the second form of the MDE to determine the actual order. This possibility exists only if, in the first form of the MDE, there are two or more terms of lower order than expected, which might cancel in the second form of the MDE, as in Eq. (7.157).

In summary, the modified differential equation (MDE) can be used to determine the consistency and order of a finite difference approximation of a differential equation. The following steps should be followed:

1. Determine the finite difference equation (FDE) to be analyzed.
2. Choose the base point for the Taylor series for the terms appearing in the FDE. If known, choose the base point for the finite difference approximations of the exact derivatives in the ODE as the base point for the MDE.
3. Substitute the Taylor series for all terms into the FDE.
4. Simplify the resulting equation by cancelling all like terms, gathering the coefficients of all similar terms, identifying all derivative terms that do not contain Δt, and identifying the remaining terms as the truncation error. This step yields the first form of the MDE, which is the actual ODE solved by the FDE.
5. Let $\Delta t \rightarrow 0$ to determine what ODE is approached by the FDE. If the exact ODE is approached, the FDE is consistent with the exact ODE. If some other ODE is approached, then the FDE is not consistent with the exact ODE.
6. Determine the second form of the MDE by repeated differentiation of the MDE itself and substitution into the first form of the MDE to eliminate time derivatives of low order.
7. Determine the order of the FDE from the second form of the MDE.
8. If the first form of the MDE has only one term containing the lowest-order power of Δt, then that term determines the order of the FDE, and the second form of the MDE is not required.

7.8 STABILITY ANALYSIS

Introduction

As discussed in Section 7.6, stability of a finite difference approximation of an ordinary differential equation that has a bounded solution is defined as follows:

> *An FDE is stable if it produces a bounded solution when the exact solution is bounded, and it is unstable if it produces an unbounded solution when the exact solution is bounded.*

The first step in the stability analysis of an FDE that approximates an ODE is to determine the behavior of the exact solution of the ODE. The solution to most physical problems is bounded. In that case, the solution to the FDE also must be bounded. If the solution of the FDE is bounded for all values of the grid size, then the FDE is *unconditionally stable*. If the solution of the FDE is bounded only for certain values of the grid size, then the FDE is *conditionally stable*. If the solution of the FDE is unbounded for all values of the grid size, then the FDE is *unconditionally unstable*. If the exact solution of the ODE is unbounded, then the solution of the FDE also must be unbounded. The concept of stability does not apply in that case, because the numerical solution is behaving in the same manner as the exact solution.

Stability analyses can be performed only for linear ODEs. Consequently, nonlinear ODEs must be linearized locally, and the FDE approximating the linearized ODE analyzed for stability. Experience has shown that the stability criteria obtained for the linearized FDE also apply to the nonlinear FDE. Instances of suspected *nonlinear instability* have been reported in the literature, but it is not clear whether those results are due to actual instabilities, inconsistent finite difference equations, excessively large grid size, or simply incorrect computations. Consequently, in this book, the stability analysis of the finite difference approximation of a linearized differential equation will be considered sufficient to determine the stability criteria for the finite difference approximation of the corresponding nonlinear differential equation.

Consider the first-order linear homogeneous ODE:

$$\bar{y}' - \bar{y} = 0, \qquad \bar{y}(0) = 1 \tag{7.162}$$

The exact solution is

$$\bar{y}(t) = e^{t} \tag{7.163}$$

which grows exponentially without bound, as illustrated in Fig. 7.17. Solving Eq. (7.162) by the explicit Euler method yields

$$y_{n+1} = y_n + \Delta t\, f_n = y_n + \alpha\, \Delta t\, y_n = (1 + \alpha\, \Delta t) y_n \tag{7.164}$$

The solutions for several values of the step size Δt are presented in Fig. 7.17. The numerical solution also grows without bound. The numerical solution is modelling

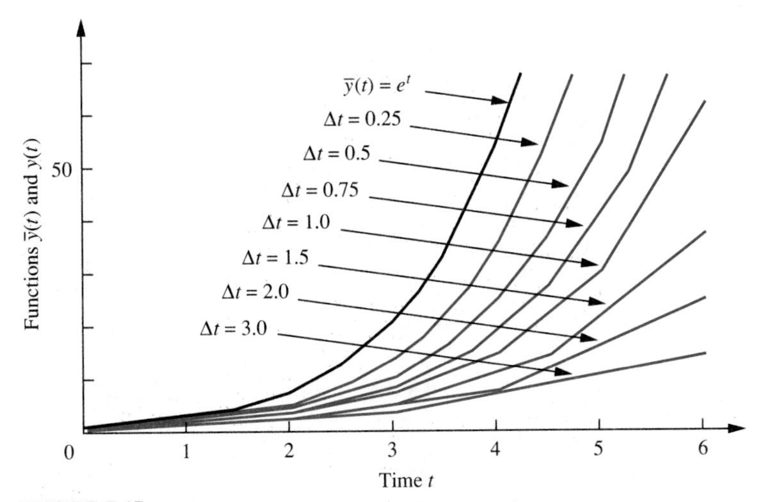

FIGURE 7.17
Solution of $\bar{y}' - \bar{y} = 0$, $\bar{y}(0) = 1$, by the explicit Euler method.

the exact solution correctly. Both are unbounded. The error increases dramatically as the step size Δt is increased. This is an accuracy problem, which can be controlled by using small step sizes, not a stability problem.

Now consider the first-order linear homogeneous ODE

$$\bar{y}' + \bar{y} = 0, \qquad \bar{y}(0) = 1 \tag{7.165}$$

The exact solution is

$$\bar{y}(t) = e^{-t} \tag{7.166}$$

which decays to $\bar{y}(\infty) = 0$ in a bounded manner, as illustrated in Fig. 7.8 in Section 7.5. Solving Eq. (7.165) by the explicit Euler method yields

$$y_{n+1} = y_n + \Delta t\, f_n = y_n - \alpha\, \Delta t\, y_n = (1 - \alpha\, \Delta t) y_n \tag{7.167}$$

The solutions for several values of the step size Δt are presented in Fig. 7.8. The behavior of Eq. (7.167) is discussed in Section 7.5, where it is shown that the explicit Euler method is conditionally stable (i.e., $\Delta t \le 2$) when used to solve Eq. (7.165).

These results demonstrate that numerical methods for solving the ODE $\bar{y}' - \alpha\bar{y} = 0$ are not subject to numerical instability, but that numerical methods for solving the ODE $\bar{y}' + \alpha\bar{y} = 0$ are subject to numerical instability. Consequently, all FDEs should be analyzed for stability when solving ODEs that have bounded solutions. That can be accomplished by applying the FDE to the first-order linear homogeneous ODE

$$\boxed{\bar{y}' + \alpha\bar{y} = 0} \tag{7.168}$$

and analyzing the behavior of the corresponding FDE. Equation (7.168) is used throughout this chapter as the model ODE for stability analysis.

The Amplification Factor G

Consider an exact ODE $\bar{y}' = \bar{f}(t, \bar{y})$ and a finite difference approximation to it, $y' = f(t, y)$. The exact solution of the FDE can be expressed as

$$\boxed{y_{n+1} = G y_n} \tag{7.169}$$

where G, which in general is a complex constant, is called the amplification factor.

The global solution of an FDE is obtained by repetitive application of the FDE, as represented by Eq. (7.169). Thus, the solution at $T = N\,\Delta t$ is given by

$$y_N = G^N y_0 \tag{7.170}$$

where $y_0 = \bar{y}(0)$. For y_N to remain bounded as $N \rightarrow \infty$,

$$\boxed{|G| \le 1} \tag{7.171}$$

Stability analysis thus reduces to the determination of the single-step exact solution of the FDE, that is, the amplification factor G, and the determination of the conditions necessary to ensure that $|G| \le 1$.

Stability Analysis of Linear ODEs

Consider the linear homogeneous first-order ODE

$$\bar{y}' + \alpha\bar{y} = 0 \tag{7.172}$$

and a finite difference approximation to it in the form

$$y' + \alpha y = 0 \tag{7.173}$$

The exact single-step solution to Eq. (7.173) is

$$y_{n+1} = G y_n \tag{7.174}$$

The necessary and sufficient condition for stability is

$$\boxed{|G| \le 1} \tag{7.175}$$

Example 7.10. Stability analysis of the explicit Euler method. Consider the explicit Euler FDE:

$$y_{n+1} = y_n + \Delta t\, f_n \tag{7.176}$$

The stability of Eq. (7.176) is investigated by applying it to the model ODE $\bar{y}'+\alpha\bar{y} = 0$. Thus,

$$y_{n+1} = y_n + \Delta t\,(-\alpha y_n) = (1 - \alpha\,\Delta t)y_n = Gy_n \tag{7.177}$$

From Eq. (7.177), the amplification factor G is

$$\boxed{G = (1 - \alpha\,\Delta t)} \tag{7.178}$$

For stability, $|G| \le 1$. Thus,

$$-1 \le (1 - \alpha\,\Delta t) \le 1 \tag{7.179}$$

The right-hand inequality is always satisfied for $\alpha\Delta t \ge 0$. The left-hand inequality is satisfied only if

$$\boxed{\alpha\,\Delta t \le 2} \tag{7.180}$$

which requires that $\Delta t \le 2/\alpha$. Consequently, the explicit Euler method is conditionally stable.

The unstable behavior of the explicit Euler method illustrated in Fig. 7.8 can now be explained. In those results, $\alpha = 1.0$. Thus Eq. (7.180) yields the stability criterion $\Delta t \le 2.0$. The results presented in Fig. 7.8 are clearly unstable for $\Delta t > 2.0$, which is in agreement with the results of the stability analysis.

Example 7.11. Stability analysis of the implicit Euler method. Consider the implicit Euler FDE:

$$y_{n+1} = y_n + \Delta t\, f_{n+1} \tag{7.181}$$

The stability of Eq. (7.181) is investigated by applying it to the model ODE $\bar{y}'+\alpha\bar{y} = 0$. Thus,

$$y_{n+1} = y_n + \Delta t\,(-\alpha y_{n+1}) \tag{7.182a}$$

$$y_{n+1} = \frac{1}{1 + \alpha\,\Delta t} y_n = Gy_n \tag{7.182b}$$

From Eq. (7.182*b*), the amplification factor G is

$$\boxed{G = \frac{1}{1 + \alpha\,\Delta t}} \tag{7.183}$$

For stability, $|G| \le 1$. This is true for all values of Δt. Consequently, the implicit Euler method is unconditionally stable.

The stability analysis of multistep methods is more complicated. The set of FDEs must be combined into a single step FDE before the stability analysis can be performed. The stability analysis of the two-step modified Euler method is presented in Example 7.12.

Example 7.12. Stability analysis of the modified Euler method. When applied to the model ODE $\bar{y}' + \alpha\bar{y} = 0$, the modified Euler predictor–corrector method can be written as a single-step FDE [see Eq. (7.155)]. For $F(t) = 0$, Eq. (7.155) yields

$$y_{n+1} = \left(1 - \alpha h + \frac{1}{2}(\alpha h)^2\right) y_n \tag{7.184}$$

where $h = \Delta t$. From Eq. (7.184), the amplification factor G is

$$\boxed{G = 1 - \alpha h + \frac{1}{2}(\alpha h)^2} \tag{7.185}$$

For stability, $|G| \leq 1$. For $\alpha h > 0$, $G > 0$. Thus, $|G| \leq 1$ if $G \leq 1$. Solving Eq. (7.185) for the stability boundary $G = 1$ gives

$$\frac{1}{2}(\alpha h)^2 - \alpha h + 1 = 1 \tag{7.186}$$

which yields

$$\alpha h \left(\frac{1}{2}\alpha h - 1\right) = 0 \tag{7.187}$$

Solving Eq. (7.187) yields $\alpha h = 2$, which is the stability boundary for Eq. (7.184). Values of $\alpha h > 2$ give $G > 1$, so the stability criteria is

$$\boxed{\alpha h \leq 2} \tag{7.188}$$

Equation (7.188) is the same stability criterion as the stability criterion of the explicit Euler method. Thus, the modified Euler predictor–corrector method inherits the stability criterion of the explicit Euler predictor.

Stability Analysis of Nonlinear ODEs

Stability analysis can be performed only for linear differential equations. Nonlinear differential equations must be linearized locally, and a stability analysis performed on the FDE that approximates the linearized differential equation. Consider the general nonlinear first-order ODE

$$\bar{y}' = \bar{f}(t, \bar{y}) \tag{7.189}$$

As shown in Section 7.2 [Eq. (7.21)], linearization of Eq. (7.189) yields

$$\boxed{\bar{y}' + \alpha \bar{y} = F(t)} \tag{7.190}$$

where

$$\alpha = -\frac{\partial \bar{f}}{\partial \bar{y}} = -\bar{f}_y = g(t, \bar{y}) \tag{7.191}$$

and $F(t)$ is defined by Eq. (7.20). The nonhomogeneous term $F(t)$ has no influence on stability.

Equation (7.190) is in the form investigated in Section 7.8, where it is shown that the necessary and sufficient condition for stability of a finite difference approximation of Eq. (7.190) is that the magnitude of the amplification factor G of the FDE satisfy $|G| \leq 1$. Applying this criterion to an FDE generally results in a limitation on the step size, which depends on the value of α. For linear ODEs, α is a constant, and the value of Δt required to ensure stability is a constant. However, for a nonlinear ODE, α is a variable that depends on the solution [see Eq. (7.191)]. Thus, the stable step size Δt must be constantly monitored as the solution is computed to ensure that stability is maintained as the solution progresses.

Experience has shown that applying the stability criteria applicable to the finite difference approximation of the linearized form of a nonlinear ODE to the corresponding nonlinear ODE yields stable numerical solutions. Experience has also shown that, for most ODEs of practical interest, the step size required to obtain the desired accuracy is smaller than the step size required for stability. Consequently, instability is generally not a problem when solving ordinary differential equations, except for stiff ODEs (see Section 7.14). Instability is a serious problem in the solution of partial differential equations.

Summary

In summary, the stability of an FDE is determined as follows:

1. Construct the FDE for the model ODE $\bar{y}' + \alpha \bar{y} = 0$.
2. Determine the amplification factor G of the FDE.
3. Determine the conditions, if any, required to ensure that $|G| \leq 1$. These conditions are the stability criteria for the FDE.

Recall that the step size Δt generally must be 50 percent or less of the stable step size to avoid overshoot.

7.9 RUNGE–KUTTA METHODS

There are numerous Runge–Kutta methods. The general approach for deriving Runge–Kutta methods was presented in Section 7.5. That procedure is illustrated in this Section by developing the second-order Runge–Kutta method. The fourth-order Runge–Kutta method, presented in Section 7.5 is analyzed and the Runge–Kutta–Fehlberg method is presented.

The Second-Order Runge–Kutta Method

Consider the general nonlinear first-order ODE

$$\bar{y}' = \bar{f}(t, \bar{y}), \qquad \bar{y}(t_0) = \bar{y}_0 \tag{7.192}$$

Assume that $\Delta y_n = (y_{n+1} - y_n)$ is a weighted sum of two $\Delta y's$:

$$y_{n+1} = y_n + C_1\,\Delta y_1 + C_2\,\Delta y_2 \tag{7.193}$$

where Δy_1 is obtained from the explicit Euler method (with $h = \Delta t$):

$$\Delta y_1 = hf(t_n, y_n) = hf_n \tag{7.194}$$

Δy_2 is based on $f(t, y)$ evaluated somewhere in the interval $t_n < t < t_{n+1}$,

$$\Delta y_2 = hf(t_n + \alpha h, y_n + \beta\,\Delta y_1) \tag{7.195}$$

and α and β are to be determined. Thus,

$$y_{n+1} = y_n + C_1 hf_n + C_2 hf(t_n + \alpha h, y_n + \beta\,\Delta y_1) \tag{7.196}$$

Expanding $\bar{f}(t, \bar{y})$ in a Taylor series gives

$$\bar{f}(t, \bar{y}) = \bar{f}_n + \bar{f}_t|_n\,\Delta t + \bar{f}_y|_n\,\Delta y + \cdots \tag{7.197}$$

Evaluating $\bar{f}(t, \bar{y})$ at $t = t_n + \alpha h$ (i.e., $\Delta t = \alpha h$) and $y = y_n + \beta\Delta y_1$ (i.e., $\Delta y = \beta\Delta y_1 = \beta h f_n$) gives

$$\bar{f}(t_n + \alpha h, y_n + \beta\,\Delta y_1) = \bar{f}_n + \alpha h \bar{f}_t|_n + \beta h \bar{f}_n \bar{f}_y|_n + \cdots \tag{7.198}$$

Truncating Eq. (7.198) and substituting the result into Eq. (7.196) yields

$$y_{n+1} = y_n + (C_1 + C_2)hf_n + h^2(\alpha C_2 f_t|_n + \beta C_2 f_n f_y|_n) \tag{7.199}$$

The four free parameters in Eq. (7.199), C_1, C_2, α, and β, can be determined by requiring Eq. (7.199) to match the Taylor series for $\bar{y}(t)$ through second-order terms. Thus,

$$\bar{y}_{n+1} = \bar{y}_n + h\bar{f}_n + \frac{1}{2}h^2(\bar{f}_t|_n + \bar{f}_n\bar{f}_y|_n) + O(h^3) \tag{7.200}$$

Comparing Eqs. (7.199) and (7.200) gives

$$C_1 + C_2 = 1, \qquad \alpha C_2 = \frac{1}{2}, \qquad \beta C_2 = \frac{1}{2} \tag{7.201}$$

There are several choices for C_1, C_2, α, and β. For example:

1. Let $C_1 = 1$, which yields $C_2 = 0$ and $\alpha = \beta = \frac{1}{2}$. This yields the first-order explicit Euler method. That is,

$$y_{n+1} = y_n + \Delta t\, f_n \tag{7.202}$$

2. Let $C_1 = \frac{1}{2}$, which yields $C_2 = \frac{1}{2}$ and $\alpha = \beta = 1$. This yields the modified Euler predictor–corrector method. That is,

$$\Delta y_1 = \Delta t\, f(t_n, y_n) = \Delta t\, f_n \tag{7.203a}$$

$$\Delta y_2 = \Delta t\, f(t_{n+1}, y_{n+1}) = \Delta t\, f_{n+1} \tag{7.203b}$$

$$y_{n+1} = y_n + \frac{1}{2}\Delta t(f_n + f_{n+1}) \tag{7.203c}$$

3. Let $C_1 = 0$, which yields $C_2 = 1$ and $\alpha = \beta = \frac{1}{2}$. This yields the midpoint predictor–corrector method. That is,

$$\Delta y_1 = \Delta t\, f(t_n, y_n) = \Delta t\, f_n \tag{7.204a}$$

$$\Delta y_2 = \Delta t\, f\left(t_n + \frac{\Delta t}{2}, y_n + \frac{\Delta y_1}{2}\right) = \Delta t\, f_{n+1/2} \tag{7.204b}$$

$$y_{n+1} = y_n + \Delta y_2 = y_n + \Delta t\, f_{n+1/2} \tag{7.204c}$$

Other methods result for other choices for C_1.

Further analysis of second-order Runge–Kutta methods shows that they are explicit, single-point, two-step methods. With the exception of Eq. (7.202), they require two derivative function evaluations per step. The single step errors are $O(\Delta t^3)$, and the global errors are $O(\Delta t^2)$. The various methods are consistent, conditionally stable (usually with $\alpha h \le 2$), and convergent.

Most Runge–Kutta formulas denote the Δy's by k's. Thus, in Eqs. (7.203) and (7.204), $k_1 = \Delta y_1$ and $k_2 = \Delta y_2$.

The Fourth-Order Runge–Kutta Method

Runge–Kutta methods of higher order have been devised. One of the most popular is the fourth-order method presented in Section 7.5. For the linear first-order homogeneous model ODE $\bar{y}' + \alpha\bar{y} = 0$, Eqs. (7.98) and (7.99) can be combined to yield the single-step FDE

$$y_{n+1} = \left(1 - \alpha h + \frac{1}{2}(\alpha h)^2 - \frac{1}{6}(\alpha h)^3 + \frac{1}{24}(\alpha h)^4\right) y_n \tag{7.205}$$

where $h = \Delta t$. The MDE corresponding to Eq. (7.205) is of the form

$$y' = -\alpha y + 0(\Delta t^5) \tag{7.206}$$

As $\Delta t \to 0$, Eq. (7.206) approaches $y' = -\alpha y$. Consequently, Eq. (7.205) is a consistent approximation of the model ODE $\bar{y}' + \alpha\bar{y} = 0$. From Eq. (7.206), Eq. (7.205) is $O(\Delta t^5)$ locally and $O(\Delta t^4)$ globally. The amplification factor G for the model ODE $\bar{y}' + \alpha\bar{y} = 0$ is:

$$G = 1 - \alpha h + \frac{1}{2}(\alpha h)^2 - \frac{1}{6}(\alpha h)^3 + \frac{1}{24}(\alpha h)^4 \tag{7.207}$$

Solving for $|G| \leq 1$ numerically shows that $|G| \leq 1$ if $\alpha h \leq 2.785\ldots$ The fourth-order Runge–Kutta method is illustrated in Example 7.5.

Other Runge–Kutta Methods

Runge–Kutta methods with more than four derivative function evaluations have been devised, in which the additional results are used for error control. The concept behind these methods is to combine two different Runge–Kutta methods so that an estimate of the error can be obtained without an excessive increase in the number of derivative function evaluations. One of the more popular methods is the Runge–Kutta–Fehlberg method [Fehlberg (1966)], which is presented below:

$$\boxed{y_{n+1} = y_n + \left(\frac{16}{135}k_1 + \frac{6656}{12825}k_3 + \frac{28561}{56430}k_4 - \frac{9}{50}k_5 + \frac{2}{55}k_6\right)} \tag{7.208}$$

$$k_1 = \Delta t\, f(t_n, y_n) \tag{7.209a}$$

$$k_2 = \Delta t\, f\left(t_n + \frac{1}{4}h,\ y_n + \frac{1}{4}k_1\right) \tag{7.209b}$$

$$k_3 = \Delta t\, f\left(t_n + \frac{3}{8}h,\ y_n + \frac{3}{32}k_1 + \frac{9}{32}k_2\right) \tag{7.209c}$$

$$k_4 = \Delta t\, f\left(t_n + \frac{12}{13}h,\ y_n + \frac{1932}{2197}k_1 - \frac{7200}{2197}k_2 + \frac{7296}{2197}k_3\right) \tag{7.209d}$$

$$k_5 = \Delta t\, f\left(t_n + h,\ y_n + \frac{439}{216}k_1 - 8k_2 + \frac{3680}{513}k_3 - \frac{845}{4104}k_4\right) \tag{7.209e}$$

$$k_6 = \Delta t\, f\left(t_n + \frac{1}{2}h,\ y_n - \frac{8}{27}k_1 + 2k_2 - \frac{3544}{2565}k_3 + \frac{1859}{4104}k_4 - \frac{11}{40}k_5\right) \tag{7.209f}$$

$$\text{Error} = \frac{1}{360}k_1 - \frac{128}{4275}k_3 - \frac{2197}{75{,}240}k_4 + \frac{1}{50}k_5 + \frac{2}{55}k_6 \tag{7.210}$$

The Runge–Kutta–Fehlberg method is explicit and requires six derivative function evaluations per step. The FDE is consistent, $O(\Delta t^6)$ locally, and $O(\Delta t^5)$ globally. The method is conditionally stable and convergent. The error term can be used for error estimation and error control in the usual manner.

7.10 MULTIPOINT METHODS

The modified Euler predictor–corrector method presented in Section 7.5 is a second-order method. Higher-order methods are desirable. Runge–Kutta methods, discussed in Section 7.9, achieve that goal by introducing intermediate points between points n and $n + 1$. Unfortunately, higher-order Runge–Kutta methods require a large number of derivative function evaluations. Higher-order methods requiring fewer derivative function evaluations are desirable. Multipoint methods, which use more than one known point, have this capability.

The basic concept behind multipoint methods is presented Section 7.5 under "The Fourth-Order Adams–Bashforth Method." The implicit fourth-order Adams–Moulton FDE is also presented in Section 7.5. Those FDEs, as well as the general class of Adams methods, are derived in this section. As shown in Section 7.5, the general approach involves fitting a Newton backward-difference polynomial to selected points and integrating over a specified interval. Thus,

$$\boxed{\int_{?}^{\bar{y}_{n+1}} d\bar{y} = \int_{?}^{t_{n+1}} P_k(t)\,dt} \tag{7.211}$$

The Fourth-Order Adams–Bashforth Method

One of the most popular multipoint methods is the fourth-order Adams–Bashforth method, which is obtained by fitting a third-degree Newton backward-difference polynomial to base point n and integrating from point n to point $n+1$, as illustrated in Figure 7.18. For these conditions, Eq. (7.211) becomes

$$\int_{\bar{y}_n}^{\bar{y}_{n+1}} d\bar{y} = \int_{t_n}^{t_{n+1}} [P_3(t)]_n\,dt \tag{7.212}$$

Recall the third-degree Newton backward-difference polynomial fitted at base point n [see Eq. (4.77)]:

$$[P_3(t)]_n = \bar{f}_n + s\,\nabla\bar{f}_n + \frac{(s+1)s}{2}\nabla^2\bar{f}_n + \frac{(s+2)(s+1)s}{6}\nabla^3\bar{f}_n + \frac{(s+3)(s+2)(s+1)s}{24}h^4\bar{f}^{(4)}(\tau) \tag{7.213}$$

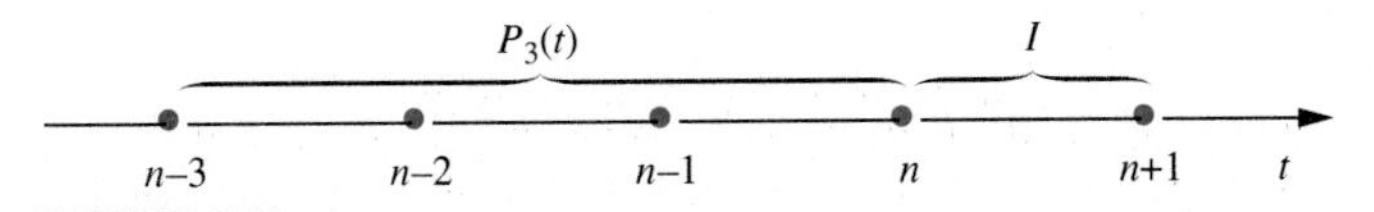

FIGURE 7.18
Finite difference grid for the fourth-order Adams–Bashforth method.

where the last term is the fourth-order error term. Equation (7.213) is actually explicit in terms of the interpolating parameter s and implicit in time t, where

$$t = t_n + sh \tag{7.214}$$

where $h = \Delta t$. Before Eq. (7.212) can be integrated, Eq. (7.213) must be expressed explicitly in terms of t through the relationship

$$s = \frac{t - t_0}{h} \tag{7.215}$$

or the integral must be expressed in terms of the interpolating parameter s by changing the independent variable from t to s and changing the limits of integration. The latter approach is simpler. Thus, differentiating Eq. (7.214) gives

$$dt = h\,ds \tag{7.216}$$

Substituting the limits of integration into Eq. (7.214) gives

$$t_n \rightarrow s = 0 \qquad \text{and} \qquad t_{n+1} \rightarrow s = 1 \tag{7.217}$$

Substituting Eqs. (7.216) and (7.217) into Eq. (7.212) gives

$$\bar{y}_{n+1} - \bar{y}_n = \int_0^1 \left(\bar{f}_n + s\,\nabla \bar{f}_n + \frac{s^2 + s}{2} \nabla^2 \bar{f}_n + \frac{s^3 + 3s^2 + 2s}{6} \nabla^3 \bar{f}_n \right) h\,ds$$
$$+ \int_0^1 \frac{s^4 + 6s^3 + 11s^2 + 6s}{24} h^4 \bar{f}^{(4)}(\tau) h\,ds \tag{7.218}$$

Integrating Eq. (7.218) gives

$$\bar{y}_{n+1} = \bar{y}_n + h \left(s\bar{f}_n + \frac{s^2}{2} \nabla \bar{f}_n + \left(\frac{s^3}{6} + \frac{s^2}{4} \right) \nabla^2 \bar{f}_n + \left(\frac{s^4}{24} + \frac{s^3}{6} + \frac{s^2}{6} \right) \nabla^3 \bar{f}_n \right) \Bigg|_0^1$$
$$+ h^5 \left(\frac{s^5}{120} + \frac{s^4}{16} + \frac{11s^3}{72} + \frac{s^2}{8} \right) \Bigg|_0^1 \bar{f}^{(4)}(\tau) \tag{7.219}$$

Evaluating Eq. (7.219) and substituting $f^{(4)}(\tau) = y^{(5)}(\tau)$ yields

$$\bar{y}_{n+1} = \bar{y}_n + h \left(\bar{f}_n + \frac{1}{2} \nabla \bar{f}_n + \frac{5}{12} \nabla^2 \bar{f}_n + \frac{3}{8} \nabla^3 \bar{f}_n \right) + \frac{251}{720} \bar{y}^{(5)}(\tau) \tag{7.220}$$

Equation (7.220) can be expressed in terms of function values rather than differences by introducing the definitions of the relevant differences from the difference table, Table 7.10. Substituting the differences from Table 7.10 into Eq. (7.220) gives

$$\bar{y}_{n+1} = \bar{y}_n + h \left(\bar{f}_n + \frac{1}{2}(\bar{f}_n - \bar{f}_{n-1}) + \frac{5}{12}(\bar{f}_n - 2\bar{f}_{n-1} + \bar{f}_{n-2}) \right.$$
$$\left. + \frac{3}{8}(\bar{f}_n - 3\bar{f}_{n-1} + 3\bar{f}_{n-2} - \bar{f}_{n-3}) \right) + \frac{251}{720} h^5 \bar{y}^{(5)}(\tau) \tag{7.221}$$

TABLE 7.10
Backward difference table

t	f	∇f	$\nabla^2 f$	$nabla^3 f$
t_{n-3}	f_{n-3}			
		$(f_{n-2} - f_{n-3})$		
t_{n-2}	f_{n-2}		$(f_{n-1} - 2f_{n-2} + f_{n-3})$	
		$(f_{n-1} - f_{n-2})$		$(f_n - 3f_{n-1} + 3f_{n-2} - f_{n-3})$
t_{n-1}	f_{n-1}		$(f_n - 2f_{n-1} + f_{n-2})$	
		$(f_n - f_{n-1})$		$(f_{n+1} - 3f_n + 3f_{n-1} - f_{n-2})$
t_n	f_n		$(f_{n+1} - 2f_n + f_{n-1})$	
		$(f_{n+1} - f_n)$		
t_{n+1}	f_{n+1}			

Collecting terms yields the fourth-order Adams–Bashforth FDE:

$$\boxed{\bar{y}_{n+1} = \bar{y}_n + \frac{h}{24}(55\bar{f}_n - 59\bar{f}_{n-1} + 37\bar{f}_{n-2} - 9\bar{f}_{n-3}) + \frac{251}{720}h^5 \bar{y}^{(5)}(\tau)} \tag{7.222}$$

Consistency and stability analyses for multipoint methods are quite tedious and complicated. It can be shown that Eq. (7.222) is consistent with $\bar{y}' = \bar{f}(t, \bar{y})$ and conditionally stable (for $\alpha\, \Delta t \lesssim 0.3$). Consequently, the method is convergent. As shown in Eq. (7.222), the local truncation error is $O(\Delta t^5)$, and the global error is $O(\Delta t^4)$.

The Fourth-Order Adams–Bashforth–Moulton Method

The fourth-order Adams–Bashforth method presented in the preceding subsection is a very accurate method. However, it has two disadvantages. First, it has a rather restrictive stable step size ($\alpha\, \Delta t \lesssim 0.3$). Second, error estimation and error control are difficult. The first problem can be reduced by developing an implicit FDE similar to the explicit fourth-order Adams–Bashforth method, by fitting the Newton backward-difference polynomial used in the integration of Eq. (7.211) to the unknown point, point $n + 1$. If the derivative function $f(t, y)$ is nonlinear, a nonlinear FDE results, which complicates the solution process. This complication can be eliminated by using an explicit FDE, such as the explicit fourth-order Adams–Bashforth FDE, as a predictor, and the implicit FDE as a corrector. The resulting two-step method will no longer be unconditionally stable, but the stability limit is generally much less restrictive than the stability limit of the predictor FDE alone.

Three additional benefits are obtained by this two-step predictor–corrector approach. First, the constant coefficient in the truncation error term is usually much smaller for the FDE based on a polynomial fitted at base point $n + 1$ than for a polynomial fitted at base point n. This is directly attributable to the increased accuracy associated with interpolation versus extrapolation. Second, the error terms associated with the predictor and corrector FDEs can be combined to yield an error estimate for step size control. Third, the error terms can be used to extrapolate the solution for improved accuracy, a process called *mop-up*. These procedures are illustrated in Section 7.5 for the fourth-order Adams–Bashforth–Moulton method.

The implicit fourth-order multipoint method is obtained by fitting a third-degree Newton backward-difference polynomial to base point $n+1$ and integrating from point n to point $n + 1$, as illustrated in Fig. 7.19. For these conditions, Eq. (7.211) becomes

$$\int_{\bar{y}_n}^{\bar{y}_{n+1}} d\bar{y} = \int_{t_n}^{t_{n+1}} [P_3(t)]_{n+1}\, dt \tag{7.223}$$

Recall the third-degree Newton backward-difference polynomial fitted at point $n + 1$ [see Eq. (4.77)]:

$$[P_3(t)]_{n+1} = \bar{f}_{n+1} + s\,\nabla\bar{f}_{n+1} + \frac{(s+1)s}{2}\nabla^2\bar{f}_{n+1} + \frac{(s+2)(s+1)s}{6}\nabla^3\bar{f}_{n+1} + \frac{(s+3)(s+2)(s+1)s}{24}h^4\bar{f}^{(4)}(\tau) \tag{7.224}$$

The relationship between time t and the interpolating parameter s is $t = t_{n+1} + sh$. Thus, $dt = h\,ds$, $t_n \to s = -1$, and $t_{n+1} \to s = 0$. Substituting these results into Eq. (7.223) gives

$$\bar{y}_{n+1} = \bar{y}_n + \int_{-1}^{0}\left(\bar{f}_{n+1} + s\nabla\bar{f}_{n+1} + \frac{s^2+s}{2}\nabla^2\bar{f}_{n+1} + \frac{s^3+3s^2+2s}{6}\nabla^3\bar{f}_{n+1}\right)h\,ds + \int_{-1}^{0}\frac{s^4+6s^3+11s^2+6s}{24}h^4\bar{f}^{(4)}(\tau)h\,ds \tag{7.225}$$

Integrating Eq. (7.225), applying the limits of integration, introducing the difference expressions from Table 7.10, and simplifying, yields the implicit fourth-order

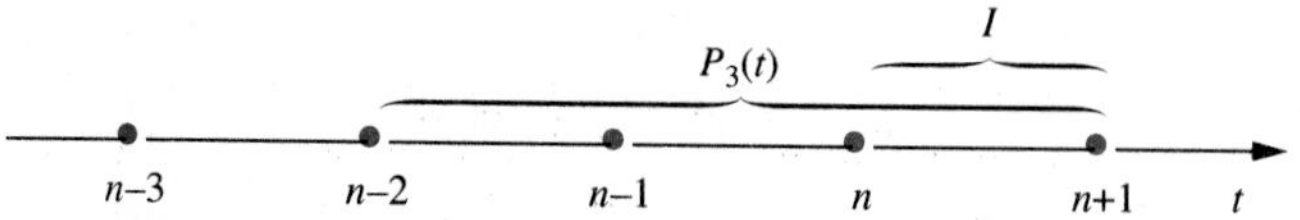

FIGURE 7.19
Finite difference grid for the fourth-order Adams–Moulton method.

Adams–Moulton FDE:

$$\overline{y}_{n+1} = \overline{y}_n + \frac{h}{24}(9\overline{f}_{n+1} + 19\overline{f}_n - 5\overline{f}_{n-1} + \overline{f}_{n-2}) - \frac{19}{720}h^5\overline{y}^{(5)}(\tau) \tag{7.226}$$

It can be shown that Eq. (7.226) is consistent with $\overline{y}' = \overline{f}(t, \overline{y})$, $O(\Delta t^5)$ locally, conditionally stable ($\alpha \, \Delta t \lesssim 3.0$), and convergent. The constant coefficient of the truncation error is $19/720$, which is approximately 13 times smaller than the coefficient of the truncation error of the explicit fourth-order Adams–Bashforth FDE [see Eq. (7.222)]. For nonlinear ODEs, Eq. (7.226) can be used as a corrector with the explicit fourth-order Adams–Bashforth FDE as a predictor. The combined predictor–corrector method is called the fourth-order Adams–Bashforth–Moulton method. This method is illustrated in Example 7.7 in Section 7.5.

Error estimation and extrapolation by combining the Adams–Bashforth predictor and the Adams–Moulton corrector is also discussed in Section 7.5.

General Adams Methods

The methods presented in the preceding subsections are fourth-order methods. Adams methods of any order can be derived by choosing different degree Newton backward-difference polynomials to fit the solution at the data points. When the range of integration is from point n to point $n + 1$, the resulting FDEs are called Adams FDEs. Those results are presented in this section. Other finite difference equations can be developed in the same manner by integrating from points ahead of point n (i.e., $n - 1$, $n - 2$, etc.) to point $n + 1$. These methods are presented in the next section.

Explicit type FDEs of the Adams type are called Adams–Bashforth FDEs. The finite difference grid for the Adams–Bashforth FDEs is illustrated in Fig. 7.20. The general formula for the explicit Adams–Bashforth FDEs is

$$\int_{\overline{y}_n}^{\overline{y}_{n+1}} d\overline{y} = h \int_0^1 [P_k(s)]_n \, ds \tag{7.227}$$

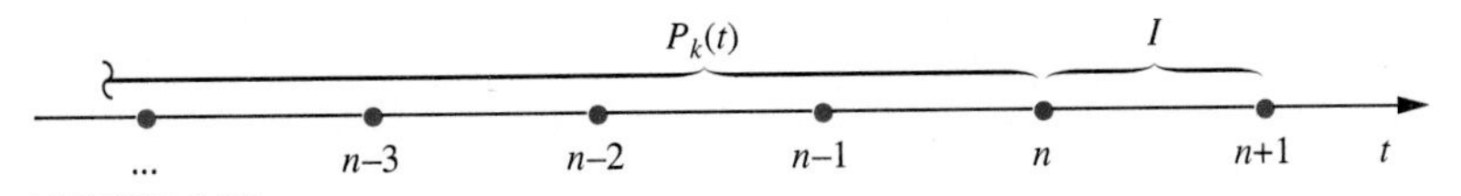

FIGURE 7.20
Finite difference grid for general Adams–Bashforth methods.

TABLE 7.11
Coefficients for the general Adams–Bashforth FDEs

k	β	α_0	α_{-1}	α_{-2}	α_{-3}	α_{-4}	α_{-5}	n	C
0	1	1						1	2.0
1	1/2	3	−1					2	1.0
2	1/12	23	−16	5				3	0.5
3	1/24	55	−59	37	−9			4	0.3
4	1/720	1901	−2774	2616	−1274	251		5	0.2
5	1/1440	4277	−7923	9982	−7298	2877	−475	6	

where k denotes the order of the Newton backward-difference polynomial fit at base point n. Integrating Eq. (7.227), evaluating the result for the limits of integration, introducing the difference expressions for point n from Table 7.10, and simplifying the results yields the general explicit Adams–Bashforth FDE:

$$y_{n+1} = y_n + \beta h(\alpha_0 f_n + \alpha_{-1} f_{n-1} + \alpha_{-2} f_{n-2} + \cdots), \qquad O(h^n), \qquad \alpha\,\Delta t \le C \tag{7.228}$$

where the coefficients β and α_i ($i = 0, -1, -2, \ldots$), the global order n, and the stability limit C are presented in Table 7.11.

Implicit-type FDEs of the Adams type are called Adams–Moulton FDEs. The finite difference grid for the Adams–Moulton FDEs is illustrated in Fig. 7.21. The general formula for the Adams–Moulton implicit FDEs is

$$\int_{\bar{y}_n}^{\bar{y}_{n+1}} d\bar{y} = h \int_{-1}^{0} [P_k(s)]_{n+1}\, ds \tag{7.229}$$

where k denotes the order of the Newton backward-difference polynomial fitted at base point $n+1$. Integrating Eq. (7.229), evaluating the results for the limits of integration, introducing the difference expressions for point $n+1$ from Table

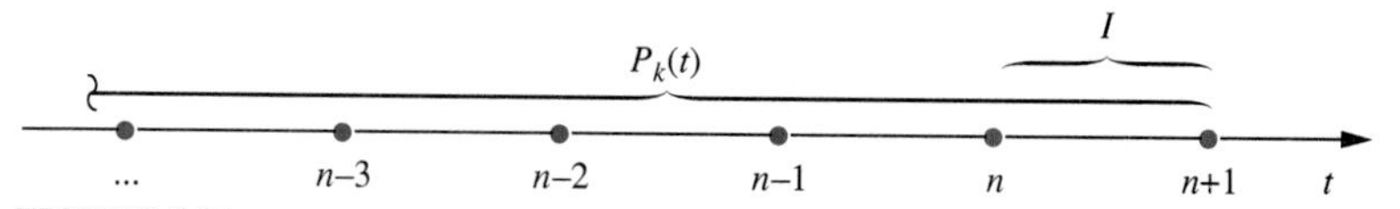

FIGURE 7.21
Finite difference grid for general Adams–Moulton methods.

TABLE 7.12
Coefficients for the general Adams–Moulton FDEs

k	B	α_1	α_0	α_{-1}	α_{-2}	α_{-3}	α_{-4}	n	C
0	1	1						1	∞
1	1/2	1	1					2	∞
2	1/12	5	8	−1				3	6.0
3	1/24	9	19	−5	1			4	3.0
4	1/720	251	646	−264	106	−19		5	1.9
5	1/1440	475	1427	−798	482	−173	27	6	

7.10, and simplifying the results yields the general implicit Adams–Moulton FDE:

$$y_{n+1} = y_n + \beta h(\alpha_1 f_{n+1} + \alpha_0 f_n + \alpha_{-1} f_{n-1} + \cdots), \qquad O(h^n), \qquad \alpha\,\Delta t \le C \tag{7.230}$$

where the coefficients β and $\alpha_i (i = 1, 0, -1, \ldots)$, the global order n, and the stability limit C are presented in Table 7.12.

General Multipoint Methods

The family of Adams multipoint methods presented in the preceding subsection is based on integrating the approximating polynomials from point n to point $n+1$. Other families of multipoint methods can be derived by integrating the approximating polynomials from points ahead of point n, for example, from points $n-1$, $n-2$, and so on. That procedure is outlined in this subsection.

Figure 7.22 illustrates the finite difference grid for the general class of explicit multipoint methods. Let the parameter q denote the lower limit of integration, $n+1-q$. Thus $q = 1 \rightarrow n$, $q = 2 \rightarrow n-1$, and so on. The general form of the FDE is

$$\int_{\bar{y}_{n+1-q}}^{\bar{y}_{n+1}} d\bar{y} = h \int_{1-q}^{1} [P_k(s)]_n \, ds \tag{7.231}$$

The Adams–Bashforth formulas correspond to $q = 1$.

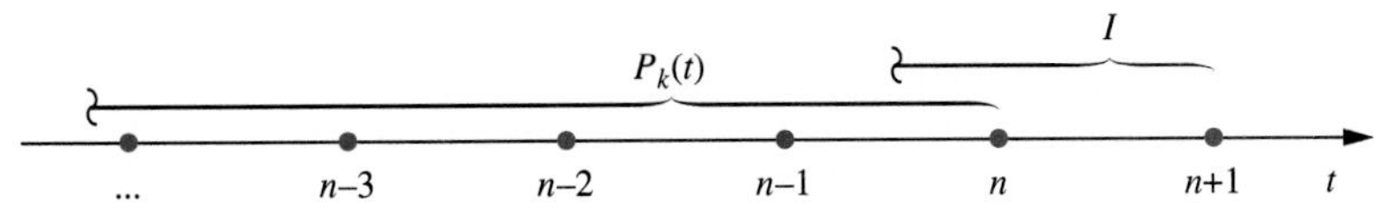

FIGURE 7.22
Finite difference grid for general explicit multipoint methods.

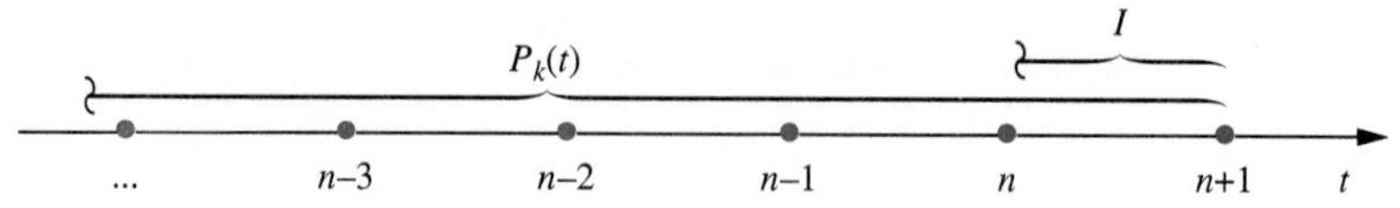

FIGURE 7.23
Finite difference grid for general implicit multipoint methods.

Figure 7.23 illustrates the finite difference grid for the general class of implicit multipoint methods, where q denotes the lower limit of integration. The general form of the FDE is

$$\int_{\bar{y}_{n+1-q}}^{\bar{y}_{n+1}} d\bar{y} = h \int_{-q}^{0} [P_k(s)]_{n+1}\, ds \tag{7.232}$$

The Adams–Moulton formulas correspond to $q = 1$.

As an example of the general multipoint formulas, consider the Milne (1953) method, for which $k = 2$ and $q = 4$ for the predictor. The predictor FDE is

$$y_{n+1}^{P} = y_{n-3} + \frac{4h}{3}(2f_n - f_{n-1} + 2f_{n-2}) \tag{7.233}$$

The predictor FDE is explicit, requires one derivative function evaluation per step, is consistent, and $O(\Delta t^4)$ globally. For the corrector, $k = 2$ and $q = 2$. The corrector FDE is

$$y_{n+1}^{C} = y_{n-1} + \frac{h}{3}(f_{n+1} + 4f_n + f_{n-1}) \tag{7.234}$$

The corrector FDE is explicit, requires one derivative function evaluation per step, is consistent, and $O(\Delta t^4)$ globally. The overall method is subject to instabilities in some cases. Hence, it is not a popular method.

7.11 NONLINEAR FINITE DIFFERENCE EQUATIONS

Several finite difference methods have been developed for solving the first-order initial-value ordinary differential equation

$$\boxed{\bar{y}' = \bar{f}(t, \bar{y}), \qquad \bar{y}(t_0) = \bar{y}_0} \tag{7.235}$$

The derivative function $\bar{f}(t, \bar{y})$ may be linear or nonlinear in $\bar{y}$. When $\bar{f}(t, \bar{y})$ is linear in $\bar{y}$, the corresponding FDE is linear in y_{n+1}, for both explicit FDEs and implicit FDEs. When $\bar{f}(t, \bar{y})$ is nonlinear in $\bar{y}$, explicit FDEs are still linear in y_{n+1}. However, implicit FDEs are nonlinear in y_{n+1}, and special procedures are required to solve for y_{n+1}. Two procedures for solving nonlinear FDEs are

1. Time linearization
2. Newton's method

These two procedures are presented in this section.

Time Linearization

One approach for solving a nonlinear FDE is *time linearization,* in which the nonlinear derivative function is expanded in a Taylor series about the known point n and truncated after the first derivative term.

To illustrate this procedure, consider the implicit Euler method [see Eq. (7.70)]:

$$y_{n+1} = y_n + \Delta t\, f_{n+1} \tag{7.236}$$

Expand $f(t, y)$ in a two-variable Taylor series. Thus,

$$f_{n+1} = f_n + f_t|_n\, \Delta t + f_y|_n (y_{n+1} - y_n) + \cdots \tag{7.237}$$

Substituting Eq. (7.237) into Eq. (7.236) yields

$$y_{n+1} = y_n + \Delta t \left(f_n + f_t|_n\, \Delta t + f_y|_n (y_{n+1} - y_n)\right) \tag{7.238}$$

Equation (7.238) is linear in y_{n+1}. Solving for y_{n+1} yields

$$\boxed{y_{n+1} = \frac{y_n + \Delta t\, f_n + \Delta t^2 f_t|_n - \Delta t\, y_n f_y|_n}{1 - \Delta t\, f_y|_n}} \tag{7.239}$$

Example 7.13. Solution by time linearization. In Example 7.3, the radiation problem presented in Section 7.1 is solved by the implicit Euler method. The FDE is

$$T_{n+1} = T_n + \Delta t\, f_{n+1} \tag{7.240}$$

and the derivative function is

$$f(t, T) = -\alpha(T^4 - T_a^4) \tag{7.241}$$

TABLE 7.13
Solution by time linearization

t_n	T_n	f_n	$f_T\|_n$	T_{exact}	Error
0.00	2500.000000	−77.117188	−0.125000		
2.00	2375.012500	−63.626828	−0.107174	2360.829988	14.182512
4.00	2270.220672	−53.117597	−0.093604	2247.247314	21.973358
6.00	2180.737446	−45.223951	−0.082966	2154.470796	26.266650
7.00	2103.161822	−39.123170	−0.074423	2074.611989	27.549924
10.00	2035.053198			2005.416366	29.636833
0.00	2500.000000	−77.117188	−0.125000		
1.00	2430.562500	−69.792468	−0.114871	2462.434874	4.127626
2.00	2367.961115	−62.874465	−0.106222	2360.829988	7.131127
⋮	⋮	⋮	⋮	⋮	⋮
9.00	2053.222779	−35.536841	−0.069247	2037.840846	14.381932
10.00	2019.987375			2005.416366	14.571009

We solve Eq. (7.240) by time linearization, using Eq. (7.239). Thus,

$$T_{n+1} = \frac{T_n + \Delta t\, f_n + \Delta t^2 f_t|_n - \Delta t\, T_n f_T|_n}{1 - \Delta t\, f_T|_n} \tag{7.242}$$

From Eq. (7.241),

$$f_t = 0 \qquad \text{and} \qquad f_T = -4\alpha T^3 \tag{7.243}$$

Let $\Delta t = 2.0$ s. For the first time step,

$$f_0 = -(2.0 \times 10^{-12})(2500^4 - 250^4) = -77.117188 \tag{7.244a}$$

$$f_T|_0 = -4(2.0 \times 10^{-12})2500^3 = -0.125000 \tag{7.244b}$$

$$T_1 = \frac{2500 + 2.0(-77.117188) - 2.0(2500)(-0.125000)}{1 - 2.0(-0.125000)} = 2375.012501 \tag{7.245}$$

These results and the results of subsequent time steps are presented in Table 7.13.

Newton's Method

Newton's method for solving nonlinear equations is presented in Section 3.5. An implicit FDE can be expressed in the form

$$y_{n+1} = F(y_{n+1}) \tag{7.246}$$

Equation (7.246) can be rearranged into the form

$$\mathcal{F}(y_{n+1}) = y_{n+1} - F(y_{n+1}) = 0 \tag{7.247}$$

Expanding $\mathcal{F}(y_{n+1})$ in a Taylor series about the value y_{n+1} and evaluating at y^*_{n+1} yields

$$\mathcal{F}(y^*_{n+1}) = \mathcal{F}(y_{n+1}) + \mathcal{F}'(y_{n+1})(y^*_{n+1} - y_{n+1}) + \cdots = 0 \tag{7.248}$$

where y_{n+1}^* is the solution of Eq. (7.246). Truncating Eq. (7.248) after the first-order term and solving for y_{n+1}^* iteratively yields, for the $(k + 1)$st interation,

$$\boxed{y_{n+1}^{(k+1)} = y_{n+1}^{(k)} - \frac{\mathcal{F}(y_{n+1}^{(k)})}{\mathcal{F}'(y_{n+1}^{(k)})}} \tag{7.249}$$

Newton's method works well for all values of $\partial F/\partial y$ and all step sizes Δt. A good initial guess may be required.

Example 7.14. Solution by Newton's method. We will illustrate Newton's method by solving the radiation problem presented in Section 7.1 and Example 7.3 by the implicit Euler method. Thus,

$$T_{n+1} = T_n + \Delta t\, f_{n+1} = F(T_{n+1}) \tag{7.250}$$

where the derivative function is

$$f(t, T) = -\alpha(T^4 - T_a^4) \tag{7.251}$$

Substituting Eq. (7.251) into Eq. (7.250) yields

$$\mathcal{F}(T_{n+1}) = T_{n+1} - T_n + \alpha\,\Delta t\,(T_{n+1}^4 - T_a^4) = 0 \tag{7.252}$$

The derivative of $\mathcal{F}(T_{n+1})$ is

$$\mathcal{F}'(T_{n+1}) = 1 + 4\alpha\,\Delta t\,T_{n+1}^3 \tag{7.253}$$

Equation (7.249) becomes

$$T_{n+1}^{(k+1)} = T_{n+1}^{(k)} - \frac{\mathcal{F}(T_{n+1}^{(k)})}{\mathcal{F}'(T_{n+1}^{(k)})} \tag{7.254}$$

Let $\Delta t = 2.0$ s. For the first time step,

$$\mathcal{F}(T_1) = T_1 - 2500 + (2.0 \times 10^{-12})(2.0)(T_1^4 - 250^4) \tag{7.255a}$$

$$\mathcal{F}'(T_1) = 1 + 4(2.0 \times 10^{-12})(2.0)T_1^3 \tag{7.255b}$$

Let $T_1^{(0)} = 2500$ K. Then

$$\mathcal{F}(T_1^{(0)}) = 2500 - 2500 + (2.0 \times 10^{-12})(2.0)(2500^4 - 250^4) = 156.234375 \tag{7.256a}$$

$$\mathcal{F}'(T_1^{(0)}) = 1 + 4(2.0 \times 10^{-12})(2.0)2500^3 = 1.250000 \tag{7.256b}$$

Substituting these values into Eq. (7.254) gives

$$T_1^{(1)} = 2500 - \frac{156.234375}{1.250000} = 2375.012500 \tag{7.256c}$$

Repeating the procedure three more times yields the converged result $T_1^{(4)} = 2373.145960$. These results and the results for subsequent time steps are presented in Table 7.4 in Example 7.3.

Summary

The results presented in Tables 7.4 and 7.13 differ due to the additional truncation error associated with time linearization. However, the differences are quite small. Time linearization is quite popular for solving implicit nonlinear FDEs corresponding to nonlinear PDEs. When the exact solution to an implicit nonlinear FDE is desired, Newton's method is recommended.

7.12 SYSTEMS OF FIRST-ORDER ORDINARY DIFFERENTIAL EQUATIONS

Sections 7.5 to 7.11 are devoted to the solution of a single first-order ordinary differential equation. In many applications in engineering and science, coupled systems of first-order ODEs governing several dependent variables arise. The methods for solving a single first-order ODE can be used to solve systems of first-order ODEs.

Consider the general system of first-order ODEs

$$\bar{y}_i' = \bar{f}_i(t, \bar{y}_1, \bar{y}_2, \ldots, \bar{y}_m) \qquad (i = 1, 2, \ldots, m) \tag{7.257a}$$

$$\bar{y}_i(0) = Y_i \qquad (i = 1, 2, \ldots, m) \tag{7.257b}$$

Each ODE in the system of ODEs can be solved by any of the methods developed for solving single ODEs. Care must be taken to ensure the proper coupling of the solutions. When predictor–corrector or multistep methods are used, each step must be applied to *all* the equations before proceeding to the next step. The step size must be the same for all of the equations.

Example 7.15. Solution of two coupled first-order ODEs. Consider the following system of two coupled ODEs from Example 7.16 in Section 7.13:

$$T' = S, \qquad T(0) = 0 \tag{7.258a}$$

$$S' = 4T, \qquad S(0) = 50 \tag{7.258b}$$

We will solve this system of equations by the fourth-order Runge–Kutta method [see Eq. (7.98)] for T(1.0) and S(1.0) with $\Delta t = 0.250$. Let $k_i (i = 1, 2, 3, 4)$ denote the increments in $T(t)$ and $\ell_i (i = 1, 2, 3, 4)$ denote the increments in $S(t)$. For two coupled ODEs, Eq. (7.98) gives

$$T_{n+1} = T_n + \frac{1}{6}(k_1 + 2k_2 + 2k_3 + k_4) \tag{2.259a}$$

$$S_{n+1} = S_n + \frac{1}{6}\left(l_1 + 2l_2 + 2l_3 + l_4\right) \tag{2.259b}$$

where k_i and l_i are given by

$$k_1 = \Delta t\, f(t_n, T_n, S_n) \qquad l_1 = \Delta t\, g(t_n, T_n, S_n) \tag{7.260a}$$

$$k_2 = \Delta t\, f\left(t_n + \frac{\Delta t}{2}, T_n + \frac{k_1}{2}, S_n + \frac{l_1}{2}\right)$$
$$l_2 = \Delta t\, g\left(t_n + \frac{\Delta t}{2}, T_n + \frac{k_1}{2}, S_n + \frac{l_1}{2}\right) \tag{7.260b}$$

$$k_3 = \Delta t\, f\left(t_n + \frac{\Delta t}{2}, T_n + \frac{k_2}{2}, S_n + \frac{l_2}{2}\right)$$
$$l_3 = \Delta t\, g\left(t_n + \frac{\Delta t}{2}, T_n + \frac{k_2}{2}, S_n + \frac{l_2}{2}\right) \tag{7.260c}$$

$$k_4 = \Delta t\, f(t_n + \Delta t, T_n + k_3, S_n + l_3)$$
$$l_4 = \Delta t\, g(t_n + \Delta t, T_n + k_3, S_n + l_3) \tag{7.260d}$$

Due to the coupling, k_1 and l_1 both must be computed before k_2 and l_2 can be computed, k_2 and l_2 both must be computed before k_3 and l_3 can be computed, and so forth.

For Eq. (7.258), the derivative functions $f(t, T, S)$ and $g(t, T, S)$ are simply $f = S$ and $g = 4T$. Thus, Eq. (7.260) reduces to

$$k_1 = \Delta t\,(S_n) \qquad l_1 = \Delta t\, 4(T_n) \tag{7.261a}$$

$$k_2 = \Delta t\left(S_n + \frac{l_1}{2}\right) \qquad l_2 = \Delta t\, 4\left(T_n + \frac{k_1}{2}\right) \tag{7.261b}$$

$$k_3 = \Delta t\left(S_n + \frac{l_2}{2}\right) \qquad l_3 = \Delta t\, 4\left(T_n + \frac{k_2}{2}\right) \tag{7.261c}$$

$$k_4 = \Delta t\,(S_n + l_3) \qquad l_4 = \Delta t\, 4(T_n + k_3) \tag{7.261d}$$

The solution is presented in Table 7.14.

TABLE 7.14
Solution of two coupled first-order ODEs

t_n t_{n1}	T_n S_n T_{n1} S_{n1}	k_1 ℓ_1	k_2 ℓ_2	k_3 ℓ_3	k_4 ℓ_4
0.000	0.000000	12.500000	12.500000	13.281250	14.062500
	50.000000	0.000000	62.250000	6.250000	13.281250
0.250	13.020833	14.095052	15.722656	16.603597	19.315592
	56.380208	13.020833	20.068359	20.882161	29.624430
0.500	29.364692	19.284481	22.955068	24.160348	29.495038
	77.137926	29.364692	39.006933	40.842226	53.525040
0.750	53.199750	29.392317	36.042286	37.879305	47.197540
	117.569267	53.199750	67.895909	71.220893	91.079056
1.000	90.605257				
	187.988002				

7.13 HIGHER-ORDER ORDINARY DIFFERENTIAL EQUATIONS

Sections 7.5 to 7.12 are devoted to the solution of first-order ordinary differential equations. Many applications in engineering and science are governed by higher-order ODEs. In general, a higher-order ODE can be replaced by a system of first-order ODEs. When a system of higher-order ODEs is involved, each single higher-order ODE can be replaced by a system of first-order ODEs, and the coupled system of higher-order ODEs can be replaced by coupled systems of first-order ODEs. The systems of first-order ODEs can be solved as described in Section 7.12.

Consider the general nth-order ODE:

$$y^{(n)} = f(t, y, y', y'', \ldots, y^{(n-1)}) \tag{7.262a}$$

$$\bar{y}(t_0) = \bar{y}_0 \quad \text{and} \quad \bar{y}^{(i)}(t_0) = \bar{y}_0^{(i)} (i = 1, 2, \ldots, n-1) \tag{7.262b}$$

Equation (7.262) can be replaced by an equivalent system of n coupled first-order ODEs by defining the n auxiliary variables:

$$y_1 = y \tag{7.263.1}$$

$$y_2 = y' = y_1' \tag{7.263.2}$$

$$y_3 = y'' = y_2' \tag{7.263.3}$$

$$\vdots \quad \vdots \quad \vdots$$

$$y_n = y^{(n-1)} = y_{n-1}' \tag{7.263.n}$$

Differentiating Eq. (2.263.n) gives

$$y_n' = y^{(n)} \tag{7.264}$$

Rearranging Eqs. (7.263.2) to (7.263.n) and substituting these results and Eq. (7.264) into Eq. (7.262a) yields the following system of n coupled first-order ODEs:

$$y_1' = y_2, \qquad y_1(0) = y_0 \tag{7.265.1}$$

$$y_2' = y_3, \qquad y_2(0) = y_0' \tag{7.265.2}$$

$$\vdots \quad \vdots \qquad \vdots \quad \vdots$$

$$y_{n-1}' = y_n, \qquad y_{n-1}(0) = y_0^{(n-2)} \tag{7.265.n − 1}$$

$$y_n' = F(t, y_1, y_2, \ldots, y_n), \qquad y_n(0) = y_0^{(n-1)} \tag{7.265.n}$$

Example 7.16. Reduction of a second-order ODE to two first-order ODEs. To illustrate the reduction of a higher-order ODE to a system of first-order ODEs, we will reduce the second-order ODE considered in Example 8.1 to two coupled first-order ODEs. From Eq. (8.35)

$$T'' - 4T = -4T_a \tag{7.266a}$$

$$T(0) = 0 \quad \text{and} \quad T'(0) = 50 \tag{7.266b}$$

Let $T' = S$. Then Eq. (7.266a) reduces to

$$T' = S, \qquad T(0) = 0 \tag{7.267a}$$

$$S' = 4(T - T_a), \qquad S(0) = 50 \tag{7.267b}$$

The solution to Eq. (7.267) by the fourth-order Runge–Kutta method is presented in Example 7.15 in Section 7.12.

7.14 STIFF ORDINARY DIFFERENTIAL EQUATIONS

A special problem arising in the numerical solution of ODEs is *stiffness*. This problem occurs in single linear and nonlinear ODEs, higher-order linear and nonlinear ODEs, and systems of linear and nonlinear ODEs. There are several definitions of stiffness:

1. An ODE is stiff if the step size required for stability is much smaller than the step size required for accuracy.
2. An ODE is stiff if the step size required for stability is so small that round-off errors become significant.
3. An ODE is stiff if it contains some transients that decay rapidly compared to the major transient of interest.
4. A system of ODEs is stiff if at least one eigenvalue of the system is negative and large compared to the other eigenvalues of the system.
5. From an economic point of view, an ODE or a system of ODEs is stiff if the step size based on cost (i.e., computational time) is too large to obtain an accurate (i.e., stable) solution.

In this section, we present an example of a single stiff ODE, an example of a system of stiff ODEs, and the Gear (1971) method for solving stiff ODEs.

A Single First-Order ODE

Although stiffness is usually associated with a system of ODEs, it can also occur in a single ODE that has more than one time scale of interest: one time scale associated with the complementary solution and one time scale associated with the particular solution. Gear (1971) considered the following ODE:

$$\boxed{\bar{y}' = \bar{f}(t, \bar{y}) = -\alpha\big(\bar{y} - F(t)\big) + F'(t), \qquad \bar{y}(t_0) = \bar{y}_0} \tag{7.268}$$

which has the exact solution

$$\boxed{\bar{y}(t) = \big(\bar{y}_0 - F(0)\big)e^{-\alpha t} + F(t)} \tag{7.269}$$

When α is a large positive constant and $F(t)$ is a smooth, slowly varying function, Eq. (7.269) exhibits two widely different time scales: a rapidly changing term associated with $\exp(-\alpha t)$ and a slowly varying term associated with $F(t)$. As an example, let $\alpha = 1000$, $F(t) = t + 2$, and $\bar{y}(0) = 1$. Equation (7.268) becomes

$$\bar{y}' = \bar{f}(t, \bar{y}) = -1000\big(\bar{y} - (t+2)\big) + 1 \tag{7.270}$$

and Eq. (7.269) becomes

$$\boxed{\bar{y}(t) = -e^{-1000t} + t + 2} \tag{7.271}$$

The exact solution at small values of t, which is dominated by the $\exp(-1000t)$ term, is presented in Fig. 7.24. The exact solution for large values of t, which is dominated by the $(t + 2)$ term, is presented in Fig. 7.25. Note how rapidly the exponential term decays.

The error is controlled by Δt, but stability is controlled by $\alpha\Delta t$. For stability of many explicit methods, $\alpha\,\Delta t \le 2$, which, for $\alpha = 1000$, gives $\Delta t < 2/\alpha = 2/1000 = 0.002$. To avoid overshoot, $\Delta t < 0.001$. To reach $t = 5$, $N = 5/0.001 = 5000$ time steps.

Example 7.17. Solution of the stiff ODE by the explicit Euler method. Solve Eq. (7.270) by the explicit Euler method [see Eq. (7.58)]:

$$y_{n+1} = y_n + \Delta t\, f_n \tag{7.272}$$

Substituting the derivative function $f(t, y)$ into Eq. (7.272) gives

$$y_{n+1} = y_n + \Delta t\Big(-1000\,(y_n - (t_n + 2)) + 1\Big) \tag{7.273}$$

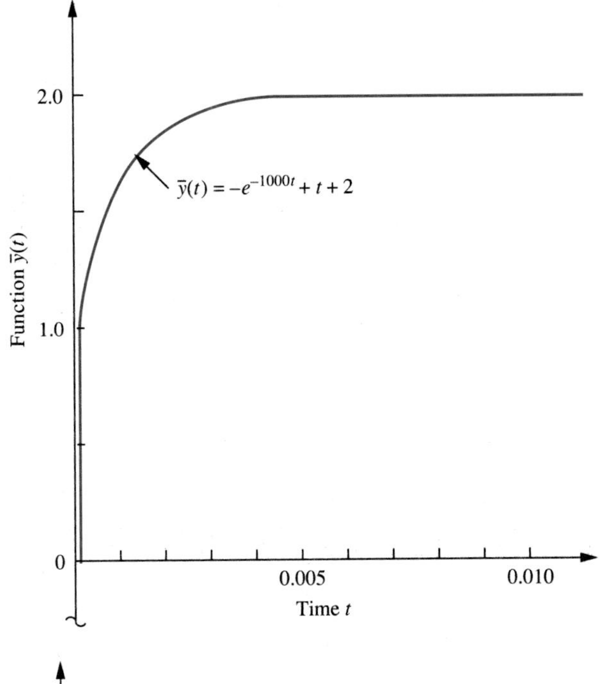

FIGURE 7.24
Exact solution of the stiff ODE at small time.

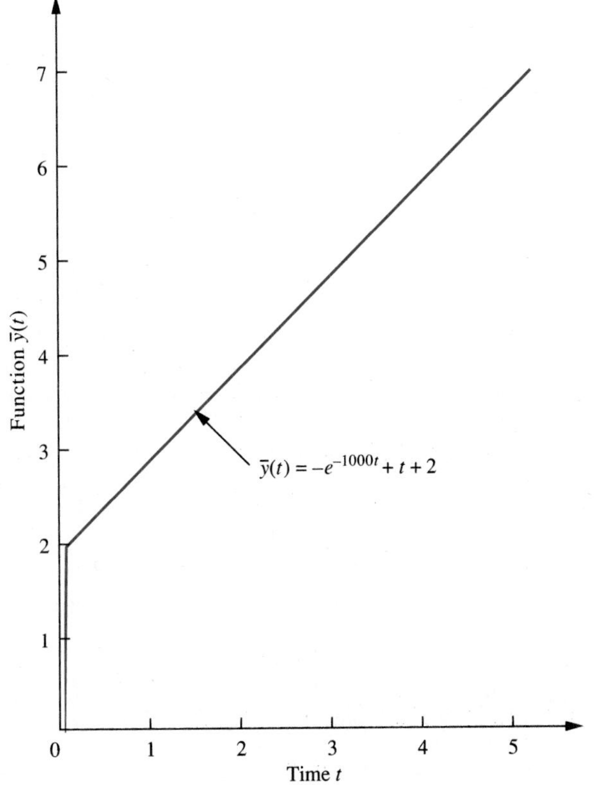

FIGURE 7.25
Exact solution of the stiff ODE at large time.

TABLE 7.15
Solution of the stiff ODE by the explicit Euler method

$\Delta t = 0.0005$			$\Delta t = 0.001$		
t_n	y_n	y_{exact}	t_n	y_n	y_{exact}
0.0000	1.000000		0.000	1.000000	
0.0005	1.500500	1.393969	0.001	2.001000	1.633121
0.0010	1.751000	1.633121	0.002	2.002000	1.866665
0.0015	1.876500	1.778370	0.003	2.003000	1.953213
0.0020	1.939500	1.866665	0.004	2.004000	1.985684
⋮	⋮	⋮	⋮	⋮	⋮
0.0100	2.009999	2.009955	0.010	2.010000	2.009955

$\Delta t = 0.002$			$\Delta t = 0.0025$		
t_n	y_n	y_{exact}	t_n	y_n	y_{exact}
0.000	1.000000		0.0000	1.000000	
0.002	3.002000	1.866665	0.0025	3.502500	1.920415
0.004	1.004000	1.985684	0.0050	−0.245000	1.998262
0.006	3.006000	2.003521	0.0075	5.382500	2.006947
0.008	1.008000	2.007665	0.0100	−3.052500	2.009955
0.010	3.010000	2.009955			

Consider four different step sizes: $\Delta t = 0.0005$, 0.001, 0.002, and 0.0025. The results are tabulated in Table 7.15 and illustrated in Fig. 7.26.

The stability limit is $\Delta t \leq 0.002$. For $\Delta t = 0.0005$, the solution is a reasonable approximation of the exact solution, although the errors are rather large. For $\Delta t = 0.001$, the solution reaches the asymptotic large-time solution $y = t + 2$ in one step. For $\Delta t = 0.002$, the solution is stable but oscillates about the asymptotic large-time solution. For $\Delta t = 0.0025$, the solution is clearly unstable.

From this example, it is obvious that the stable step size is controlled by the rapid transient associated with the exponential term. At large times, that transient has completely died out and the solution is given totally by the asymptotic large-time solution $y = t+2$. If an accurate small-time solution is required, then the small step size required for stability may be larger than the small step size required for accuracy. In that case, explicit methods can be used. However, if the early transient solution is of no interest, and an accurate asymptotic large-time solution is required, explicit methods are unsuitable due to the small stable step size.

Example 7.17 clearly illustrates the effect of stiffness of the ODE on the numerical solution by the explicit Euler method. In Example 7.18, the implicit Euler method is used to reduce the problems associated with stiffness.

Example 7.18. Solution of the stiff ODE by the implicit Euler method. Solve Eq. (7.270) by the implicit Euler method [see Eq. (7.70)]:

$$y_{n+1} = y_n + \Delta t\, f_{n+1} \tag{7.274}$$

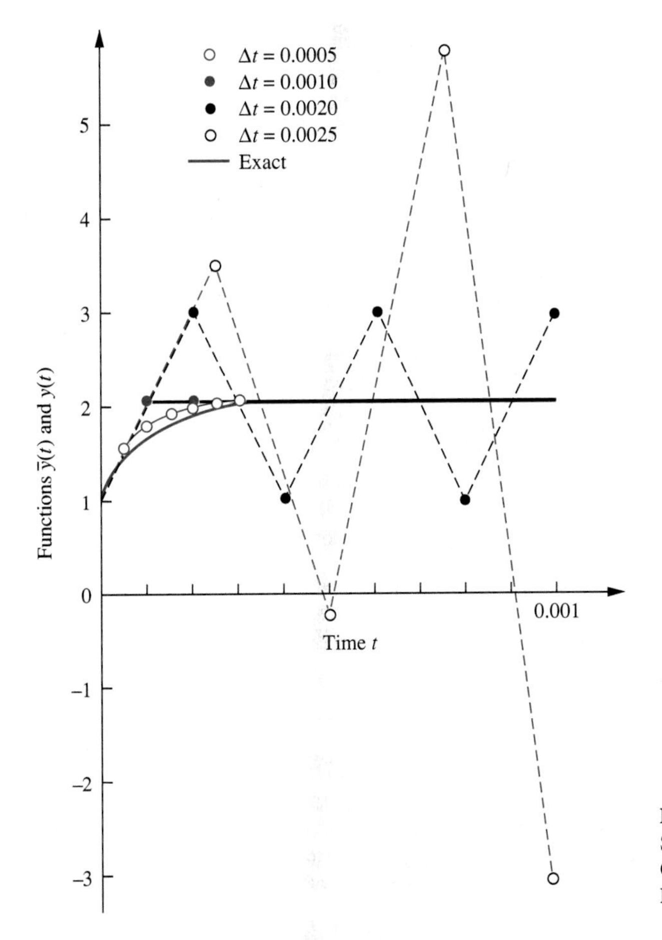

FIGURE 7.26
Solution of the stiff ODE by the explicit Euler method.

Substituting the derivative function $f(t, y)$ into Eq. (7.274) yields

$$y_{n+1} = y_n + \Delta t\Big(- 1000\,(y_{n+1} - (t_{n+1} + 2)) + 1\Big) \tag{7.275}$$

Equation (7.275) is implicit in y_{n+1}. However, since $f(t, y)$ is linear in y, Eq. (7.275) is linear in y_{n+1}, and it can be rearranged to give

$$y_{n+1} = \left(\frac{1}{1 + 1000\Delta t}\right)\Big(y_n + 1000(t_{n+1} + 2)\,\Delta t + \Delta t\Big) \tag{7.276}$$

Consider four different step sizes: 0.01, 0.05, 0.10, and 0.5. The results for the three small time steps are tabulated in Table 7.16, and the results for $\Delta t = 0.5$ are illustrated in Fig. 7.27.

The implicit Euler method is unconditionally stable. Consequently, there is no limit on the stable step size. As illustrated in Table 7.16 and Fig. 7.27, the solutions are all stable. However, as the step size is increased, the accuracy of the early-time transient due to the exponential term suffers. In fact, the entire early-time transient is completely lost for large values of Δt. However, even in those cases, the asymptotic large-time solution is predicted quite accurately. If the early-time transient is of interest, then a small step size is required for accuracy. If only the large-time solution is of interest, then implicit methods can be employed to reduce the computational effort.

TABLE 7.16
Solution of the stiff ODE by the implicit Euler method

$\Delta t = 0.01$			$\Delta t = 0.05$		
t_n	y_n	y_{exact}	t_n	y_n	y_{exact}
0.00	1.000000		0.00	1.000000	
0.01	1.919091	2.009955	0.05	2.030392	2.050000
0.02	2.011736	2.020000	0.10	2.099616	2.100000
0.03	2.029249	2.030000			
0.04	2.039932	2.040000	$\Delta t = 0.1$		
...	......	......			
0.10	2.100000	2.100000	t_n	y_n	y_{exact}
			0.0	1.000000	
			0.1	2.090099	2.100000

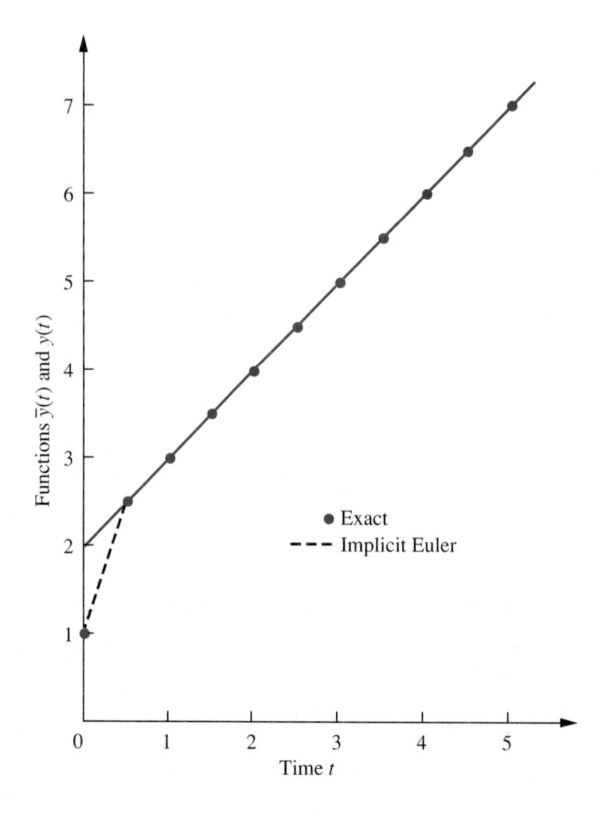

FIGURE 7.27
Solution of the stiff ODE by the implicit Euler method.

Systems of First-Order ODEs

Consider the general system of first-order ODEs discussed in Section 7.12 [see Eq. (7.257*a*)]:

$$\bar{y}_i' = \bar{f}_i(t, \bar{y}_1, \bar{y}_2, \ldots, \bar{y}_m) \qquad (i = 1, 2, \ldots, m) \tag{7.277}$$

For a system of coupled linear ODEs, Eq. (7.277) can be expressed as

$$\bar{\mathbf{y}}' = \mathbf{A}\bar{\mathbf{y}} + \mathbf{F} \tag{7.278}$$

where $\mathbf{y}^{\mathrm{T}} = (\bar{y}_1 \bar{y}_2 \ldots \bar{y}_m)$, $\mathbf{A}$ is an $m \times m$ matrix, and $\mathbf{F}^{\mathrm{T}} = (F_1 F_2 \ldots F_m)$. Stability and stiffness are related to the eigenvalues α_i $(i = 1, \ldots, m)$ of the matrix $\mathbf{A}$. For stability, $|\alpha_i| \leq 1$ $(i = 1, \ldots, m)$. A system of ODEs is stiff if at least one eigenvalue has a large negative real part, which causes the corresponding component of the solution to vary rapidly compared to the typical scale of variation displayed by the rest of the solution. The stiffness ratio is defined as

$$\text{Stiffness ratio} = \frac{\text{Max}\,|\,\text{Re}(\alpha_i)|}{\text{Min}\,|\,\text{Re}(\alpha_i)|} \tag{7.279}$$

A system of coupled linear ODEs can be uncoupled to yield a system of uncoupled linear ODEs. Consider the system of two coupled linear ODEs:

$$u' = F(t, u, v) \tag{7.280a}$$

$$v' = G(t, u, v) \tag{7.280b}$$

These two ODEs can be uncoupled to yield

$$y' = f(t, y) \tag{7.281a}$$

$$z' = g(t, z) \tag{7.281b}$$

Consider the uncoupled system of ODEs:

$$y' = -y, \qquad y(0) = 1 \tag{7.282a}$$

$$z' = -1000z, \qquad z(0) = 1 \tag{7.282b}$$

which corresponds to some coupled system of ODEs in terms of the variables u and v. Equations (7.282*a*) and (7.282*b*) can be analyzed separately for stability. Consider an explicit finite difference method for which the stability limit is $\alpha\Delta t \leq C$, where C is a constant of order unity. For Eq. (7.282), $\alpha_1 = 1$ and $\alpha_2 = 1000$. Thus, for $C = 1$,

$$\Delta t_1 \leq \frac{C}{1} = 1 \qquad \text{and} \qquad \Delta t_2 \leq \frac{C}{1000} = 0.001 \tag{7.283}$$

If the coupled system, Eq. (7.280), represented by the uncoupled ODEs, Eq. (7.282), is solved by an explicit method, the common time step must be the smaller of the two values given by Eq. (7.283), that is, $\Delta t = \Delta t_2 \leq 0.001$. The exact solutions of Eq. (7.282) are

$$y(t) = e^{-t} \tag{7.284a}$$

$$z(t) = e^{-1000t} \tag{7.284b}$$

The function $z(t)$ decays to a negligible value after a few time steps, during which time the function $y(t)$ has changed only slightly. Small time steps must still be taken in the solution for $y(t)$ because of the stability limit associated with $z(t)$.

When a system of ODEs can be uncoupled, as in the previous paragraph, each ODE can be solved by a method appropriate to its own peculiarities. However, when the system of ODEs cannot be uncoupled, the problem of stiffness of the system becomes critical. In such cases, implicit finite difference methods are useful. However, when the derivative function is nonlinear, nonlinear FDEs result.

Higher-Order Implicit Methods

The problems of stiffness illustrated in the previous sections occur for both single ODEs and systems of ODEs. When even the most rapid transient component of the solution is of interest, small time steps are required for accuracy as well as stability, and explicit finite difference methods can be used to generate the solution. However, when the effects of the rapid transients have decayed to insignificant levels, small time steps must still be employed due to the stability limit, not accuracy requirements. In that case, implicit finite difference methods can be used to take larger time steps.

The implicit Euler method is unconditionally stable. However, it is only first-order accurate. The implicit trapezoid rule is also unconditionally stable, but it is only second-order accurate. Higher-order methods are desirable.

Any of the Adams–Moulton FDEs can be used to devise a higher-order implicit method. However, the stability limits of these FDEs are quite restrictive when applied to stiff ODEs. Gear (1971) has devised a series of implicit FDEs that has much larger stability limits. The Gear formulas are presented below:

$$y_{n+1} = \gamma\Big(\beta h f_{n+1} + (\alpha_0 y_n + \alpha_{-1} y_{n-1} + \alpha_{-2} y_{n-2} + \cdots)\Big) \tag{7.285}$$

where the coefficients γ, β, and α_i ($i = 0, 1, 2, \ldots$) are presented in Table 7.17, and k denotes the order of the FDE.

TABLE 7.17
Coefficient for the Gear FDE's

k	γ	β	α_0	α_{-1}	α_{-2}	α_{-3}	α_{-4}	α_{-5}
1	1	1	1					
2	1/3	2	4	−1				
3	1/11	6	18	−9	2			
4	1/25	12	48	−36	16	−3		
5	1/137	60	300	−300	200	−75	12	
6	1/147	60	360	−450	400	−225	72	−10

The Gear FDEs are implicit. When the derivative function is nonlinear, the Gear FDEs are nonlinear. These nonlinear FDEs must be solved iteratively. Newton's method is the preferred procedure. Gear (1971) discusses this procedure in some detail.

SUMMARY

Methods for solving one-dimensional initial-value ordinary differential equations are presented in this chapter. Procedures for discretizing the continuous solution domain and representing exact derivatives by finite difference approximations are discussed. The concepts of consistency, order, stability, and convergence are defined and discussed. A procedure for investigating consistency and determining order by developing and analyzing a modified differential equation is presented. A procedure for determining stability criteria by analyzing the amplification factor G, the single-step exact solution of a finite difference equation, is presented.

Numerous explicit and implicit finite difference methods are presented for solving first-order ODEs. Systems of ODEs and higher-order ODEs can be solved by the same methods. Numerous examples illustrate the advantages and disadvantages of most of the methods considered. For most first-order initial-value ODEs, the fourth-order Adams–Bashforth–Moulton predictor–corrector method with a fourth-order Runge–Kutta starter is recommended. The problems of stiff ODEs are introduced briefly.

Overall, this chapter presents a sound fundamental basis for solving initial-value ODEs, illustrates the concepts with numerous examples, and develops a solid basis for the numerical solution of the initial-value ODEs that occur in engineering and science.

PROBLEMS

Section 7.1 Introduction

1. Derive the exact solution of the radiation problem presented in Section 7.1, Eq. (7.4).
2. Use the secant method to determine the exact solution of Eq. (7.4) for the times presented in Table 7.1.

Section 7.2 General Features of Initial-Value Ordinary Differential Equations

3. Derive the exact solution of Eq. (7.5).
4. Derive the exact solution of the ODE

$$\bar{y}' = a\bar{y} + b + ct + dt^2, \qquad \bar{y}(t_0) = \bar{y}_0$$

5. Derive the exact solution of Eq. (7.12). Plot the solution from $t = 0$ to $t = 5$ for $\alpha = 1$ and 10.
6. Work Problem 5 for Eq. (7.13).

7. Consider the nonlinear ODE

$$\bar{y}' = \bar{y}^2 \sin t + 10, \qquad \bar{y}(0) = \bar{y}_0$$

Express this ODE in the linearized form of Eq. (7.21).

8. Work Problem 7 for the nonlinear ODE

$$\bar{y}' = \bar{y}^3 t + t^2, \qquad \bar{y}(0) = \bar{y}_0$$

Section 7.3 The Taylor Series Method

9. Solve the example radiation problem by the Taylor series method including the fifth derivative term. Compare the results with the results presented in Table 7.2.

10. Work Problem 9 including the sixth derivative term.

11. Solve the following ODE by the Taylor series method including the fourth derivative term for $t = 0$ to 10 in increments of $\Delta t = 1.0$. Compare the results with the exact solution.

$$\bar{y}' = t + \bar{y}, \qquad \bar{y}(0) = 1$$

12. Work Problem 11 for the ODE

$$\bar{y}' = t - \bar{y}, \qquad \bar{y}(0) = 1$$

Section 7.4 Finite Difference Grids and Finite Difference Approximations

13. Using the Taylor series approach, derive the following finite difference approximations (FDAs) of $\bar{y}' = d\bar{y}/dt$, including the leading truncation error term: (*a*) $y'|_n$, $O(\Delta t)$, (*b*) $y'|_{n+1}$, $O(\Delta t)$, (*c*) $y'|_n$, $O(\Delta t^2)$, and (*d*) $y'|_{n+1/2}$, $O(\Delta t^2)$.

14. Using Taylor series, determine what derivative is represented by the following FDA and the leading truncation error term.

$$\text{FDA} = \frac{y_{n+1} + 3y_n - 6y_{n-1} + y_{n-2}}{6\Delta t}$$

Section 7.5 Finite Difference Equations

Problems 15 to 91 involve the numerical solution of initial-value ODEs. These problems can be worked by hand calculation or computer programs. Carry at least six digits after the decimal place in all calculations. For the Adams–Bashforth and Adams–Bashforth–Moulton methods, use the exact solution as starting values unless otherwise specified.

An infinite variety of additional problems can be obtained from Problems 15 to 91 by (*a*) changing the coefficients in the ODEs, (*b*) changing the initial conditions, (*c*) changing the step size, (*d*) changing the range of integration, and (*e*) combinations of the above changes.

15. Solve the following ODE by the explicit Euler method from $t = 0.0$ to 1.0 with $\Delta t = 0.2$ and 0.1. The general exact solution and the particular exact solution are presented below. Compare the errors and calculate the ratio of the errors at $t = 1.0$.

$$\bar{y}' = 2 - 2t + 4t^2 - 4t^3 - 4t^4, \qquad \bar{y}(0) = 1$$

$$\bar{y}(t) = y_0 + 2(t - t_0) - (t^2 - t_0^2) + \frac{4}{3}(t^3 - t_0^3) - (t^4 - t_0^4) - \frac{4}{5}(t^5 - t_0^5) \qquad \text{(P7.15)}$$

$$\bar{y}(t) = 1 + 2t - t^2 + \frac{4}{3}t^3 - t^4 - \frac{4}{5}t^5$$

16. Work Problem 15 by the implicit Euler method. Solve the FDE directly.

17. Work Problem 15 by the modified Euler method without iteration.

18. Work Problem 15 by the fourth-order Runge–Kutta method.

19. Work Problem 15 by the fourth-order Adams–Bashforth method.

20. Work Problem 15 by the fourth-order Adams–Bashforth–Moulton method.

21. Work Problem 15 by the fourth-order Adams–Bashforth–Moulton method with mop-up.

* **22.** Solve the following ODE by the explicit Euler method from $t = 0.0$ to 1.0 with $\Delta t = 0.2$ and 0.1. The general exact solution and the particular exact solution are presented below. Compare the errors and calculate the ratio of the errors at $t = 1.0$.

$$\bar{y}' = 1 - \bar{y}, \qquad \bar{y}(0) = 0$$
$$\bar{y}(t) = (y_0 - 1)e^{(t-t_0)} + 1, \qquad \bar{y}(t) = 1 - e^{-t} \tag{P7.22}$$

* **23.** Work Problem 22 by the implicit Euler method. Solve the FDE directly.

* **24.** Work Problem 22 by the modified Euler method without iteration.

* **25.** Work Problem 22 by the fourth-order Runge–Kutta method.

* **26.** Work Problem 22 by the fourth-order Adams–Bashforth method.

* **27.** Work Problem 22 by the fourth-order Adams–Bashforth–Moulton method.

* **28.** Work Problem 22 by the fourth-order Adams–Bashforth–Moulton method with mop-up.

29. Solve the following ODE by the explicit Euler method from $t = 0.0$ to 1.0 with $\Delta t = 0.2$ and 0.1. The general exact solution and the particular exact solution are presented below. Compare the errors and calculate the ratio of the errors at $t = 1.0$.

$$\bar{y}' = t + \bar{y}, \qquad \bar{y}(0) = 1$$
$$\bar{y}(t) = (y_0 + t_0 + 1)e^{(t-t_0)} - t - 1, \qquad \bar{y}(t) = 2e^t - t - 1 \tag{P7.29}$$

30. Work Problem 29 by the implicit Euler method. Solve the FDE directly.

31. Work Problem 29 by the modified Euler method without iteration.

32. Work Problem 29 by the fourth-order Runge–Kutta method.

33. Work Problem 29 by the fourth-order Adams–Bashforth method.

34. Work Problem 29 by the fourth-order Adams–Bashforth–Moulton method.

35. Work Problem 29 by the fourth-order Adams–Bashforth–Moulton method with mop-up.

36. Solve the following ODE by the explicit Euler method from $t = 0.0$ to 1.0 with $\Delta t = 0.2$ and 0.1. The general exact solution and the particular exact solution are presented below. Compare the errors and calculate the ratio of the errors at $t = 1.0$.

$$\bar{y}' = e^{-t} + \bar{y}, \qquad \bar{y}(0) = 0$$
$$\bar{y}(t) = \left(y_0 + \frac{1}{2}e^{-t_0}\right)e^{(t-t_0)} - \frac{1}{2}e^{-t}, \qquad \bar{y}(t) = \frac{1}{2}\left(e^t - e^{-t}\right) \tag{P7.36}$$

37. Work Problem 36 by the implicit Euler method. Solve the FDE directly.

38. Work Problem 36 by the modified Euler method without iteration.

39. Work Problem 36 by the fourth-order Runge–Kutta method.

40. Work Problem 36 by the fourth-order Adams–Bashforth method.

41. Work Problem 36 by the fourth-order Adams–Bashforth–Moulton method.

42. Work Problem 36 by the fourth-order Adams–Bashforth–Moulton method with mop-up.

43. Solve the following ODE by the explicit Euler method from $t = 0.0$ to 1.0 with $\Delta t = 0.2$ and 0.1. The general exact solution and the particular exact solution are presented below. Compare the errors and calculate the ratio of the errors at $t = 1.0$.

$$\bar{y}' = t^2\bar{y}, \qquad \bar{y}(0) = 1$$
$$\bar{y}(t) = y_0 e^{(t^3 - t_0^3)/3}, \qquad \bar{y}(t) = e^{t^3/3} \tag{P7.43}$$

44. Work Problem 43 by the implicit Euler method. Solve FDE directly.
45. Work Problem 43 by the modified Euler method without iteration.
46. Work Problem 43 by the fourth-order Runge–Kutta method.
47. Work Problem 43 by the fourth-order Adams–Bashforth method.
48. Work Problem 43 by the fourth-order Adams–Bashforth–Moulton method.
49. Work Problem 43 by the fourth-order Adams–Bashforth–Moulton method with mop-up.
50. Solve the following ODE by the explicit Euler method from $t = 0.0$ to 1.0 with $\Delta t = 0.2$ and 0.1. The general exact solution and the particular exact solution are presented below. Compare the errors and calculate the ratio of the errors at $t = 1.0$.

$$\bar{y}' = 2\sin t + \bar{y}, \qquad \bar{y}(0) = 1$$
$$\bar{y}(t) = e^{(t-t_0)}\left(y_0 + \frac{1}{2}\sin t_0 + \frac{1}{2}\cos t_0\right) - \frac{1}{2}\sin t - \frac{1}{2}\cos t \tag{P7.50}$$
$$\bar{y}(t) = \frac{3}{2}e^t - \frac{1}{2}\sin t - \frac{1}{2}\cos t$$

51. Work Problem 50 by the implicit Euler method. Solve FDE directly.
52. Work Problem 50 by the modified Euler method without iteration.
53. Work Problem 50 by the fourth-order Runge–Kutta method.
54. Work Problem 50 by the fourth-order Adams–Bashforth method.
55. Work Problem 50 by the fourth-order Adams–Bashforth–Moulton method.
56. Work Problem 50 by the fourth-order Adams–Bashforth–Moulton method with mop-up.
57. Solve the following ODE by the explicit Euler method from $t = 0.0$ to 1.0 with $\Delta t = 0.2$ and 0.1. The general exact solution and the particular exact solution are presented below. Compare the errors and calculate the ratio of the errors at $t = 1.0$.

$$\bar{y}' = 2\cos t + \bar{y}, \qquad \bar{y}(0) = 1$$
$$\bar{y}(t) = e^{(t-t_0)}\left(y_0 + \frac{1}{2}\sin t_0 - \frac{1}{2}\cos t_0\right) + \frac{1}{2}\sin t - \frac{1}{2}\cos t \tag{P7.57}$$
$$\bar{y}(t) = \frac{3}{2}e^t + \frac{1}{2}\sin t - \frac{1}{2}\cos t$$

58. Work Problem 57 by the implicit Euler method. Solve the FDE directly.
59. Work Problem 57 by the modified Euler method without iteration.
60. Work Problem 57 by the fourth-order Runge–Kutta method.
61. Work Problem 57 by the fourth-order Adams–Bashforth method.
62. Work Problem 57 by the fourth-order Adams–Bashforth–Moulton method.

63. Work Problem 57 by the fourth-order Adams–Bashforth–Moulton method with mop-up.

* 64. Solve the following ODE by the explicit Euler method from $t = 0.0$ to 1.0 with $\Delta t = 0.2$ and 0.1. The general exact solution and the particular exact solution are presented below. Compare the errors and calculate the ratio of the errors at $t = 1.0$.

$$\bar{y}' = 1 + 0.5\bar{y}^2, \qquad \bar{y}(0) = 0.5$$

$$\bar{y}(t) = \tan\left(t + \tan^{-1}(y_0) - t_0\right), \qquad \bar{y}(t) = \frac{1}{\sqrt{0.5}}\tan\left(\sqrt{0.5}t + \frac{1}{\sqrt{0.5}}\tan^{-1}(0.25)\right) \tag{P7.64}$$

* 65. Work Problem 64 by the modified Euler method without iteration.

* 66. Work Problem 64 by the fourth-order Runge–Kutta method.

* 67. Work Problem 64 by the fourth-order Adams–Bashforth method.

* 68. Work Problem 64 by the fourth-order Adams–Bashforth–Moulton method.

* 69. Work Problem 64 by the fourth-order Adams–Bashforth–Moulton method with mop-up.

70. Solve the following ODE by the explicit Euler method from $t = 0.0$ to 1.0 with $\Delta t = 0.2$ and 0.1. The general exact solution and the particular exact solution are presented below. Compare the errors and calculate the ratio of the errors at $t = 1.0$.

$$\bar{y}' = t\sqrt{\bar{y}}, \qquad \bar{y}(0) = 1$$

$$\bar{y}(t) = \frac{1}{4}\left(\frac{1}{2}(t - t_0) + 2\sqrt{y_0}\right), \qquad \bar{y}(t) = \frac{1}{4}\left(\frac{1}{2}t^2 + 2\right) \tag{P7.70}$$

71. Work Problem 70 by the modified Euler method without iteration.

72. Work Problem 70 by the fourth-order Runge–Kutta method.

73. Work Problem 70 by the fourth-order Adams–Bashforth method.

74. Work Problem 70 by the fourth-order Adams–Bashforth–Moulton method.

75. Work Problem 70 by the fourth-order Adams–Bashforth–Moulton method with mop-up.

76. Solve the following ODE by the explicit Euler method from $t = 0.0$ to 1.0 with $\Delta t = 0.2$ and 0.1. The general exact solution and the particular exact solution are presented below. Compare the errors and calculate the ratio of the errors at $t = 1.0$.

$$\bar{y}' = t\bar{y}^2, \qquad \bar{y}(0) = 1$$

$$\bar{y}(t) = -\frac{2}{t^2 - t_0^2 - 2/y_0}, \qquad \bar{y}(t) = -\frac{2}{t^2 - 2} \tag{P7.76}$$

77. Work Problem 76 by the modified Euler method without iteration.

78. Work Problem 76 by the fourth-order Runge–Kutta method.

79. Work Problem 76 by the fourth-order Adams–Bashforth method.

80. Work Problem 76 by the fourth-order Adams–Bashforth–Moulton method.

81. Work Problem 76 by the fourth-order Adams–Bashforth–Moulton method with mop-up.

82. Solve the following ODE by the explicit Euler method from $t = 0.0$ to 1.0 with $\Delta t = 0.2$ and 0.1. The general exact solution and the particular exact solution are presented below. Compare the errors and calculate the ratio of the errors at $t = 1.0$.

$$\bar{y}' = \frac{1}{t + \bar{y}}, \qquad \bar{y}(0) = 1$$

$$e^{(y - y_0)}(t_0 + y_0 + 1) - \bar{y} - 1 = t, \qquad 2e^{(\bar{y} - 1)} - \bar{y} - 1 = t \tag{P7.82}$$

83. Work Problem 82 by the modified Euler method without iteration.

84. Work Problem 82 by the fourth-order Runge–Kutta method.

85. Work Problem 82 by the fourth-order Adams–Bashforth method.

86. Work Problem 82 by the fourth-order Adams–Bashforth–Moulton method.

87. Work Problem 82 by the fourth-order Adams–Bashforth–Moulton method with mop-up.

88. Work Problem 64 by the Adams–Bashforth–Moulton method using the fourth-order Runge–Kutta method to obtain starting values. Compare the results with the results of Problem 68.

89. Work Problem 70 by the procedure described in Problem 88. Compare the results with the results of Problem 74.

90. Work Problem 76 by the procedure described in Problem 88. Compare the results with the results of Problem 80.

91. Work Problem 82 by the procedure described in Problem 88. Compare the results with the results of Problem 86.

Section 7.6 Consistency, Order, Stability, and Convergence

* **92.** The order of a finite difference equation is the order of the leading truncation error term. Order can be estimated numerically by solving an ODE that has an exact solution with two different step sizes and comparing the ratio of the errors. For step size halving, the ratio of the errors, as $\Delta t \to 0$, is given by

$$\frac{\text{Error}(h)}{\text{Error}(h/2)} = 2^n$$

where n is the order of the FDE. For ODEs that do not have an exact solution, order can be estimated by solving the ODE numerically for three step sizes, each one being one-half the previous one, letting the most accurate solution (the solution for the smallest step size) be an approximation of the exact solution, and applying the procedure described above. Use this procedure to estimate the order of the solution to Problem 64.

* **93.** Apply the procedure described in Problem 92 to Problem 65.

* **94.** Apply the procedure described in Problem 92 to Problem 66.

* **95.** Apply the procedure described in Problem 92 to Problem 67.

* **96.** Apply the procedure described in Problem 92 to Problem 68.

* **97.** Apply the procedure described in Problem 92 to Problem 69.

98. Apply the procedure described in Problem 92 to Problem 76.

99. Apply the procedure described in Problem 92 to Problem 77.

100. Apply the procedure described in Problem 92 to Problem 78.

101. Apply the procedure described in Problem 92 to Problem 79.

102. Apply the procedure described in Problem 92 to Problem 80.

103. Apply the procedure described in Problem 92 to Problem 81.

Section 7.7 The Modified Differential Equation

104. Develop the explicit Euler approximation of the linear first-order ODE $\bar{y}' + \alpha\bar{y} = F(t)$. Derive the corresponding MDE, including the first two truncation error terms. Investigate consistency and order.

105. Work Problem 104 using the implicit Euler method.

106. Work Problem 104 using the modified Euler method.

107. Work Problem 104 using the midpoint finite difference equation.

108. Work Problem 104 using the trapezoid method.

109. Apply the fourth-order Runge–Kutta method to the linear first-order homogeneous ODE $\bar{y}' + \alpha\bar{y} = 0$. Develop a single-step FDE for this problem. Derive the corresponding MDE, including the first truncation error term. Investigate consistency and order.

Section 7.8 Stability Analysis

110. Perform a von Neumann stability analysis of the explicit Euler approximation of the model ODE $\bar{y}' + \alpha\bar{y} = 0$, Eq. (7.58).

111. Work Problem 110 for the implicit Euler method, Eq. (7.70).

112. Work Problem 110 for the midpoint method, Eq. (7.82).

113. Work Problem 110 for the trapezoid method, Eq. (7.86).

114. Work Problem 110 for the modified Euler method, Eq. (7.87). The predictor and corrector FDEs must be combined into a single step FDE.

115. Work Problem 110 for the fourth-order Runge–Kutta method, Eq. (7.98). The four-step FDEs must be combined into a single step FDE.

116. Perform a von Neumann stability analysis of the midpoint leapfrog FDE

$$y_{n+1} = y_{n-1} + 2\Delta t f_n$$

Use the relationship $G = y_{n+1}/y_n = y_n/y_{n-1}$ to obtain a quadratic equation for G. Investigate the stability boundaries $G = 1$ and $G = -1$.

117. Perform a von Neumann stability analysis of the fourth-order Adams–Bashforth FDE, Eq. (7.108).

118. Perform a von Neumann stability analysis of the nth-order Adams–Bashforth FDEs for (*a*) $n = 1$, (*b*) $n = 2$, and (*c*) $n = 3$ (see Table 7.11).

119. Work Problem 118 for (*a*) $n = 5$ and (*b*) $n = 6$.

120. Perform a von Neumann stability analysis of the fourth-order Adams–Moulton FDE, Eq. (7.111).

121. Perform a von Neumann stability analysis of the nth-order Adams–Moulton FDEs for (*a*) $n = 1$, (*b*) $n = 2$, and (*c*) $n = 3$ (see Table 7.12).

122. Work Problem 121 for (*a*) $n = 5$ and (*b*) $n = 6$.

Section 7.9 Runge–Kutta Methods

123. Derive the general second-order Runge–Kutta method described by Eqs. (7.193) and (7.201).

124. Derive the general third-order Runge–Kutta method:

$$y_{n+1} = y_n + C_1 k_1 + C_2 k_2 + C_3 k_3$$

Show that one such method is given by

$$y_{n+1} = y_n + \frac{1}{4}(k_1 + 3k_2 + k_3), \qquad k_1 = \Delta t f(t_n, y_n)$$

$$k_2 = \Delta t f\left(t_n + \frac{1}{3}\Delta t,\ y_n + \frac{1}{3}k_1\right), \qquad k_3 = \Delta t f\left(t_n + \frac{2}{3}\Delta t,\ y_n + \frac{2}{3}k_2\right)$$

125. Derive the general fourth-order Runge–Kutta method. Show that Eq. (7.98) is one such method.

***126.** Work Problem 76 by the Runge–Kutta–Fehlberg method. Compare the results with the results of Problem 78. Evaluate the error at each step.

127. Work Problem 82 by the Runge–Kutta–Fehlberg method. Compare the results with the results of Problem 84. Evaluate the error at each step.

128. The Runge–Kutta–Merson method is

$$y_{n+1} = y_n + \frac{1}{6}(k_1 + 4k_4 + k_5), \qquad k_1 = \Delta t f(t_n, y_n)$$

$$k_2 = \Delta t f\left(t_n + \frac{1}{3}\Delta t, y_n + \frac{1}{3}k_1\right)$$

$$k_3 = \Delta t f\left(t_n + \frac{1}{3}\Delta t, y_n + \frac{1}{6}k_1 + \frac{1}{6}k_2\right)$$

$$k_4 = \Delta t f\left(t_n + \frac{1}{2}\Delta t, y_n + \frac{1}{8}k_1 + \frac{3}{8}k_3\right)$$

$$k_5 = \Delta t f\left(t_n + \Delta t, y_n + \frac{1}{2}k_1 - \frac{3}{2}k_3 + 2k_4\right)$$

$$\text{Error} = \frac{1}{30}(2k_1 - 9k_3 + 8k_4 - k_5)$$

Work Problem 126 by the Runge–Kutta–Merson method.

129. Work Problem 127 by the Runge–Kutta–Merson method.

Section 7.10 Multipoint Methods

130. Derive the fourth-order Adams–Bashforth FDE, Eq. (7.222), including the leading truncation error term.

131. Derive the nth-order Adams–Bashforth FDEs for (*a*) $n = 1$, (*b*) $n = 2$, and (*c*) $n = 3$.

132. Derive the nth-order Adams–Bashforth FDEs for (*a*) $n = 5$ and (*b*) $n = 6$.

133. Derive the fourth-order Adams–Moulton FDE, Eq. (7.226), including the leading truncation error term.

134. Derive the nth-order Adams–Moulton FDEs for (*a*) $n = 1$, (*b*) $n = 2$, and (*c*) $n = 3$.

135. Derive the nth-order Adams–Moulton FDEs for (*a*) $n = 5$ and (*b*) $n = 6$.

136. Develop a formula for error estimation for the fourth-order Adams–Bashforth–Moulton method.

137. Work Problem 136 for (*a*) $n = 1$, (*b*) $n = 2$, and (*c*) $n = 3$.

138. Work Problem 136 for (*a*) $n = 5$ and (*b*) $n = 6$.

Section 7.11 Nonlinear Finite Difference Equations

139. Work Problem 15 by the implicit Euler method using (*a*) time linearization and (*b*) Newton's method.

***140.** Work Problem 22 by the implicit Euler method using (*a*) time linearization and (*b*) Newton's method.

141. Work Problem 29 by the implicit Euler method using (*a*) time linearization and (*b*) Newton's method.

142. Work Problem 36 by the implicit Euler method using (*a*) time linearization and (*b*) Newton's method.

143. Work Problem 43 by the implicit Euler method using (*a*) time linearization and (*b*) Newton's method.

144. Work Problem 50 by the implicit Euler method using (*a*) time linearization and (*b*) Newton's method.

145. Work Problem 57 by the implicit Euler method using (*a*) time linearization and (*b*) Newton's method.

***146.** Work Problem 64 by the implicit Euler method using (*a*) time linearization and (*b*) Newton's method.

147. Work Problem 70 by the implicit Euler method using (*a*) time linearization and (*b*) Newton's method.

148. Work Problem 76 by the implicit Euler method using (*a*) time linearization and (*b*) Newton's method.

149. Work Problem 82 by the implicit Euler method using (*a*) time linearization and (*b*) Newton's method.

Section 7.12 Systems of First-Order Ordinary Differential Equations

***150.** Solve the following pair of initial-value ODEs by the explicit Euler method from $t = 0.0$ to 1.0 with $\Delta t = 0.2$ and 0.1.

$$\bar{y}' = 2\bar{y} + \bar{z} + 1, \bar{y}(0) = 1, \qquad \bar{z}' = \bar{y} + \bar{z} + 1, \bar{z}(0) = 1 \tag{P7.150}$$

***151.** Solve Problem 150 by the modified Euler method without iteration.

***152.** Solve Problem 150 by the fourth-order Runge–Kutta method.

153. Solve the following pair of initial-value ODEs by the explicit Euler method from $t = 0.0$ to 1.0 with $\Delta t = 0.2$ and 0.1.

$$\bar{y}' = 2\bar{y} + \bar{z} + t, \quad \bar{y}(0) = 1, \qquad \bar{z}' = \bar{y} + \bar{z} + t, \quad \bar{z}(0) = 1 \tag{P7.153}$$

154. Solve Problem 153 by the modified Euler method without iteration.

155. Solve Problem 153 by the fourth-order Runge–Kutta method.

156. Solve the following pair of initial-value ODEs by the explicit Euler method from $t = 0.0$ to 1.0 with $\Delta t = 0.2$ and 0.1.

$$\bar{y}' = 2\bar{y} + \bar{z} + e^t, \quad \bar{y}(0) = 1, \qquad \bar{z}' = \bar{y} + \bar{z} + 1, \quad \bar{z}(0) = 1 \tag{P7.156}$$

157. Solve Problem 156 by the modified Euler method without iteration.

158. Solve Problem 156 by the fourth-order Runge–Kutta method.

159. Solve the following pair of initial-value ODEs by the explicit Euler method from $t = 0.0$ to 1.0 with $\Delta t = 0.2$ and 0.1.

$$\bar{y}' = 2\bar{y} + \bar{z} + e^t + 1 + t, \quad \bar{y}(0) = 0, \qquad \bar{z}' = \bar{y} + \bar{z} + t, \quad \bar{z}(0) = 1 \tag{P7.159}$$

160. Solve Problem 159 by the modified Euler method without iteration.

161. Solve Problem 159 by the fourth-order Runge–Kutta method.

162. Solve the following pair of initial-value ODEs by the explicit Euler method from $t = 0.0$ to 1.0 with $\Delta t = 0.2$ and 0.1.

$$\bar{y}' = \bar{z},\ \bar{y}(0) = 1, \qquad \bar{z}' = -4\bar{y} - 5\bar{z} + 1 + t + e^t,\ \bar{z}(0) = 1 \tag{P7.162}$$

163. Solve Problem 162 by the modified Euler method without iteration.

164. Solve Problem 162 by the fourth-order Runge–Kutta method.

165. Solve the following pair of initial-value ODEs by the explicit Euler method from $t = 0.0$ to 1.0 with $\Delta t = 0.2$ and 0.1.

$$\bar{y}' = \bar{z},\ \bar{y}(0) = 1, \qquad \bar{z}' = -6.25\bar{y} - 4\bar{z} + 1 + t + 2e^t,\ \bar{z}(0) = 1 \tag{P7.165}$$

166. Solve Problem 165 by the modified Euler method without iteration.

167. Solve Problem 165 by the fourth-order Runge–Kutta method.

168. Solve the following pair of initial-value ODEs by the explicit Euler method from $t = 0.0$ to 1.0 with $\Delta t = 0.2$ and 0.1.

$$\bar{y}' = \bar{z}^2 + 1,\ \bar{y}(0) = 1, \quad \text{and} \quad \bar{z}' = \bar{y}^2 + \bar{z}^2,\ \bar{z}(0) = 1 \tag{P7.168}$$

169. Solve Problem 168 by the modified Euler method without iteration.

170. Solve Problem 168 by the fourth-order Runge–Kutta method.

Section 7.13 Higher-Order Ordinary Differential Equations

171. Reduce the following ODE to a pair of first-order ODEs:

$$ay'' + by' + cy = d, \qquad y(0) = y_0 \quad \text{and} \quad y'(0) = y'_0$$

172. Reduce the following ODE to a pair of first-order ODEs:

$$ay'' + b|y'|y' + cy = F(t), \qquad y(0) = y_0 \quad \text{and} \quad y'(0) = y'_0$$

173. Reduce the following ODE to a set of first-order ODEs:

$$ay''' + by'' + cy' + dy = e, \qquad y(0) = y_0, \qquad y'(0) = y'_0, \qquad \text{and} \quad y''(0) = y''_0$$

174. Reduce the following pair of ODEs to a set of first-order ODEs:

$$ay'' + by' + cz' + dy + ez = F(t), \qquad y(0) = y_0 \quad \text{and} \quad y'(0) = y'_0$$

$$Az'' + By' + Cz' + Dy + Ez = G(t), \qquad z(0) = z_0 \quad \text{and} \quad z'(0) = z'_0$$

175. The ODE governing the displacement x(t) of a mass–damper-spring system is

$$x'' + Cx' + Kx = F(t), \qquad x(0) = x_0 \quad \text{and} \quad x'(0) = x'_0$$

Reduce this second-order ODE to a pair of coupled first-order ODEs.

176. The ODE governing the current $i(t)$ in a series L (inductance), R (resistance), and C (capacitance) circuit is

$$Li'' + Ri' + \frac{1}{C}i = \frac{dV}{dt}, \qquad i(0) = i_0 \quad \text{and} \quad i'(0) = i'_0$$

Reduce this second-order ODE to two coupled first-order ODEs.

177. The angular displacement $\theta(t)$ of a frictionless pendulum is governed by the ODE

$$\theta'' + \frac{g}{L}\sin\theta = 0, \qquad \theta(0) = \theta_0 \quad \text{and} \quad \theta'(0) = \theta_0'$$

Reduce this second-order ODE to a pair of first-order ODEs.

178. The governing equation for the displacement $y(t)$ of a projectile shot vertically is

$$my'' + C|V|V = -mg, \qquad y(0) = 0, \quad V(0) = V_0$$

where $V = dy/dt$ is the projectile velocity, C is a drag parameter, and g is the acceleration of gravity. Reduce this second-order ODE to a pair of first-order ODEs.

179. The governing ODEs for the position [$x(t)$ and $y(t)$] of a projectile shot at an angle α with respect to the horizontal are

$$mx'' + C|V|V\cos\theta = 0, \qquad x(0) = 0, \quad x'(0) = V_0\cos\alpha$$

$$my'' + C|V|V\sin\theta = -mg, \qquad y(0) = 0, \quad y'(0) = V_0\sin\alpha$$

where $\theta = \tan^{-1}(v/u)$, $u = dx/dt$, $v = dy/dt$, and C and g are defined in Problem 178. Reduce this pair of coupled second-order ODEs to a set of four first-order ODEs.

180. The governing equation for the laminar boundary layer over a flat plate is (see Problem 8.82)

$$\frac{d^3f}{d\eta^3} + \frac{1}{2}f\frac{d^2f}{d\eta^2} = 0, \qquad f(0) = 1, \quad f'(0) = 0, \quad \text{and} \quad f'(\eta) \to 1 \quad \text{as} \quad \eta \to \infty$$

Reduce this ODE to a set of first-order ODEs.

181. The governing equation for a laminar mixing layer is (see Problem 8.83)

$$\frac{d^3f}{d\eta^3} + f\frac{df}{d\eta} + \left(\frac{df}{dn}\right)^2 = 0, \qquad f(0) = 0, \quad f'(0) = 0, \quad \text{and} \quad f'(\eta) \to 0 \quad \text{as} \quad \eta \to \infty$$

Reduce this ODE to a set of first-order ODEs.

Section 7.14 Stiff Ordinary Differential Equations

The following problems involving stiff ODEs require small step sizes and large numbers of steps. Consequently, these problems should be worked by writing computer programs to perform the calculations.

182. Consider the model stiff ODE

$$\bar{y}' = -1000\left(\bar{y} - (t+2)\right) + 1, \quad \bar{y}(0) = 1 \qquad \text{(P7.182)}$$

Solve this ODE by the explicit Euler method from $t = 0$ to 0.01 with $\Delta t = 0.0005$, 0.0001, 0.002, and 0.0025. Compare the solution with the exact solution.

183. Solve Problem 182 by the implicit Euler method from $t = 0$ to 0.1 with $\Delta t = 0.01$, 0.05, and 0.1.

184. Work Problem 182 by the modified Euler method without iteration.

185. Solve Problem 182 by the trapezoid method from $t = 0$ to 0.1 with $\Delta t = 0.01$, 0.05, and 0.1.

***186.** Solve Problem 182 by the second-order Gear method from $t = 0$ to 0.1 with $\Delta t = 0.01$ and 0.05. Use the exact solution for starting values.

187. Solve Problem 182 by the fourth-order Gear method from $t = 0$ to 0.1 with $\Delta t = 0.01$. Use the exact solution for starting values.

188. Solve Problem 187 using the first-, second-, and third-order Gear methods to obtain the starting values.

189. Solve the second-order ODE

$$\epsilon \bar{y}'' + \bar{y}' + \bar{y} = 1, \quad \bar{y}(0) = 0 \qquad \text{and} \quad \bar{y}'(0) = 1 \tag{P7.189}$$

by the explicit Euler method from $t = 0$ to 1.0 for $\epsilon = 0.01$. Choose Δt appropriately.

190. Work Problem 189 by the implicit Euler method. In addition, solve for $y(1.0)$ with $\Delta t =$ 0.1 and 1.0.

191. Work Problem 189 by the modified Euler method without iteration.

192. Work Problem 189 by the trapezoid method.

193. Work Problem 189 by the fourth-order Gear method. Use the first-, second-, and third-order Gear methods to obtain the starting values.

***194.** Consider the pair of ODEs

$$\bar{y}' = -\bar{y}, \quad \bar{y}(0) = 1 \qquad \text{and} \qquad \bar{z}' = -100\bar{z}, \quad \bar{z}(0) = 1 \tag{P7.194}$$

Assume that these two equations must be solved simultaneously with the same Δt as part of a larger problem. Solve these equations by the explicit Euler method from $t = 0$ to 1.0.

195. Work Problem 194 by the implicit Euler method.

196. Work Problem 194 by the modified Euler method without iteration.

197. Work Problem 194 by the trapezoid method.

198. Work Problem 194 by the fourth-order Gear method. Use the first-, second-, and third-order Gear methods to obtain the starting values.

***199.** Consider the coupled pair of ODEs:

$$\bar{y}' = 998\bar{y} + 1998\bar{z}, \qquad \bar{y}(0) = 1 \tag{P7.199a}$$

$$\bar{z}' = -999\bar{y} - 1999\bar{z}, \qquad \bar{z}(0) = 1 \tag{P7.199b}$$

Solve these two equations by the explicit Euler method from $t = 0$ to 0.1.

200. Work Problem 199 by the implicit Euler method.

201. Work Problem 199 by the modified Euler method without iteration.

202. Work Problem 199 by the trapezoid method.

203. Work Problem 199 by the fourth-order Gear method. Use the first-, second-, and third-order Gear methods to obtain the starting values.

204. Solve the coupled pair of ODEs

$$\bar{y}' = -\bar{y} + 0.999\bar{z}, \qquad \bar{y}(0) = 1 \tag{P7.204a}$$

$$\bar{z}' = -0.001\bar{z}, \qquad \bar{z}(0) = 1 \tag{P7.204b}$$

by the explicit Euler method from $t = 0$ to 0.1.

205. Work Problem 204 by the implicit Euler method.

206. Work Problem 204 by the modified Euler method without iteration.

207. Work Problem 204 by the trapezoid method.

208. Work Problem 204 by the fourth-order Gear method. Use the first-, second-, and third-order Gear methods to obtain the starting values.

***209.** Solve the coupled pair of ODEs

$$\bar{y}' = -\bar{y} + 0.999\bar{z}, \qquad \bar{y}(0) = 2 \qquad \text{(P7.209}a\text{)}$$

$$\bar{z}' = -0.001\bar{z}, \qquad \bar{z}(0) = 0 \qquad \text{(P7.209}b\text{)}$$

by the explicit Euler method from $t = 0$ to 0.1.

210. Work Problem 209 by the implicit Euler method.

211. Work Problem 209 by the modified Euler method without iteration.

212. Work Problem 209 by the trapezoid method.

213. Work Problem 209 by the fourth-order Gear method. Use the first-, second-, and third-order Gear methods to obtain the starting values.

Applied Problems

Several applied problems from various disciplines are presented in this section. These problems can be solved by any of the methods presented in this chapter. An infinite variety of exercises can be constructed by changing the numerical values of the parameters, the step size Δt, and so forth.

Most of these problems require a large amount of computation to obtain accurate answers. Consequently, it is recommended that they be solved by computer programs.

214. Population growth of any species is frequently modeled by an ODE of the form

$$\frac{dN}{dt} = aN - bN^2, \qquad N(0) = N_0 \qquad \text{(P7.214)}$$

where N is the population, aN represents the birth rate, and bN^2 represents the death rate due to all causes, such as disease, competition for food supplies, and so on. If $N_0 =$ 100,000, $a = 0.1$, and $b = 0.0000008$, calculate $N(t)$ for $t = 0$ to 20 years.

215. A lumped mass m initially at the temperature T_0 is cooled by convection to its surroundings at the temperature T_a. From Newton's law of cooling, $\dot{q}_{\text{conv}} = hA(T - T_a)$, where h is the convective cooling coefficient and A is the surface area of the mass. The energy E stored in the mass is $E = mCT$, where C is the specific heat. From an energy balance, the rate of change of E must equal the rate of cooling due to convection $\dot{q}_{\text{conv}}$. Thus,

$$\frac{dT}{dt} = -\frac{hA}{mC}(T - T_a), \qquad T(0) = T_0 \qquad \text{(P7.215)}$$

Consider a sphere of radius $r = 1.0$ cm made of an alloy for which $\rho = 3000$ kg/m^3 and $C = 1000$ J/(kg-K). If h $= 500$ J/(s-m^2-K), $T(0) = 500$ C, and $T_a = 50$ C, calculate $T(t)$ for $t = 0$ to 10 s.

216. Consider the radiation problem presented in Part II.5, Eq. (II.20):

$$\frac{dT}{dt} = -\frac{A\epsilon\sigma}{mC}\left(T^4 - T_a^4\right), \qquad T(0) = T_0 \qquad \text{(P7.216)}$$

Consider a sphere of radius $r = 1.0$ cm made of an alloy for which $\rho = 8000$ kg/m^3 and $C = 500$ J/(kg-K). If $\epsilon = 0.5$, $T(0) = 2500$ K, and $T_a = 100$ K, calculate $T(t)$ for $t = 0$ to 10 s. The Stefan–Boltzmann constant $\sigma = 5.67 \times 10^{-8}$ J/(s-m^2-K^4).

217. Extend Problems 7.215 and 7.216 to consider simultaneous cooling by radiation and convection. For the situation described in Problem 216, the convective cooling coefficient

$h = 600$ J/(s-m^2-K). Calculate $T(t)$ for $t = 0$ to 10 s and compare the results with the results of Problem 7.216.

218. When an ideal gas flows in a variable-area passage in the presence of friction and heat transfer, the Mach number M is governed by the ODE [see Eq. (9.112) in Zucrow and Hoffman (1975)]

$$\frac{dM}{dx} = \frac{M\left(1 + \frac{\gamma-1}{2}M^2\right)}{1 - M^2}\left(-\frac{1}{A}\frac{dA}{dx} + \frac{1}{2}\gamma M^2 \frac{4f}{D} + \frac{1}{2}(1 + \gamma M^2)\frac{1}{T}\frac{dT}{dx}\right) \tag{P7.218}$$

where x is distance along the passage (cm), γ is the ratio of specific heats (dimensionless), A is the cross-sectional flow area (cm^2), f is the friction coefficient (dimensionless), D is the diameter of the passage (cm), and T is the stagnation temperature (K). For a conical flow passage with a circular cross section, $A = \pi D^2/4$, where $D(x) = D_i + \alpha x$, where D_i is the inlet diameter. Thus,

$$\frac{dA}{dx} = \frac{d}{dx}\left(\frac{\pi}{4}D^2\right) = \frac{\pi}{4}\frac{d}{dx}(D_i + \alpha x)^2 = \frac{\pi}{2}(D_i + \alpha x)\alpha = \alpha\frac{\pi}{2}D$$

The stagnation temperature T is given by

$$T(x) = T_i + \frac{Q(x)}{C}$$

where $Q(x)$ is the heat transfer along the flow passage (J/m) and C is the specific heat (kJ/kg-K). Thus,

$$\frac{dT}{dx} = \frac{1}{C}\frac{dQ}{dx}$$

For a linear heat transfer rate, $Q = Q_i + \beta x$, and

$$\frac{dT}{dx} = \frac{1}{C}\frac{d}{dx}(Q_i + \beta x) = \frac{\beta}{C}$$

The friction coefficient f is an empirical function of the Reynolds number and passage surface roughness. It is generally assumed to be constant for a specific set of flow conditions. Consider a problem where $f = \beta = 0$, $\alpha = 0.25$ cm/cm, $\gamma = 1.4$, and $D_i = 1.0$ cm. Calculate $M(x)$ for $x = 0$ to 5 cm for (*a*) $M_i = 0.7$ and (*b*) $M_i = 1.5$.

219. For the fluid mechanics problem described in Problem 7.218, let $\alpha = \beta = 0$, $f = 0.005$, $\gamma = 1.4$, and $D_i = 1.0$ cm. Calculate $M(x)$ for $x = 0$ to 5 cm for (*a*) $M_i = 0.7$ and (*b*) $M_i = 1.5$.

220. For the fluid mechanics problem described in Problem 7.218, let $\alpha = f = 0$, $T_i = 1000$ K, $\beta = 50$ J/cm, C = 1.0 kJ/(kg-K), and $D_i = 1.0$ cm. Calculate $M(x)$ for $x = 0$ to 5 cm for (*a*) $M_i = 0.5$ and (*b*) $M_i = 2.0$.

221. Work Problem 7.220 for $\beta = -50$ J/cm.

222. Consider combined area change and friction in the fluid mechanics problem described in Problem 7.218. Solve Problem 7.218 with the addition of $f = 0.005$.

223. Consider combined friction and heat transfer in the fluid mechanics problem described in Problem 7.220. Work Problem 7.220 with the addition of $f = 0.005$.

224. The governing equation for a projectile shot vertically upward is

$$m\frac{d^2y}{dt^2} = -mg - C|V|V, \qquad y(0) = 0 \quad \text{and} \quad y'(0) = V_0 \tag{P7.224}$$

where m is the mass of the projectile (kg), $y(t)$ is the height (m), g is the acceleration of gravity (9.80665 m/s^2), C is an aerodynamic drag parameter, and $V = dy/dt$ is the velocity. For $m = 10$ kg, $C = 0.1$ N-s^2/m^2, and $V_0 = 500$ m/s, calculate (*a*) the maximum height attained by the projectile, (*b*) the time required to reach the maximum height, and (*c*) the time required to return to the original elevation.

225. A machine of mass m (kg) rests on a support that exerts both a damping force and a spring force on the machine. The support is subjected to the displacement $y(t) = Y_0 \sin \omega t$. From Newton's second law of motion

$$m\frac{d^2y}{dt^2} = -C\left(\frac{dy}{dt} - \frac{dY}{dt}\right) - K(y - Y) \qquad \text{(P7.225)}$$

where $(y - Y)$ is the relative displacement between the machine and the support, C is the damping coefficient, and K is the spring constant. Determine the motion of the machine during the first cycle of oscillation of the support for $m = 1000$ kg, $C = 5000$ N-s/m, $K = 50{,}000$ N/m, $Y_0 = 1.0$ cm, $\omega = 100$ rad/s, and $y(0) = y'(0) = 0.0$.

226. The current $i(t)$ in a series *L-R-C* circuit is governed by the ODEs

$$L\frac{di}{dt} + Ri + \frac{1}{C}q = V(t), \qquad i(0) = i_0 \qquad \text{(P7.226)}$$

$$\frac{dq}{dt} = i, \qquad q(0) = q_0$$

where i is the current (amps), q is the charge (coulombs), L is the inductance (henrys), C is the capacitance (farads), and V is the applied voltage (volts). Let $L = 100$ mH, $R = 10$ ohms, $C = 1$ mf, $V = 10$ volts, $i_0 = 0$, and $q(0) = 0$. Calculate $i(t)$ and $q(t)$ for $t = 0$ to 0.1 s. What is the maximum current, and at what time does it occur?

227. Solve Problem 7.226 for $V = 10\sin(\omega t)$, where ω is the frequency (1/s) of the applied voltage, which is given by $\omega = 2\pi f$, where $f = 60$ cycles/s.

228. The angular displacement θ(t) (radians) of a frictionless pendulum is governed by the equation

$$\frac{d^2\theta}{dt^2} + \frac{g}{L}\sin\theta = 0, \qquad \theta(0) = \theta_0 \quad \text{and} \quad \theta'(0) = \theta_0' \qquad \text{(P7.228}a\text{)}$$

where g is the acceleration of gravity (9.80665 m/s^2) and L is the length of the pendulum (m). For small θ, the governing equation simplifies to

$$\frac{d^2\theta}{dt^2} + \frac{g}{L}\theta = 0 \qquad \text{(P7.228}b\text{)}$$

Solve for $\theta(t)$ for one period of oscillation for $\theta(0) = 0.1$ and 0.5 radians, $\theta'(0) = 0$, and $L = 0.1$, 1.0, and 10.0 m, using the simplified equation.

229. Solve Problem 7.228 using the exact governing equation. Compare the results with the results of Problem 7.228.

230. The population of two species competing for the same food supply can be modeled by the pair of ODEs

$$\frac{dN_1}{dt} = N_1(A_1 - B_1N_1 - C_1N_2), \qquad N_1(0) = N_{1,0} \qquad \text{(P7.230}a\text{)}$$

$$\frac{dN_2}{dt} = N_2(A_2 - B_2N_2 - C_2N_1), \qquad N_2(0) = N_{2,0} \qquad \text{(P7.230}b\text{)}$$

where AN is the birth rate, BN^2 models the death rate due to disease, and CN_1N_2 models the death rate due to competition for the food supply. If $N_1(0) = N_2(0) = 100{,}000$, $A_1 = 0.1$, $B_1 = 0.0000008$, $C_1 = 0.000001$, $A_2 = 0.1$, $B_2 = 0.0000008$, and $C_2 = 0.0000001$, calculate $N_1(t)$ and $N_2(t)$ for $t = 0$ to 10 years.

231. Consider a projectile of mass m (kg) shot upward at the angle α (radians) with respect to the horizontal at the initial velocity V_0 (m/s). The two ODEs that govern the displacement $x(t)$ and $y(t)$ (m) of the projectile from the launch location are

$$m\frac{d^2x}{dt^2} = -C|V|V\cos\theta, \qquad x(0) = 0 \quad \text{and} \quad x'(0) = V_0\cos\alpha \tag{P7.231a}$$

$$m\frac{d^2y}{dt^2} = -C|V|V\sin\theta - mg, \qquad y(0) = 0 \quad \text{and} \quad y'(0) = V_0\sin\alpha \tag{P7.231b}$$

where the vector velocity $\mathbf{V} = \mathbf{i}u + \mathbf{j}v$, $u = dx/dt$ and $v = dy/dt$, C is a drag parameter, $\theta = \tan^{-1}(v/u)$, and g is the acceleration of gravity (9.80665 m/s^2). For $m = 10$ kg, $C = 0.1$ N-s^2/m^2, $V_0 = 500$ m/s, $\alpha = 1.0$ radian, and a level terrain, calculate (a) the maximum height attained by the projectile, (b) the corresponding time, (c) the maximum range of the projectile, (d) the corresponding time, and (e) the velocity $\mathbf{V}$ at impact.

232. The inherent features of finite-rate chemical reactions can be modeled by the prototype rate equation

$$\frac{dC}{dt} = \frac{C_e - C}{\tau}, \qquad C(0) = C_0 \tag{P7.232}$$

where C is the nonequilibrium mass fraction of the species under consideration, C_e is its equilibrium mass fraction corresponding to the local conditions, and τ has the character of a chemical relaxation time. Assume that C_e varies quadratically with time. That is, $C_e = C_{e,0} + \alpha t^2$. Let $C(0) = 0.0$, $C_{e,0} = 0.1$, $\alpha = 0.5$, and $\tau = 0.0001$. Solve for $C(t)$ from $t = 0$ to 0.01.

CHAPTER 8

ONE-DIMENSIONAL BOUNDARY-VALUE PROBLEMS

Section

Example

8.1 INTRODUCTION

The general features of *boundary-value* ordinary differential equations (ODEs) are discussed in Section II.6. In that section it is shown that boundary-value ODEs govern *equilibrium* problems, which are boundary-value problems in *closed* domains. Consequently, boundary-value ODEs are solved numerically by *relaxation* methods. This chapter is devoted to presenting the basic properties of finite difference methods for solving boundary-value (i.e., equilibrium) problems and to developing several specific methods for solving boundary-value ODEs.

Numerous boundary-value ordinary differential equations arise in engineering and science. Single ODEs governing a single dependent variable are quite common. Coupled systems of ODEs governing several dependent variables are also quite common. Boundary-value ODEs may be linear or nonlinear, second- or higher-order, and homogeneous or nonhomogeneous. In this chapter, the majority of attention is devoted to the general nonlinear second-order boundary-value ODE and the linear second-order boundary-value ODE:

$$y'' + P(x, y)y' + Q(x, y)y = F(x) \tag{8.1a}$$

$$y'' + Py' + Qy = F(x) \tag{8.1b}$$

Several numerical methods for solving Eq. (8.1) are developed. Procedures for solving higher-order ODEs and systems of ODEs, based on the methods for solving Eq. (8.1), are discussed. The solution to Eq. (8.1) is the function $y(x)$. This function must satisfy two boundary conditions at the boundaries of the solution domain. The solution domain $D(x)$ is closed, that is, $x_1 \leq x \leq x_2$.

There are two completely different methods for solving boundary-value ODEs:

1. The shooting (initial-value) method
2. The equilibrium (boundary-value) method

The shooting method transforms the boundary-value ODE into a system of first-order ODEs, which can be solved by any of the initial-value methods developed in Chapter 7. The boundary conditions on one side of the closed domain can be used as initial conditions. Unfortunately, however, the boundary conditions on the other side of the closed domain cannot be used as initial conditions. The additional initial conditions are assumed, the initial-value problem is solved, and the solution at the other boundary is compared to the known boundary conditions on that boundary. An iterative approach, called shooting, is employed to vary the assumed initial conditions until the boundary conditions at the other boundary are satisfied.

The equilibrium method constructs a finite difference approximation of the exact ODE at each point in the closed solution domain, including the boundaries.

A system of coupled finite difference equations results, which must be solved simultaneously, thus relaxing the entire solution, including the boundary conditions, simultaneously.

Equation (8.1) applies to many problems in engineering and science. Most people have some physical understanding of heat transfer, due to its presence in many aspects of our daily life. Consequently, the second-order ODE governing steady one-dimensional heat transfer in a rod, presented in Section II.6, is considered in this chapter to illustrate numerical methods for solving second-order boundary-value ODEs (Fig. 8.1). That equation, Eq. (II.35), is

$$T'' - \alpha^2 T = -\alpha^2 T_a \tag{8.2}$$

where T is the temperature of the rod, $\alpha^2 = hP/kA$ (h, P, k, and A are defined in Section II.6), and T_a is the ambient (i.e., surrounding) temperature. The exact solution of Eq. (8.2) is

$$T(x) = Ae^{\alpha x} + Be^{-\alpha x} + T_a \tag{8.3}$$

which can be demonstrated by direct substitution. Consider a rod 1.0 unit long with $T(0) = 0$ and $T(1.0) = 100$. Let $\alpha = 2.0$ and $T_a = 0$. For these conditions, Eq. (8.3) yields

$$T(x) = 13.786028(e^{2x} - e^{-2x}) \tag{8.4}$$

The exact solution at selected values of x is tabulated in Table 8.1 and illustrated in Fig. 8.2.

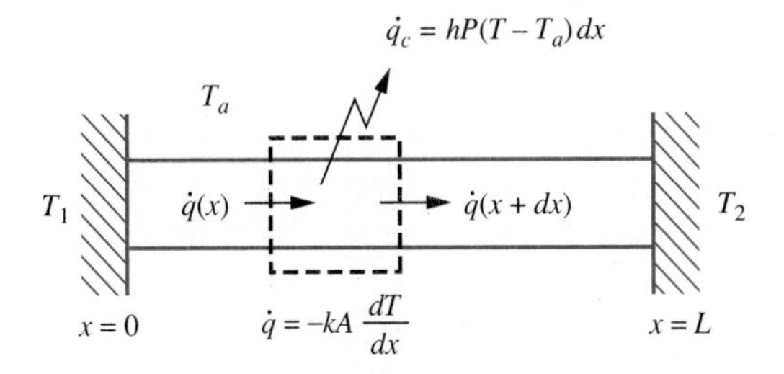

FIGURE 8.1
Steady one-dimensional heat transfer in a rod.

TABLE 8.1
Exact solution of the heat transfer problem.

x	$T(x)$	x	$T(x)$
0.000	0.000000	0.625	14.168203
0.125	6.965041	0.750	58.708613
0.250	14.367669	0.875	76.937463
0.375	22.672963	1.000	100.000000
0.500	32.402714		

8.2 GENERAL FEATURES OF BOUNDARY-VALUE ORDINARY DIFFERENTIAL EQUATIONS

Several general features of boundary-value ordinary differential equations are discussed in this section. The linear second-order ODE is discussed in some detail. Nonlinear second-order ODEs, systems of ODEs, and higher-order ODEs are discussed briefly.

The Linear Second-Order ODE

The general nonlinear second-order boundary-value ODE is given by:

$$y'' + P(x, y)y' + Q(x, y)y = F(x) \tag{8.5}$$

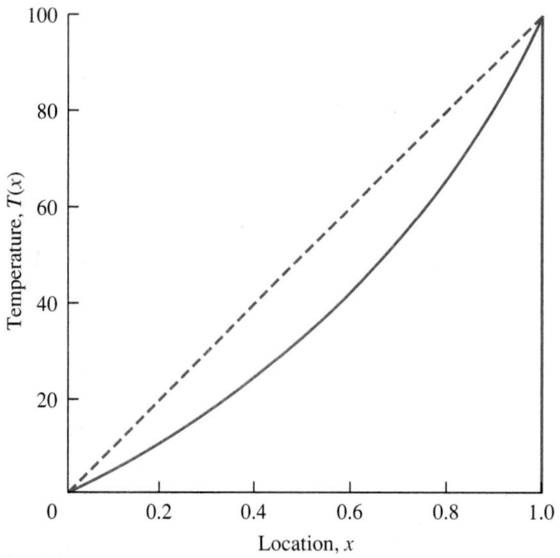

FIGURE 8.2
Exact solution of the hear transfer problem.

The linear second-order boundary-value ODE is given by:

$$y'' + Py' + Qy = F(x) \tag{8.6}$$

where P and Q are constants.

As discussed in Section 7.2 for initial-value ODEs, the exact solution of an ordinary differential equation is the sum of the complementary solution $y_c(x)$ of the homogeneous ODE and the particular solution $y_p(x)$ of the nonhomogeneous ODE. The complementary solution $y_c(x)$ has the form

$$y_c(x) = Ae^{\lambda x} \tag{8.7}$$

Substituting Eq. (8.7) into Eq. (8.6) with $F(x) = 0$ yields the characteristic equation:

$$\lambda^2 + P\lambda + Q = 0 \tag{8.8}$$

Equation (8.8) has two solutions, λ_1 and λ_2, which may be both real or a complex conjugate pair. Thus, the complementary solution is

$$y_c(x) = Ae^{\lambda_1 x} + Be^{\lambda_2 x} \tag{8.9}$$

As discussed in Section 7.2, the particular solution has the form

$$y_p(x) = B_0 F(x) + B_1 F'(x) + \cdots \tag{8.10}$$

where the terms $F'(x)$, and so on are the derivatives of the function $F(x)$. Thus, the total solution is

$$y(x) = Ae^{\lambda_1 x} + Be^{\lambda_2 x} + B_0 F(x) + B_1 F'(x) + \cdots \tag{8.11}$$

The constants of integration, A and B, can be determined by requiring Eq. (8.11) to satisfy the two boundary conditions.

The Nonlinear Second-Order ODE

The general nonlinear second-order boundary-value ODE is given by

$$y'' + P(x, y)y' + Q(x, y)y = F(x) \tag{8.12}$$

where the coefficients $P(x, y)$ and $Q(x, y)$ may themselves be nonlinear functions of y. When solved by the shooting method, which is based on methods for solving initial-value ODEs, the nonlinear terms pose no special problems. However, when solved by the equilibrium method, in which the exact ODE is replaced by an algebraic finite difference approximation that is applied at each point in a discrete finite difference grid, a system of nonlinear finite difference equations results. Solving such systems of nonlinear finite difference equations can be quite difficult.

Systems of Second-Order ODEs

Systems of coupled second-order boundary-value ODEs can be solved by replacing each second-order ODE by two first-order ODEs, and solving the coupled systems of first-order ODEs by the shooting method. Alternatively, each second-order ODE can be solved by the equilibrium method, and the coupling between the systems of second-order ODEs can be accomplished by relaxation. By either approach, solving coupled systems of second-order ODEs can be quite difficult.

Higher-Order ODEs

Higher-order boundary-value ODEs can be replaced by a system of first-order ODEs, which can then be solved by the shooting method. Some higher-order ODEs can be reduced to systems of second-order ODEs, which can be solved by the equilibrium method. Direct solution of higher-order ODEs by the equilibrium method is quite difficult.

Boundary Conditions

Boundary conditions are required at the boundaries of the closed solution domain. Three types of boundary conditions are possible: (a) the function y may be specified (Dirichlet boundary condition), (b) the derivative y' may be specified (Neumann boundary condition), or (c) a combination of y and y' may be specified (mixed boundary condition). The terminology *Dirichlet, Neumann*, and *mixed*, when applied to boundary conditions, is borrowed from partial differential equation (PDE) terminology. The procedures for implementing these three types of boundary conditions are the same for ODEs and PDEs. Consequently, the same terminology is used to identify these three types of boundary conditions for both ODEs and PDEs.

Summary

Four types of boundary-value ODEs have been considered:

1. Linear second-order boundary-value ODEs
2. Nonlinear second-order boundary-value ODEs
3. Systems of second-order boundary-value ODEs
4. Higher-order boundary-value ODEs

Solution methods for Types (2), (3), and (4) are based on the solution methods for Type (1). Consequently, Chapter 8 is devoted to the development of solution methods for the linear second-order boundary-value ODE

$$\boxed{y'' + Py' + Qy = F(x)} \tag{8.13}$$

Keep in mind that equilibrium problems are steady state problems in closed solution domains. Equilibrium problems are not unsteady, time-dependent problems.

8.3 FINITE DIFFERENCE GRIDS AND FINITE DIFFERENCE APPROXIMATIONS

The objective of a finite difference method for solving an ordinary differential equation (ODE) is to transform a calculus problem into an algebra problem by

1. Discretizing the continuous solution domain
2. Approximating the exact derivatives in the ODE by algebraic finite difference approximations (FDAs)
3. Substituting the FDAs into the ODE to obtain an algebraic finite difference equation (FDA)

Discretizing the continuous solution domain and approximating the exact derivatives by finite difference approximations are discussed in Section 7.4 for initial-value ODEs. That discussion is directly applicable to boundary-value ODEs, with minor modifications. Consequently, Section 7.4 should be reviewed and considered part of the present discussion. Initial-value problems are time (or time-like) marching problems in open domains. Boundary-value problems are steady equilibrium problems in closed domains.

The solution domain $D(x)$ is illustrated in Fig. 8.3. The solution domain must be discretized by a one-dimensional set of discrete *grid points*, called the finite difference grid. When solving boundary-value problems by the shooting method, the solution domain is open in the marching direction, and the discussion in Section 7.4 is applicable. When solving boundary-value problems by the equilibrium method, the closed solution domain is discretized by a set of uniformly

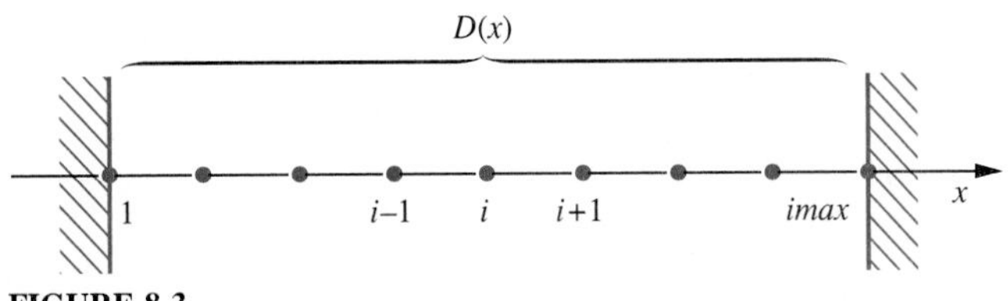

FIGURE 8.3
Solution domain and finite difference grid.

spaced grid points, as illustrated in Figure 8.3. Nonuniform grids in which Δx is variable are discussed in Chapter 13. The subscript i is used to denote the physical grid points, that is, x_i. Thus, grid point i corresponds to location x_i in the solution domain $D(x)$. The total number of grid points is denoted by *imax*.

The dependent variable at a grid point is denoted by the same subscript notation that is used to denote the grid points themselves. Thus, the function $y(x)$ at grid point i is denoted by

$$y(x_i) = y_i \tag{8.14}$$

In a similar manner, derivatives are denoted by

$$y'(x_i) = y'|_i \qquad \text{and} \qquad y''(x_i) = y''|_i \tag{8.15}$$

Now that the finite difference grid has been specified, finite difference approximations of the exact derivatives in the ODE must be obtained. That procedure is discussed in detail in Section 7.4 for initial-value ODEs. Those results are extended to boundary-value ODEs in this section. As discussed in Section 7.4, a distinction must be made between the exact solution of the differential equation and the approximate solution obtained from the FDE. Thus,

$$\bar{y}(x) = \text{exact solution}$$
$$y(x) = \text{approximate solution}$$

This precise distinction between the exact solution and the approximate solution of a differential equation is required for studies of consistency, order, and convergence.

Exact derivatives, such as $\bar{y}'$ and $\bar{y}''$, can be approximated at a grid point in terms of the values of $\bar{y}$ at that grid point and adjacent grid points in a number of ways. In the following discussion, FDAs of $\bar{y}'$ and $\bar{y}''$ are obtained from Taylor series (see the Appendix) with base point i. Thus,

$$\bar{y}_{i+1} = \bar{y}_i + \bar{y}'|_i\,\Delta x + \frac{1}{2}\bar{y}''|_i\,\Delta x^2 + \cdots \tag{8.16}$$

$$\bar{y}_{i-1} = \bar{y}_i - \bar{y}'|_i\,\Delta x + \frac{1}{2}\bar{y}''|_i\,\Delta x^2 - \cdots \tag{8.17}$$

Equation (8.16) can be written as

$$\bar{y}_{i+1} = \bar{y}_i + \bar{y}'|_i\,\Delta x + \frac{1}{2}\bar{y}''|_i\,\Delta x^2 + \ldots + \frac{1}{n!}\bar{y}^{(n)}|_i\,\Delta x^n + R_{n+1} \tag{8.18}$$

where the remainder term R_{n+1} (see the Appendix) is given by

$$R_{n+1} = \frac{1}{(n+1)!}y^{(n+1)}(\xi_+)\Delta x^{n+1} \tag{8.19}$$

where $x_i \le \xi_+ \le x_{i+1}$. Equation (8.17) can be written as

$$\bar{y}_{i-1} = \bar{y}_i - \bar{y}'|_i\,\Delta x + \frac{1}{2}\bar{y}''|_i\,\Delta x^2 - \cdots + \frac{1}{n!}\bar{y}^{(n)}|_i\,\Delta x^n + R_{n+1} \tag{8.20}$$

where the remainder term R_{n+1} is given by

$$R_{n+1} = \frac{1}{(n+1)!}y^{(n+1)}(\xi_-)\,\Delta x^{n+1} \tag{8.21}$$

where $x_{i-1} \le \xi_- \le x_i$. When the Taylor series is truncated after the nth derivative to obtain an approximation of $\bar{y}_{i+1}$, the remainder term R_{n+1} is the error associated with the truncated Taylor series. Our main concern is the *order* of the error term, which is the rate at which the error goes to zero as $\Delta x \to 0$.

When solving boundary-value ODEs by the shooting method, the FDAs presented in Section 7.4 are employed. When solving boundary-value ODEs by the equilibrium method, centered-difference approximations are used. Subtracting Eq. (8.20) from Eq. (8.18) and solving for $\bar{y}'|_i$ gives

$$\bar{y}'|_i = \frac{\bar{y}_{i+1} - \bar{y}_{i-1}}{2\,\Delta x} - \frac{1}{3}\bar{y}'''(\xi)\,\Delta x^2 \tag{8.22}$$

where $x_{i-1} \le \xi \le x_{i+1}$. Equation (8.22) can be written as

$$\bar{y}'|_i = \frac{\bar{y}_{i+1} - \bar{y}_{i-1}}{2\,\Delta x} + O(\Delta x^2) \tag{8.23}$$

where the $O(\Delta x^2)$ term denotes the remainder term and specifies its order. A second-order finite difference approximation for $\bar{y}'|_i$ is obtained by neglecting the remainder term. Thus,

$$y'|_i = \frac{y_{i+1} - y_{i-1}}{2\,\Delta x} \tag{8.24}$$

Adding Eqs. (8.18) and (8.20) and solving for $\bar{y}''|_i$ yields

$$\bar{y}''|_i = \frac{\bar{y}_{i+1} - 2\bar{y}_i + \bar{y}_{i-1}}{\Delta x^2} - \frac{1}{12}\bar{y}^{(4)}(\xi)\,\Delta x^2 \tag{8.25}$$

where $x_{i-1} \le \xi \le x_{i+1}$. Equation (8.25) can be written as

$$\bar{y}''|_i = \frac{\bar{y}_{i+1} - 2\bar{y}_i + \bar{y}_{i-1}}{\Delta x^2} + O(\Delta x^2) \tag{8.26}$$

A second-order finite difference approximation for $\bar{y}''|_i$ is obtained by neglecting the remainder term. Thus,

$$y''|_i = \frac{y_{i+1} - 2y_i + y_{i-1}}{\Delta x^2} \tag{8.27}$$

Finite difference approximations of higher-order derivatives and higher-order approximations of $y|'$ and $y|''$ can be obtained in a similar manner. Several such approximations are presented in Table 5.1 in Section 5.5.

8.4 THE SHOOTING (INITIAL-VALUE) METHOD

The shooting method transforms the boundary-value ODE into a system of first-order ODEs, which can be solved by any of the initial-value methods presented in Chapter 7. The boundary conditions on one side of the closed domain $D(x)$ can be used as initial conditions for the system of initial-value ODEs. Unfortunately, however, the boundary conditions on the other side of the closed domain cannot be used as initial conditions on the first side of the closed domain. The unknown additional initial conditions must be assumed. The initial-value problem can then be solved, and the solution at the other boundary can be compared to the known boundary conditions on that side of the closed solution domain. An iterative approach, called *shooting*, is employed to vary the assumed initial conditions until the specified boundary conditions are satisfied. In this section, the shooting method is applied to the general second-order nonlinear boundary-value ODE with known function (i.e., Dirichlet) boundary conditions. A brief discussion of the solution of higher-order boundary-value ODEs by the shooting method is presented.

When solving boundary-value ODEs by the shooting method, consistency, order, stability, and convergence of the initial-value ODE solution method must be considered. These requirements are discussed thoroughly in Chapter 7 for marching methods for solving initial-value problems. Identical results are obtained when solving boundary-value problems by marching methods. Consequently, no further attention is given to these concepts in this section.

The Second-Order Boundary-Value Problem

Consider the general second-order nonlinear boundary-value ODE with Dirichlet boundary conditions:

$$\bar{y}'' = f(x, \bar{y}, \bar{y}'), \qquad \bar{y}(a) = A \text{ and } \bar{y}(b) = B \tag{8.28}$$

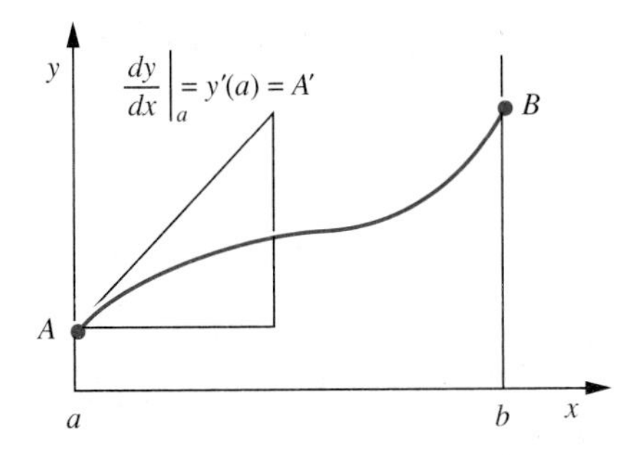

FIGURE 8.4
Solution of the general second-order boundary-value problem.

The solution of Eq. (8.28) is illustrated in Fig. 8.4. The boundary conditions $y(a) = A$ and $y(b) = B$ are both satisfied. The first derivative $\bar{y}'(a) = A'$ is not specified as a boundary condition, but it does have a unique value, which is obtained as part of the solution.

Rewrite the second-order ODE, Eq. (8.28), as two first-order ODEs:

$$\bar{y}' = \bar{z}, \qquad \bar{y}(a) = A \tag{8.29}$$

$$\bar{z}' = f(x, \bar{y}, \bar{z}), \qquad \bar{z}(a) = \bar{y}'(a) = ? \tag{8.30}$$

Create an initial-value problem by assuming a value for $\bar{z}(a) = \bar{y}'(a)$:

$$\bar{z}(a) = \bar{y}'(a) = A' \tag{8.31}$$

Choose an initial estimate for A', denoted by $(A')^{(1)}$, and integrate the two coupled first-order ODEs, Eqs. (8.29) and (8.30), by any initial-value ODE integration method (e.g., Runge–Kutta or Adams–Bashforth–Moulton). The solution is illustrated in Fig. 8.5. The solution at $x = b$ is $y(b) = B^{(1)}$, which is not equal to the specified boundary condition $\bar{y}(b) = B$. Assume a second value for $\bar{z}(a) = (A')^{(2)}$, and repeat the process to obtain $y(b) = B^{(2)}$, which again is not equal to $\bar{y}(b) = B$. This procedure is continued until the value $\bar{z}(a) = A'$ is determined for which $y(b) = B$.

For a nonlinear ODE, this is a zero-finding problem for the function

$$\boxed{y(b) = f\big(z(a)\big) = B} \tag{8.32}$$

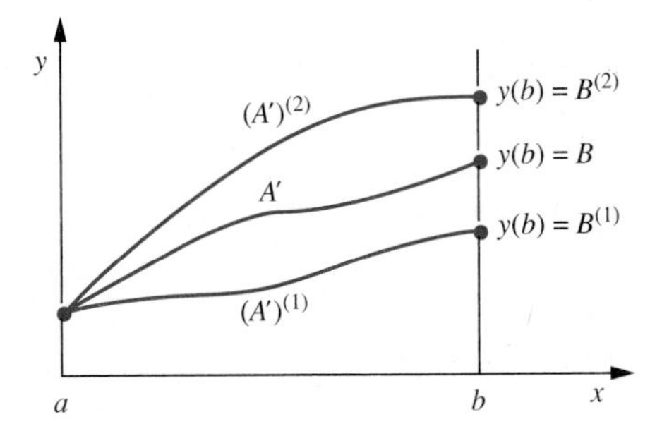

FIGURE 8.5
Iterative solution for the boundary condition.

which can be solved by the secant method (see Section 3.6). Thus,

$$\frac{B - B^{(n)}}{(A')^{(n+1)} - (A')^{(n)}} = \frac{B^{(n)} - B^{(n-1)}}{(A')^{(n)} - (A')^{(n-1)}} = \text{Slope} \tag{8.33}$$

$$\boxed{(A')^{(n+1)} = (A')^{(n)} + \frac{\left(B - (B)^{(n)}\right)}{\text{Slope}}} \tag{8.34}$$

The entire initial-value problem is reworked with $\overline{z}(a) = (A')^{(n+1)}$ until $(A')^{(n+1)}$ approaches A' within a specified tolerance, that is, until $y(b) \to B$ within a specified tolerance.

Example 8.1. Solution by the shooting method with iteration. As an example of the shooting method, we will solve the heat transfer problem presented in Section 8.1. The boundary-value ODE is [see Eq. (8.2)]:

$$T'' - \alpha^2 T = -\alpha^2 T_a = 0, \qquad T(0) = 0 \quad \text{and} \quad T(1.0) = 100 \tag{8.35}$$

Let $T_a = 0$, and rewrite the second-order ODE, Eq. (8.35), as two first-order ODEs:

$$T' = S, \qquad T(0) = 0.0 \tag{8.36}$$

$$S' = \alpha^2 T, \qquad S(0) = T'(0) \tag{8.37}$$

Solve Eqs. (8.36) and (8.37) by the modified Euler method [see Eq. (7.87)]:

$$T_{i+1}^P = T_i + \Delta t\, S_i \qquad S_{i+1}^P = S_i + \Delta t\, \alpha^2 T_i \tag{8.38}$$

$$T_{i+1}^C = T_i + \frac{1}{2}\Delta t (S_i + S_{i+1}^P) \qquad S_{i+1}^C = S_i + \frac{1}{2}\Delta t\, \alpha^2 (T_i + T_{i+1}^P) \tag{8.39}$$

Let $\Delta x = 0.250$, $S(0.0)^{(1)} = 50.0$, and $S(0.0)^{(2)} = 100.0$. The solution for $S(0.0)^{(1)} = 50.0$ is presented in Table 8.2. From Table 8.2, $T(1.0)^{(1)} = 85.253906$, which does

TABLE 8.2
First solution for $S(0)^{(1)} = T'(0) = 50.0$

x_i x_{i+1}	T_i T_{i+1}^P T_{i+1}^C	S_i S_{i+1}^P S_{i+1}^C	T_i' $(T')_{i+1}^P$	S_i' $(S')_{i+1}^P$
0.000	0.000000	50.000000	50.000000	0.000000
	12.500000	50.000000	50.000000	50.000000
0.250	12.500000	56.250000	56.250000	50.000000
	26.562500	68.750000	68.750000	106.250000
0.500	28.125000	75.781250	75.781250	112.500000
	47.070313	103.906250	103.906250	188.281250
0.750	50.585938	113.378906	113.378906	202.343750
	78.930664	163.964844	163.964844	315.722656
1.000	85.253906	178.137207		

TABLE 8.3
Third solution for $S(0)^{(3)} = 58.648339$

x_i x_{i+1}	T_i T_{i+1}^P T_{i+1}^C	S_i S_{i+1}^P S_{i+1}^C	T_i' $(T')_{i+1}^P$	S_i' $(S')_{i+1}^P$
0.000	0.000000	58.648339	58.648339	0.000000
	14.662085	58.648339	58.648339	58.648339
0.250	14.662085	65.979381	65.979381	58.648339
	31.156930	80.641466	80.641466	124.627721
0.500	32.989691	88.888889	88.888889	131.958763
	55.211913	121.878580	121.878580	220.847652
0.750	59.335624	132.989691	132.989691	237.342497
	92.583047	192.325315	192.325315	370.332188
1.000	100.000000	208.949026		

not equal the specified boundary condition $T(1.0) = 100.0$. Repeating the solution with $S(0)^{(2)} = 100.0$ yields $T(1.0)^{(2)} = 170.507813$, which also does not equal 100.0 Applying the secant method yields

$$\text{Slope} = \frac{T(1.0)^{(2)} - T(1.0)^{(1)}}{S(0.0)^{(2)} - S(0.0)^{(1)}} = \frac{170.507813 - 85.253906}{100.0 - 50.0} = 1.705078 \tag{8.40}$$

$$S(0.0)^{(3)} = S(0.0)^{(2)} + \frac{100.0 - T(1.0)^{(2)}}{\text{Slope}} = 58.648339 \tag{8.41}$$

The solution with $S(0.0)^{(3)} = 58.648339$ is presented in Table 8.3. For this linear problem, $T(1.0)^{(3)} = 100.0$, which is the desired value. The final solution is presented in Table 8.4. Repeating the solution for $\Delta x = 0.125$ yields the results presented in Table 8.5.

The ratios of the errors at the three common points in the two grids (i.e., $x = 0.25$, 0.50, and 0.75) are 2.7, 3.0, and 3.1, respectively, which suggests that the method is second-order (the ratio of errors is 4.0 for a second-order method in the limit as $\Delta x \to 0$).

The errors in Table 8.5 are rather large, indicating that a smaller step size or a higher-order method is needed. The errors are plotted in Fig. 8.6, which also presents the errors for the fourth-order Runge–Kutta shooting method. For the Runge–Kutta method, the ratios of the errors at the three common points in the grid are 10.0, 11.3, and 12.0, which demonstrates the fourth-order accuracy of the method.

TABLE 8.4
Final solution for $\Delta x = 0.250$

x	T	T_{exact}	Error
0.000	0.000000	0.000000	
0.250	14.662085	14.367669	0.294416
0.500	32.989691	32.402714	0.586977
0.750	59.335624	58.708613	0.627011
1.000	100.000000	100.000000	

TABLE 8.5
Final solution for $\Delta x = 0.125$

x	T	T_{exact}	**Error**
0.000	0.000000	0.000000	
0.125	7.019052	6.965041	0.054011
0.250	14.476794	14.367669	0.109125
0.375	22.832482	22.672963	0.159519
0.500	32.601062	32.402714	0.198349
0.625	44.384911	44.168203	0.216708
0.750	58.910981	58.708613	0.202367
0.875	77.075642	76.937463	0.138179
1.000	100.000000	100.000000	

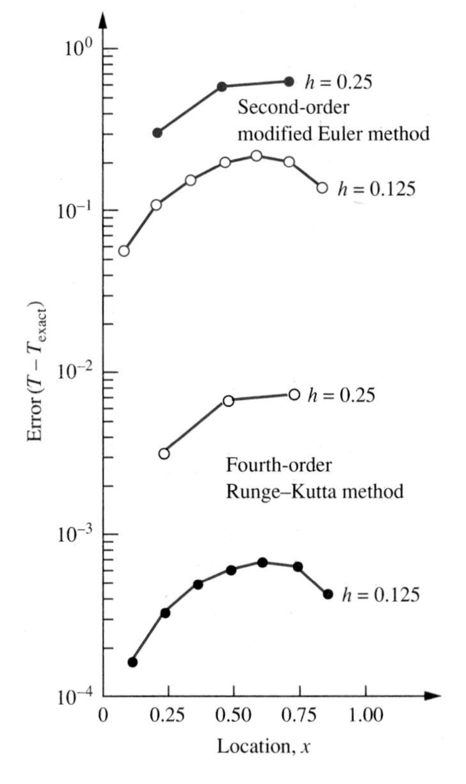

FIGURE 8.6
Errors in the solution by the shooting method.

For a linear ODE, the principle of superposition applies. Compute two solutions for $\bar{z}(a) = (A')^{(1)}$ and $\bar{z}(a) = (A')^{(2)}$, denoted by $y_1(x)$ and $y_2(x)$, respectively. Thus,

$$y_1(x) \text{ for } (A')^{(1)} \quad \text{and} \quad y_2(x) \text{ for } (A')^{(2)} \tag{8.42}$$

Form a linear combination of these two solutions:

$$\boxed{y(x) = C_1 y^{(1)}(x) + C_2 y^{(2)}(x)} \tag{8.43}$$

Apply Eq. (8.43) at $x = a$ and $x = b$. Thus,

$$\text{At } x = a\text{: } A = C_1 A + C_2 A \rightarrow C_1 + C_2 = 1 \tag{8.44}$$

$$\text{At } x = b\text{: } B = C_1 B^{(1)} + C_2 B^{(2)} = C_1 B^{(1)} + (1 - C_1) B^{(2)} \tag{8.45}$$

Solving Eqs. (8.44) and (8.45) for C_1 and C_2 yields

$$\boxed{C_1 = \frac{B - B^{(2)}}{B^{(1)} - B^{(2)}} \quad \text{and} \quad C_2 = \frac{B^{(1)} - B}{B^{(1)} - B^{(2)}}} \tag{8.46}$$

No iteration is required for linear ODEs.

Example 8.2. Solution by the shooting method with superposition. The heat transfer problem considered in Example 8.1 is governed by a linear boundary-value ODE. Consequently, the solution can be obtained by making two solutions for two assumed values of $\bar{z}(a) = \bar{y}'(a)$ and superimposing those solutions. The results of the first two solutions by the modified Euler method with $\Delta x = 0.250$ are presented in Table 8.6. From Table 8.6, $B^{(1)} = 85.253906$ and $B^{(2)} = 170.507813$. The specified value of $y(1.0)$ is 100.0. Substituting these values into Eq. (8.46) gives

$$C_1 = \frac{100.000000 - 170.507813}{85.253906 - 170.507813} = 0.827033 \tag{8.47}$$

$$C_2 = \frac{85.253906 - 100.000000}{85.253906 - 170.507813} = 0.172967 \tag{8.48}$$

TABLE 8.6
Solution by superposition for $\Delta x = 0.250$

x_i	$y_i^{(1)}$	$y_i^{(2)}$	y_i
0.00	0.000000	0.000000	0.000000
0.25	12.500000	25.000000	14.662085
0.50	28.125000	56.250000	32.989691
0.75	50.585938	101.171875	59.335624
1.00	85.253906	170.507813	100.000000

Substituting these results into Eq. (8.43) yields

$$\boxed{y(x) = 0.827033y^{(1)}(x) + 0.172967y^{(2)}(x)} \tag{8.49}$$

Solving Eq. (8.49) for $y(x)$ gives the values presented in the final column of Table 8.6, which are the same as the values presented in Table 8.4.

Higher-Order Boundary-Value Problems

Consider the third-order boundary-value problem

$$\boxed{\bar{y}''' = f(x, \bar{y}, \bar{y}', \bar{y}''), \qquad \bar{y}(a) = A, \ \bar{y}'(a) = A', \ \text{and} \ \bar{y}(b) = B} \tag{8.50}$$

Rewriting Eq. (8.50) as three first-order ODEs gives:

$$\bar{y}' = \bar{z}, \qquad \bar{y}(a) = A \tag{8.51}$$

$$\bar{z}' = \bar{y}'' = \bar{w}, \qquad \bar{z}(a) = \bar{y}'(a) = A' \tag{8.52}$$

$$\bar{w}' = \bar{y}''' = f(x, \bar{y}, \bar{z}, \bar{w}), \qquad \bar{w}(a) = \bar{y}''(a) = ? \tag{8.53}$$

Create an initial-value problem by assuming a value for $\bar{w}(a) = \bar{y}''(a) = A''$. Assume values for A'' and proceed as discussed for the second-order boundary-value problem.

For fourth- and higher-order boundary-value problems, proceed in a similar manner. In these cases, more than one boundary condition may have to be iterated. In such cases, use Newton's method for systems of nonlinear equations (see Section 3.8) to conduct the iteration.

The solution of higher-order linear boundary-value problems can be determined by superposition. For an nth-order boundary-value problem, n solutions are linearly combined:

$$y(x) = C_1 y^{(1)}(x) + C_2 y^{(2)}(x) + \cdots + C_n y^{(n)}(x) \tag{8.54}$$

The weighting factors C_i $(i = 1, 2, \ldots, n)$ are determined by substituting the boundary conditions into Eq. (8.54), as illustrated in Eq. (8.49) for the second-order boundary-value problem.

8.5 THE EQUILIBRIUM (BOUNDARY-VALUE) METHOD

The equilibrium (boundary-value) method for solving boundary-value ODEs constructs a finite difference approximation of the exact ODE at each point in the discretized solution domain, including the boundaries. A system of coupled finite difference equations results, which must be solved simultaneously, thus relaxing the entire solution, including the boundary points, simultaneously. In this section, the equilibrium method is applied to the linear second-order boundary-value ODE with known function (i.e., Dirichlet) boundary conditions.

When solving boundary-value problems by the equilibrium method, consistency, order, and convergence of the solution method must be considered. Stability is not an issue, since a relaxation procedure, not a marching procedure, is employed. Consistency and order are determined from the modified differential equation (MDE), which is discussed in Section 7.7 for marching methods. The same procedure is applicable to relaxation methods. Convergence is guaranteed for consistent finite difference approximations of a boundary-value ODE, as long as the system of FDEs can be solved. This can always be accomplished by direct solution methods, such as Gauss elimination. Consequently, consistency, order, and convergence are determined from the MDE.

Consider the linear second-order boundary-value problem with Dirichlet boundary conditions:

$$\boxed{\bar{y}'' + P(x)\bar{y}' + Q(x)\bar{y} = F(x), \qquad \bar{y}(a) = A \text{ and } \bar{y}(b) = B} \tag{8.55}$$

The discrete finite difference grid for solving Eq. (8.55) by the equilibrium method is illustrated in Figure 8.3. Recall the second-order centered-difference approximations of $\bar{y}'$ and $\bar{y}''$ developed in Section 8.3 [Eqs. (8.23) and (8.26), respectively]:

$$\bar{y}'|_i = \frac{\bar{y}_{i+1} - \bar{y}_{i-1}}{2\,\Delta x} + O(\Delta x^2) \tag{8.56}$$

$$\bar{y}''|_i = \frac{\bar{y}_{i+1} - 2\bar{y}_i + \bar{y}_{i-1}}{\Delta x^2} + O(\Delta x^2) \tag{8.57}$$

Substituting Eqs. (8.56) and (8.57) into Eq. (8.55) and evaluating the coefficients at base point i yields

$$\left(\frac{\bar{y}_{i+1} - 2\bar{y}_i + \bar{y}_{i-1}}{\Delta x^2} + O(\Delta x^2)\right) + P_i\left(\frac{\bar{y}_{i+1} - \bar{y}_{i-1}}{2\,\Delta x} + O(\Delta x^2)\right) + Q_i\bar{y}_i = F_i \tag{8.58}$$

All of the approximated terms in Eq. (8.58) are $O(\Delta x^2)$. Rearranging Eq. (8.58), multiplying through by Δx^2, and gathering terms yields

$$\boxed{\left(1 - \frac{\Delta x}{2}P_i\right)\bar{y}_{i-1} + (-2 + \Delta x^2 Q_i)\bar{y}_i + \left(1 + \frac{\Delta x}{2}P_i\right)\bar{y}_{i+1} = \Delta x^2 F_i + \Delta x^2 O(\Delta x^2)} \tag{8.59}$$

Neglecting the remainder terms in Eq. (8.59) yields the FDE:

$$\left(1 - \frac{\Delta x}{2}P_i\right)\bar{y}_{i-1} + (-2 + \Delta x^2 Q_i)\bar{y}_i + \left(1 + \frac{\Delta x}{2}P_i\right)\bar{y}_{i+1} = \Delta x^2 F_i \tag{8.60}$$

Applying Eq. (8.60) at each point in a discrete finite difference grid gives a tridiagonal system of FDEs, which can be solved by the Thomas algorithm (see Section 1.5).

Example 8.3. Solution by the equilibrium method. Solve the heat transfer problem presented in Section 8.1 by the second-order equilibrium method. The boundary-value ODE is [see (Eq. 8.2)]:

$$\bar{T}'' - \alpha^2 \bar{T} = -\alpha^2 T_a, \qquad T(0) = 0 \text{ and } T(1.0) = 100 \tag{8.61}$$

Replacing T'' by the second-order centered-difference approximation [Eq. (8.57)] and evaluating all the terms at grid point i gives

$$\frac{\bar{T}_{i+1} - 2\bar{T}_i + \bar{T}_{i-1}}{\Delta x^2} + O(\Delta x^2) - \alpha^2 \bar{T}_i = -\alpha^2 T_a \tag{8.62}$$

Multiplying through by Δx^2 and neglecting the remainder term yields the FDE:

$$T_{i-1} - (2 + \alpha^2 \Delta x^2) T_i + T_{i+1} = -\alpha^2 \Delta x^2 T_a \tag{8.63}$$

Let $\Delta x = 0.25$, $\alpha = 2.0$, and $T_a = 0.0$. Then, Eq. (8.63) becomes

$$T_{i-1} - 2.25T_i + T_{i+1} = 0 \tag{8.64}$$

Applying Eq. (8.64) at the three interior grid points gives:

$$x = 0.25: \quad T_0 - (2.25)T_1 + T_2 = 0.0, \qquad T_0 = 0.0 \tag{8.65a}$$

$$x = 0.50: \quad T_1 - (2.25)T_2 + T_3 = 0.0 \tag{8.65b}$$

$$x = 0.75: \quad T_2 - (2.25)T_3 + T_4 = 0.0, \qquad T_4 = 100.0 \tag{8.65c}$$

Transferring T_0 and T_4 to the right-hand sides of Eqs. (8.65a) and (8.65c), respectively, yields the following tridiagonal system of FDEs:

$$\begin{bmatrix} -2.25 & 1.0 & 0 \\ 1.0 & -2.25 & 1.0 \\ 0 & 1.0 & -2.25 \end{bmatrix} \begin{bmatrix} T_1 \\ T_2 \\ T_3 \end{bmatrix} = \begin{bmatrix} 0 \\ 0 \\ -100 \end{bmatrix} \tag{8.66}$$

Solving Eq. (8.66) by the Thomas algorithm yields the results presented in Table 8.7. The exact solution and the errors are presented for comparison. Repeating the solution for $\Delta x = 0.125$ yields the results presented in Table 8.8.

TABLE 8.7
Solution for $\Delta x = 0.250$

x_i	T_i	T_{exact}	Error
0.000	0.000000		
0.250	14.512472	14.367669	0.144803
0.500	32.653061	32.402713	0.250348
0.750	58.956916	58.708612	0.248304
1.000	100.000000		

The ratios of the errors at the three common points in the two grids (i.e., $x = 0.25, 0.50$, and 0.75) are 3.9, 3.9, and 3.9, which demonstrates that the method is second-order.

The errors in Table 8.8 are about one-third the magnitude of the errors in Table 8.5, which presents the solution by the second-order shooting method. The errors can be decreased by using a smaller step size or a higher-order method. The errors are presented in Fig. 8.7, which also presents the errors for the compact three-point fourth-order equilibrium method presented in Section 8.9 and Example 8.7. For the fourth-order method, the ratios of the errors at the three common points in the grid are 15.9, 15.9, and 15.9, which demonstrates the fourth-order accuracy of the method.

8.6 DERIVATIVE BOUNDARY CONDITIONS

The boundary-value problems considered so far in this chapter have all had Dirichlet (i.e., known function value) boundary conditions. Many problems in engineering and science have derivative (i.e., Neumann) boundary conditions. Procedures for implementing derivative boundary conditions for one-dimensional boundary-value problems are developed in this section. These procedures are directly applicable to derivative boundary conditions for elliptic and parabolic partial differential equations, which are discussed in Sections 9.6 and 11.7, respectively. Implementation of derivative boundary conditions by both the shooting method and the equilibrium method are discussed in this section. The heat transfer prob-

TABLE 8.8
Solution for $\Delta x = 0.125$

x_i	T_i	T_{exact}	Error
0.000	0.000000		
0.125	6.984033	6.965041	0.018992
0.250	14.404569	14.367669	0.036900
0.375	22.725390	22.672963	0.052427
0.500	32.466548	32.402713	0.063835
0.625	44.236865	44.168203	0.068662
0.750	58.771987	58.708612	0.063375
0.875	76.980357	76.937461	0.042896
1.000	100.000000		

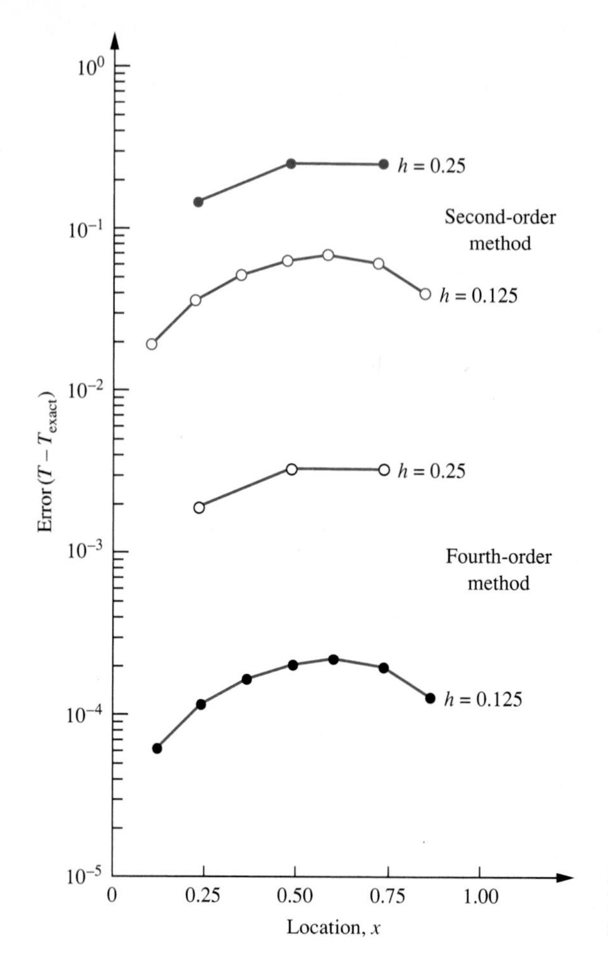

FIGURE 8.7
Errors in the solution by the equilibrium method.

lem presented in Section 8.1 is modified to create a derivative boundary condition by insulating the right end of the rod, so $T_x(1.0) = 0.0$.

Consider steady heat transfer in a rod with $T(0) = 0.0$ and $T_x(1.0) = 0.0$, as illustrated in Fig. 8.8. The boundary-value problem is specified by

$$T_{xx} - \alpha^2 T = -\alpha^2 T_a, \qquad T(0) = T_1 \text{ and } T_x(L) = 0 \tag{8.67}$$

The general solution of Eq. (8.67) is [see Eq. (8.3)]

$$T(x) = Ae^{\alpha x} + Be^{-\alpha x} + T_a \tag{8.68}$$

Substituting the boundary conditions specified in Eq. (8.67) into Eq. (8.68) yields

$$A = (T_1 - T_a)(1 + e^{2\alpha L})^{-1} \qquad \text{and} \qquad B = (T_1 - T_a)e^{2\alpha L}(1 + e^{2\alpha L})^{-1} \tag{8.69}$$

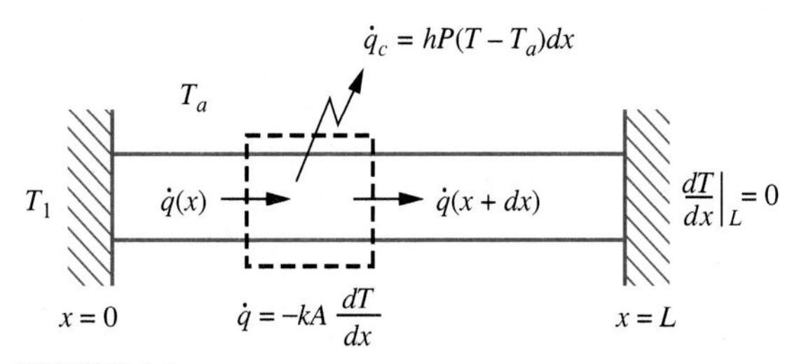

FIGURE 8.8
Heat transfer in a rod with an insulated end.

Let $T(0) = 100$, $T_x(1) = 0$, $T_a = 0$, $\alpha = 2$, and $L = 1.0$. Substituting these values into Eq. (8.69) and the results into Eq. (8.68) gives the exact solution:

$$T(x) = 1.798621(e^{2x} + 54.598150e^{-2x}) \qquad (8.70)$$

The solution at intervals of $\Delta x = 0.1$ is tabulated in Table 8.9 and illustrated in Fig. 8.9.

The Shooting Method

The shooting method for derivative boundary conditions is analogous to the shooting method for Dirichlet boundary conditions, except that we are shooting for the value of the derivative instead of the value of the function at the boundary. As an example, consider the boundary-value problem

$$\bar{y}'' + P\bar{y}' + Q\bar{y} = F(x), \qquad \bar{y}(a) = A \quad \text{and} \quad \bar{y}'(b) = B' \qquad (8.71)$$

TABLE 8.9
Exact solution for a rod with an insulated end

x	$T(x)$	x	$T(x)$
0.000	100.000000	0.625	34.412970
0.125	78.788786	0.750	29.972549
0.250	62.527572	0.875	27.415190
0.375	50.194728	1.000	26.580223
0.500	41.015427		

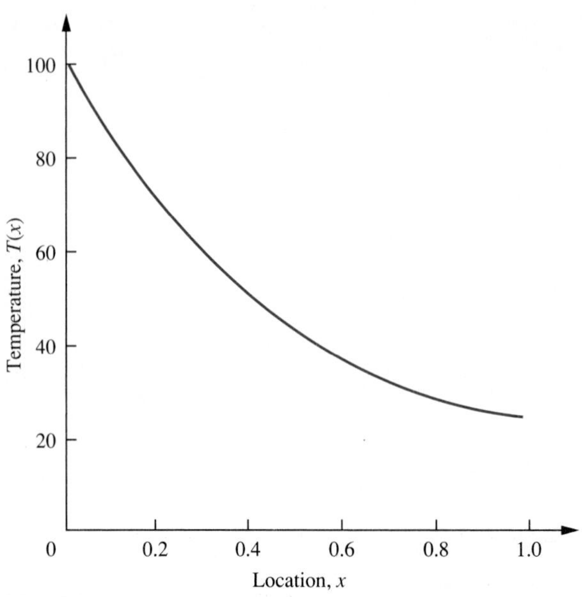

FIGURE 8.9
Exact solution for a rod with an insulated end.

Rewrite Eq. (8.71) as a system of two first-order ODEs:

$$\bar{y}' = z, \qquad \bar{y}(a) = A \tag{8.72a}$$

$$\bar{z}' = F(x) - P\bar{z} - Q\bar{y}, \qquad \bar{z}(a) = \bar{y}'(a) = ? \tag{8.72b}$$

The derivative boundary condition, $\bar{y}'(b) = B'$, yields

$$\bar{z}(b) = B' \tag{8.73}$$

Consequently, the shooting procedure described in Section 8.4 applies exactly, with the single exception that we are shooting for $\bar{z}(b) = B'$ rather than for $\bar{y}(b) = B$.

The Equilibrium Method

If the equilibrium method is to be used to solve a boundary-value problem with a derivative boundary condition, a finite difference procedure must be developed to solve for the value of the function at the boundary where the derivative boundary condition is imposed. Consider the linear second-order boundary-value problem:

$$\boxed{\bar{y}'' + P\bar{y}' + Q\bar{y} = F(x), \qquad \bar{y}(a) = A \text{ and } \bar{y}'(b) = B'} \tag{8.74}$$

An FDE must be developed to evaluate $y(b)$. Consider the finite difference grid in the neighborhood of point b, which is illustrated in Fig. 8.10. Two procedures for determining $y(b)$ are presented below. The first procedure applies the interior point finite difference equation at point b. The second procedure extrapolates the interior point solution to point b. Several variations of these two procedures are possible. In all cases, the boundary condition at point b must be satisfied.

INTERIOR POINT FDE AT THE BOUNDARY. The second-order centered-difference approximation of Eq. (8.74) at boundary point I is obtained by introducing Eqs. (8.56) and (8.57). Thus,

$$\left(\frac{\bar{y}_{I+1} - 2\bar{y}_I + \bar{y}_{I-1}}{\Delta x^2} + O(\Delta x^2)\right) + P_I\left(\frac{\bar{y}_{I+1} - \bar{y}_{I-1}}{2\,\Delta x} + O(\Delta x^2)\right) + Q_I\bar{y}_I = F_I \tag{8.75}$$

where point $I+1$ is outside of the solution domain. The value of $\bar{y}_{I+1}$ is unknown. It can be determined by expressing the derivative boundary condition at point I in finite difference form as follows. From Eq. (8.56),

$$\bar{y}'|_I = \frac{\bar{y}_{I+1} - \bar{y}_{I-1}}{2\,\Delta x} + O(\Delta x^2) \tag{8.76}$$

Solving Eq. (8.76) for $\bar{y}_{I+1}$ gives

$$\boxed{\bar{y}_{I+1} = \bar{y}_{I-1} + 2\,\Delta x\,\bar{y}'|_I + \Delta x\; O(\Delta x^2)} \tag{8.77}$$

Substituting Eq. (8.77) for $\bar{y}_{I+1}$ into the FDE at the boundary point, Eq. (8.75), gives:

$$\left(\frac{[\bar{y}_{I-1} + 2\,\Delta x\,\bar{y}'|_I + \Delta x\;O(\Delta x^2)] - 2\bar{y}_I + \bar{y}_{I-1}}{\Delta x^2} + O(\Delta x^2)\right)$$
$$+P_I\left(\frac{[\bar{y}_{I-1} + 2\,\Delta x\,\bar{y}'|_I + \Delta x\;O(\Delta x^2)] - \bar{y}_{I-1}}{2\,\Delta x} + O(\Delta x^2)\right) + Q_I\bar{y}_I = F_I \tag{8.78}$$

The remainder term in the finite difference approximation of $\bar{y}''|_I$ is now $O(\Delta x)$. This procedure reduces the finite difference equation at point I to $O(\Delta x)$. This may

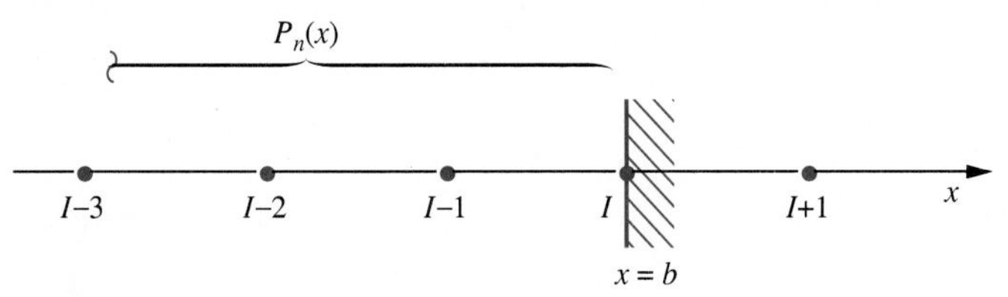

FIGURE 8.10
Finite difference grid at the boundary.

be undesirable. Rearranging the difference equation and dropping the remainder terms yields

$$2y_{I-1} + (\Delta x^2 Q_I - 2)y_I = \Delta x^2 F_I - \Delta x(2 + \Delta x\, P_I)\bar{y}'|_I = b_I \tag{8.79}$$

When used in conjunction with the centered difference equation at the interior points, a tridiagonal system of equations results, which can be solved by the Thomas algorithm. One potential problem exists: the FDE at the boundary is $O(\Delta x)$. This may not create problems if the solution is well-behaved and slowly varying at the boundary. A method for evaluating y_I to $O(\Delta x^2)$ and $O(\Delta x^3)$ is presented in the next section.

EXTRAPOLATION. Consider the finite difference grid illustrated in Figure 8.10. Let's fit a Newton backward-difference polynomial at point I and extrapolate the solution at point I from the interior. Recall Eq. (5.40):

$$\bar{y}'(x_I + s\Delta x) = \frac{1}{\Delta x}\left(\nabla \bar{y}_I + \frac{2s+1}{2}\nabla^2 \bar{y}_I + \frac{3s^2+6s+2}{6}\nabla^3 \bar{y}_I + \cdots\right) \tag{8.80}$$

At point I, $s = 0.0$. Thus, Eq. (8.80) yields

$$\bar{y}'|_I = \frac{1}{\Delta x}\left(\nabla \bar{y}_I + \frac{1}{2}\nabla^2 \bar{y}_I + \frac{1}{3}\nabla^3 \bar{y}_I + \cdots\right) \tag{8.81}$$

Recall that the error term in the truncated Newton backward-difference polynomial is obtained from the first truncated term by the substitution $\nabla^n \bar{y}_I \rightarrow \Delta x^n\, \bar{y}^{(n)}(\xi)$. Formulas of any order can be determined from Eq. (8.81) by truncating the polynomial after any term. Results for first-, second-, and third-order extrapolation are presented in the following discussion.

1. First-order extrapolation

$$\bar{y}'|_I = \frac{1}{\Delta x}\left(\nabla \bar{y}_I + O(\Delta x^2)\right) = \frac{1}{\Delta x}(\bar{y}_I - \bar{y}_{I-1}) + O(\Delta x) \tag{8.82}$$

$$y_I = y_{I-1} + \Delta x\, \bar{y}'|_I, \qquad \Delta x\, O(\Delta x) \tag{8.83}$$

2. Second-order extrapolation

$$\bar{y}'|_I = \frac{1}{\Delta x}\left(\nabla \bar{y}_I + \frac{1}{2}\nabla^2 \bar{y}_I + O(\Delta x^3)\right) \tag{8.84a}$$

$$\bar{y}'|_I = \frac{1}{\Delta x}\left((\bar{y}_I - \bar{y}_{I-1}) + \frac{1}{2}(\bar{y}_I - 2\bar{y}_{I-1} + \bar{y}_{I-2})\right) + O(\Delta x^2) \tag{8.84b}$$

$$y_I = \frac{1}{3}(4y_{I-1} - y_{I-2} + 2\Delta x\, \overline{y}'|_I), \qquad \Delta x\, O(\Delta x^2) \tag{8.85}$$

3. Third-order extrapolation

$$\overline{y}'|_I = \frac{1}{\Delta x}\left(\nabla \overline{y}_I + \frac{1}{2}\nabla^2 \overline{y}_I + \frac{1}{3}\nabla^3 \overline{y}_I + O(\Delta x^4)\right) \tag{8.86}$$

$$y_I = \frac{1}{11}(18y_{I-1} - 9y_{I-2} + 2y_{I-3} + 6\Delta x\, \overline{y}'|_I), \qquad \Delta x\, O(\Delta x^3) \tag{8.87}$$

In general, extrapolation yields an FDE for $\overline{y}_I$ of the form

$$\overline{y}_I = y_I + \Delta x\, O(\Delta x^n) \tag{8.88}$$

where n is the order of the extrapolation. How does the error at point I affect the solution at point $I-1$? The FDE, Eq. (8.75), when applied at point $I-1$, yields

$$\left(\frac{\overline{y}_I - 2\overline{y}_{I-1} + \overline{y}_{I-2}}{\Delta x^2} + O(\Delta x^2)\right) + P_I\left(\frac{\overline{y}_I - \overline{y}_{I-2}}{2\Delta x} + O(\Delta x^2)\right) + Q_{I-1}y_{I-1} = F_{I-1} \tag{8.89}$$

Substituting for $\overline{y}_I$ from Eq. (8.88) yields

$$\left(\frac{[y_I + \Delta x\, O(\Delta x^n)] - 2\overline{y}_{I-1} + \overline{y}_{I-2}}{\Delta x^2} + O(\Delta x^2)\right)$$

$$+P_I\left(\frac{[y_I + \Delta x\, O(\Delta x^n)] - \overline{y}_{I-2}}{2\Delta x} + O(\Delta x^2)\right) + Q_{I-1}y_{I-1} = F_{I-1} \tag{8.90}$$

The remainder term in the finite difference approximation of $\overline{y}''|_{I-1}$ is now $O(\Delta x^{n-1})$. Thus, to achieve $O(\Delta x^2)$, $n = 3$, which requires third-order extrapolation.

Equations (8.83), (8.85), and (8.87) can be expressed in the form

$$y_I = a_{I-1}y_{I-1} + a_{I-2}y_{I-2} + a_{I-3}y_{I-3} + b\overline{y}'|_I \tag{8.91a}$$

where the coefficients $a_i (i = I-1$, etc.) and b for each equation can be determined by inspection. The interior point FDE, Eq. (8.60), has the form

$$l_i y_{i-1} + d_i y_i + u_i y_{i+1} = b_i \tag{8.91b}$$

Applying Eq. (8.91a) at grid point I and Eq. (8.91b) at grid points $I-1, I-2$, and $I-3$, yields the matrix equation:

$$\begin{bmatrix} \cdots & \cdots & \cdots & \cdots & \cdots & \cdots \\ \vdots & \vdots & \vdots & \vdots & \vdots & \vdots \\ \cdots & l_{I-3} & d_{I-3} & u_{I-3} & 0 & 0 \\ \cdots & 0 & l_{I-2} & d_{I-2} & u_{I-2} & 0 \\ \cdots & 0 & 0 & l_{I-1} & d_{I-2} & u_{I-1} \\ \cdots & 0 & a_{I-3} & a_{I-2} & a_{I-1} & a_I \end{bmatrix} \begin{bmatrix} \cdots \\ \vdots \\ y_{I-3} \\ y_{I-2} \\ y_{I-1} \\ y_I \end{bmatrix} = \begin{bmatrix} \cdots \\ \vdots \\ b_{I-3} \\ b_{I-2} \\ b_{I-1} \\ b_I \end{bmatrix} \tag{8.92}$$

For first-order extrapolation, $a_{I-2} = a_{I-3} = 0$, and Eq. (8.92) is tridiagonal. For second-order extrapolation, $a_{I-3} = 0$, but $a_{I-2} \neq 0$, thus, destroying the tridiagonality of the matrix. However, rows I and $I-1$ can be combined explicitly to eliminate the a_{I-2} term. The a_{I-1}, a_I, and b_I terms also change. For third-order extrapolation, a_{I-3} and a_{I-2} are both present. Rows I and $I-2$ can be combined explicitly to eliminate a_{I-3}, and row I and modified row $I-1$ can then be explicitly combined to eliminate modified coefficient a_{I-2}. This procedure preserves the tridiagonality of the matrix, so the Thomas algorithm can be employed.

TABLE 8.10
Solution for $\Delta x = 0.125$

	Method 1		Method 2	
x_i	T_i	Error	T_i	Error
0.000	100.000000		100.000000	
0.125	78.846006	0.057220	79.099275	0.310489
0.250	62.619887	0.092316	63.142254	0.614682
0.375	50.307512	0.112784	51.131624	0.936897
0.500	41.139356	0.123929	42.316721	1.301294
0.625	34.542409	0.129439	36.146613	1.733642
0.750	30.104364	0.131814	32.235668	2.263118
0.875	27.547840	0.132650	30.339452	2.924262
1.000	26.713057	0.132835	30.339452	3.759229

	Method 3		Method 4	
x_i	T_i	Error	T_i	Error
0.000	100.000000		100.000000	
0.125	78.838840	0.050054	78.853361	0.064575
0.250	62.605108	0.077536	62.635056	0.107485
0.375	50.284195	0.089467	50.331443	0.136716
0.500	41.106044	0.090617	41.173545	0.158118
0.625	34.497021	0.084051	34.588994	0.176023
0.750	30.044062	0.071513	30.166254	0.193705
0.875	27.468987	0.053667	27.628906	0.213716
1.000	26.610455	0.030232	26.818364	0.238141

Example 8.4. Solution by the equilibrium method with a derivative boundary condition. Solve the heat transfer problem in a rod with an insulated end by the four methods presented in this section. The interior point FDE is presented in Example 8.3 [see Eq. (8.63)]:

$$T_{i-1} - (2 + \alpha^2\,\Delta x^2)T_i + T_{i+1} = -\alpha^2\,\Delta x^2\,T_a \tag{8.93}$$

Let $\Delta x = 0.125$, $\alpha = 2.0$, $T_a = 0$, and $\overline{T}_x(1.0) = 0$. Eq. (8.93) yields

$$T_{i-1} - 2.062500T_i + T_{i+1} = 0 \tag{8.94}$$

Consider the four boundary condition methods:

$$\text{Method 1}: T_{I+1} = T_{I-1} + 2\,\Delta x\,\overline{T}_x|_I \tag{8.95}$$

$$\text{Method 2}: T_I = T_{I-1} + \Delta x\,\overline{T}_x|_I \tag{8.96}$$

$$\text{Method 3}: T_I = \frac{1}{3}(4T_{I-1} - T_{I-2} + 2\,\Delta x\,\overline{T}_x|_I) \tag{8.97}$$

$$\text{Method 4}: T_I = \frac{1}{11}(18T_{I-1} - 9T_{I-2} + 2T_{I-3} + 6\,\Delta x\,\overline{T}_x|_I) \tag{8.98}$$

For each method, the system of FDEs was modified to yield a tridiagonal system, which was solved by the Thomas algorithm. The results are presented in Table 8.10 and illustrated in Fig. 8.11. Method 1, applying the FDE at the boundary, and Methods

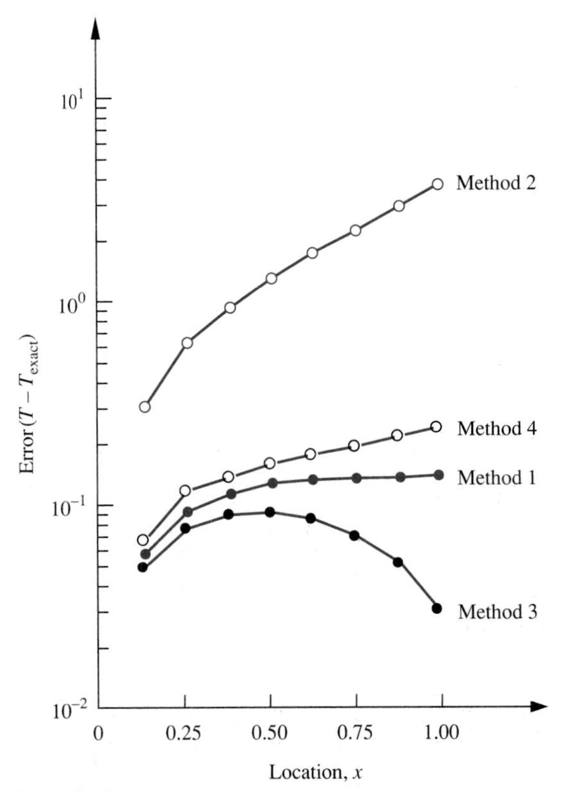

FIGURE 8.11
Errors in the solution of the insulated rod problem.

3 and 4, quadratic and cubic extrapolation, respectively, yield acceptable results. Method 2, linear extrapolation, is unacceptable. Method 3, quadratic extrapolation, yields more accurate results that Method 4, cubic extrapolation. This is probably due to an unfavorable error interaction when the boundary point solution depends on a larger set of data (i.e., points I to $I-3$) than the solution at the first interior point (i.e., I to $I-2$).

8.7 OTHER BOUNDARY CONDITIONS

Function (i.e., Dirichlet) boundary conditions and derivative (i.e., Neumann) boundary conditions for a finite domain are considered in Sections 8.4 to 8.6. This section presents a brief introduction to other types of boundary conditions.

Mixed Boundary Conditions

A mixed boundary condition has the form

$$\boxed{A\bar{y}(b) + B\bar{y}'(b) = C} \tag{8.99}$$

Mixed boundary conditions are implemented in the same manner as derivative boundary conditions, with minor modifications.

If the PDE is applied at the boundary point I illustrated in Fig. 8.10, a value for y_{I+1} is required. The boundary condition, Eq. (8.99), can be written in finite difference form by approximating $\bar{y}'(b)$ by the second-order centered-difference approximation. Thus,

$$A\bar{y}_I + B\frac{\bar{y}_{I+1} - \bar{y}_{I-1}}{2\,\Delta x} + O(\Delta x^2) = C \tag{8.100}$$

Solving Eq. (8.100) for $\bar{y}_{I+1}$ and neglecting the third-order remainder term yields

$$\boxed{y_{I+1} = y_{I-1} + \frac{2\,\Delta x}{B}(C - Ay_I), \quad O(\Delta x^3)} \tag{8.101}$$

Extrapolation can also be used to implement a mixed boundary condition. Recall Eq. (8.81):

$$\bar{y}'|_I = \frac{1}{\Delta x}\left(\nabla\bar{y}_I + \frac{1}{2}\nabla^2\bar{y}_I + \frac{1}{3}\nabla^3\bar{y}_I + \cdots\right) \tag{8.102}$$

Substituting Eq. (8.102) into the boundary condition, Eq. (8.99), gives

$$A\bar{y}_I + B\frac{1}{\Delta x}\left(\nabla\bar{y}_I + \frac{1}{2}\nabla^2\bar{y}_I + \frac{1}{3}\nabla^2\bar{y}_I + \cdots\right) = C \tag{8.103}$$

Equation (8.103) can be solved for $\bar{y}_I$ by choosing the order of extrapolation, substituting for the backward differences in terms of function values, and simplifying.

For example, for second-order extrapolation, Eq. (8.103) becomes

$$A\bar{y}_I + B\frac{1}{\Delta x}\left((\bar{y}_I - \bar{y}_{I-1}) + \frac{1}{2}(\bar{y}_I - 2\bar{y}_{I-1} + \bar{y}_{I-2}) + O(\Delta x^3)\right) = C \quad (8.104)$$

Solving Eq. (8.104) for $\bar{y}_I$ and neglecting the third-order remainder term gives

$$y_I = \left(\frac{1}{A\,\Delta x + 1.5B}\right)\left(C\,\Delta x + 2By_{I-1} + \frac{1}{2}By_{I-2}\right) \quad (8.105)$$

Boundary Condition at Infinity

Occasionally one boundary condition is given at infinity, as illustrated in Figure 8.12. For example, for bodies moving through the atmosphere, infinity simply means very far away. In such a case, the boundary conditions might be

$$\bar{y}(0) = A \qquad \text{and} \qquad \bar{y}(\infty) = B \quad (8.106)$$

Derivative boundary conditions can also be specified at infinity. Two procedures for implementing boundary conditions at infinity are (a) replacing ∞ with a large value of $x = X$, and (b) an asymptotic solution at large values of x.

FINITE DOMAIN. In this approach, the boundary condition at $x = \infty$ is simply replaced by the same boundary condition applied at a finite location $x = X$. Thus,

$$\bar{y}(\infty) = B \rightarrow \bar{y}(X) = B, \qquad \text{large X} \quad (8.107)$$

This procedure is illustrated in Fig. 8.13. The boundary-value problem is then solved in the usual manner.

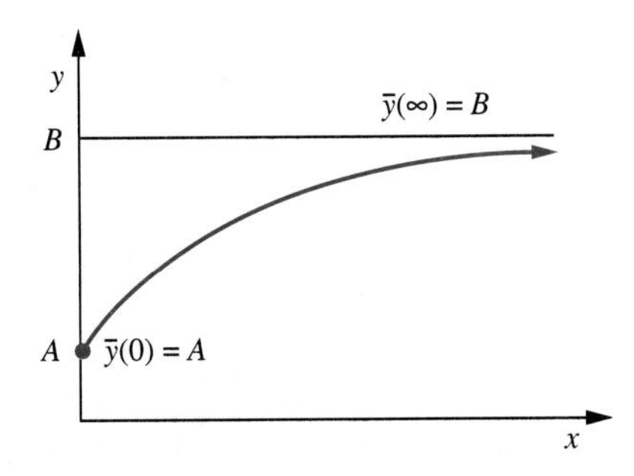

FIGURE 8.12
Boundary condition at infinity.

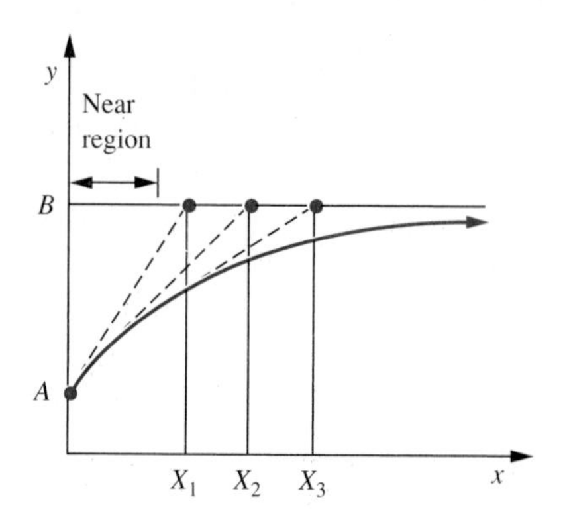

FIGURE 8.13
Finite domain approximation.

The major problem with this approach is determining what value of X, if any, yields a reasonable solution to the original problem. In most cases, our interest is in the near region far away from infinity. In that case, successively larger values of X, denoted by X_1, X_2, and so on, can be chosen, and the boundary-value problem is solved for each value of X. The solution in the near region can be monitored as X increases, until successive solutions in the region of interest change by less than some prescribed tolerance.

ASYMPTOTIC SOLUTION. A second approach for implementing boundary conditions at infinity is based on an asymptotic solution for large values of x. In many problems, the behavior of the solution near ∞ behaves in a much simpler manner than the behavior in the near region. The governing differential equation can be simplified, perhaps linearized, and the simplified differential equation can be solved exactly, including the boundary condition at infinity, to yield the solution

$$\bar{y}_{\text{asymptotic}}(x) = F(x), \qquad X \leq x \leq \infty \tag{8.108}$$

The boundary condition for the solution of the original differential equation is determined by choosing a finite location $x = X$ and substituting that value of x into Eq. (8.108) to obtain

$$\bar{y}_{\text{asymptotic}}(X) = F(X) = Y \tag{8.109}$$

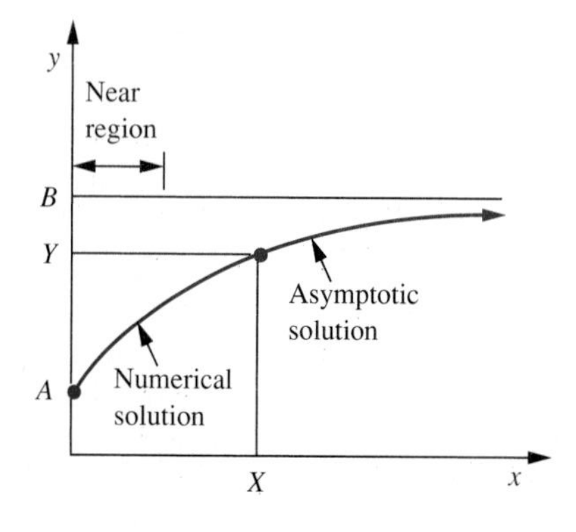

FIGURE 8.14
Asymptotic solution approximation.

The boundary condition $\bar{y}(\infty) = B$ is replaced by the boundary condition $\bar{y}(X) = Y$, as illustrated in Figure 8.14. As discussed in the previous subsection, the value of X can be varied to determine its effect on the solution in the near region.

8.8 NONLINEAR BOUNDARY-VALUE PROBLEMS

Consider the general nonlinear second-order boundary-value ODE:

$$\bar{y}'' + P(x, \bar{y})\bar{y}' + Q(x, \bar{y})\bar{y} = F(x) \tag{8.110}$$

The solution of Eq. (8.110) by the shooting method, as discussed in Section 8.4, is straightforward. The shooting method is based on finite difference methods for solving initial-value problems. Explicit methods, such as the Runge–Kutta and Adams–Bashforth–Moulton methods, solve nonlinear initial-values ODEs directly. Implicit methods require the solution of a nonlinear FDE at each step.

The solution of Eq. (8.110) by the equilibrium method is complicated, since the corresponding FDE is nonlinear, which yields a system of nonlinear FDEs. Two procedures for solving nonlinear boundary-value ODEs by the equilibrium method are presented in this section: iteration and Newton's method.

Iteration

The iteration procedure for solving nonlinear boundary-value ODEs is similar to the fixed-point iteration concept presented in Section 3.4 for solving nonlinear equations. In that method, the problem $f(x) = 0$ is rearranged into the form $x = g(x)$, and an initial value of x is assumed and substituted into $g(x)$ to give the next approximation for x.

The solution of a nonlinear boundary-value ODE by iteration proceeds in the following steps.

1. Develop a finite difference approximation of the ODE. Linearize the ODE by lagging all the coefficients. Preserve the general character of the ODE by lagging the lowest-order terms in a group of terms. For example,

$$\bar{y}''\bar{y}'y^{1/2} \rightarrow (\bar{y}'')^{(k+1)}(\bar{y}')^{(k)}(\bar{y}^{1/2})^{(k)} \tag{8.111}$$

   Choose finite difference approximations for the derivatives and construct the linearized FDE.

2. Assume an initial approximation for the solution: $y^{(0)}(x)$. A good initial approximation can reduce the number of iterations. A bad initial approximation may not converge. Choose the initial approximation similar in form to the expected form of the solution. For example, for the Dirichlet boundary conditions $\bar{y}(a) = A$ and $\bar{y}(b) = B$, the initial approximation $y^{(0)}(x)$ could be a

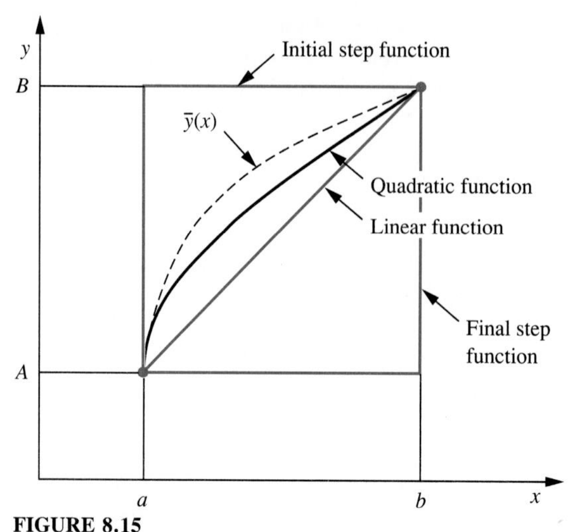

FIGURE 8.15
Initial approximations for iteration.

step function at $x = a$, a step function at $x = b$, a linear variation from a to b, or a quadratic variation from a to b, as illustrated in Fig. 8.15. The step functions are obviously less desirable than the linear or quadratic variations. The linear variation is quite acceptable in most cases. If additional insight into the problem suggests a quadratic variation, it should be used.

3. Calculate the lagged coefficients $P(x, y) = P[x, y^{(0)}(x)] = P^{(0)}(x)$, and so on.
4. Solve the system of linear FDEs to obtain $y^{(1)}(x)$.
5. Calculate the lagged coefficients based on the new solution $y^{(n)}(x)$.
6. Repeat Steps 4 and 5 to convergence.

Example 8.5. Linearization of a nonlinear ODE. Consider the nonlinear boundary-value ODE:

$$\overline{y}'' + P(x)\overline{y}^2\overline{y}' + Q(x)\overline{y}^2 = F(x) \tag{8.112}$$

Lag the nonlinear coefficients in Eq. (8.112) to linearize the ODE:

$$(\overline{y}'')^{(k+1)} + P(x)(\overline{y}^{(k)})^2(\overline{y}')^{(k+1)} + Q(x)\overline{y}^{(k)}\overline{y}^{(k+1)} = F(x) \tag{8.113}$$

Approximating $\overline{y}''$ and $\overline{y}'$ by second-order centered-difference approximations and neglecting the remainder terms yields

$$\left(\frac{y_{i+1} - 2y_i + y_{i-1}}{\Delta x^2}\right)^{(k+1)} + P_i(y_i^{(k)})^2\left(\frac{y_{i+1} - y_{i-1}}{2\,\Delta x}\right)^{(k+1)} + Q_i y_i^{(k)} y_i^{(k+1)} = F_i \tag{8.114}$$

Multiplying by Δx^2 and rearranging yields the FDE:

$$y_{i-1}^{(k+1)}\left(1 - \frac{\Delta x}{2}P_i(y_i^{(k)})^2\right) + y_i^{(k+1)}(-2 + \Delta x^2\,Q_i y_i^{(k)})$$
$$+ y_{i+1}^{(k+1)}\left(1 + \frac{\Delta x}{2}P_i(y_i^{(k)})^2\right) = \Delta x^2\,F_i \tag{8.115}$$

Newton's Method

Newton's method for solving nonlinear boundary-value problems by the equilibrium method consists of choosing an approximate solution $Y_0(x)$ to the problem and assuming that the exact solution $\bar{y}(x)$ is the sum of the approximate solution $Y_0(x)$ and a small perturbation $\eta(x)$. Thus,

$$\boxed{\bar{y}(x) = Y_0(x) + \eta(x)} \tag{8.116}$$

Equation (8.116) is substituted into the nonlinear ODE, and terms involving products of $\eta(x)$ and its derivatives are assumed to be negligible compared to linear terms in $\eta(x)$ and its derivatives. This process yields a linear ODE for $\eta(x)$, which can be solved by the equilibrium method. The solution is not exact, since higher-order terms in $\eta(x)$ and its derivatives were neglected. The procedure is repeated, with the approximate solution

$$Y_1(x) = Y_0(x) + \eta(x) \tag{8.117}$$

This procedure is applied repetitively until $\eta(x)$ changes by less than some prescribed tolerance at each point in the finite difference grid. The general iteration algorithm is

$$\boxed{Y_{i+1}(x) = Y_i(x) + \eta_i(x)} \tag{8.118}$$

Newton's method converges quadratically. Convergence is faster if a good initial approximation is available. The procedure can diverge for a poor (i.e., unrealistic) initial approximation. Newton's method, with its quadratic convergence, is especially useful if, for example, the same boundary-value problem must be worked many times with different boundary conditions or grid sizes.

Example 8.6. Newton's method for a nonlinear ODE. We will illustrate Newton's method by applying it to the nonlinear boundary-value ODE

$$\bar{y}'' - 2\bar{y}^2\bar{y}' = F(x), \qquad \bar{y}(a) = A \quad \text{and} \quad \bar{y}(b) = B \tag{8.119}$$

Let $Y_0(x)$ be an approximate solution. Then,

$$\bar{y}(x) = Y_0(x) + \eta(x) \tag{8.120}$$

$$\bar{y}' = Y_0' + \eta' \quad \text{and} \quad \bar{y}'' = Y_0'' + \eta'' \tag{8.121}$$

Substituting Eqs. (8.120) and (8.121) into Eq. (8.119) gives

$$(Y_0'' + \eta'') - 2(Y_0 + \eta)^2(Y_0' + \eta') = F \tag{8.122}$$

Expanding the nonlinear term yields

$$(Y_0'' + \eta'') - 2(Y_0^2 Y_0' + Y_0^2\eta' + \eta^2 Y_0' + \eta^2\eta' + 2Y_0\eta Y_0' + 2Y_0\eta\eta') = F \tag{8.123}$$

Neglecting nonlinear terms in η in Eq. (8.123) yields the linear ODE

$$\boxed{\eta'' - 2Y_0^2\eta' - 4Y_0Y_0'\eta = F - Y_0'' + 2Y_0^2Y_0' = G(x)} \tag{8.124}$$

The boundary conditions on $\bar{y}(x)$ must be transformed to boundary conditions on $\eta(x)$. At $x = a$,

$$\eta(a) = \bar{y}(a) - Y_0(a) = A - A = 0 \tag{8.125}$$

since the approximate solution $Y_0(x)$ must also satisfy the boundary condition. In a similar manner, $\eta(b) = 0$.

Equation (8.124), with the boundary conditions $\eta(a) = \eta(b) = 0$, can be solved by the equilibrium method to yield $Y_1(x) = Y_0(x) + \eta(x)$. The procedure is applied repetitively to convergence.

8.9 HIGHER-ORDER METHODS

Consider the general second-order nonlinear boundary-value ODE:

$$\boxed{\bar{y}'' + P(x, \bar{y})\bar{y}' + Q(x, \bar{y})\bar{y} = F(x)} \tag{8.126}$$

When solving ODEs such as Eq. (8.126) by the shooting method, it is quite easy to develop higher-order methods (e.g., the fourth-order Runge–Kutta and the fourth-order Adams–Bashforth–Moulton methods). However, it is quite complicated to develop equilibrium methods higher than second order. Two procedures for obtaining fourth-order equilibrium methods are presented in this section: the five-point method, and the compact three-point method.

The Five-Point Fourth-Order Method

Consider the five-point finite difference grid illustrated in Fig. 8.16. Fourth-order approximations for $\bar{y}'$ and $\bar{y}''$ require five grid points: $i-2$ to $i+2$. The sixth-order Taylor series for $\bar{y}(x)$ at these points with base point n are given by

$$\bar{y}_{i+2} = \bar{y}_i + \bar{y}'|_i\,(2\,\Delta x) + \frac{1}{2}\bar{y}''|_i\,(2\,\Delta x)^2 + \frac{1}{6}\bar{y}'''|_i\,(2\,\Delta x)^3 + \frac{1}{24}\bar{y}^{(4)}|_i\,(2\,\Delta x)^4 + \frac{1}{120}\bar{y}^{(5)}|_i\,(2\,\Delta x)^5 + \frac{1}{720}\bar{y}^{(6)}|_i\,(2\,\Delta x)^6 + \cdots \tag{8.127}$$

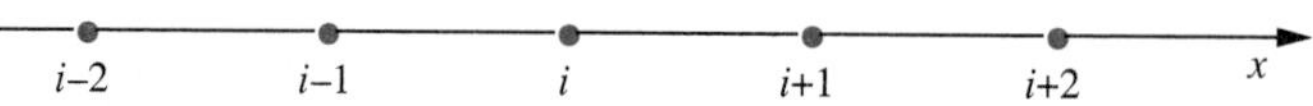

FIGURE 8.16
Five-point finite difference grid.

$$\bar{y}_{i+1} = \bar{y}_i + \bar{y}'|_i\,\Delta x + \frac{1}{2}\bar{y}''|_i\,\Delta x^2 + \frac{1}{6}\bar{y}'''|_i\,\Delta x^3 + \frac{1}{24}\bar{y}^{(4)}|_i\,\Delta x^4 + \frac{1}{120}\bar{y}^{(5)}|_i\,\Delta x^5 + \frac{1}{720}\bar{y}^{(6)}|_i\,\Delta x^6 + \cdots \quad (8.128)$$

$$\bar{y}_{i-1} = \bar{y}_i - \bar{y}'|_i\,\Delta x + \frac{1}{2}\bar{y}''|_i\,\Delta x^2 - \frac{1}{6}\bar{y}'''|_i\,\Delta x^3 + \frac{1}{24}\bar{y}^{(5)}k|_i\,\Delta x^4 - \frac{1}{120}\bar{y}^{(5)}|_i\,\Delta x^{(5)} + \frac{1}{720}\bar{y}^{5}|_i\,\Delta x^6 - \cdots \quad (8.129)$$

$$\bar{y}_{i-2} = \bar{y}_i - \bar{y}'|_i(2\Delta x) + \frac{1}{2}\bar{y}''|_i(2\Delta x)^2 - \frac{1}{6}\bar{y}'''|_i(2\Delta x)^3 + \frac{1}{24}\bar{y}^{(4)}|_i(2\Delta x)^4 - \frac{1}{120}\bar{y}^{(5)}|_i(2\Delta x)^5 + \frac{1}{720}\bar{y}^{(6)}|_i(2\Delta x)^6 - \cdots \quad (8.130)$$

An approximation for $\bar{y}'|_i$ can be obtained by forming the combination $-\bar{y}_{i+2} + 8\bar{y}_{i+1} - 8\bar{y}_{i-1} + \bar{y}_{i-2}$. Thus,

$$\boxed{\bar{y}'|_i = \frac{-\bar{y}_{i+2} + 8\bar{y}_{i+1} - 8\bar{y}_{i-1} + \bar{y}_{i-2}}{12\Delta x} + \frac{48}{120}\bar{y}^{(5)}(\xi)\Delta x^4} \quad (8.131)$$

An approximation for $\bar{y}''|_i$ can be obtained by forming the combination $-\bar{y}_{i+2} + 16\bar{y}_{i+1} - 30\bar{y}_i + 16\bar{y}_{i-1} - \bar{y}_{i-2}$. The result is

$$\boxed{\bar{y}''|_i = \frac{-\bar{y}_{i+2} + 16\bar{y}_{i+1} - 30\bar{y}_i + 16\bar{y}_{i-1} - \bar{y}_{i-2}}{12\Delta x^2} + \frac{96}{720}\bar{y}^{(6)}(\xi)\Delta x^4} \quad (8.132)$$

These FDAs can be substituted into the boundary-value ODE to give an $O(\Delta x^4)$ FDE.

Problems arise at points just inside the boundaries, where the centered fourth-order FDE cannot be applied. Nonsymmetrical fourth-order FDEs can be used at these points, or second-order FDEs can be used with some loss of accuracy. A pentadiagonal matrix results. A method similar to the Thomas algorithm for tridiagonal matrices can be used to give an efficient solution of the system of FDEs.

The Compact Three-Point Fourth-Order Method

Implicit three-point fourth-order FDAs can be devised. When the overall algorithm is implicit, as it is when solving boundary-value problems by the equilibrium method, implicitness is already present in the FDEs. Subtract the Taylor series for

$\bar{y}_{i-1}$, Eq. (8.129), from the Taylor series for $\bar{y}_{i+1}$, Eq. (8.128).

$$\bar{y}_{i+1} - \bar{y}_{i-1} = 2\,\Delta x\,\bar{y}'|_i + \frac{1}{3}\,\Delta x^3\,\bar{y}'''|_i + \frac{1}{60}\,\Delta x^5\,\bar{y}^{(5)}|_i + O(\Delta x^7) \tag{8.133}$$

Rearranging Eq. (8.133) gives

$$\frac{\bar{y}_{i+1} - \bar{y}_{i-1}}{2\,\Delta x} = \bar{y}'|_i + \frac{1}{6}\,\Delta x^2\,\bar{y}'''|_i + O(\Delta x^4) \tag{8.134}$$

Write Taylor series for $\bar{y}'|_{i+1}$ and $\bar{y}'|_{i-1}$. Thus,

$$\bar{y}'|_{i+1} = \bar{y}'|_i + \bar{y}''|_i\,\Delta x + \frac{1}{2}\bar{y}'''|_i\,\Delta x^2 + \frac{1}{6}\bar{y}^{(4)}|_i\,\Delta x^3 + \frac{1}{24}\bar{y}^{(5)}|_i\,\Delta x^4 + \cdots \tag{8.135}$$

$$\bar{y}'|_{i-1} = \bar{y}'|_i - \bar{y}''|_i\,\Delta x + \frac{1}{2}\bar{y}'''|_i\,\Delta x^2 - \frac{1}{6}\bar{y}^{(4)}|_i\,\Delta x^3 + \frac{1}{24}\bar{y}^{(5)}|_i\,\Delta x^4 - \cdots \tag{8.136}$$

Adding Eqs. (8.135) and (8.136) yields

$$\bar{y}'|_{i+1} - 2\bar{y}'|_i + \bar{y}'|_{i-1} = \Delta x^2\,\bar{y}'''|_i + O(\Delta x^4) \tag{8.137}$$

Adding and subtracting $6\bar{y}'|_i$ from Eq. (8.137) and rearranging gives

$$\frac{1}{6}(\bar{y}'|_{i+1} + 4\bar{y}'|_i + \bar{y}'|_{i-1}) = \bar{y}'_i + \frac{1}{6}\Delta x^2\bar{y}'''|_i + O(\Delta x^4) \tag{8.138}$$

The right-hand sides of Eqs. (8.134) and (8.138) are identical. Equating the left-hand sides of those two equations gives

$$\boxed{\frac{1}{6}(\bar{y}'|_{i+1} + 4\bar{y}'|_i + \bar{y}'|_{i-1}) = \frac{\bar{y}_{i+1} - \bar{y}_{i-1}}{2\,\Delta x} + O(\Delta x^4)} \tag{8.139}$$

Neglecting the remainder term, Eq. (8.139) can be written in matrix form as

$$\mathbf{C}\mathbf{y}' = \mathbf{D}\mathbf{y} \tag{8.140}$$

Solving for $\mathbf{y}'$ yields

$$\boxed{\mathbf{y}' = \mathbf{C}^{-1}\mathbf{D}\mathbf{y}} \tag{8.141}$$

Adding the Taylor series for $\bar{y}_{i+1}$, Eq. (8.128), and $\bar{y}_{i-1}$, Eq. (8.129), gives

$$\bar{y}_{i+1} - 2\bar{y}_i + \bar{y}_{i-1} = \Delta x^2\,\bar{y}''|_i + \frac{1}{12}\,\Delta x^4\,\bar{y}^{(4)}|_i + O(\Delta x^6) \tag{8.142}$$

Rearranging Eq. (8.142) gives

$$\frac{\bar{y}_{i+1} - 2\bar{y}_i + \bar{y}_{i-1}}{\Delta x^2} = \bar{y}''|_i + \frac{1}{12}\,\Delta x^2\,\bar{y}^{(4)}|_i + O(\Delta x^4) \tag{8.143}$$

Write Taylor series for $\bar{y}''|_{i+1}$ and $\bar{y}''|_{i-1}$. Thus,

$$\bar{y}''|_{i+1} = \bar{y}''|_i + \bar{y}'''|_i\,\Delta x + \frac{1}{2}\bar{y}^{(4)}|_i\,\Delta x^2 + \frac{1}{6}\bar{y}^{(5)}|_i\,\Delta x^3 + \frac{1}{24}\bar{y}^{(6)}|_i\,\Delta x^4 + \cdots \tag{8.144}$$

$$\bar{y}''|_{i-1} = \bar{y}''|_i - \bar{y}'''|_i\,\Delta x + \frac{1}{2}\bar{y}^{(4)}|_i\,\Delta x^2 - \frac{1}{6}\bar{y}^{(5)}|_i\,\Delta x^3 + \frac{1}{24}\bar{y}^{(6)}|_i\,\Delta x^4 - \cdots \tag{8.145}$$

Adding Eqs. (8.144) and (8.145) gives

$$\bar{y}''|_{i+1} - 2\bar{y}''|_i + \bar{y}''|_{i-1} = \Delta x^2\,\bar{y}^{(4)}|_i + O(\Delta x^4) \tag{8.146}$$

Adding and subtracting $12\bar{y}''|_i$ from Eq. (8.146) and rearranging gives

$$\frac{1}{12}(\bar{y}''|_{i+1} + 10\bar{y}''|_i + \bar{y}''|_{i-1}) = \bar{y}''|_i + \frac{1}{12}\Delta x^2\,\bar{y}^{(4)}|_i + O(\Delta x^4) \tag{8.147}$$

The right-hand sides of Eqs. (8.143) and (8.147) are identical. Equating the left-hand sides of those equations gives

$$\boxed{\frac{1}{12}(\bar{y}''|_{i+1} + 10\bar{y}''|_i + \bar{y}''|_{i-1}) = \frac{1}{\Delta x^2}(\bar{y}_{i+1} - 2\bar{y}_i + \bar{y}_{i-1}) + O(\Delta x^4)} \tag{8.148}$$

Neglecting the remainder term, Eq. (8.148) can be written in matrix form as

$$\mathbf{Ay}'' = \mathbf{By} \tag{8.149}$$

Solving for $\mathbf{y}''$ gives

$$\boxed{\mathbf{y}'' = \mathbf{A}^{-1}\mathbf{By}} \tag{8.150}$$

Consider the boundary-value ODE:

$$\bar{y}'' + P(x,\bar{y})\bar{y}' + Q(x,\bar{y})\bar{y} = F(x) \tag{8.151}$$

Substituting Eqs. (8.141) and (8.150) into Eq. (8.151) yields the matrix equation

$$\boxed{\mathbf{A}^{-1}\mathbf{By} + \mathbf{P(x, y)C}^{-1}\mathbf{Dy} + \mathbf{Q(x, y)y} = \mathbf{F}} \tag{8.152}$$

If $\mathbf{P}$ and $\mathbf{Q}$ depend on $\mathbf{y}$, the system of FDEs is nonlinear. If not, the system is linear.

Example 8.7. Solution by the compact fourth-order method. As an example of the compact fourth-order method, we will solve the heat transfer problem presented in

TABLE 8.11
Solution by the compact fourth-order method

x_i	T_i	T_{exact}	Error
0.00	0.000000		
0.25	14.365830	14.367669	−0.001840
0.50	32.399531	32.402714	−0.003183
0.75	58.705452	58.708613	−0.003161
1.00	100.000000		

Section 8.1. Thus,

$$T'' - \alpha^2 T = -\alpha^2 T_a, \qquad T(0) = 0 \text{ and } T(1.0) = 100 \tag{8.153}$$

Substituting Eq. (8.150) into Eq. (8.153) gives

$$\mathbf{A}^{-1}\mathbf{B}\mathbf{T} = \boldsymbol{\alpha}^2(\mathbf{T} - T_a) \tag{8.154}$$

Multiplying Eq. (8.154) by **A** yields

$$\mathbf{B}\ \mathbf{T} = \mathbf{A}\boldsymbol{\alpha}^2(\mathbf{T} - T_a) \tag{8.155}$$

Substituting for **A** and **B** from Eq. (8.148) into Eq. (8.155) gives

$$\frac{1}{\Delta x^2}(T_{i-1} - 2T_i + T_{i+1}) = \frac{\alpha^2}{12}\Big((T - T_a)_{i-1} + 10(T - T_a)_i + (T - T_a)_{i+1}\Big) \tag{8.156}$$

Rearranging Eq. (8.156) yields

$$\boxed{(1 - \beta)T_{i-1} - (2 + 10\beta)T_i + (1 - \beta)T_{i+1} = -12\beta T_a} \tag{8.157}$$

where $\beta = \alpha^2\,\Delta x^2/12$.

Let $\Delta x = 0.25, \alpha = 2.0$, and $T_a = 0.0$, which gives $\beta = (2.0)^2(0.25)^2/12 = 0.020833$. Equation (8.157) becomes

$$\boxed{0.979167T_{i-1} - 2.208333T_i + 0.979167T_{i+1} = 0} \tag{8.158}$$

Applying Eq. (8.158) at the three interior grid points, transferring the boundary conditions to the right-hand side of the equations, and solving the tridiagonal system of FDEs by the Thomas algorithm yields the results presented in Table 8.11. The errors for $\Delta x = 0.250$ and 0.125 are presented in Fig. 8.11 in Section 8.5, where the errors for the second-order equilibrium method are also presented.

8.10 EIGENPROBLEMS

Eigenproblems are equilibrium problems in which the solution exists only for special values (i.e., eigenvalues) of a parameter of the problem. Eigenproblems occur when homogeneous boundary-value ODEs also have homogeneous boundary conditions. The eigenvalues are to be determined in addition to the corresponding equilibrium configuration of the system. Shooting methods are not well suited for solving eigenproblems. Consequently, eigenproblems are generally solved by the equilibrium method.

Exact Solution

Consider the linear homogeneous boundary-value problem

$$\boxed{\bar{y}'' + k^2\bar{y} = 0, \qquad \bar{y}(0) = \bar{y}(1) = 0} \tag{8.159}$$

The exact solution to this problem is

$$\bar{y}(x) = A\sin(kx) + B\cos(kx) \tag{8.160}$$

where k is an unknown parameter to be determined. Substituting the boundary values into Eq. (8.160) gives

$$\bar{y}(0) = A\sin(k0) + B\cos(k0) = 0 \quad \rightarrow B = 0 \tag{8.161}$$

$$\bar{y}(1) = A\sin(k1) = 0 \tag{8.162}$$

Either $A = 0$ (undesired) or $\sin(k) = 0$, for which

$$\boxed{k = \pm n\pi, \qquad n = 1, 2, \ldots} \tag{8.163}$$

The values of k are the eigenvalues of the problem. There are an infinite number of eigenvalues. The solution of the differential equation is

$$\boxed{\bar{y}(x) = A\sin(n\pi x)} \tag{8.164}$$

The value of A is not uniquely determined.

The Equilibrium Finite Difference Method

We can solve Eq. (8.159) by the equilibrium finite difference method. Choose an equally spaced grid with four interior points, as illustrated in Fig. 8.17. Approximate $\bar{y}''$ with the second-order centered-difference approximation, Eq. (8.57). The corresponding finite difference equation is:

$$\frac{\bar{y}_{i+1} - 2\bar{y}_i + \bar{y}_{i-1}}{\Delta x^2} + O(\Delta x^2) + k^2\bar{y}_i = 0 \tag{8.165}$$

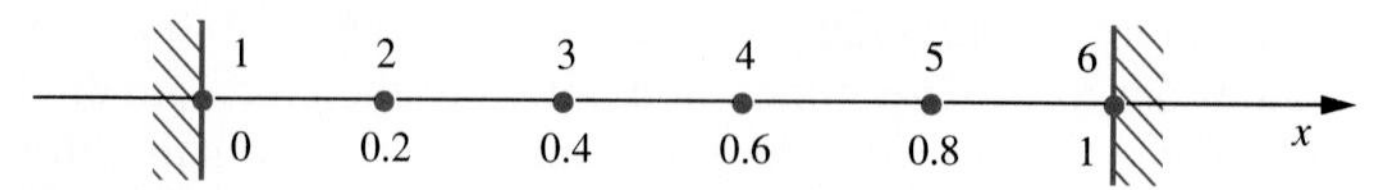

FIGURE 8.17
Finite difference grid for the eigenproblem.

Multiplying by Δx^2, neglecting the remainder term, and rearranging gives the FDE

$$\boxed{y_{i-1} - (2 - \Delta x^2\, k^2) y_i + y_{i+1} = 0} \tag{8.166}$$

Apply the FDE, with $\Delta x = 0.2$, at the four interior points:

$$x = 0.2: \quad y_1 - (2 - 0.04k^2) y_2 + y_3 = 0, \qquad y_1 = 0 \tag{8.167a}$$

$$x = 0.4: \quad y_2 - (2 - 0.04k^2) y_3 + y_4 = 0 \tag{8.167b}$$

$$x = 0.6: \quad y_3 - (2 - 0.04k^2) y_4 + y_5 = 0 \tag{8.167c}$$

$$x = 0.8: \quad y_4 - (2 - 0.04k^2) y_5 + y_6 = 0, \qquad y_6 = 0 \tag{8.167d}$$

Writing Eq. (8.167) in matrix form gives

$$\begin{bmatrix} (2 - 0.04k^2) & -1 & 0 & 0 \\ -1 & (2 - 0.04k^2) & -1 & 0 \\ 0 & -1 & (2 - 0.04k^2) & -1 \\ 0 & 0 & -1 & (2 - 0.04k^2) \end{bmatrix} [y_i] = 0 \tag{8.168}$$

which can be expressed as

$$\boxed{(\mathbf{A} - \lambda \mathbf{I})\mathbf{y} = \mathbf{0}} \tag{8.169}$$

where $\lambda = 0.04k^2$ and $\mathbf{A}$ is defined as

$$\mathbf{A} = \begin{bmatrix} 2 & -1 & 0 & 0 \\ -1 & 2 & -1 & 0 \\ 0 & -1 & 2 & -1 \\ 0 & 0 & -1 & 2 \end{bmatrix} \tag{8.170}$$

This is a classical eigenproblem. The characteristic equation is given by

$$\det(\mathbf{A} - \lambda \mathbf{I}) = \mathbf{0} \tag{8.171}$$

Define $Z = (2 - 0.04k^2)$. The characteristic equation is determined by expanding

TABLE 8.12
Solution of the eigenproblem

Z	k	k(exact)	Error, percent
1.618	± 3.090	$\pm\ \pi = \pm\ 3.142$	$\mp\ 1.66$
0.618	± 5.878	$\pm 2\pi = \pm\ 6.283$	$\mp\ 6.45$
−0.618	± 8.090	$\pm 3\pi = \pm\ 9.425$	∓ 14.16
−1.618	± 9.511	$\pm 4\pi = \pm 12.566$	∓ 24.31

the determinant. Thus,

$$Z^4 - 3Z^2 + 1 = 0 \tag{8.172}$$

which is quadratic in Z^2. Solving Eq. (8.172) by the quadratic formula yields

$$Z = (2 - 0.04k^2) = \pm 1.618\ldots, \pm 0.618\ldots \tag{8.173}$$

The values of Z, k, k(exact), and percent error are presented in Table 8.12.

The first eigenvalue is reasonably accurate. The higher-order eigenvalues become less and less accurate. To improve the accuracy of the eigenvalues and to obtain higher-order eigenvalues, more grid points are required. This is not without disadvantages, however. Expanding the determinant becomes more difficult, and finding the zeros of high-order polynomials is more difficult. Numerical methods, which are introduced in Chapter 2, for finding the eigenvalues may be used to determine the eigenvalues for large systems of FDEs.

SUMMARY

Two procedures are presented in this chapter for solving boundary-value ordinary differential equations: the shooting method and the equilibrium method. The advantages and disadvantages of these methods are summarized in this section.

The shooting method is based on marching methods for solving initial-value ODEs. The advantages of the shooting method are as follows:

1. Any initial-value ODE solution method can be used.
2. Nonlinear ODEs are solved directly.
3. It is easy to achieve fourth- or higher-order accuracy.
4. There is no system of FDEs to solve.

The disadvantages of the shooting method are:

1. One or more boundary conditions must be satisfied iteratively (by shooting).
2. Shooting for more than one boundary condition is time-consuming.
3. Nonlinear problems require an iterative procedure (e.g., the secant method) to satisfy the boundary conditions.

The equilibrium method is based on relaxing a system of FDEs simultaneously, including the boundary conditions. The major advantage of the equilibrium method is that the boundary conditions are applied directly and automatically satisfied. The disadvantages of the equilibrium method are:

1. It is difficult to achieve higher than second-order accuracy.
2. A system of FDEs must be solved.
3. Nonlinear ODEs yield a system of nonlinear FDEs, which must be solved by iterative methods.

No rigid guidelines exist for choosing between the shooting method and the equilibrium method. Experience is the best guide. Shooting methods work well for nonsmooth problems and oscillatory problems where their error control and variable grid size capacity are of great value. Equilibrium methods work well for problems that have extraneous solutions that satisfy the boundary conditions, but do not appear in the final solution and pollute the solution of an initial-value problem. Equilibrium methods also work well for problems with complicated or delicate boundary conditions. Shooting methods frequently require more computational effort, but they are generally more certain of producing a solution.

PROBLEMS

Section 8.1 Introduction

1. Derive the exact solution of the heat transfer problem presented in Section 8.1, Eq. (8.4). Calculate the solution presented in Table 8.1.

Section 8.2 General Features of Boundary-Value Ordinary Differential Equations

2. Derive the exact solution of the linear second-order boundary-value ODE given by Eq. (8.6), where $y(x_1) = y_1$, $y(x_2) = y_2$, and $F(x) = a\exp(bx) + c + dx$.
3. Evaluate the solution of Problem 8.2 for $P = 5$, $Q = 4$, $F = 1$, $y(0) = 0$, and $y(1) = 1$. Tabulate the solution for $x = 0$ to 1 at intervals $\Delta x = 0.125$. Plot the solution.

Section 8.3 Finite Difference Grids and Finite Difference Approximations

4. Using the Taylor series approach, derive the second-order centered-space finite difference approximation (FDA) of $\bar{y}'(x) = d\bar{y}/dx$, including the leading truncation error term.
5. Using the Taylor series approach, derive the second-order centered-space finite difference approximation of $\bar{y}''(x) = d^2\bar{y}/dx^2$, including the leading truncation error term.
6. Using Taylor series, determine what derivative is represented by the following FDA, and the leading truncation error term:

$$\text{FDA} = \frac{-11y_i + 18y_{i+1} - 9y_{i+2} + 2f_{i+3}}{6\Delta x}$$

The following problems involve the numerical solution of boundary-value ODEs. These problems can be worked by hand calculation or computer programs. Carry at least six digits after the decimal place in all calculations.

An infinite variety of additional problems can be obtained from these problems by (*a*) changing the coefficients in the ODEs, (*b*) changing the boundary conditions, (*c*) changing the step size, (*d*) changing the range of integration, and (*e*) combinations of these changes.

For all problems solved by a shooting method, let $y'(0) = 0.0$ and 1.0 for the first two guesses, unless otherwise noted.

For all problems solved by an equilibrium method, let the first approximation for $y(x)$ be a linear variation consistent with the boundry conditions.

Section 8.4 The Shooting (Initial-Value) Method

7. Solve the following ODE by the shooting method using the first-order explicit Euler method with (*a*) $\Delta x = 0.25$, (*b*) $\Delta x = 0.125$, and (*c*) $\Delta x = 0.0625$. Compare the errors and calculate the ratio of the errors at $x = 0.5$.

$$\bar{y}'' + 5\bar{y}' + 4\bar{y} = 1, \qquad \bar{y}(0) = 0 \text{ and } \bar{y}(1) = 1 \tag{P8.7}$$

8. Work Problem 7 by the second-order modified Euler method without iteration.

9. Work Problem 7 by the fourth-order Runge–Kutta method.

10. Solve the following ODE by the shooting method using the first-order explicit Euler method with (*a*) $\Delta x = 0.25$, (*b*) $\Delta x = 0.125$, and (*c*) $\Delta x = 0.0625$. Compare the errors and calculate the ratio of the errors at $x = 0.5$.

$$\bar{y}'' + 4\bar{y}' + 6.25\bar{y} = 1, \qquad \bar{y}(0) = 0 \text{ and } \bar{y}(1) = 1 \tag{P8.10}$$

11. Work Problem 10 by the second-order modified Euler method without iteration.

12. Work Problem 10 by the fourth-order Runge–Kutta method.

13. Solve the following ODE by the shooting method using the first-order explicit Euler method with (*a*) $\Delta x = 0.25$, (*b*) $\Delta x = 0.125$, and (*c*) $\Delta x = 0.0625$. Compare the errors and calculate the ratio of the errors at $x = 0.5$.

$$\bar{y}'' + 5\bar{y}' + 4\bar{y} = e^x, \qquad \bar{y}(0) = 0 \text{ and } \bar{y}(1) = 1 \tag{P8.13}$$

14. Work Problem 13 by the second-order modified Euler method without iteration.

15. Work Problem 13 by the fourth-order Runge–Kutta method.

16. Solve the following ODE by the shooting method using the first-order explicit Euler method with (*a*) $\Delta x = 0.25$, (*b*) $\Delta x = 0.125$, and (*c*) $\Delta x = 0.0625$. Compare the errors and calculate the ratio of the errors at $x = 0.5$.

$$\bar{y}'' + 4\bar{y}' + 6.25\bar{y} = e^x, \qquad \bar{y}(0) = 0 \text{ and } \bar{y}(1) = 1 \tag{P8.16}$$

17. Work Problem 16 by the second-order modified Euler method without iteration.

18. Work Problem 16 by the fourth-order Runge–Kutta method.

19. Solve the following ODE by the shooting method using the first-order explicit Euler method with (*a*) $\Delta x = 0.25$, (*b*) $\Delta x = 0.125$, and (*c*) $\Delta x = 0.0625$. Compare the errors and calculate the ratio of the errors at $x = 0.5$.

$$\bar{y}'' + 5\bar{y}' + 4\bar{y} = 2e^{x/2} + 1 + x, \qquad \bar{y}(0) = 0 \text{ and } \bar{y}(1) = 1 \tag{P8.19}$$

20. Work Problem 19 by the second-order modified Euler method without iteration.

21. Work Problem 19 by the fourth-order Runge–Kutta method.

22. Solve the following ODE by the shooting method using the first-order explicit Euler method with (*a*) $\Delta x = 0.25$, (*b*) $\Delta x = 0.125$, and (*c*) $\Delta x = 0.0625$. Compare the errors and calculate the ratio of the errors at $x = 0.5$.

$$\bar{y}'' + 4\bar{y}' + 6.25\bar{y} = 2e^{x/2} + 1 + x, \qquad \bar{y}(0) = 0 \text{ and } \bar{y}(1) = 1 \tag{P8.22}$$

23. Work Problem 22 by the second-order modified Euler method without iteration.

24. Work Problem 22 by the fourth-order Runge–Kutta method.

25. Solve the following ODE by the shooting method using the first-order explicit Euler method with (*a*) $\Delta x = 0.25$, (*b*) $\Delta x = 0.125$, and (*c*) $\Delta x = 0.0625$. Compare the errors and calculate the ratio of the errors at $x = 0.5$.

$$\bar{y}'' + (1 + x)\bar{y}' + (1 + x)\bar{y} = 1, \qquad \bar{y}(0) = 0 \text{ and } \bar{y}(1) = 1 \tag{P8.25}$$

26. Work Problem 25 by the second-order modified Euler method without iteration.

27. Work Problem 25 by the fourth-order Runge–Kutta method.

28. Solve the following ODE by the shooting method using the first-order explicit Euler method with (*a*) $\Delta x = 0.25$, (*b*) $\Delta x = 0.125$, and (*c*) $\Delta x = 0.0625$. Compare the errors and calculate the ratio of the errors at $x = 0.5$.

$$\bar{y}'' + (1 + x)\bar{y}' + (1 + x)\bar{y} = e^{x}, \qquad \bar{y}(0) = 0 \text{ and } \bar{y}(1) = 1 \tag{P8.28}$$

29. Work Problem 28 by the second-order modified Euler method without iteration.

30. Work Problem 28 by the fourth-order Runge–Kutta method.

31. Solve the following ODE by the shooting method using the first-order explicit Euler method with (*a*) $\Delta x = 0.25$, (*b*) $\Delta x = 0.125$, and (*c*) $\Delta x = 0.0625$. Compare the errors and calculate the ratio of the errors at $x = 0.5$.

$$\bar{y}'' + (1 + x)\bar{y}' + (1 + x)\bar{y} = 2e^{x/2} + 1 + x, \qquad \bar{y}(0) = 0 \text{ and } \bar{y}(1) = 1 \tag{P8.31}$$

32. Work Problem 31 by the second-order modified Euler method without iteration.

33. Work Problem 31 by the fourth-order Runge–Kutta method.

34. Solve the following third-order boundary-value ODE by the shooting method using the first-order explicit Euler method with (*a*)$\Delta x = 0.25$ and (*b*) $\Delta x = 0.125$. Compare the solutions.

$$\bar{y}''' - 7\bar{y}'' + 14\bar{y}' - 8\bar{y} = 1, \qquad \bar{y}(0) = 0,\ \bar{y}'(0) = 1, \text{ and } \bar{y}(1) = 1 \tag{P8.34}$$

35. Work Problem 34 by the second-order modified Euler method without iteration.

36. Work Problem 34 by the fourth-order Runge–Kutta method.

37. Solve the following third-order boundary-value ODE by the shooting method using the first-order explicit Euler method with (*a*) $\Delta x = 0.25$ and (*b*) $\Delta x = 0.125$. Compare the solutions.

$$\bar{y}''' - 7\bar{y}'' + 14\bar{y}' - 8\bar{y} = 2e^{x/2} + 1 + x, \qquad \bar{y}(0) = 0,\ \bar{y}'(0) = 1, \text{ and } \bar{y}(1) = 1 \tag{P8.37}$$

38. Work Problem 37 by the second-order modified Euler method without iteration.

39. Work Problem 37 by the fourth-order Runge–Kutta method.

Section 8.5 The Equilibrium (Boundary-Value) Method

40. Work Problem 7 by the second-order equilibrium method.

41. Work Problem 10 by the second-order equilibrium method.

42. Work Problem 13 by the second-order equilibrium method.
43. Work Problem 16 by the second-order equilibrium method.
44. Work Problem 19 by the second-order equilibrium method.
45. Work Problem 22 by the second-order equilibrium method.
46. Work Problem 25 by the second-order equilibrium method.
47. Work Problem 28 by the second-order equilibrium method.
48. Work Problem 31 by the second-order equilibrium method.
49. Work Problem 34 by letting $\bar{z} = \bar{y}'$, thus reducing the third-order ODE to a second-order ODE for $\bar{z}(x)$. Solve this system of two coupled ODEs by solving the second-order ODE for $\bar{z}(x)$ by the second-order equilibrium method and the first-order ODE for $\bar{y}(x)$ by the second-order modified Euler method. Solve the problem for (*a*) $\Delta x = 0.25$ and (*b*) $\Delta x = 0.125$.
50. Work Problem 37 by the procedure described in Problem 49.

Section 8.6 Derivative Boundary Conditions

51. Solve the following second-order boundary-value ODE by the shooting method using the second-order modified Euler method without iteration with $\Delta x = 0.125$.

$$\bar{y}'' + 5\bar{y}' + 4\bar{y} = 1, \qquad \bar{y}(0) = 1 \text{ and } \bar{y}'(1) = 0 \tag{P8.51}$$

Implement the derivative boundary condition (*a*) by applying the PDE at the boundary, (*b*) by linear extrapolation, (*c*) by quadratic extrapolation, and (*d*) by cubic extrapolation.

52. Work Problem 51 for the ODE

$$\bar{y}'' + 4\bar{y}' + 6.25\bar{y} = 1, \qquad \bar{y}(0) = 1 \text{ and } \bar{y}'(1) = 0 \tag{P8.52}$$

53. Work Problem 51 for the ODE

$$\bar{y}'' + 5\bar{y}' + 4\bar{y} = e^x, \qquad \bar{y}(0) = 1 \text{ and } \bar{y}'(1) = 0 \tag{P8.53}$$

54. Work Problem 51 for the ODE

$$\bar{y}'' + 4\bar{y}' + 6.25\bar{y} = e^x, \qquad \bar{y}(0) = 1 \text{ and } \bar{y}'(1) = 0 \tag{P8.54}$$

55. Work Problem 51 for the ODE

$$\bar{y}'' + (1 + x)\bar{y}' + (1 + x)\bar{y} = 1, \qquad \bar{y}(0) = 1 \text{ and } \bar{y}'(1) = 0 \tag{P8.55}$$

56. Work Problem 51 for the ODE

$$\bar{y}'' + (1 + x)\bar{y}' + (1 + x)\bar{y} = 2e^{x/2} + 1 + x, \qquad \bar{y}(0) = 1 \text{ and } \bar{y}'(1) = 0 \tag{P8.56}$$

In problems 57 to 62, implement the derivative boundary condition (*a*) by applying the PDE at the boundary and (*b*) by quadratic extrapolation.

57. Solve Problem 51 by the second-order equilibrium method.
58. Solve Problem 52 by the second-order equilibrium method.
59. Solve Problem 53 by the second-order equilibrium method.
60. Solve Problem 54 by the second-order equilibrium method.
61. Solve Problem 55 by the second-order equilibrium method.
62. Solve Problem 56 by the second-order equilibrium method.

Section 8.7 Other Boundary Conditions

63. Solve the following second-order boundary-value ODE by the shooting method using the first-order explicit Euler method with (*a*) $\Delta x = 0.25$ and (*b*) $\Delta x = 0.125$.

$$\bar{y}'' + 5\bar{y}' + 4\bar{y} = 1, \qquad \bar{y}(0) = 0 \text{ and } \bar{y}(1) - 0.5\bar{y}'(1) = 0.5 \tag{P8.63}$$

64. Work Problem 63 by the second-order modified Euler method without iteration.

65. Work Problem 63 by the fourth-order Runge–Kutta method.

66. Work Problem 63 for the ODE

$$\bar{y}'' + 4\bar{y}' + 6.25\bar{y} = e^x, \qquad \bar{y}(0) = 0 \text{ and } \bar{y}(1) - 0.5\bar{y}'(1) = 0.5 \tag{P8.66}$$

67. Work Problem 66 by the second-order modified Euler method without iteration.

68. Work Problem 66 by the fourth-order Runge–Kutta method.

69. Solve Problem 63 by the second-order equilibrium method. Implement the mixed boundary condition by applying the PDE at the boundary.

70. Solve Problem 66 by the second-order equilibrium method. Implement the mixed boundary condition by applying the PDE at the boundary.

71. Solve the following ODE by the shooting method using the first-order explicit Euler method with (*a*) $\Delta x = 0.25$ and (*b*) $\Delta x = 0.125$.

$$\bar{y}'' - \bar{y} = 0 \qquad \bar{y}(0) = 1 \text{ and } \bar{y}(\infty) = 0 \tag{P8.71}$$

Let $y'(0) = 0$ and -1 for the first two passes. Implement the boundary condition at infinity by applying that BC at $x = 2, 5, 10$, and so on, until the solution at $x = 1.0$ changes by less than 0.001.

72. Work Problem 71 by the second-order modified Euler method without iteration.

73. Work Problem 71 by the fourth-order Runge–Kutta method.

74. Work Problem 71 for the ODE

$$\bar{y}'' + \bar{y}' - 2\bar{y} = 1, \qquad \bar{y}(0) = 1 \text{ and } \bar{y}(\infty) = 0 \tag{P8.74}$$

75. Work Problem 74 by the second-order modified Euler method without iteration.

76. Work Problem 74 by the fourth-order Runge–Kutta method.

77. Solve Problem 71 by the second-order equilibrium method.

78. Solve Problem 74 by the second-order equilibrium method.

Section 8.8 Nonlinear Boundary-Value Problems

79. Solve the following ODE by the shooting method using the first-order explicit Euler method with (*a*) $\Delta x = 0.25$, (*b*) $\Delta x = 0.125$, and (*c*) $\Delta x = 0.0625$. Compare the errors and calculate the ratio of the errors at $x = 0.5$.

$$\bar{y}'' + (1 + \bar{y})\bar{y}' + (1 + \bar{y})\bar{y} = 1, \qquad \bar{y}(0) = 0 \text{ and } \bar{y}(1) = 1 \tag{P8.79}$$

80. Work Problem 79 by the second-order modified Euler method without iteration.

81. Work Problem 79 by the fourth-order Runge–Kutta method.

82. Solve the following ODE by the shooting method using the first-order explicit Euler method with (*a*) $\Delta x = 0.25$, (*b*) $\Delta x = 0.125$, and (*c*) $\Delta x = 0.0625$. Compare the errors and calculate the ratio of the errors at $x = 0.5$.

$$\bar{y}'' + (1 + x + \bar{y})\bar{y}' + (1 + x + \bar{y})\bar{y} = 2e^{x/2} + 1 + x, \qquad \bar{y}(0) = 0 \text{ and } \bar{y}(1) = 1 \tag{P8.82}$$

83. Work Problem 82 by the second-order modified Euler method without iteration.

84. Work Problem 82 by the fourth-order Runge–Kutta method.

85. Work Problem 79 by the second-order equilibrium method by (*a*) iteration and (*b*) Newton's method.

86. Work Problem 82 by the second-order equilibrium method by (*a*) iteration and (*b*) Newton's method.

Section 8.9 Higher-Order Methods

87. Solve Problem 7 using the five-point fourth-order equilibrium method for $\Delta x = 0.125$. Use the three-point second-order equilibrium method at points adjacent to the boundaries.

88. Solve Problem 10 by the procedure described in Problem 87.

89. Solve Problem 13 by the procedure described in Problem 87.

90. Solve Problem 16 by the procedure described in Problem 87.

91. Compact three-point fourth-order finite difference approximations are presented in Section 8.9 for $\bar{y}''(x)$ and $\bar{y}'(x)$. When these are used in a second-order boundary-value ODE, a matrix equation, Eq. (8.152), is obtained. This equation is straightforward in concept but difficult to implement numerically. When the first derivative $\bar{y}'(x)$ does not appear in the ODE, however, a simple FDE can be developed, such as Eq. (8.157) in Example 8.7. Apply this procedure to solve the following ODE:

$$\bar{y}'' + \bar{y} = 1, \qquad \bar{y}(0) = 0 \text{ and } \bar{y}(1) = 1$$

92. Solve the following ODE by the procedure described in Problem 91:

$$\bar{y}'' + \bar{y} = 1 + x + e^x, \qquad \bar{y}(0) = 0 \text{ and } \bar{y}(1) = 1$$

93. Solve the following ODE by the procedure described in Problem 91:

$$\bar{y}'' - \bar{y} = 1, \qquad \bar{y}(0) = 0 \text{ and } \bar{y}(1) = 1$$

94. Solve the following ODE by the procedure described in Problem 91:

$$\bar{y}'' - \bar{y} = 1 + x + e^x, \qquad \bar{y}(0) = 0 \text{ and } \bar{y}(1) = 1$$

Section 8.10 Eigenproblems

95. Consider the eigenproblem described by Eq. (8.159). The finite difference equation corresponding to the eigenproblem is given by Eq. (8.166). The exact solution of this eigenproblem is $k = \pm n\pi$ $(n = 1, 2, \ldots)$. The numerical solution of this eigenproblem for $\Delta x = \frac{1}{5}$ is presented in Table 8.12. Determine the solution to this eigenproblem for (*a*) $\Delta x = \frac{1}{6}$ and (*b*) $\Delta x = \frac{1}{8}$. Compare the three sets of results in normalized form, that is, k/π.

96. Consider the eigenproblem

$$\bar{y}'' - k^2\bar{y} = 0, \qquad \bar{y}(0) = \bar{y}(1) = 0$$

This problem has no solution except the trivial solution $\bar{y}(x) = 0$. (*a*) Demonstrate this result analytically. (*b*) Illustrate this result numerically by setting up a system of second-order finite difference equations with $\Delta x = 0.2$, and show that there are no real values of k.

97. Consider the eigenproblem

$$\bar{y}'' + \bar{y}' + k^2\bar{y} = 0, \qquad \bar{y}(0) = \bar{y}(1) = 0$$

Estimate the first three eigenvalues by setting up a system of second-order finite difference equations with $\Delta x = 0.25$.

98. Work Problem 97 for the eigenproblem

$$\bar{y}'' + (1 + x)\bar{y}' + k^2\bar{y} = 0, \qquad \bar{y}(0) = \bar{y}(1) = 0$$

99. Work Problem 97 for the eigenproblem

$$\bar{y}'' + \bar{y}' + k^2(1 + x)\bar{y} = 0, \qquad \bar{y}(0) = \bar{y}(1) = 0$$

Applied Problems

Several applied problems from various disciplines are presented in this section. All these problems can be solved by any of the methods presented in this chapter. An infinite variety of exercises can be constructed by changing the numerical values of the parameters, the grid size Δx, and so on.

100. The temperature distribution in the wall of a pipe through which a hot liquid is flowing is given by the ODE

$$\frac{d^2T}{dr^2} + \frac{1}{r}\frac{dT}{dr} = 0, \qquad T(1) = 100 \text{ C and } T(2) = 0 \text{ C}$$

Determine the temperature distribution in the wall.

101. The pipe described in Problem 100 is cooled by convection on the outer surface. Thus, the heat conduction, $\dot{q}_{\text{cond}}$, at the outer wall is equal to the heat convection, $\dot{q}_{\text{conv}}$, to the surroundings:

$$\dot{q}_{\text{cond}} = -kA\frac{dT}{dr} = \dot{q}_{\text{conv}} = hA(T - T_a)$$

where the thermal conductivity $k = 100$ J/(s-m-K), the convective cooling coefficient $h = 500$ J/(s-m^2-K), and $T_a = 0$ C is the temperature of the surroundings. Determine the temperature distribution in the wall.

102. The temperature distribution in a cylindrical rod made of a radioactive isotope is governed by the ordinary differential equation

$$\frac{d^2T}{dr^2} + \frac{1}{r}\frac{dT}{dr} = 1 + \left(\frac{r}{R}\right)^2, \qquad T'(0) = 0 \text{ and } T(R) = 0$$

Solve this problem for $T(r)$, where $R = 1.0$.

103. The velocity distribution in the laminar boundary layer formed when an incompressible fluid flows over a flat plate is related to the solution of the ordinary differential equation

$$\frac{d^3f}{d\eta^3} + \frac{1}{2}f\frac{d^2f}{d\eta^2} = 0, \qquad f(0) = 1,\ f'(0) = 0, \quad \text{and} \quad f'(\eta) \to 1 \text{ as } \eta \to \infty$$

where f is a dimensionless stream function, the velocity u is proportional to $f'(\eta)$, and η is proportional to distance normal to the plate. Solve this problem for $f(\eta)$.

104. The velocity distribution in the mixing layer that forms when a laminar free jet issues into a stagnant atmosphere is related to the solution of the ordinary differential equation

$$\frac{d^3 f}{d\eta^3} + f\frac{df}{d\eta} + \left(\frac{df}{d\eta}\right)^2 = 0, \qquad f(0) = 0,\ f'(0) = 0,\ \text{and } f'(\eta) \rightarrow 0 \text{ as } \eta \rightarrow \infty$$

Solve this problem for $f(\eta)$.

105. The deflection of a simply supported and uniformly loaded beam is governed by the ordinary differential equation (for small deflections)

$$EI\frac{d^2 y}{dx^2} = -\frac{qLx}{2} + \frac{qx^2}{2}, \qquad y(0) = 0 \text{ and } y(L) = 0$$

where q is the uniform load per unit length, L is the length of the beam, I is the moment of inertia of the beam cross section, and E is the modulus of elasticity. For a rectangular beam, $I = wh^3/12$, where w is the width and h is the height. Consider a wooden beam (E = 10,000 kN/m^2) 5.0 m long, 5 cm wide, and 10 cm high, which is subjected to the uniform load q = 1500 N/m on the 5 cm face. Solve for the deflection $y(x)$.

106. When the load on the beam described in Problem 105 is applied on the 10 cm face, the deflection will be large. In that case, the governing differential equation is

$$\frac{EI(d^2y/dx^2)}{\left(1 + (dy/dx)^2\right)^{3/2}} = -\frac{qLx}{2} + \frac{qx^2}{2}$$

For the properties specified in Problem 105, determine $y(x)$.

PART III

PARTIAL DIFFERENTIAL EQUATIONS

Section

III.1 INTRODUCTION

Partial differential equations (PDEs) arise in all fields of engineering and science. Most real physical processes are governed by partial differential equations. In many cases, simplifying approximations are made to reduce the governing PDEs to ordinary differential equations (ODEs) or even to algebraic equations. However, because of the ever increasing requirement for more accurate modeling of physical processes, engineers and scientists are more and more required to solve the actual PDEs that govern the physical problem being investigated. Part III of this book is devoted to the solution of partial differential equations by *finite difference* methods.

Some general features of partial differential equations are discussed in this section. The three classes of PDEs (i.e., elliptic, parabolic, and hyperbolic PDEs) are introduced. The two types of physical problems (i.e., equilibrium and propagation problems) are discussed.

The objectives of Part III are (a) to present the general features of partial differential equations, (b) to discuss the relationship between the type of physical problem being solved, the classification of the corresponding governing PDE, and the type of numerical method required, and (c) to present examples to illustrate these concepts.

III.2 GENERAL FEATURES OF PARTIAL DIFFERENTIAL EQUATIONS

A partial differential equation (PDE) is an equation stating a relationship between a function of several independent variables and the partial derivatives of this function with respect to these independent variables. The symbol f represents a generic dependent variable throughout Part III. In most problems in engineering and science, the independent variables are either space (x, y, z) or space and time (x, y, z, t). The dependent variable depends on the physical problem being modeled. Examples of three simple partial differential equations having two independent variables are presented below:

$$\frac{\partial^2 f}{\partial x^2} + \frac{\partial^2 f}{\partial y^2} = 0 \tag{III.1}$$

$$\frac{\partial f}{\partial t} = \alpha \frac{\partial^2 f}{\partial x^2} \tag{III.2}$$

$$\frac{\partial^2 f}{\partial t^2} = c^2 \frac{\partial^2 f}{\partial x^2} \tag{III.3}$$

Equation (III.1) is the *Laplace* equation, Equation (III.2) is the *diffusion* equation, and Equation (III.3) is the *wave* equation. For simplicity of notation, Eqs. (III.1) to (III.3) usually will be written as

$$f_{xx} + f_{yy} = 0 \tag{III.4}$$

$$f_t = \alpha f_{xx} \tag{III.5}$$

$$f_{tt} = c^2 f_{xx} \tag{III.6}$$

where the subscripts denote partial differentiation.

The solution of a partial differential equation is that particular function $f(x, y)$ or $f(x, t)$ that satisfies the PDE in the domain of interest $D(x, y)$ or $D(x, t)$, respectively, and satisfies the conditions (initial-value, boundary-value, or both) specified on the boundaries of the domain of interest. In a very few special cases, the solution of a PDE can be expressed in closed form. In the majority of problems in engineering and science, the solution must be obtained by numerical methods. Such problems are the subject of Part III of this book.

Equations (III.4) to (III.6) are examples of partial differential equations in two independent variables, x and y, or x and t. Equation (III.4), which is the Laplace equation, in three independent variables is

$$f_{xx} + f_{yy} + f_{zz} = \nabla^2 f = 0 \tag{III.7}$$

where ∇^2 is the Laplacian operator, which in Cartesian coordinates is

$$\nabla^2 = \frac{\partial^2}{\partial x^2} + \frac{\partial^2}{\partial y^2} + \frac{\partial^2}{\partial z^2} \tag{III.8}$$

Equation (III.5), which is the diffusion equation, in four independent variables is

$$f_t = \alpha(f_{xx} + f_{yy} + f_{zz}) = \alpha\nabla^2 f \tag{III.9}$$

The parameter α is the *diffusion coefficient*. Equation III.6, which is the wave equation, in four independent variables is

$$f_{tt} = c^2(f_{xx} + f_{yy} + f_{zz}) = c^2\nabla^2 f \tag{III.10}$$

The parameter c is the wave propagation speed. Problems in two, three, and four independent variables occur throughout engineering and science.

Equations (III.4) to (III.10) are all *second-order* partial differential equations. The order of a PDE is determined by the highest-order derivative appearing in the equation. A large number of physical problems are governed by second-order PDEs. Some physical problems are governed by a first-order PDE of the form

$$af_t + bf_x = 0 \tag{III.11}$$

where a and b are constants. Other physical problems are governed by fourth-order PDEs such as

$$f_{xxxx} + f_{xxyy} + f_{yyyy} = 0 \tag{III.12}$$

Equations (III.4) to (III.12) are all *linear* partial differential equations. A linear PDE is one in which all the partial derivatives appear in linear form and none of the coefficients depends on the dependent variable. The coefficients may be functions of the independent variables, in which case the PDE is a linear, variable-coefficient PDE. For example,

$$af_t + bxf_x = 0 \tag{III.13}$$

where a and b are constants, is a variable-coefficient linear PDE, whereas Eq.

(III.4) to (III.12) are all linear PDEs. If the coefficients depend on the dependent variable, or the derivatives appear in a nonlinear form, then the PDE is nonlinear. For example,

$$ff_x + bf_y = 0 \tag{III.14}$$

$$af_x^2 + bf_y = 0 \tag{III.15}$$

are nonlinear PDEs.

Equations (III.4) to (III.15) are all *homogeneous* partial differential equations. An example of a nonhomogeneous PDE is given by

$$f_{xx} + f_{yy} + f_{zz} = \nabla^2 f = F(x, y, z) \tag{III.16}$$

Equation (III.16) is the *nonhomogeneous* Laplace equation, which is known as the *Poisson* equation. The nonhomogeneous term $F(x, y, z)$ is a forcing function, a source term, or a dissipation function, depending on the application. The appearance of a nonhomogeneous term in a partial differential equation does not change the general features of the PDE, nor does it usually change or complicate the numerical method of solution.

Equations (III.4) to (III.16) are all examples of a single partial differential equation with one dependent variable. Many physical problems are governed by a system of PDEs involving several dependent variables. For example, the two PDEs

$$af_t + bg_x = 0 \tag{III.17a}$$

$$Ag_t + Bf_x = 0 \tag{III.17b}$$

comprise a system of two partial differential equations in two independent variables (x and t) for determining the two functions $f(x, t)$ and $g(x, t)$. Systems containing many PDEs occur frequently, and systems containing higher-order PDEs occur occasionally. Systems of PDEs are generally more difficult to solve numerically than a single PDE.

As illustrated in the preceding discussion, a wide variety of partial differential equations exists. Each problem has its own special governing equation or equations and its own peculiarities, which must be considered individually. However, useful insights into the general features of PDEs can be obtained by studying three special cases. The first special case is the general quasi-linear (i.e., linear in the highest-order derivative) second-order nonhomogeneous PDE in two independent variables, which is

$$\boxed{Af_{xx} + Bf_{xy} + Cf_{yy} + Df_x + Ef_y + Ff = G} \tag{III.18}$$

where the coefficients A to C may depend on x, y, f, f_x, and f_y, the coefficients D to F may depend on x, y, and f, and the nonhomogeneous term G may depend on x and y. The second special case is the general quasi-linear first-order nonhomogeneous PDE in two independent variables

$$af_t + bf_x = c \tag{III.19}$$

where a, b, and c may depend on x, t, and f. The third special case is the system of two general quasi-linear first-order nonhomogeneous PDEs in two independent variables, which can be written as

$$af_t + bf_x + cg_t + dg_x = e \tag{III.20a}$$

$$Af_t + Bf_x + Cg_t + Dg_x = E \tag{III.20b}$$

where the coefficients a to d and A to D and the nonhomogeneous terms e and E may depend on x, t, f, and g. The general features of these three special cases are similar to the general features of all the PDEs discussed in this book. Consequently, these three special cases are studied thoroughly in the following sections.

III.3 CLASSIFICATION OF PARTIAL DIFFERENTIAL EQUATIONS

Physical problems are governed by many different partial differential equations. A few problems are governed by a single first-order PDE. Numerous problems are governed by a system of first-order PDEs. Some problems are governed by a single second-order PDE, and numerous problems are governed by a system of second-order PDEs. A few problems are governed by fourth-order PDEs. The classification of PDEs is most easily explained for a single second-order PDE. Consequently, in the following discussion, the general quasi-linear (i.e., linear in the highest-order derivative) second-order nonhomogeneous PDE in two independent variables [i.e., Eq. (III.18)] is classified first. The classification of the general quasi-linear first-order nonhomogeneous PDE in two independent variables [i.e., Eq. (III.19)] is studied next. Finally, the classification of the system of two quasi-linear first-order nonhomogeneous PDEs [i.e., Eq. (III.20)] is studied. The classification of higher-order PDEs, larger systems of PDEs, and PDEs having more than two independent variables is considerably more complicated.

The general quasi-linear second-order nonhomogeneous partial differential equation in two independent variables is [see Eq. (III.18)]

$$Af_{xx} + Bf_{xy} + Cf_{yy} + Df_x + Ef_y + Ff = G \tag{III.21}$$

The classification of Eq. (III.21) depends on the sign of the discriminant $B^2 - 4AC$

as follows:

$B^2 - 4AC$	**Classification**
negative	elliptic
zero	parabolic
positive	hyperbolic

The terminology *elliptic, parabolic,* and *hyperbolic* chosen to classify PDEs reflects the analogy between the form of the discriminant $B^2 - 4AC$ for PDEs and the form of the discriminant $B^2 - 4AC$ that classifies conic sections. Conic sections are described by the general second-order algebraic equation

$$Ax^2 + Bxy + Cy^2 + Dx + Ey + F = 0 \tag{III.22}$$

The type of curve represented by Eq. (III.22) depends on the sign of the discriminant $B^2 - 4AC$ as follows:

$B^2 - 4AC$	**Type of Curve**
negative	ellipse
zero	parabola
positive	hyperbola

The analogy to the classification of PDEs is obvious. There is no other significance to the terminology.

What is the significance of the above classification? What impact, if any, does the classification of a PDE have on the allowable or required initial and boundary conditions? Does the classification of a PDE have any effect on the choice of numerical method employed to solve the equation? These questions are discussed in this section, and the results are applied to physical problems in the next section.

The classification of a PDE is intimately related to the *characteristics* of the PDE. Characteristics are $(n - 1)$-dimensional hypersurfaces in n-dimensional hyperspace (where n is the number of independent variables) that have some very special features. The prefix *hyper* is used to denote spaces that can be of more than three dimensions, such as, $xyzt$ spaces, and curves and surfaces within those spaces. In two-dimensional space, which is the case considered here, characteristics are lines (curved, in general) in the solution domain along which signals, or information, propagate. In other words, information propagates through the solution domain along the characteristic curves. Discontinuities in the derivatives of the dependent variable (if they exist) propagate along the characteristic curves. If a PDE possesses real characteristics, then information propagates along these characteristics. If no real characteristics exist, then there are no preferred paths of information propagation. Consequently, the presence or absence of characteristics has a significant impact on the solution of a PDE (by both analytical and numerical methods).

A simple physical example can be used to illustrate the physical significance of characteristic curves. *Convection* is the process in which a physical property is carried (i.e., convected) through space by the motion of the medium occupying the space. Fluid flow is a common example of convection. The convection of a property, f, of a fluid particle in one dimension is governed by the convection equation

$$f_t + uf_x = 0 \tag{III.23}$$

where u is the convection velocity. A moving fluid particle carries (convects) its mass, momentum, and energy with it as it moves through space. The location $x(t)$ of the fluid particle is related to its velocity $u(t)$ by the relationship

$$\frac{dx}{dt} = u \tag{III.24}$$

The path of the fluid particle, called its *pathline,* is given by

$$x = x_0 + \int_{t_0}^{t} u(t)\,dt \tag{III.25}$$

The pathline is illustrated in Fig. III.1*a*.

Along the pathline, the convection equation [i.e., Eq. (III.23)] can be written as

$$f_t + uf_x = f_t + \frac{dx}{dt} f_x = \frac{df}{dt} = 0 \tag{III.26}$$

which can be integrated to yield f = Constant. Consequently, the fluid property f is convected along the pathline, which is the characteristic path associated with the convection equation. Equation (III.24), which is generally called the *characteristic* equation, is the differential equation of the characteristic curve. The physical significance of the pathline (i.e., the characteristic curve) as the path of propagation of the fluid property f is quite apparent for fluid convection.

To illustrate further the property of a characteristic curve as the path of propagation in a convection problem, consider the triangular property distribution illustrated in Figure III.1*b*. As the fluid particles move to the right at the constant convection velocity u, each particle carries with it its value of the property f.

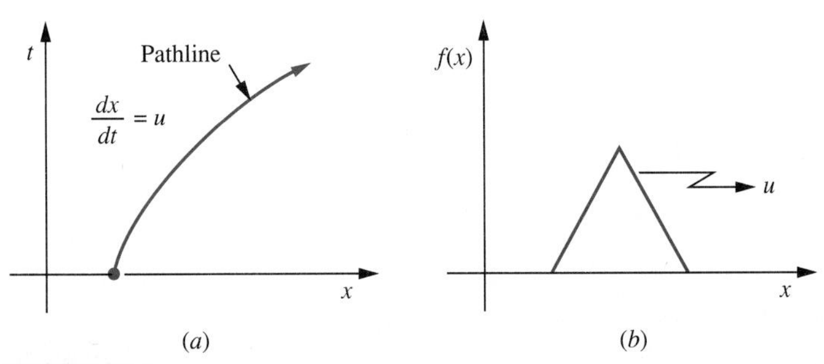

FIGURE III.1
Pathline as the characteristic for the convection equation: (*a*) pathline; (*b*) triangular property distribution.

Consequently, the triangular property distribution simply moves (i.e., convects) to the right at the constant convection velocity u, unchanged in magnitude and shape. The apex of the triangle, which is a point of discontinuous slope, convects as a discontinuity in slope at the convection velocity u. This simple convection example illustrates the significance of characteristic curves.

Let us return to the classification of Eq. (III.21). Several procedures exist for determining the characteristics, and hence the classification, of PDEs. Because discontinuities in the derivatives of the solution, if they exist, must propagate along the characteristics, one approach is to answer the following question: Are there any paths in the solution domain $D(x, y)$ passing through a general point P along which the second derivatives of $f(x, y)$, that is, f_{xx}, f_{xy}, and f_{yy}, are multivalued or discontinuous? Such paths, if they exist, are the paths of information propagation, that is, the characteristics.

One relationship for determining the three second derivatives of $f(x, y)$ is given by the partial differential equation itself, Eq. (III.21). Two more relationships are obtained by applying the chain rule to determine the total derivatives of f_x and f_y, which are themselves functions of x and y. Thus,

$$d(f_x) = f_{xx}\,dx + f_{xy}\,dy \tag{III.27a}$$

$$d(f_y) = f_{yx}\,dx + f_{yy}\,dy \tag{III.27b}$$

Equations (III.21) and (III.27) can be written in matrix form as follows:

$$\begin{bmatrix} A & B & C \\ dx & dy & 0 \\ 0 & dx & dy \end{bmatrix} \begin{bmatrix} f_{xx} \\ f_{xy} \\ f_{yy} \end{bmatrix} \begin{bmatrix} -Df_x - Ef_y - F + G \\ d(f_x) \\ d(f_y) \end{bmatrix} \tag{III.28}$$

Equation (III.28) can be solved by Cramer's rule to yield unique finite values of f_{xx}, f_{xy}, and f_{yy}, unless the determinant of the coefficient matrix vanishes. In that case, the second derivatives of $f(x, y)$ are either infinite, which is physically meaningless, or they are indeterminate, and thus multivalued or discontinuous.

Setting the determinant of the coefficient matrix of Eq. (III.28) equal to zero yields

$$A(dy)^2 - B(dx)(dy) + C(dx)^2 = 0 \tag{III.29}$$

Equation (III.29) is the *characteristic* equation corresponding to Eq. (III.21). Equation (III.29) can be solved by the quadratic formula to yield

$$\boxed{\frac{dy}{dx} = \frac{B \pm \sqrt{B^2 - 4AC}}{2A}} \tag{III.30}$$

Equation (III.30) is the differential equation for two families of curves in the xy plane, corresponding to the $\pm$ signs. Along these two families of curves, the second derivatives of $f(x, y)$ may be multivalued or discontinuous. These two families of curves, if they exist, are the characteristic curves of the original PDE, Eq. (III.21).

The two families of characteristic curves may be complex, real and repeated, or real and distinct, according to whether the discriminant $B^2 - 4AC$ is negative, zero, or positive, respectively. Accordingly, Eq. (III.21) is classified as follows:

$B^2 - 4AC$	**Characteristic Curves**	**Classification**
negative	complex	elliptic
zero	real and repeated	parabolic
positive	real and distinct	hyperbolic

Consequently, elliptic PDEs have no real characteristic curves, parabolic PDEs have one real repeated characteristic curve, and hyperbolic PDEs have two real distinct characteristic curves.

The presence of characteristic curves in the solution domain leads to the concepts of *domain of dependence* and *range of influence*. Consider a point P in the solution domain $D(x, y)$. The domain of dependence of point P is defined as the region of the solution domain upon which the solution at point P, $f(x_P, y_P) = f_P$, depends. In other words, f_P depends on everything that has happened in the domain of dependence. The range of influence of point P is defined as the region of the solution domain in which the solution $f(x, y)$ is influenced by the solution at point P. In other words, f_P influences the solution at all points in the range of influence.

Recall that parabolic and hyperbolic PDEs have real characteristic curves. Consequently, they have specific domains of dependence and ranges of influence. Elliptic PDEs, on the other hand, do not have real characteristic curves. Consequently, they have no specific domains of dependence or ranges of influence. In effect, the entire solution domain of an elliptic PDE is both the domain of dependence and the range of influence of every point in the solution domain. Figure III.2 illustrates the concepts of domain of dependence and range of influence for elliptic, parabolic, and hyperbolic PDEs.

Unlike the second-order PDE just discussed, a single first-order PDE is always hyperbolic. Consider the classification of the single general quasi-linear first-order nonhomogeneous PDE [Eq. (III.19)]

$$af_t + bf_x = c \tag{III.31}$$

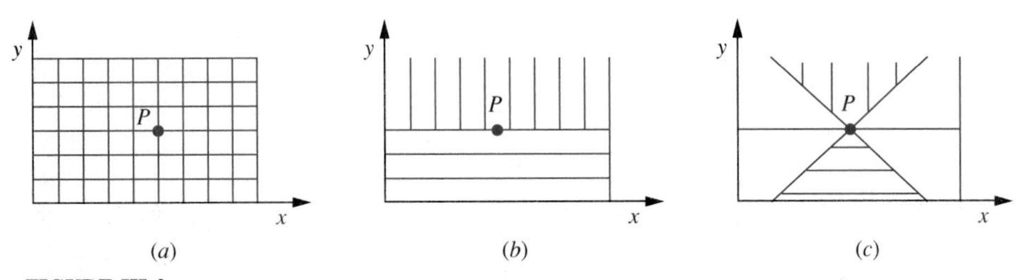

FIGURE III.2
Domain of dependence (horizontal hatching) and range of influence (vertical hatching) of PDEs: (*a*) elliptic PDE; (*b*) parabloic PDE; (*c*) hyperbolic PDE.

The characteristic curves, if they exist, are determined by answering the following question: Are there any paths in the solution domain $D(x, t)$ passing through a general point P along which the first derivatives of $f(x, t)$ are not uniquely determined? Such curves, if they exist, are the characteristics of Eq. (III.31).

One relationship for determining f_t and f_x is given by Eq. (III.31). Another relationship is given by the total derivative of $f(t, x)$:

$$df = f_t\,dt + f_x\,dx \tag{III.32}$$

Equations (III.31) and (III.32) can be written in matrix form as

$$\begin{bmatrix} a & b \\ dt & dx \end{bmatrix} \begin{bmatrix} f_t \\ f_x \end{bmatrix} = \begin{bmatrix} c \\ df \end{bmatrix} \tag{II.33}$$

As before, the partial derivatives f_t and f_x are uniquely determined unless the determinant of the coefficient matrix of Eq. (III.33) is zero. Setting that determinant equal to zero gives the characteristic equation, which is

$$a\,dx - b\,dt = 0 \tag{III.34}$$

Solving Eq. (III.34) for dx/dt gives

$$\boxed{\frac{dx}{dt} = \frac{b}{a}} \tag{III.35}$$

Equation (III.35) is the differential equation for a family of curves in the solution domain along which f_t and f_x may be multivalued. Since a and b are real functions, the characteristic curves always exist. Consequently, a single quasi-linear first-order PDE is always hyperbolic. The convection equation, Eq. (III.23), is an example of such a PDE.

As a third example, consider the classification of the system of two general quasi-linear first-order nonhomogeneous partial differential equations, Eq. (III.20):

$$af_t + bf_x + cg_t + dg_x = e \tag{III.36a}$$

$$Af_t + Bf_x + Cg_t + Dg_x = E \tag{III.36b}$$

The characteristic curves, if they exist, are determined by answering the following question: Are there any paths in the solution domain $D(x, t)$ that pass through a general point P along which the first derivatives of $f(x, t)$ and $g(x, t)$ are not uniquely determined? Such paths, if they exist, are the characteristics of Eq. (III.36).

Two relationships for determining the four first derivatives of $f(x, t)$ and $g(x, t)$ are given by Eq. (III.36). Two more relationships are given by the total derivatives of f and g:

$$df = f_t\,dt + f_x\,dx \tag{III.37a}$$

$$dg = g_t\,dt + g_x\,dx \tag{III.37b}$$

Equations (III.36) and (III.37), which comprise a system of four equations for determining f_t, f_x, g_t, and g_x, can be written in matrix form as follows:

$$\begin{bmatrix} a & b & c & d \\ A & B & C & D \\ dt & dx & 0 & 0 \\ 0 & 0 & dt & dx \end{bmatrix} \begin{bmatrix} f_t \\ f_x \\ g_t \\ g_x \end{bmatrix} = \begin{bmatrix} e \\ E \\ df \\ dg \end{bmatrix}$$

As before, the partial derivatives are uniquely determined unless the determinant of the coefficient matrix of Eq. (III.38) is zero. Setting that determinant equal to zero yields the characteristic equation, which is

$$(aC - Ac)(dx)^2 - (aD - Ad + bC - Bc)(dx)(dt) + (bD - Bd)(dt)^2 = 0 \quad \text{(III.39)}$$

Equation (III.39), which is a quadratic equation in dx/dt, may be written as

$$\overline{A}(dx)^2 - \overline{B}(dx)(dt) + \overline{C}(dt)^2 = 0 \quad \text{(III.40)}$$

where $\overline{A} = (aC - Ac)$, $\overline{B} = (aD - Ad + bC - Bc)$, and $\overline{C} = (bD - Bd)$. Equation (III.40) can be solved by the quadratic formula to yield

$$\boxed{\frac{dx}{dt} = \frac{\overline{B} \pm \sqrt{\overline{B}^2 - 4\overline{A}\,\overline{C}}}{2\overline{A}}} \quad \text{(III.41)}$$

Equation (III.41) is the differential equation for two families of curves in the xt plane, corresponding to the $\pm$ signs. Along these two families of curves, the first derivatives of $f(x, t)$ and $g(x, t)$ may be multivalued. These two families of curves, if they exist, are the characteristic curves of the original system of PDEs, Eq. (III.36). The slopes of the two families of characteristic curves may be complex, real and repeated, or real and distinct, according to whether the discriminant $\overline{B}^2 - 4\overline{A}\,\overline{C}$ is negative, zero, or positive, respectively. Accordingly, Eq. (III.36) is classified as follows:

$\overline{B}^2 - 4\overline{A}\,\overline{C}$	**Classification**
negative	elliptic
zero	parabolic
positive	hyperbolic

In summary, the physical interpretation of the classification of a partial differential equation can be explained in terms of its characteristics.

If real characteristics exist, preferred paths of information propagation exist. The speed of propagation of information through the solution domain depends on the slopes of the characteristic curves. Specific domains of dependence and ranges of influence exist for every point in the solution domain. Physical problems governed by PDEs that have real characteristics are *propagation* problems. Thus, parabolic and hyperbolic PDEs govern propagation problems.

If the slopes of the characteristics are complex, then no real characteristics exist and there are no preferred paths of information propagation. The domain of dependence and range of influence of every point is the entire solution domain. The solution at every point depends on the solution at all the other points, and the solution at each point influences the solution at all the other points. Since there are no curves along which the derivatives may be discontinuous, the solution throughout the entire solution domain must be continuous. Physical problems governed by PDEs that have complex characteristics are *equilibrium* problems. Thus, elliptic PDEs govern equilibrium problems. These concepts are related to the classification of physical problems in the next section.

III.4 CLASSIFICATION OF PHYSICAL PROBLEMS

Physical problems fall into one of the following three general classifications:

1. Equilibrium problems
2. Eigenproblems
3. Propagation problems

Each of these three types of physical problems has its own special features, its own particular type of governing partial differential equation, and its own special numerical solution methods. A clear understanding of these concepts is essential if meaningful numerical solutions are to be obtained.

Equilibrium Problems

Equilibrium problems are *steady state* problems in *closed* domains, $D(x, y)$, in which the solution $f(x, y)$ is governed by an elliptic PDE subject to boundary conditions specified at each point on the boundary B of the domain. Equilibrium problems are *jury* problems, in which the entire solution is passed on by a "jury" that requires satisfaction of all internal requirements (i.e., the PDE) and all the boundary conditions simultaneously.

As illustrated in the previous section, elliptic PDEs have no real characteristics. Thus, the solution at every point in the solution domain is influenced by the solution at all the other points, and the solution at each point influences the solution at all the other points. Consequently, equilibrium problems are solved numerically by *relaxation* methods.

A classical example of an equilibrium problem governed by an elliptic PDE is steady heat conduction in a solid (see Section III.5). The governing PDE is the Laplace equation

$$\nabla^2 T = 0 \tag{III.42}$$

where T is the temperature of the solid. In two dimensions, Eq. (III.42) is

$$T_{xx} + T_{yy} = 0 \tag{III.43}$$

Figure III.3 illustrates the closed solution domain $D(x, y)$ and its boundary B. Along the boundary B, the temperature T is subject to the boundary condition

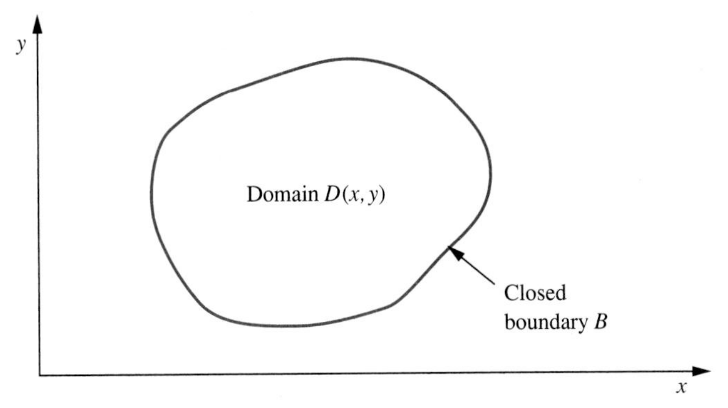

FIGURE III.3
Solution domain for an equilibrium problem governed by the elliptic Laplace equation.

$$aT + bT_n = c \tag{III.44}$$

at each point on the boundary, where T_n denotes the derivative normal to the boundary.

Equilibrium problems arise in all fields of engineering and science. Equilibrium problems in partial differential equations are analogous to boundary-value problems in ordinary differential equations, which are considered in Chapter 8.

Eigenproblems

Eigenproblems are special equilibrium problems in which the solution exists only for special values (i.e., *eigenvalues*) of a parameter of the problem. The eigenvalues are to be determined in addition to the corresponding equilibrium configuration of the system. Eigenproblems for PDEs are analogous to eigenproblems for ODEs, which are considered in Section 8.10. Eigenproblems for PDEs are not considered in this book.

Propagation Problems

Propagation problems are *initial-value* problems in *open* domains (open with respect to one of the independent variables) in which the solution $f(x, t)$ in the domain of interest $D(x, t)$ is marched forward from the initial state, guided and modified by boundary conditions. Propagation problems are governed by parabolic or hyperbolic PDEs. Propagation problems in PDEs are analogous to initial-value problems in ODEs, which are considered in Chapter 7.

The majority of propagation problems are unsteady problems. The diffusion equation, Eq. (III.5), is an example of an unsteady propagation problem, in which the initial property distribution at time t_0, $f(x, t_0) = F(x)$, is marched forward in time. A few propagation problems are steady problems. An example of a steady propagation problem is

$$f_y = \beta f_{xx} \tag{III.45}$$

in which the initial property distribution at location y_0, $f(x, y_0) = F(x)$, is marched forward in space in the y direction. The general features of these two PDEs are identical, with the space coordinate y in Eq. (III.45) taking on the character of the time coordinate t in the diffusion equation. Consequently, the marching direction in a steady, space-propagation problem is called the *time-like* direction, and the corresponding coordinate is called the *time-like* coordinate. The space direction in which diffusion occurs [i.e., the x direction in Eqs. (III.5) and (III.45)] is called the *space-like* direction, and the corresponding coordinate is called the *space-like* coordinate. In the present discussion, unsteady and steady propagation problems are considered simultaneously by considering the time coordinate t in the diffusion equation, Eq. (III.5), to be a *time-like* coordinate, so that Eq. (III.5) models both unsteady and steady propagation problems.

The solution of a propagation problem is subject to initial conditions specified at a particular value of the time-like coordinate, and boundary conditions, specified at each point on the space-like boundary. The domain of interest $D(x, t)$ is open in the direction of the time-like coordinate. Propagation problems are therefore initial-value problems, which are solved by marching methods.

A classical example of a propagation problem governed by a *parabolic* PDE is unsteady heat conduction in a solid (see Section III.6). The governing PDE is the diffusion equation

$$T_t = \alpha \nabla^2 T \tag{III.46}$$

where T is the temperature and α is the thermal diffusivity of the solid. In one space dimension, Eq. (III.46) is

$$T_t = \alpha T_{xx} \tag{III.47}$$

Figure III.4 illustrates the open solution domain $D(x, t)$ and its boundary B, which is composed of the initial time boundary and two physical boundaries. Since Eq. (III.47) is first-order in time, values of T must be specified along the initial time boundary. Since Eq. (III.47) is second-order in space, values of T must be specified along both space boundaries.

Parabolic PDEs have real repeated characteristics. As shown in Section III.6 for the diffusion equation, parabolic PDEs have specific domains of dependence and ranges of influence and infinite signal propagation speed. Thus, the solution at each point in the solution domain depends on a specific domain of dependence and influences the solution in a specific range of influence.

In two variables (e.g., space x and time t), parabolic PDEs have two real repeated families of characteristics. As illustrated in Fig. III.4, both families of characteristics have zero slope in the xt-plane, which corresponds to an infinite signal propagation speed. Consequently, parabolic PDEs behave like hyperbolic PDEs in the limit where the signal propagation speed is infinite. Thus, the solution at point P depends on the entire solution domain upstream of and including the horizontal line through point P itself. The solution at point P influences the entire solution domain downstream of and including the horizontal line through point P itself. However, the solution at point P does not depend on the solution

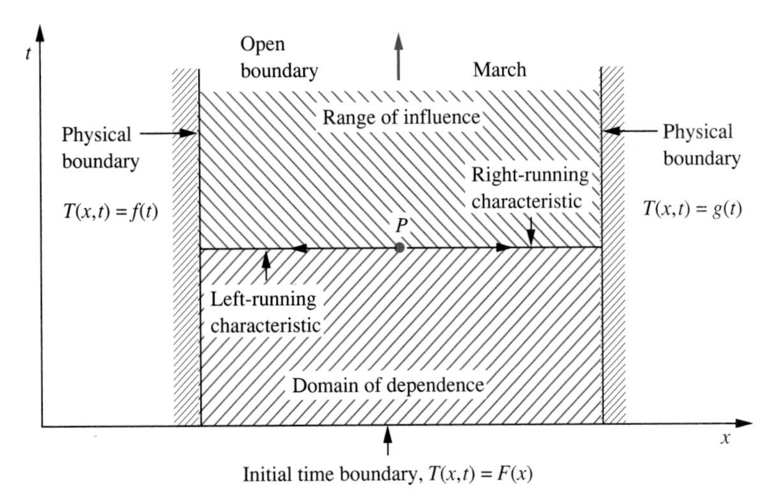

FIGURE III.4
Solution deomain for a propagation problem governed by the parabolic diffusion equation.

downstream of the horizontal line through point P, nor does the solution at point P influence the solution upstream of the horizontal line through point P. Numerical methods for solving propagation problems governed by parabolic PDEs must take the infinite signal propagation speed into account.

A classical example of a propagation problem governed by a *hyperbolic* PDE is acoustic wave propagation (see Section III.7). The governing PDE is the wave equation

$$P'_{tt} = a^2 \nabla^2 P' \tag{III.48}$$

where P' is the acoustic pressure (i.e., the pressure disturbance) and a is the speed of propagation of small disturbances (i.e., the speed of sound). In one space dimension, Eq. (III.48) is

$$P'_{tt} = a^2 P'_{xx} \tag{III.49}$$

Figure III.5 illustrates the open solution domain $D(x, t)$ and its boundary B, which is composed of the initial time boundary and two physical boundaries. Since Eq. (III.49) is second-order in time, initial values of both P' and P'_t must be specified along the initial time boundary. Since Eq. (III.49) is second-order in space, values of P' must be specified along both space boundaries.

Hyperbolic PDEs have real distinct characteristics. As shown in Section III.7 for the wave equation, hyperbolic PDEs have finite domains of dependence and ranges of influence and finite signal propagation speed. Thus, the solution at each point in the solution domain depends only on the solution in a finite domain of dependence and influences the solution only in a finite range of influence.

In two variables (e.g., space x and time t), hyperbolic PDEs have two real and distinct families of characteristics. For acoustic fields, these two real families of characteristics are the right-running (i.e., in the positive x direction) and left-

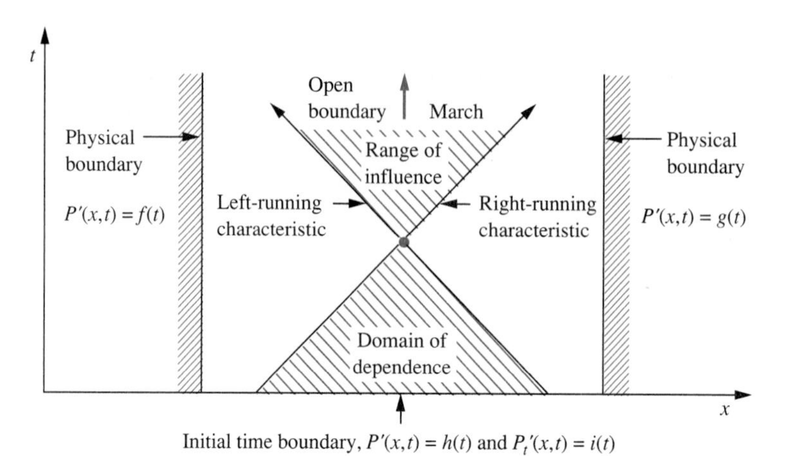

FIGURE III.5
Solution domain for a propagation problem governed by the hyperbolic wave equation.

running (i.e., in the negative x direction) acoustic waves. These characteristics are illustrated in Fig. III.5 at a particular point P. The characteristics have finite signal propagation speed, thus giving rise to a finite domain of dependence and a finite range of influence for each point in the solution domain. The solution at point P depends only on the solution within the domain of dependence defined by the characteristics from the upstream portion of the solution domain. The solution at point P influences only the solution within the range of influence defined by the downstream propagating characteristics. The portion of the solution domain outside the domain of dependence and the range of influence of point P neither influences the solution at point P nor depends on the solution at point P. Numerical methods for solving propagation problems governed by hyperbolic PDEs must take the finite signal propagation speed into account.

From the above discussion, it is seen that propagation problems are governed by either a parabolic or a hyperbolic PDE. These two types of PDEs exhibit many similarities (e.g., an open boundary, initial data, boundary data, domains of dependence, and ranges of influence). Both types of problems are solved numerically by marching methods. However, there are significant differences in propagation problems governed by parabolic PDEs and hyperbolic PDEs, due to the infinite signal propagation speed associated with parabolic PDEs and the finite signal propagation speed associated with hyperbolic PDEs. These differences must be accounted for when applying marching methods to these two types of partial differential equations.

Propagation problems arise in all fields of engineering and science. Propagation problems governed by hyperbolic PDEs are somewhat analogous to initial-value problems in ODEs, while propagation problems governed by parabolic PDEs share some of the features of both initial-value and boundary-value problems in ODEs. Table III.1 summarizes the general features of the PDEs presented in this section.

TABLE III.1
General features of partial differential equations

	Elliptic	Parabolic	Hyberbolic
Type of physical problem	Equilibrium	Propagation	Propagation
Characteristics	Complex	Real repeated	Real distinct
Signal propagation speed	Undefined	Infinite	Finite
Domain of dependence	Entire solution domain	Present and entire past solution domain	Past solution domain between characteristics
Range of influence	Entire solution domain	Present and entire future solution domain	Future solution domain between characteristics
Type of numerical method	Relaxation	Marching	Marching

III.5 ELLIPTIC PARTIAL DIFFERENTIAL EQUATIONS

A classical example of an elliptic PDE is the Laplace equation:

$$\nabla^2 f = 0 \tag{III.50}$$

The Laplace equation applies to problems in such areas as ideal fluid flow, mass diffusion, heat conduction, and electrostatics. In the following discussion, the general features of the Laplace equation are illustrated for the problem of steady two-dimensional heat conduction in a solid.

Consider the differential cube of solid material illustrated in Fig. III.6. Heat flow in a solid is governed by Fourier's law of conduction, which states that

$$\dot{q} = -kA\frac{dT}{dn} \tag{III.51}$$

where $\dot{q}$ is the energy transfer per unit time (J/s), T is the temperature (K), A is the area across which the energy flows (m^2), dT/dn is the temperature gradient normal to the area A (K/m), and k is the thermal conductivity of the solid (J/m-s-K), which is a physical property of the solid material. The net rate of flow of energy into the solid in the x direction is

$$\dot{q}_{\text{Net},x} = \dot{q}(x) - \dot{q}(x+dx) = \dot{q}(x) - \left(\dot{q}(x) + \frac{\partial \dot{q}(x)}{\partial x}dx\right) = -\frac{\partial \dot{q}(x)}{\partial x}dx \tag{III.52}$$

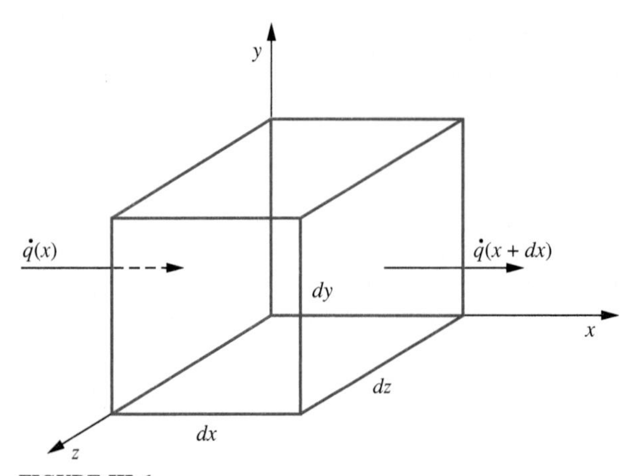

FIGURE III.6
Physical model of heat conduction.

Introducting Eq. (III.51) into Eq. (III.52) yields

$$\dot{q}_{\text{Net},x} = -\frac{\partial}{\partial x}\left(-kA\frac{\partial T}{\partial x}\right)dx = \frac{\partial}{\partial x}\left(k\frac{\partial T}{\partial x}\right)d\mathcal{V} \tag{III.53}$$

where $d\mathcal{V} = A\,dx$ is the volume of the differential cube of solid material. Similarly,

$$\dot{q}_{\text{Net},y} = \frac{\partial}{\partial y}\left(k\frac{\partial T}{\partial y}\right)d\mathcal{V} \tag{III.54}$$

$$\dot{q}_{\text{Net},z} = \frac{\partial}{\partial z}\left(k\frac{\partial T}{\partial z}\right)d\mathcal{V} \tag{III.55}$$

For steady heat flow, there is no net change in the amount of energy stored in the solid, so the sum of the net rate of flow of energy in the three directions is zero. Thus,

$$\frac{\partial}{\partial x}\left(k\frac{\partial T}{\partial x}\right) + \frac{\partial}{\partial y}\left(k\frac{\partial T}{\partial y}\right) + \frac{\partial}{\partial z}\left(k\frac{\partial T}{\partial z}\right) = 0 \tag{III.56}$$

Equation (III.56) governs the steady conduction of heat in a solid. When the thermal conductivity k is constant (i.e., neither a function of temperature nor location), Eq. (III.56) simplifies to

$$\boxed{T_{xx} + T_{yy} + T_{zz} = \nabla^2 T = 0} \tag{III.57}$$

which is the Laplace equation.

For steady two-dimensional heat conduction, Eq. (III.57) becomes

$$T_{xx} + T_{yy} = 0 \tag{III.58}$$

In terms of the general second-order PDE defined by Eq. (III.21), $A = 1$, $B = 0$, and $C = 1$. The discriminant $B^2 - 4AC$ is

$$B^2 - 4AC = 0^2 - 4(1)(1) = -4 < 0 \tag{III.59}$$

Consequently, Eq. (III.58) is an elliptic PDE.

The characteristics associated with Eq. (III.58) are determined by performing a characteristic analysis. In this case, Eq. (III.28) becomes

$$\begin{bmatrix} 1 & 0 & 1 \\ dx & dy & 0 \\ 0 & dx & dy \end{bmatrix} \begin{bmatrix} T_{xx} \\ T_{xy} \\ T_{yy} \end{bmatrix} = \begin{bmatrix} 0 \\ d(T_x) \\ d(T_y) \end{bmatrix} \tag{III.60}$$

The characteristic equation corresponding to Eq. (III.58) is determined by setting the determinant of the coefficient matrix of Eq. (III.60) equal to zero and solving the resulting equation for the slopes of the characteristic curves. Thus,

$$(1)(dy)^2 + (1)(dx)^2 = 0 \tag{III.61}$$

$$\frac{dy}{dx} = \pm\sqrt{-1} \tag{III.62}$$

Equation (III.62) shows that there are no real characteristics associated with the steady two-dimensional heat conduction equation. Physically, this implies that there are no preferred paths of signal propagation, and that the domain of dependence and range of influence of every point is the entire solution domain. The temperature at every point depends on the temperature at all the other points, including the boundaries of the solution domain, and the temperature at each point influences the temperature at all the other points. The temperature distribution is continuous throughout the solution domain because there are no paths along which the derivative of temperature may be discontinuous. The domain of dependence and the range of influence of point P are illustrated schematically in Fig. III.7.

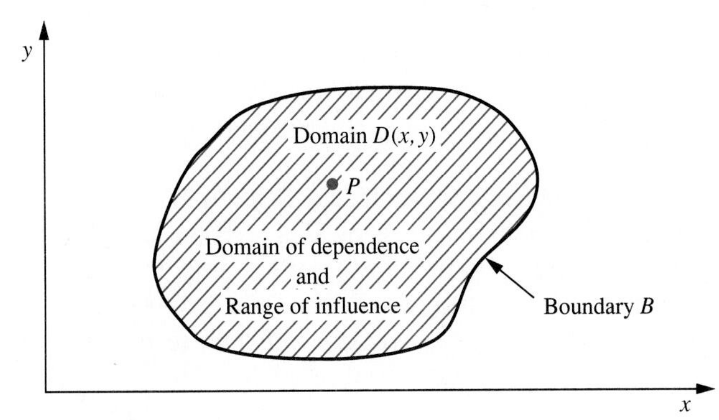

FIGURE III.7
Solution domain for an elliptic problem.

Another classical example of an elliptic PDE is the Poisson equation, which is the nonhomogeneous Laplace equation. Consider the probelm of steady heat conduction in a solid with internal energy generation $\dot{E}$(J/s) given by

$$\dot{E} = \dot{Q}(x, y, z)\, d\mathcal{V} \tag{III.63}$$

where $\dot{Q}$ is the energy generation rate per unit volume (J/m^3-s). For steady heat flow, the sum of the energy transferred to the solid by conduction and the internal energy generation must equal zero. Thus, Eq. (III.56) becomes

$$\frac{\partial}{\partial x}\left(k\frac{\partial T}{\partial x}\right) + \frac{\partial}{\partial y}\left(k\frac{\partial T}{\partial y}\right) + \frac{\partial}{\partial z}\left(k\frac{\partial T}{\partial z}\right) + \dot{Q} = 0 \tag{III.64}$$

When the thermal conductivity k is constant (i.e., neither a function of temperature nor location), Eq. (III.64) becomes

$$\boxed{T_{xx} + T_{yy} + T_{zz} = \nabla^2 T = -\frac{\dot{Q}}{k}} \tag{III.65}$$

Equation (III.65) is the Poisson equation. The presence of the nonhomogeneous (i.e., source) term $\dot{Q}/k$ does not affect the classification of the nonhomogeneous Laplace equation. All of the general features of the Laplace equation discussed above apply to the Poisson equation.

In summary, steady heat conduction is an equilibrium problem and must be solved by relaxation methods. The PDE governing steady heat conduction is a classical example of an elliptic PDE.

III.6 PARABOLIC PARTIAL DIFFERENTIAL EQUATIONS

A classical example of a parabolic PDE is the diffusion equation:

$$f_t = \alpha \nabla^2 f \tag{III.66}$$

The diffusion equation applies to problems in such areas as mass diffusion, momentum diffusion, and heat conduction. The general features of the diffusion equation are illustrated for the problem of unsteady one-dimensional heat conduction in a solid.

Consider the heat conduction analysis presented in Section III.5. The net flow of heat in the x, y, and z directions is given by Eqs. (III.53) to (III.55), respectively. For steady heat flow, there is no net change in the amount of energy stored in the solid, so the sum of the net heat flow components is zero. In an unsteady situation, however, there can be a net change with time in the amount of energy stored in the solid. The energy dE (J) stored in the solid mass dm (kg) is given by

$$dE_{\text{stored}} = dm\, CT = \rho\, d\mathcal{V} CT = \rho CT\, d\mathcal{V} \tag{III.67}$$

where ρ is the density of the solid material (kg/m^3), T is the temperature (K), $d\mathcal{V}$ is the volume (m^3), and C is the specific heat (J/kg-K), which is a physical property of the solid material. The sum of the net heat flow components must equal the time rate of change of the stored energy. Thus,

$$\frac{\partial(\rho CT)}{\partial t} = \frac{\partial}{\partial x}\left(k\frac{\partial T}{\partial x}\right) + \frac{\partial}{\partial y}\left(k\frac{\partial T}{\partial y}\right) + \frac{\partial}{\partial z}\left(k\frac{\partial T}{\partial z}\right) \tag{III.68}$$

Equation (III.68) governs the unsteady conduction of heat in a solid. When the thermal conductivity k, density ρ, and specific heat C are all constant (i.e., neither functions of temperature nor position), Eq. (III.68) simplifies to

$$\boxed{T_t = \alpha(T_{xx} + T_{yy} + T_{zz}) = \alpha\nabla^2 T} \tag{III.69}$$

where $\alpha = (k/\rho C)$ is the thermal diffusivity (m^2/s). Equation (III.69) is the diffusion equation.

For unsteady one-dimensional heat conduction, Eq. (III.69) becomes

$$T_t = \alpha T_{xx} \tag{III.70}$$

In terms of the general second-order PDE defined by Eq. (III.21), $A = \alpha$, $B = 0$, and $C = 0$. The discriminant $B^2 - 4AC$ is

$$B^2 - 4AC = 0^2 - 4(\alpha)(0) = 0 \tag{III.71}$$

Consequently, Eq. (III.70) is a parabolic PDE.

The characteristics associated with Eq. (III.70) are determined by performing a characteristic analysis. In this case, Eq. (III.28) becomes

$$\begin{bmatrix} \alpha & 0 & 0 \\ dx & dt & 0 \\ 0 & dx & dt \end{bmatrix} \begin{bmatrix} T_{xx} \\ T_{xt} \\ T_{tt} \end{bmatrix} = \begin{bmatrix} T_t \\ d(T_x) \\ d(T_t) \end{bmatrix} \tag{III.72}$$

The characteristic equation corresponding to Eq. (III.70) is determined by setting the determinant of the coefficient matrix of Eq. (III.72) equal to zero and solving for the slopes of the characteristic curves. In the present case, this yields

$$\alpha\, dt^2 = 0 \tag{III.73}$$

$$dt = \pm 0 \tag{III.74}$$

$$t = \text{Constant} \tag{III.75}$$

Equation (III.74) shows that there are two real repeated roots associated with the characteristic equation, and Eq. (III.75) shows that the characteristics are lines of constant time. The speed of propagation of information along these characteristic curves is

$$c = \frac{dx}{dt} = \frac{dx}{\pm 0} = \pm\infty \tag{III.76}$$

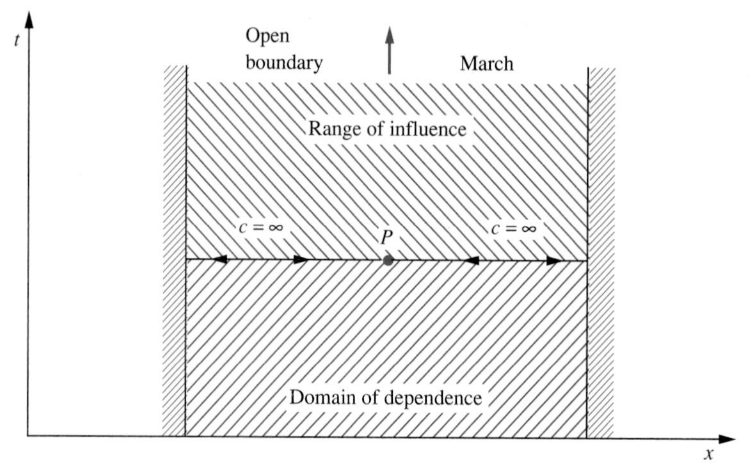

FIGURE III.8
Solution domain for a hyperbolic problem.

Consequently, signals propagate at an infinite speed along lines of constant time. This situation is illustrated schematically in Fig. III.8. The information at point P propagates at an infinite speed in both directions. Consequently, the temperature at point P depends on the temperature at all other points in physical space at all times preceding and including the current time, and the temperature at point P influences the temperature at all other points in physical space at all times after and including the current time. In other words, the domain of dependence of point P is the finite region ahead of and including the current time line. The range of influence of point P is the semi-infinite region after and including the current time line. In this regard, the diffusion equation behaves somewhat like an elliptic PDE at each time level.

In summary, unsteady heat conduction is a propagation problem which must be solved by marching methods. The PDE governing unsteady heat conduction is a classical example of a parabolic PDE.

III.7 HYPERBOLIC PARTIAL DIFFERENTIAL EQUATIONS

A classical example of a hyperbolic PDE is the wave equation

$$f_{tt} = c^2 \nabla^2 f \tag{III.77}$$

The wave equation applies to problems in such areas as vibrations, electrostatics, gas dynamics, and acoustics. The general features of the wave equation are illustrated for the problem of unsteady one-dimensional acoustic wave propagation.

Fluid flow is governed by the law of conservation of mass (the continuity equation), Newton's second law of motion (the momentum equation), and the first law of thermodynamics (the energy equation). As shown in any text on fluid dynamics [e.g., Fox and McDonald (1985) or Zucrow and Hoffman (1976)], those basic physical laws yield the following system of quasi-linear first-order PDEs:

$$\rho_t + \nabla \cdot (\rho \mathbf{V}) = 0 \tag{III.78}$$

$$\rho \mathbf{V}_t + \rho(\mathbf{V} \cdot \nabla)\mathbf{V} + \nabla P = 0 \tag{III.79}$$

$$P_t + \mathbf{V} \cdot \nabla P - a^2(\rho_t + \mathbf{V} \cdot \nabla \rho) = 0 \tag{III.80}$$

where ρ is the fluid density (kg/m^3), $\mathbf{V}$ is the fluid velocity vector (m/s), P is the static pressure (N/m^2), and a is the speed of propagation of small disturbances (m/s) (i.e., the speed of sound). Equations (III.78) to (III.80) are restricted to the flow of a pure substance with no body forces or transport phenomena (i.e., no mass, momentum, or energy diffusion). For unsteady one-dimensional flow, Eqs. (III.78) to (III.80) are

$$\rho_t + \rho u_x + u \rho_x = 0 \tag{III.81}$$

$$\rho u_t + \rho u u_x + P_x = 0 \tag{III.82}$$

$$P_t + u P_x - a^2(\rho_t + u \rho_x) = 0 \tag{III.83}$$

Equations (III.81) to (III.83) are more general examples of the simple one-dimensional convection equation

$$f_t + u f_x = 0 \tag{III.84}$$

where the property f is being convected by the velocity u through the solution domain $D(x, t)$. Equation (III.84) in three independent variables is

$$f_t + u f_x + v f_y + w f_z = f_t + \mathbf{V} \cdot \nabla f = \frac{Df}{Dt} = 0 \tag{III.85}$$

where u, v, and w are the velocity components in the x, y, and z directions, respectively, and the vector operator D/Dt is called the *substantial derivative*:

$$\frac{D}{Dt} = \frac{\partial}{\partial t} + u \frac{\partial}{\partial x} + v \frac{\partial}{\partial y} + w \frac{\partial}{\partial z} = \frac{\partial}{\partial t} + \mathbf{V} \cdot \nabla \tag{III.86}$$

Equations (III.81) and (III.83) are frequently combined to eliminate the derivatives of density. Thus,

$$P_t + u P_x + \rho a^2 u_x = 0 \tag{III.87}$$

Equations (III.81) to (III.83), or Eqs. (III.82) and (III.87), are classical examples of a system of nonlinear first-order PDEs.

Acoustics is the science devoted to the study of the motion of small amplitude disturbances in a fluid medium. Consider the classical case of infinitesimally small perturbations in velocity, pressure, and density in a stagnant fluid. In that case,

$$u = u_0 + u' = u', \qquad P = P_0 + P', \qquad \rho = \rho_0 + \rho', \qquad a = a_0 + a' \tag{III.88}$$

where u_0, P_0, ρ_0, and a_0 are the undisturbed properties of the fluid, and u', P', ρ', and a' are infinitesimal perturbations. For a stagnant fluid, $u_0 = 0$. Substituting Eq. (III.88) into Eqs. (III.82) and (III.87) and neglecting all products of perturbation quantities yields the following system of linear PDEs:

$$\rho_o u'_t + P'_x = 0 \tag{III.89}$$

$$P'_t + \rho_0 a_0^2 u'_x = 0 \tag{III.90}$$

Equations (III.89) and (III.90) can be combined to solve explicitly for either the pressure perturbation P' or the velocity perturbation u'. Differentiating Eq. (III.89) with respect to x and Eq. (III.90) with respect to t and combining the results to eliminate u'_{xt} yields the wave equation for the pressure perturbation P'

$$\boxed{P'_{tt} = a_0^2 P'_{xx}} \tag{III.91}$$

Differentiating Eq. (III.89) with respect to t and Eq. (III.90) with respect to x and combining the results to eliminate P'_{xt} yields the wave equation for the velocity perturbation u':

$$\boxed{u'_{tt} = a_0^2 u'_{xx}} \tag{III.92}$$

Equations (III.91) and (III.92) show that the properties of a linearized acoustic field are governed by the wave equation. In terms of the general second-order PDE defined by Eq. (III.21), $A = 1$, $B = 0$, and $C = -a_0^2$. The discriminant $B^2 - 4AC$ is

$$B^2 - 4AC = 0 - 4(1)(-a_0^2) = 4a_0^2 > 0 \tag{III.93}$$

Consequently, Eqs. (III.91) and (III.92) are hyperbolic PDEs.

Since Eqs. (III.91) and (III.92) both involve the same differential operators [i.e., $()_{tt} = a_0^2()_{xx}$], they have the same characteristics. Consequently, it is necessary to study only one of them, so Eq. (III.91) is chosen. The characteristics associated with Eq. (III.91) are determined by performing a characteristic analysis. In this case, Eq. (III.28) becomes

$$\begin{bmatrix} 1 & 0 & -a_0^2 \\ dt & dx & 0 \\ 0 & dt & dx \end{bmatrix} \begin{bmatrix} P'_{tt} \\ P'_{xt} \\ P'_{xx} \end{bmatrix} = \begin{bmatrix} 0 \\ d(P'_x) \\ d(P'_t) \end{bmatrix} \tag{III.94}$$

The characteristic equation corresponding to Eq. (III.91) is determined by setting the determinant of the coefficient matrix of Eq. (III.94) to zero and solving for the slopes of the characteristic curves. This yields

$$(dx)^2 - a_0^2(dt)^2 = 0 \tag{III.95}$$

Equation (III.95) is a quadratic equation for dx/dt. Solving for dx/dt gives

$$\frac{dx}{dt} = \pm a_0 \tag{III.96}$$

$$x = x_0 \pm a_0 t \tag{III.97}$$

Equation (III.96) shows that there are two distinct real roots associated with the characteristic equation, and Eq. (III.97) shows that the characteristics are straight lines having the slopes $\pm 1/a_0$ in the xt-plane. The speed of propagation of information along these characteristic lines is

$$c = \frac{dx}{dt} = \pm a_0 \tag{III.98}$$

Consequently, signals propagate at the acoustic speed a_0 along the characteristic lines. This situation is illustrated schematically in Fig. III.9. Information at point P propagates at a finite rate in physical space. Consequently, the perturbation pressure at point P depends only upon the solution within the finite domain of dependence illustrated in Fig. III.9. Likewise, the perturbation pressure at point P influences the solution only within the finite range of influence illustrated in Fig. III.9. The finite speed of propagation of information and the finite domain of dependence and range of influence must be accounted for when solving hyperbolic PDEs.

Equations (III.89) and (III.90) are examples of a system of two coupled first-order convection equations of the general form

$$f_t + a g_x = 0 \tag{III.99a}$$

$$g_t + a f_x = 0 \tag{III.99b}$$

Differentiating Eq. (III.99*a*) with respect to t, differentiating Eq. (III.99*b*) with

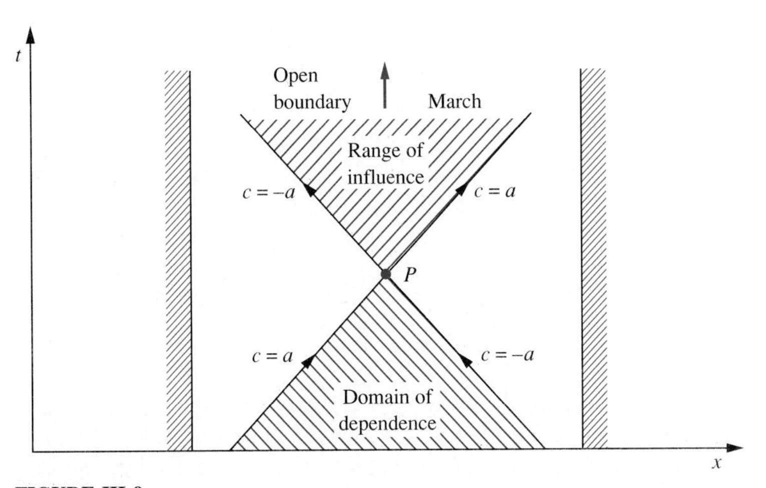

FIGURE III.9
Solution domain for a hyperbolic problem.

respect to x and multiplying by a, and subtracting yields the wave equation:

$$f_{tt} = a^2 f_{xx} \tag{III.100}$$

Consequently, the second-order wave equation can be interpreted as a coupled system of two first-order convection equations.

Nonlinear one-dimensional wave motion in a flowing fluid is governed by Eqs. (III.82) and (III.87), which are renumbered and repeated below:

$$\rho u_t + \rho u u_x + P_x = 0 \tag{III.101a}$$

$$\rho a^2 u_x + P_t + u P_x = 0 \tag{III.101b}$$

Equation (III.101) comprises two equations for determining the partial derivatives of u and P. Two more relationships are given by the total derivatives of u and P:

$$\begin{aligned} du &= u_t\,dt + u_x\,dx \\ dP &= P_t\,dt + P_x\,dx \end{aligned} \tag{III.102}$$

Writing Eqs. (III.101) and (III.102) in matrix form yields

$$\begin{bmatrix} \rho & \rho u & 0 & 1 \\ 0 & \rho a^2 & 1 & u \\ dt & dx & 0 & 0 \\ 0 & 0 & dt & dx \end{bmatrix} \begin{bmatrix} u_t \\ u_x \\ P_t \\ P_x \end{bmatrix} = \begin{bmatrix} 0 \\ 0 \\ du \\ dP \end{bmatrix} \tag{III.103}$$

The characteristic equation is determined by setting the determinant of the coefficient matrix of Eq. (III.103) equal to zero. The result is

$$-\rho(dx)(dx - u\,dt) + (dt)\big(\rho u(dx - u\,dt) + \rho a^2 dt\big) = 0 \tag{III.104}$$

Equation (III.104) is a quadratic equation for dx/dt. Rearranging Eq. (III.104) yields

$$(dx)^2 - 2u(dx)(dt) + (u^2 - a^2)(dt)^2 = 0 \tag{III.105}$$

Solving Eq. (III.105) for dx/dt by the quadratic formula gives

$$\frac{dx}{dt} = u \pm a \tag{III.106}$$

Equation (III.106) shows that there are two distinct real roots associated with the characteristic equation. However, in the nonlinear fluid flow case, u and a are not constant, so the characteristics are curved lines that depend on the solution itself. The speed of propagation of information along the characteristic curves is

$$c = \frac{dx}{dt} = u \pm a \tag{III.107}$$

Consequently, at each point in the flow, signals propagate at the local acoustic speed a with respect to the local fluid velocity u, and at the absolute local speeds $u \pm a$ with respect to the fixed coordinate system. The concepts illustrated in Fig. III.9 still apply in a qualitative sense, but the straight characteristic lines are replaced by the curved characteristic lines.

In summary, unsteady wave motion is a propagation problem, which must be solved by marching methods. The wave equation governing unsteady wave motion is a classical example of a hyperbolic PDE.

III.8 THE CONVECTION-DIFFUSION EQUATION

The Laplace and Poisson equations, the diffusion equation, and the convection and wave equations, presented in Sections III.5 to III.7, respectively, model many physical processes in engineering and science. The Laplace and Poisson equations and the diffusion equation govern steady and unsteady diffusion processes, respectively. The convection and wave equations govern convection processes. When convection and diffusion are both present in a physical process, the convection–diffusion equation models the physical process. Thus,

$$\boxed{f_t + \mathbf{V} \cdot \nabla f = \alpha \nabla^2 f} \tag{III.108}$$

For an unsteady one-dimensional convection–diffusion problem, Eq. (III.108) yields

$$f_t + u f_x = \alpha f_{xx} \tag{III.109}$$

which is a second-order PDE. In terms of the general second-order PDE defined by Eq. (III.21), $A = \alpha$, $B = 0$, and $C = 0$. The discriminant $B^2 - 4AC = 0$. Consequently, Eq. (III.109) is a parabolic PDE. These results are the same as the results obtained in Section III.6 for the diffusion equation. Performing a characteristic analysis of Eq. (III.109) yields $dt = \pm 0$, which is the same result obtained in Eq. (III.74) for the diffusion equation. However, as shown in Section III.3, convection is a hyperbolic process with the distinct characteristic curve

$$\frac{dx}{dt} = u \tag{III.110}$$

This result is not found in a classical characteristic analysis of the convection–diffusion equation, but the convection process is obviously present. How is this apparent loss of the convection characteristic explained?

The explanation is straightforward. In the classical approach to classifying a PDE, the question asked is: Are there any paths along which the highest-order derivatives can be discontinuous? If so, information is propagated along those paths by the highest-order derivatives, which in the case of the convection–diffusion equation are the second derivatives. A second question must also be asked: Are there any paths along which the lower-order derivatives can be discontinuous if they alone are present? If so, information can be propagated along those paths by the lower-order derivatives, which in the case of the convection–diffusion equation are the first derivatives. With this expanded interpretation, it is clear that the convection–diffusion equation, although formally parabolic, propagates information by both convection and diffusion.

III.9 INITIAL VALUES AND BOUNDARY CONDITIONS

A differential equation governs a family of solutions. A particular member of the family of solutions is specified by the auxiliary conditions imposed on the differential equation.

For steady equilibrium problems, the auxiliary conditions consist of boundary conditions on the entire boundary of the closed solution domain. Three types of boundary conditions can be imposed:

1. *Dirichlet* boundary condition: the value of the function is specified.

$$f \text{ is specified on the boundary} \tag{III.111}$$

2. *Neumann* boundary condition: the value of the derivative normal to the boundary is specified.

$$\frac{\partial f}{\partial n} \text{ is specified on the boundary} \tag{III.112}$$

3. *Mixed* boundary condition: a combination of the function and its normal derivative is specified on the boundary.

$$af + b\frac{\partial f}{\partial n} \text{ is specified on the boundary} \tag{III.113}$$

One of the above types of boundary conditions must be specified on each boundary of the solution domain. Different types of boundary conditions can be specified on different portions of the boundary.

For unsteady or steady propagation problems, the auxiliary conditions consist of an initial condition (or conditions) along the time (or time-like) boundary and boundary conditions on the physical boundaries of the solution domain. No auxiliary conditions can be applied on the open boundary in the time (or time-like) direction. For a PDE containing a first-order time (or time-like) derivative, one initial condition is required along the time (or time-like) boundary:

$$f(x, y, z, 0) = F(x, y, z) \text{ on the time boundary} \tag{III.114}$$

For a PDE containing a second-order time (or time-like) derivative, two initial conditions are required along the time (or time-like) boundary:

$$f(x, y, z, 0) = F(x, y, z) \text{ on the time boundary} \tag{III.115a}$$

$$f_t(x, y, z, 0) = G(x, y, z) \text{ on the time boundary} \tag{III.115b}$$

The required boundary conditions on the physical boundaries of the solution domain can be of the Dirichlet type [Eq. (III.111)], the Neumann type [Eq. (III.112)], or the mixed type [Eq. (III.113)]. Different types of boundary conditions can be specified on different portions of the boundary.

Proper specifications of the type and number of auxiliary conditions is a necessary condition to obtain a well-posed problem, as discussed in Section III.10.

III.10 WELL-POSED PROBLEMS

The general features of partial differential equations are discussed in the preceding sections. Elliptic PDEs govern equilibrium problems in closed domains, where no real characteristics exist. Parabolic PDEs govern propagation problems in open domains where real repeated characteristics exist. Hyperbolic PDEs govern propagation problems in open domains where real distinct characteristics exist. In all three cases, auxiliary conditions (i.e., initial values and boundary conditions) are required to specify a particular solution of a PDE. The interrelationship between the type of PDE, the auxiliary data, and whether or not a solution exists and is unique, gives rise to the concept of a *well-posed* problem.

Hadamard (1923) states that a physical problem is well-posed if its solution exists, is unique, and depends continuously on the boundary data and (for propogation problems) the initial data.

For an elliptic PDE, the solution domain $D(x, y)$ must be closed, and continuous boundary conditions must be specified along the entire physical boundary B. The boundary conditions may be of three types: Dirichlet boundary conditions, Neumann boundary conditions, or mixed boundary conditions.

For a parabolic PDE, the solution domain $D(x, t)$ must be open in the time (or time-like) direction, initial data must be specified along the time (or time-like) boundary, and continuous boundary conditions must be specified along the physical boundaries of the solution domain. The boundary conditions can be of the Dirichlet type, the Neumann type, or the mixed type.

For a hyperbolic PDE, the solution domain $D(x, t)$ must be open in the time (or time-like) direction, initial data must be specified along the time (or time-like) boundary, and continuous boundary conditions must be specified along the physical boundaries of the solution domain. The boundary conditions can be of the Dirichlet type, the Neumann type, or the mixed type. For a hyperbolic PDE, the initial data cannot be specified along only one characteristic curve (or surface). A pure initial-value problem (the Cauchy problem) can be defined for a hyperbolic PDE by specifying initial data along several characteristic curves (or surfaces). An initial–boundary-value problem is defined by specifying initial data along a noncharacteristic curve and boundary conditions along the physical boundaries of the solution domain.

Care must be exercised to ensure that a problem is well-posed. Only well-posed problems are considered in this book.

SUMMARY

The general features of partial differential equations have been presented, and the concept of characteristics has been introduced. Characteristics are the physical paths along which information propagates. Partial differential equations are classified as elliptic, parabolic, or hyperbolic, according to whether there are no real characteristics, real repeated characteristics, or real distinct characteristics, respectively. Examples of several partial differential equations that arise in engineering and science have been presented.

The Laplace equation is a classical example of an elliptic PDE, which must be solved by relaxation methods:

$$\nabla^2 f = 0 \tag{III.116}$$

Chapter 9 is devoted to the solution of the Laplace equation. The diffusion equation is a classical example of a parabolic PDE, which must be solved by marching methods:

$$f_t = \alpha \nabla^2 f \tag{III.117}$$

Chapter 11 is devoted to the solution of the diffusion equation. The convection equation is a classical example of a hyperbolic PDE, which must be solved by marching methods:

$$f_t + \mathbf{V} \cdot \nabla f = 0 \tag{III.118}$$

Chapter 12 is devoted to the solution of the convection equation. When convection and diffusion are both present, the process is governed by the convection–diffusion equation:

$$f_t + \mathbf{V} \cdot \nabla f = \alpha \nabla^2 f \tag{III.119}$$

The convection–diffusion equation is a more complicated example of a parabolic PDE, which must be solved by marching methods. Chapter 14 is devoted to the solution of the convection–diffusion equation. Some physical problems are governed by a system of convection equations. In some cases, they can be recast as the wave equation:

$$f_{tt} = c^2 \nabla^2 f \tag{III.120}$$

The wave equation is a more complicated example of a hyperbolic PDE, which must be solved by marching methods. Chapter 15 is devoted to the solution of the wave equation.

CHAPTER 9

ELLIPTIC PARTIAL DIFFERENTIAL EQUATIONS

The Laplace Equation

Section

Example

9.1 INTRODUCTION

The general features of elliptic partial differential equations (PDEs) are discussed in Section III.5. In that section it is shown that elliptic PDEs govern equilibrium problems, which are boundary-value problems in closed domains. Consequently, elliptic PDEs are solved numerically by relaxation methods.

Problems governed by elliptic PDEs have no real characteristics. Physically, this implies that there are no preferred paths of signal propagation and that the domain of dependence and the range of influence of every point is the entire solution domain. The solution at every point depends on the solution at all other points, including the boundaries of the solution domain, and the solution at every point influences the solution at all other points. The solution is continuous throughout the solution domain, since there are no curves along which the derivatives of the solution may be discontinuous. The closed solution domain for an elliptic PDE is illustrated schematically in Fig. 9.1.

The basic properties of finite difference methods for solving equilibrium problems governed by elliptic PDEs are presented in this Chapter. A finite difference grid must be superimposed on the continuous solution domain, and finite difference approximations (FDAs) of the individual exact partial derivatives appearing in the PDE must be chosen. These FDAs are substituted into the PDE to yield an algebraic finite difference equation (FDE). For elliptic PDEs, the solution at every point depends on the solution at all the other points, including the boundaries. Thus, the FDE for the solution at every point is coupled to the FDEs at all the other points. Consequently, a system of FDEs must be solved simultaneously. Such finite difference methods are called *implicit* methods, because the solution at each point is *implicitly* specified in terms of the unknown solutions at

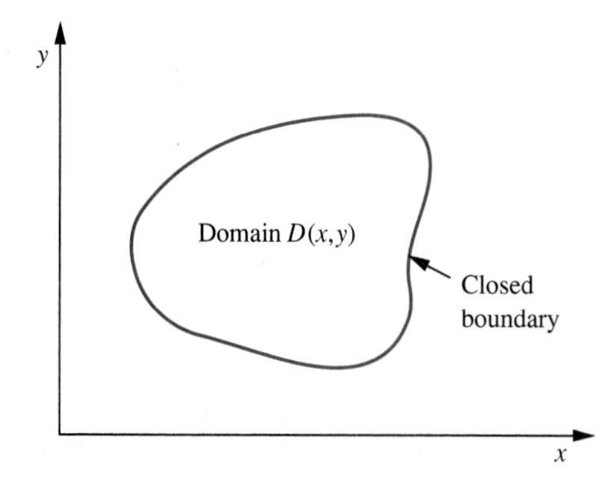

FIGURE 9.1
Solution domain for an elliptic partial differential equation.

neighboring points. Implicit methods, in which the solutions at all the points are coupled together, model the physical behavior of equilibrium problems correctly.

Numerous elliptic partial differential equations arise in engineering and science. Two of the more common ones are the *Laplace* equation and the *Poisson* equation, presented below for the generic dependent variable $f(x, y)$:

$$f_{xx} + f_{yy} = 0 \tag{9.1}$$

$$f_{xx} + f_{yy} = F(x, y) \tag{9.2}$$

where $F(x, y)$ is a known nonhomogeneous term. The Poisson equation is simply the *nonhomogeneous* Laplace equation. The presence of the nonhomogeneous term $F(x, y)$ can greatly complicate the closed-form solution of the Poisson equation. However, the presence of this term does not complicate the numerical solution of the Poisson equation. The nonhomogeneous term is simply evaluated at each physical location and added to the finite difference approximations of the exact partial derivatives. Consequently, the present chapter is devoted mainly to the numerical solution of the Laplace equation. All the results apply directly to the numerical solution of the Poisson equation.

The Laplace equation applies to problems in such areas as mass diffusion, heat diffusion (i.e., conduction), neutron diffusion, eletrostatics, and inviscid incompressible fluid flow. In fact, the Laplace equation governs the potential of many quantities where the rate of flow of a particular property is proportional to the gradient of the potential. Most people have some physical understanding of heat conduction, due to its presence in many aspects of our daily life. Consequently, the Laplace equation governing steady heat conduction is considered in this chapter to demonstrate numerical methods for solving the Laplace equation. That equation is derived in Section III.5, Eq. (III.57), which is repeated and renumbered below:

$$\nabla^2 T = T_{xx} + T_{yy} + T_{zz} = 0 \tag{9.3}$$

where T is the temperature (C). For two-dimensional heat conduction, Eq. (9.3) becomes

$$T_{xx} + T_{yy} = 0 \tag{9.4}$$

The solution to Eq. (9.4) is the function $T(x, y)$. This function must satisfy a set of boundary conditions on the boundaries of the physical domain. The boundary conditions may be of the Dirichlet type (i.e., specified temperature),

$$T(x, y) = G(x, y) \qquad \text{(on the boundaries)} \tag{9.5}$$

the Neumann type (i.e., specified temperature gradient),

$$T_n(x, y) = G(x, y) \qquad \text{(on the boundaries)} \tag{9.6}$$

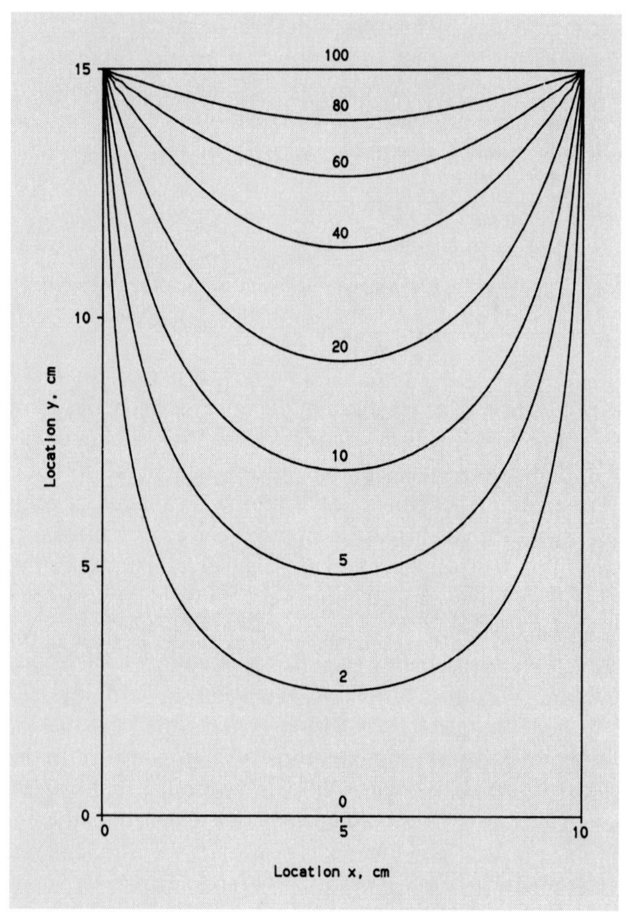

FIGURE 9.2
Exact solution of the heat conduction problem.

where $T_n = \partial T/\partial n$ is the temperature gradient normal to the boundary, or the mixed type (i.e., some specified combination of temperature and temperature gradient),

$$aT(x, y) + bT_n(x, y) = G(x, y) \qquad \text{(on the boundaries)} \tag{9.7}$$

The following simple problem is considered in this chapter to illustrate the numerical solution of the Laplace equation. A rectangular plate of height $h = 15$ cm, width $w = 10$ cm, and thickness $t = 1$ cm is insulated on both faces so that no heat flows in the direction of the thickness t. The temperature on the top edge of the plate is held at 100 C, and the temperatures on the left, right, and bottom edges of the plate are held at 0 C. The plate and the boundary conditions as well as selected isotherms (i.e., lines of constant temperature) are illustrated in Fig. 9.2. The temperature distribution $T(x, y)$ in the plate is required. The

TABLE 9.1
Exact solution of the heat conduction problem

	Temperature $T(x, y)$, C				
y	$x = 0.00$	$x = 1.25$	$x = 2.50$	$x = 3.75$	$x = 5.00$
15.00	100.000	100.000	100.000	100.000	100.000
13.75	0.000	48.361	67.025	73.814	75.611
12.50	0.000	26.410	43.483	51.944	54.449
11.25	0.000	16.200	28.519	35.690	37.996
10.00	0.000	10.472	18.945	24.260	26.049
8.75	0.000	6.922	12.669	16.400	17.684
7.50	0.000	4.611	8.483	11.036	11.924
6.25	0.000	3.067	5.657	7.376	7.978
5.00	0.000	2.018	3.725	4.863	5.261
3.75	0.000	1.288	2.379	3.107	3.362
2.50	0.000	0.761	1.405	1.836	1.987
1.25	0.000	0.353	0.652	0.851	0.922
0.00	0.000	0.000	0.000	0.000	0.000

exact solution to this linear PDE is obtained by assuming a product solution of the form $T(x, y) = X(x)Y(y)$, separating variables, integrating the resulting two ordinary differential equations, applying the boundary conditons at $x = 0$, $x = w$, and $y = 0$, and superimposing an infinite number of solutions to obtain the general solution. The coefficients of the general solution are choosen to satisfy the boundary condition at $y = h$. The result is

$$T(x, y) = \frac{400}{\pi} \sum_{n=1,3,\ldots}^{\infty} \frac{1}{n \sinh (n\pi h/w)} \sinh\left(\frac{n\pi y}{w}\right) \sin\left(\frac{n\pi x}{w}\right) \tag{9.8}$$

The exact solution at selected locations for $h = 15$ cm and $w = 10$ cm is tabulated in Table 9.1 for the left half of the plate. The solution is symmetrical about the vertical centerline.

9.2 FINITE DIFFERENCE APPROXIMATIONS

There are several choices that must be made when developing a finite difference solution to a partial differential equation. Foremost among these are the choice of the discrete finite difference grid used to represent the continuous solution domain and the choice of the finite difference approximations used to represent the exact partial derivatives in the partial differential equation. Some general characteristics of finite difference grids and finite difference approximations for equilibrium (i.e., elliptic) problems are discussed in this section.

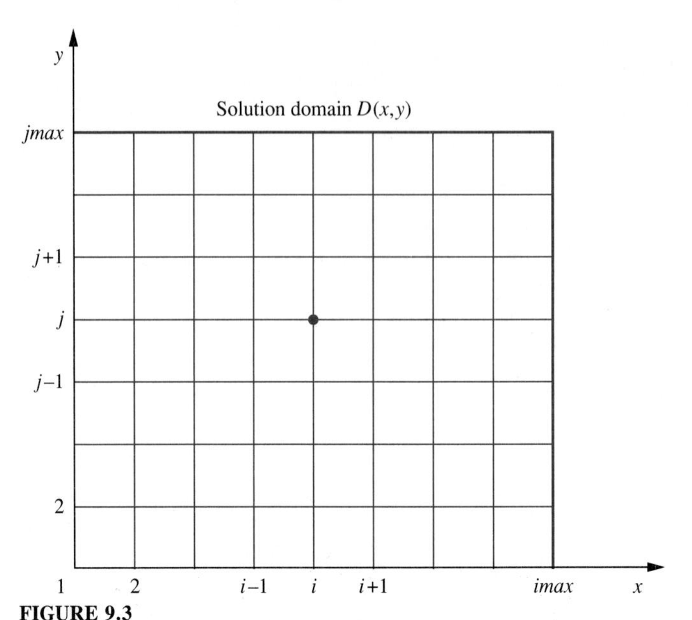

FIGURE 9.3
Solution domain $D(x, y)$ and finite difference grid.

The solution domain $D(x, y)$ in xy space for a two-dimensional equilibrium problem is illustrated in Fig. 9.3. The solution domain must be covered by a two-dimensional grid of lines, called the finite difference grid. The intersections of these grid lines are the grid points at which the finite difference solution to the partial differential equation is to be obtained. For the present, let these grid lines be equally spaced lines, perpendicular to the x and y axes and having uniform spacings Δx and Δy, respectively, but with Δx and Δy not necessarily equal. The resulting finite difference grid is illustrated in Fig. 9.3. Nonuniform grids, in which Δx and Δy are variable, and generalized grids, in which the grid lines are not parallel to the coordinate axes, are discussed in Chapter 13. The subscript i is used to denote the physical grid lines corresponding to constant values of x [i.e., $x_i = (i - 1)\,\Delta x$], and the subscript j is used to denote the physical grid lines corresponding to constant values of y [i.e., $y_j = (j - 1)\,\Delta y$]. Thus, grid point (i, j) corresponds to location (x_i, y_j) in the solution domain $D(x, y)$. The total number of x grid lines is denoted in the figure by *imax*, and the total number of y grid lines is denoted by *jmax*.

Three-dimensional physical spaces can be covered in a similar manner by a three-dimensional grid of planes perpendicular to the coordinate axes, where the subscripts i, j, and k denote the physical grid planes perpendicular to the x, y, and z axes, respectively. Thus, grid point (i, j, k) corresponds to location (x_i, y_j, z_k) in the solution domain $D(x, y, z)$.

The dependent variable at a grid point is denoted by the same subscript notation that is used to denote the grid points themselves. Thus, the function $f(x, y)$ at grid point (i,j) is denoted by

$$f(x_i, y_j) = f_{i,j} \tag{9.9}$$

In a similar manner, derivatives are denoted by

$$\frac{\partial f(x_i, y_j)}{\partial x} = \left.\frac{\partial f}{\partial x}\right|_{i,j} = f_x\big|_{i,j} \quad \text{and} \quad \frac{\partial^2 f(x_i, y_j)}{\partial x^2} = \left.\frac{\partial^2 f}{\partial x^2}\right|_{i,j} = f_{xx}\big|_{i,j} \tag{9.10}$$

Similar results apply in three-dimensional problems. For example,

$$f(x_i, y_j, z_k) = f_{i,j,k} \tag{9.11}$$

Now that the finite difference grid has been defined, finite difference approximations of the exact partial derivatives appearing in the partial differential equation must be developed. That is accomplished by using Taylor series expansions of the dependent variable about grid point (*i,j*). This is done in Chapter 5 for functions of one variable, where approximations of various types (i.e., forward, backward, and centered) having various orders of accuracy (first-order, second-order, etc.) are developed for various derivatives (first derivative, second derivative, etc.). Selected portions of those results are presented in Table 5.1.

In the development of finite difference methods, a distinction must be made between the exact solution of the partial differential equation and the approximate solution of the partial differential equation. For the remainder of this chapter, exact solutions will be denoted by an overbar on the symbol for the dependent variable [e.g., $\bar{f}(x, y)$], and the approximate solution will be denoted by the symbol for the dependent variable without an overbar [e.g., $f(x, y)$]. This very precise distinction between the exact solution and the approximate solution of a partial differential equation is required for studies of consistency, order, and convergence.

Exact derivatives such as $\bar{f}_{xx}$ may be approximated at grid point (*i,j*) in terms of the values of f at grid point (*i, j*) itself and adjacent grid points in a number of ways. For example, consider the partial derivative $\bar{f}_{xx}$. Writing the Taylor series (see the Appendix) for $\bar{f}_{i+1,j}$ and $\bar{f}_{i-1,j}$ using grid point (*i,j*) as the base point gives

$$\bar{f}_{i+1,j} = \bar{f}_{i,j} + \bar{f}_x\big|_{i,j}\,\Delta x + \frac{1}{2}\bar{f}_{xx}\Big|_{i,j}\,\Delta x^2 + \frac{1}{6}\bar{f}_{xxx}\Big|_{i,j}\,\Delta x^3 + \frac{1}{24}\bar{f}_{xxxx}\Big|_{i,j}\,\Delta x^4 + \cdots \tag{9.12}$$

$$\bar{f}_{i-1,j} = \bar{f}_{i,j} - \bar{f}_x\big|_{i,j}\,\Delta x + \frac{1}{2}\bar{f}_{xx}\Big|_{i,j}\,\Delta x^2 - \frac{1}{6}\bar{f}_{xxx}\Big|_{i,j}\,\Delta x^3 + \frac{1}{24}\bar{f}_{xxxx}\Big|_{i,j}\,\Delta x^4 + \cdots \tag{9.13}$$

where the convention $(\Delta x)^n \rightarrow \Delta x^n$ has been used for compactness. Equations (9.12) and (9.13) can be expressed as Taylor formulas with remainders (see the

Appendix). Thus,

$$\bar{f}_{i+1,j} = \bar{f}_{i,j} + \bar{f}_x\Big|_{i,j} \Delta x + \frac{1}{2}\bar{f}_{xx}\Big|_{i,j} \Delta x^2 + \frac{1}{6}\bar{f}_{xxx}\Big|_{i,j} \Delta x^3 + \frac{1}{24}\bar{f}_{xxxx}\Big|_{i,j} \Delta x^4 + R_{n+1}(\xi_+) \quad (9.14)$$

$$\bar{f}_{i-1,j} = \bar{f}_{i,j} - \bar{f}_x\Big|_{i,j} \Delta x + \frac{1}{2}\bar{f}_{xx}\Big|_{i,j} \Delta x^2 - \frac{1}{6}\bar{f}_{xxx}\Big|_{i,j} \Delta x^3 + \frac{1}{24}\bar{f}_{xxxx}\Big|_{i,j} \Delta x^4 + R_{n+1}(\xi_-) \quad (9.15)$$

where the remainder term R_{n+1} is given by

$$R_{n+1} = \frac{1}{(n+1)!}\frac{\partial^{n+1}\bar{f}(\xi)}{\partial x^{n+1}} \Delta x^{n+1} \quad (9.16)$$

where $x_i \le \xi_+ \le x_{i+1}$ and $x_{i-1} \le \xi_- \le x_i$. If the infinite Taylor series are truncated after the nth derivative to obtain approximations of $\bar{f}_{i+1,j}$ and $\bar{f}_{i-1,j}$, then the remainder term R_{n+1} is the error associated with the truncated Taylor series. In many cases, our main concern will be the *order* of the error, which is the rate at which the error goes to zero as $\Delta x \to 0$. The remainder term depends on Δx^{n+1}. Consequently, as $\Delta x \to 0$, the error goes to zero as Δx^{n+1}. Thus, the order of the truncated Taylor series approximation of $\bar{f}_{xx}\big|_{i,j}$ is $n+1$, which is denoted by the symbol $O(\Delta x^{n+1})$.

Adding Eqs. (9.12) and Eq. (9.13) and solving for $\bar{f}_{xx}\big|_{i,j}$ yields

$$\bar{f}_{xx}\Big|_{i,j} = \frac{\bar{f}_{i+1,j} - 2\bar{f}_{i,j} + \bar{f}_{i-1,j}}{\Delta x^2} - \frac{1}{12}\bar{f}_{xxxx}\,|_{i,j}\,\Delta x^2 + \cdots \quad (9.17)$$

Equivalently, from Eqs. (9.14) and (9.15),

$$\bar{f}_{xx}\,|_{i,j} = \frac{\bar{f}_{i+1,j} - 2\bar{f}_{i,j} - \bar{f}_{i-1,j}}{\Delta x^2} + \frac{R_{n+2}}{\Delta x^2} \quad (9.18)$$

which can be written as

$$\bar{f}_{xx}\,|_{i,j} = \frac{\bar{f}_{i+1,j} - 2\bar{f}_{i,j} + \bar{f}_{i-1,j}}{\Delta x^2} + \cdots + O(\Delta x^n) \quad (9.19)$$

where

$$\frac{R_{n+2}}{\Delta x^2} = \frac{1}{(n+2)!}\frac{\partial^{n+2}\bar{f}(\bar{\xi})}{\partial x^{n+2}}\frac{\Delta x^{n+2}}{\Delta x^2} = O(\Delta x^n) \quad (9.20)$$

where $x_{i-1} \le \bar{\xi} \le x_{i+1}$. If the Taylor series is truncated after the second derivative term (i.e., $n = 2$), then Eqs. (11.18) and (11.19) give

$$\bar{f}_{xx}\big|_{i,j} = \frac{\bar{f}_{i+1,j} - 2\bar{f}_{i,j} + \bar{f}_{i-1,j}}{\Delta x^2} - \frac{1}{12}\bar{f}_{xxxx}(\xi)\,\Delta x^2 \tag{9.21}$$

which can be written as

$$\begin{aligned} \bar{f}_{xx}\big|_{i,j} &= \frac{\bar{f}_{i+1,j} - 2\bar{f}_{i,j} + \bar{f}_{i-1,j}}{\Delta x^2} + E(\bar{f}_{xx}\big|_{i,j}) \\ &= \frac{\bar{f}_{i+1,j} - 2\bar{f}_{i,j} + \bar{f}_{i-1,j}}{\Delta x^2} + O(\Delta x^2) \end{aligned} \tag{9.22}$$

where the remainder term $E(\bar{f}_{xx}\big|_{i,j})$ is given by

$$E(\bar{f}_{xx}\big|_{i,j}) = -\frac{1}{12}\bar{f}_{xxxx}(\bar{\xi})\,\Delta x^2 = O(\Delta x^2) \tag{9.23}$$

A finite difference approximation of $\bar{f}_{xx}\big|_{i,j}$, which will be denoted by $f_{xx}\big|_{i,j}$, can be obtained from Eq. (9.22) by neglecting the remainder term. Thus,

$$f_{xx}\big|_{i,j} = \frac{f_{i+1,j} - 2f_{i,j} + f_{i-1,j}}{\Delta x^2} \tag{9.24}$$

The remainder term which has been neglected in Eq. (9.24) is called the *truncation error* of the finite difference approximation of $\bar{f}_{xx}\big|_{i,j}$. Equation (9.24) is a *second-order centered-difference* approximation of $\bar{f}_{xx}$ at grid point (i, j).

First-order one-sided approximations of $\bar{f}_{xx}$ at grid point (i, j) can be obtained by writing Taylor series for $\bar{f}_{i+2,j}$ and $\bar{f}_{i-2,j}$ using grid point (i, j) as the base point and proceeding in a similar manner. The results are

$$\bar{f}_{xx}\big|_{i,j} = \frac{\bar{f}_{i+2,j} - 2\bar{f}_{i+1,j} + \bar{f}_{i,j}}{\Delta x^2} + O(\Delta x) \tag{9.25}$$

$$\bar{f}_{xx}\big|_{i,j} = \frac{\bar{f}_{i,j} - 2\bar{f}_{i-1,j} + \bar{f}_{i-2,j}}{\Delta x^2} + O(\Delta x) \tag{9.26}$$

The terms $O(\Delta x)$ and $O(\Delta x^2)$ are truncation error terms. The notation $O(\Delta x)$, read as order Δx, denotes that the truncation error is proportional to

Δx (i.e, first-order). Similarly, the notation $O(\Delta x^2)$, read as order Δx^2, denotes a second-order truncation error. In some cases, our only concern will be with the order of the truncation error. In other cases, we will need to know the exact form of the truncation error. Equation (9.25) is a first-order forward-difference approximation and Eq. (9.26) is a first-order backward-difference approximation. They are rarely used, except at boundaries. Equation (9.22) is a second-order centered-difference approximation. It is the most commonly used finite difference approximation of a second spatial derivative.

Performing the analogous procedures in the y direction yields the following results:

$$\bar{f}_{yy}\Big|_{i,j} = \frac{\bar{f}_{i,j+1} - 2\bar{f}_{i,j} + \bar{f}_{i,j-1}}{\Delta y^2} - \frac{1}{12}\bar{f}_{yyyy}(\bar{\eta})\,\Delta y^2 \tag{9.27}$$

$$\bar{f}_{yy}\Big|_{i,j} = \frac{\bar{f}_{i,j+2} - 2\bar{f}_{i,j+1} + \bar{f}_{i,j}}{\Delta y^2} + O(\Delta y) \tag{9.28}$$

$$\bar{f}_{yy}\Big|_{i,j} = \frac{\bar{f}_{i,j} - 2\bar{f}_{i,j-1} + \bar{f}_{i,j-2}}{\Delta y^2} + O(\Delta y) \tag{9.29}$$

Finite difference solutions of a partial differential equation are obtained by replacing the exact partial derivatives in the partial differential equation by finite difference approximations, such as Eqs. (9.22) and (9.27), to obtain a finite difference equation that approximates the partial differential equation.

Example 9.1. Finite difference approximation of the Laplace equation. Consider the steady two-dimensional Laplace equation:

$$\bar{f}_{xx} + \bar{f}_{yy} = 0 \tag{9.30}$$

Replacing $\bar{f}_{xx}$ and $\bar{f}_{yy}$ by the second-order centered-difference approximations at grid point (i, j), Eqs. (9.22) and (9.27), respectively, yields

$$\frac{\bar{f}_{i+1,j} - 2\bar{f}_{i,j} + \bar{f}_{i-1,j}}{\Delta x^2} + O(\Delta x^2) + \frac{\bar{f}_{i,j+1} - 2\bar{f}_{i,j} + \bar{f}_{i,j-1}}{\Delta y^2} + O(\Delta y^2) = 0 \tag{9.31}$$

Equation (9.31) is a second-order centered-difference representation of Eq. (9.30). Equation (9.31) can be written as

$$\frac{\bar{f}_{i+1,j} - 2\bar{f}_{i,j} + \bar{f}_{i-1,j}}{\Delta x^2} + \frac{\bar{f}_{i,j+1} - 2\bar{f}_{i,j} + \bar{f}_{i,j-1}}{\Delta y^2} + E_{i,j} = 0 \tag{9.32}$$

where $E_{i,j}$ is the *truncation error* of the finite difference approximation of the partial differential equation. For Eq. (9.32),

$$E_{i,j} = O(\Delta x^2) + O(\Delta y^2) \tag{9.33}$$

The truncation error $E_{i,j}$ is second order in Δx and Δy. Define the *grid aspect ratio* β as

$$\boxed{\beta = \frac{\Delta x}{\Delta y}} \tag{9.34}$$

Multiplying Eq. (9.31) by Δx^2 and introducing Eq. (9.34) yields

$$\bar{f}_{i+1,j} + \beta^2 \bar{f}_{i,j+1} + \bar{f}_{i-1,j} + \beta^2 \bar{f}_{i,j-1} - 2(1 + \beta^2)\bar{f}_{i,j} + \Delta x^2 \big(O(\Delta x^2) + O(\Delta y^2)\big) = 0 \tag{9.35}$$

Equation (9.35) may be written as

$$\bar{f}_{i+1,j} + \beta^2 \bar{f}_{i,j+1} + \bar{f}_{i-1,j} + \beta^2 \bar{f}_{i,j-1} - 2(1 + \beta^2)\bar{f}_{i,j} + e_{i,j} = 0 \tag{9.36}$$

where $e_{i,j}$ is the *discretization error* of the finite difference equation. For Eq. (9.36), the discretization error is

$$e_{i,j} = \Delta x^2 \big(O(\Delta x^2) + O(\Delta y^2)\big) \tag{9.37}$$

Dropping the discretization error $e_{i,j}$ from Eq. (9.36) yields the five-point finite difference equation (FDE):

$$\boxed{f_{i+1,j} + \beta^2 f_{i,j+1} + f_{i-1,j} + \beta^2 f_{i,j-1} - 2(1 + \beta^2) f_{i,j} = 0} \tag{9.38}$$

Solving Eq. (9.38) for $f_{i,j}$ yields

$$\boxed{f_{i,j} = \frac{f_{i+1,j} + \beta^2 f_{i,j+1} + f_{i-1,j} + \beta^2 f_{i,j-1}}{2(1 + \beta^2)}} \tag{9.39}$$

The implicit nature of the finite difference equation is apparent in Eq. (9.39). The solution at every grid point depends on the solutions at the four neighboring grid points, which are not known until the entire solution is known. This implicit behavior of the finite difference equation is typical of the numerical solution of elliptic partial differential equations, which govern equilibrium physical problems.

In the special case where $\Delta x = \Delta y$, the grid aspect ratio β is unity, and Eqs. (9.38) and (9.39) become

$$\boxed{f_{i+1,j} + f_{i,j+1} + f_{i-1,j} + f_{i,j-1} - 4 f_{i,j} = 0} \tag{9.40}$$

$$\boxed{f_{i,j} = \frac{1}{4}(f_{i+1,j} + f_{i,j+1} + f_{i-1,j} + f_{i,j-1})} \tag{9.41}$$

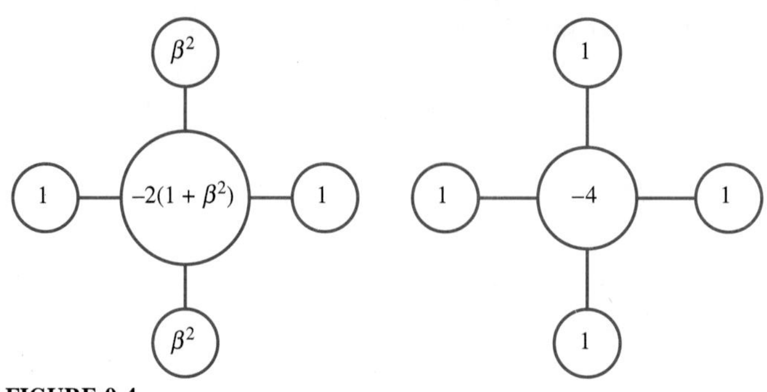

FIGURE 9.4
Finite difference stencils.

Although there is no formal mathematical advantage when β is unity, large values of the grid aspect ratio β tend to produce less accurate solutions than values of β in the neighborhood of unity.

Equation (9.41) has a very simple physical interpretation. It shows that, for a unity grid aspect ratio, the solution at every point is the arithmetic average of the solutions at the four neighboring points. This result applies only to the Laplace equation (i.e., no nonhomogeneous term).

The finite difference solution of a partial differential equation is obtained by solving a finite difference equation, such as Eq. (9.38) or Eq. (9.40), at every point in the solution domain.

A finite difference equation can be illustrated pictorially by a *finite difference stencil*, which is a picture of that part of the finite difference grid used to develop the finite difference equation at a point. The neighboring grid points employed in the finite difference approximations of the exact partial derivatives are denoted by open circles each containing the weighting factor associated with its grid point. The finite difference stencils for Eqs. (9.38) and (9.40) are illustrated in Fig. 9.4.

The rate at which the truncation errors of the finite difference solution approach zero as Δx and Δy go to zero is called the order of the finite difference equation. The total error at any point in the solution domain is directly related to the local truncation errors throughout the entire solution domain. Consequently, the total error at a given point depends on Δx and Δy in exactly the same manner as the local truncation errors depend on Δx and Δy. Thus, the order of a finite difference solution to a partial differential equation is the order of the truncation errors of the finite difference approximations to the exact partial derivatives in the partial differential equation. For example, for Eqs. (9.38) and (9.40), the truncation error is $O(\Delta x^2) + O(\Delta y^2)$ [see Eq. (9.33)]. Consequently, the total error at a point decreases quadratically as Δx and $\Delta y \rightarrow O$. The finite difference solution is second-order accurate in space. The order of the finite difference solution of a partial differential equation is an important property of a finite difference method.

9.3 CONSISTENCY, ORDER, AND CONVERGENCE

There are three important properties of finite difference equations for equilibrium problems that must be considered before numerical computations are made.

1. Consistency
2. Order
3. Convergence

These three concepts are discussed in this section.

First consider the concept of *consistency*.

> *A finite difference equation is consistent with a partial differential equation if the difference between the FDE and the PDE (i.e., the truncation error) vanishes as the sizes of the grid spacings go to zero independently.*

When the truncation errors of the finite difference approximations of the individual exact partial derivatives are known, proof of consistency is straightforward. When the truncation errors of the finite difference approximations of the individual exact partial derivatives are not known, the complete finite difference equation must be analyzed for consistency. That is accomplished by expressing each term in the finite difference equation [i.e., $f(x, y)$, not $\bar{f}(x, y)$] in a Taylor series expansion about grid point (i, j). The resulting equation, which is called the *modified differential equation* (MDE), can then be simplified to yield the exact form of the truncation error of the complete finite difference equation. Consistency can then be investigated by letting the grid spacings go to zero.

The modified differential equation (MDE) is the actual PDE that is solved by the FDE. The MDE differs from the exact PDE by the truncation error. The MDE can be used to investigate consistency and order.

Consider the Laplace equation and a corresponding FDE:

$$\bar{f}_{xx} + \bar{f}_{yy} = 0 \rightarrow \bar{f}(x, y) \text{ exact solution}$$

$$f_{xx} + f_{yy} = 0 \rightarrow f(x, y) \text{ approximate solution}$$

All values of $f(x, y)$ in the FDE can be expanded in a Taylor series expansion of $f(x, y)$ about some base point [e.g., point (i, j)]. Substituting those expressions into the FDE gives the MDE. Thus,

$$f_{xx} + f_{yy} = \sum_{m} A_m \frac{\partial^m f}{\partial x^m} + \sum_{m,n} B_{mn} \frac{\partial^{m+n} f}{\partial x^m \partial y^n} + \sum_{n} C_n \frac{\partial^n f}{\partial y^n} \tag{9.42}$$

The MDE is a PDE of infinite order. It is the actual PDE that is solved by the FDE.

Example 9.2. Consistency analysis of the five-point method. As an example, consider the Laplace equation, Eq. (9.1),

$$\bar{f}_{xx} + \bar{f}_{yy} = 0 \tag{9.43}$$

and the five-point finite difference approximation for $\Delta x = \Delta y$, Eq. (9.40):

$$f_{i+1,j} + f_{i,j+1} + f_{i-1,j} + f_{i,j-1} - 4f_{i,j} = 0 \tag{9.44}$$

Equation (9.44) can be rearranged as follows:

$$(f_{i+1,j} + f_{i-1,j}) + (f_{i,j+1} + f_{i,j-1}) - 4f_{i,j} = 0 \tag{9.45}$$

Write Taylor series about grid point (i, j) for all values of $f(x, y)$ appearing in Eq. (9.45). Thus,

$$f_{i\pm 1,j} = f_{i,j} \pm f_x\big|_{i,j}\,\Delta x + \frac{1}{2}f_{xx}\big|_{i,j}\,\Delta x^2 \pm \frac{1}{6}f_{xxx}\big|_{i,j}\,\Delta x^3 + \frac{1}{24}f_{xxxx}\big|_{i,j}\,\Delta x^4 + \cdots \tag{9.46}$$

$$f_{i,j\pm 1} = f_{i,j} \pm f_y\big|_{i,j}\,\Delta y + \frac{1}{2}f_{yy}\big|_{i,j}\,\Delta y^2 \pm \frac{1}{6}f_{yyy}\big|_{i,j}\,\Delta y^3 + \frac{1}{24}f_{yyyy}\big|_{i,j}\,\Delta y^4 + \cdots \tag{9.47}$$

Dropping the notation $\big|_{i,j}$ for clarity and substituting Eqs. (9.46) and (9.47) into Eq. (9.45) gives

$$\left(2f + f_{xx}\,\Delta x^2 + \frac{1}{12}f_{xxxx}\,\Delta x^4 + \cdots\right) + \left(2f + f_{yy}\,\Delta y^2 + \frac{1}{12}f_{yyyy}\,\Delta y^4 + \cdots\right) - 4f = 0 \tag{9.48}$$

Cancelling zero-order terms, dividing through by $\Delta x = \Delta y$, and rearranging terms yields the MDE:

$$\boxed{f_{xx} + f_{yy} = -\frac{1}{12}f_{xxxx}\,\Delta x^2 - \cdots - \frac{1}{12}f_{yyyy}\,\Delta y^2 - \cdots} \tag{9.49}$$

As $\Delta x \to 0$ and $\Delta y \to 0$, Eq. (9.49) approaches $f_{xx} + f_{yy} = 0$, which is the Laplace equation. Consequently, Eq. (9.44) is a consistent approximation of the Laplace equation.

Next consider the concept of *order*, which is introduced in Section 9.2.

> *The order of a finite difference approximation of a partial differential equation is the rate at which the global error of the finite difference solution approaches zero as the sizes of the grid spacings approach zero.*

As discussed in Section 9.2, the global order of a finite difference equation is the order of the truncation error terms in the finite difference approximations of the individual exact partial derivatives in the PDE. The order of an FDE is an extremely important property of the FDE.

When the truncation errors of the finite difference approximations of the individual exact partial derivatives are known, as in Eqs. (9.21) and (9.27), the order of the FDE is obvious. When the truncation errors of the finite difference approximations of the individual exact partial derivatives are not known, the order can be determined from the modified differential equation. For example, the order of the five-point finite difference approximation of the Laplace equation, Eq. (9.44), can be obtained from the corresponding MDE, Eq. (9.49). From Eq. (9.49), Eq. (9.44) is an $0(\Delta x^2) + 0(\Delta y^2)$ approximation of the Laplace equation.

Finally, consider the concept of *convergence*.

> *A finite difference method is convergent if the solution of the finite difference equation approaches the exact solution of the partial differential equation as the sizes of the grid spacings go to zero.*

Let $\bar{f}_{i,j}$ denote the exact solution of the partial differential equation, $f_{i,j}$ denote the exact solution of the finite difference equation, and $e_{i,j}$ denote the difference between them. The statement of convergence is

$$f_{i,j} - \bar{f}_{i,j} = e_{i,j} \rightarrow 0 \quad \text{as} \quad \Delta x \rightarrow 0 \text{ and } \Delta y \rightarrow 0 \tag{9.50}$$

The proof of convergence of a finite difference solution is in the domain of the mathematician. We shall not attempt to prove convergence directly. Numerous discussions of convergence appear in the literature, for example, Forsythe and Wasow (1960).

As discussed in Section 9.2, finite difference approximations of elliptic partial differential equations yield systems of finite difference equations. If the partial differential equation is linear, then a system of linear finite difference equations results. For our purposes, it is sufficient to know that the solution of the system of linear finite difference equations converges to the solution of the partial differential equation if the finite difference equation is consistent with the partial differential equation. Thus, the question of convergence of a finite difference solution can be answered by a study of the consistency of the finite difference equation used to approximate the partial differential equation. If the system of FDEs is solved iteratively, by the SOR method for example (see Section 1.8), then the coefficient matrix of the system of FDEs must be diagonally dominant to ensure convergence of the iterative process.

The above conclusions apply strictly to linear equilibrium problems. Many problems in engineering and science are not linear. There are no equivalent general conclusions for such problems. Experience has shown, however, that numerical algorithms that are consistent and whose system of linearized finite difference equations is diagonally dominant generally converge, even for nonlinear equilibrium problems. When the system of difference equations is not diagonally dominant, the question of convergence is more difficult to answer. In this book we shall consider only finite difference approximations that yield diagonally dominant systems of finite difference equations.

As shown in Section 9.4, when Eq. (9.38) or Eq. (9.40) is used to solve the Laplace equation numerically, the system of finite difference equations is diagonally dominant. This result, along with the proof of consistency presented above, guarantees that the numerical solution of the finite difference equations converges to the exact solution of the partial differential equation as the sizes of the grid spacings approach zero.

In summary, the concepts of consistency, order, and convergence must always be considered when solving an elliptic partial differential equation by finite difference methods. Consistency can be demonstrated by direct substitution of Taylor series into the finite difference equation to determine the truncation error, which must go to zero as the grid spacings approach zero. Diagonal dominance of the system of finite difference equations can be obtained by careful choice of the finite difference approximations of the individual exact partial derivatives. For example, second-order centered-difference approximations always result in diagonally dominant systems of finite difference equations. Thus, convergence of the finite difference solution to the exact solution of the partial differential equation can be ensured by demonstrating consistency and diagonal dominance.

9.4 FINITE DIFFERENCE SOLUTION OF THE LAPLACE EQUATION

In this section the steady two-dimensional Laplace equation is solved using the finite difference equations developed in Section 9.2. Two approaches are available for solving the system of FDEs: the direct approach (e.g., Gauss elimination) and the iterative approach (e.g., Gauss–Seidel or successive overrelaxation (SOR)). The direct approach requires an excessive amount of computational effort if the number of grid points is very large. For sparse matrices, the iterative approach is much more efficient. Both approaches are discussed below.

For purposes of discussion, consider the heat conduction problem described in Section 9.1. The rectangular physical domain is 10 cm wide and 15 cm high. Discretizing the domain into a 5×7 finite difference grid yields the grid illustrated in Fig. 9.5. For this grid, the grid aspect ratio β is unity, so Eq. (9.40)

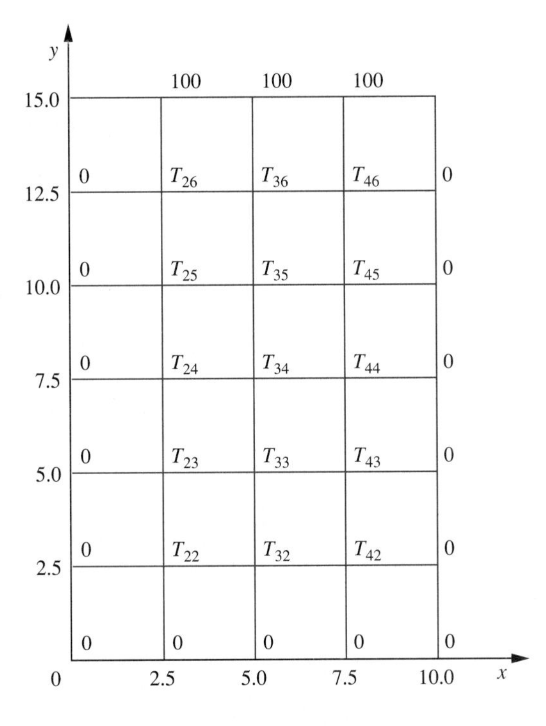

FIGURE 9.5
Finite difference grid for $\Delta x = \Delta y = 2.5$ cm.

is the relevant FDE. The temperatures across the top of the plate are 100 C, and the temperatures on the other three sides of the plate are 0 C. The temperatures at the four corners of the plate are not required by the five-point FDE.

Applying Eq. (9.40) at every point in the finite difference grid yields the following system of FDEs:

$$
\begin{aligned}
-4T_{22} + T_{23} + T_{32} &= 0 \\
T_{22} - 4T_{23} + T_{24} + T_{33} &= 0 \\
T_{23} - 4T_{24} + T_{25} + T_{34} &= 0 \\
T_{24} - 4T_{25} + T_{26} + T_{35} &= 0 \\
T_{25} - 4T_{26} + T_{36} &= -100 \\
T_{22} - 4T_{32} + T_{33} + T_{42} &= 0 \\
T_{23} + T_{32} - 4T_{33} + T_{34} + T_{43} &= 0 \\
T_{24} + T_{33} - 4T_{34} + T_{35} + T_{44} &= 0 \\
T_{25} + T_{34} - 4T_{35} + T_{36} + T_{45} &= 0 \\
T_{26} + T_{35} - 4T_{36} + T_{46} &= -100 \\
T_{32} - 4T_{42} + T_{43} &= 0 \\
T_{33} + T_{42} - 4T_{43} + T_{44} &= 0 \\
T_{34} + T_{43} - 4T_{44} + T_{45} &= 0
\end{aligned}
\tag{9.51}
$$

$$T_{35} + T_{44} - 4T_{45} + T_{46} = 0$$

$$T_{36} + T_{45} - 4T_{46} = -100$$

where the subscripts i, j have been written as ij for simplicity. Equation (9.51) consists of 15 FDEs. Equation (9.51) can be written in the matrix form:

$$\begin{bmatrix}
-4 & 1 & & & & 1 & & & & & & & & & \\
1 & -4 & 1 & & & & 1 & & & & & & & & \\
 & 1 & -4 & 1 & & & & 1 & & & & & & & \\
 & & 1 & -4 & 1 & & & & 1 & & & & & & \\
 & & & 1 & -4 & & & & & 1 & & & & & \\
1 & & & & & -4 & 1 & & & & 1 & & & & \\
 & 1 & & & & 1 & -4 & 1 & & & & 1 & & & \\
 & & 1 & & & & 1 & -4 & 1 & & & & 1 & & \\
 & & & 1 & & & & 1 & -4 & 1 & & & & 1 & \\
 & & & & 1 & & & & 1 & -4 & & & & & 1 \\
 & & & & & 1 & & & & & -4 & 1 & & & \\
 & & & & & & 1 & & & & 1 & -4 & 1 & & \\
 & & & & & & & 1 & & & & 1 & -4 & 1 & \\
 & & & & & & & & 1 & & & & 1 & -4 & 1 \\
 & & & & & & & & & 1 & & & & 1 & -4
\end{bmatrix}
\begin{bmatrix} T_{22} \\ T_{23} \\ T_{24} \\ T_{25} \\ T_{26} \\ T_{32} \\ T_{33} \\ T_{34} \\ T_{35} \\ T_{36} \\ T_{42} \\ T_{43} \\ T_{44} \\ T_{45} \\ T_{46} \end{bmatrix}
=
\begin{bmatrix} 0 \\ 0 \\ 0 \\ 0 \\ -100 \\ 0 \\ 0 \\ 0 \\ 0 \\ -100 \\ 0 \\ 0 \\ 0 \\ 0 \\ -100 \end{bmatrix}
\tag{9.52}$$

which is in the general form

$$\mathbf{AT} = \mathbf{b} \tag{9.53}$$

where $\mathbf{A}$ is the 15×15 coefficient matrix, $\mathbf{T}$ and $\mathbf{b}$ are 15×1 column vectors, and all the missing terms are zero. Equation (9.52) can be solved by Gauss elimination.

Consider an iterative solution by the SOR method. Applying Eq. (9.41) at grid point (i, j) yields

$$T_{i,j} = \frac{1}{4}\left(T_{i+1,j} + T_{i,j+1} + T_{i-1,j} + T_{i,j-1}\right) \tag{9.54}$$

Equation (9.54) can be rewritten in the form required for iteration by the SOR method by adding $\pm T_{i,j}$ to the right-hand side, rearranging, assuming a sweep strategy, and introducing the overrelaxation factor ω. The resulting relaxation equation is:

$$T_{i,j}^{k+1} = T_{i,j}^{k} + \omega\, \Delta T_{i,j}^{k} \tag{9.55}$$

where $\Delta T_{i,j}^{k}$ is given by

$$\Delta T_{i,j}^{k} = \frac{1}{4}\left(T_{i+1,j}^{k} + T_{i,j+1}^{k} + T_{i-1,j}^{k+1} + T_{i,j-1}^{k+1} - 4T_{i,j}^{k}\right) \tag{9.56}$$

The sweep strategy used in Eq. (9.56) is illustrated in Fig. 9.6. Letting the overrelaxation factor $\omega = 1.0$ yields the Gauss–Seidel method. Iterative methods of solution are discussed in more detail in Section 9.5

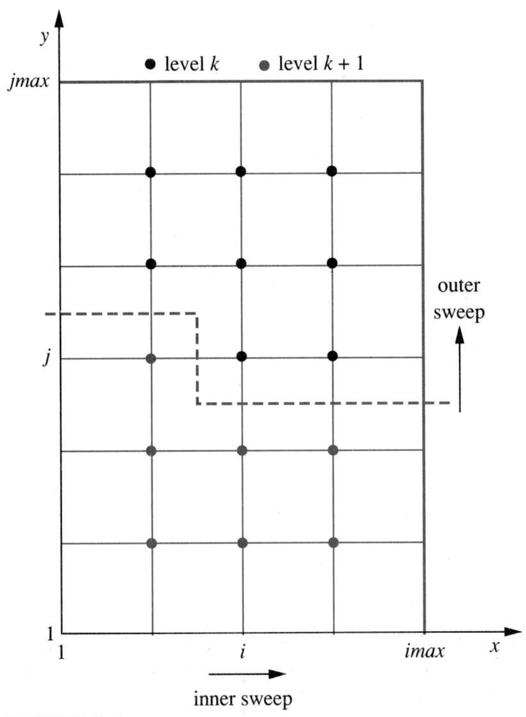

FIGURE 9.6
Sweep strategy for the Gauss–Seidel method.

Example 9.3. Numerical solution on a 3 × 4 grid. Solve the steady two-dimensional heat conduction problem described in Section 9.1 to illustrate the numerical solution of the Laplace equation. First, we will solve the problem using an extremely coarse finite difference grid. Let $\Delta x = \Delta y = 5$ cm, which gives $imax = 3$ and $jmax = 4$. For this grid, there are only two unknown temperatures, T_{22} and T_{23}. For $\Delta x = \Delta y$, the grid aspect ratio β is unity, so Eq. (9.40) is the appropriate finite difference equation. Writing Eq. (9.40) at grid points (2,2) and (2,3), respectively, yields

$$T_{32} + T_{23} + T_{12} + T_{21} - 4T_{22} = 0 \tag{9.57a}$$

$$T_{33} + T_{24} + T_{13} + T_{22} - 4T_{23} = 0 \tag{9.57b}$$

Substituting the known boundary values into Eq. (9.57) gives

$$0 + T_{23} + 0 + 0 - 4T_{22} = 0 \tag{9.58a}$$

$$0 + 100 + 0 + T_{22} - 4T_{23} = 0 \tag{9.58b}$$

which reduces to

$$-4T_{22} + T_{23} = 0 \tag{9.59a}$$

$$T_{22} - 4T_{23} = -100 \tag{9.59b}$$

Equation (9.59) can be solved by elimination to yield

$$T_{22} = 6.667 \qquad \text{and} \qquad T_{23} = 26.667 \tag{9.60}$$

TABLE 9.2
Solution on the 3×4 grid

Location (x,y)	T	$\overline{T}$	ΔT
(5.0, 10.0)	26.667	26.049	0.618
(5.0, 5.0)	6.667	5.261	1.406

Table 9.2 presents a comparison of the numerical solution with the exact solution for the 3 × 4 grid. The numerical solution is qualitatively correct, but the errors are rather large. Even more serious is the coarseness of the solution.

The numerical solution presented in Example 9.3 for the 3 × 4 grid is quite coarse. Figure 9.5 illustrates a 5 × 7 grid corresponding to $\Delta x = \Delta y = 2.5$ cm. For this grid, there are 15 unknown temperatures, T_{22} to T_{46}. Writing Eq. (9.40) at the 15 interior grid points, introducing the known boundary conditions, and simplifying, yields Eq. (9.51). Example 9.4 presents the solution of Eq. (9.51) for the 5 × 7 grid.

Example 9.4. Numerical solution on a 5×7 grid. Now we rework the heat conduction problem on the 5 × 7 grid illustrated in Fig. 9.5 by solving Eq. (9.51). The solution is tabulated in Table 9.3, where the numerical solution is compared with the exact solution. The values for $i = 4$ are the same as those for $i = 2$ because of symmetry, so the values for $i = 4$ are not presented. The errors are considerably smaller than the errors for the 3×4 grid presented in Table 9.2.

Table 9.4 compares the solutions obtained for the two different grid sizes at the common locations of the two grids. The solution for the 5×7 grid is considerably more accurate than the solution for the 3×5 grid, as expected. The truncation error of the finite difference equation is second-order, so the errors should decrease by a factor of 4.0 as the grid sizes are halved. The error at location (5.0,5.0) decreases by a factor of approximately 3.0, and the error at location (5.0,10.0) decreases by a factor of approximately 3.5. Although these

TABLE 9.3
Solution on the 5×7 grid

Location (x,y)	T	$\overline{T}$	ΔT
(2.5, 12.5)	43.193	43.483	−0.290
(2.5, 10.0)	19.620	18.945	0.675
(2.5, 7.5)	9.057	8.483	0.574
(2.5, 5.0)	4.092	3.725	0.367
(2.5, 2.5)	1.578	1.405	0.173
(5.0, 12.5)	53.154	54.449	−1.295
(5.0, 10.0)	26.228	26.049	0.179
(5.0, 7.5)	12.518	11.924	0.594
(5.0, 5.0)	5.731	5.261	0.470
(5.0, 2.5)	2.222	1.987	0.235

TABLE 9.4
Comparison of the solutions on the 3×4 and 5×7 grids

		5×7 grid		9×13 grid	
Location (x,y)	$\bar{T}$	T	ΔT	T	ΔT
(5.0, 10.0)	26.049	26.667	0.618	26.228	0.179
(5.0, 5.0)	5.261	6.667	1.406	5.731	0.470

factors are not exactly 4.0, they are considerably larger than 2.0, which is the theoretical factor for a first-order method. The present method is clearly a second-order accurate method. The value of 4.0 for the ratio of errors when the grid sizes are halved applies in the limit as the grid sizes approach zero. For finite grid sizes, some of the higher-order truncation error terms are still significant.

To further illustrate the improvement in accuracy as the grid sizes are reduced, the solution for a 9 × 13 grid is presented in Example 9.5.

Example 9.5. Numerical solution on a 9 × 13 grid. As a final example, we will rework the heat conduction problem with $\Delta x = \Delta y = 1.25$ cm. In this case, $imax = 9$ and $jmax = 13$, and there are $(imax - 2) \times (jmax - 2) = 7 \times 11 = 77$ unknown temperatures. The solution for the 9 × 13 grid is obtained as before. The amount of computational effort is considerably increased because of the increased number of equations to be solved. The results are presented in Fig. 9.7, where the numerical solution is indicated by the dashed lines. The numerical solution is obviously a good approximation of the exact solution.

Table 9.5 compares the numerical solutions obtained for the 5 × 7 and 9 × 13 grids at the common locations of the two grids along the vertical centerline of the plate. The errors for the 9 × 13 grid are approximately one-fourth the size of the errors for the 5 × 7 grid at the points in the bottom half of the plate, where the gradients are relatively small. In the top half of the plate, where the gradients are relatively large, the errors for the 9 × 13 grid are closer to one-third the size of the errors for the 5 × 7 grid. The second-order accuracy of the finite difference equation is quite apparent.

The numerical solution obtained on the 9×13 grid is sufficiently accurate for most practical applications. If a more accurate solution is required, it can be obtained by decreasing the grid size even more and repeating the solution. In principle, this process can be repeated forever. However, in practice, the amount of computational effort increases rapidly as the sizes of the grid spacings decrease (or conversely, as the number of grid points increases).

The results presented in this section were obtained by Gauss–Seidel iteration. Gauss elimination could have been used. However, as mentioned in Section 1.3, the number of operations N required for Gauss elimination to solve the system of finite difference equations is given by

$$N = \frac{1}{3}n^3 + n^2 - \frac{1}{3}n \tag{9.61}$$

where n is the number of equations to be solved. Thus, the amount of compu-

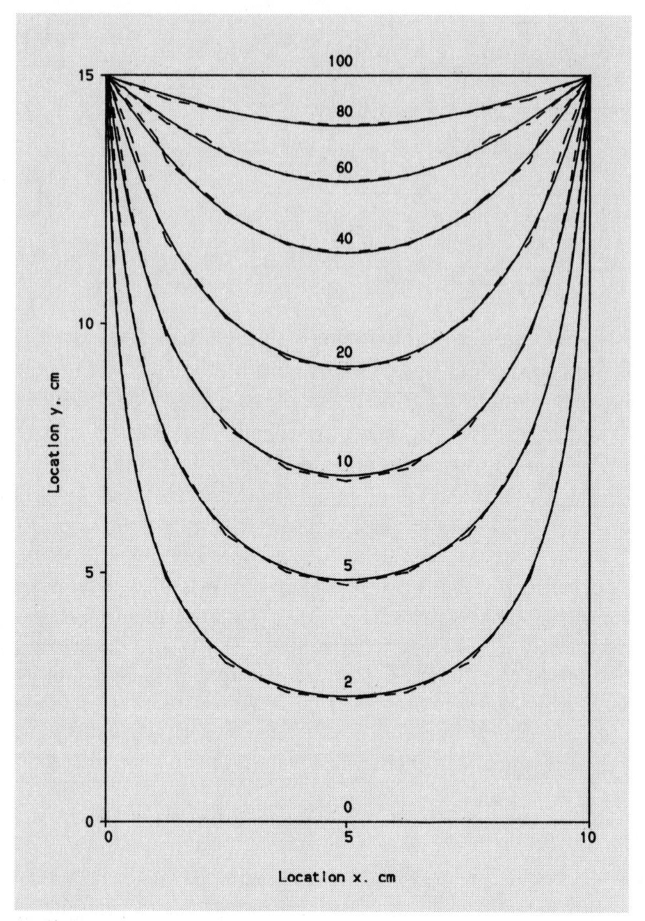

FIGURE 9.7
Numerical solution of the heat conduction problem.

TABLE 9.5
Comparison of the solutions on the 5×7 and 9×13 grids

		5×7 grid		9×13 grid	
Location (x, y)	$\overline{T}$	T	ΔT	T	ΔT
(5.0, 12.5)	54.449	53.154	−1.295	54.024	−0.425
(5.0, 10.0)	26.049	26.228	0.179	26.095	0.046
(5.0, 7.5)	11.924	12.518	0.594	12.093	0.169
(5.0, 5.0)	5.261	5.731	0.470	5.390	0.129
(5.0, 2.5)	1.987	2.222	0.235	2.050	0.063

tational effort increases approximately as the cube of the number of grid points. For a two-dimensional problem, the number of grid points increases as the square of the reciprocal of the grid size (assuming that the grid aspect ratio β remains constant as the grid size is reduced). Consequently, the amount of computational effort increases approximately as the sixth power of the reciprocal of the grid size. For the three grid sizes chosen in this section to solve the heat conduction problem (i.e., 5.0, 2.5, and 1.25 cm), the number of operations $N = 6$, 1345, and 158,081, respectively. Clearly the amount of computational effort increases at an alarming rate.

Equation (9.61) is applicable to Gauss elimination for a full coefficient matrix. The coefficient matrices arising in the numerical solution of partial differential equations are banded matrices, as illustrated in Eq. (9.52). When such systems are solved by Gauss elimination, all the zero coefficients outside of the outer bands remain zero and do not need to be computed. A significant amount of computational effort can be saved by modifying the Gauss elimination algorithm to omit the calculation of those terms. However, the bands of zeros between the central tridiagonal band of coefficients and the outer bands fill up with nonzero coefficients, which must be computed. Consequently, even when the banded nature of the coefficient matrix is accounted for, Gauss elimination still requires a large amount of computational effort for large systems of equations. In that case, iterative methods, which are discussed in Section 9.5, should be employed.

Another problem that arises in the direct solution of systems of equations is the large amount of computer memory required to store the coefficient matrix. From Eq. (9.52), it is apparent that many of the elements in the 15×15 coefficient matrix are zero. In fact only 59 of the 225 elements are nonzero, that is, 26 percent. For the 77×77 coefficient matrix associated with the 9×13 grid, only 169 of the 5929 elements are nonzero, that is, 2.9 percent. The percent of nonzero elements decreases dramatically as the size of the coefficient matrix increases, since the total number of elements is n^2, whereas the number of nonzero elements is somewhat less than $5n$. To illustrate this point more dramatically, if $\Delta x = \Delta y = 0.1$ cm, then $imax = 101$ and $jmax = 151$, and there are $n = 99 \times 149 = 14{,}751$ interior grid points. The coefficient matrix for the corresponding system of finite difference equations would contain $14{,}751 \times 14{,}751 = 217{,}592{,}001$ elements. This exceeds the memory of all but the most advanced supercomputer and clearly cannot be considered. However, each finite difference equation contains at most five nonzero elements. Thus, the minimum amount of computer memory in which the coefficient matrix can be stored is $5n$, not n^2. However, if Gauss elimination is used to solve the system of FDEs, then computer memory must be reserved for all the nonzero elements of the coefficient matrix within and including the outer bands.

Iterative methods, on the other hand, use only the nonzero elements of the coefficient matrix. As shown in Eq. (9.38), these nonzero elements are 1, β^2, 1, β^2, and $-2(1 + \beta^2)$, corresponding to grid points $(i + 1, j)$, $(i, j + 1)$, $(i - 1, j)$, $(i, j - 1)$, and (i, j), respectively. These five coefficients are the same for all the finite difference equations. Thus, there is no need to store even these $5n$ coefficients if iterative methods are used. Only the $n = (imax)\times(jmax)$ values of $T_{i,j}$, the solution array itself, must be stored. Consequently, iterative methods, which are discussed in Section 9.5, should be employed when the number of grid points is large.

9.5 ITERATIVE METHODS OF SOLUTION

Direct solutions of the Laplace equation for the steady two-dimensional heat conduction problem are presented in Section 9.4. As discussed at the end of that section, direct solutions require excessive computational effort and computer memory as the number of grid points increases. In such cases, iterative methods should be employed.

Several iterative methods are discussed in Sections 1.6 to 1.8:

1. Jacobi iteration
2. Gauss–Seidel iteration
3. relaxation
4. successive overrelaxation (SOR)

As discussed in those sections, iterative methods require *diagonal dominance* to guarantee convergence. Diagonal dominance requires that

$$|a_{ii}| \geq \sum_{j=1, j\neq i}^{n} |a_{ij}| \qquad (i = 1, \ldots, n) \tag{9.62}$$

with the inequality satisfied for at least one equation. The system of finite difference equations arising from the five-point second-order centered-difference approximation of the Laplace equation is always diagonally dominant, as illustrated by the finite difference stencils presented in Fig. 9.4 and the coefficient matrix presented in Eq. (9.52). Consequently, iterative methods can be employed to solve the Laplace equation.

The Jacobi method converges slowly, so it will not be used here. The relaxation method is most suitable for hand calculation, so it will not be used here. The Gauss–Seidel method, which is the limiting case of the SOR method, will be used to demonstrate the general features of iterative methods. However, successive overrelaxation (SOR) is the recommended method and should be used in general.

The Gauss–Seidel Method

The Gauss–Seidel method, applied to the finite difference solution of the Laplace equation, is obtained by adding the term $\pm f_{i,j}$ to Eq. (9.39) and rearranging as follows:

$$f_{i,j}^{k+1} = f_{i,j}^{k} + \Delta f_{i,j}^{k+1} \tag{9.63}$$

$$\Delta f_{i,j}^{k+1} = \frac{f_{i+1,j}^{k} + \beta^2 f_{i,j+1}^{k} + f_{i-1,j}^{k+1} + \beta^2 f_{i,j-1}^{k+1} - 2(1+\beta^2) f_{i,j}^{k}}{2(1+\beta^2)} \tag{9.64}$$

where the superscript $k(k = 0, 1, 2, \ldots)$ denotes the iteration number. The term $\Delta f_{i,j}$ is called the *residual* in the relaxation method. Equation (9.64) is based on the sweep directions illustrated in Fig. 9.6. The order of the sweeps is irrelevant, but once chosen, it should be maintained.

An initial approximation ($k = 0$) must be made for $f_{i,j}$ to start the process. Several choices are available, such as the following:

1. Let $f_{i,j} = 0.0$ at all of the interior points.
2. Approximate $f_{i,j}$ by some weighted average of the boundary values.
3. Construct a solution on a coarser grid, then interpolate for starting values on a finer grid. This procedure can be repeated on finer and finer grids.

Iterative methods do not yield the exact solution of the finite difference equations directly. They approach the exact solution asymptotically as the number of iterations increases. When the number of iterations increases without bound, the iterative solution yields the exact solution of the finite difference equations, within the round-off limit of the computer. However, in most practical problems, such extreme precision is not warranted. Consequently, the iterative process is usually terminated when some form of convergence criterion has been achieved. Various convergence criteria are possible. For example:

$$\left|\Delta f_{i,j}^{k+1}\right| < \epsilon \quad \text{(for all } i, j) \qquad \left|\Delta f_{i,j}^{k+1}\right| < \epsilon \left|f_{i,j}^{k}\right| \quad \text{(for all } i, j) \tag{9.65}$$

$$\sum_{i,j}^{n} \left|\Delta f_{i,j}^{k+1}\right| < \epsilon \qquad \sum_{i,j}^{n} \left|\frac{\Delta f_{i,j}^{k+1}}{f_{i,j}^{k}}\right| < \epsilon \tag{9.66}$$

$$\left(\sum_{i,j}^{n} \left(\Delta f_{i,j}^{k+1}\right)^2\right)^{1/2} < \epsilon \qquad \left(\sum_{i,j}^{n} \left(\frac{\Delta f_{i,j}^{k+1}}{f_{i,j}^{k}}\right)^2\right)^{1/2} < \epsilon \tag{9.67}$$

where ϵ is the convergence tolerance. The three criteria on the left are absolute criteria and are useful when the magnitude of the solution is known, so that a meaningful value of ϵ can be specified. The three criteria on the right are relative criteria and are useful when the magnitude of the solution is not known, in which case a meaningful absolute convergence tolerance cannot be specified. Caution in the use of relative criteria is necessary if any of the $f_{i,j}$ are close to zero in magnitude.

Example 9.6. Numerical solution by the Gauss–Seidel method. Solve the steady two-dimensional heat conduction problem presented in Section 9.1 by the Gauss–Seidel method, using the 5×7 finite difference grid illustrated in Fig. 9.5. Let $T_{i,j} = 0.0$ be the initial guess. The solution at selected iteration steps is presented in Table 9.6 for selected grid points, along with the maximum value of $\left|\Delta T_{i,j}\right| = \left|\Delta T\right|_{\max}$. The solution has converged to five significant figures on the 20th iteration. The maximum residual continues to decrease as the iterative process continues, but no changes occur in the solution in the first five significant digits. The solution (converged to 13 significant digits) is presented in the third from the last line. The exact solution is presented in the next to the last line of Table 9.5. The difference between the converged solution of the

TABLE 9.6
Temperatures at selected grid points as a function of iteration number k

Iteration number k	Grid point location (x,y) (2.5, 12.5)	(5.0, 12.5)	(5.0, 10.0)	(5.0, 7.5)	(7.5, 12.5)	$\lvert\Delta T\rvert_{max}$
0	0.000	0.000	0.000	0.000	0.000	
1	25.000	31.250	9.375	2.734	32.813	3.28E + 01
2	34.375	44.141	17.188	6.226	38.672	1.29E + 01
3	38.867	48.682	21.155	8.595	40.869	4.54E + 00
4	40.900	50.731	23.279	10.087	41.904	2.12E + 00
5	41.909	51.773	24.472	11.014	42.446	1.19E + 00
6	42.447	52.342	25.167	11.588	42.479	6.95E − 01
7	42.749	52.666	25.581	11.943	42.925	4.14E − 01
8	42.925	52.858	25.831	12.162	43.030	2.50E − 01
9	43.030	52.973	25.983	12.298	43.093	1.53E − 01
10	43.093	53.042	26.077	12.382	43.132	9.37E − 02
15	43.184	53.144	26.214	12.506	43.188	8.40E − 03
20	43.193	53.153	26.227	12.517	43.193	7.61E − 04
25	43.193	53.154	26.228	12.518	43.193	6.89E − 05
30	...	...	...	...	...	6.25E − 06
35	...	...	...	...	...	5.66E − 07
40	...	...	...	...	...	5.13E − 08
	...	...	...	...	...	
∞	43.193	53.154	26.228	12.518	43.193	
Exact	43.483	54.449	26.049	11.924	43.483	
Error	− 0.290	− 1.295	0.179	0.594	− 0.290	

finite difference equations and the exact solution of the partial differential equation is the truncation error of the finite difference method, which is presented in the last line of Table 9.6.

The maximum residual $|\Delta T|_{max}$ is presented in Fig. 9.8 as a function of the iteration number k. The curve labeled "Gauss–Seidel" corresponds to the results presented in Table 9.6. The curves labeled "SOR" are discussed later in this section. The maximum residual decreases exponentially with increasing k. The linear portion of the curve can be fit to the equation

$$|\Delta T|_{\max} = Ae^{-Bk} \tag{9.68}$$

For the data presented in Fig. 9.8, Eq. (9.68) becomes

$$|\Delta T|_{\max} = 11.289e^{-0.4802k} \tag{9.69}$$

The rate of convergence is given by

$$\frac{d\,|\Delta T|_{\max}}{|\Delta T|_{\max}} = d\left(\ln|\Delta T|_{\max}\right) = -Bk \tag{9.70}$$

Thus, B is the logarithmic rate of decrease of $|\Delta T|_{\max}$ with the number of itera-

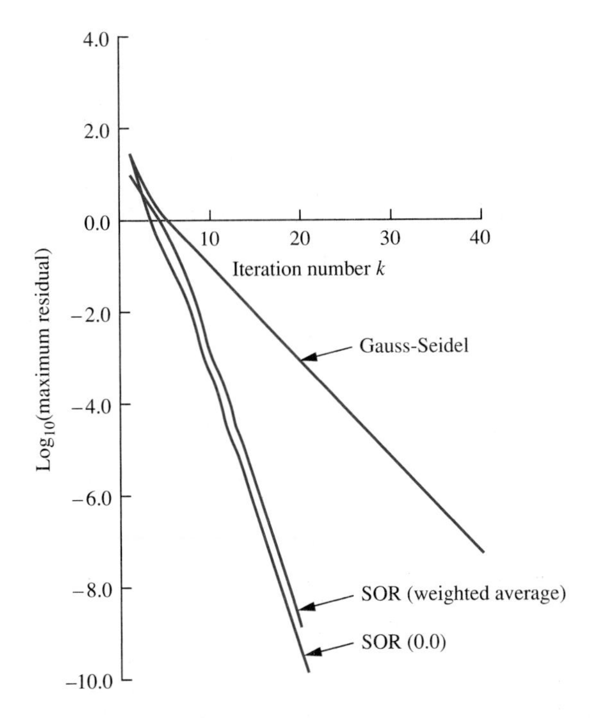

FIGURE 9.8
Maximum residual as a function of the iteration number k.

tions. For the Gauss–Seidel method applied to the heat conduction problem using a 5×7 grid, $B = 0.4802$.

The Successive Overrelaxation (SOR) Method

The convergence rate of the relaxation method can be greatly increased by using overrelaxation. The Gauss–Seidel method, Eq. (9.63), becomes overrelaxation simply by overrelaxing the residual $\Delta f_{i,j}^{k+1}$ by the overrelaxation factor ω. Thus,

$$f_{i,j}^{k+1} = f_{i,j}^{k} + \omega \, \Delta f_{i,j}^{k+1} \tag{9.71}$$

where the residual $\Delta f_{i,j}^{k+1}$ is given by Eq. (9.64), as before. When Eq. (9.71) is applied repetitively, it is called the successive overrelaxation (SOR) method. When $\omega = 1.0$, the SOR method reduces to the Gauss–Seidel method. The maximum rate of convergence is achieved for some optimum value of ω, denoted by ω_{opt}, which lies between 1.0 and 2.0.

Example 9.7. Numerical solution by the SOR method. The optimum overrelaxation factor ω_{opt} cannot be predicted theoretically except for some very special cases. However, ω_{opt} can be determined experimentally by reworking a given problem repetitively for a range of values of ω and monitoring the convergence rate. Table 9.7 presents the results of such a study for the present problem, for the 5×7 and 9×13 grids, for an absolute convergence tolerance $\epsilon = 0.000001$. For the 5×7 grid, 34 iterations are required for the

TABLE 9.7
Effects of the overrelaxation factor ω on the number of iterations k.

ω	Number of iterations k	
	5×7 grid	9×13 grid
1.00	34	130
1.10	27	106
1.20	19	85
1.30	15	67
1.40	21	50
1.50	26	31
1.60	35	36
1.70	50	50
1.80	78	78
1.90	165	165

TABLE 9.8
Numerical evaluation of ω_{opt}.

ω	Number of iterations k	
	5×7 grid	9×13 grid
1.00	30	108
1.10	23	89
1.20	17	72
1.30	15	58
1.40	18	44
1.50	23	29
1.60	29	31
1.70	40	45
1.80	63	69
1.90	133	134

Gauss–Seidel method ($\omega = 1.0$), whereas only 15 iterations are required for $\omega = 1.30$. This is a decrease of approximately 56 percent in the computational effort. The value of ω_{opt} is in the neighborhood of 1.30. For the 9×13 grid, 130 iterations are required for the Gauss–Seidel method ($\omega = 1.0$), whereas only 31 iterations are required for $\omega = 1.50$. This is a decrease of approximately 76 percent in the computational effort. The value of ω_{opt} is in the neighborhood of 1.50. The savings in computational effort increases dramatically as the number of grid points (i.e., the number of finite difference equations) increases.

The determination of an optimum value of the overrelaxation factor ω can be accomplished numerically. Example 9.8 illustrates the procedure.

Example 9.8. Numerical evaluation of ω_{opt}. Numerical evaluation of the optimum overrelaxation factor ω_{opt} is worthwhile only when a problem is to be worked repetitively—for example, for a series of different boundary conditions or nonhomogeneous terms. A straightforward procedure for determining ω_{opt} numerically for a specific finite difference grid is to set all the boundary values to 0.0 and all the interior values to 100.0, and then vary ω from 1.0 to 2.0 in increments until ω_{opt} is determined. Table 9.8 presents the results of such a study for the 5×7 and 9×13 grids, for $\epsilon = 0.000001$. Comparing Tables 9.7 and 9.8 shows that the same values of ω_{opt} are obtained for the two different sets of initial and boundary conditions, but that the number of iterations required to converge is considerably different.

In some special cases, the optimum overrelaxation factor ω_{opt} can be predicted theoretically. For a rectangular region with Dirichlet boundary conditions (i.e., specified values of the dependent variable), ω_{opt} can be estimated from [Frankel (1950)]

$$\omega_{opt} = 2\left(\frac{1 - \sqrt{1 - \xi}}{\xi}\right) \tag{9.72}$$

TABLE 9.9
Values of ω_{opt} for several grid sizes

Grid Size	ω_{opt}
3×4	1.01613323
5×7	1.23647138
9×13	1.50676003
17×25	1.71517254
33×49	1.84615581
65×97	1.91993173

where

$$\xi = \left(\frac{\cos(\pi/I) + \beta^2 \cos(\pi/J)}{1 + \beta^2} \right)^2 \tag{9.73}$$

where $I = (imax-1)$ is the number of spatial increments in the x direction, $J = (jmax - 1)$ is the number of spatial increments in the y direction, and $\beta = \Delta x/\Delta y$ is the grid aspect ratio. Values of ω_{opt} for the 10 cm by 15 cm physical space considered in the heat conduction problem are presented in Table 9.9 for several grid sizes.

Example 9.9. Numerical solution by the SOR method using ω_{opt}. Table 9.10 presents the solution to the heat conduction problem presented in Section 9.1 for the 5×7 grid using the SOR method with $\omega_{opt} = 1.23647138$. The convergence history is illustrated in Fig. 9.8. The curve labeled "SOR (0.0)" uses $T_{i,j} = 0.0$ as the initial guess. The curve labeled "SOR (weighted average)" uses the linearly weighted average of the four

TABLE 9.10
Temperatures at selected grid points as a function of iteration number k

	Grid point location (x,y)					
Iteration number k	(2.5, 12.5)	(5.0, 12.5)	(5.0, 10.0)	(5.0, 7.5)	(7.5, 12.5)	$\lvert\Delta T\rvert_{max}$
0	0.000	0.000	0.000	0.000	0.000	
1	30.912	40.467	15.463	5.693	43.421	3.51E + 01
2	39.065	51.620	24.481	11.033	42.227	9.02E + 00
3	42.425	52.440	25.427	11.944	42.886	2.75E + 00
4	42.936	52.900	25.961	12.356	43.085	4.32E − 01
5	43.078	53.062	26.144	12.477	43.158	1.63E − 01
6	43.157	53.127	26.209	12.506	43.184	7.10E − 02
7	43.185	53.149	26.223	12.515	43.192	2.31E − 02
8	43.192	53.152	26.226	12.518	43.193	5.35E − 03
9	43.193	53.153	26.227	12.518	43.193	9.21E − 04
10	43.193	53.154	26.228	12.518	43.193	3.43E − 04
15	...	...	...	...	...	3.82E − 07
20	...	...	...	...	...	3.82E − 10
	...	...	...	...	...	
∞	43.193	53.154	26.228	12.518	43.193	
Exact	43.483	54.449	26.049	11.924	43.483	

corresponding boundary values as the initial guess. As illustrated in Fig. 9.8, the initial guess has little effect on the convergence rate. Comparing Tables 9.6 and 9.10 shows that the solution converges more rapidly using the SOR method. In fact, the solution has converged to five significant digits by the 10th iteration, as compared to 20 iterations for the Gauss–Seidel method. Figure 9.8 presents the maximum residual $|\Delta T|_{max}$ as a function of iteration number k for the SOR method with ω_{opt}, for comparison with the results of the Gauss–Seidel method. The linear portion of the curve can be fitted to the equation

$$|\Delta T|_{max} = 307.98e^{-1.3708k} \tag{9.74}$$

The logarithmic convergence rate for these results is $B = 1.3708$ [see Eq. (9.70)], compared to $B = 0.4802$ for the Gauss–Seidel method.

Further insights into the SOR method are illustrated in Figs. 9.9 and 9.10. Both figures apply to the heat conduction problem. Figure 9.9 presents the value of $|\Delta T|_{max}$, for the 9×13 grid, after 50, 100, and 200 iterations, as a function of the overrelaxation factor ω. Figure 9.10 presents the number of iterations k required to achieve convergence tolerances of $\epsilon = 0.001$, 0.0001, 0.00001, and 0.000001 for the 5×7, 9×13, and 17×25 grids, as a function of the overrelaxation factor ω. Both of these figures demonstrate the advantages of the SOR method and the desirability of using the optimum value of ω.

All of the results presented so far used $T_{i,j} = 0.0$ as the initial guess. Fig. 9.8 also presents the maximum residual $|\Delta T|_{max}$ for the solution for the

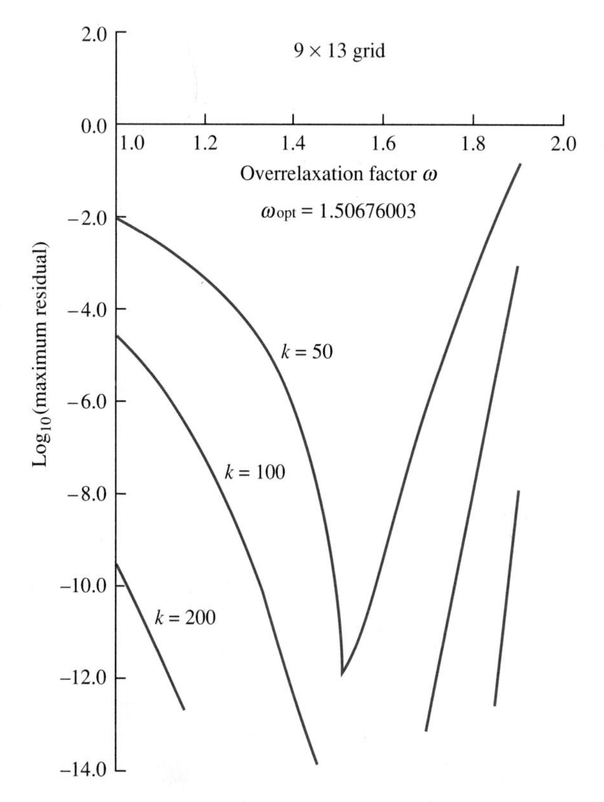

FIGURE 9.9
Maximum residual as a function of the overrelaxation factor ω.

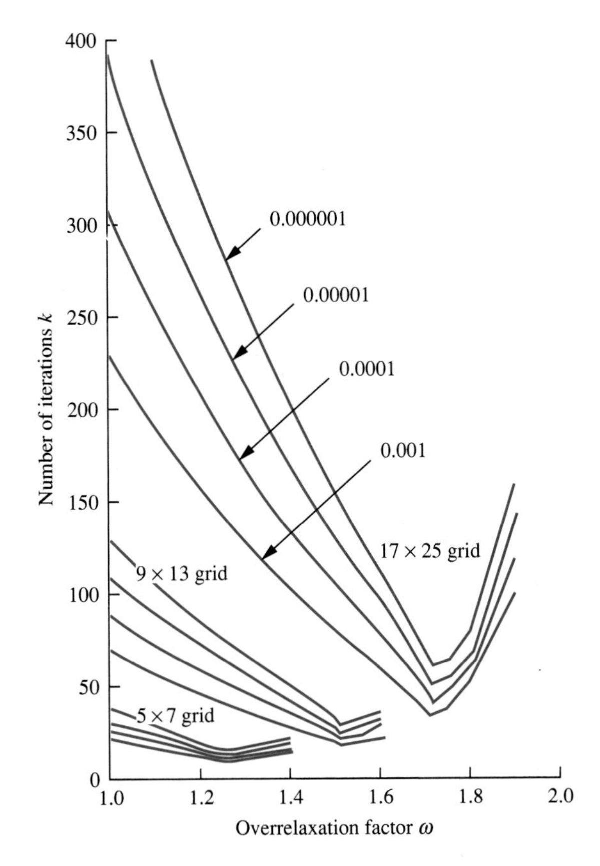

FIGURE 9.10
Number of iterations k as a function of the overrelaxation factor ω.

5×7 grid obtained by the SOR method using ω_{opt}, where the initial guess is the weighted average of the four corresponding boundary conditions. The initial errors are smaller, and the errors for the first three iterations are smaller. However, the errors for the remaining iterations are larger than those for the 0.0 initial guess. Evidently, the weighted average initial guess is slightly less effective than the 0.0 initial guess.

The Line Successive Overrelaxation (LSOR) Method

The Gauss–Seidel and SOR methods are both *point* relaxation methods, in which each point is relaxed in succession. *Block* relaxation methods, in which a block of points is relaxed simultaneously, can also be employed. *Line relaxation* is a common form of block relaxation. Point relaxation, illustrated in Fig. 9.6, is specified by Eqs. (9.63) and (9.64). In Eq. (9.64), two values of f are specified at iteration number $k + 1$ ($f_{i-1,j}$ and $f_{i,j-1}$) and three values of f are specified at iteration number k ($f_{i+1,j}$, $f_{i,j+1}$, and $f_{i,j}$).

In line relaxation by rows, the entire solution row is specified at iteration number $k + 1$, leaving only $f_{i,j+1}$ specified at iteration number k. Figure 9.11 illustrates line relaxation by rows. For line relaxation by rows, Eq. (9.64)

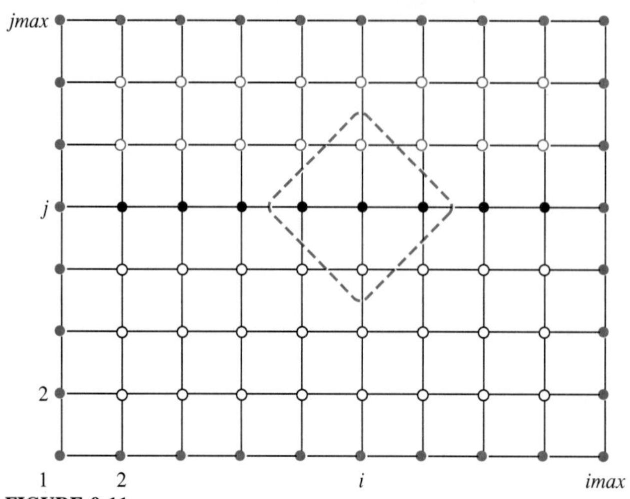

FIGURE 9.11
Sweep strategy for line relaxation.

becomes

$$\Delta f_{i,j}^{k+1} = \frac{f_{i+1,j}^{k+1} + \beta^2 f_{i,j+1}^{k} + f_{i-1,j}^{k+1} + \beta^2 f_{i,j-1}^{k+1} - 2(1+\beta^2) f_{i,j}^{k+1}}{2(1+\beta^2)} \tag{9.75}$$

Substituting Eq. (9.75) into Eq. (9.63) and rearranging yields

$$f_{i-1,j}^{k+1} - 2(1+\beta^2) f_{i,j}^{k+1} + f_{i+1,j}^{k+1} = -\beta^2 \left(f_{i,j-1}^{k+1} + f_{i,j+1}^{k} \right) \tag{9.76}$$

Equation (9.76) is an implicit finite difference equation containing three unknown values at each grid point: $f_{i+1,j}^{k+1}$, $f_{i,j}^{k+1}$, and $f_{i-1,j}^{k+1}$. The value of $f_{i,j-1}^{k+1}$ is known from the just completed sweep of line $j-1$, and the value of $f_{i,j+1}^{k}$ is known from the previous iteration.

In line relaxation by columns, sweeping from column $i = 2$ to $i = imax - 1$, the entire solution column is specified at iteration number $k+1$, leaving only $f_{i+1,j}$ specified at iteration number k. For line relaxation by columns,

$$\Delta f_{i,j}^{k+1} = \frac{f_{i+1,j}^{k} + \beta^2 f_{i,j+1}^{k+1} + f_{i-1,j}^{k+1} + \beta^2 f_{i,j-1}^{k+1} - 2(1+\beta^2) f_{i,j}^{k+1}}{2(1+\beta^2)} \tag{9.77}$$

Substituting Eq. (9.77) into Eq. (9.63) and rearranging yields

$$f_{i,j-1}^{k+1} - \frac{2(1+\beta^2)}{\beta^2} f_{i,j}^{k+1} + f_{i,j+1}^{k+1} = -\frac{1}{\beta^2} \left(f_{i-1,j}^{k+1} - f_{i+1,j}^{k} \right) \tag{9.78}$$

Equation (9.78) is an implicit finite difference equation containing three unknown values at each grid point: $f_{i,j-1}^{k+1}$, $f_{i,j}^{k+1}$, and $f_{i,j+1}^{k+1}$. The value of $f_{i-1,j}^{k+1}$ is known from the just completed sweep of column $i-1$, and the value of $f_{i+1,j}^{k}$ is known from the previous iteration.

When the implicit finite difference equation [Eq. (9.76) or (9.78)] is applied at all of the interior grid points on one line (i.e., row or column, respectively), a tridiagonal system of equations results. That system can be solved directly by the Thomas algorithm (see Section 1.5).

After the solution for $f_{i,j}^{k+1}$ has been computed along the line, it can be overrelaxed by applying Eq. (9.71) at every point along the line. Thus,

$$\left(f_{i,j}^{k+1}\right)_{\text{overrelaxed}} = f_{i,j}^{k} + \omega\left(f_{i,j}^{k+1} - f_{i,j}^{k}\right) \tag{9.79}$$

Ames (1969) states that the line SOR method converges in fewer iterations than the point SOR method by the factor $1/\sqrt{2}$ in the limit as Δx and $\Delta y \to 0$. However, each iteration requires more computational effort because of the solution of the tridiagonal system. Consequently, the overall gain in computational efficiency, if any, may be small and not worth the increased complexity of the overall algorithm.

Another approach to line SOR is to include the overrelaxation factor ω in Eqs. (9.76) and (9.78). The value of ω may be considerably different in this approach.

The Alternating-Direction Line SOR (ADLSOR) Method

The line SOR method described in the previous section can be modified to sweep first across the rows, as illustrated in Fig. 9.11 and specified in Eq. (9.76), and then along the columns, as specified by Eq. (9.78). Subsequent pairs of sweeps are performed until the procedure converges. This procedure is known as the alternating-direction line successive overrelaxation (ADLSOR) method. The advantage of this procedure, like the LSOR procedure, is that the influence of the boundary conditions is spread over the entire solution domain more rapidly. The overall gain in computational efficiency, if any, may be small and not worth the increased complexity of the overall algorithm.

9.6 DERIVATIVE BOUNDARY CONDITIONS

All the finite difference solutions to the Laplace equation presented thus far have been for Dirichlet boundary conditions, that is, the values of $\bar{f}(x, y)$ are specified on the boundaries. In this section, several procedures for implementing derivative, or Neumann, boundary conditions are presented. We will solve the steady two-dimensional heat conduction problem presented in Section 9.1 by recognizing that the vertical midplane of the rectangular plate considered in that problem is a plane of symmetry. Thus, no heat crosses the midplane, and the temperature gradient at that location is zero. This is true only when the boundary conditions on the edges of the plate are symmetrical, which is the case in this particular problem.

The formal statement of the problem is as follows. A rectangular plate of height $h = 15$ cm, width $w = 5$ cm, and thickness $t = 1$ cm, is insulated on both faces so that no heat flows in the direction of the thickness t. The temperature on the top edge of the plate is held at 100 C, and the temperatures on the left and bottom edges of the plate are held at 0 C. The right edge of the plate is insulated so that $\partial T/\partial x = 0$ along that edge. This boundary condition is formally stated as

$$\overline{T}_x(5.0, y) = 0 \tag{9.80}$$

The temperature distribution $\overline{T}(x, y)$ in the plate is required.

The exact solution to this problem is the same as the exact solution to the problem presented in Section 9.1, which is given by Eq. (9.8). The plate, the boundary conditions, and the exact solution are presented in Fig. 9.12 for selected isotherms.

In this section, we will solve this problem numerically using the finite difference method developed in Section 9.4, modified to account for the derivative boundary condition along the right edge of the plate, Eq. (9.80). The following two approaches for applying the derivative boundary condition will be implemented:

1. Application of the interior point FDE at the boundary point
2. Extrapolation of the interior point solution to the boundary point

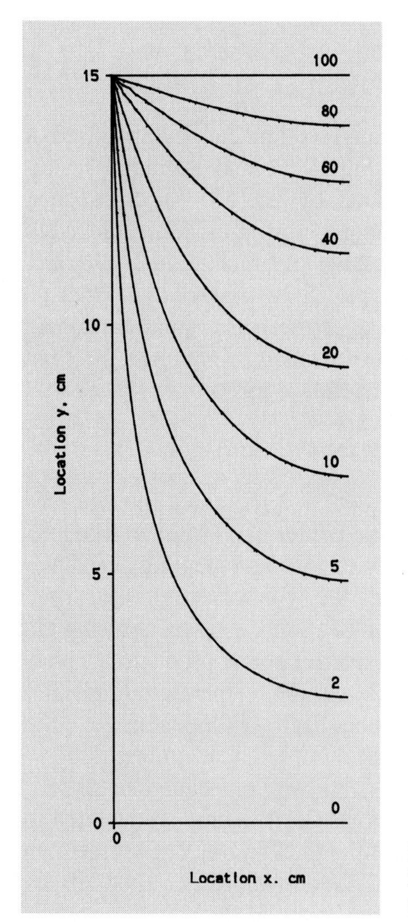

FIGURE 9.12
Exact solution of the heat conduction problem with a derivative boundary condition.

In both cases, careful attention will be given to the order of the truncation error of the finite difference approximation of the partial differential equation and to the order of the discretization error of the corresponding finite difference equation.

Interior Point FDE at the Boundary

First, let us apply the interior point finite difference equation (FDE) at grid point (I, j) on the right edge of the plate, as illustrated in Fig. 9.13. The FDE is [Eq. (9.35)]:

$$\bar{f}_{I+1,j}+\beta^2\bar{f}_{I,j+1}+\bar{f}_{I-1,j}+\beta^2\bar{f}_{I,j-1}-2(1+\beta^2)\bar{f}_{I,j}+\Delta x^2\left(O(\Delta x^2)+O(\Delta y)^2\right)=0 \tag{9.81}$$

where the terms $\Delta x^2\,[O(\Delta x^2)+O(\Delta y^2)]$ are discretization errors. Grid point $(I+1, j)$ is outside of the solution domain, so $\bar{f}_{I+1,j}$ is not defined. However, a value for $\bar{f}_{I+1,j}$ can be determined from the derivative boundary condition on the right edge of the plate.

The finite difference approximations employed in Eq. (9.81) for the space derivatives $\bar{f}_{xx}$ and $\bar{f}_{yy}$ are second-order. It is desirable to match this truncation error by using a second-order centered-difference finite difference approximation for the derivative boundary condition, $\bar{f}_x|_{I,j}$ = known. Thus,

$$\bar{f}_x|_{I,j} = \frac{\bar{f}_{I+1,j}-\bar{f}_{I-1,j}}{2\,\Delta x} + O(\Delta x^2) \tag{9.82}$$

Solving Eq. (9.82) for $\bar{f}_{I+1,j}$ gives

$$\bar{f}_{I+1,j} = \bar{f}_{I-1,j} + 2\bar{f}_x|_{I,j}\,\Delta x + \Delta x\; O(\Delta x^2) \tag{9.83}$$

Substituting this result into Eq. (9.81) yields

$$\left(\bar{f}_{I-1,j} + 2\bar{f}_x|_{I,j}\,\Delta x + \Delta x O(\Delta x^2)\right) + \beta^2\bar{f}_{I,j+1} + \bar{f}_{I-1,j} + \beta^2\bar{f}_{I,j-1}$$
$$-2(1+\beta^2)\bar{f}_{I,j} + \Delta x^2\left(O(\Delta x^2)+O(\Delta y^2)\right) = 0 \tag{9.84}$$

Dropping the discretization error terms gives the finite difference equation appli-

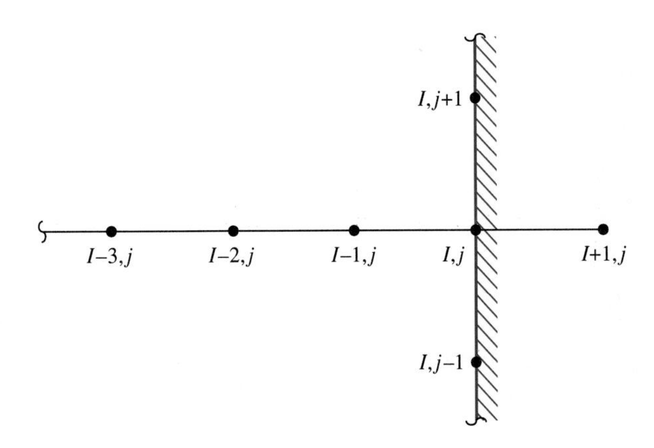

FIGURE 9.13
Finite difference grid at the boundary.

cable along the right edge of the plate:

$$\beta^2 f_{I,j+1} + 2f_{I-1,j} + \beta^2 f_{I,j-1} - 2(1+\beta^2)f_{I,j} = -2\bar{f}_x|_{I,j}\,\Delta x \tag{9.85}$$

In the present problem, $\bar{f}_x|_{I,j} = 0$. However, Eq. (9.85) is applicable in the general case where $\bar{f}_x|_{I,j} \neq 0$.

Before applying Eq. (9.85) in a numerical example, let us examine the discretization errors in Eq. (9.84) to see whether they are compatible. The discretization errors are

$$e_{I,j} = \Delta x\, O(\Delta x^2) + \Delta x^2 \left(O(\Delta x^2) + O(\Delta y^2)\right) \tag{9.86}$$

The first term, $\Delta x\, O(\Delta x^2)$, which is a consequence of the manner in which the boundary condition is implemented, is one order lower in Δx than the other terms that arise from the discretization of the partial derivatives in the partial differential equation. This result is also illustrated in Eq. (8.78). Consequently, even though the truncation error of the finite difference approximation of $\bar{f}_x$ at the boundary is of the same order as the truncation errors of the finite difference approximations

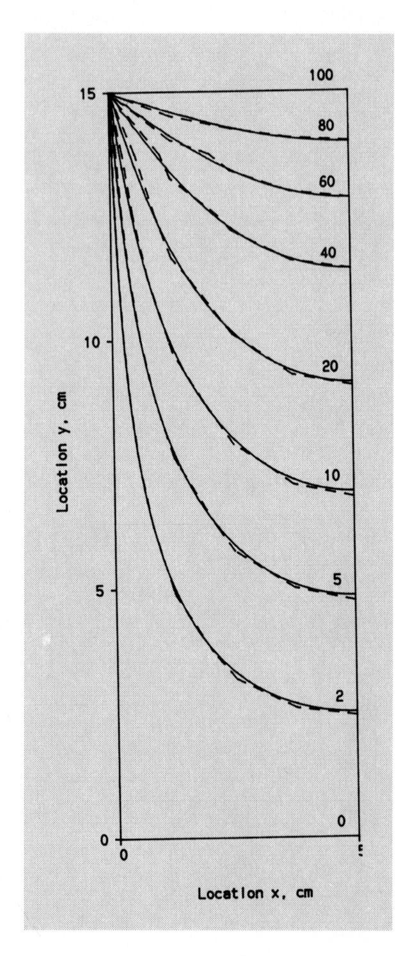

FIGURE 9.14a
Numerical solution with a derivative BC: (*a*) PDE at the boundary.

of $\overline{f}_{xx}$ and $\overline{f}_{yy}$ in the partial differential equation, the corresponding discretization error is of lower order. This mismatch in the orders of the discretization errors always occurs when the orders of the partial derivatives being approximated are different (i.e., $\overline{f}_x$, $\overline{f}_{xx}$, and $\overline{f}_{yy}$ in the present case). This may or may not be acceptable, depending on the problem. For example, if the solution is well-behaved near the boundary and the gradients are small, the mismatch in discretization errors may not affect the accuracy of the overall solution significantly. That is the case in the present example. In other problems where the solution is less well-behaved near the boundary and the gradients there are large, this mismatch in discretization errors may cause a significant loss of accuracy.

Example 9.10. Numerical solution using the PDE at the boundary. As an example, we will work the steady two-dimensional heat conduction problem on a 5×13 grid using Eq. (9.85) along the right edge of the plate. The results are presented in Fig. 9.14*a*, where the numerical solution is indicated by the dashed lines. The numerical solution is obviously a good approximation of the exact solution. The temperatures along the right edge of the plate are presented in Table 9.11 under the heading PDE. These results are comparable to the results illustrated in Fig. 9.7 and tabulated in Table 9.5 for the 9×13 grid for the full plate solution.

TABLE 9.11
Temperatures* along the right edge of the plate

			Extrapolation		
Location (x,y)	**Exact**	**PDE**	**Linear**	**Quadratic**	**Cubic**
(5,0, 15.00)	100.000	100.000	100.000	100.000	100.000
(5,0, 13.75)	75.611	75.122	71.038	75.972	73.752
		−0.489	−4.573	0.361	−1.859
(5,0, 12.50)	54.449	54.024	48.045	54.729	53.240
		−0.425	−6.404	0.280	−1.209
(5,0, 11.25)	37.996	37.838	31.678	38.224	37.507
		−0.158	−6.318	0.228	−0.489
(5,0, 10.00)	26.049	26.095	20.615	26.251	25.996
		0.046	−5.434	0.202	−0.053
(5,0, 8.75)	17.684	17.828	13.322	17.858	17.833
		0.144	−4.362	0.174	0.149
(5,0, 7.50)	11.924	12.093	8.567	12.065	12.139
		0.169	−3.357	0.141	0.215
(5,0, 6.25)	7.978	8.134	5.478	8.085	8.190
		0.156	−2.500	0.107	0.212
(5,0, 5.00)	5.261	5.390	3.464	5.340	5.442
		0.129	−1.797	0.079	0.181
(5,0, 8.75)	3.362	3.458	2.133	3.417	3.500
		0.096	−1.229	0.055	0.138
(5,0, 2.50)	1.987	2.050	1.224	2.021	2.078
		0.063	−0.763	0.034	0.091
(5,0, 1.25)	0.999	0.952	0.557	0.938	0.967
		−0.047	−0.442	−0.061	−0.032
(5,0, 0.00)	0.000	0.000	0.000	0.000	0.000

* Errors are listed below the solution values.

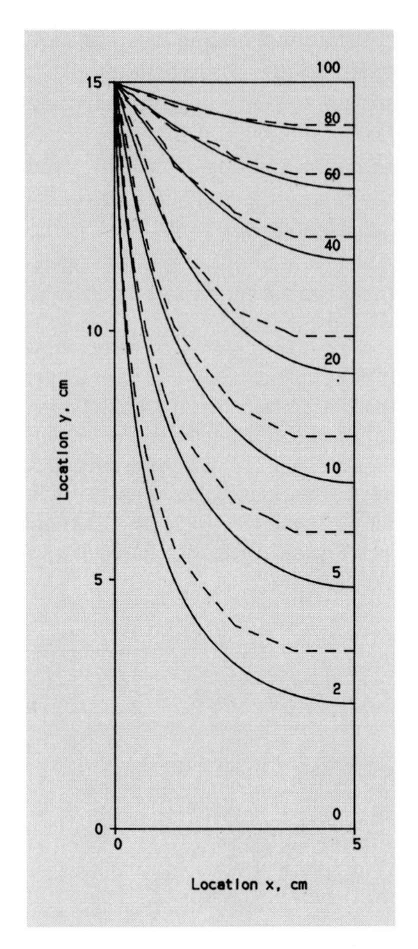

FIGURE 9.14*b*
Numerical solution with a derivative BC: (*b*) Linear extrapolation.

Extrapolation

Next, let us consider a procedure for implementing a derivative boundary condition by *extrapolating* the solution at the boundary point from the solution at the adjacent interior points. The finite difference grid is illustrated in Fig. 9.13. A Newton backward-difference polynomial with base point at grid point (I, j) is fitted to the data along grid line j. This polynomial is then differentiated and solved for the derivative at the boundary point. The known derivative boundary condition is then substituted into that equation, which is then solved for $f_{I,j}$ at the boundary point.

This procedure is presented in Section 8.6 for a one-dimensional equilibrium problem in terms of the variable $y(x)$. The results obtained there apply here directly with y_i replaced by $f_{i,j}$. Recall Eqs. (8.83) for linear extrapolation,

$$f_{I,j} = f_{I-1,j} + \overline{f}_x|_{I,j}\, \Delta x, \qquad \Delta x\ O(\Delta x) \tag{9.87}$$

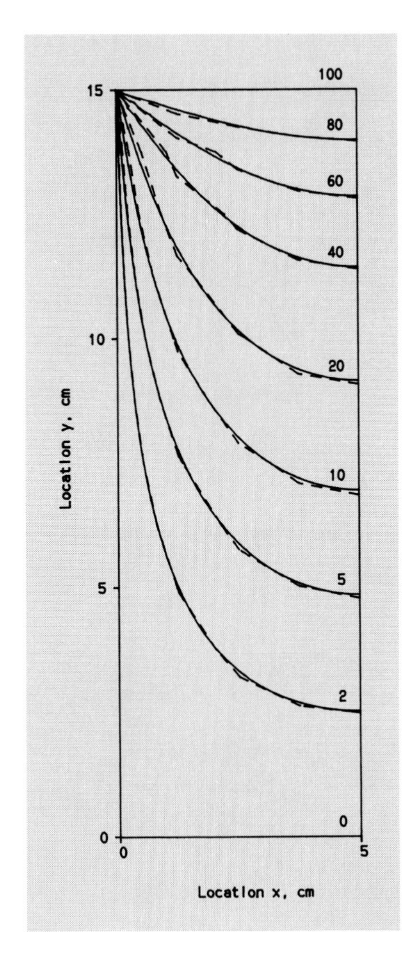

FIGURE 9.14*c*
Numerical solution with a derivative BC: (*c*) Quadratic extrapolation.

Eq. (8.85) for quadratic extrapolation,

$$f_{I,j} = \frac{1}{3}\left(4f_{I-1,j} - f_{I-2,j} - 2\overline{f}_x|_{I,j}\ \Delta x\right), \qquad \Delta x\ O(\Delta x^2) \tag{9.88}$$

and Eq. (8.87) for cubic extrapolation:

$$f_{I,j} = \frac{1}{11}\left(18f_{I-1,j} - 9f_{I-2,j} + 2f_{I-3,j} + 6\overline{f}_x|_{I,j}\ \Delta x\right), \qquad \Delta x\ O(\Delta x^3) \tag{9.89}$$

Equations (9.87) to (9.89) must be examined for consistency with the Laplace equation. From Eq. (9.35), the discretization error of the five-point finite difference approximation of the Laplace equation is $\Delta x^2[O(\Delta x^2) + O(\Delta y^2)]$.

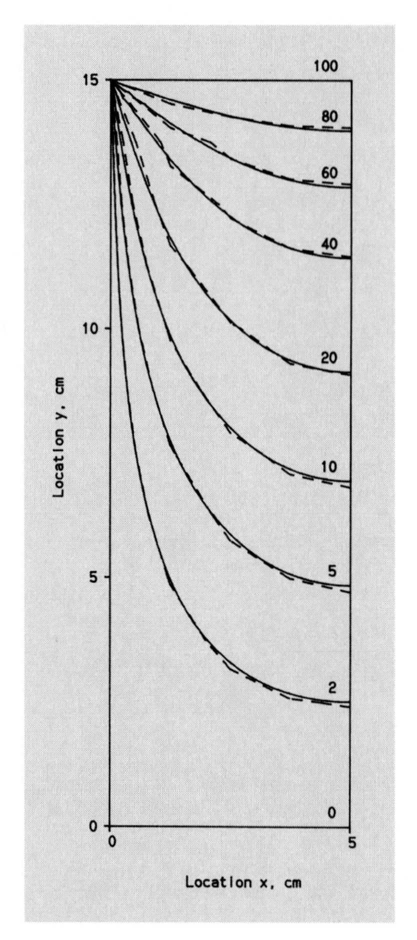

FIGURE 9.14*d*
Numerical solution with a derivative BC: (*d*) Cubic extrapolation.

Equation (9.87) is two-orders lower in Δx, Eq. (9.88) is one order lower in Δx, and Eq. (9.89) is the same order in Δx. The two-order mismatch of Eq. (9.87) is a serious problem. As discussed in the preceding subsection, the one-order mismatch in Eq. (9.88) may or may not be acceptable, depending on the problem being solved. Equation (9.89) is the same order as Eq. (9.35). An undesirable feature of Eq. (9.89) is that $f_{I,j}$ depends on a larger range of points (i.e., $I - 3$ to I) than $f_{I-1,j}$ (i.e., $I - 2$ to I).

Example 9.11. Numerical solution using extrapolation. Let us work the heat conduction problem with a derivative BC using the extrapolation method. The results are presented in Figs. 9.14*b* to 9.14*d*. The temperatures along the right edge of the plate are presented in Table 9.11. For linear extrapolation, Fig. 9.14*b* shows that, although the solution is not completely unrealistic, the solution is not a good approximation of the exact solution. This is not surprising, since Eq. (9.87) is two orders less accurate in Δx than the FDE at the interior points. For quadratic extrapolation, Fig. 9.14*c* shows that the results are comparable to the results presented in Fig. 9.14*a* for the PDE method, and they are considerably better than the results presented in Fig. 9.14*b* for linear extrapolation. The results presented in Fig. 9.14*d* for cubic extrapolation are comparable to the results obtained with quadratic extrapolation and the PDE method.

All the numerical results presented in this section were obtained by Gauss elimination for a 5×13 grid. The objective of the numerical studies presented in this section was to demonstrate procedures for implementing derivative boundary conditions. Accuracy and computational efficiency were not of primary interest. As demonstrated in Sections 9.4 and 9.5, more accurate solutions can be obtained using finer grids. When a large number of grid points are considered, iterative methods should be employed.

9.7 FINITE DIFFERENCE SOLUTION OF THE POISSON EQUATION

The numerical solution of the Laplace equation is considered in Sections 9.2 to 9.6. In this section, the numerical solution of the Poisson equation is discussed. The Poisson equation is simply the nonhomogeneous Laplace equation. It applies to problems in such areas as mass diffusion, heat diffusion (i.e., conduction), and incompressible fluid flow, in which a nonhomogeneous term is present. Most people have some physical understanding of heat conduction. Consequently, the Poisson equation governing steady heat conduction with internal energy generation is considered in this section to demonstrate numerical methods for solving the Poisson equation. That equation is derived in Section III.5 [Eq. (III.65)]:

$$\nabla^2 \overline{T} + \frac{\dot{Q}}{k} = \overline{T}_{xx} + \overline{T}_{yy} + \overline{T}_{zz} + \frac{\dot{Q}}{k} = 0 \tag{9.90}$$

where $\overline{T}$ is the temperature (C), k is the thermal conductivity of the solid (J/cm-s-C), and $\dot{Q}$ is the energy generation rate per unit volume (J/s-cm^3). For two-dimensional heat conduction, Eq. (9.90) becomes

$$\boxed{\overline{T}_{xx} + \overline{T}_{yy} + \frac{\dot{Q}}{k} = 0} \tag{9.91}$$

The solution to Eq. (9.91) is the function $\overline{T}(x, y)$. This function must satisfy a set of boundary conditions on the boundaries of the physical domain. The boundary conditions may be of the Dirichlet type (i.e., specified temperature), the Neumann type (i.e., specified temperature gradient), or the mixed type (i.e., some specified combination of temperature and temperature gradient).

The following simple problem is considered in this section to illustrate the numerical solution of the Poisson equation. A rectangular rod of a copper alloy (k = 4.0 J/cm-s-C) has a height h = 1.5 cm and a width w = 1.0 cm. Negligible heat flows along the length of the rod, which is being used as an electrical conductor. Energy is being generated within the rod by electrical heating at the

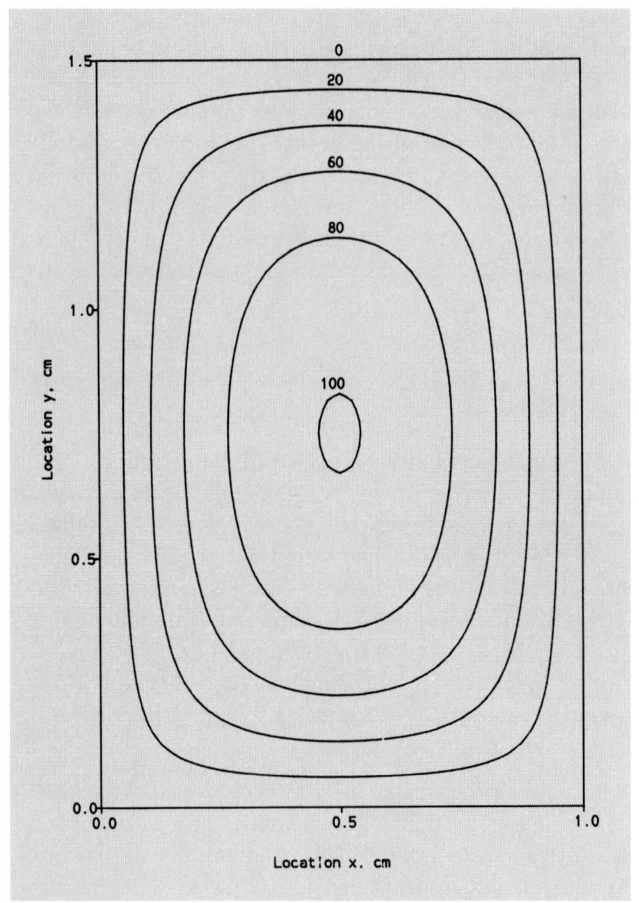

FIGURE 9.15
Exact solution of the Poisson equation.

rate $\dot{Q} = 40$ J/cm^3-s. The four sides of the rod are held at 0 C. The rod cross section and boundary conditions, as well as selected isotherms, are illustrated in Fig. 9.15. The temperature distribution $\overline{T}(x, y)$ in the rod cross section is required. The exact solution to this problem is

$$\overline{T}(x, y) = \frac{(\dot{Q}/k)(a^2 - x^2)}{2} - \frac{16a^2(\dot{Q}/k)}{\pi^3} \sum_{n=0}^{\infty} \frac{(-1)^n \cos\big((2n+1)\pi x/2a\big)\cosh\big((2n+1)\pi y/2a\big)}{(2n+1)^3 \cosh\big((2n+1)\pi b/2a\big)} \tag{9.92}$$

where $a = w/2$, $b = h/2$, and x and y are measured from the center of the rod. The exact solution for $a = 0.5$ cm and $b = 0.75$ cm is presented in Fig. 9.15, for selected isotherms.

In this section the steady two-dimensional heat conduction problem with internal energy generation is solved using the finite difference equations developed in Sections 9.2 and 9.3 for solving the Laplace equation. Those equations must be modified to include the nonhomogeneous (i.e., source) term.

Example 9.12. Finite difference approximation of the Poisson equation. Consider the steady two-dimensional heat conduction equation with internal energy generation, Eq. (9.91). Replacing $\overline{T}_{xx}$ and $\overline{T}_{yy}$ by the second-order centered-difference approximations at grid point (i, j), Eqs. (9.22) and (9.27), respectively, evaluating $\dot{Q}$ at grid point (i, j), multiplying by Δx^2, and introducing the grid aspect ratio β [Eq. (9.34)], yields

$$T_{i+1,j} + \beta^2 T_{i,j+1} + T_{i-1,j} + \beta^2 T_{i,j-1} - 2(1 + \beta^2)T_{i,j} = -\Delta x^2\left(\frac{\dot{Q}_{i,j}}{k}\right) \tag{9.93}$$

Solving Eq. (9.93) for $T_{i,j}$ gives

$$T_{i,j} = \frac{T_{i+1,j} + \beta^2 T_{i,j+1} + T_{i-1,j} + \beta^2 T_{i,j-1} + \Delta x^2(\dot{Q}_{i,j}/k)}{2(1 + \beta^2)} \tag{9.94}$$

In the special case where $\Delta x = \Delta y$, the grid aspect ratio β is unity, and Eqs. (9.93) and (9.94) become

$$T_{i+1,j} + T_{i,j+1} + T_{i-1,j} + T_{i,j-1} - 4T_{i,j} = -\Delta x^2(\dot{Q}_{i,j}/k) \tag{9.95}$$

$$T_{i,j} = \frac{T_{i+1,j} + T_{i,j+1} + T_{i-1,j} + T_{i,j-1} + \Delta x^2(\dot{Q}_{i,j}/k)}{4} \tag{9.96}$$

Equations (9.93) to (9.96) are analogous to Eqs. (9.38) to (9.41) presented in Example 9.1 for solving the Laplace equation numerically. All the general features of the numerical solution of the Laplace equation presented in Sections 9.2 to 9.6 apply directly to the numerical solution of the Poisson equation.

Example 9.13. Numerical solution on a 9×13 grid. As an example, let us solve the steady two-dimensional heat conduction problem with internal energy generation, described at the beginning of this section, on a 9×13 grid. For this grid, there are $7 \times 11 = 77$ interior points and 77 corresponding finite difference equations. This system of equations is solved by Gauss elimination. The results are presented in Fig. 9.16, where the numerical solution is indicated by the dashed lines. The numerical solution is a good approximation of the exact solution. No special problems arise due to the presence of the source term.

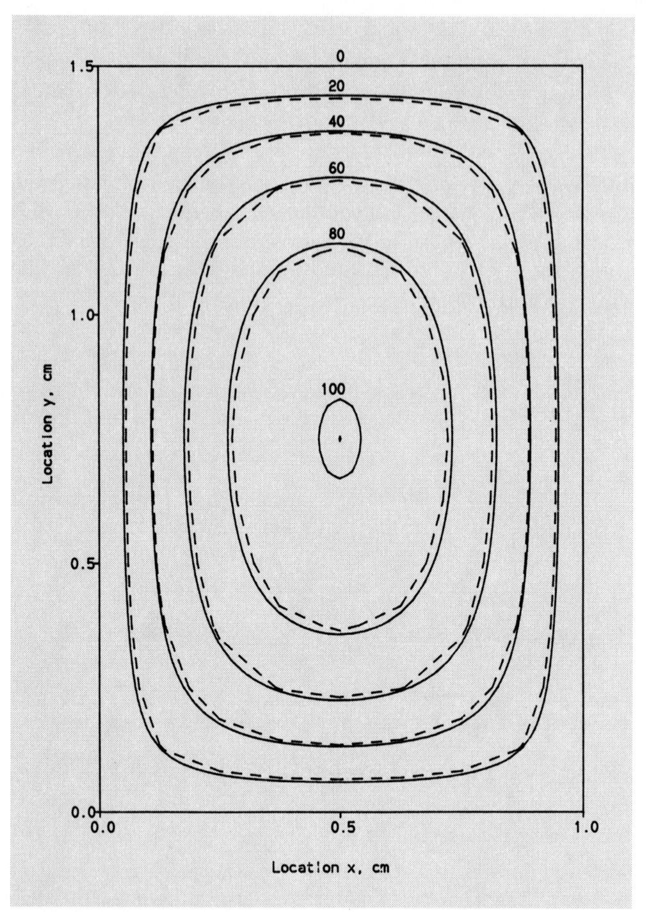

FIGURE 9.16
Numerical solution of the Poisson equation.

9.8 THE ALTERNATING-DIRECTION IMPLICIT (ADI) METHOD

As will be discussed in Section 11.9, steady equilibrium problems can be solved as the asymptotic solution at large time of an appropriate unsteady propagation problem. For the steady Laplace equation,

$$\bar{f}_{xx} + \bar{f}_{yy} = 0 \tag{9.97}$$

the appropriate unsteady PDE is the diffusion equation:

$$\bar{f}_t = \alpha(\bar{f}_{xx} + \bar{f}_{yy}) \tag{9.98}$$

where the boundary conditions of the unsteady problem are the boundary conditions of the steady problem.

Since the asymptotic steady state is desired, a numerical method that can take large time steps is desired. From numerical stability considerations, unconditionally stable implicit finite difference methods are the obvious choice. Implicit finite difference methods yield systems of coupled finite difference equations, which must be solved simultaneously. For one space dimension, tridiagonal systems of equations result, which can be solved very efficiently by the Thomas algorithm (see Section 1.5). However, for more than one space dimension, as in the present case, banded systems of equations result, which require a large amount of effort to solve. As discussed in Section 11.8, alternating-direction implicit (ADI) methods can be used to solve such problems more efficiently. ADI methods are the obvious choice for solving the steady Laplace equation as the asymptotic solution in time of the unsteady diffusion equation.

The finite difference equations for the ADI solution of the unsteady diffusion equation are presented in Section 11.8, Eqs. (11.60) and (11.61). Applying those equations for time step $\Delta t/2$ yields

$$\frac{f_{i,j}^{n+1/2} - f_{i,j}^{n}}{(\Delta t/2)} = \alpha\left(f_{xx}\big|_{i,j}^{n+1/2} + f_{yy}\big|_{i,j}^{n}\right) \tag{9.99}$$

$$\frac{f_{i,j}^{n+1} - f_{i,j}^{n+1/2}}{(\Delta t/2)} = \alpha\left(f_{xx}\big|_{i,j}^{n+1/2} + f_{yy}\big|_{i,j}^{n+1}\right) \tag{9.100}$$

Replacing the exact spatial derivatives by the second-order centered-difference finite difference approximations [Eqs. (9.24) and (9.27)] and introducing the grid aspect ratio $\beta = \Delta x/\Delta y$, Eqs. (9.99) and (9.100) become

$$f_{i,j}^{n+1/2} - f_{i,j}^{n} = \frac{\alpha\,\Delta t}{2\,\Delta x^2}\left(\left(f_{i+1,j}^{n+1/2} - 2f_{i,j}^{n+1/2} + f_{i-1,j}^{n+1/2}\right) + \beta^2\left(f_{i,j+1}^{n} - 2f_{i,j}^{n} + f_{i,j-1}^{n}\right)\right) \tag{9.101}$$

$$f_{i,j}^{n+1} - f_{i,j}^{n+1/2} = \frac{\alpha\,\Delta t}{2\,\Delta x^2}\left(\left(f_{i+1,j}^{n+1/2} - 2f_{i,j}^{n+1/2} + f_{i-1,j}^{n+1/2}\right) + \beta^2\left(f_{i,j+1}^{n+1} - 2f_{i,j}^{n+1} + f_{i,j-1}^{n+1}\right)\right) \tag{9.102}$$

The asymptotic steady-state solution of Eqs. (9.101) and (9.102) is the desired solution of the Laplace equation.

Equations (9.101) and (9.102) can be expressed in terms of the *diffusion number d*, which is directly proportional to Δt:

$$d = \frac{\alpha\,\Delta t}{\Delta x^2} \tag{9.103}$$

That is the approach taken in Chapter 11. When solving elliptic PDEs by the ADI method, Eqs. (9.101) and (9.102) are generally expressed in terms of the iteration parameter ρ,

$$\boxed{\rho = \frac{2\,\Delta x^2}{\alpha\,\Delta t}} \tag{9.104}$$

which is inversely proportional to Δt. Introducing ρ into Eqs. (9.101) and (9.102) and rearranging yields the two FDEs:

$$f_{i-1,j}^{n+1/2} - (2+\rho)f_{i,j}^{n+1/2} + f_{i+1,j}^{n+1/2} = -\beta^2\left(f_{i,j-1}^{n} - \left(2 - \frac{\rho}{\beta^2}\right)f_{i,j}^{n} + f_{i,j+1}^{n}\right) \tag{9.105}$$

$$f_{i,j-1}^{n+1} - \left(2+\frac{\rho}{\beta^2}\right)f_{i,j}^{n+1} + f_{i,j+1}^{n+1} = -\frac{1}{\beta^2}\left(f_{i-1,j}^{n+1/2} - (2-\rho)f_{i,j}^{n+1/2} + f_{i+1,j}^{n+1/2}\right) \tag{9.106}$$

When applied at every point in a finite difference grid, Eq. (9.105) yields a tridiagonal system of equations along each row of grid points (i.e., along lines of constant j), and Eq. (9.106) yields a tridiagonal system of equations along each column of grid points (i.e., along lines of constant i). These tridiagonal systems of equations can be solved by the Thomas algorithm, as discussed in Section 1.5.

Since only the asymptotic steady-state solution is desired, it might appear that the solution can be obtained most efficiently by taking extremely large time steps. However, this is not the case. A repeated sequence of time steps, Δt_k, or equivalently, a repeated sequence of iteration parameters, ρ_k, yields the most rapidly converging solution. A discussion of these concepts is beyond the scope of this book. These concepts are discussed by Peaceman and Rachford (1955), Douglas (1962), Wachpress (1966), Lynch and Rice (1968), and many others. Additional discussions are presented in the books of Ames (1969), Mitchell (1969), and Ferziger (1981).

The ADI method is quite efficient when the optimum iteration parameter sequence, ρ_k, can be found. At present, such sequences can be found only for extremely simple problems. The search for such sequences is the subject of ongoing research. The SOR method is generally just as effective as the ADI method for a fixed value of ρ or for a nonoptimum sequence ρ_k, especially when the additional complexity of the ADI method is considered. Consequently, in most practical applications, SOR is the method of choice.

9.9 NONLINEAR EQUATIONS AND THREE-DIMENSIONAL PROBLEMS

All the partial differential equations considered so far in this chapter are linear. Consequently, the corresponding finite difference equations are linear. All of the examples considered so far are for two-dimensional problems. Some of the problems that arise for nonlinear partial differential equations and for three-dimensional problems are discussed briefly in this section.

Nonlinear PDEs

When a nonlinear elliptic partial differential equation is solved by finite difference methods, a system of nonlinear finite difference equations results. Several approaches can be used to solve the system of nonlinear equations.

Two procedures are presented in Section 8.8 for solving the systems of nonlinear finite difference equations that arise when one-dimensional boundaryvalue problems are solved by the equilibrium method:

1. Iteration
2. Newton's method

In both approaches, the finite difference equations are linearized and the system of linearized finite difference equations is solved by an iterative technique, such as SOR. Both of these approaches can be extended to solve nonlinear elliptic partial differential equations in two or three space dimensions.

This approach involves a two-step procedure. Step 1 involves the evaluation of the nonlinear coefficients in the system of finite difference equations, based on the current estimate of the solution. These coefficients are updated periodically, typically by underrelaxation. Step 2 involves the solution of the system of linearized FDEs by an iterative technique. Steps 1 and 2 are repeated until the system of nonlinear FDEs converges to the desired tolerance. It is not necessary to solve the linearized equations to a small tolerance during the early stages of the overall two-step procedure. As the two-step procedure approaches convergence, the tolerance of the linear equation solver should be decreased towards the desired final tolerance.

The multigrid method discussed by Brandt (1977) can be applied directly to solve nonlinear elliptic partial differential equations. Unfortunately, this method is beyond the scope of this text. Any serious effort to solve nonlinear elliptic PDEs should consider the multigrid method very seriously. It works equally well for linear and nonlinear PDEs and for one, two, or three space dimensions. The book by Hackbusch (1980) presents a comprehensive discussion of the multigrid method.

Three-Dimensional Problems

Three-dimensional problems can be solved by the same methods that are used to solve two-dimensional problems, by including the finite difference approximations of the exact partial derivatives in the third direction. The major complication is that the size of the system of FDEs increases dramatically. The line successive overrelaxation (LSOR) method and the alternating-direction line successive overrelaxation (ADLSOR) method which are presented in Section 9.5, possibly can be used to some advantage. The alternating-direction implicit (ADI) method discussed in Section 9.8 is also a possibility. The multigrid method can also be applied to three-dimensional problems. It is probably the most efficient procedure for solving three-dimensional elliptic PDEs, both linear and nonlinear.

SUMMARY

The numerical solution of elliptic partial differential equations by finite difference methods is discussed in this chapter. Elliptic PDEs govern equilibrium problems, which have no preferred paths of signal propagation. The domain of dependence and range of influence of every point is the entire solution domain. They are solved numerically by relaxation methods. The two-dimensional Laplace equation, $\bar{f}_{xx} + \bar{f}_{yy} = 0$, is considered as the model elliptic PDE in this chapter.

Finite difference methods, as typified by the five-point method, yield systems of finite difference equations, which must be solved by relaxation methods. The successive overrelaxation (SOR) method is generally the method of choice. Line SOR (LSOR) and alternating-direction line SOR (ADLSOR) also can be employed. The alternating-direction implicit (ADI) method potentially can increase the rate of convergence, but the inability to determine the optimum sequence of the relaxation parameter ρ_k has made this approach unpopular. The multigrid method shows the best potential for rapid convergence.

Nonlinear partial differential equations yield nonlinear finite difference equations. Systems of nonlinear FDEs can be extremely difficult to solve. The multigrid method can be applied directly to nonlinear PDEs. Three-dimensional problems represented by three-dimensional PDEs are approximated simply by including the finite difference approximations of the spatial derivatives in the third direction. The relaxation techniques used to solve two-dimensional problems generally can be used to solve three-dimensional problems, at the expense of a considerable increase in computational effort.

PROBLEMS

Section 9.1 Introduction

1. Consider the two-dimensional Laplace equation $\bar{f}_{xx} + \bar{f}_{yy} = 0$. Classify this PDE. Determine the characteristic curves. Discuss the significance of these results as regards domain of dependence, range of influence, signal propagation speed, auxiliary conditions, and numerical solution procedures.
2. Develop the exact solution of the heat conduction problem presented in Section 9.1, Eq. (9.8).
3. By hand, calculate the exact solution for $T(5.0, 12.5)$.
4. Write a computer program to evaluate the exact solution of the heat conduction problem. Use the program to reproduce Table 9.1.

Section 9.2 Finite Difference Approximations

5. Develop the second-order centered-space approximations for $\bar{f}_{xx}$ and $\bar{f}_{yy}$, Eqs. (9.21) and (9.27), respectively, including the leading truncation error terms.
6. Develop the five-point finite difference approximation of the Laplace equation: (*a*) for $\Delta x = \Delta y$, and (*b*) for $\Delta x/\Delta y = \beta \neq 1$.
7. Develop a second-order centered-space approximation of the mixed partial derivative $\bar{f}_{xy}$ for the finite difference grid illustrated in Figure 9.3.

Section 9.3 Consistency, Order, and Convergence

8. Derive the MDE for the five-point approximation of the Laplace equation with $\Delta x = \Delta y$, Eq. (9.49). Discuss consistency and order of this FDE.

9. Consider the following finite difference approximations of the Laplace equation:

$$(a)\ f_{i+1,j+1} + f_{i+1,j} + f_{i+1,j-1} + f_{i,j+1} + f_{i,j-1} + f_{i-1,j+1} + f_{i-1,j} + f_{i-1,j-1} - 8f_{i,j} = 0 \qquad \text{(P9.9}a\text{)}$$

$$(b)\ f_{i+1,j+1} + 2f_{i+1,j} + f_{i+1,j-1} + 2f_{i,j+1} + 2f_{i,j-1} + f_{i-1,j+1} + 2f_{i-1,j} + f_{i-1,j-1} - 12f_{i,j} = 0 \qquad \text{(P9.9}b\text{)}$$

$$(c)\ -f_{i+2,j} + 16f_{i+1,j} - f_{i,j+2} + 16f_{i,j+1} + 16f_{i,j-1} - f_{i,j-2} + 16f_{i-1,j} - f_{i-2,j} - 60f_{i,j} = 0 \qquad \text{(P9.9}c\text{)}$$

$$(d)\ f_{i+1,j+1} + 4f_{i+1,j} + f_{i+1,j-1} + 4f_{i,j+1} + 4f_{i,j-1} + f_{i-1,j+1} + 4f_{i-1,j} + f_{i-1,j-1} - 20f_{i,j} = 0 \qquad \text{(P9.9}d\text{)}$$

Derive the MDE for each of these FDEs. Discuss consistency and order.

Section 9.4 Finite Difference Solution of the Laplace Equation

10. Solve the heat conduction problem that is presented in Section 9.1 using the five-point method with $\Delta x = \Delta y = 5.0$ cm. Compare the results with the exact solution in Table 9.1.

11. Solve Problem 10 with $\Delta x = \Delta y = 2.5$ cm using Gauss elimination. Compare the results with the exact solution in Table 9.1. Compare the errors and the ratio of the errors with the results of Problem 10.

12. Modify the heat conduction problem presented in Section 9.1 by letting $T = 0$ C on the top boundary and $T = 100$ C on the right boundary. Solve this problem using the five-point method with $\Delta x = \Delta y = 5.0$ cm.

13. Solve Problem 12 with $\Delta x = \Delta y = 2.5$ using Gauss elimination.

14. Consider steady heat conduction in the unit square $0 \le x \le 1$ and $0 \le y \le 1$. Let $T(0, y) = T(x, 0) = 100$ and $T(1, y) = T(x, 1) = 0$. Solve this problem using the five-point method with $\Delta x = \Delta y = 0.25$ using Gauss elimination.

15. Solve Problem 14 with $\Delta x = \Delta y = 0.1$.

16. Write a computer program to solve the Laplace equation in a rectangle with Dirichlet boundary conditions using Gauss elimination. Solve the heat conduction problem presented in Section 9.1 with $\Delta x = \Delta y = 1.25$ cm and compare the results with Tables 9.1 and 9.5.

17. Solve Problem 15 with the program developed in Problem 16.

18. Work Problem 10 using Eq. (P9.9*d*) from Problem 9.9.

19. Work Problem 11 using Eq. (P9.9*d*) from Problem 9.9.

20. Modify the computer program written in Problem 16 to use Eq. (P9.9*d*) from Problem 9.9. Work Problem 16 with the modified program. Compare the errors with the results of Problem 16.

Section 9.5 Iterative Methods of Solution

21. Solve the heat conduction problem presented in Section 9.1 using the five-point method with $\Delta x = \Delta y = 2.5$ cm using Gauss-Seidel iteration. Iterate until $|\Delta T_{max}| \le \epsilon = 1.0$.

22. Write a computer program to solve the Laplace equation in a rectangle with Dirichlet boundary conditions using SOR. Solve Problem 21 with $\omega = 1.0$ and $\epsilon = 0.000001$. Compare with the results presented in Table 9.6.

23. Solve Problem 22 with $\omega = \omega_{opt}$ from Eq. (9.72). Compare the rates of convergence of Problems 22 and 23.

24. Solve Problem 14 with $\Delta x = \Delta y = 0.1$ using the program developed in Problem 22 with (*a*) $\omega = 1.0$, and (*b*) $\omega = \omega_{opt}$ from Eq. (9.72), both for $\epsilon = 0.000001$.

25. Modify the computer program written in Problem 22 to use line SOR along either vertical lines or horizontal lines. Solve Problem 22 (*a*) with LSOR along vertical lines and (*b*) with LSOR along horizontal lines. Let $\omega = 1.0$.

26. Solve Problem 22 using the alternating-direction LSOR method.

27. Solve Problem 22 using the ADI method.

28. Use the computer program written in Problem 22 to determine ω_{opt} numerically for the unit square $0 \le x \le 1$ and $0 \le y \le 1$. Let $\Delta = \Delta x = \Delta y$ and $\epsilon = 0.000001$. For $\Delta =$ 0.25, 0.125, and 0.0025, calculate ω_{opt} and compare with the values obtained from Eq. (9.72).

Section 9.6 Derivative Boundary Conditions

29. Work Example 9.10 with $\Delta x = \Delta y = 2.5$ cm using Gauss elimination.

30. Consider steady heat conduction in the unit square $0 \le x \le 1$ and $0 \le y \le 1$. Let $T(0, y) = T(x, 0) = 100$ and $T_x(1, y) = T_y(x, 1) = 0.0$. Solve this problem using the five-point method with $\Delta x = \Delta y = 0.25$ and the derivative BC method based on Eq. (9.85) using Gauss elimination.

31. Solve Problem 30 where the derivative BC is enforced by (*a*) linear extrapolation, Eq. (9.87); (*b*) quadratic extrapolation, Eq. (9.88); and (*c*) cubic extrapolation, Eq. (9.89).

32. Consider steady heat conduction in the unit square $0 \le x \le 1$ cm and $0 \le y \le 1$ cm. Let $T(x, 0) = 0$, $T(x, 1) = 100$, and $T_x(1, 0) = 0$. The left side of the square is cooled by convection to the surroundings. For steady conditions, the rate of convection, $\dot{q}_{conv}$, must equation the rate of conduction, $\dot{q}_{cond}$, at the boundary. Thus,

$$\dot{q}_{conv} = hA(T - T_a) = \dot{q}_{cond} = kA\frac{\partial T}{\partial x} \qquad \text{(P9.32)}$$

(*a*) Develop a finite difference approximation of the convection boundary condition, Eq. (P9.32). Let $h = 100$ J/(s-m^2-K), $k = 5$ J/(s-m-K), and $T_a = 10$ C. Solve this problem for $\Delta x = \Delta y = 0.25$ cm using Gauss elimination.

33. Modify the computer program written in Problem 22 to implement a derivative BC along the right side of the rectangle. Implement the BC by the procedure based on Eq. (9.85). Solve Example 9.10 using this program. Compare with the results presented in Table 9.11.

Section 9.7 Finite Difference Solution of the Poisson Equation

34. Develop the five-point finite difference approximation of the Poisson equation (*a*) for $\Delta x = \Delta y$ and (*b*) for $\Delta x/\Delta y = \beta \ne 1$.

35. Derive the MDE for the five-point approximation of the Poisson equation with $\Delta x = \Delta y$. Discuss consistency and order of the FDE.

36. Solve the heat conduction problem presented in Section 9.7 using the five-point method with $\Delta x = \Delta y = 5.0$ cm.

37. Solve Problem 36 with $\Delta x = \Delta y = 2.5$ cm using Gauss elimination.

38. Write a computer program to solve the Poisson equation in a rectangle with Dirichlet boundary conditions using SOR. This program is a straightforward modification of the program written in Problem 9.22. Solve the heat conduction problem presented in Section 9.7 with $\omega = 1.0$ and $\epsilon = 0.000001$.

39. Work Problem 38 with $\omega = \omega_{\text{opt}}$ from Eq. (9.72).

40. Work Problem 28 for the Poisson equation with $F(x, y) = 10.0$.

Section 9.8 The Alternating-Direction Implicit (ADI) Method

41. Solve Problem 10 with $\Delta x = \Delta y = 2.5$ cm by the ADI method with $\epsilon = 1.0$.

42. Solve Problem 36 with $\Delta x = \Delta y = 2.5$ cm by the ADI method with $\epsilon = 1.0$.

Section 9.9 Nonlinear Equations and Three-Dimensional Problems

43. Grid generation using elliptic partial differential equations yields a set of nonlinear elliptic PDEs with Dirichlet BCs, as discussed in Section 13.6, Eqs. (13.76) and (13.77). Derive the five-point finite difference approximations of these PDEs. Develop a strategy to solve these FDEs by: (*a*) relaxation, and (*b*) Newton's method.

44. Work Example 13.2 by hand calculation for $1 \le \xi \le 5$ and $1 \le \eta \le 3$, using Gauss elimination and updating the coefficients after each pass.

45. Derive the five-point finite difference approximation of the three-dimensional Laplace equation with $\Delta x = \Delta y = \Delta z$.

46. Consider steady heat conduction in the unit cube $0 \le x \le 1$, $0 \le y \le 1$, and $0 \le z \le 1$. Let $T = 100$ on the surface $z = 1$ and $T = 0$ on the other five surfaces. Solve this problem by the five-point method with $\Delta x = \Delta y = \Delta z = 1/2$.

47. Solve Problem 46 with $\Delta x = \Delta y = \Delta z = 1/3$ using Gauss elimination.

48. Solve Problem 46 with $\Delta x = \Delta y = \Delta z = 1/4$ using Gauss-Seidel iteration with $\epsilon = 0.1$. Let $T_{i,j,k}^{(0)} = 0.0$.

CHAPTER 10

INTRODUCTION TO FINITE DIFFERENCE METHODS FOR SOLVING PROPAGATION PROBLEMS

Section

Example

10.1 INTRODUCTION

The general features of parabolic and hyperbolic partial differential equations (PDEs) are discussed in Sections III.6 and III.7, respectively. In those sections it is shown that parabolic and hyperbolic PDEs govern propagation problems, which are initial-boundary-value problems in open domains. Consequently, parabolic and hyperbolic PDEs are solved numerically by marching methods. In view of the similarities between parabolic and hyperbolic PDEs (both govern propagation problems and are solved by marching methods), Chapter 10 is devoted to presenting the basic properties of finite difference methods for solving propagation problems.

Parabolic partial differential equations frequently arise in engineering and science. Two of the more common ones are the diffusion equation and the convection–diffusion equation, presented below for the generic dependent variable $f(x, t)$:

$$f_t = \alpha f_{xx} \quad \text{(diffusion equation)} \tag{10.1}$$

$$f_t + u f_x = \alpha f_{xx} \quad \text{(convection–diffusion equation)} \tag{10.2}$$

where α is the diffusion coefficient and u is the convection velocity. Since the classification of a partial differential equation is determined by the coefficients of its highest-order derivatives, the presence of the first-order convection term $u f_x$ in the convection–diffusion equation does not affect its classification. However, that term does have a major influence on the numerical solution procedure. The diffusion equation is considered in this chapter to illustrate the basic features of the numerical solution of parabolic PDEs. A more complete discussion of the numerical solution of the diffusion equation is presented in Chapter 11. A discussion of the numerical solution of the convection–diffusion equation is presented in Chapter 14.

Hyperbolic partial differential equations also arise frequently in engineering and science. Two of the more common ones are the convection equation and the wave equation, presented below for the generic dependent variable $f(x, t)$:

$$f_t + u f_x = 0 \quad \text{(convection equation)} \tag{10.3}$$

$$f_{tt} = c^2 f_{xx} \quad \text{(wave equation)} \tag{10.4}$$

where u is the convection velocity and c is the wave propagation speed. The wave equation applies to problems of vibrating systems, such as a vibrating string or an acoustic field. In such problems, waves travel in both directions. The convection equation is a simple first-order equation that has propagation properties similar to the propagation properties of the wave equation. The convection equation models a wave traveling in only one direction. Thus, the convection equation models the essential features of the more complex wave motion governed by the wave equation. The general features of the numerical solution of the convection equation also apply to the numerical solution of the wave equation. Consequently, the convection equation is studied in this chapter to illustrate the basic features of the numerical solution of hyperbolic PDEs. Chapter 12 is devoted to a more complete discussion of the numerical solution of the convection equation. The numerical solution of the wave equation is discussed in Chapter 15.

10.2 FUNDAMENTAL CONSIDERATIONS

Propagation problems are initial-boundary-value problems in open domains (open with respect to one of the independent variables) in which the solution in the domain of interest is marched forward from the initial state, guided and modified by the boundary conditions. Propagation problems are governed by parabolic or hyperbolic partial differential equations. The general features of parabolic and hyperbolic PDEs are discussed in Part III. Those features that are relevant to the finite difference solution of parabolic and hyperbolic PDEs are summarized in this section.

From a characteristic analysis, it is shown in Section III.6 that problems governed by *parabolic* PDEs have an infinite physical signal propagation speed $c = dx/dt$. As a result, the solution at a particular point P at time level n depends on the solution at all other points in the solution domain at all times preceding and including time level n, and the solution at a particular point P at time level n influences the solution at all other points in the solution domain at all times including and after time level n. These general features of parabolic PDEs are illustrated in Fig. 10.1.

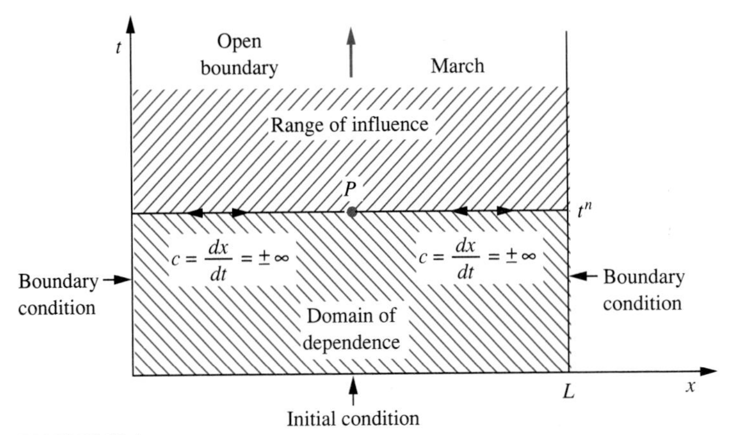

FIGURE 10.1
Domain of dependence and range of influence for a parabolic PDE.

The objective of the numerical solution of a parabolic PDE is to march the solution at time level n forward in time to time level $n + 1$, as illustrated in Fig. 10.2, where the physical domain of dependence of the PDE is illustrated. In view of the infinite *physical* signal propagation speed associated with parabolic PDEs, the solution at point P at time level $n + 1$ should depend on the solution at all the other points at time level $n + 1$. This in turn requires an infinite *numerical* signal propagation speed $c_n = \Delta x / \Delta t$.

From a characteristic analysis, it is shown in Section III.7 that problems governed by *hyperbolic* PDEs have finite physical signal propagation speed $c = dx/dt$. As a result, the solution at a particular point P at time level n depends on the solution only within a finite domain of dependence in the solution domain at times preceding time level n. Likewise, the solution at a particular point P at time level n influences the solution only within a finite range of influence in the solution domain at times after time level n. These general features of hyperbolic PDEs are illustrated in Fig. 10.3.

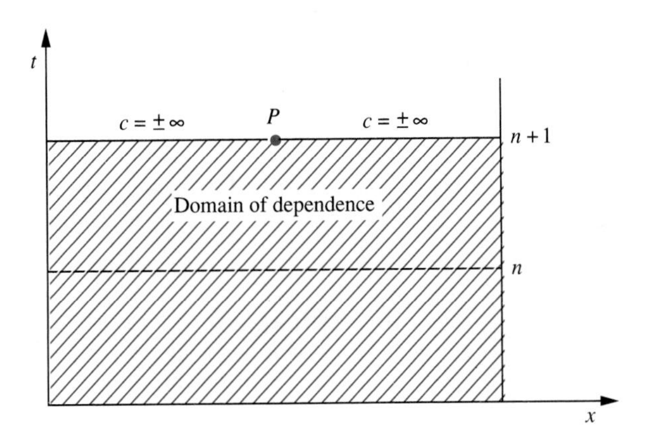

FIGURE 10.2
Physical domain of dependence for a parabolic PDE.

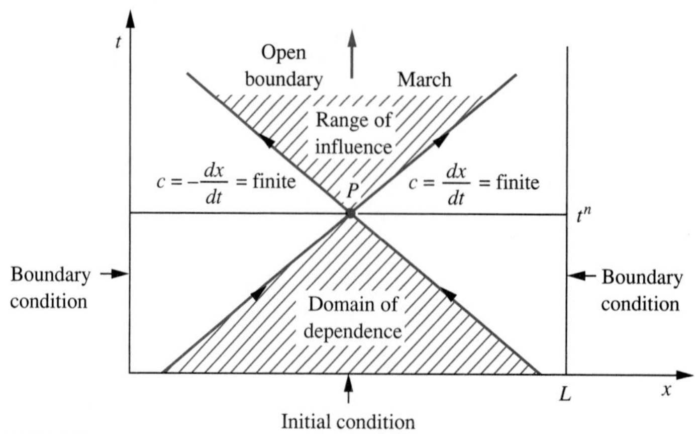

FIGURE 10.3
Domain of dependence and range of influence for a hyperbolic PDE.

The objective of the numerical solution of a hyperbolic PDE is to march the solution at time level n forward in time to time level $n + 1$, as illustrated in Fig. 10.4, where the physical domain of dependence of the PDE is illustrated. In view of the finite physical signal propagation speed associated with hyperbolic PDEs, the solution at point P at time level $n + 1$ should not depend on the solution at any of the other points at time level $n + 1$. This in turn requires a finite *numerical* signal propagation speed $c_n = \Delta x / \Delta t$.

The similarities and differences between parabolic and hyperbolic PDEs are illustrated in Figs. 10.1 to 10.4. The major similarity is that both are propagation problems, which require marching methods to obtain a numerical solution. The major difference is that the physical signal propagation speed for a parabolic PDE is infinite, whereas the physical signal propagation speed for a hyperbolic PDE is finite.

Finite difference methods in which the solution at point P at time level $n + 1$ depends only on the solution at neighboring points at time level n have finite numerical signal propagation speed $c_n = \Delta x / \Delta t$. Such finite difference methods are called *explicit* methods, because the solution at each point is specified ex-

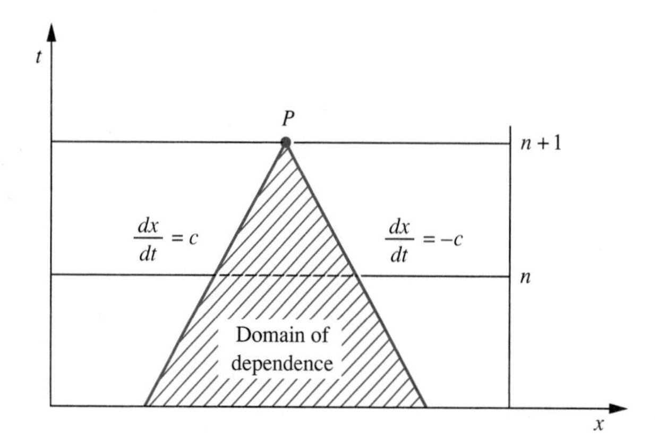

FIGURE 10.4
Physical domain of dependence for a hyperbolic PDE.

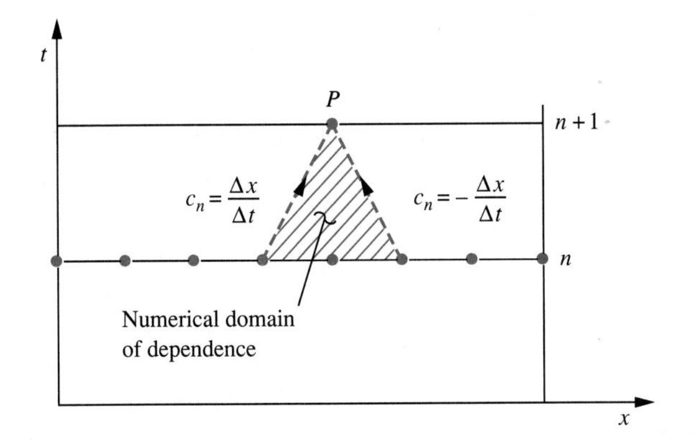

FIGURE 10.5
Numerical domain of dependence of explicit methods.

plicitly in terms of the known solution at neighboring points at time level n. This situation is illustrated in Fig. 10.5, which resembles the domain of dependence for a hyperbolic PDE. The numerical signal propagation speed $c_n = \Delta x/\Delta t$ is finite.

Finite difference methods in which the solution at point P at time level $n+1$ depends on the solution at neighboring points at time level $n + 1$ have infinite numerical signal propagation speed $c_n = \Delta x/\Delta t$. Such methods couple the finite difference equations at time level $n + 1$ and result in a system of equations, which must be solved at each time level. The solution procedure at each time level is analogous to the solution procedure for elliptic PDEs. Such finite difference methods are called *implicit* methods, because the solution at each point is specified implicitly in terms of the unknown solution at neighboring points at time level $n + 1$. This situation is illustrated in Fig. 10.6, which resembles the domain of dependence for a parabolic PDE. The numerical signal propagation speed $c_n = \Delta x/\Delta t$ is infinite.

The similarities of and the differences between explicit and implicit numerical marching methods are illustrated in Figs. 10.5 and 10.6. The major similarity is that both march the numerical solution forward from one time level to the next. The major difference is that the numerical signal propagation speed for explicit marching methods is finite, whereas the numerical signal propagation speed for implicit marching methods is infinite.

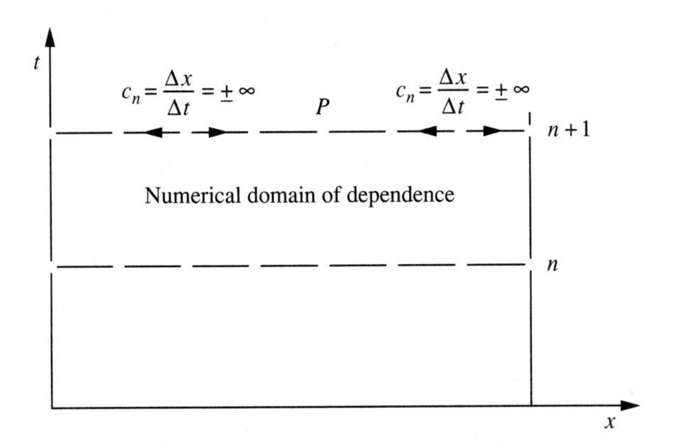

FIGURE 10.6
Numerical domain of dependence of implicit methods.

Explicit methods are computationally faster than implicit methods, because there are no systems of equations to solve. Thus, explicit methods might appear to be superior to implicit methods. However, the finite numerical signal propagation speed of explicit methods does not model the infinite physical signal propagation speed associated with parabolic PDEs, whereas the infinite numerical signal propagation speed of implicit methods correctly models the infinite physical signal propagation speed of parabolic PDEs. Thus, implicit methods appear to be well-suited for solving parabolic PDEs, and explicit methods might appear to be unsuitable for solving parabolic PDEs. In actuality, only an infinitesimal quantity of information propagates at the infinite physical signal propagation speed of a parabolic PDE; the bulk of the information travels at a finite physical signal propagation speed. Experience has shown that explicit methods can be employed to solve parabolic PDEs.

The finite numerical signal propagation speed of explicit methods correctly models the finite physical signal propagation speed associated with hyperbolic PDEs, whereas the infinite numerical signal propagation speed of implicit methods does not correctly model the finite physical signal propagation speed of hyperbolic PDEs. Thus, explicit methods appear to be well-suited for solving hyperbolic PDEs, and implicit methods might appear to be unsuitable for solving hyperbolic PDEs. In actuality, only an infinitesimal quantity of information propagates at the infinite numerical signal propagation speed of an implicit method; the bulk of the information travels at a finite numerical signal propagation speed. Consequently, some success has been achieved using implicit methods to solve hyperbolic PDEs. However, explicit methods match the physics more accurately, and the majority of numerical methods for solving hyperbolic PDEs are explicit methods.

10.3 GENERAL FEATURES OF CONVECTION, DIFFUSION, AND DISPERSION

Most real physical processes involve either convection, diffusion, or combined convection and diffusion. A few real physical processes involve dispersion. The truncation errors associated with the finite difference solutions of PDEs also exhibit diffusive and dispersive behavior. Consequently, the general features of pure convection, pure diffusion, and pure dispersion are presented in this section to aid in understanding the numerical solution of partial differential equations.

Convection

In a propagation problem, pure convection is governed by the convection equation:

$$\boxed{f_t + u f_x = 0} \tag{10.5}$$

where u is the convection velocity. The general features of pure convection can be illustrated by studying the propagation of a wave in space and time. Consider the single wave specified by the complex Fourier component

$$F(x,t) = Ce^{st}e^{Ikx} = \mathrm{Re}\big(F(x,t)\big) + I\,\mathrm{Im}\big(F(x,t)\big) \tag{10.6}$$

where C is the amplitude, s is the complex frequency,

$$s = \sigma + I\omega \tag{10.7}$$

$I = \sqrt{-1}$, and k is the wave number. The real or imaginary part of $F(x,t)$ is chosen to satisfy the initial condition. Substituting Eq. (10.7) into Eq. (10.6) gives

$$\boxed{F(x,t) = Ce^{\sigma t}e^{I(kx+\omega t)}} \tag{10.8}$$

Substituting Eq. (10.8) into Eq. (10.5) yields

$$(\sigma + I\omega)Ce^{\sigma t}e^{I(kx+\omega t)} + u(Ik)Ce^{\sigma t}e^{I(kx+\omega t)} = 0 \tag{10.9}$$

which gives

$$\sigma + I(\omega + uk) = 0 \tag{10.10}$$

from which

$$\sigma = 0 \qquad \text{and} \qquad \omega = -uk \tag{10.11}$$

Substituting Eq. (10.11) into Eq. (10.8) gives the exact solution of the convection equation:

$$\boxed{F(x,t) = Ce^{Ik(x-ut)}} \tag{10.12}$$

Consider the sinusoidal initial property distribution

$$f(x,0) = A_m \sin mx \tag{10.13}$$

where $m = 1, 2, \ldots$ From Eq. (10.12),

$$F(x,0) = Ce^{Ikx} = C(\cos kx + I \sin kx) = A_m \sin mx \tag{10.14}$$

Consequently, $C = A_m$, $k = m$, and $f(x,t) = \mathrm{Im}[F(x,t)]$, which gives

$$f(x,t) = A_m \sin\big(k(x - ut)\big) \tag{10.15}$$

Equation (10.15) can be written as

$$\boxed{f(x,t) = A_m \sin k\xi = F(\xi)} \tag{10.16}$$

where the *phase* ξ is defined as

$$\xi = (x - ut) \qquad \text{phase} \tag{10.17}$$

and the *phase velocity* or *wave velocity* c is given by

$$c = u \qquad \text{wave velocity} \tag{10.18}$$

Equation (10.16) shows that the sine wave moves at the constant wave velocity $c = u$, unchanged in magnitude or shape.

Arbitrary wave shapes can be described by a linear superposition of sine and cosine waves of different amplitudes and wavelengths, that is, by a complex Fourier series representation of the arbitrary wave shape (see the Appendix). Equations (10.16) to (10.18) show that all the Fourier components propagate unchanged in magnitude and shape at the unique wave velocity $c = u$. Thus, the arbitrary wave shape propagates unchanged in magnitude and shape at the wave velocity $c = u$. Consequently, pure convection simply propagates the initial property distribution with the convection velocity u.

Example 10.1. Exact solution of the convection equation. We will illustrate the general features of pure convection by considering four initial data distributions: two sinusoidal distributions and two triangular distributions. The results are presented in Fig. 10.7 for $u = 0.1$ at $t = 0, 2, 4, 6, 8,$ and 10.

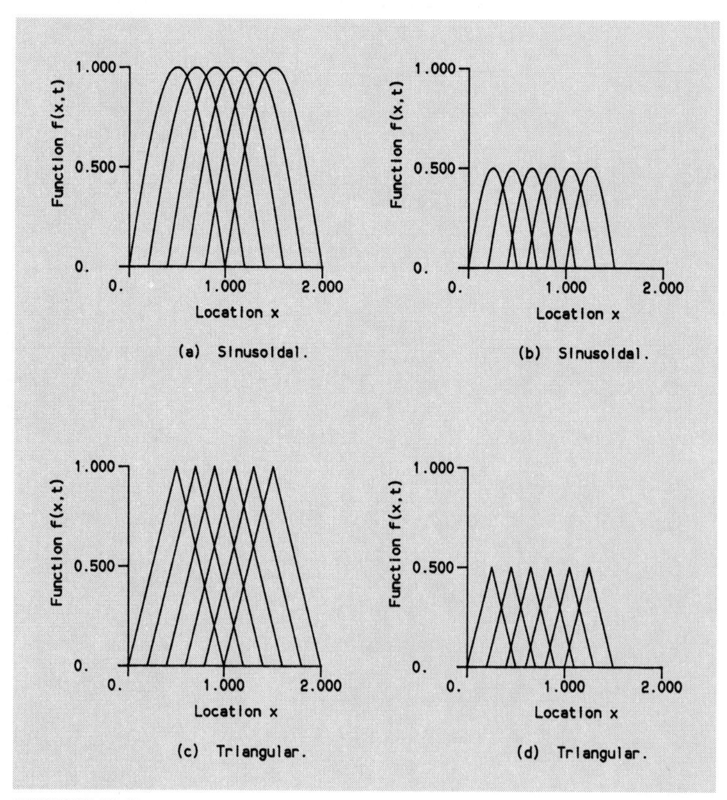

FIGURE 10.7
Exact solutions of the convection equation: (*a*) and (*b*) sinusoidal; (*c*) and (*d*) triangular.

Figure 10.7*a* presents the solution for a sinusoidal wave with an amplitude of 1.0 and a period of 1.0, for which the wave number $k = \pi$. As illustrated, the sine wave propagates unchanged in shape at the wave velocity $c = u = 0.1$. Figure 10.7*b* presents analogous results for a sinusoidal wave with an amplitude of 0.5 and a period of 0.5, for which $k = 2\pi$. This wave also propagates unchanged in shape at the wave velocity $c = u = 0.1$.

Figure 10.7*c* presents the solution for a triangular wave with an amplitude of 1.0 and a period of 1.0, for which $k_1 = \pi$ and $k_m = m\pi$. The solution is obtained by expressing the initial data distribution in a Fourier series, obtaining the solution for the propagation of each Fourier component, and superimposing those solutions to obtain the overall solution. For pure convection, the wave velocity does not depend on the wave number. Consequently, each Fourier component propagates at the unique wave velocity $c = u$. Thus, as illustrated in Fig. 10.7*c*, the triangular wave propagates unchanged in shape at the wave velocity $c = u = 0.1$. Fig. 10.7*d* presents analogous results for a triangular wave with an amplitude of 0.5 and a period of 0.5, for which $k_1 = 2\pi$ and $k_m = 2m\pi$. This wave also propagates unchanged in shape at the wave velocity $c = u = 0.1$.

Figure 10.7 clearly demonstrates that convection propagates a wave in space and time unchanged in magnitude and shape with the constant wave velocity $c = u$. The wave velocity does not depend on the magnitude or period of the wave.

Diffusion

Next consider pure diffusion, which is governed by the diffusion equation:

$$\boxed{f_t = \alpha f_{xx}} \tag{10.19}$$

where α is the diffusion coefficient. Substituting Eq. (10.8) into Eq. (10.19) yields

$$(\sigma + I\omega)Ce^{\sigma t}e^{I(kx+\omega t)} = \alpha(Ik)^2 Ce^{\sigma t}e^{I(kx+\omega t)} \tag{10.20}$$

which gives

$$\sigma + I\omega = -\alpha k^2 \tag{10.21}$$

from which

$$\sigma = -\alpha k^2 \qquad \text{and} \qquad \omega = 0 \tag{10.22}$$

Substituting Eq. (10.22) into Eq. (10.8) gives the exact solution of the diffusion equation:

$$\boxed{F(x, t) = Ce^{-\alpha k^2 t}e^{Ikx}} \tag{10.23}$$

Consider the sinusoidal initial property distribution

$$f(x,0) = A_m \sin mx \tag{10.24}$$

From Eq. (10.23),

$$F(x,0) = C(\cos kx + I \sin kx) = A_m \sin mx \tag{10.25}$$

Consequently, $C = A_m$, $k = m$, and $f(x,t) = \text{Im}[F(x,t)]$, which gives

$$f(x,t) = A_m e^{-\alpha k^2 t} \sin mx = e^{-\alpha k^2 t}(A_m \sin mx) = e^{-\alpha k^2 t} f(x,0) \tag{10.26}$$

Equation (10.26) shows that the initial property distribution simply decays with time at the exponential rate $\exp(-\alpha k^2 t)$. Thus, the rate of decay depends on the square of the wave number k. The initial property distribution does not propagate in space.

For an arbitrary initial property distribution represented by a complex Fourier series, Eq. (10.26) shows that each Fourier component simply decays exponentially, but at a rate that depends on the square of the wave number k. Thus, the property distribution changes shape. Consequently, pure diffusion causes the initial property distribution to decay and change shape, but the wave does not propagate in space.

Example 10.2. Exact solution of the diffusion equation. We will illustrate the general features of pure diffusion by considering four initial data distributions: two sinusoidal distributions and two triangular distributions. The results are presented in Fig. 10.8 for $\alpha = 0.1/\pi^2$ at $t = 0, 2, 4, 6, 8$, and 10.

Figure 10.8*a* presents the solution for a sinusoidal initial data distribution with an amplitude of 1.0 and a period of 1.0, for which the wave number $k = \pi$. As demonstrated by Eq. (10.26), the shape of the property distribution remains unchanged (i.e., it remains a sinusoidal shape) and the amplitude decays exponentially as $\exp(-\alpha k^2 t)$. Figure 10.8*b* presents analogous results for a sinusoidal initial data distribution with an amplitude of 0.5 and a period of 0.5, for which $k = 2\pi$. The shape of this property distribution also remains unchanged and decays exponentially as $\exp(-\alpha k^2 t)$. Consequently, the second case decays faster than the first case, due to the effect of the larger wave number (i.e., $k = 2\pi$). The value of the wave number has no effect on the shape of the property distribution.

Figure 10.8*c* presents the solution for a triangular initial data distribution with an amplitude of 1.0 and a period of 1.0, for which $k_1 = \pi$ and $k_m = m\pi$. The solution is obtained by expressing the initial data distribution in a Fourier series, obtaining the time-decaying solution for each Fourier component, and superimposing those solutions to obtain the overall solution. As demonstrated by Eq. (10.26), the exponential decay rate depends on the square of the wave number k_m [i.e., $\exp(-\alpha k_m^2 t)$]. Consequently, each Fourier component decays at a different rate, and the shape of the property distribution changes with time, as illustrated in Figure 10.8*c*. The larger-wave-number components decay more rapidly, leaving the smaller-wave-number components. In fact, the property distribution approaches a pure sine wave having a period of 1.0 and a wave number $k_1 = \pi$ as time increases. Figure 10.8*d* presents analogous results for a triangular initial data distribution with an amplitude of 0.5 and a period of 0.5, for which $k_1 = 2\pi$ and $k_m = 2m\pi$. The behavior of this case is similar to the previous case. However, the wave numbers of the corresponding components are twice those of the first case, because the

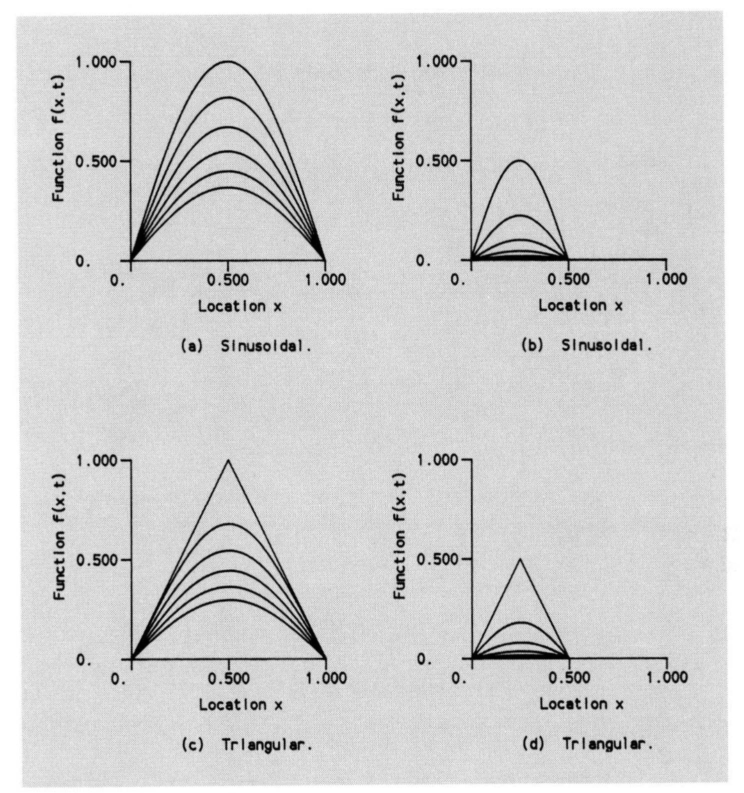

FIGURE 10.8
Exact solutions of the diffusion equation: (*a*) and (*b*) sinusoidal; (*c*) and (*d*) triangular.

period is one-half that of the first case. Consequently, the solution decays more rapidly as time increases.

Figure 10.8 clearly demonstrates that diffusion causes an initial data distribution to decay exponentially with time at a rate that depends on the square of the wave number. Consequently, the shape of the solution changes with time if the initial data distribution is not sinusoidal. The exponential decay rate does not depend on the magnitude of the solution.

Dispersion

Now consider pure dispersion, which is governed by the dispersion equation:

$$\boxed{f_t = \beta f_{xxx}} \tag{10.27}$$

where β is the dispersion coefficient. Substituting Eq. (10.8) into Eq. (10.27) yields

$$(\sigma + I\omega)Ce^{\sigma t}e^{I(kx+\omega t)} = \beta(Ik)^3 Ce^{\sigma t}e^{I(kx+\omega t)} \tag{10.28}$$

which gives

$$\sigma + I\omega = -I\beta k^3 \tag{10.29}$$

from which

$$\sigma = 0 \qquad \text{and} \qquad \omega = -\beta k^3 \tag{10.30}$$

Substituting Eq. (10.30) into Eq. (10.8) gives the exact solution of the dispersion equation:

$$\boxed{F(x,t) = Ce^{Ik(x-\beta k^2 t)}} \tag{10.31}$$

Consider the sinusoidal initial property distribution

$$f(x,0) = A_m \sin mx \tag{10.32}$$

From Eq. (10.31),

$$F(x,0) = C(\cos kx + I \sin kx) = A_m \sin mx \tag{10.33}$$

Consequently, $C = A_m$, $k = m$, and $f(x,t) = \text{Im}[F(x,t)]$, which gives

$$f(x,t) = A_m \sin\left(k(x - \beta k^2 t)\right) \tag{10.34}$$

Equation (10.34) can be written as

$$\boxed{f(x,t) = A_m \sin(k\xi) = F(\xi)} \tag{10.35}$$

where the *phase* ξ is defined as

$$\xi = (x - \beta k^2 t) \qquad \text{phase} \tag{10.36}$$

and the *phase velocity* or *wave velocity* c is given by

$$c = \beta k^2 \qquad \text{wave velocity} \tag{10.37}$$

Equation (10.35) shows that the sine wave moves at the constant wave velocity $c = \beta k^2$, which depends on the square of the wave number k, unchanged in magnitude or shape. By comparison, in pure convection the sine wave moves at the constant wave velocity $c = u$ [see Eq. (10.18)], which is independent of the wave number.

For an arbitrary wave shape represented by a Fourier series, each component propagates unchanged in magnitude and shape, but at a different wave velocity, which depends on the square of the wave number k. Thus, the wave shape changes as the wave propagates. Consequently, pure dispersion propagates the initial property distribution in space and changes the wave shape due to the dependence of the wave velocity c on the wave number k.

Example 10.3. Exact solution of the dispersion equation. We will demonstrate the general features of pure dispersion by considering four initial data distributions: two sinusoidal distributions and two triangular distributions. The results are presented in Fig. 10.9 for $\beta = 0.001/\pi^2$ at $t = 0$ to 20 at increments of 2.0.

Figure 10.9*a* presents the solution for a sinusoidal wave with an amplitude of 1.0 and a period of 1.0, for which the wave number $k = \pi$. As illustrated, the sine wave propagates unchanged in shape at the wave velocity $c = \beta k^2 = 0.001$. Figure 10.9*b* presents analogous results for a sinusoidal wave with an amplitude of 0.5 and a period of 0.5, for which the wave number $k = 2\pi$. This wave also propagates unchanged in shape, but at the wave velocity $c = \beta k^2 = 0.004$, which is four times the wave velocity of the first case.

Figure 10.9*c* presents the solution for a triangular wave with an amplitude of 1.0 and a period of 1.0, for which $k_1 = \pi$ and $k_m = m\pi$. The solution is obtained by expressing the initial data distribution in a Fourier series, obtaining the solution for the propagation of each Fourier component at its own wave velocity $c_m = \beta k_m^2$, and superimposing those solutions to obtain the overall solution. The amplitude and shape of each Fourier component is unchanged as it propagates, but the wave velocity depends on the square of the wave number k. Consequently, considerable wave distortion occurs

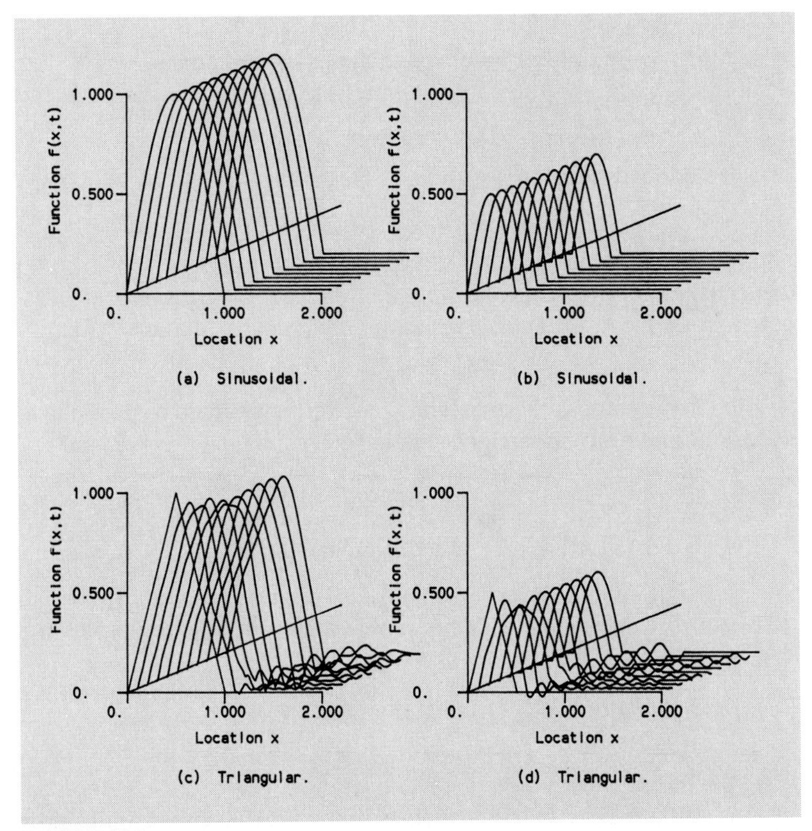

FIGURE 10.9
Exact solutions of the dispersion equation: (*a*) and (*b*) sinusoidal; (*c*) and (*d*) triangular.

as the wave propagates, as illustrated in Figure 10.9*c*. For a triangular wave, only the odd terms in the Fourier series are nonzero, that is, the components corresponding to $m = 1$, 3, 5, and so on. Consequently, the wave speeds of the higher-order components increase very rapidly, and they propagate much faster than the fundamental wave. After a very short time (depending on the value of β), the triangular wave separates into its Fourier components, which continually spread farther and farther apart. Eventually, the original wave consists only of the fundamental sine component, as illustrated in Figure 10.9*c*. Figure 10.9*d* presents analogous results for a triangular wave with an amplitude of 0.5 and a period of 0.5, for which $k_1 = 2\pi$ and $k_m = 2m\pi$. The propagation characteristics of this wave are similar to the previous case, except that all the wave velocities are four times as large.

Figure 10.9 clearly demonstrates that dispersion distorts the shape of an initially nonsinusoidal wave as it propagates. The wave velocity depends on the square of the wave number (i.e., $c_m = \beta k_m^2$) but does not depend on the wave amplitude.

In summary, pure convection propagates waves in space unchanged in magnitude and shape, pure diffusion causes the initial property distribution to decay with time and change shape, and pure dispersion propagates waves in space and changes the wave shape. These general features of convection, diffusion, and dispersion should be expected when solving more complicated convection, diffusion, and dispersion problems.

Many physical problems involve simultaneous combinations of convection, diffusion, and dispersion. Note, for example, the convection–diffusion equation

$$f_t + u f_x = \alpha f_{xx} \tag{10.38}$$

and the convection–dispersion equation

$$f_t + u f_x = \beta f_{xxx} \tag{10.39}$$

Equation (10.38) is the linearized form of the Burgers equation, and Eq. (10.39) is the linearized form of the Korteweg–de Vries equation. Although it is not a very common problem, all three processes could occur simultaneously:

$$f_t + u f_x = \alpha f_{xx} + \beta f_{xxx} \tag{10.40}$$

Complex problems such as these exhibit some of the features of pure convection, pure diffusion, and pure dispersion, simultaneously.

10.4 FINITE DIFFERENCE GRIDS AND FINITE DIFFERENCE APPROXIMATIONS

The objective of a finite difference method for solving a partial differential equation (PDE) is to transform a calculus problem into an algebra problem by the following steps:

1. Discretizing the continuous physical domain
2. Approximating the exact partial derivatives by algebraic finite difference approximations (FDAs)
3. Substituting the FDAs into the PDE to obtain an algebraic finite difference equation (FDE)

Discretizing the continuous physical domain and approximating exact partial derivatives by finite difference approximations are discussed in this section. The development of finite difference equations is discussed in the next section.

There are several choices which must be made when developing a finite difference solution to a partial differential equation. Foremost among these are the choice of the discrete finite difference grid used to represent the continuous solution domain and the choice of the finite difference approximations used to represent the individual exact partial derivatives in the partial differential equation. Some general properties of finite difference grids and finite difference approximations, for both parabolic and hyperbolic PDEs, are discussed in this section.

Finite Difference Grids

The solution domain $D(x, t)$ in xt space for an unsteady one-dimensional propagation problem is illustrated in Fig. 10.10. The solution domain must be covered by a two-dimensional grid of lines, called the finite difference grid. The intersections of these grid lines are the grid points, at which the finite difference solution to the partial differential equation is to be obtained. For the present, let the spatial grid lines be equally spaced lines perpendicular to the x axis having uniform spacing. The resulting finite difference grid is also illustrated in Fig. 10.10. Nonuniform grids in which Δx is variable, and transformed grids, in which the spatial grid lines are not parallel to the coordinate axes, are discussed in Chapter 13. The subscript i is used to denote the physical grid lines [i.e., $x_i = (i - 1)\Delta x$], and

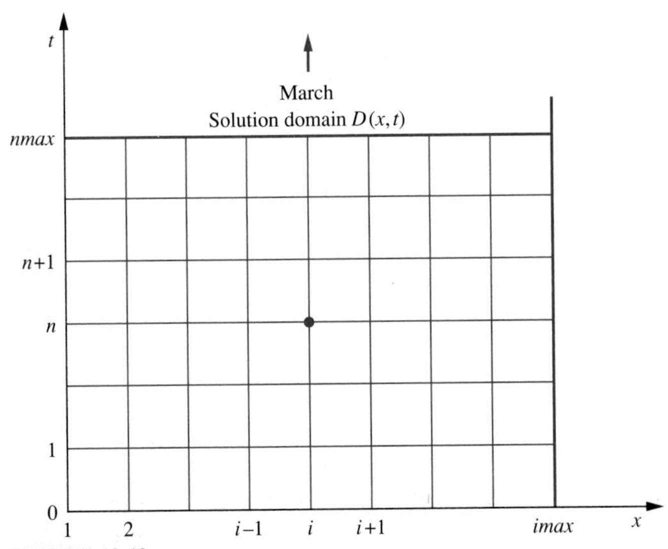

FIGURE 10.10
Solution domain $D(x, t)$ and finite difference grid.

the superscript n is used to denote the time grid lines (i.e., $t^n = n\,\Delta t$). Thus, grid point (i, n) corresponds to location (x_i, t^n) in the solution domain $D(x, t)$. The total number of x grid lines is denoted in the figure by *imax*, and the total number of time steps is denoted by *nmax*.

Two-dimensional physical spaces can be covered in a similar manner by a three-dimensional grid of planes perpendicular to the coordinate axes, where the subscripts i and j denote the physical grid planes perpendicular to the x and y axes, respectively, and the superscript n denotes time planes. Thus, grid point (i, j, n) corresponds to location (x_i, y_j, t^n) in the solution domain $D(x, y, t)$. Similarly, in three-dimensional physical space, grid point (i, j, k, n) corresponds to location (x_i, y_j, z_k, t^n) in the solution domain $D(x, y, z, t)$.

In multidimensional problems, the boundaries of the physical domain usually do not fall on the coordinate lines of a Cartesian coordinate system. In that case, the physical domain must be transformed to a body-fitted uniform orthogonal computational space, in which the boundaries of the physical domain fall on the boundaries of the computational space. That process is discussed in Chapter 13.

The dependent variable at a grid point is denoted by the same subscript–superscript notation that is used to denote the grid points themselves. Thus, the function $f(x, t)$ at grid point (i, n) is denoted by

$$f(x_i, t^n) = f_i^n \tag{10.41}$$

In a similar manner, derivatives are denoted by

$$\frac{\partial f(x_i, t^n)}{\partial t} = \left.\frac{\partial f}{\partial t}\right|_i^n = f_t|_i^n \quad \text{and} \quad \frac{\partial^2 f(x_i, t^n)}{\partial x^2} = \left.\frac{\partial^2 f}{\partial x^2}\right|_i^n = f_{xx}|_i^n \tag{10.42}$$

Similar results apply in two- and three-dimensional spaces. Thus,

$$f(x_i, y_j, t^n) = f_{i,j}^n \quad \text{and} \quad f(x_i, y_j, z_k, t^n) = f_{i,j,k}^n \tag{10.43}$$

Finite Difference Approximations

Now that the finite difference grid has been specified, finite difference approximations of the individual exact partial derivatives in the partial differential equation must be obtained. This is accomplished by using Taylor series expansions of the dependent variable about a particular grid point. This has been done in Chapter 5 for functions of one variable, where approximations of various types (i.e., forward, backward, and centered) of various orders (first-order, second-order, etc.) are developed for various derivatives (first derivative, second derivative, etc.). Those results are presented in Table 5.1.

In the development of finite difference approximations, a distinction must be made between the *exact* solution of the partial differential equation and the solution of the finite difference equation, which is an *approximation* of the partial differential equation. For the remainder of this book, the exact solution of the PDE is denoted by an overbar over the symbol for the dependent variable [e.g.,

$\bar{f}(x, t)$], and the approximate solution is denoted by the symbol for the dependent variable without an overbar [e.g., $f(x, t)$]. Thus,

$$\bar{f}(x, t) = \text{exact solution}$$
$$f(x, t) = \text{approximate solution}$$

This very precise distinction between the exact solution and the approximate solution of a partial differential equation is required for studies of consistency, order, stability, and convergence, which are discussed in Section 10.6.

TIME DERIVATIVES. Exact partial derivatives, such as $\bar{f}_t$, $\bar{f}_x$, and $\bar{f}_{xx}$, can be approximated at a grid point in terms of the values of f at that grid point and adjacent grid points in several ways. For example, consider the partial derivative $\bar{f}_t$. Writing the Taylor series for $\bar{f}_i^{n+1}$ using grid point (i, n) as the base point gives

$$\bar{f}_i^{n+1} = \bar{f}_i^n + \bar{f}_t|_i^n \, \Delta t + \frac{1}{2}\bar{f}_{tt}|_i^n \, \Delta t^2 + \cdots \tag{10.44}$$

where the convention $(\Delta t)^m \to \Delta t^m$ is employed for compactness. Equation (10.44) can be expressed as the Taylor formula with remainder (see the Appendix)

$$\bar{f}_i^{n+1} = \bar{f}_i^n + \bar{f}_t|_i^n \, \Delta t + \frac{1}{2}\bar{f}_{tt}|_i^n \, \Delta t^2 + \cdots + \frac{1}{m!}\frac{\partial^m \bar{f}}{\partial t^m}\bigg|_i^n \Delta t^m + R^{m+1} \tag{10.45}$$

where the remainder term R^{m+1} is given by

$$R^{m+1} = \frac{1}{(m+1)!}\frac{\partial^{m+1}\bar{f}(\tau)}{\partial t^{m+1}}\Delta t^{m+1} \tag{10.46}$$

where $t \le \tau \le t + \Delta t$. If the infinite Taylor series is truncated after the mth derivative term to obtain an approximation of $\bar{f}_i^{n+1}$, then the remainder term R^{m+1} is the error associated with the truncated Taylor series. In many cases, our main concern will be the *order* of the error, which is the rate at which the error goes to zero as $\Delta \to 0$. The remainder term R^{m+1} depends on Δt^{m+1}. Consequently, as $\Delta t \to 0$, the error goes to zero as Δt^{m+1}. Thus, the order of the truncated Taylor series approximation of $\bar{f}_i^{n+1}$ is $m + 1$, which is denoted by the symbol $O(\Delta t^{m+1})$.

Solving Eq. (10.44) for $\bar{f}_t|_i^n$ yields

$$\bar{f}_t|_i^n = \frac{\bar{f}_i^{n+1} - \bar{f}_i^n}{\Delta t} - \frac{1}{2}\bar{f}_{tt}|_i^n \, \Delta t - \cdots \tag{10.47}$$

Equivalently, from Eq. (10.45),

$$\bar{f}_t|_i^n = \frac{\bar{f}_i^{n+1} - \bar{f}_i^n}{\Delta t} - \frac{1}{2}\bar{f}_{tt}|_i^n \, \Delta t - \cdots - \frac{R^{m+1}}{\Delta t} \tag{10.48}$$

which can be written as

$$\bar{f}_t|_i^n = \frac{\bar{f}_i^{n+1} - \bar{f}_i^n}{\Delta t} - \cdots - O(\Delta t^m) \tag{10.49}$$

where

$$\frac{R^{m+1}}{\Delta t} = \frac{1}{(m+1)!} \frac{\partial^{m+1}\bar{f}(\tau)}{\partial t^{m+1}} \frac{\Delta t^{m+1}}{\Delta t} = O(\Delta t^m) \tag{10.50}$$

If the Taylor series is truncated after the first derivative term (i.e., $m = 1$), then Eqs. (10.48) and (10.50) give

$$\bar{f}_t|_i^n = \frac{\bar{f}_i^{n+1} - \bar{f}_i^n}{\Delta t} - \frac{1}{2}\bar{f}_{tt}(\tau)\Delta t \tag{10.51}$$

which can be written as

$$\boxed{\bar{f}_t|_i^n = \frac{\bar{f}_i^{n+1} - \bar{f}_i^n}{\Delta t} + E(\bar{f}_t|_i^n) = \frac{\bar{f}_i^{n+1} - \bar{f}_i^n}{\Delta t} + O(\Delta t)} \tag{10.52}$$

where the error term $E(\bar{f}_t|_i^n)$ is given by

$$\boxed{E(\bar{f}_t|_i^n) = -\frac{1}{2}\bar{f}_{tt}(\tau)\Delta t = O(\Delta t)} \tag{10.53}$$

A finite difference approximation for $\bar{f}_t|_i^n$, which will be denoted by $f_t|_i^n$, can be obtained from Eq. (10.52) by neglecting the error term. Thus,

$$\boxed{f_t|_i^n = \frac{f_i^{n+1} - f_i^n}{\Delta t}} \tag{10.54}$$

The error term, which has been neglected in Eq. (10.54), is called the truncation error of the finite difference approximation of $\bar{f}_t|_i^n$. Equation (10.54) is a first-order forward-difference approximation of $\bar{f}_t$ at grid point (i, n).

A first-order backward-difference approximation of $\bar{f}_t$ at grid point $(i, n+1)$ can be obtained by writing the Taylor series for $\bar{f}_i^n$ using grid point $(i, n+1)$ as the base point. Thus,

$$\bar{f}_i^n = \bar{f}_i^{n+1} + \bar{f}_t|_i^{n+1}(-\Delta t) + \frac{1}{2}\bar{f}_{tt}|_i^{n+1}(-\Delta t)^2 + \cdots \tag{10.55}$$

Solving Eq. (10.55) for $\bar{f}_t|_i^{n+1}$ gives

$$\bar{f}_t|_i^{n+1} = \frac{\bar{f}_i^{n+1} - \bar{f}_i^n}{\Delta t} + \frac{1}{2}\bar{f}_{tt}|_i^{n+1}\,\Delta t + \cdots \tag{10.56a}$$

Truncating the Taylor series after the first derivative term (i.e., $m = 1$) gives

$$\bar{f}_t|_i^{n+1} = \frac{\bar{f}_i^{n+1} - \bar{f}_i^n}{\Delta t} + \frac{1}{2}\bar{f}_{tt}(\tau)\,\Delta t \tag{10.56b}$$

Neglecting the error term yields the finite difference approximation

$$\boxed{f_t|_i^{n+1} = \frac{f_i^{n+1} - f_i^n}{\Delta t}} \tag{10.57}$$

A second-order centered-difference approximation of $\bar{f}_t$ at grid point $(i, n + \frac{1}{2})$ can be obtained by writing Taylor series for $\bar{f}_i^{n+1}$ and $\bar{f}_i^n$ about grid point $(i, n + \frac{1}{2})$, subtracting them, and solving for $\bar{f}_t|_i^{n+1/2}$ to obtain

$$\bar{f}_t|_i^{n+1/2} = \frac{\bar{f}_i^{n+1} - \bar{f}_i^n}{\Delta t} - \frac{1}{24}\bar{f}_{ttt}|_i^{n+1/2}\,\Delta t^2 - \cdots \tag{10.58a}$$

Truncating the Taylor series after the second derivative term (i.e., $m = 2$) gives

$$\bar{f}_t|_i^{n+1/2} = \frac{\bar{f}_i^{n+1} - \bar{f}_i^n}{\Delta t} - \frac{1}{24}\bar{f}_{ttt}(\tau)\,\Delta t^2 \tag{10.58b}$$

Neglecting the error term yields the finite difference approximation

$$\boxed{f_t|_i^{n+1/2} = \frac{f_i^{n+1} - f_i^n}{\Delta t}} \tag{10.59}$$

A second-order centered-difference approximation of $\bar{f}_t$ at grid point (i, n) can be obtained by writing Taylor series for $\bar{f}_i^{n+1}$ and $\bar{f}_i^{n-1}$ about grid point (i, n), subtracting them, and solving for $\bar{f}_t|_i^n$ to obtain

$$\bar{f}_t|_i^n = \frac{\bar{f}_i^{n+1} - \bar{f}_i^{n-1}}{2\Delta t} - \frac{1}{6}\bar{f}_{ttt}|_i^n\,\Delta t^2 - \cdots \tag{10.60a}$$

Truncating the Taylor series after the second derivative term (i.e., $m = 2$) gives

$$\bar{f}_t|_i^n = \frac{\bar{f}_i^{n+1} - \bar{f}_i^{n-1}}{2\Delta t} - \frac{1}{6}\bar{f}_{ttt}(\tau)\,\Delta t^2 \tag{10.60b}$$

Neglecting the error term yields the finite difference approximation

$$f_t|_i^n = \frac{f_i^{n+1} - f_i^{n-1}}{2\Delta t} \tag{10.61}$$

Equations (10.54), (10.57), and (10.59) involve the function $f(x,t)$ at two adjacent time levels: n and $n+1$. Equation (10.61) also involves $f(x,t)$ at two time levels: $n-1$ and $n+1$. However, three time levels are involved, because levels $n-1$ and $n+1$ are separated by $2\Delta t$. Finite difference approximations involving $f(x,t)$ at two adjacent time levels are called *two-level* methods; finite difference approximations involving $f(x,t)$ at three time levels are called *three-level* methods. The number of time levels employed in a finite difference approximation can have a significant impact on the amount of computer storage required to solve the resulting finite difference equation in a computer program. Consequently, the number of time levels is an important property of a finite difference method.

SPACE DERIVATIVES. In a similar manner, the following five finite difference approximations of $\bar{f}_x$ can be obtained:

$$\bar{f}_x|_i^n = \frac{\bar{f}_{i+1}^n - \bar{f}_i^n}{\Delta x} - \frac{1}{2}\bar{f}_{xx}(\xi^n)\Delta x \tag{10.62a}$$

$$f_x|_i^n = \frac{f_{i+1}^n - f_i^n}{\Delta x} \tag{10.62b}$$

$$\bar{f}_x|_i^n = \frac{\bar{f}_i^n - \bar{f}_{i-1}^n}{\Delta x} + \frac{1}{2}\bar{f}_{xx}(\xi^n)\Delta x \tag{10.63a}$$

$$f_x|_i^n = \frac{f_i^n - f_{i-1}^n}{\Delta x} \tag{10.63b}$$

$$\bar{f}_x|_i^n = \frac{\bar{f}_{i+1}^n - \bar{f}_{i-1}^n}{2\Delta x} - \frac{1}{6}\bar{f}_{xxx}(\xi^n)\Delta x^2 \tag{10.64a}$$

$$f_x|_i^n = \frac{f_{i+1}^n - f_{i-1}^n}{2\Delta x} \tag{10.64b}$$

$$\bar{f}_x|_i^{n+1} = \frac{\bar{f}_{i+1}^{n+1} - \bar{f}_{i-1}^{n+1}}{2\Delta x} - \frac{1}{6}\bar{f}_{xxx}(\xi^{n+1})\Delta x^2 \tag{10.65a}$$

$$f_x|_i^{n+1} = \frac{f_{i+1}^{n+1} - f_{i-1}^{n+1}}{2\Delta x} \tag{10.65b}$$

$$\bar{f}_x\Big|_i^{n+1/2} = \frac{1}{2}\left(\frac{\bar{f}_{i+1}^{n+1} - \bar{f}_{i-1}^{n+1}}{2\Delta x} + \frac{\bar{f}_{i+1}^{n} - \bar{f}_{i-1}^{n}}{2\Delta x}\right) - \frac{1}{12}\left(\bar{f}_{xxx}(\xi^{n+1}) + \bar{f}_{xxx}(\xi^{n})\right)\Delta x^2 \tag{10.66a}$$

$$f_x\Big|_i^{n+1/2} = \frac{1}{2}\left(\frac{f_{i+1}^{n+1} - f_{i-1}^{n+1}}{2\Delta x} + \frac{f_{i+1}^{n} - f_{i-1}^{n}}{2\Delta x}\right) \tag{10.66b}$$

where the convention $(\Delta x)^m \to \Delta x^m$ is employed for compactness, and ξ lies within the range of values of x employed in the Taylor series expansions. Equations (10.62*b*) to (10.64*b*) all involve the function $f(x, t)$ at time level n only. Equation (10.62*b*) is a first-order forward-difference approximation, and Eq. (10.63*b*) is a first-order backward-difference approximation. Due to their poor accuracy [i.e., $O(\Delta x)$], they are rarely used, except at boundaries. Equation (10.64*b*) is a second-order centered-difference approximation. It is the most commonly used finite difference approximation of a first spatial derivative. Equations (10.65*b*) and (10.66*b*) both involve $f(x, t)$ at time level $n + 1$. Both of these finite difference approximation are used frequently.

Similarly, the following five finite difference approximations of $\bar{f}_{xx}$ can be obtained:

$$\bar{f}_{xx}\Big|_i^n = \frac{\bar{f}_{i+2}^n - 2\bar{f}_{i+1}^n + \bar{f}_i^n}{\Delta x^2} - \bar{f}_{xxx}(\xi^n)\,\Delta x \tag{10.67a}$$

$$f_{xx}\Big|_i^n = \frac{f_{i+2}^n - 2f_{i+1}^n + f_i^n}{\Delta x^2} \tag{10.67b}$$

$$\bar{f}_{xx}\Big|_i^n = \frac{\bar{f}_i^n - 2\bar{f}_{i-1}^n + \bar{f}_{i-2}^n}{\Delta x^2} + \bar{f}_{xxx}(\xi^n)\,\Delta x \tag{10.68a}$$

$$f_{xx}\Big|_i^n = \frac{f_i^n - 2f_{i-1}^n + f_{i-2}^n}{\Delta x^2} \tag{10.68b}$$

$$\bar{f}_{xx}\Big|_i^n = \frac{\bar{f}_{i+1}^n - 2\bar{f}_i^n + \bar{f}_{i-1}^n}{\Delta x^2} - \frac{1}{12}\bar{f}_{xxxx}(\xi^n)\,\Delta x^2 \tag{10.69a}$$

$$f_{xx}\Big|_i^n = \frac{f_{i+1}^n - 2f_i^n + f_{i-1}^n}{\Delta x^2} \tag{10.69b}$$

$$\bar{f}_{xx}\Big|_i^{n+1} = \frac{\bar{f}_{i+1}^{n+1} - 2\bar{f}_i^{n+1} + \bar{f}_{i-1}^{n+1}}{\Delta x^2} - \frac{1}{12}\bar{f}_{xxxx}(\xi^{n+1})\,\Delta x^2 \tag{10.70a}$$

$$f_{xx}\Big|_i^{n+1} = \frac{f_{i+1}^{n+1} - 2f_i^{n+1} + f_{i-1}^{n+1}}{\Delta x^2} \tag{10.70b}$$

$$\bar{f}_{xx}\Big|_i^{n+1/2} = \frac{1}{2}\left(\frac{\bar{f}_{i+1}^{n+1} - 2\bar{f}_i^{n+1} + \bar{f}_{i-1}^{n+1}}{\Delta x^2} + \frac{\bar{f}_{i+1}^n - 2\bar{f}_i^n + \bar{f}_{i-1}^n}{\Delta x^2}\right) - \frac{1}{24}\left(\bar{f}_{xxxx}(\xi^n) + \bar{f}_{xxxx}(\xi^{n+1})\right)\Delta x^2 \tag{10.71a}$$

$$f_{xx}\Big|_i^{n+1/2} = \frac{1}{2}\left(\frac{f_{i+1}^{n+1} - 2f_i^{n+1} + f_{i-1}^{n+1}}{\Delta x^2} + \frac{f_{i+1}^n - 2f_i^n + f_{i-1}^n}{\Delta x^2}\right) \tag{10.71b}$$

Equations (10.67*b*) to (10.69*b*) involve $f(x, t)$ at time level n only. Equation (10.67*b*) is a first-order forward-difference approximation; Eq. (10.68*b*) is a first-order backward-difference approximation. As discussed previously, first-order approximations are rarely used, except at boundaries. Equation (10.69*b*) is a second-order centered-difference approximation. It is the most commonly used finite difference approximation of a second spatial derivative. Equations (10.70*b*) and (10.71*b*) both involve $f(x, t)$ at time level $n + 1$. Both of these finite difference approximations are used frequently.

10.5 FINITE DIFFERENCE EQUATIONS

Finite difference solutions of partial differential equations are obtained by replacing the individual exact partial derivatives in the partial differential equations by finite difference approximations (such as Eqs. (10.54), (10.57), (10.59), and (10.61) for time derivatives and Eqs. (10.62*b*) to (10.71*b*) for space derivatives) to obtain a finite difference approximation of the entire partial differential equation. Such approximations are called *finite difference equations*. Example 10.4 presents the *forward-time centered-space* (FTCS) approximation of the parabolic diffusion equation; Example 10.5 presents the approximation of the hyperbolic convection equation by the method developed by Lax and Wendroff (1960); and Example 10.6 presents the *backward-time centered-space* (BTCS) approximation of the parabolic convection-diffusion equation.

Example 10.4. The FTCS approximation of the parabolic diffusion equation. Consider the unsteady one-dimensional diffusion equation $\bar{f}_t = \alpha \bar{f}_{xx}$. Replacing $\bar{f}_t$ by the first-order forward-difference approximation at grid point (i, n), Eq. (10.54), and $\bar{f}_{xx}$ by the second-order centered-difference approximation at grid point (i, n), Eq. (10.69*b*), yields

$$\frac{f_i^{n+1} - f_i^n}{\Delta t} = \alpha \frac{f_{i+1}^n - 2f_i^n + f_{i-1}^n}{\Delta x^2} \tag{10.72}$$

The truncation errors of these finite difference approximations are $E(\bar{f}_t|_i^n) = O(\Delta t)$ and $E(\bar{f}_{xx}|_i^n) = O(\Delta x^2)$. Consequently, the truncation error of Eq. (10.72) is $O(\Delta t) + O(\Delta x^2)$. Equation (10.72) can be solved explicitly for f_i^{n+1}. Thus,

$$\boxed{f_i^{n+1} = f_i^n + d(f_{i+1}^n - 2f_i^n + f_{i-1}^n)} \tag{10.73}$$

where d, which is called the *diffusion number*, is defined as

$$\boxed{d = \frac{\alpha\, \Delta t}{\Delta x^2}} \tag{10.74}$$

Equation (10.73) is the FTCS approximation of the parabolic diffusion equation.

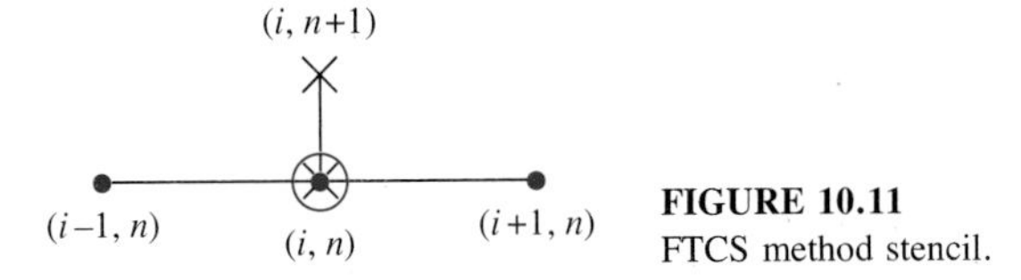

FIGURE 10.11
FTCS method stencil.

A finite difference equation can be illustrated pictorially by a *finite difference stencil*, which is a picture of the part of the finite difference grid used to develop the finite difference equation. The base point for the finite difference approximations of the individual exact partial derivatives is denoted by an open circle. The grid points involved in the finite difference approximations of the exact partial derivatives $\bar{f}_t$, $\bar{f}_x$, and $\bar{f}_{xx}$ are denoted by the symbols $\times$, an open square, and a solid circle, respectively. The finite difference stencil for Eq. (10.73) is presented in Fig. 10.11.

Two-level finite difference equations can be expressed in the general form

$$\sum_i a_i f_i^{n+1} = \sum_i b_i f_i^n \tag{10.75}$$

which can be written as

$$\boxed{a_i f_i^{n+1} = b_i f_i^n} \tag{10.76}$$

where the repeated subscript i denotes summation over the appropriate range of the spatial grid index. For example, the FTCS approximation of the diffusion equation [Eq. (10.73)] can be represented by letting i range from $i - 1$ to $i + 1$ and defining a_i and b_i as follows:

$$a_{i-1} = 0, \qquad a_i = 1, \qquad a_{i+1} = 0 \tag{10.77a}$$

$$b_{i-1} = d, \qquad b_i = (1 - 2d), \qquad b_{i+1} = d \tag{10.77b}$$

The equation $a_i f_i^{n+1} = b_i f_i^n$ is a convenient general representation of a two-level finite difference equation. Similar expressions can be written for multilevel FDEs.

The global error of the finite difference solution of a PDE at every point in the solution domain is of great interest. The error itself cannot be determined. However, the rate at which the error approaches zero as the sizes of the grid spacings Δt and Δx approach zero can be determined. This rate is called the *order* of the finite difference equation. The order of the global error of the finite difference solution is the same as the order of the truncation error of the finite difference approximations of the individual exact partial derivatives in the exact PDE. An investigation of the global order of the FTCS approximation of the diffusion equation is presented in the next paragraph.

Consider the diffusion equation $\bar{f}_t = \alpha \bar{f}_{xx}$. Applying the diffusion equation at grid point (i, n) gives

$$\bar{f}_t|_i^n = \alpha \bar{f}_{xx}|_i^n \tag{10.78}$$

Let $\bar{f}_t|_i^n$ be represented by Eq. (10.51) and $\bar{f}_{xx}|_i^n$ by Eq. (10.69a). Substituting these expressions into Eq. (10.78) yields

$$\frac{\bar{f}_i^{n+1} - \bar{f}_i^n}{\Delta t} - \frac{1}{2}\bar{f}_{tt}(\tau)\,\Delta t = \alpha\left(\frac{\bar{f}_{i+1}^n - 2\bar{f}_i^n + \bar{f}_{i-1}^n}{\Delta x^2} - \frac{1}{12}\bar{f}_{xxxx}(\xi^n)\,\Delta x^2\right) \tag{10.79a}$$

Solving for $\Delta\bar{f}_i^n = \bar{f}_i^{n+1} - \bar{f}_i^n$ yields

$$\Delta\bar{f}_i^n = d(\bar{f}_{i+1}^n - 2\bar{f}_i^n + \bar{f}_{i-1}^n) + \left(\frac{1}{2}\bar{f}_{tt}(\tau)\,\Delta t - \frac{1}{12}\alpha\bar{f}_{xxxx}(\xi^n)\,\Delta x^2\right)_i^n \Delta t \tag{10.79b}$$

The global solution at grid point $(i, T) = (i, N\Delta t)$ is

$$\bar{f}_i^N = \bar{f}_i^0 + \sum_{n=0}^{N-1} \Delta f_i^n + \sum_{n=0}^{N-1}\left(\frac{1}{2}\bar{f}_{tt}(\tau)\,\Delta t - \frac{1}{12}\alpha\bar{f}_{xxxx}(\xi^n)\,\Delta x^2\right)_i^n \Delta t \tag{10.80}$$

where $\Delta f_i^n = d(\bar{f}_{i+1}^n - 2\bar{f}_i^n + \bar{f}_{i-1}^n)$. Equation (10.80) can be written as

$$\bar{f}_i^N = \bar{f}_i^0 + \Delta f + N\left(\frac{1}{2}\bar{f}_{tt}(\bar{\tau})\,\Delta t - \frac{1}{12}\alpha\bar{f}_{xxxx}(\bar{\xi})\,\Delta x^2\right)\Delta t \tag{10.81}$$

where Δf represents the first summation and $\bar{\tau}$ and $\bar{\xi}$ are evaluated somewhere in the solution domain. The number of time steps N required to march to the final time T is $N = T/\Delta t$. Consequently, Eq. (10.81) becomes

$$\bar{f}_i^N = \bar{f}_i^0 + \Delta f + T\left(\frac{1}{2}\bar{f}_{tt}(\bar{\tau})\,\Delta t - \frac{1}{12}\alpha\bar{f}_{xxxx}(\bar{\xi})\,\Delta x^2\right) \tag{10.82}$$

Equation (10.82) can be written as

$$\boxed{\bar{f}_i^N = \bar{f}_i^0 + \Delta\bar{f} + O(\Delta t) + O(\Delta x^2)} \tag{10.83}$$

Equation (10.83) shows that the global error of the FTCS approximation of the diffusion equation is $O(\Delta t) + O(\Delta x^2)$, which is the same order as the order of the finite difference approximations of the exact partial derivatives $\bar{f}_t$ and $\bar{f}_{xx}$, respectively. This correspondence between the order of the truncation error of the finite difference approximations of the individual exact partial derivatives in the PDE and the order of the global solution of the FDE occurs for all finite difference approximations of all PDEs.

Example 10.4 presents the FTCS approximation of the parabolic diffusion equation. When applied to the hyperbolic convection equation, the FTCS approximation yields an unstable finite difference equation (see Section 12.3). Consequently, the method developed by Lax and Wendroff (1960) is applied to the hyperbolic convection equation in Example 10.5 to illustrate a finite difference approximation of that equation.

Example 10.5. The Lax–Wendroff approximation of the hyperbolic convection equation. Consider the unsteady one-dimensional convection equation $\bar{f}_t + u\bar{f}_x = 0$. The function to be determined is $\bar{f}(x, t)$. Lax and Wendroff (1960) proposed a method based on expanding $\bar{f}(x, t)$ in a Taylor series in time about grid point (i, n):

$$\bar{f}_i^{n+1} = \bar{f}_i^n + \bar{f}_t|_i^n \,\Delta t + \frac{1}{2}\bar{f}_{tt}|_i^n \,\Delta t^2 + O(\Delta t^3) \tag{10.84}$$

The first derivative $\bar{f}_t|_i^n$ is determined from the partial differential equation: $\bar{f}_t = -u\bar{f}_x$. The second derivative $\bar{f}_{tt}|_i^n$ is determined by differentiating the partial differential equation with respect to time. Thus,

$$\bar{f}_{tt} = (\bar{f}_t)_t = (-u\bar{f}_x)_t = -u(\bar{f}_t)_x = -u(-u\bar{f}_x)_x = u^2\bar{f}_{xx} \tag{10.85}$$

Substituting for $\bar{f}_t|_i^n$ and $\bar{f}_{tt}|_i^n$ in Eq. (10.84) yields

$$\bar{f}_i^{n+1} = \bar{f}_i^n - u\bar{f}_x|_i^n \,\Delta t + \frac{1}{2}u^2\bar{f}_{xx}|_i^n \,\Delta t^2 + O(\Delta t^3) \tag{10.86}$$

Replacing $\bar{f}_x|_i^n$ and $\bar{f}_{xx}|_i^n$ by second-order centered-difference approximations [Eqs. (10.64*b*) and (10.69*b*), respectively] gives

$$\bar{f}_i^{n+1} = \bar{f}_i^n - u\left(\frac{\bar{f}_{i+1}^n - \bar{f}_{i-l}^n}{2\Delta x} + O(\Delta x^2)\right)\Delta t$$
$$+ \frac{1}{2}u^2\left(\frac{\bar{f}_{i+1}^n - 2\bar{f}_i^n + \bar{f}_{i-1}^n}{\Delta x^2} + O(\Delta x^2)\right)\Delta t^2 + O(\Delta t^3) \tag{10.87}$$

Dropping the truncation error terms yields

$$f_i^{n+1} = f_i^n - \frac{c}{2}(f_{i+1}^n - f_{i-1}^n) + \frac{c^2}{2}(f_{i+1}^n - 2f_i^n + f_{i-1}^n) \tag{10.88}$$

where c, which is called the *convection number*, is defined as

$$c = \frac{u\,\Delta t}{\Delta x} \tag{10.89}$$

Equation (10.88) is the Lax–Wendroff approximation of the convection equation. The finite difference stencil is presented in Fig. 10.12.

The truncation error, and hence the order, of Eq. (10.88) is not readily apparent. The finite difference approximations of $\bar{f}_x$ and $\bar{f}_{xx}$ are obviously $O(\Delta x^2)$. From Eq.

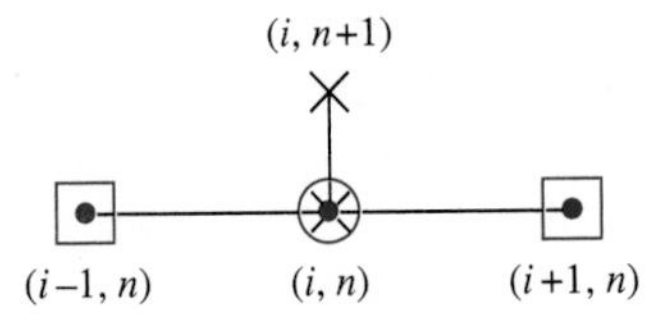

FIGURE 10.12
Lax–Wendroff one-step method stencil.

(10.84), it is apparent that the error of the truncated Taylor series expansion of $\bar{f}(x,t)$ is $O(\Delta t^3)$. However, to march to a given time T with a time step Δt requires $N = T/\Delta t$ time steps. Thus,

$$\bar{f}_i^N = \sum_{n=0}^{N-1}(\bar{f}_i^{n+1} - \bar{f}_i^n) + \sum_{n=0}^{N-1} O(\Delta t^3) \tag{10.90}$$

The total error is the sum of $N = T/\Delta t$ terms of $O(\Delta t^3)$, which is $O(\Delta t^2)$. Consequently, the global error of the Lax–Wendroff approximation of the convection equation is $O(\Delta t^2) + O(\Delta x^2)$.

The Lax–Wendroff approximation of the convection equation [i.e., Eq. (10.88)] can be expressed in the general form $a_i f_i^{n+1} = b_i f_i^n$ by letting i range from $i-1$ to $i+1$ and defining a_i and b_i as follows:

$$a_{i-1} = 0, \qquad a_i = 1, \qquad a_{i+1} = 0 \tag{10.91a}$$

$$b_{i-1} = \left(\frac{c}{2} + \frac{c^2}{2}\right), \qquad b_i = (1 - c^2), \qquad b_{i+1} = \left(-\frac{c}{2} + \frac{c^2}{2}\right) \tag{10.91b}$$

When the finite difference approximations of the individual exact partial derivatives in the PDE contain f^{n+1} only at physical location x_i (i.e., f_i^{n+1}), the corresponding FDE can be solved explicitly for f_i^{n+1} in terms of $f(x,t)$ at known time levels. Such finite difference equations are called *explicit* FDEs. The FTCS approximation of the diffusion equation and the Lax-Wendroff approximation of the convection equation are examples of explicit FDEs.

When the finite difference approximations of the individual exact partial derivatives in the PDE contain values of f^{n+1} at physical locations other than x_i (e.g., f_{i+1}^{n+1} and f_{i-1}^{n+1}), the solution for f_i^{n+1} from the corresponding FDE is implicitly specified in terms of f^{n+1} at neighboring physical locations. Such finite difference equations are called *implicit* FDEs. Implicit finite difference approximations result in systems of finite difference equations, which must be solved simultaneously. Whether an FDE is explicit or implicit is an important property of the FDE. Example 10.6 develops the implicit backward-time centered-space (BTCS) approximation of the parabolic convection–diffusion equation.

Example 10.6. The BTCS approximation of the parabolic convection–diffusion equation. Consider the unsteady one-dimensional convection–diffusion equation $\bar{f}_t + u\bar{f}_x = \alpha \bar{f}_{xx}$. Replacing $\bar{f}_t$ by the first-order backward-difference approximation at grid point $(i, n+1)$ [Eq. (10.56*b*)], $\bar{f}_x$ by the second-order centered-difference approximation at grid point $(i, n+1)$ [Eq. (10.65*a*)], and $\bar{f}_{xx}$ by the second-order centered-difference approximation at grid point $(i, n+1)$ [Eq. (10.70*a*)], yields

$$\frac{\bar{f}_i^{n+1} - \bar{f}_i^n}{\Delta t} + O(\Delta t) + u\frac{\bar{f}_{i+1}^{n+1} - \bar{f}_{i-1}^{n+1}}{2\Delta x} + O(\Delta x^2) = \alpha \frac{\bar{f}_{i+1}^{n+1} - 2\bar{f}_i^{n+1} + \bar{f}_{i-1}^{n+1}}{\Delta x^2} + O(\Delta x^2) \tag{10.92}$$

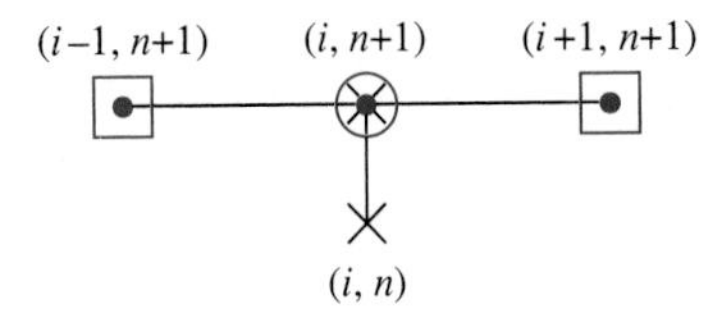

FIGURE 10.13
BTCS method stencil.

Dropping the truncation error terms and rearranging yields

$$-\left(\frac{c}{2}+d\right)f_{i-1}^{n+1}+(1+2d)f_i^{n+1}+\left(\frac{c}{2}-d\right)f_{i+1}^{n+1}=f_i^n \tag{10.93}$$

where $c = u\Delta t/\Delta x$ is the convection number and $d = \alpha\Delta t/\Delta x^2$ is the diffusion number. Equation (10.93) is the BTCS approximation of the convection–diffusion equation. The global error of the BTCS approximation of the convection–diffusion equation is $O(\Delta t) + O(\Delta x^2)$. The finite difference stencil is presented in Fig. 10.13.

The BTCS approximation of the convection–diffusion equation can be expressed in the general form $a_i f_i^{n+1} = b_i f_i^n$ by letting i range from $i-1$ to $i+1$ and defining a_i and b_i as follows:

$$a_{i-1}=-\left(\frac{c}{2}+d\right),\qquad a_i=(1+2d),\qquad a_{i+1}=\left(\frac{c}{2}-d\right) \tag{10.94a}$$

$$b_{i-1}=0,\qquad b_i=1,\qquad b_{i+1}=0 \tag{10.94b}$$

Another important property of a finite difference equation is the number of *steps* required to advance the solution one time level. A *single-step* method is one in which the solution at time level $n+1$ is obtained in one step. The forward-time centered-space (FTCS) method, the Lax–Wendroff method, and the backward-time centered-space (BTCS) method are all single-step methods. A *two-step* method is one in which the solution at time level $n+1$ is obtained in two steps. *Predictor-corrector* methods, such as the modified Euler method presented in Section 7.5 for the numerical solution of ordinary differential equations, are two-step methods. *Multistep* methods, such as the fourth-order Runge–Kutta method presented in Section 7.5, are methods in which several steps are required to advance the solution one time level. The number of steps in a numerical method has a direct influence on the computational efficiency of the method.

In summary, four important properties of the finite difference equations that approximate partial differential equations have been identified.

1. Whether the finite difference equations are explicit or implicit
2. The order of the finite difference equation
3. The number of time levels used to compute the next time level
4. The number of steps required to advance the solution one time level

For example, the forward-time centered-space (FTCS) approximation of the diffusion equation is an explicit, $O(\Delta t) + O(\Delta x^2)$, two-level, single-step, finite difference equation; the Lax–Wendroff approximation of the convection equation is an explicit, $O(\Delta t^2) + O(\Delta x^2)$, two-level, single-step, finite difference equation; and the backward-time centered-space (BTCS) approximation of the convection–diffusion equation is an implicit, $O(\Delta t) + O(\Delta x^2)$, two-level, single-step, finite difference equation.

Partial differential equations that govern propagation problems can be expressed in the general form

$$\bar{f}_t + \mathcal{L}_x(\bar{f}) = 0 \tag{10.95}$$

where $\mathcal{L}_x$ is the spatial derivative operator

$$\mathcal{L}_x = A_1 \frac{\partial}{\partial x} + A_2 \frac{\partial^2}{\partial x^2} + \cdots + A_n \frac{\partial^n}{\partial x^n} \tag{10.96}$$

A finite difference equation that represents Eq. (10.95) can be expressed in the general form

$$f_t + \mathcal{L}_x(f) = 0 \tag{10.97}$$

These compact forms for denoting PDEs and FDEs are useful in general discussions.

10.6 CONSISTENCY, ORDER, STABILITY, AND CONVERGENCE

Several important properties of finite difference equations for propagation problems governed by parabolic and hyperbolic PDEs must be considered before we can choose a specific approach. They are

1. Consistency
2. Order
3. Stability
4. Convergence

These concepts are defined and discussed in this section.

First, consider the concept of consistency.

A finite difference equation is consistent with a partial differential equation if the difference between the FDE and the PDE (i.e., the truncation error) vanishes as the sizes of the grid spacings go to zero independently.

When the truncation errors of the finite difference approximations of the individual exact partial derivatives are known, proof of consistency is straightforward. When the truncation errors of the individual finite difference approximations are not known, the complete finite difference equation must be analyzed for consistency. That is accomplished by expressing each term in the finite difference equation [i.e., $f(x, t)$, not $\bar{f}(x, t)$] by a Taylor series about a particular grid point. The resulting equation, which is called the modified differential equation (MDE), can be simplified to yield the exact form of the truncation error of the complete finite difference equation. Consistency can be investigated by letting the grid spacings go to zero. Examples of this approach are presented in Section 10.7.

Next, consider the concept of order, which is introduced in Section 10.5.

> *The order of a finite difference approximation of a partial differential equation is the rate at which the global error of the finite difference solution approaches zero as the sizes of the grid spacings approach zero.*

As shown in Section 10.5 [see Eq. (10.83)], the global order of a finite difference equation is the order of the truncation error terms in the finite difference approximations of the individual exact partial derivatives in the PDE. The order of an FDE is an extremely important property of the FDE.

Next, consider the concept of stability. First, the general behavior of the exact solution of the PDE must be considered. If the exact solution of the PDE is unbounded, then the numerical solution also must be unbounded. The concept of stability does not apply in that case. However, if the exact solution of the PDE is bounded, then the numerical solution must also be bounded. The concept of stability applies in this latter case. Several definitions of stability are in common use. In this book, stability is defined as follows:

> *When applied to a partial differential equation that has a bounded solution, a finite difference equation is stable if it produces a bounded solution and is unstable if it produces an unbounded solution.*

Several methods have been devised to analyze the stability of a finite difference approximation of a PDE. Three methods for analyzing the stability of FDEs are introduced in Section 10.8:

1. The discrete perturbation method
2. The von Neumann method
3. The matrix method

All three of these methods are demonstrated for the forward-time centered-space (FTCS) approximation of the diffusion equation in Section 10.8. In subsequent chapters, the results of the von Neumann method are presented for all the finite difference equations developed in this book.

Finally, consider the concept of *convergence*.

> *A finite difference method is convergent if the solution of the finite difference equation approaches the exact solution of the partial differential equation as the sizes of the grid spacings go to zero.*

Let $\bar{f}_i^n$ denote the exact solution of the partial differential equation, f_i^n the solution of the finite difference equation, and E_i^n the difference between them (i.e., the global error). The statement of convergence is

$$f_i^n - \bar{f}_i^n = E_i^n \rightarrow 0 \qquad \text{as } \Delta t \rightarrow 0 \text{ and } \Delta x \rightarrow 0$$

The proof of convergence of a finite difference solution is in the domain of the mathematician. We shall not attempt to prove convergence directly. However, the convergence of a finite difference method is related to the consistency and stability of the finite difference equation.

The *Lax equivalence theorem* [Lax (1954)] states:

> *Given a properly posed linear initial-value problem and a finite difference approximation to it that is consistent, stability is the necessary and sufficient condition for convergence.*

Thus, the question of convergence of a finite difference method is answered by a study of the consistency and stability of the finite difference equation. If the finite difference equation is consistent and stable, then the finite difference method is convergent.

The Lax equivalence theorem applies to well-posed linear initial-value problems. Many problems in engineering and science are not linear, and nearly all problems involve boundary conditions in addition to the initial conditions. There is no equivalence theorem for such problems. Nonlinear PDEs must be linearized locally, and the FDE that approximates the linearized PDE is analyzed for stability. Experience has shown that the stability criteria obtained for the linearized FDE also apply to the nonlinear FDE, and that FDEs that are consistent and whose linearized equivalent is stable generally converge, even for nonlinear initial-boundary-value problems.

In summary, the concepts of consistency, order, stability, and convergence must always be considered when solving a partial differential equation by finite difference methods. Consistency and order can be determined from the modified differential equation. Stability can be investigated by applying the von Neumann method. Convergence can be ensured through the Lax equivalence theorem by demonstrating consistency and stability.

10.7 THE MODIFIED DIFFERENTIAL EQUATION

Several important properties of finite difference equations that approximate partial differential equations are introduced in the preceding sections, in particular, consistency, order, stability, and convergence. Warming and Hyett (1974) developed a convenient technique for evaluating these properties. The technique involves determining the actual partial differential equation that is solved by the finite difference equation; that is the modified differential equation (MDE). Following Warming and Hyett, the MDE is determined by expressing each term in the finite difference equation in a Taylor series at some base point. Effectively, this changes the FDE back into a PDE. Time derivatives higher than first-order, and mixed time and space derivatives, are eliminated by differentiation of the MDE itself.

Terms appearing in the MDE that do not appear in the original partial differential equation are truncation error terms. Analysis of the truncation error terms leads directly to the determination of consistency and order. A study of these terms can also yield insight into the stability of the finite difference equation. However, that approach to stability analysis is not presented in this book.

Consider the general linear partial differential equation

$$\boxed{\bar{f}_t + \mathcal{L}_x(\bar{f}) = 0} \tag{10.98}$$

where $\bar{f}$ denotes the exact solution and $\mathcal{L}_x$ represents the spatial derivatives in x. The general spatial differential operator $\mathcal{L}_x$ is given by

$$\mathcal{L}_x = \sum_{q=1}^{n} A_q \frac{\partial^q}{\partial x^q} = A_1 \frac{\partial}{\partial x} + A_2 \frac{\partial^2}{\partial x^2} + \cdots + A_n \frac{\partial^n}{\partial x^n} \tag{10.99}$$

where n is the order of the PDE. For example, for the one-dimensional convection equation, $\mathcal{L}_x(\bar{f}) = u\bar{f}_x$; for the one-dimensional diffusion equation, $\mathcal{L}_x(\bar{f}) = -\alpha\bar{f}_{xx}$; and for the one-dimensional convection-diffusion equation, $\mathcal{L}_x(\bar{f}) = u\bar{f}_x - \alpha\bar{f}_{xx}$.

The finite difference equation that approximates the exact partial differential equation is obtained by replacing the exact partial derivatives $\bar{f}_t$ and $\mathcal{L}_x(\bar{f})$ by the finite difference approximations f_t and $\mathcal{L}_x(f)$, respectively. Thus, the FDE is

$$\boxed{f_t + \mathcal{L}_x(f) = 0} \tag{10.100}$$

The modified differential equation (MDE) is the actual PDE that is solved by the FDE. Let $f(x, t)$ be the exact solution of the FDE, Eq. (10.100). Each term in Eq. (10.100) can be expressed in a Taylor series for the approximate solution $f(x, t)$ about some base point. Substituting those Taylor series into Eq. (10.100) yields

$$f_t + \mathscr{L}_x(f) = \sum_r^\infty A_r \frac{\partial^r f}{\partial t^r} + \sum_{u,v}^\infty C_{u,v} \frac{\partial^{u+v} f}{\partial t^u \partial x^v} + \sum_s^\infty B_s \frac{\partial^s f}{\partial x^s} \tag{10.101}$$

Equation (10.101) is the actual PDE that is solved by the FDE, that is, it is the modified differential equation. The MDE must contain all of the terms appearing in the exact PDE [i.e., $\bar{f}_t + \mathscr{L}_x(\bar{f})$]. However, it also contains an infinite number of higher-order time and space derivatives. If all of the terms involving these higher-order derivatives vanish as $\Delta t \to 0$ and $\Delta x \to 0$ independently, then the MDE becomes identical to the exact PDE in the limit of infinitesimal-size grid spacings. In that case, the FDE is a consistent approximation of the exact PDE. If one or more of the terms involving these higher-order derivatives does not vanish as $\Delta t \to 0$ and $\Delta x \to 0$ independently, then the FDE is not a consistent approximation of the exact PDE. However, at finite size grid spacings, the MDE always differs from the exact PDE.

Example 10.7. The MDE for the FTCS approximation of the diffusion equation. As an example, consider the diffusion equation $\bar{f}_t = \alpha \bar{f}_{xx}$. The FTCS approximation of the diffusion equation is [see Eq. (10.73)]

$$f_i^{n+1} = f_i^n + d(f_{i+1}^n - 2f_i^n + f_{i-1}^n) \tag{10.102}$$

where $d = \alpha \Delta t / \Delta x^2$ is the diffusion number. Let grid point (i, n) be the base point, and write Taylor series for all of the terms in Eq. (10.102). Thus,

$$f_i^{n+1} = f_i^n + f_t|_i^n \Delta t + \frac{1}{2} f_{tt}|_i^n \Delta t^2 + \frac{1}{6} f_{ttt}|_i^n \Delta t^3 + \cdots \tag{10.103a}$$

$$f_{i\pm1}^n = f_i^n \pm f_x|_i^n \Delta x + \frac{1}{2} f_{xx}|_i^n \Delta x^2 \pm \frac{1}{6} f_{xxx}|_i^n \Delta x^3 + \frac{1}{24} f_{xxxx}|_i^n \Delta x^4$$
$$\pm \frac{1}{120} f_{xxxxx}|_i^n \Delta x^5 + \frac{1}{720} f_{xxxxxx}|_i^n \Delta x^6 \pm \cdots \tag{10.103b}$$

Dropping the notation $|_i^n$ for clarity and substituting the above expressions into Eq. (10.102) gives

$$f + f_t \Delta t + \frac{1}{2} f_{tt} \Delta t^2 + \frac{1}{6} f_{ttt} \Delta t^3 + \cdots$$
$$= f + \frac{\alpha \Delta t}{\Delta x^2} \left(2f + f_{xx} \Delta x^2 + \frac{1}{12} f_{xxxx} \Delta x^4 + \frac{1}{360} f_{xxxxxx} \Delta x^6 + \cdots - 2f \right) \tag{10.104}$$

Cancelling zero-order terms, dividing through by Δt, and rearranging terms yields the *first* form of the MDE:

$$\boxed{f_t = \alpha f_{xx} - \frac{1}{2} f_{tt}\,\Delta t - \frac{1}{6} f_{ttt}\,\Delta t^2 - \cdots + \frac{1}{12}\alpha f_{xxxx}\Delta x^2 + \frac{1}{360}\alpha f_{xxxxxx}\Delta x^4 + \cdots} \tag{10.105}$$

As $\Delta t \to 0$ and $\Delta x \to 0$, Eq. (10.105) approaches $f_t = \alpha f_{xx}$, which is the diffusion equation. Consequently, Eq. (10.102) is a consistent approximation of the diffusion equation. The truncation error may be determined from the first form of the MDE. From Eq. (10.105) [noting that $\mathscr{L}_x(\bar{f}) = -\alpha \bar{f}_{xx}$, so that the second line on the right-hand side of Eq. (10.105) is actually $-E(\bar{f}_{xx}|_i^n)$],

$$E(\bar{f}_t|_i^n) = -\frac{1}{2}\bar{f}_{tt}|_i^n\,\Delta t - \cdots \qquad \text{and} \qquad E(\bar{f}_{xx}|_i^n) = -\frac{1}{12}\bar{f}_{xxxx}|_i^n\,\Delta x^2 - \cdots \tag{10.106}$$

which agrees with Eq. (10.47) and Eq. (10.69*a*). Consequently, Eq. (10.102) is $O(\Delta t) + O(\Delta x^2)$.

The *second* form of the modified differential equation (MDE) is obtained by eliminating the higher-order time derivatives and the mixed time and space derivatives from the first form of the MDE [Eq. (10.105)] by repeated differentiation of the MDE itself. The derivative f_{tt} can be obtained by differentiating Eq. (10.105) with respect to time to yield

$$f_{tt} = \alpha f_{xxt} - \frac{1}{2} f_{ttt}\,\Delta t - \frac{1}{6} f_{tttt}\,\Delta t^2 - \cdots + \frac{1}{12}\alpha f_{xxxxt}\,\Delta x^2 + \frac{1}{360}\alpha f_{xxxxxxt}\,\Delta x^4 + \cdots \tag{10.107a}$$

The mixed derivative f_{xxt} can be determined by differentiating Eq. (10.105) twice with respect to x to give

$$f_{xxt} = \alpha f_{xxxx} - \frac{1}{2} f_{xxtt}\,\Delta t - \frac{1}{6} f_{xxttt}\,\Delta t^2 - \cdots + \frac{1}{12}\alpha f_{xxxxxx}\,\Delta x^2 + \frac{1}{360}\alpha f_{xxxxxxxx}\,\Delta x^4 + \cdots \tag{10.107b}$$

Combining Eqs. (10.107*a*) and (10.107*b*) gives

$$\begin{aligned} f_{tt} = \Bigg(&\alpha^2 f_{xxxx} - \frac{1}{2}\alpha f_{xxtt}\,\Delta t - \frac{1}{6}\alpha f_{xxttt}\,\Delta t^2 - \cdots + \frac{1}{12}\alpha^2 f_{xxxxxx}\,\Delta x^2 \\ &+ \frac{1}{360}\alpha^2 f_{xxxxxxxx}\,\Delta x^4 + \cdots\Bigg) - \frac{1}{2} f_{ttt}\,\Delta t - \frac{1}{6} f_{tttt}\,\Delta t^2 - \cdots \\ &+ \frac{1}{12}\alpha f_{xxxxt}\,\Delta x^2 + \frac{1}{360}\alpha f_{xxxxxxt}\,\Delta x^4 + \cdots \end{aligned} \tag{10.107c}$$

The remaining higher-order time derivatives and the mixed time and space derivatives can be obtained in a similar manner. Thus, through sixth-order spatial derivatives,

$$f_{ttt} = \alpha^3 f_{xxxxxx} + \cdots \tag{10.108a}$$

$$f_{xxtt} = \alpha^2 f_{xxxxxx} + \cdots \tag{10.108b}$$

$$f_{xxxxt} = \alpha f_{xxxxxx} + \cdots \tag{10.108c}$$

Substituting all of the above results into the first form of the MDE, Eq. (10.105), yields

$$\boxed{\begin{aligned} f_t = \alpha f_{xx} &+ \left(\frac{1}{12}\alpha\,\Delta x^2 - \frac{1}{2}\alpha^2\,\Delta t\right) f_{xxxx} \\ &+ \left(\frac{1}{360}\alpha\,\Delta x^4 - \frac{1}{12}\alpha^2\,\Delta t\,\Delta x^2 + \frac{1}{3}\alpha^3\,\Delta t^2\right) f_{xxxxxx} + \cdots \end{aligned}} \tag{10.109}$$

Equation (10.109) is the second form of the MDE. In the second form of the MDE, all the truncation error terms are expressed in terms of spatial derivatives. Equation (10.109) can be written in the form

$$\boxed{f_t + \mathscr{L}_x(f) = \sum_m^{\infty} C_m \frac{\partial^m f}{\partial x^m}} \tag{10.110}$$

where the terms $C_m(\partial^m f/\partial x^m)$ represent the spatial derivative terms in Eq. (10.109).

The consistency and order of a finite difference equation can be determined from the MDE. For example, in Eq. (10.105), as $\Delta t \to 0$ and $\Delta x \to 0$, Eq. (10.105) approaches $f_t = \alpha f_{xx}$, which is the diffusion equation. Consequently, Eq. (10.102) is a consistent approximation of that equation. The order of the individual truncation error terms can be determined from the first form of the MDE. For example, from Eq. (10.105), the order is $O(\Delta t) + O(\Delta x^2)$. In some FDEs, however, the leading truncation error terms in Δt and Δx may cancel exactly, which results in a higher-order FDE. Such cancellations, if they occur, occur when the time derivatives are replaced by spatial derivatives, as in the second form of the MDE. Examination of Eq. (10.109) shows that such cancellations did not occur in this example. An example of such cancellations is presented in Example 10.8. However, the leading truncation error terms may cancel numerically for specific choices of Δx and Δt.

The leading truncation error terms in Eq. (10.109) can be rearranged as follows:

$$\left(\frac{1}{12}\alpha\,\Delta x^2 - \frac{1}{2}\alpha^2\,\Delta t\right) f_{xxxx} = \frac{1}{2}\alpha\,\Delta x^2 \left(\frac{1}{6} - d\right) f_{xxxx} \tag{10.111}$$

where d is the diffusion number. When $d = \frac{1}{6}$, this term is zero, and the MDE becomes

$$f_t = \alpha f_{xx} + O(\Delta t^2) + O(\Delta t\,\Delta x^2) + O(\Delta x^4) \tag{10.112}$$

Thus, for $d = \frac{1}{6}$, the truncation error of the FTCS approximation of the diffusion equation is higher order than for all other values of d.

An alternate approach for determining the second form of the MDE has been employed by several authors. In that approach, the time derivatives higher than first order and the mixed time and space derivatives are determined by differentiating the *exact* partial differential equation. That approach is incorrect, however, since a solution of the finite difference equation does not satisfy the exact PDE. The MDE is the actual PDE that is solved by the finite difference equation. Applying this incorrect approach to eliminate the higher-order time derivatives in Eq. (10.105) yields

$$f_{tt} = \alpha^2 f_{xxxx} + \cdots \tag{10.113a}$$

$$f_{ttt} = \alpha^3 f_{xxxxxx} + \cdots \tag{10.113b}$$

Substituting the above equations into Eq. (10.105) gives

$$f_t = \alpha f_{xx} + \left(\frac{1}{12}\alpha\,\Delta x^2 - \frac{1}{2}\alpha^2\,\Delta t\right) f_{xxxx} + \left(\frac{1}{360}\alpha\,\Delta x^4 - \frac{1}{6}\alpha^3\,\Delta t^2\right) f_{xxxxxx} + \cdots \tag{10.114}$$

The leading truncation error term in Eq. (10.114) is the same as in the correct MDE, Eq. (10.109). This is generally the case. The remaining truncation error terms in Eq. (10.114) involve the same spatial derivatives as in the correct MDE, but the coefficients are different. This is always the case. This incorrect approach for obtaining the second form of the MDE does show whether or not any low-order truncation error terms cancel exactly.

Example 10.8. The MDE for the Lax–Wendroff approximation of the convection equation. As a second example, we will develop the MDE for the Lax–Wendroff approximation of the convection equation $\bar{f}_t + u\bar{f}_x = 0$ [see Eq. (10.88)]:

$$f_i^{n+1} = f_i^n - \frac{c}{2}(f_{i+1}^n - f_{i-1}^n) + \frac{c^2}{2}(f_{i+1}^n - 2f_i^n + f_{i-1}^n) \tag{10.115}$$

Let grid point (i, n) be the base point. Substituting Taylor series for $f(x, t)$ into Eq. (10.115) and simplifying yields the first form of the DE:

$$\begin{aligned} f_t + uf_x = &-\frac{1}{2}f_{tt}\,\Delta t - \frac{1}{6}f_{ttt}\,\Delta t^2 - \frac{1}{24}f_{tttt}\,\Delta t^3 - \cdots \\ &- \frac{1}{6}uf_{xxx}\,\Delta x^2 - \cdots \\ &+ \frac{1}{2}u^2 f_{xx}\,\Delta t + \frac{1}{24}u^2 f_{xxxx}\,\Delta x^2\,\Delta t + \cdots \end{aligned} \tag{10.116}$$

The second form of the MDE is obtained by eliminating the higher-order time derivatives and the mixed time and space derivatives from the first form of the MDE by repeated differentiation of the MDE itself. The result is

$$f_t + u f_x = \left(-\frac{1}{6} u\,\Delta x^2 + \frac{1}{6} u^3\,\Delta t^2\right) f_{xxx} + \left(-\frac{1}{8} u^2\,\Delta x^2\,\Delta t + \frac{1}{8} u^4\,\Delta t^3\right) f_{xxxx} + \cdots \tag{10.117}$$

As $\Delta t \to 0$ and $\Delta x \to 0$, Eq. (10.116) approaches $f_t + u f_x = 0$. Consequently, Eq. (10.115) is a consistent approximation of the convection equation. Equation (10.116) suggests that the truncation error is $O(\Delta t) + O(\Delta x^2)$. However, Eq. (10.117) shows that the truncation error is actually $O(\Delta t^2) + O(\Delta x^2)$, due to exact cancellation of the leading truncation error terms in Eq. (10.116) for all values of Δx and Δt.

Examples 10.7 and 10.8 illustrate the derivation of the MDEs for finite difference aproximations of pure diffusion and pure convection, respectively. The derivation of the MDE for an FDE involving combined convection and diffusion is illustrated in the next example.

Example 10.9. The MDE for the BTCS approximation of the convection–diffusion equation. As a final example, let us determine the MDE for the BTCS approximation of the convection–diffusion equation $\bar{f}_t + u\bar{f}_x = \alpha \bar{f}_{xx}$ [see Eq. (10.93)]:

$$-\left(\frac{c}{2} + d\right) f_{i-1}^{n+1} + (1 + 2d) f_i^{n+1} + \left(\frac{c}{2} - d\right) f_{i+1}^{n+1} = f_i^n \tag{10.118}$$

Let grid point $(i, n+1)$ be the base point. Substituting Taylor series for $f(x, t)$ into Eq. (10.118) and simplifying yields the first form of the MDE:

$$f_t + u f_x = \alpha f_{xx} + \frac{1}{2} f_{tt}\,\Delta t - \frac{1}{6} f_{ttt}\,\Delta t^2 - \cdots - \frac{1}{6} u f_{xxx}\,\Delta x^2$$
$$- \frac{1}{120} u f_{xxxxx}\,\Delta x^4 - \cdots + \frac{1}{12} \alpha f_{xxxx}\,\Delta x^4 + \frac{1}{360} \alpha f_{xxxxxx}\,\Delta x^4 + \cdots \tag{10.119}$$

The second form of the MDE is:

$$f_t + u f_x = \alpha f_{xx} + \left(\frac{1}{2} u^2\,\Delta t\right) f_{xx} + \left(-\frac{1}{6} u\,\Delta x^2 + u\alpha\,\Delta t - \frac{1}{3} u^3\,\Delta t^2\right) f_{xxx} + \cdots \tag{10.120}$$

As $\Delta t \to 0$ and $\Delta x \to 0$, Eq. (10.119) approaches $f_t + u f_x = \alpha f_{xx}$. Consequently, Eq. (10.118) is a consistent approximation of the convection–diffusion equation. From Eqs. (10.119) and (10.120), the truncation error is $O(\Delta t) + O(\Delta x^2)$.

The following steps should be followed to obtain the MDE, from which consistency and order of an FDE can be determined.

1. Determine the finite difference equation (FDE) to be analyzed.
2. Choose the base point for the Taylor series for $f(x, t)$ for the terms appearing in the FDE. If known, choose the base point for the finite difference approximations of the exact partial derivatives in the PDE as the base point for the MDE.

3. Substitute the Taylor series for all terms into the FDE.
4. Simplify the resulting equation by cancelling all like terms, gathering the coefficients of all similar terms, identifying all partial derivative terms that do not contain Δt or Δx, and identifying the remaining terms as the truncation error. This step yields the first form of the MDE, which is the actual PDE represented by the FDE.
5. Let $\Delta t \to 0$ and $\Delta x \to 0$ to determine what PDE is approached by the FDE. If the exact PDE is approached, the FDE is consistent with the exact PDE. If some other PDE is approached, then the FDE is not consistent with the exact PDE.
6. Determine the second form of the MDE by repeated differentiation of the MDE itself and substitution into the first form of the MDE to eliminate all time derivatives and mixed time and space derivatives of low order.
7. Determine the order of the FDE from the second form of the MDE.
8. If the first form of the MDE has only one term containing the lowest-order power of Δt, then that term determines the order of the FDE, and the second form of the MDE is not needed.

In summary, the modified differential equation (MDE) can be used to determine the consistency and order of a finite difference approximation of a partial differential equation. As discussed by Warming and Hyett (1974), the MDE also can be employed to investigate stability. That approach to stability analysis is not presented in this book. The more straightforward von Neumann method presented in Section 10.8 is used.

10.8 STABILITY ANALYSIS

As discussed in Section 10.6, stability of a finite difference approximation of a partial differential equation which has a bounded solution is defined as follows:

> *A finite difference equation is stable if it produces a bounded solution and is unstable if it produces an unbounded solution.*

This definition of stability for FDEs that approximate PDEs is analogous to the definition of stability presented in Section 7.8 for FDEs that approximate ODEs.

The first step in the stability analysis of an FDE that approximates a PDE is to determine the behavior of the exact solution of the PDE. The solution to most physical problems is bounded. This is demonstrated in Section 10.3 for pure convection, pure diffusion, and pure dispersion. In that case, the solution to the FDE also must be bounded. If the solution of the FDE is bounded for all values of the grid spacings, then the FDE is *unconditionally stable*. If the solution of the FDE is bounded only for certain values of the grid spacings, then the FDE is *conditionally stable*. If the solution of the FDE is unbounded for all values of the grid spacings, then the FDE is *unconditionally unstable*. If the exact solution of the PDE is unbounded, then the solution of the FDE also must be unbounded. The concept of stability does not apply in that case, because the numerical solution is behaving in the same manner as the exact solution.

Stability analyses can be performed only for linear PDEs. Consequently, nonlinear PDEs must be linearized locally, and the FDE approximating the linearized PDE is analyzed for stability. Experience has shown that the stability criteria obtained for the FDE approximating the linearized PDE also apply to the FDE approximating the nonlinear PDE. Instances of suspected *nonlinear instabilities* have been reported in the literature, but it is not clear whether those phenomena are due to actual instabilities, inconsistent finite difference equations, excessively large grid spacings, inadequate treatment of boundary conditions, or simply incorrect computations. Consequently, in this book, the stability analysis of the finite difference equation that approximates a linearized PDE will be considered sufficient to determine the stability criteria for the FDE, even for nonlinear partial differential equations.

Three methods for analyzing the stability of a finite difference equation that approximates a partial differential equation are presented in this book:

1. The discrete perturbation method
2. The von Neumann method
3. The matrix method

All three of these methods are illustrated by applying them to the forward-time centered-space (FTCS) approximation of the diffusion equation, $\bar{f}_t = \alpha \bar{f}_{xx}$, which is [see Eq. (10.73)]

$$\boxed{f_i^{n+1} = f_i^n + d(f_{i+1}^n - 2f_i^n + f_{i-1}^n)} \tag{10.121}$$

Discrete Perturbation Method

First consider the *discrete perturbation method*. In this method, an arbitrary distribution of the dependent variable $f(x, t)$ is assumed to exist at time level n. The behavior of this arbitrary property distribution is analyzed to determine what conditions, or criteria, must be satisfied to ensure that the numerical solution remains bounded.

Example 10.10. Discrete perturbation stability analysis of the FTCS approximation of the diffusion equation. We will perform a discrete perturbation stability analysis of Eq. (10.121). Assume that the function $f(x, t)$ is zero everywhere except at point (i, n), where $f_i^n = \epsilon$. Use Eq. (10.121) to determine the solution at time level $n + 1$.

Thus,

$$f_{i-1}^{n+1} = 0 + d[0 - 2(0) + \epsilon] = (d)\epsilon \tag{10.122a}$$

$$f_{i}^{n+1} = \epsilon + d[0 - 2(\epsilon) + 0] = (1 - 2d)\epsilon \tag{10.122b}$$

$$f_{i+1}^{n+1} = 0 + d[\epsilon - 2(0) + 0] = (d)\epsilon \tag{10.122c}$$

The requirement for stability is that the magnitude of the perturbation ϵ introduced at point i at time level n must be bounded as n increases. Thus, at time level $n + 1$,

$$|f_i^{n+1}/f_i^n| = |(1 - 2d)\epsilon/\epsilon| = |1 - 2d| \le 1 \tag{10.123}$$

For stability,

$$-1 \le 1 - 2d \le 1 \tag{10.124}$$

The right-hand inequality is always satisfied if d is greater than or equal to zero, which it must be for positive Δt. The left-hand inequality is satisfied if $d \le 1$. Thus, the criterion $0 \le d \le 1$ guarantees that a perturbation at point i will not amplify during one time step.

However, $d \le 1$ is not the complete answer. From Eq. (10.122), we see that the perturbation $f_i^n = \epsilon$ not only propagates a contribution forward at point i, but it also propagates a contribution laterally to points $i - 1$ and $i + 1$ equal to $(d)\epsilon$ at both locations. These terms will contribute to the solution at point i at time level $n + 2$. Thus,

$$f_i^{n+2} = (1 - 2d)\epsilon + d\Big((d)\epsilon - 2(1 - 2d)\epsilon + (d)\epsilon\Big) = (6d^2 - 4d + 1)\epsilon \tag{10.125}$$

For stability,

$$-1 \le 6d^2 - 4d + 1 \le 1 \tag{10.126}$$

Equation (10.126) is satisfied if

$$0 \le d \le \frac{2}{3} \tag{10.127}$$

This process must be repeated at subsequent time levels until the asymptotic limit is obtained. The required algebra becomes excessively tedious, so it is not shown here. In the present case, the asymptotic limit is

$$\boxed{0 \le d \le \frac{1}{2}} \tag{10.128}$$

It is instructive to consider the physical implications of the perturbation analysis. A perturbation ϵ corresponds to a finite amount of the physical property f. Once this perturbation in f is introduced, it must diffuse through the physical domain until it passes out through the boundaries into the surroundings, just as the true physical property is diffused to the boundaries. This diffusion of the perturbation is governed by the finite difference equation, Eq. (10.121). Consequently, the propagation of the perturbation can be determined by solving Eq. (10.121) numerically.

As an example, let us introduce the perturbation $f(0.5, 0.0) = 1.0$ in the physical domain $0.0 \le x \le 1.0$. Let $\Delta x = 0.1$. This perturbation should diffuse through the solution domain and pass out through the boundaries to the surroundings. The sum of the perturbations should be 1.0 at succeeding time levels until the perturbations reach the boundaries, after which the sum should smoothly decrease to 0.0. Table 10.1 presents the exact solution of Eq. (10.121) for $d = 0.5$. Since the solution is symmetrical about $x = 0.5$, the solution for $x > 0.5$ is not presented. At time level 0, the sum of the perturbations is 1.0. The sum remains 1.0 for the first four time steps, during which no information reaches the boundaries. At time step 5, some of the perturbation passes out through the boundaries, and the sum of the perturbations at the interior points is less than 1.0. As time increases, more of the perturbation passes out through the boundaries, and the sum of the perturbations at the interior points approaches 0.0. The results presented in Table 10.1 clearly demonstrate that the FTCS approximation of the diffusion equation is stable when $d = 0.5$.

Consider now the case with $d = 1.0$. The solution is presented in Table 10.2. At each time level, the sum of the perturbations is 1.0. However, the perturbations are growing rapidly (even exponentially) and oscillating. This situation is unstable. Consequently, the FTCS approximation of the diffusion equation is unstable when $d = 1.0$.

The discrete perturbation method of stability analysis yields useful insights into the behavior of a finite difference equation, but it may not lead to precise stability criteria without an excessive amount of algebraic work. The numerical approach illustrated in Tables 10.1 and 10.2 gives the exact stability criteria only by numerical trial and error. Consequently, the discrete perturbation analysis is useful to enhance physical understanding, but a simpler, more straightforward method is desired for formal stability analysis.

TABLE 10.1
Solution of the perturbation equation for $d = 0.5$

		Perturbation f_i^n					
n	t	$x = 0.0$	$x = 0.1$	$x = 0.2$	$x = 0.3$	$x = 0.4$	$x = 0.5$
0	0.0	0	0	0	0	0	1
1	0.5	0	0	0	0	1/2	0
2	1.0	0	0	0	1/4	0	2/4
3	1.5	0	0	1/8	0	3/8	0
4	2.0	0	1/16	0	4/16	0	6/16
5	2.5	0	0	5/32	0	10/32	0
6	3.0	0	5/64	0	15/64	0	20/64
7	3.5	0	0	20/128	0	35/128	0
8	4.0	0	20/256	0	55/256	0	70/256
9	4.5	0	0	65/512	0	125/512	0
10	5.0	0	65/1024	0	190/1024	0	250/1024

TABLE 10.2
Solution of the perturbation equation for $d = 1.0$

		Perturbation f_i^n					
n	t	$x = 0.0$	$x = 0.1$	$x = 0.2$	$x = 0.3$	$x = 0.4$	$x = 0.5$
0	0.0	0	0	0	0	0	1
1	1.0	0	0	0	0	1	−1
2	2.0	0	0	0	1	−2	3
3	3.0	0	0	1	−3	6	−7
4	4.0	0	1	−4	10	−16	19
5	5.0	0	−5	15	−30	45	−51
6	6.0	0	20	−50	90	−126	141
7	7.0	0	−70	160	−226	357	−393

von Neumann Method

The preferred procedure for performing a stability analysis is the von Neumann method. In this method, the exact solution of the finite difference equation is obtained for the general Fourier component of a complex Fourier series representation of the initial property distribution. If the solution for the general Fourier component is bounded (either conditionally or unconditionally), then the finite difference equation is stable. If the solution for the general Fourier component is unbounded, then the finite difference equation is unstable.

As an example, consider the diffusion equation $\bar{f}_t = \alpha \bar{f}_{xx}$. As shown in Section 10.3 [see Eq. (10.23)], the exact solution of the diffusion equation for a general Fourier component (the overbars have been added to denote the exact solution) is

$$\bar{F}(x, t) = \bar{C} e^{-\alpha \bar{k}^2 t} e^{I \bar{k} x} \tag{10.129}$$

Equation (10.129) represents a time-decaying solution, which is clearly bounded as time increases.

Consider the numerical solution of the diffusion equation by the FTCS method [see Eq. (10.121)]:

$$f_i^{n+1} = f_i^n + d(f_{i+1}^n - 2f_i^n + f_{i-1}^n) \tag{10.130}$$

The exact solution of Eq. (10.130) for a single step can be expressed as

$$\boxed{f_i^{n+1} = G f_i^n} \tag{10.131}$$

where G, which is called the *amplification factor*, is in general a complex constant. The solution of the FDE at time $T = N\Delta t$ is then

$$f_i^N = G^N f_i^0 \tag{10.132}$$

where $f_i^0 = f(x_i, 0)$. For f_i^N to remain bounded,

$$\boxed{|G| \le 1} \tag{10.133}$$

Stability analysis thus reduces to the determination of the single-step exact solution of the finite difference equation, that is, the amplification factor G, and an investigation of the conditions necessary to ensure that $|G| \le 1$.

From Eq. (10.130), it is seen that f_i^{n+1} depends not only on f_i^n, but also on f_{i-1}^n and f_{i+1}^n. Consequently, f_{i-1}^n and f_{i+1}^n must be related to f_i^n, so that Eq. (10.130) can be solved explicitly for G. That is accomplished by expressing $f(x, t^n) = F(x)$ in a Fourier series. Each component of the Fourier series is propagated forward in time independently of all of the other Fourier components. The complete solution at any subsequent time is simply the sum of the individual Fourier components at that time.

Consider the arbitrary property distribution illustrated in Fig. 10.14. The fundamental period of the property distribution is $2L$. The von Neumann method assumes that the boundary conditions are periodic. The Fourier series for an arbitrary property distribution having a fundamental period of 2π is

$$F(z) = \frac{a_0}{2} + \sum_{m=1}^{\infty} a_m \cos mz + \sum_{m=1}^{\infty} b_m \sin mz \tag{10.134}$$

When the fundamental period is $2L$ instead of 2π, the transformation

$$x = \frac{2L}{2\pi} z \qquad \text{and} \qquad z = \frac{2\pi}{2L} x \tag{10.135}$$

transforms Eq. (10.134) into the form

$$F(x) = \frac{a_0}{2} + \sum_{m=1}^{\infty} a_m \cos\left(\frac{2\pi m}{2L} x\right) + \sum_{m=1}^{\infty} b_m \sin\left(\frac{2\pi m}{2L} x\right) \tag{10.136}$$

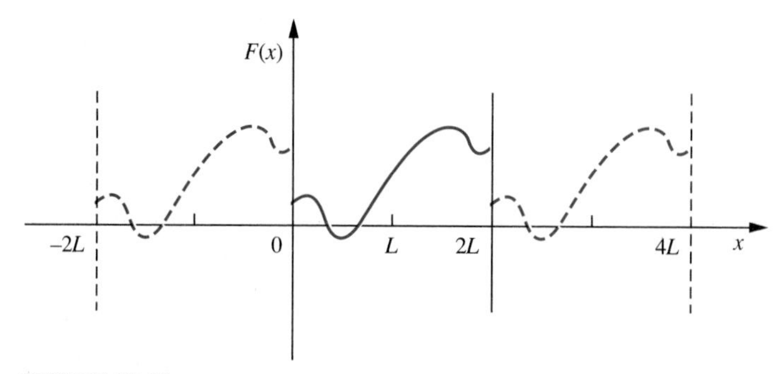

FIGURE 10.14
Arbitrary property distribution.

The wave number k_m is defined as

$$\boxed{k_m = \frac{2\pi m}{2L}} \tag{10.137}$$

Then Eq. (10.136) can be written as

$$F(x) = \frac{a_0}{2} + \sum_{m=1}^{\infty} a_m \cos k_m x + \sum_{m=1}^{\infty} b_m \sin k_m x \tag{10.138}$$

Recall the relationships between the cosine, sine, and exponential functions:

$$\cos k_m x = \frac{e^{Ik_m x} + e^{-Ik_m x}}{2} \quad \text{and} \quad \sin k_m x = \frac{e^{Ik_m x} - e^{-Ik_m x}}{2I} \tag{10.139}$$

where $I = \sqrt{-1}$. Substituting Eq. (10.139) into Eq. (10.138) yields

$$F(x) = \frac{c_0}{2} + \sum_{m=1}^{\infty} c_m e^{Ik_m x} + \sum_{m=1}^{\infty} c_{-m} e^{-Ik_m x} \tag{10.140}$$

where

$$c_0 = a_0, \qquad c_m = \frac{a_m - Ib_m}{2}, \qquad c_{-m} = \frac{a_m + Ib_m}{2I} \tag{10.141}$$

Equation (10.140) can be written in the general form

$$\boxed{F(x) = \sum_{m=-\infty}^{\infty} c_m e^{Ik_m x}} \tag{10.142}$$

The essence of the von Neumann method of stability analysis is as follows. The arbitrary property distribution, $f(x, t^n) = F(x)$, is expressed in a complex Fourier series by Eq. (10.142). The significance of Eq. (10.142) is that it permits the values of $f(x, t^n)$ to be determined explicitly for any value of x. In particular, $f_{i\pm1}^n$ can be determined. These values can be substituted into the finite difference equation, Eq. (10.130), to determine the exact solution, Eq. (10.131), which can then be analyzed for stability.

This procedure is simplified by considering the general term F_m of the Fourier series:

$$F_m = c_m e^{Ik_m x} = c_m e^{Ik_m (i\,\Delta x)} = c e^{Ii(k\,\Delta x)} \tag{10.143}$$

where $x = i\Delta x$ and the subscript m has been dropped for clarity. Thus,

$$f_i^n = ce^{Ii(k\,\Delta x)} \tag{10.144a}$$

$$f_{i\pm1}^n = ce^{I(i\pm1)(k\,\Delta x)} = ce^{Ii(k\,\Delta x)}e^{\pm I(k\,\Delta x)} = f_i^n e^{\pm I(k\,\Delta x)} \tag{10.144b}$$

Substituting Eq. (10.144) into the FDE allows f_i^{n+1} to be expressed in terms of f_i^n only, which enables the exact solution, Eq. (10.131), to be determined.

The steps for performing a von Neumann stability analysis of a finite difference equation (FDE) are summarized below:

1. Determine the FDE to be analyzed.
2. Substitute the complex Fourier components for $f_{i\pm1}^n$ and $f_{i\pm1}^{n+1}$ into the FDE.
3. Express $\exp(k\,\Delta x)$ in terms of $\sin k\,\Delta x$ and $\cos k\,\Delta x$ and determine the amplification factor G.
4. Analyze G (i.e., $|G| \le 1$) to determine the stability criteria for the FDE.

Example 10.11. von Neumann stability analysis of the FTCS approximation of the diffusion equation. As an example of the von Neumann method of stability analysis, we will perform a stability analysis of the FTCS approximation of the diffusion equation, Eq. (10.121). The required Fourier components are given by Eq. (10.144). Substituting Eq. (10.144) into Eq. (10.121) gives

$$f_i^{n+1} = f_i^n + d(f_i^n e^{I(k\,\Delta x)} - 2f_i^n + f_i^n e^{-I(k\,\Delta x)}) \tag{10.145}$$

which can be written as

$$f_i^{n+1} = f_i^n\Big(1 + d(e^{I(k\,\Delta x)} + e^{-I(k\,\Delta x)} - 2)\Big) \tag{10.146}$$

Introducing the relationship between the cosine and exponential functions and setting $f_i^{n+1} = Gf_i^n$ yields

$$f_i^{n+1} = f_i^n\Big(1 + 2d(\cos k\,\Delta x - 1)\Big) = Gf_i^n \tag{10.147}$$

where the amplification factor G is defined as

$$G = 1 + 2d(\cos k\,\Delta x - 1) \tag{10.148}$$

The amplication factor G is the single-step exact solution of the finite difference equation for the general Fourier component, which must be less than unity in magnitude to ensure a bounded solution. For a specific wave number k_m and grid spacing Δx, Eq.

(10.148) can be analyzed to determine the range of values of the diffusion number d for which $|G| \leq 1$. In the infinite Fourier series representation of the property distribution, $k_m = (2\pi m/2L)$ ranges from $-\infty$ to $+\infty$ as m goes from $-\infty$ to $+\infty$. The grid spacing Δx can range from zero to any finite value up to $2L$. Consequently, the product $(k_m \Delta x)$ ranges continuously from $-\infty$ to $+\infty$. To ensure that the FDE is stable for an arbitrary property distribution and arbitrary Δx, Eq. (10.148) must be analyzed to determine the range of values of d for which $|G| \leq 1$ as $(k\,\Delta x)$ ranges continuously from $-\infty$ to $+\infty$.

Solving Eq. (10.148) for $|G| \leq 1$ yields

$$-1 \leq 1 + 2d(\cos k\,\Delta x - 1) \leq 1 \tag{10.149}$$

The upper limit is always satisfied for $d \geq 0$, because $[\cos k\Delta x - 1]$ varies between -2 and 0 as $(k\Delta x)$ ranges from $-\infty$ to $+\infty$. From the lower limit,

$$d \leq \frac{1}{(1 - \cos k\,\Delta x)} \tag{10.150}$$

The minimum value of d corresponds to the maximum value of $(1 - \cos k\,\Delta x)$. As $(k\,\Delta x)$ ranges from $-\infty$ to $+\infty$, $(1 - \cos k\,\Delta x)$ varies between 0 and 2. Consequently, the minimum value of d is $\frac{1}{2}$. Thus, $|G| \leq 1$ if

$$\boxed{0 \leq d \leq \frac{1}{2}} \tag{10.151}$$

Consequently, the FTCS approximation of the diffusion equation is conditionally stable.

The behavior of the amplification factor G can also be determined by graphical methods. Equation (10.148) can be written in the form

$$G = (1 - 2d) + 2d \cos k\,\Delta x \tag{10.152}$$

In the complex plane, Eq. (10.152) represents an oscillation on the real axis, centered at $[(1 - 2d), 0]$ with an amplitude of $2d$, as illustrated in Fig. 10.15. For G to remain inside the stability boundary $-1 \leq |G| \leq 1$ as $(k\,\Delta x)$ varies from $-\infty$ to $+\infty$, $0 \leq 2d \leq 1$. The graphical approach is very useful when G is a complex function.

The von Neumann stability analysis, presented in Example 10.11 for the FTCS approximation of the diffusion equation, is the most straightforward procedure for determining the stability criteria for a finite difference equation. Example 10.12 presents the von Neumann stability analysis of the Lax–Wendroff approximation of the convection equation.

The complex exponentials in Eq. (10.144) {i.e., $\exp[\pm I(k\,\Delta x)]$} represent sine and cosine functions, which have a period of 2π. Consequently, the values of these exponentials repeat themselves with a period of 2π. Thus, it is only necessary to investigate the behavior of the amplification factor G over the range $0 \leq k\,\Delta x \leq 2\pi$. In view of this behavior, the term $k\,\Delta x$ will be denoted simply

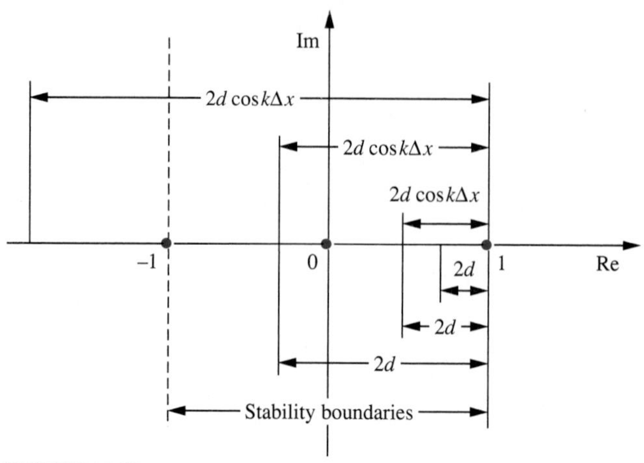

FIGURE 10.15
Locus of G for the FTCS approximation of the diffusion equation.

as θ, and Eq. (10.144) can be written as

$$f_i^n = ce^{Ii\theta} \quad \text{and} \quad f_{i\pm1}^n = f_i^n e^{\pm I\theta} \tag{10.153}$$

Example 10.12. von Neumann stability analysis of the Lax–Wendroff approximation of the convection equation. The Lax–Wendroff approximation of the convection equation is Eq. (10.88):

$$f_i^{n+1} = f_i^n - \frac{c}{2}(f_{i+1}^n - f_{i-1}^n) + \frac{c^2}{2}(f_{i+1}^n - 2f_i^n + f_{i-1}^n) \tag{10.154}$$

Substituting the general Fourier components, Eq. (10.153), into Eq. (10.154), dividing by f_i^n, and setting $f_i^{n+1} = Gf_i^n$ yields

$$G = 1 - \frac{c}{2}(e^{I\theta} - e^{-I\theta}) + \frac{c^2}{2}(e^{I\theta} - 2 + e^{-I\theta}) \tag{10.155}$$

Introducing the relationships between the exponential function and the sine and cosine functions gives

$$G = 1 - Ic\sin\theta + c^2(\cos\theta - 1) \tag{10.156}$$

Rearranging Eq. (10.156) yields

$$G = \Big((1 - c^2) + c^2\cos\theta\Big) - Ic\sin\theta \tag{10.157}$$

Equation (10.157) represents an ellipse in the complex plane, as illustrated in Fig. 10.16. The center of the ellipse is at $(1 - c^2)$ on the real axis, and the axes of the ellipse are c and c^2. For stability, $|G| \le 1$, which requires that the ellipse lie on or within the unit circle. From Fig. 10.16, three conditions are apparent. Both axes c and c^2 must be less

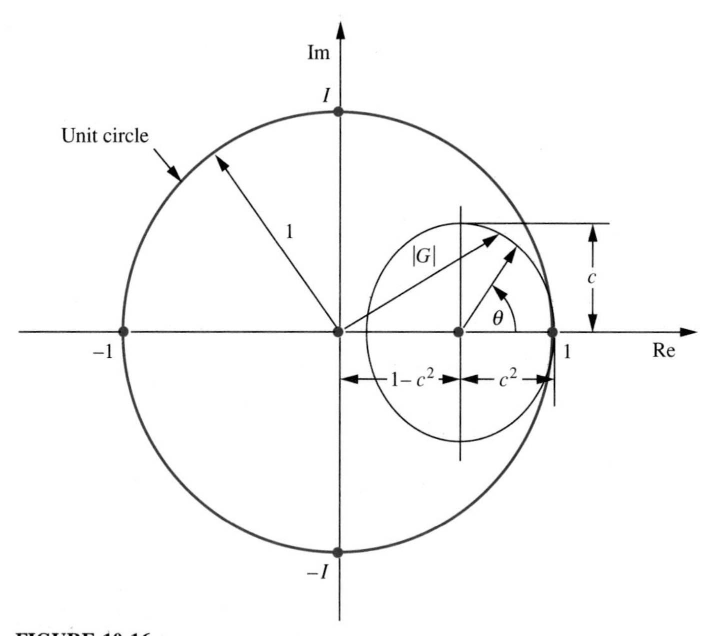

FIGURE 10.16
Locus of G for the Lax–Wendroff approximation of the convection equation.

than or equal to unity. In addition, at point (1,0), the curvature of the unit circle must be less than the curvature of the ellipse. With some additional analysis, it can be shown that this condition is satisfied if $c^2 \le 1$. All three necessary conditions are satisfied by the single sufficient condition

$$\boxed{c = \frac{u\,\Delta t}{\Delta x} \le 1} \tag{10.158}$$

Thus, the Lax–Wendroff approximation of the convection equation is conditionally stable.

Examples 10.11 and 10.12 illustrate the von Neumann stability analysis for two explicit finite difference equations. Example 10.13 illustrates the von Neumann stability analysis for an implicit finite difference equation.

Example 10.13. von Neumann stability analysis of the BTCS approximation of the convection–diffusion equation. We will apply the von Neumann method to analyze the stability of the BTCS approximation of the convection–diffusion equation, Eq. (10.93):

$$-\left(\frac{c}{2} + d\right)f_{i-1}^{n+1} + (1 + 2d)f_i^{n+1} + \left(\frac{c}{2} - d\right)f_{i+1}^{n+1} = f_i^n \tag{10.159}$$

Substituting the general Fourier components, Eqs. (10.153), into Eq. (10.159), dividing by f_i^n, and setting $f_i^{n+1} = Gf_i^n$ gives

$$-\left(\frac{c}{2} + d\right)e^{-I\theta}G + (1 + 2d)G + \left(\frac{c}{2} - d\right)e^{I\theta}G = 1 \tag{10.160}$$

Grouping terms involving c and terms involving d into two groups, introducing the relationships between the exponential function and the sine and cosine functions, and rearranging gives

$$G = \frac{1}{1 + 2d(1 - \cos\theta) + Ic\sin\theta} \tag{10.161}$$

The term $(1 - \cos\theta) \geq 0$ for all values of θ. Consequently, $|G| \leq 1$ for all values of c and d, and Eq. (10.159) is unconditionally stable.

Matrix Method

A third method of stability analysis, the matrix method, involves a study of the *eigenvalues* of the *amplification matrix* of the system of finite difference equations for the entire solution domain. A complete development of this method is beyond the scope of this book. However, the general features of the method are introduced briefly. One advantage of the matrix method is that it can be applied to a finite solution domain, including the boundaries. Consequently, the effect of boundary condition treatment on stability can be determined.

Consider the finite difference grid illustrated in Fig. 10.17. When the FDE is applied at every point in the finite difference grid (including the boundaries, if appropriate), the following system of finite difference equations is obtained:

$$\boxed{\mathbf{A}\mathbf{f}^{n+1} = \mathbf{B}\mathbf{f}^{n}} \tag{10.162}$$

where $\mathbf{f}^n$ is the column vector of known properties at time level n, $\mathbf{f}^{n+1}$ is the column vector of unknown properties at time level $n + 1$, and $\mathbf{A}$ and $\mathbf{B}$ are $imax \times imax$ coefficient matrices, where $imax$ is the number of finite difference equations. Multiplying Eq. (10.162) by the inverse of $\mathbf{A}$ yields

$$\mathbf{f}^{n+1} = \mathbf{A}^{-1}\mathbf{B}\mathbf{f}^{n} \tag{10.163}$$

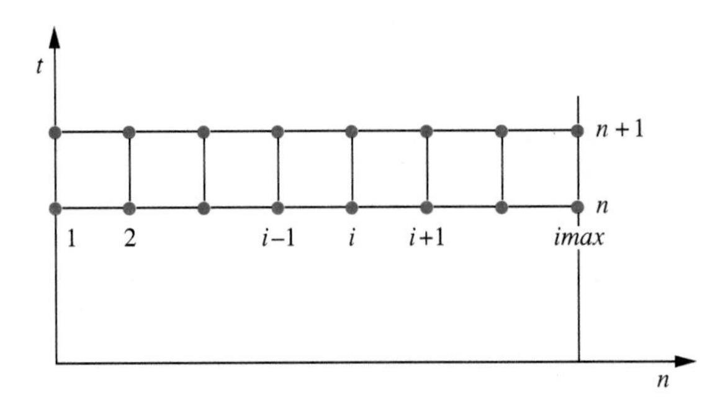

FIGURE 10.17
Finite difference grid for implicit methods.

TABLE 10.3
Effect of eigenvalues on stability

Case	Value of λ_i	Behavior of the solution
1	$1 < \lambda_i$	No oscillations, steady unbounded growth, $\lvert f^{n+1}\rvert > \lvert f^n\rvert$, unstable.
2	$0 \leq \lambda_i \leq 1$	No oscillations, steady decay, $\lvert f^{n+1}\rvert \leq \lvert f^n\rvert$, stable.
3	$-1 \leq \lambda_i \leq 0$	Oscillations, oscillatory decay, $\lvert f^{n+1}\rvert \leq \lvert f^n\rvert$, stable.
4	$\lambda_i < -1$	Oscillations, oscillatory unbounded growth, $\lvert f^{n+1}\rvert > \lvert f^n\rvert$, unstable.

The matrix $\mathbf{A}^{-1}\mathbf{B}$ is called the amplification matrix of the system of finite difference equations, which is analogous to the amplification factor G for a single FDE. It has *imax* eigenvalues. If the magnitude of any of these eigenvalues is greater than 1.0 in magnitude, then some component of the solution can grow without bound. Consequently, the stability analysis of the system of finite difference equations reduces to a study of the eigenvalues of the amplification matrix $\mathbf{A}^{-1}\mathbf{B}$.

The eigenvalues of $\mathbf{A}^{-1}\mathbf{B}$ are determined by solving the characteristic equation

$$\det(\mathbf{A}^{-1}\mathbf{B} - \lambda\mathbf{I}) = 0 \tag{10.164}$$

This equation can be simplified by the following two steps. First, multiply Eq. (10.164) by det($\mathbf{A}$) to obtain

$$\det(\mathbf{A})\det(\mathbf{A}^{-1}\mathbf{B} - \lambda\mathbf{I}) = 0 \tag{10.165}$$

The product of the determinants of two matrices is equal to the determinant of the product of the two matrices. Thus,

$$\det(\mathbf{B} - \lambda\mathbf{A}) = 0 \tag{10.166}$$

Equation (10.166) is in the standard form of an eigenproblem and can be solved for the eigenvalues λ_i ($i = 1, \ldots, imax$) by the procedures presented in Chapter 2.

Four types of behavior of the solution are possible, depending on the value of the eigenvalues λ_i. They are summarized in Table 10.3. Cases 1 and 4 are obviously unacceptable. Case 3, although stable, is undesirable, because physical phenomena do not oscillate in this manner. Case 2 is the desired situation.

Example 10.14. Matrix method stability analysis of the FTCS approximation of the diffusion equation. We will apply the matrix method to the FTCS approximation of the diffusion equation, Eq. (10.121), with Dirichlet boundary conditions (i.e., f is specified on the boundaries). Applying Eq. (10.121) at all interior points ($i = 2, \ldots, imax - 1$) yields the following results for $\mathbf{A}$ and $\mathbf{B}$:

$$\mathbf{A} = \mathbf{I} \tag{10.167}$$

$$\mathbf{B} = \begin{bmatrix} (1-2d) & d & & & \cdots & & \\ d & (1-2d) & d & & \cdots & & \\ & d & (1-2d) & d & \cdots & & \\ \vdots & \vdots & \vdots & \vdots & \vdots & \vdots & \vdots \\ & & & & & d & (1-2d) \end{bmatrix} \tag{10.168}$$

where all the terms not shown are zero. Consider the case with two interior points:

$$\mathbf{A} = \begin{bmatrix} 1 & 0 \\ 0 & 1 \end{bmatrix} \qquad \mathbf{B} = \begin{bmatrix} (1-2d) & d \\ d & (1-2d) \end{bmatrix} \tag{10.169}$$

and the matrix $(\mathbf{B} - \lambda\mathbf{A})$ is

$$(\mathbf{B} - \lambda\mathbf{A}) = \begin{bmatrix} (1-2d-\lambda) & d \\ d & (1-2d-\lambda) \end{bmatrix} \tag{10.170}$$

Setting the determinant of $(\mathbf{B} - \lambda\mathbf{A})$ equal to zero yields

$$(1-2d-\lambda)^2 - d^2 = 0 \tag{10.171}$$

Solving Eq. (10.171) yields the two eigenvalues

$$\lambda_1 = 1 - d \qquad \text{and} \qquad \lambda_2 = 1 - 3d \tag{10.172}$$

The behavior of the two eigenvalues is illustrated in Fig. 10.18. Neither eigenvalue can be greater than 1.0. However, both can be less than -1.0. The eigenvalue λ_2 decreases more rapidly, so it is the critical eigenvalue in this case. For stability, $|\lambda_2|$ must be ≤ 1. From Eq. (10.172), the stability criterion for the system of finite difference equations is $0 \leq d \leq \frac{2}{3}$. Recall that the von Neumann stability analysis of this FDE (Example 10.12) resulted in the stability criterion $0 \leq d \leq \frac{1}{2}$. The value $d \leq \frac{2}{3}$ applies only for a system of two finite difference equations. Repeating this analysis for one FDE yields the value $d \leq 1.0$. As the number of FDEs increases, d decreases and approaches the limiting value $d \leq \frac{1}{2}$ as the number of FDEs becomes infinite.

For values of λ_i between 0 and -1.0, the Fourier components oscillate. To avoid such oscillations, λ_i must be greater than or equal to zero. For the critical eigenvalue λ_2, this requires $d \leq \frac{1}{3}$.

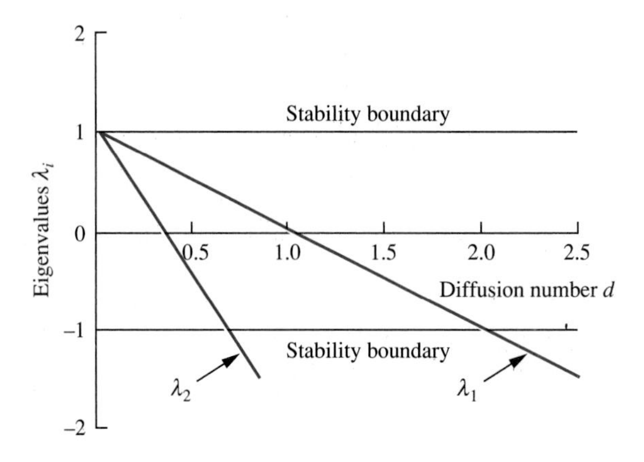

FIGURE 10.18
Eigenvalues of the FTCS approximation of the diffusion equation.

The matrix method for determining the stability of a finite difference equation is considerably more complicated than the von Neumann method. Consequently, the von Neumann method is generally preferred. However, the matrix method can be used to investigate the effects of boundary conditions, and it does explain the occurrence of stable solutions in which the solution behaves in an oscillatory manner.

The definition presented at the beginning of this section for stability of a finite difference equation is expressed in terms of the behavior of the solution of the FDE. Stability can also be expressed in terms of the behavior of errors in the solution of the FDE. Errors arise from four sources: algebraic errors, round-off errors, the single-step truncation error, and inherited error from previous steps. Algebraic errors are assumed to be nonexistent. The remaining three types of errors are always present. The stability of an FDE that is a discrete approximation of a PDE that has a bounded solution can also be defined as follows:

A finite difference equation is stable if errors introduced into the solution remain bounded and is unstable if the errors are unbounded.

Let $\overline{f}_i^n$ denote the exact solution of the PDE and f_i^n denote the numerical solution of the FDE. Then

$$\zeta_i^n = f_i^n - \overline{f}_i^n \tag{10.173}$$

where ζ_i^n represents the cumulative effects of all errors introduced at all grid points at all preceding time levels up to and including time level n. Subtracting the exact solution term by term from the FDE and introducing ζ_i^n gives the finite difference equation that governs the propagation of errors, which is called the *error equation*. For example, for the FTCS approximation of the diffusion equation, Eq. (10.121), the error equation is

$$\boxed{\zeta_i^{n+1} = \zeta_i^n + d(\zeta_{i+1}^n - 2\zeta_i^n + \zeta_{i-1}^n)} \tag{10.174}$$

Equation (10.174) is identical in form to Eq. (10.121). Consequently, error propogation is governed by the same FDE that governs the numerical solution of the PDE. This equivalence of an FDE and its corresponding error equation occurs for all FDEs. Obviously, a stability analysis of the error equation will yield the same stability criteria as a stability analysis of the finite difference equation.

In summary, three methods for performing the stability analysis of a finite difference equation have been presented:

1. The discrete perturbation method
2. The von Neumann method
3. The matrix method

The discrete perturbation method gives a good physical interpretation of the concept of stability. However, it is quite tedious to implement. The matrix method permits the investigation of the effects of boundary conditions and explains the oscillatory behavior of some numerical solutions. However, it is also quite complicated to implement. The von Neumann method does not furnish the insights furnished by the other two methods, but it gives the necessary and sufficient stability criteria in a straightforward and uncomplicated manner. Consequently, the von Neumann method of stability analysis is employed throughout this book.

10.9 IMPLICIT NUMERICAL DIFFUSION AND DISPERSION

Implicit numerical diffusion and *dispersion* are errors that arise in the numerical solution of a partial differential equation, due to the behavior of the truncation error terms in the finite difference equation. Implicit numerical diffusion and dispersion can be understood most easily by analogy to the transfer function concept in linear stability theory. In essence, an arbitrary continuous function is represented by an infinite Fourier series. Each component of the Fourier series is acted on by the transfer function of the system. In general, transfer functions are complex functions of frequency that have both magnitude and phase. Consequently, each component of the Fourier series representation of the continuous function may have a different change in magnitude and phase as it passes through the transfer function. When the continuous output signal is reconstructed as the sum of the modified Fourier components, the shape of the signal may be changed. Changes in the amplitude of the Fourier components yield amplitude distortion, and changes in the phase of the Fourier components yield phase distortion.

A partial differential equation acts similarly to a transfer function. The PDE propagates the initial data forward in time:

$$\bar{f}(x,0) \quad \rightarrow \boxed{\text{PDE}} \rightarrow \quad \bar{f}(x,t) \tag{10.175}$$

The amplification factor, or transfer function, corresponding to this process is denoted by $\bar{G}$, which in general is a complex number. Thus,

$$\bar{G} = \bar{G}_R + I\bar{G}_I = |\bar{G}|e^{I\bar{\phi}} \tag{10.176}$$

where $I = \sqrt{-1}$, $\bar{G}_R$ and $\bar{G}_I$ are the real and imaginary components of $\bar{G}$, $|\bar{G}|$ is its magnitude, and $\bar{\phi}$ is its phase.

In a similar manner, a finite difference equation acts like a transfer function. The FDE propagates the initial data forward in time:

$$f(x,t) \quad \rightarrow \boxed{\text{FDE}} \rightarrow \quad f(x,t+\Delta t) \tag{10.177}$$

The amplification factor, or transfer function, corresponding to this process is denoted by G, which in general is a complex constant. Thus,

$$G = G_R + IG_I = |G|e^{I\phi} \tag{10.178}$$

where G_R and G_I are the real and imaginary components of G, $|G|$ is its magnitude, and ϕ is its phase.

As discussed in Section 10.8, any initial property distribution can be represented by a complex Fourier series. Each component of the Fourier series is acted on by the amplification factor. The total effect of the amplification factor on the initial property distribution is obtained by summing the responses of the individual Fourier components. In general, the amplification factor is dependent on the wave number, or frequency, of the individual Fourier components.

When $|G| \neq |\overline{G}|$, an *amplitude* error results. If the amplitude error is frequency (i.e., wave number)-dependent, then *amplitude distortion* occurs. Amplitude error and distortion in the numerical solution of a PDE by an FDE are called *implicit numerical diffusion*.

When $\phi \neq \overline{\phi}$, a *phase* error results. If the phase error is frequency (i.e., wave number)-dependent, then *phase* distortion occurs. Phase error and distortion in the numerical solution of a PDE by an FDE are called *implicit numerical dispersion*.

Consider the linear initial-value problem specified by the partial differential equation

$$\overline{f}_t + \mathcal{L}_x(\overline{f}) = 0 \tag{10.179}$$

with the initial condition

$$\overline{f}(x, 0) = F(x) \tag{10.180}$$

The spatial differential operator $\mathcal{L}_x$ is given by

$$\mathcal{L}_x = \sum_{q=1}^{n} A_q \frac{\partial^q}{\partial x^q} = A_1 \frac{\partial}{\partial x} + A_2 \frac{\partial^2}{\partial x^2} + \cdots + A_n \frac{\partial^n}{\partial x^n} \tag{10.181}$$

where n is the order of the PDE. The amplification factor of the PDE is denoted by $\overline{G}$. Consider the finite difference approximation of the PDE specified by the FDE

$$f_t + \mathcal{L}_x(f) = 0 \tag{10.182}$$

The amplification factor of the FDE is denoted by G. Implicit numerical diffusion results when $|G| \neq |\overline{G}|$, and implicit numerical dispersion results when $\phi \neq \overline{\phi}$. Consequently, to determine the implicit numerical diffusion and dispersion of a finite difference approximation to a PDE, both $\overline{G}$ for the PDE and G for the FDE must be determined.

The general solution of the exact PDE, Eq. (10.179), can be written in terms of the complex Fourier component $\overline{F}(x, t)$ [see Eq. (10.6)], which is

$$\overline{F}(x, t) = \overline{C} e^{\overline{s}t} e^{I\overline{k}x} = \text{Re}\left(\overline{F}(x, t)\right) + I\,\text{Im}\left(\overline{F}(x, t)\right) \tag{10.183}$$

where $\overline{C}$ is the amplitude, $\overline{s}$ is the complex frequency

$$\overline{s} = \overline{\sigma} + I\overline{\omega} \tag{10.184}$$

and $\bar{k}$ is the wave number. The real or imaginary part of $\bar{F}(x, t)$ is chosen to satisfy the initial condition. Substituting Eq. (10.184) into Eq. (10.183) gives

$$\boxed{\bar{F}(x, t) = \bar{C} e^{\bar{\sigma} t} e^{I(\bar{k}x + \bar{\omega} t)}} \tag{10.185}$$

which is the general form of the exact solution.

The amplification factor $\bar{G}$ of the PDE is

$$\bar{G} = \frac{\bar{f}(x, t)}{\bar{f}(x, 0)} = \frac{\bar{C} e^{\bar{s}(t)} e^{I\bar{k}x}}{\bar{C} e^{s(0)} e^{I\bar{k}x}} = e^{\bar{s}t} \tag{10.186}$$

Introducing Eq. (10.184) gives

$$\bar{G} = e^{\bar{\sigma} t} e^{I\bar{\omega} t} = |\bar{G}| e^{I\bar{\phi}} \tag{10.187}$$

where

$$\boxed{|\bar{G}| = e^{\bar{\sigma} t} \qquad \text{and} \qquad \bar{\phi} = \bar{\omega} t} \tag{10.188}$$

From Eq. (10.188), it is seen that $\bar{\sigma}$ governs the magnitude of the solution and $\bar{\omega}$ governs the phase of the solution.

Equation (10.185) must also satisfy the initial condition, Eq. (10.180). Thus,

$$\bar{F}(x, 0) = \bar{f}(x, 0) = F(x) = \bar{C} e^{\bar{s}(0)} e^{I\bar{k}x} = \bar{C} e^{I\bar{k}x} \tag{10.189}$$

which gives

$$F(x) = \bar{C} e^{I\bar{k}x} \tag{10.190}$$

The values of $\bar{C}$ and $\bar{k}$ can be determined from Eq. (10.190).

The amplification factor G of the finite difference equation can be determined by a similar analysis of the modified differential equation (MDE), which is the actual PDE that is solved by the FDE. The second form of the MDE is given by Eq. (10.110). Thus,

$$f_t + \mathcal{L}_x(f) = \sum_{m}^{\infty} C_m \frac{\partial^m f}{\partial x^m} \tag{10.191}$$

where the terms $C_m(\partial^m f / \partial x^m)$ denote the truncation error terms. Equation (10.191) can be separated into odd and even derivative terms to yield

$$f_t = \sum_{m=1}^{\infty} A_{2m} \frac{\partial^{2m} f}{\partial x^{2m}} + \sum_{m=0}^{\infty} B_{2m+1} \frac{\partial^{2m+1} f}{\partial x^{2m+1}} \tag{10.192}$$

where the terms represented by $\mathscr{L}_x(f)$ have been included in the summations on the right-hand side by appropriate definitions of the leading coefficients.

The general solution of Eq. (10.192) can be expressed in terms of the complex Fourier series

$$f(x,t) = F(x,t) = Ce^{st}e^{Ikx} = \mathrm{Re}\big(F(x,t)\big) + I\,\mathrm{Im}\big(F(x,t)\big) \tag{10.193}$$

where C is the amplitude, s is the complex frequency

$$s = \sigma + I\omega \tag{10.194}$$

and k is the wave number. Equation (10.193) can be differentiated to yield

$$f_t = s(Ce^{st}e^{Ikx}) = sf \tag{10.195a}$$

$$\frac{\partial^{2m} f}{\partial x^{2m}} = (Ik)^{2m}(Ce^{st}e^{Ikx}) = (-1)^m k^{2m} f \tag{10.195b}$$

$$\frac{\partial^{2m+1} f}{\partial x^{2m+1}} = (Ik)^{2m+1}(Ce^{st}e^{Ikx}) = I(-1)^m k^{2m+1} f \tag{10.195c}$$

Substituting Eq. (10.195) into Eq. (10.192) yields

$$s = \sigma + I\omega = \sum_{m=1}^{\infty}(-1)^m k^{2m} A_{2m} + I\sum_{m=0}^{\infty}(-1)^m k^{2m+1} B_{2m+1} \tag{10.196}$$

From Eq. (10.196),

$$\sigma = \sum_{m=1}^{\infty}\sigma_m = \sum_{m=1}^{\infty}(-1)^m k^{2m} A_{2m} \tag{10.197}$$

$$\omega = \sum_{m=0}^{\infty}\omega_m = \sum_{m=0}^{\infty}(-1)^m k^{2m+1} B_{2m+1} \tag{10.198}$$

Each σ_m term contributes to σ, which governs the magnitude of the solution. The σ_m terms arise from the even derivatives in the MDE. Consequently, all truncation error terms containing even derivatives contribute to errors in the magnitude of the solution, that is, implicit numerical diffusion. If the first even derivative error term contains f_{xx}, then this term acts like real physical diffusion αf_{xx}.

Each ω_m term contributes to ω, which governs the phase of the solution. The ω_m terms arise from the odd derivatives in the MDE. Consequently, all truncation error terms containing odd derivatives contribute to errors in the phase of the solution, that is, implicit numerical dispersion. If the first odd derivative error term contains f_{xxx}, then this term acts like real physical dispersion βf_{xxx}.

Let us apply the concepts presented above to a particular situation to illustrate the concepts. Two problems are considered: the Lax–Wendroff approximation of the convection equation and the FTCS approximation of the diffusion equation.

Example 10.15. Implicit numerical diffusion and dispersion of the Lax–Wendroff approximation of the convection equation. Consider the convection equation $\bar{f}_t + u\bar{f}_x = 0$. As shown in Section 10.3 [see Eq. (10.12)], the exact solution is

$$\bar{F}(x, t) = \bar{C}e^{I\bar{k}(x-ut)} \tag{10.199}$$

which gives $\bar{\sigma} = 0$ and $\bar{\omega} = -u\bar{k}$. From Eq. (10.188),

$$\boxed{|\bar{G}| = 1 \qquad \text{and} \qquad \bar{\phi} = -u\bar{k}t} \tag{10.200}$$

Consequently, the exact solution is a traveling wave which moves at the constant wave velocity $c = u$, unchanged in magnitude or shape.

Consider the case where the initial condition is

$$\bar{f}(x, 0) = F(x) = A\sin \pi x, \qquad 0 \le x \le 1 \tag{10.201}$$

From Eq. (10.14), $\bar{C} = A$, $\bar{k} = \pi$, and $\bar{f}(x, t) = \text{Im}(F(x, t))$. Equation (10.199) yields

$$\bar{f}(x, t) = A\sin[\pi(x - ut)] \tag{10.202}$$

As a specific example, let $u = 0.1$ and $t = 10.0$. Equation (10.202) becomes

$$\boxed{\bar{f}(x, 10.0) = A\sin[\pi(x - 1.0)]} \tag{10.203}$$

Now consider the Lax–Wendroff approximation of the convection equation. The finite difference equation is Eq. (10.88), and the amplification factor G is [see Eq. (10.157)]

$$G = \Big((1 - c^2) + c^2\cos\theta)\Big) - Ic\sin\theta \tag{10.204}$$

From Eq. (10.204),

$$|G| = \sqrt{\Big((1 - c^2) + c^2\cos\theta\Big)^2 + c^2\sin^2\theta} \tag{10.205a}$$

$$\phi = \tan^{-1}\left(-\frac{c\sin\theta}{[(1 - c^2) + c^2\cos\theta]}\right) \tag{10.205b}$$

For $c = 1.0$, $|G| = 1.0$, and $\phi = -\theta = -k\,\Delta x = -ku\,\Delta t$, which is the exact solution given by Eq. (10.200). For all other values of c, $|G| \neq |\bar{G}|$ and $\phi \neq \bar{\phi}$.

Consider the initial condition given by Eq. (10.201). In this case, the initial condition is completely specified by one Fourier component ($m = 1$) having the wave number $k_1 = \pi$. Let $u = 0.1$ and $\Delta x = 0.1$, for which $\theta = k\,\Delta x = 0.1\pi$. Calculate $f(x, 10.0)$ and compare with Eq. (10.203). Let $\Delta t = 0.5$, so $nmax = (10.0/0.5) = 20$ time steps and

$$c = \frac{u\,\Delta t}{\Delta x} = \frac{(0.1)(0.5)}{0.1} = 0.5 \tag{10.206}$$

Equation (10.205) gives

$$|G| = \sqrt{\{[1 - (0.5)^2] + (0.5)^2 \cos(0.1\pi)\}^2 + (0.5)^2 \sin^2(0.1\pi)} = 0.999775 \tag{10.207a}$$

$$\phi = \tan^{-1}\left(-\frac{(0.5)\sin(0.1\pi)}{[1 - (0.5)^2] + (0.5)^2 \cos(0.1\pi)}\right) = -0.049391\pi \tag{10.207b}$$

The solution after 20 time steps is

$$f(x, 10.0) = G^{20} f(x, 0) = |G|^{20} e^{I20\phi} A \sin \pi x \tag{10.208a}$$

$$f(x, 10.0) = (0.999775)^{20} e^{I20(-0.049391\pi)} A \sin \pi x \tag{10.208b}$$

which gives

$$\boxed{f(x, 10.0) = 0.995510\, A \sin[\pi(x - 0.987820)]} \tag{10.209}$$

Comparing Eqs. (10.209) and (10.203) shows that there is an amplitude error of -0.45 percent and a phase error of 0.012180π. These are reasonably small errors.

Repeating the calculations for $\Delta x = 0.05$ and $\Delta t = 0.25$, so $\theta = k\,\Delta x = 0.05\pi$, $nmax = 40$, and $c = 0.5$, gives $|G| = 0.999986$ and $\phi = -0.024923\pi$. This gives

$$f(x, 10.0) = 0.999440\, A \sin[\pi(x - 0.996920)] \tag{10.210}$$

In this case, the amplitude error is -0.06 percent and the phase error is 0.003080π.

These results suggest that the Lax–Wendroff method is an excellent method for solving the convection equation.

Thus far we have considered the effects of the implicit numerical diffusion and dispersion inherent in a finite difference equation on the numerical solution of a partial differential equation when the initial data consist of a pure sine wave. What effects do implicit numerical diffusion and dispersion have on the numerical solution of a PDE when the initial data distribution is arbitrary?

For a linear PDE, the solution can be obtained as the superposition of simpler solutions, specifically, exponential functions (i.e., sines and cosines). Consequently, arbitrary initial data can be expressed in a complex Fourier series, and each component of the Fourier series can be analyzed to determine how it is affected by the implicit numerical diffusion and dispersion in the FDE. The response of the arbitrary initial data can then be obtained as the sum of the responses of the individual Fourier components.

Each Fourier component may have an amplitude error (i.e., $|G| \neq |\overline{G}|$) and a phase error (i.e., $\phi \neq \overline{\phi}$). If $|G|$ is constant [i.e., $|G| \neq f(k_m)$], then all Fourier components have the same fractional amplitude error, and pure amplitude error occurs. However, if $|G|$ depends on the wave number k_m of the Fourier components, then amplitude distortion occurs. Similarly, if ϕ is constant [i.e., $\phi \neq f(k_m)$], then all Fourier components have the same phase error, and pure phase error occurs. However, if ϕ depends on the wave number k_m, then phase distortion occurs.

Example 10.15 presents a detailed investigation of the effects of implicit numerical diffusion and dispersion in the Lax–Wendroff approximation of the convection equation when the initial property distribution is a pure sine wave. However, the effects of an arbitrary initial data distribution can be determined only by investigating that particular distribution. Figure 10.19 presents the numerical solution of the convection equation for a triangular initial data distribution for $\Delta x = 0.05$. The solution is presented at times from 1.0 to 5.0 for $c = 0.5$, and at $t = 10.0$ for $c = 0.1$, 0.5, 0.9, and 1.0. When $c = 1.0$, the numerical solution is identical to the exact solution, for the linear convection equation. This is not true for the nonlinear convection equation. When $c = 0.5$, the amplitude of the solution is damped slightly, and the sharp peak becomes rounded. However, the wave shape is maintained quite well. The results at $t = 10.0$, for $c = 0.1$, 0.5, and 0.9, are all reasonable approximations of the exact solution. There is a slight decrease in the numerical convection velocity. Slight *wiggles* appear in the

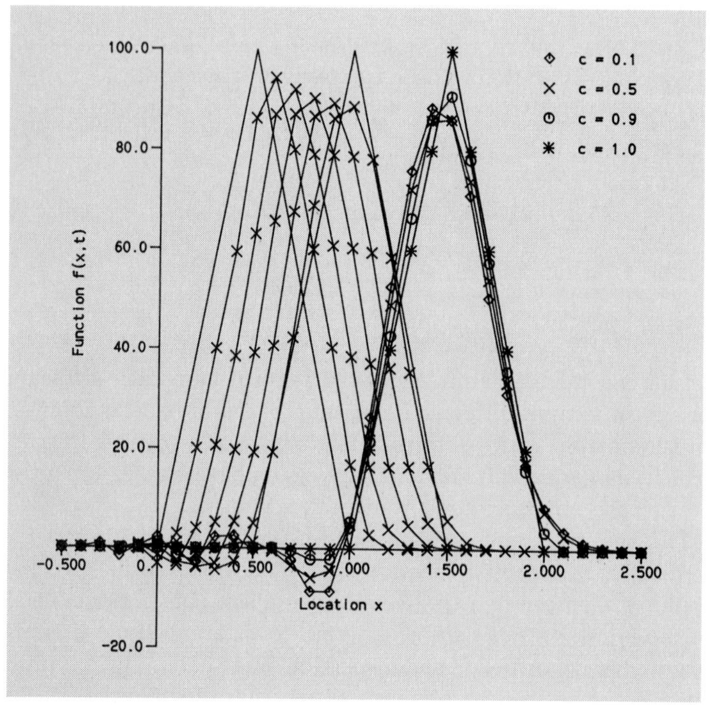

FIGURE 10.19
Solution of the convection equation by the Lax–Wendroff one-step method.

trailing portion of the wave due to implicit numerical dispersion. Such wiggles are a common feature of finite difference approximations of convection terms. Overall, the Lax–Wendroff method is a good method for solving the convection equation.

Example 10.16. Implicit numerical diffusion and dispersion of the FTCS approximation of the diffusion equation. Consider the diffusion equation $\bar{f}_t = \alpha \bar{f}_{xx}$. As shown in Section 10.3 [see Eq. (10.23)], the exact solution is

$$\bar{F}(x, t) = \bar{C} e^{-\alpha \bar{k}^2 t} e^{I\bar{k}x} \tag{10.211}$$

which gives $\bar{\sigma} = -\alpha \bar{k}^2$ and $\bar{\omega} = 0$. From Eq. (10.188)

$$\boxed{|\bar{G}| = e^{-\alpha \bar{k}^2 t} \qquad \text{and} \qquad \bar{\phi} = 0} \tag{10.212}$$

Consequently, the exact solution is a decaying exponential with zero phase.

Consider the case where the initial condition is

$$\bar{f}(x, 0) = F(x) = A \sin \pi x, \qquad 0 \leq x \leq 1 \tag{10.213}$$

From Eq. (10.25), $\bar{C} = A$, $k = \pi$, and $\bar{f}(x, t) = \text{Im}\,(\bar{F}(x, t))$. Equation (10.211) yields

$$\bar{f}(x, t) = e^{-\alpha \pi^2 t} A \sin \pi x \tag{10.214}$$

As a specific example, let $\alpha = 0.01$ and $t = 10.0$. Equation (10.214) becomes

$$\boxed{\bar{f}(x, 10.0) = 0.372708\, A \sin \pi x} \tag{10.215}$$

Next, consider the FTCS approximation of the diffusion equation. The finite difference equation is Eq. (10.73), and the amplification factor G is [see Eq. (10.148)]

$$G = 1 + 2d(\cos\theta - 1) \tag{10.216}$$

From Eq. (10.216),

$$\boxed{|G| = 1 + 2d(\cos\theta - 1) \qquad \text{and} \qquad \phi = 0} \tag{10.217}$$

Comparing Eqs. (10.212) and (10.217) shows that $|G| \neq |\bar{G}|$, but that $\phi = \bar{\phi}$. Consequently, there will be magnitude errors but no phase errors.

Consider the initial condition given by Eq. (10.213). In this case, the initial condition is completely specified by one Fourier component ($m = 1$) having the wave number $k_1 = \pi$. Let $\alpha = 0.01$ and $\Delta x = 0.1$, for which $\theta = k\,\Delta x = 0.1\pi$. Calculate $f(x, 10.0)$ and compare with Eq. (10.215). Let $\Delta t = 0.5$, so $nmax = (10.0/0.5) = 20$ time steps, and

$$d = \frac{\alpha\,\Delta t}{\Delta x^2} = \frac{(0.01)(0.5)}{(0.1)^2} = 0.5 \tag{10.218}$$

From Eq. (10.217),

$$|G| = 1 + 2(0.5)[\cos(0.1\pi) - 1.0] = 0.951057 \tag{10.219}$$

and $\phi = 0$. The solution after 20 time steps is

$$f(x, 10.0) = G^{20} f(x, 0) = |G|^{20} e^{I20\phi} A \sin \pi x = (0.951057)^{20} e^{I20(0)} A \sin \pi x \tag{10.220}$$

which gives

$$\boxed{f(x, 10.0) = 0.366544\, A \sin \pi x} \tag{10.221}$$

Comparing Eqs. (10.215) and (10.221) shows that there is an amplitude error of approximately 1.65 percent, but no phase error. Repeating the calculations for $\Delta t = 0.25$, so $nmax = 40$ and $d = 0.25$, gives $|G| = 0.975528$ and $\phi = 0$. This gives

$$f(x, 10.0) = 0.371188 A \sin \pi x \tag{10.222}$$

For this case, the amplitude error is approximately 0.40 percent.

These results show that the FTCS method is a reasonably good method for solving the diffusion equation.

Example 10.16 presents a detailed investigation of the effects of implicit numerical diffusion in the FTCS approximation of the diffusion equation when the initial property distribution is a pure sine wave. However, the effects on a specific initial data distribution can be determined only by investigating that particular distribution. Figure 10.20 presents the numerical solution of the diffusion equation for a triangular initial-data distribution for $\Delta x = 0.1$ and $\Delta t = \frac{1}{6}$ and 0.5, which correspond to $d = \frac{1}{6}$ and 0.5, respectively. The solid lines are the exact solution, the open circles are the numerical solution for $d = \frac{1}{6}$, and the asterisks are the numerical solution for $d = 0.5$. The numerical solution for $d = \frac{1}{6}$ is extremely accurate, showing almost no effect of implicit numerical diffusion. The numerical solution for $d = 0.5$ is reasonably accurate, but the effects of implicit numerical diffusion are noticeable.

Note that with a finite number of discrete grid points, only a finite Fourier series can be constructed. Consequently, even the initial data cannot be represented exactly. This error in the discretization of the initial data obviously affects the numerical solution of a PDE by an FDE. For example, if a solution domain is discretized with 11 points (10 intervals), as illustrated in Fig. 10.21, only the first five harmonics of the Fourier series can be represented. Property variations

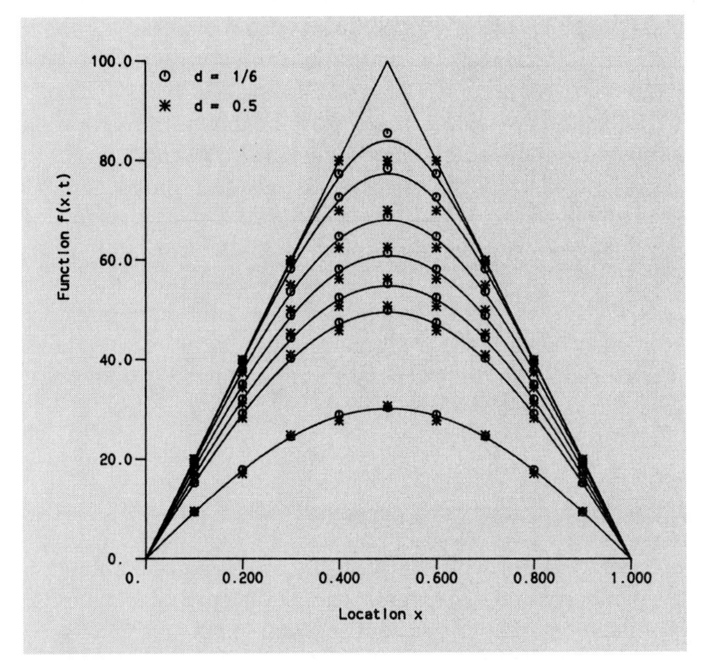

FIGURE 10.20
Solution of the diffusion equation by the FTCS method.

occurring on a scale of the order of the spatial grid size Δx are completely lost in the finite difference approximation of the continuous property distribution.

Summarizing, implicit numerical diffusion and dispersion are present in the finite difference approximation of a partial differential equation. These effects are caused by the truncation error terms, which can be determined from the modified differential equation. Implicit numerical diffusion acts on the magnitude of the Fourier components of the solution and results in magnitude error and distortion. Implicit numerical dispersion results in phase error and distortion. Even derivatives in the truncation error contribute to implicit numerical diffusion; odd derivatives contribute to implicit numerical dispersion. Implicit numerical

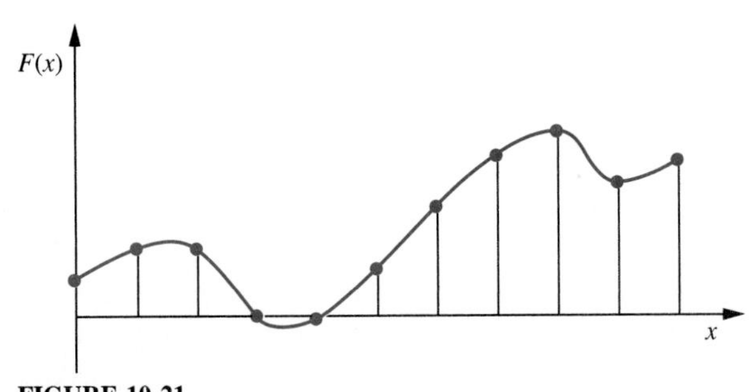

FIGURE 10.21
Eleven-point discretization.

diffusion and dispersion behave like real physical diffusion and dispersion, which are discussed in Section 10.3. In fact, if the leading truncation error term contains f_{xx}, that term numerically acts like real physical diffusion; this correspondence explains the choice of the name *implicit numerical diffusion* for this portion of the truncation error. Likewise, if the leading truncation error term contains f_{xxx}, that term numerically acts like real physical dispersion; this correspondence explains the choice of the name *implicit numerical dispersion* for this portion of the truncation error. These names are generally applied to all the truncation error terms, not just the leading term. In general, if the leading truncation error term contains an even space derivative, the truncation error will exhibit predominately diffusive behavior. On the other hand, if the leading truncation error term contains an odd space derivative, the truncation error will exhibit predominately dispersive behavior.

10.10 ASYMPTOTIC STEADY STATE SOLUTION OF PROPAGATION PROBLEMS

Marching methods are employed for solving unsteady propagation problems, which are governed by parabolic and hyperbolic partial differential equations. The emphasis in those problems is on the transient solution itself.

Marching methods are also used to solve steady equilibrium problems and steady mixed problems as the asymptotic solution in time of an appropriate unsteady propagation problem. Steady equilibrium problems are governed by elliptic PDEs. Steady mixed problems are governed by PDEs that change classification from elliptic to parabolic or hyperbolic in some portion of the solution domain, or by systems of PDEs which are a mixed set of elliptic and parabolic or hyperbolic PDEs. Mixed problems present serious numerical difficulties, due to the different types of solution domains (closed domains for equilibrium problems and open domains for propagation problems) and different types of auxiliary conditions (boundary conditions for equilibrium problems and boundary conditions and initial conditions for propagation problems). Consequently, it may be easier to obtain the solution of a steady mixed problem by re-posing the problem as an unsteady parabolic or hyperbolic problem and using marching methods to obtain the asymptotic steady state solution. That approach to solving steady state problems is discussed in this section.

The appropriate unsteady propagation problem must be governed by a parabolic or hyperbolic PDE having the same spatial derivatives as the steady equilibrium problem or the mixed problem and the same boundary conditions (BCs). As an example, consider the steady convection–diffusion equation:

$$u\hat{f}_x = \alpha\hat{f}_{xx} \tag{10.223}$$

The solution to Eq. (10.223) is the function $\hat{f}(x)$, which must satisfy two boundary conditions. The BCs may be of the Dirichlet type (i.e., specified values of $\hat{f}$), the Neumann type (i.e., specified values of $\hat{f}_x$), or the mixed type (i.e., specified combinations of $\hat{f}$ and $\hat{f}_x$).

An appropriate unsteady propagation problem for solving Eq. (10.223) as the asymptotic solution in time is the unsteady convection–diffusion equation

$$\bar{f}_t + u\bar{f}_x = \alpha\bar{f}_{xx} \tag{10.224}$$

The solution to Eq. (10.224) is the function $\bar{f}(x, t)$, which must satisfy an initial condition $\bar{f}(x, 0) = F(x)$ and two boundary conditions. If the boundary conditions for $\bar{f}(x, t)$ are the same as the boundary conditions for $\hat{f}(x)$, then

$$\boxed{\hat{f}(x) = \lim_{t\to\infty} \bar{f}(x, t) = \bar{f}(x, \infty)} \tag{10.225}$$

As long as the asymptotic solution converges, the particular choice for the initial condition, $\bar{f}(x, 0) = F(x)$, should not affect the steady state solution. However, the steady state solution may be reached in fewer time steps if the initial condition is a reasonable approximation of the general features of the steady state solution.

The solution of equilibrium problems as the asymptotic solution in time of appropriate unsteady propagation problems is illustrated in Section 11.9 for the diffusion equation.

SUMMARY

The basic features of finite difference methods for solving propagation problems are presented in this chapter. The following steps should be followed to develop a finite difference solution of partial differential equations governing propagation problems:

1. Specify the discrete finite difference grid.
2. Choose finite difference approximations for the individual exact partial derivatives in the PDE.
3. Determine the finite difference equation (FDE).
4. Derive the first and second forms of the modified differential equation (MDE) that is actually solved by the FDE.
5. Analyze the first form of the MDE for consistency and order.
6. If the first form of the MDE contains truncation errors that might cancel exactly, analyze the second form of the MDE for order.
7. Analyze the second form of the MDE to determine whether the truncation error is diffusive, dispersive, or both, and which predominates if both are present.
8. Perform a von Neumann stability analysis of the FDE to determine the stability criteria.
9. From the consistency analysis and the stability analysis, determine whether the finite difference method is convergent.

In the following chapters, the above steps are applied to obtain finite difference methods for solving the diffusion equation (Chapter 11), the convection equation (Chapter 12), the convection–diffusion equation (Chapter 14), and the wave equation (Chapter 15).

PROBLEMS

Section 10.2 Fundamental Considerations

1. Discuss the general features of parabolic PDEs.
2. Discuss the general features of hyperbolic PDEs.
3. Discuss the major similarities of parabolic and hyperbolic PDEs.
4. Discuss the major differences between parabolic and hyperbolic PDEs.
5. Classify the unsteady one-dimensional diffusion equation, Eq. (10.1). Derive the characteristic equation. Determine the characteristic curves. Discuss the significance of the characteristic curves.
6. Work Problem 5 for the convection-diffusion equation, Eq. (10.2).
7. Work Problem 5 for the convection equation, Eq. (10.3).
8. Work Problem 5 for the pair of coupled convection equations $f_t + ag_x = 0$ and $g_t + af_x = 0$.

Section 10.3 General Features of Convection, Diffusion, and Dispersion

9. Develop the exact solution of the convection equation, Eq. (10.12).
10. Discuss the significance of Eq. (10.12) as regards the general behavior of convection problems. Explain the results presented in Fig. 10.7.
11. Develop the exact solution of the diffusion equation, Eq. (10.23).
12. Discuss the significance of Eq. (10.23) as regards the general behavior of diffusion problems. Explain the results presented in Fig. 10.8.
13. Develop the exact solution of the dispersion equation, Eq. (10.31).
14. Discuss the significance of Eq. (10.31) as regards the general behavior of dispersion problems. Explain the results presented in Fig. 10.9.

Section 10.4 Finite Difference Grids and Finite Difference Approximations

15. Derive the following finite difference approximations of $\bar{f}_t$ including the leading truncation error terms: (*a*) first-order forward-difference $f_t|^n$, (*b*) first-order backward-difference $f_t|^n$, (*c*) second-order centered difference $f_t|^n$, and (*d*) second-order centered-difference $f_t|^{n+1/2}$.
16. Derive the following finite difference approximations of $\bar{f}_x$, including the leading truncation error terms: (*a*) first-order forward-difference $f_x|_i$, first-order backward-difference $f_x|_i$, and (*c*) second-order centered-difference $f_x|_i$.
17. Derive the following finite difference approximations of $\bar{f}_{xx}$, including the leading truncation error terms: (*a*) first-order forward-difference $f_{xx}|_i$, (*b*) first-order backward-difference $f_{xx}|_i$, and (*c*) second-order centered-difference $f_{xx}|_i$.

Section 10.5 Finite Difference Equations

18. Derive the forward-time centered-space approximation of the diffusion equation, including the leading truncation error terms.

19. Derive the backward-time centered-space approximation of the diffusion equation, including the leading truncation error terms.

20. Derive the Crank–Nicolson approximation of the diffusion equation, which is obtained by replacing $\bar{f}_t$ by the second-order centered-difference approximation $f_t|_i^{n+1/2}$ and $\bar{f}_{xx}$ by the average of the second-order centered-difference approximations of $\bar{f}_{xx}$ at grid points (i, n) and $(i, n+1)$. Include the leading truncation error terms.

21. Work Problem 18 for the convection-diffusion equation.

22. Work Problem 19 for the convection-diffusion equation.

23. Work Problem 20 for the convection-diffusion equation.

24. Work Problem 18 for the convection equation.

25. Work Problem 19 for the convection equation.

26. Work Problem 20 for the convection equation.

27. Derive the upwind approximation of the convection equation for $u > 0$ by replacing $\bar{f}_t$ by the first-order forward-difference approximation $f_t|_i^n$ and $\bar{f}_x$ by the first-order backward-difference approximation $f_x|_i^n$. Include the leading truncation error terms. Repeat the analysis for $u < 0$.

28. Derive the upwind approximation of the convection-diffusion equation for $u > 0$ by replacing $\bar{f}_t$ by the first-order forward-difference approximation $f_t|_i^n$, $\bar{f}_x$ by the first-order backward-difference approximation $f_x|_i^n$, and $\bar{f}_{xx}$ by the second-order centered-difference approximation $f_{xx}|_i^n$. Include the leading truncation error terms. Repeat the analysis for $u < 0$.

Section 10.7 The Modified Differential Equation

29. Derive the first and approximate second forms of the MDE for the FDE derived in Problem 18. Investigate consistency and determine the order of the FDE.

30. Work Problem 29 for the FDE derived in Problem 19.

31. Work Problem 29 for the FDE derived in Problem 20.

32. Work Problem 29 for the FDE derived in Problem 21.

33. Work Problem 29 for the FDE derived in Problem 22.

34. Work Problem 29 for the FDE derived in Problem 23.

35. Work Problem 29 for the FDE derived in Problem 24.

36. Work Problem 29 for the FDE derived in Problem 25.

37. Work Problem 29 for the FDE derived in Problem 26.

38. Work Problem 29 for the FDE derived in Problem 27.

39. Work Problem 29 for the FDE derived in Problem 28.

Section 10.8 Stability Analysis

40. Perform a von Neumann stability analysis of the FDE derived in Problem 18.

41. Perform a von Neumann stability analysis of the FDE derived in Problem 19.

42. Perform a von Neumann stability analysis of the FDE derived in Problem 20.

43. Perform a von Neumann stability analysis of the FDE derived in Problem 24.

44. Perform a von Neumann stability analysis of the FDE derived in Problem 25.
45. Perform a von Neumann stability analysis of the FDE derived in Problem 26.
46. Perform a von Neumann stability analysis of the FDE derived in Problem 27.

Section 10.9 Implicit Numerical Diffusion and Dispersion

47. From the MDE for the FDE derived in Problem 18, determine whether or not implicit numerical diffusion or dispersion are present in the FDE and which is dominant.
48. Work Problem 47 for the FDE derived in Problem 19.
49. Work Problem 47 for the FDE derived in Problem 20.
50. Work Problem 47 for the FDE derived in Problem 21.
51. Work Problem 47 for the FDE derived in Problem 22.
52. Work Problem 47 for the FDE derived in Problem 23.
53. Work Problem 47 for the FDE derived in Problem 24.
54. Work Problem 47 for the FDE derived in Problem 25.
55. Work Problem 47 for the FDE derived in Problem 26.
56. Work Problem 47 for the FDE derived in Problem 27.
57. Work Problem 47 for the FDE derived in Problem 28.

Applied Problems

In a practical problem, a particular PDE is approximated by a specific FDE. That FDE must be analyzed for consistency, order, stability, convergence, and the effects of implicit numerical diffusion and dispersion. These analyses comprise a complete analysis of the FDE. Perform complete analyses of the following FDEs:

58. The FDE derived in Problem 18.
59. The FDE derived in Problem 19.
60. The FDE derived in Problem 20.
61. The FDE derived in Problem 24.
62. The FDE derived in Problem 25.
63. The FDE derived in Problem 26.
64. The FDE derived in Problem 27.

CHAPTER 11

PARABOLIC PARTIAL DIFFERENTIAL EQUATIONS

The Diffusion Equation

Section

Example

11.1 INTRODUCTION

The general features of *parabolic* partial differential equations (PDEs) are discussed in Section III.6. In that section it is shown that parabolic PDEs govern propagation problems, which are initial-boundary-value problems in open domains. Consequently, parabolic PDEs are solved numerically by marching methods.

From a characteristic analysis, it is shown in Section III.6 that problems governed by parabolic PDEs have an infinite physical signal propagation speed $c = dx/dt$. As a result, the solution at a given point P at time level n depends on the solution at all other points in the solution domain at all times preceding and including time level n, and the solution at a given point P at time level n influences the solution at all other points in the solution domain at all times including and after time level n. These general features of parabolic PDEs are illustrated in Fig. 11.1.

The basic features of finite difference methods for solving propagation problems are discussed in Chapter 10. A finite difference grid must be superimposed on the continuous solution domain, and finite difference approximations (FDAs) of the individual exact partial derivatives appearing in the PDE must be chosen. These FDAs are substituted into the PDE to yield an algebraic finite difference equation (FDE). The finite difference equation must be analyzed for consistency, order, stability, and convergence. The effects of implicit numerical diffusion and dispersion on the solution must be considered. These properties are discussed in Chapter 10.

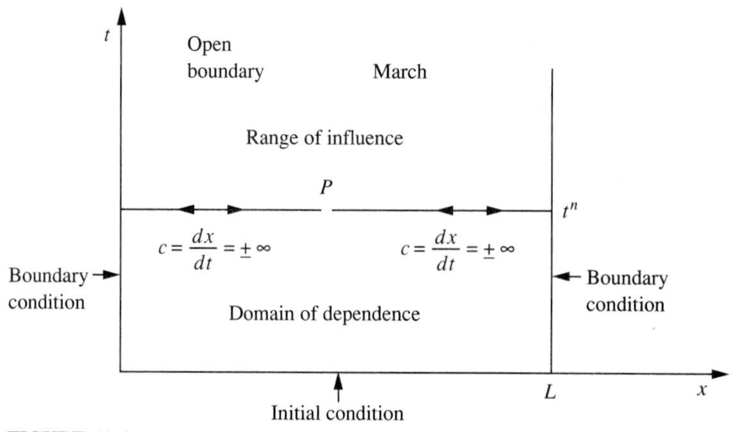

FIGURE 11.1
Domain of dependence and range of influence for a parabolic PDE.

The present chapter is devoted to the numerical solution of the unsteady one-dimensional parabolic diffusion equation:

$$\boxed{\bar{f}_t = \alpha \bar{f}_{xx}} \tag{11.1}$$

It is shown in Section III.6 that the diffusion equation has a zero discriminant, that the characteristic equation is $dt = \pm 0$, and that the characteristics are the lines (or surfaces) of constant time.

The numerical solution of Eq. (11.1) by several numerical methods is presented in this chapter. For each method, the modified differential equation (MDE) is presented; consistency and order are investigated; the amplification factor G, obtained from a von Neumann stability analysis, is presented and stability is analyzed; convergence is investigated; and the influence of implicit numerical diffusion and dispersion is determined.

The solution of Eq. (11.1) is the function $\bar{f}(x, t)$. This function must satisfy an initial condition at $t = 0$, $\bar{f}(x, 0) = F(x)$. The time coordinate has an unspecified (i.e., open) final value. Since Eq. (11.1) is second-order in the spatial coordinate x, two boundary conditions are required. These may be of the Dirichlet type (i.e., specified values of $\bar{f}$), the Neumann type (i.e., specified values of $\bar{f}_x$), or the mixed type (i.e., specified combinations of $\bar{f}$ and $\bar{f}_x$).

The diffusion equation applies to problems in such areas as mass diffusion, momentum diffusion, heat diffusion (i.e., conduction), and neutron diffusion. Most people have some physical understanding of heat conduction, due to its presence in many aspects of our daily life. Consequently, the diffusion equation governing heat conduction is considered in this chapter to illustrate numerical methods for solving the diffusion equation. That equation is derived in Section III.6, Eq. (III.69). For unsteady one-dimensional heat conduction, Eq. (III.69) becomes

$$T_t = \alpha T_{xx} \tag{11.2}$$

where T is temperature (C) and α is the thermal diffusivity (cm^2/s). The solution to Eq. (11.2) is the function $T(x, t)$. This function must satisfy an initial condition at time $t = 0$, $T(x, 0) = F(x)$, and a set of boundary conditions at $x = 0$ and $x = L$.

The following simple problem is considered in this chapter to illustrate the behavior of several numerical integration methods applied to the diffusion equation. The plate illustrated in Fig. 11.2 has a thickness $L = 1.0$ cm, and the thermal diffusivity $\alpha = 0.01$ cm^2/s. The initial temperature distribution in the plate is specified by

$$T(x, 0) = 200x \qquad 0.0 \le x \le 0.5 \tag{11.3}$$

$$T(x, 0) = 200(1 - x) \qquad 0.5 \le x \le 1.0 \tag{11.4}$$

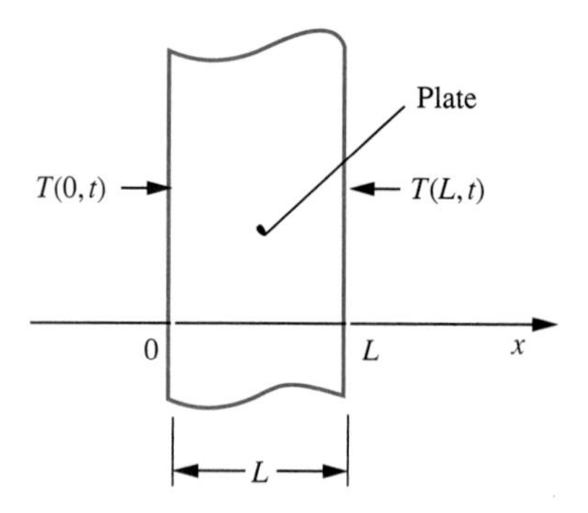

FIGURE 11.2
Heat conduction in a plate.

where T is measured in degrees centigrade (C). This initial temperature distribution is illustrated by the top curve in Fig. 11.3. The temperatures on the two faces of the plate are held at 0.0 C for all time. Thus,

$$T(0.0, t) = T(1.0, t) = 0.0 \tag{11.5}$$

The temperature distribution $T(x, t)$ in the plate is required. The exact solution to this problem is obtained by assuming a product solution of the form $T(x, t) = X(x)\tilde{T}(t)$, separating variables, integrating the resulting two ordinary differential equations, applying the boundary conditions at $x = 0$ and $x = L$, and superimposing an infinite number of solutions to obtain the general solution.

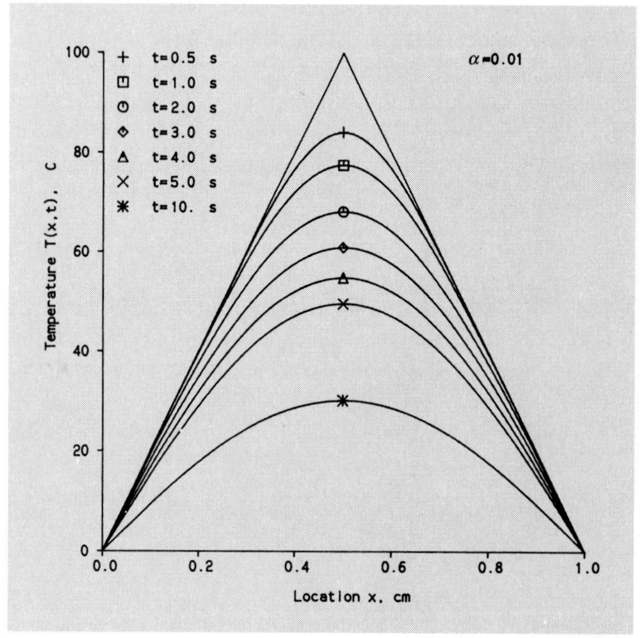

FIGURE 11.3
Exact solution of the heat conduction problem.

TABLE 11.1
Exact solution of the heat conduction problem

	Temperature $T(x, t)$, C					
t, s	$x = 0.0$	$x = 0.1$	$x = 0.2$	$x = 0.3$	$x = 0.4$	$x = 0.5$
0.0	0.00	20.00	40.00	60.00	80.00	100.00
0.5	0.00	20.00	39.98	59.66	76.67	84.04
1.0	0.00	19.96	39.66	57.99	72.01	77.43
2.0	0.00	19.35	37.66	53.34	64.18	68.08
3.0	0.00	18.12	34.84	48.57	57.70	60.91
4.0	0.00	16.67	31.86	44.11	52.10	54.88
5.0	0.00	15.21	28.99	40.00	47.13	49.59
10.0	0.00	9.33	17.76	24.44	28.73	30.21
20.0	0.00	3.48	6.62	9.11	10.71	11.26
50.0	0.00	0.18	0.34	0.47	0.55	0.56
∞	0.00	0.00	0.00	0.00	0.00	0.00

The coefficients of the general solution are chosen to satisfy the initial condition at $t = 0$. The result is

$$T(x, t) = \frac{800}{\pi^2} \sum_{m=0}^{\infty} \frac{(-1)^m}{(2m + 1)^2} \sin\big((2m + 1)\pi x\big) e^{-\left((2m+1)^2\pi^2\alpha^2\right)t} \tag{11.6}$$

The exact solution at selected values of time is tabulated in Table 11.1 and illustrated in Fig. 11.3. The solution is symmetrical about the midplane of the plate. The solution smoothly approaches the asymptotic steady state solution $T(x, \infty) = 0.0$.

11.2 THE FORWARD-TIME CENTERED-SPACE METHOD

In this section the unsteady one-dimensional parabolic diffusion equation $\bar{f}_t = \alpha \bar{f}_{xx}$ is solved numerically by the forward-time centered-space (FTCS) method. In the FTCS method, the base point for the finite difference approximation (FDA) of the partial differential equation (PDE) is point (i, n). As shown in Example 10.4, the finite difference equation (FDE) that approximates the partial differential equation is obtained by replacing the partial derivative $\bar{f}_t$ by the first-order forward-difference approximation [Eq. (10.54)] and the partial derivative $\bar{f}_{xx}$ by the second-order centered-difference approximation [Eq. (10.69b)]. The resulting FDE is [see Eq. (10.73)]

$$f_i^{n+1} = f_i^n + d(f_{i+1}^n - 2f_i^n + f_{i-1}^n) \tag{11.7}$$

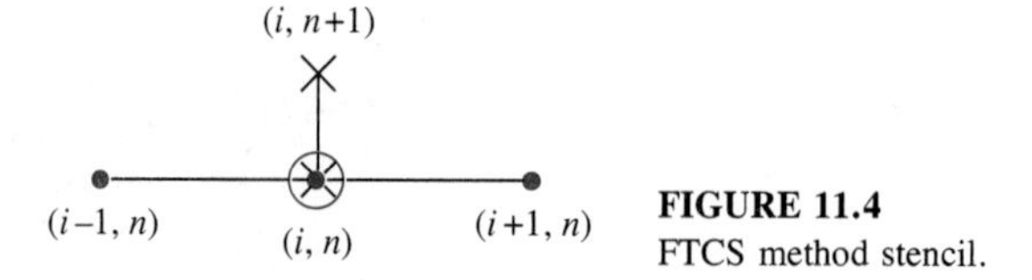

FIGURE 11.4
FTCS method stencil.

where $d = \alpha\,\Delta t/\Delta x^2$ is the diffusion number. Equation (11.7) is the FTCS approximation of the one-dimensional diffusion equation. The finite difference stencil is illustrated in Fig. 11.4.

The first form of the modified differential equation (MDE) is [see Eq. (10.105)]

$$f_t = \alpha f_{xx} - \frac{1}{2}f_{tt}\,\Delta t - \frac{1}{6}f_{ttt}\,\Delta t^2 - \cdots + \frac{1}{12}\alpha f_{xxxx}\,\Delta x^2 + \frac{1}{360}\alpha f_{xxxxxx}\,\Delta x^4 + \cdots \tag{11.8}$$

and the second form of the MDE is [see Eq. (10.109)]

$$f_t = \alpha f_{xx} + \left(\frac{1}{12}\alpha\,\Delta x^2 - \frac{1}{2}\alpha^2\,\Delta t\right)f_{xxxx} + \left(\frac{1}{360}\alpha\,\Delta x^4 - \frac{1}{12}\alpha^2\,\Delta t\,\Delta x^2 + \frac{1}{3}\alpha^3\,\Delta t^2\right)f_{xxxxxx} + \cdots \tag{11.9}$$

As $\Delta t \to 0$ and $\Delta x \to 0$, Eq. (11.8) approaches $f_t = \alpha f_{xx}$. Thus, Eq. (11.7) is a consistent approximation of the diffusion equation. From Eq. (11.8), the truncation error is $O(\Delta t) + O(\Delta x^2)$. As shown by Eq. (10.112), when $d = \frac{1}{6}$, the truncation error is $O(\Delta t^2) + O(\Delta t\,\Delta x^2) + O(\Delta x^4)$. Equation (11.9) shows that the truncation error contains only even derivative terms. Consequently, implicit numerical diffusion will be present in the numerical solution, but there will not be any implicit numerical dispersion. The amplification factor G corresponding to Eq. (11.7) is [see Eq. (10.148)]

$$G = 1 + 2d\left(\cos\theta - 1\right) \tag{11.10}$$

As shown in Example 10.11, $|G| \leq 1$ if

$$\boxed{d \leq \frac{1}{2}} \tag{11.11}$$

Consequently, Eq. (11.7) is conditionally stable. The FTCS approximation of the diffusion equation is consistent and conditionally stable. Consequently, by the Lax equivalence theorem, the numerical solution of the diffusion equation by the FTCS method converges to the true solution of the exact PDE as $\Delta t \to 0$ and $\Delta x \to 0$. In other words, the method is convergent.

The general features of the FTCS approximation of the diffusion equation can be illustrated by applying it to solve the heat transfer problem described in Section 11.1. Several solutions are presented in Example 11.1.

Example 11.1. Solution by the FTCS method. We will solve the heat conduction problem described in Section 11.1 by the FTCS method with $\Delta x = 0.1$ cm. Let $\Delta t = 0.1$ s, so $d = \alpha\,\Delta t/\Delta x^2 = (0.01)(0.1)/(0.1)^2 = 0.1$. The numerical solution, $T(x, t)$, and errors, $T(x, t) - \overline{T}(x, t)$, at selected times are presented in Table 11.2 and illustrated in Fig. 11.5. Due to the symmetry of the solution, results are tabulated only for $x = 0.0$ to 0.5 cm. It is apparent that the numerical solution is a good approximation of the exact solution. The error at the midpoint (i.e., $x = 0.5$ cm) is the largest error at each time level. This is a direct result of the discontinuity in the slope of the initial temperature distribution at that point. However, the magnitude of this error decreases rapidly as the solution progresses, and the initial discontinuity in the slope is smoothed out. The errors at the remaining locations grow initially, due to the accumulation of truncation errors, and reach a maximum value. As the solution progresses, however, the numerical solution approaches the exact asymptotic solution $T(x, \infty) = 0.0$, so the errors decrease and approach zero. The numerical results presented in Table 11.2 present a very favorable impression of the FTCS approximation of the diffusion equation.

The results obtained with $d = 0.1$ are quite good. However, a considerable amount of computational effort is required. The following question naturally arises: Can acceptable results be obtained with larger values of Δt, thus requiring less computational effort? To answer this question, we will rework the problem with $d = 0.5$ (i.e., $\Delta t = 0.5$ s), which requires only one-fifth of the computational effort to reach a given time level. The results at selected times are illustrated in Fig. 11.6. Although the solution is still reasonable, it is apparent that the solution is no longer smooth. A slight oscillation about

TABLE 11.2
Numerical solution and errors* for $d = 0.1$

	$T(x, t)$, C					
t, s	$x = 0.0$	$x = 0.1$	$x = 0.2$	$x = 0.3$	$x = 0.4$	$x = 0.5$
0.0	0.00	20.00	40.00	60.00	80.00	100.00
0.5	0.00	20.00	39.98	59.71	77.32	85.97
		0.00	0.00	0.05	0.65	1.93
1.0	0.00	19.96	39.68	58.22	72.81	78.67
		0.00	0.02	0.23	0.80	1.24
2.0	0.00	19.39	37.81	53.73	64.87	68.91
		0.04	0.15	0.39	0.69	0.83
3.0	0.00	18.21	35.06	48.99	58.30	61.58
		0.09	0.22	0.42	0.60	0.67
4.0	0.00	16.79	32.12	44.51	52.63	55.45
		0.12	0.26	0.40	0.53	0.57
5.0	0.00	15.34	29.25	40.39	47.61	50.11
		0.13	0.26	0.39	0.48	0.52
10.0	0.00	9.44	17.96	24.72	29.07	30.56
		0.11	0.20	0.28	0.34	0.35

* The errors, $T(x, t) - \overline{T}(x, t)$, are listed below the solution values.

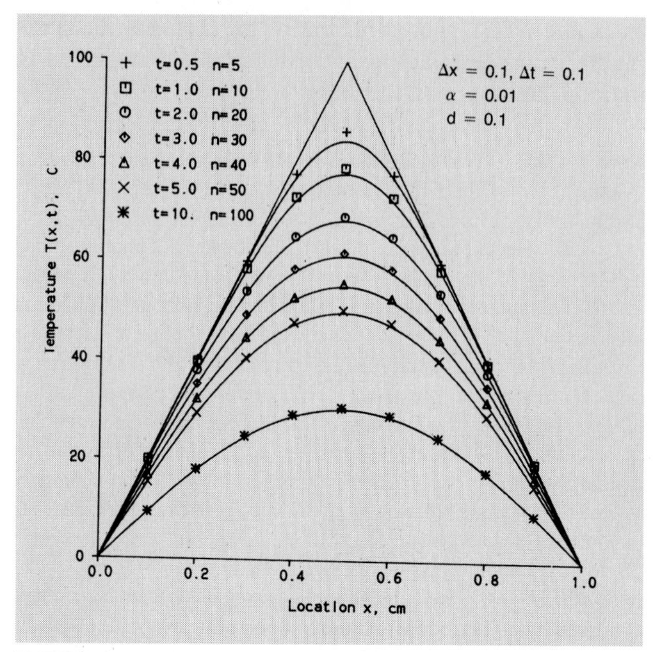

FIGURE 11.5
Solution by the FTCS method with $d = 0.1$.

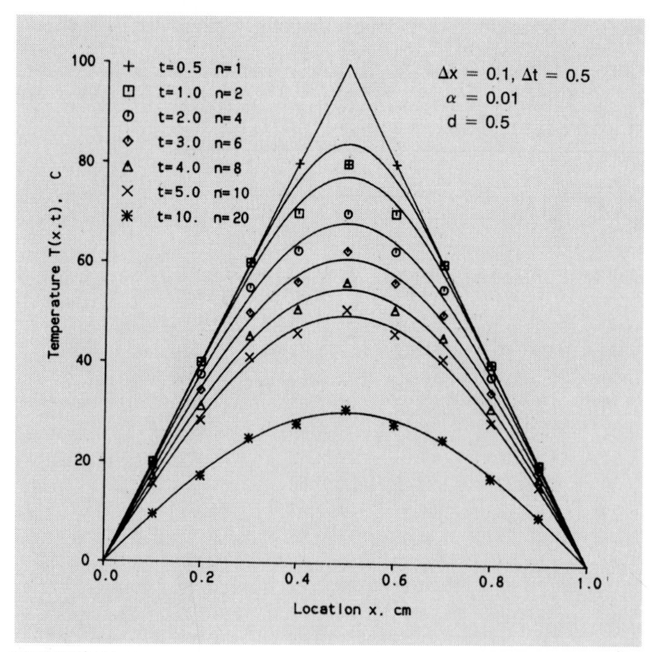

FIGURE 11.6
Solution by the FTCS method with $d = 0.5$.

the exact solution is apparent. Every numerically computed point is on the opposite side of the exact solution from its two neighbors.

Let us rework the problem again with $d = 1.0$. This time step violates the stability criterion specified by Eq. (11.11). The results after each of the first three time steps are illustrated in Fig. 11.7. That result is obviously physically incorrect. Severe oscillations have developed in the solution. These oscillations grow larger and larger as time increases. Values of $T(x, t)$ greater than the initial value of 100 and less than the boundary value of 0 are predicted. Both of these results are physically impossible.

The results presented in Fig. 11.6, while qualitatively correct, appear on the verge of behaving like the results presented in Fig. 11.7. The value $d = 0.5$ appears to be the boundary between physically meaningful results for d less than 0.5 and physically meaningless results for d greater than 0.5. To check out this supposition, let us rework the problem for two more values of d: $d = 0.4$ and $d = 0.6$. These results are illustrated in Fig. 11.8 at $t = 6.0$ s. The numerical solution with $d = 0.4$ is obviously modeling physical reality, while the solution with $d = 0.6$ is not. These results support the conclusion that the value $d = 0.5$, which is the theoretical stability limit, is the boundary between physically correct solutions and physically incorrect solutions.

The stability restriction $d \leq \frac{1}{2}$ imposes a serious limitation on the usefulness of the FTCS method for solving the diffusion equation. One procedure for deciding whether or not a solution is accurate enough is to cut Δx in half and repeat the solution up to the same specified time level to see if the solution changes significantly. For the FTCS method, cutting Δx in half while holding d constant decreases Δt by a factor of four. Thus, four times as many time steps are required

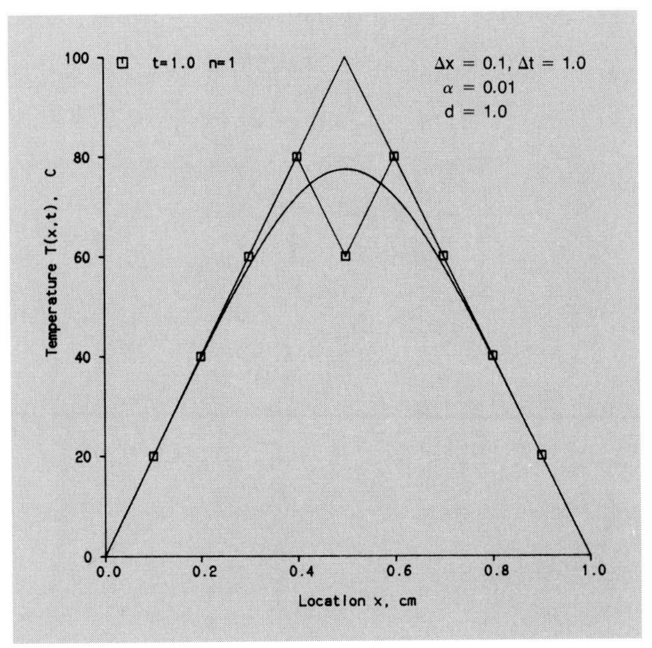

FIGURE 11.7*a*
Solution by the FTCS method with $d = 1.0$. (*a*) First step.

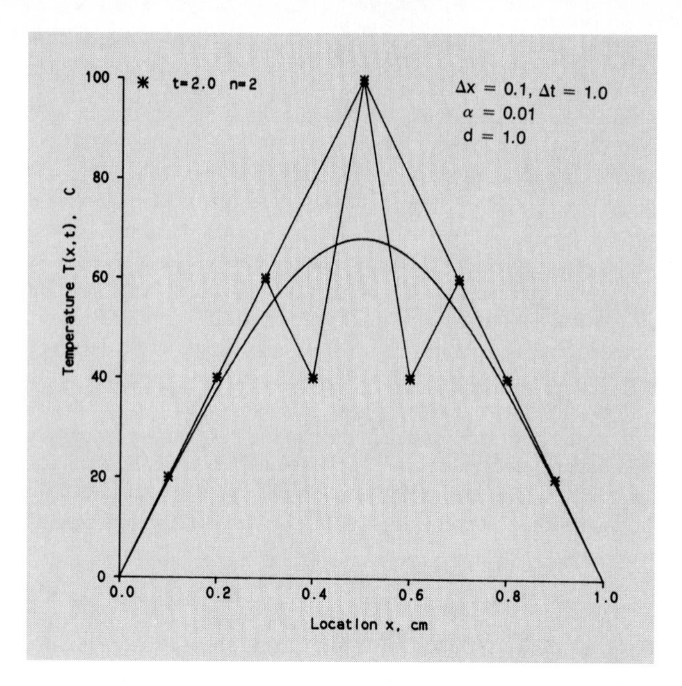

FIGURE 11.7*b*
Solution by the FTCS method with $d = 1.0$. (*b*) Second step.

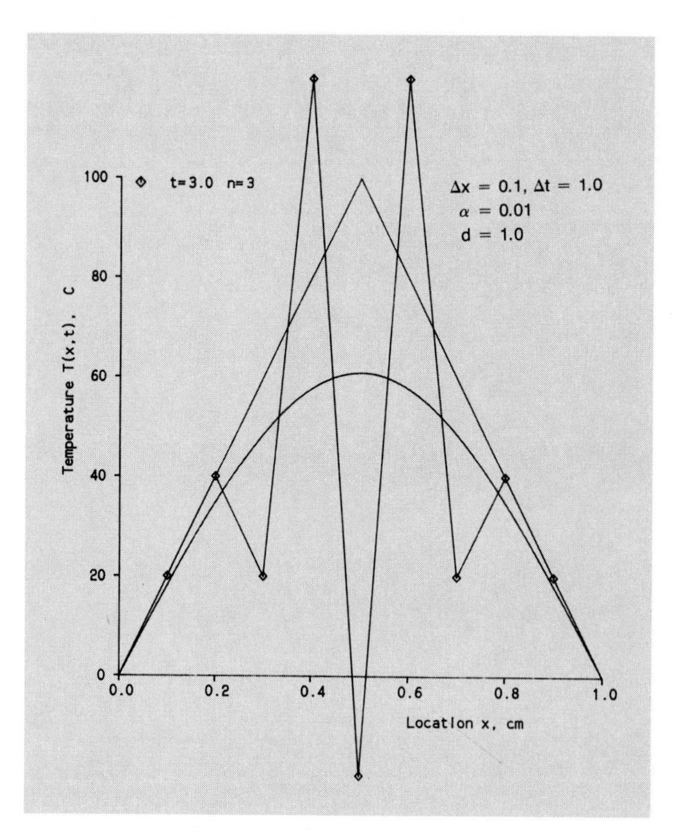

FIGURE 11.7*c*
Solution by the FTCS method with $d = 1.0$. (*c*) Third step.

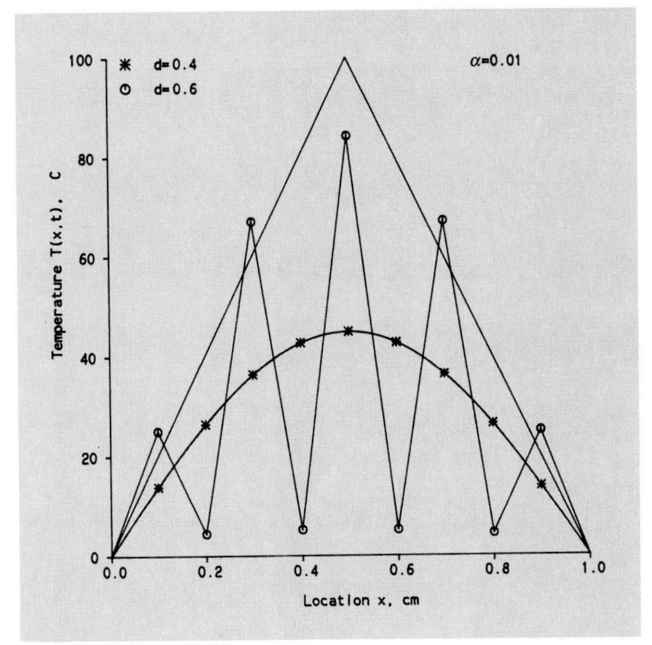

FIGURE 11.8
Solution at $t = 6.0$ s by the FTCS method.

to reach the previously specified time level, and twice as much work is required for each time step, since twice as many physical grid points are involved. Thus, the total computational effort increases by a factor of *eight*!

The forward-time centered-space method has an interesting feature when $d = \frac{1}{6}$. In that special case, the $O(\Delta t)$ and the $O(\Delta x^2)$ truncation error terms cancel exactly, and the method becomes $O(\Delta t^2) + O(\Delta t\, \Delta x^2) + O(\Delta x^4)$ [see Eq. (10.112)]. Let us rework the heat conduction problem with $d = \frac{1}{6}$ to illustrate the improved accuracy. The results are presented in Table 11.3 for $d = \frac{1}{6}$. Comparing these results with the results presented in Table 11.2 shows that the errors for the two computations are about the same size. The errors at the midpoint are smaller throughout the computation with $d = \frac{1}{6}$. The errors at the other points are slightly larger at early times, but slightly smaller at later times. The results presented in Table 11.3 were obtained with only 60 percent of the computational effort required to obtain the results obtained in Table 11.2 [i.e., $(0.1)/(1/6) = 0.60$].

Next, consider a parametric study in which the temperature at $x = 0.4$ cm and $t = 5.0$ s, $T(0.4, 5.0)$, is calculated using values of $\Delta x = 0.1$, 0.05, 0.025, and 0.0125 cm, for values of $d = 0.1$, $\frac{1}{6}$, and 0.5. The value of Δt for each solution is determined by the specified values of Δx and d. The exact solution is $\bar{T}(0.4, 5.0) = 47.12550$ C. The results are presented in Table 11.4. The truncation error of the FTCS method is $O(\Delta t) + O(\Delta x^2)$. For a constant value of d, $\Delta t = d\, \Delta x^2/\alpha$. Thus, as Δx is successively halved, Δt is quartered. Consequently, both the $O(\Delta t)$ term and the $O(\Delta x^2)$ term should decrease by a

TABLE 11.3
Numerical solution and errors for $d = \frac{1}{6}$

	$T(x, t)$, C					
t, s	$x = 0.0$	$x = 0.1$	$x = 0.2$	$x = 0.3$	$x = 0.4$	$x = 0.5$
0.0	0.00	20.00	40.00	60.00	80.00	100.00
0.5	0.00	20.00	40.00	59.81	77.41	85.56
		0.00	0.02	0.15	0.74	1.52
1.0	0.00	19.98	39.75	58.31	72.75	78.43
		0.02	0.09	0.34	0.74	1.00
2.0	0.00	19.43	37.87	53.73	64.77	68.77
		0.08	0.21	0.39	0.59	0.69
3.0	0.00	18.24	35.08	48.96	58.21	61.46
		0.12	0.24	0.39	0.51	0.55
4.0	0.00	16.79	32.10	44.47	52.54	55.35
		0.12	0.24	0.36	0.44	0.47
5.0	0.00	15.33	29.22	40.33	47.52	50.01
		0.12	0.23	0.33	0.39	0.42
10.0	0.00	9.41	17.90	24.64	28.97	30.46
		0.08	0.14	0.20	0.24	0.25

factor of approximately four as Δx is halved for a constant value of d. This result is clearly evident from the results presented in Table 11.4.

The forward-time centered-space (FTCS) method has a finite numerical signal propagation speed. Numerically, information propagates one physical grid space during each time step. The diffusion equation has an infinite physical signal propagation speed. Consequently, the FTCS method does not correctly model the signal propagation speed of the diffusion equation. However, the bulk of the information propagates at a finite speed, and the FTCS method yields a reasonable representation of the exact solution of the diffusion equation. For example, consider the results presented in this section. The solution at $t = 5.0$ s is presented in Table 11.5 for $d = 0.1$, $\frac{1}{6}$, and 0.5. The grid spacing $\Delta x = 0.1$ cm

TABLE 11.4
Parametric Study of $T(0.4, 5.0)$

	$T(0.4, 5.0)$, C		
Δx, cm	$d = 0.1$	$d = \frac{1}{6}$	$d = 0.5$
0.1	47.60697	47.52022	45.89844
	0.48147	0.39472	−1.22706
0.05	47.24488	47.22360	47.41171
	0.11938	0.09810	0.28621
0.025	47.15528	47.14999	47.19700
	0.02978	0.02449	0.07150
0.0125	47.13294	47.13162	47.14337
	0.00744	0.00612	0.01787

TABLE 11.5
Numerical solution at $t = 5.0$ s

			$T(x, 5.0)$, C			
d	$x = 0.0$	$x = 0.1$	$x = 0.2$	$x = 0.3$	$x = 0.4$	$x = 0.5$
0.1	0.00	15.34	29.25	40.39	47.61	50.11
		0.13	0.26	0.39	0.48	0.52
$\frac{1}{6}$	0.00	15.33	29.22	40.33	47.52	50.01
		0.12	0.23	0.33	0.39	0.42
0.5	0.00	15.63	28.32	41.02	45.90	50.78
		0.42	−0.67	0.02	−1.23	1.19

is the same for all three solutions, and the time step $\Delta t = d\,\Delta x^2/\alpha$. Thus, the numerical signal propagation speed c_n is given by

$$c_n = \frac{\Delta x}{\Delta t} = \frac{\alpha\,\Delta x}{d\,\Delta x^2} = \frac{0.01}{d(0.1)} = \frac{0.1}{d}\ \text{cm/s} \tag{11.12}$$

Thus, $c_n = 1.0$ cm/s for $d = 0.1$, 0.6 cm/s for $d = \frac{1}{6}$, and 0.2 cm/s for $d = 0.5$. Consequently, the numerical signal propagation speed varies by a factor of five for the results presented in Table 11.5. Those results show very little influence of this large change in the numerical signal propagation speed, thus supporting the observation that the bulk of the physical information travels at a finite rate.

The explicit FTCS method can be applied to nonlinear PDEs simply by evaluating the nonlinear coefficients at base point (i, n). Systems of PDEs can be solved simply by solving the corresponding system of FDEs. Multidimensional problems can be solved simply by adding on the finite difference approximations of the y and z partial derivatives. A von Neumann stability analysis shows that $d_x + d_y + d_z \le \frac{1}{2}$, where d_x, d_y, and d_z are the component diffusion numbers (i.e., $d_x = \alpha\,\Delta t/\Delta x^2$, etc.). Consequently, the FTCS method can be used to solve nonlinear PDEs, systems of PDEs, and multidimensional problems by a straightforward extension of the procedure presented in this section. The solution of nonlinear equations and multidimensional problems is discussed further in Section 11.8.

In summary, the forward-time centered-space (FTCS) approximation of the diffusion equation is explicit, two-level, single-step, $O(\Delta t) + O(\Delta x^2)$, conditionally stable, and convergent. It is somewhat inefficient, because the time step varies as the square of the spatial grid spacing.

11.3 THE RICHARDSON (LEAPFROG) METHOD

The forward-time centered-space (FTCS) approximation of the diffusion equation, $\bar{f}_t = \alpha \bar{f}_{xx}$, presented in Section 11.2, has several desirable features. It is an explicit, two-level, single-step method. The finite difference approximation of the spatial derivative is second-order. However, the finite difference approximation of the time derivative is only first-order. An obvious improvement would be to use a second-order finite difference approximation of the time derivative.

Richardson (1910) proposed replacing the partial derivative $\bar{f}_t$ by the three-level second-order centered-difference approximation [see Eq. (10.61)] and the partial derivative $\bar{f}_{xx}$ by the second-order centered-difference approximation [Eq. (10.69*b*)]. The corresponding finite difference stencil is presented in Fig. 11.9. The resulting finite difference approximation to the diffusion equation is

$$\frac{f_i^{n+1} - f_i^{n-1}}{2\,\Delta t} = \alpha \frac{f_{i+1}^n - 2f_i^n + f_{i-1}^n}{\Delta x^2} \tag{11.13}$$

Solving Eq. (11.13) for f_i^{n+1} yields

$$\boxed{f_i^{n+1} = f_i^{n-1} + 2d(f_{i+1}^n - 2f_i^n + f_{i-1}^n)} \tag{11.14}$$

where $d = \alpha\,\Delta t/\Delta x^2$ is the diffusion number.

The Richardson method appears to be a significant improvement over the FTCS method, because of the increased accuracy of the finite difference approximation of $\bar{f}_t$. However, Eq. (11.14) is unconditionally unstable. Performing a von Neumann stability analysis of Eq. (11.14) (where $f_i^n = Gf_i^{n-1}$) yields

$$G = \frac{1}{G} + 4d(\cos\theta - 1) \tag{11.15}$$

which yields

$$G^2 + bG - 1 = 0 \tag{11.16}$$

where $b = -4d(\cos\theta - 1) = 8d\,\sin^2(\theta/2)$. Solving Eq. (11.16) by the quadratic formula yields

$$G = \frac{-b \pm \sqrt{b^2 + 4}}{2} \tag{11.17}$$

When $b = 0$, $|G| = 1$. For all other values of b, $|G| > 1$. Consequently, the Richardson method is unconditionally unstable when applied to the diffusion equation.

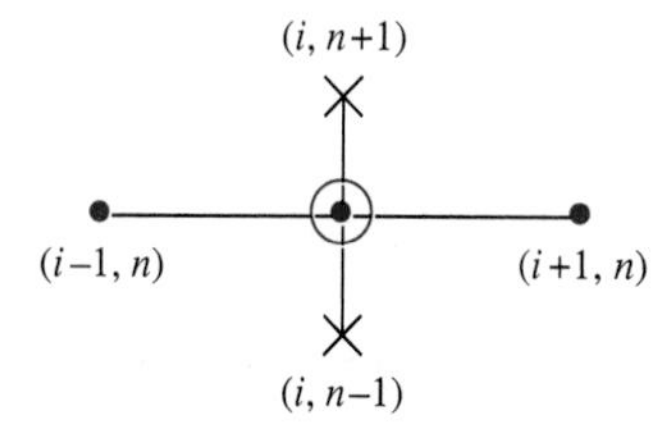

FIGURE 11.9
Richardson (leapfrog) method stencil.

Since the Richardson method is unconditionally unstable when applied to the diffusion equation, it cannot be used to solve that equation. This conclusion applies only to the parabolic diffusion equation. The combination of a three-level centered-difference approximation of $\bar{f}_t$ combined with a centered-difference approximation of a spatial derivative may be stable when applied to other partial differential equations. For example, when applied to the hyperbolic convection equation, where it is known simply as the leapfrog method, a conditionally stable finite difference method is obtained (see Section 12.7). However, when applied to the convection–diffusion equation (see Section 14.3), an unconditionally unstable finite difference equation is again obtained. Such occurrences of diametrically opposing results require the numerical analyst to be constantly alert when applying finite difference approximations to solve partial differential equations.

11.4 THE DUFORT–FRANKEL METHOD

DuFort and Frankel (1953) proposed a modification to the Richardson method for the diffusion equation $\bar{f}_t = \alpha \bar{f}_{xx}$ that removes the unconditional instability. The central grid point value f_i^n in the second-order centered-difference approximation of $\bar{f}_{xx}|_i^n$ is replaced by the average of f_i at time levels $n+1$ and $n-1$, that is, $f_i^n = (f_i^{n+1} + f_i^{n-1})/2$. Thus, Eq. (11.13) becomes

$$\frac{f_i^{n+1} - f_i^{n-1}}{2\Delta t} = \alpha \frac{f_{i+1}^n - (f_i^{n+1} + f_i^{n-1}) + f_{i-1}^n}{\Delta x^2} \tag{11.18}$$

At this point, it is not obvious how the truncation error is affected by this replacement. The value f_i^{n+1} appears on both sides of Eq. (11.18). However, it appears linearly, so Eq. (11.18) can be solved explicitly for f_i^{n+1}. Thus,

$$\boxed{(1 + 2d) f_i^{n+1} = (1 - 2d) f_i^{n-1} + 2d(f_{i+1}^n + f_{i-1}^n)} \tag{11.19}$$

where $d = \alpha \Delta t / \Delta x^2$ is the diffusion number.

The addition of a third time level to a finite difference method has two potential disadvantages:

1. All three time levels may have to be stored in the computer, thus increasing the storage requirements by 50 percent.
2. A special starting procedure is required for the first time step.

The additional time level is not a problem in the DuFort–Frankel method, because f_i^{n+1} can be stored in place of f_i^{n-1}, so only two levels of computer storage are required. The starting problem can be solved by using a two-level method, such as the FTCS method (see Section 11.2) or the Crank–Nicolson method (see Section 11.6), to calculate the solution at time level 1.

The first form of the modified differential equation (MDE) is

$$f_t = \alpha f_{xx} - \frac{1}{6} f_{ttt}\,\Delta t^2 - \cdots - \alpha f_{tt}\frac{\Delta t^2}{\Delta x^2} - \frac{1}{12}\alpha f_{tttt}\frac{\Delta t^4}{\Delta x^2} + \cdots$$
$$+ \frac{1}{12}\alpha f_{xxxx}\,\Delta x^2 + \frac{1}{360}\alpha f_{xxxxxx}\,\Delta x^4 + \cdots \tag{11.20}$$

and the second form of the MDE is

$$f_t = \alpha f_{xx} + \left(\frac{1}{12}\alpha\,\Delta x^2 - \alpha^3\frac{\Delta t^2}{\Delta x^2}\right) f_{xxxx}$$
$$+ \left(\frac{1}{360}\alpha\,\Delta x^4 - \frac{1}{3}\alpha^3\,\Delta t^2 + 2\alpha^5\frac{\Delta t^4}{\Delta x^4}\right) f_{xxxxxx} + \cdots \tag{11.21}$$

As $\Delta t \to 0$ and $\Delta x \to 0$, the terms involving the ratio $(\Delta t/\Delta x)^2$ do not go to zero. In fact, they become indeterminate. Consequently, Eq. (11.19) is not a consistent approximation of the diffusion equation. However, if the ratio $(\Delta t/\Delta x)^2$ is held constant as $\Delta t \to 0$ and $\Delta x \to 0$, for example at the value $\beta = (\Delta t/\Delta x)^2$, then Eq. (11.20) approaches the equation

$$f_t = \alpha f_{xx} - \alpha\beta f_{tt} \tag{11.22}$$

Equation (11.22) is a hyperbolic PDE. In spite of this inconsistency, physically meaningful results can be obtained with the DuFort–Frankel method for small values of Δt if not too many time steps are taken. From Eq. (11.21), the DuFort–Frankel approximation of the diffusion equation is $O(\Delta t^2) + O(\Delta x^2) + O(\Delta t^2/\Delta x^2)$. From Eq. (11.21), it is seen that there are only even spatial derivatives in the truncation error. Hence, implicit numerical diffusion is present, but there is no implicit numerical dispersion. The amplification factor G corresponding to Eq. (11.19) is

$$(1 + 2d)G^2 - (4d\cos\theta)G - (1 - 2d) = 0 \tag{11.23}$$

Solving Eq. (11.23) by the quadratic formula gives

$$G = \frac{2d\cos\theta \pm \sqrt{1 - 4d^2\sin^2\theta}}{(1 + 2d)} \tag{11.24}$$

Three cases exist, depending on whether the term $(1 - 4d^2\sin^2\theta)$ is greater than, equal to, or less than zero. For all three cases, further analysis shows that $|G| \le 1$ for all values of d. Consequently, the DuFort–Frankel method is unconditionally stable when applied to the diffusion equation. Thus, Δt may be chosen as large as desired and a stable solution will be obtained. However, because of the consistency problem described above and because the truncation error increases as Δt increases, the step size Δt must be limited to achieve the desired accuracy. Even though the DuFort–Frankel approximation of the diffusion equation is unconditionally stable, there is some question as to its consistency with the diffusion equation, and thus with convergence.

Example 11.2. Solution by the DuFort–Frankel method. We will solve the heat conduction problem, described in Section 11.1, by the DuFort–Frankel method with $\Delta x = 0.1$ cm, using the exact solution for the first step. Let $\Delta t = 0.5$ s, so $d = 0.5$. The results at selected times are presented in Fig. 11.10. Although these results are in general agreement with the trends of the exact solution, they are not very good.

The DuFort–Frankel method is unconditionally stable. Consequently, the time step Δt is chosen to satisfy accuracy requirements, not stability criteria. To demonstrate these concepts, let us solve the example problem at $t = 10.0$ s with $\Delta t = 1.0$, 2.5, and 5.0 s, for which $d = 1.0$, 2.5, and 5.0, respectively. The results are presented in Fig. 11.11. The results are stable, but they are physically incorrect. These results suggest that large values of the diffusion number d lead to unacceptable solutions.

The unsatisfactory results presented in Fig. 11.11 are caused by using a large time step in an unconditionally stable explicit finite difference method. In an explicit finite difference method, numerical information can propagate only one spatial grid point during each time step. Consequently, for large time steps, the numerical signal propagation speed $c_n = \Delta x / \Delta t$ is much too small, and results such as presented in Fig. 11.11 are obtained. Even though the method is unconditionally stable, the diffusion number cannot be much larger than the stability limit $d \leq \frac{1}{2}$ associated with the FTCS method if accurate results are to

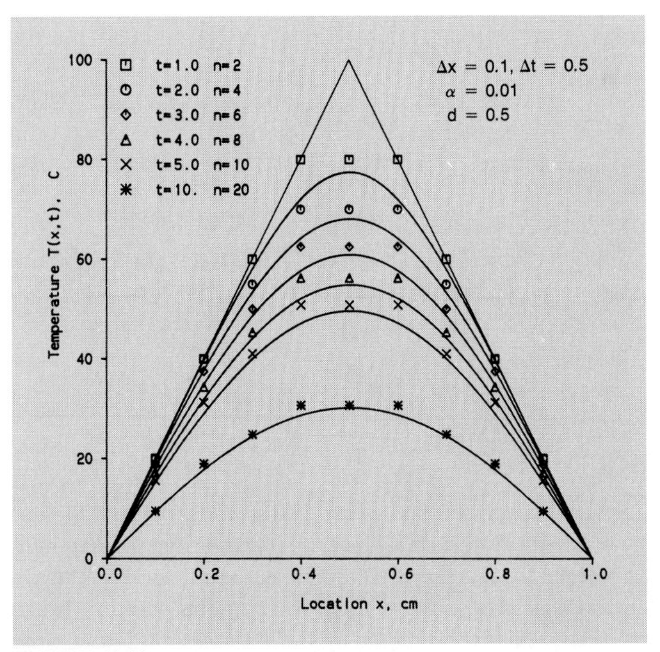

FIGURE 11.10
Solution by the DuFort–Frankel method with $d = 0.5$.

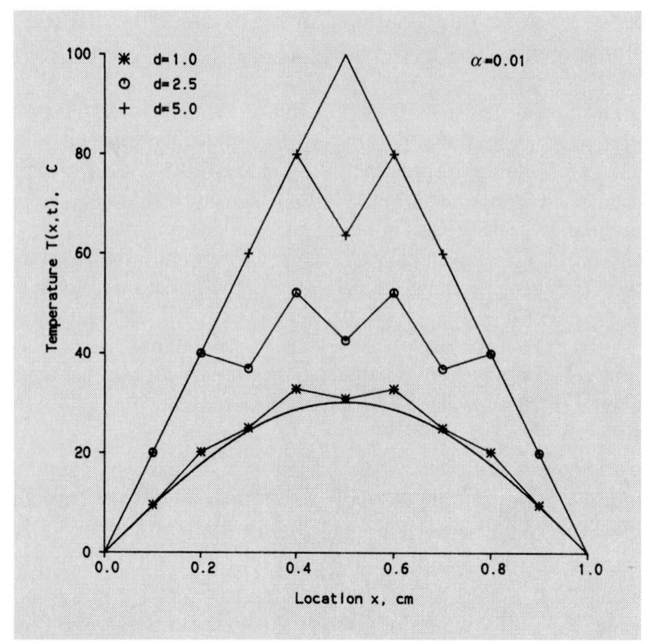

FIGURE 11.11
Solution at $t = 10.0$ s by the DuFort–Frankel method.

be obtained. On the other hand, implicit finite difference methods have an infinite numerical signal propagation speed, which eliminates the problem illustrated in Fig. 11.11.

The explicit DuFort–Frankel method can be applied in a straightforward manner to solve nonlinear PDEs, systems of PDEs, and multidimensional problems, as discussed at the end of Section 11.3 for the FTCS method. Further discussion is presented in Section 11.8.

In summary, the DuFort–Frankel approximation of the diffusion equation is explicit, three-level, single-step, $O(\Delta t^2) + O(\Delta x^2) + O(\Delta t^2/\Delta x^2)$, and unconditionally stable. A starting procedure is required for the first time step. For large values of the diffusion number d, it yields unsatisfactory results because of the small numerical signal propagation speed.

11.5 THE BACKWARD-TIME CENTERED-SPACE METHOD

The forward-time centered-space method is an example of an explicit finite difference method, in which the finite difference approximations of the individual exact partial derivatives in the partial differential equation are evaluated at the known time level n, so that the solution at a point at the solution time level, $n + 1$, can be expressed explicitly in terms of the known solution at time level n. Explicit finite difference methods have many desirable features. However, they share one undesirable feature: they are only conditionally stable, or, as in the case of the DuFort–Frankel method, they are not consistent with the partial differential equation. Consequently, the allowable time step is generally quite small, and the amount of computational effort required to obtain the solution to some problems is prohibitive. Some procedure for avoiding the time step limitation is obviously desirable.

Implicit finite difference methods furnish such a procedure. In implicit methods, the finite difference approximations of the individual exact partial derivatives in the partial differential equation are evaluated at the solution time level, $n + 1$. Fortuitously, implicit finite difference methods are unconditionally stable. There is no limit on the allowable time step required to achieve a numerically stable solution. There is, of course, some practical limit on the time step required to maintain the truncation errors within reasonable limits, but this is not a stability consideration—it is an accuracy consideration.

Implicit methods do have some disadvantages, however. The foremost disadvantage is that the solution at a point at the solution time level depends on the solution at neighboring points at the solution time level, which are also unknown. Consequently, the solution is implied in terms of other unknown solutions, and a system of equations must be solved to obtain the solution at each time level. Additional complexities arise when the partial differential equations are nonlinear. This gives rise to nonlinear finite difference equations, which must be solved by some manner of linearization, iteration, or both.

In spite of their disadvantages, the advantage of unconditional stability makes implicit finite difference methods attractive. Consequently, two implicit finite difference methods are presented in this chapter. The backward-time centered-space (BTCS) method is presented in this section, and the Crank–Nicolson (1947) method is presented in Section 11.6.

In this section the unsteady one-dimensional diffusion equation $\bar{f}_t = \alpha \bar{f}_{xx}$ is solved by the backward-time centered-space (BTCS) method. This method is also called the fully implicit method. The finite difference equation that approximates the partial differential equation is obtained by replacing the exact partial derivative $\bar{f}_t$ by the first-order backward-difference approximation [Eq. (10.57)] and the exact partial derivative $\bar{f}_{xx}$ by the second-order centered-difference approximation [Eq. (10.70b)]. The finite difference stencil is illustrated in Fig. 11.12. Thus,

$$\frac{f_i^{n+1} - f_i^n}{\Delta t} = \alpha \frac{f_{i+1}^{n+1} - 2f_i^{n+1} + f_{i-1}^{n+1}}{\Delta x^2} \tag{11.25}$$

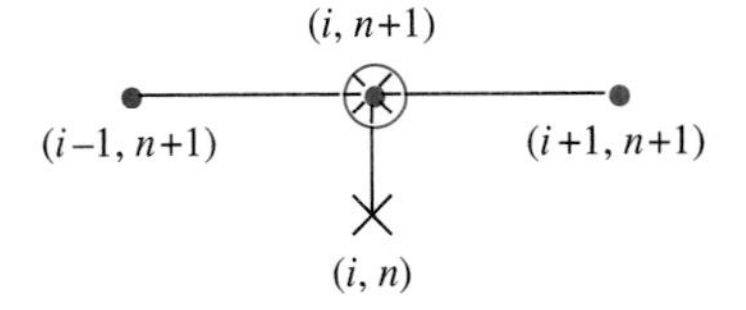

FIGURE 11.12
BTCS method stencil.

Rearranging Eq. (11.25) yields

$$\boxed{-d f_{i-1}^{n+1} + (1+2d) f_i^{n+1} - d f_{i+1}^{n+1} = f_i^n} \tag{11.26}$$

where $d = \alpha\, \Delta t / \Delta x^2$ is the diffusion number.

Equation (11.26) cannot be solved explicitly for f_i^{n+1}, because the two unknown neighboring values, f_{i-1}^{n+1} and f_{i+1}^{n+1}, also appear in the equation. The value of f_i^{n+1} is implied in Eq. (11.26), however. Finite difference equations in which the unknown value f_i^{n+1} is implied in terms of its unknown neighbors rather than being explicitly given in terms of known initial values are implicit FDEs.

The first form of the modified differential equation (MDE) is

$$f_t = \alpha f_{xx} + \frac{1}{2} f_{tt}\, \Delta t - \frac{1}{6} f_{ttt}\, \Delta t^2 + \cdots$$
$$+ \frac{1}{12} \alpha f_{xxxx}\, \Delta x^2 + \frac{1}{360} \alpha f_{xxxxxx}\, \Delta x^4 + \cdots \tag{11.27}$$

and the second form of the MDE is

$$f_t = \alpha f_{xx} + \left(\frac{1}{2} \alpha^2\, \Delta t + \frac{1}{12} \alpha\, \Delta x^2 \right) f_{xxxx}$$
$$+ \left(\frac{1}{3} \alpha^3\, \Delta t^2 + \frac{1}{12} \alpha^2\, \Delta t\, \Delta x^2 + \frac{1}{360} \alpha\, \Delta x^4 \right) f_{xxxxxx} + \cdots \tag{11.28}$$

As $\Delta t \to 0$ and $\Delta x \to 0$, all the truncation error terms go to zero, and Eq. (11.27) approaches $f_t = \alpha f_{xx}$. Consequently, Eq. (11.26) is consistent with the diffusion equation. From Eq. (11.28), the FDE is $O(\Delta t) + O(\Delta x^2)$. Implicit numerical diffusion is indicated by the even-order spatial derivatives in Eq. (11.28), but the absence of odd-order spatial derivatives indicates that there is no implicit numerical dispersion. The amplification factor G is

$$G = \frac{1}{1 + 2d(1 - \cos\theta)} \tag{11.29}$$

The term $(1 - \cos\theta)$ is greater than or equal to zero for all values of $\theta = k\,\Delta x$. Consequently, $|G| \le 1$ for all positive values of d, and Eq. (11.26) is unconditionally stable. The BTCS approximation of the diffusion equation is consistent and unconditionally stable. Consequently, by the Lax equivalence theorem, the method is convergent.

Consider now the solution of the unsteady one-dimensional diffusion equation by the BTCS method. The finite difference grid for advancing the solution from time level n to time level $n+1$ is illustrated in Fig. 11.13. For Dirichlet boundary conditions (i.e., the value of the function is specified at the boundaries), the finite difference equation must be applied only at the interior points, points 2

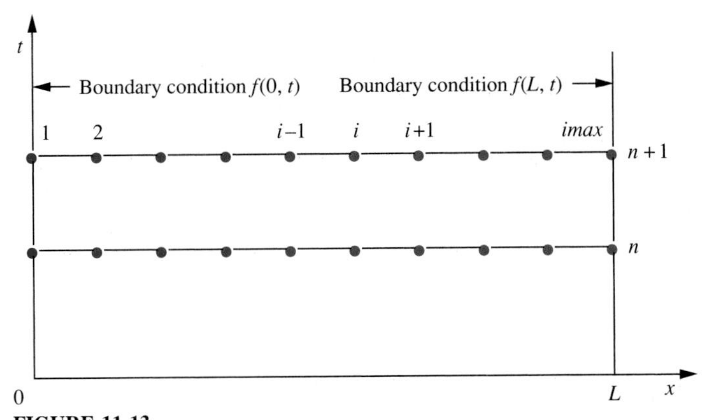

FIGURE 11.13
Finite difference grid for implicit methods.

to $imax - 1$. Equation (11.26) applies directly at points 3 to $imax - 2$. At points 2 and $imax - 1$, Eq. (11.26) is modified by transferring the known values $\bar{f}(0, t)$ and $\bar{f}(L, t)$, respectively, to the right-hand side of the equation. The following set of simultaneous linear equations is obtained:

$$\begin{aligned}
(1 + 2d)f_2^{n+1} - df_3^{n+1} &= b_2 \\
-df_2^{n+1} + (1 + 2d)f_3^{n+1} - df_4^{n+1} &= b_3 \\
-df_3^{n+1} + (1 + 2d)f_4^{n+1} - df_5^{n+1} &= b_4 \\
&\vdots \\
-df_{imax-2}^{n+1} + (1 + 2d)f_{imax-1}^{n+1} &= b_{imax-1}
\end{aligned} \tag{11.30}$$

where the nonhomogeneous terms b_i are given by

$$\begin{aligned}
b_2 &= f_2^n + d\bar{f}(0, t^{n+1}) \\
b_3 &= f_3^n \\
b_4 &= f_4^n \\
&\vdots \\
b_{imax-1} &= f_{imax-1}^n + d\bar{f}(L, t^{n+1})
\end{aligned} \tag{11.31}$$

Equation (11.30) comprises a tridiagonal system of linear equations. That system of equations may be written as

$$\mathbf{A}\mathbf{f}^{n+1} = \mathbf{b} \tag{11.32}$$

where $\mathbf{A}$ is the $(imax - 2) \times (imax - 2)$ coefficient matrix, $\mathbf{f}^{n+1}$ is the $(imax - 2) \times 1$ solution column vector, and $\mathbf{b}$ is the $(imax - 2) \times 1$ column vector of nonhomogeneous terms. Equation (11.32) can be solved very efficiently by the Thomas algorithm presented in Section 1.5. Since the coefficient matrix $\mathbf{A}$ does not change from one time level to the next, **LU** decomposition can be employed with the Thomas algorithm to reduce the computational effort even further.

The FTCS method and the BTCS method are both first-order in time and second-order in space. So what advantage, if any, does the BTCS method have over the FTCS method? The BTCS method is unconditionally stable. The time step can be much larger than the time step for the FTCS method. Consequently, the solution at a given time level can be reached with much less computational effort by taking time steps much larger than those allowed for the FTCS method. In fact, the time step is limited only by accuracy requirements.

Example 11.3. Solution by the BTCS method. We will solve the heat conduction problem, described in Section 11.1, by the BTCS method with $\Delta x = 0.1$ cm. As the first example, let $\Delta t = 0.5$ s, so $d = 0.5$. The results at selected time levels are presented in Fig. 11.14. It is obvious that the numerical solution is a good approximation of the exact solution. The general features of the numerical solution presented in Fig. 11.14 are qualitatively similar to the numerical solution obtained by the FTCS method for $\Delta t = 0.5$ s and $d = 0.5$, which is presented in Fig. 11.6. Although the results obtained by the BTCS method are smoother, there is no major difference. Consequently, there is no significant advantage to the BTCS method for $d = 0.5$.

The numerical solution at $t = 10.0$ s, obtained with $\Delta t = 1.0$, 2.5, 5.0, and 10.0 s, for which $d = 1.0$, 2.5, 5.0, and 10.0, respectively, is presented in Fig. 11.15. These results clearly demonstrate the unconditional stability of the BTCS method. However, the numerical solution lags the exact solution seriously for the larger values of d. The advantage of the BTCS method over explicit methods is now apparent. If the

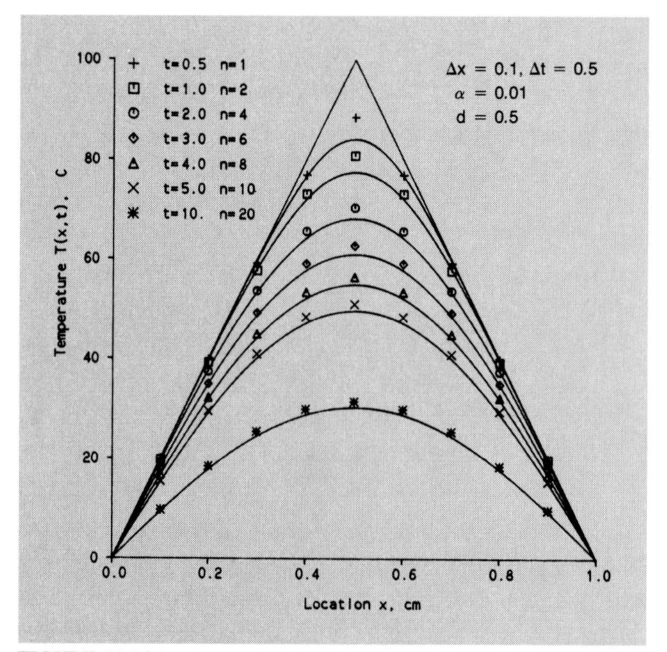

FIGURE 11.14
Solution by the BTCS method with $d = 0.5$.

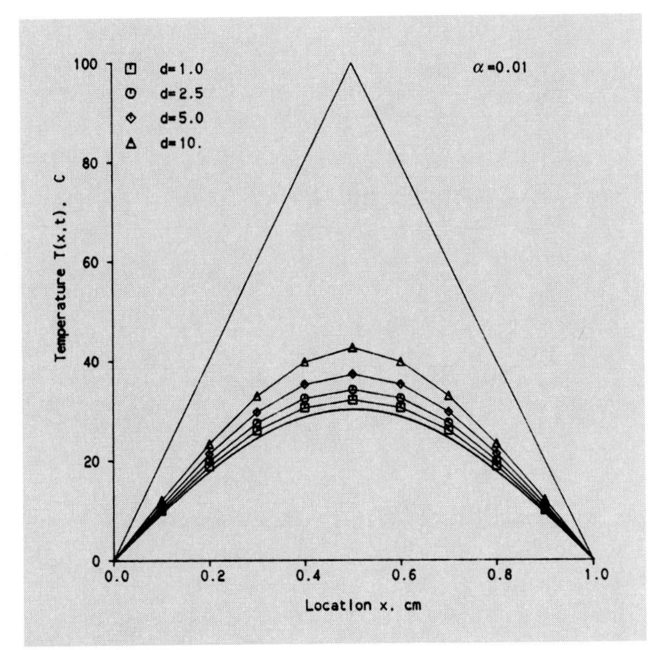

FIGURE 11.15
Solution at $t = 10.0$ s by the BTCS method.

decreased accuracy associated with the larger time steps is acceptable, then the solution can be obtained with less computational effort with the BTCS method than with the FTCS method. However, the results presented in Fig. 11.15 suggest that large values of the diffusion number d lead to serious decreases in the accuracy of the solution.

A matrix method stability analysis of the FTCS approximation of the diffusion equation is presented in Example 10.14 for a finite difference grid with two interior points. The resulting eigenvalues are presented in Fig. 10.18. Performing a similar stability analysis for the BTCS method gives the results presented in Fig. 11.16. These results show that the eigenvalues are always in the range $0 \leq \lambda_i \leq 1$, which demonstrates unconditional stability. The eigenvalues are always positive, so overshoot does not occur. As the diffusion number d increases, the eigenvalues decrease, which causes the numerical solution to lag the exact solution.

The final results presented for the BTCS method are those of a parametric study in which the value of $T(0.4, 5.0)$ is calculated using values of $\Delta x = 0.1$, 0.05, 0.025, and 0.0125 cm, for values of $d = 0.5$, 1.0, 2.0, and 5.0. The value of Δt for each solution is determined by the specified values of Δx and d. The exact solution is $\overline{T}(0.4, 5.0) = 47.12550$ C. The results are presented in Table 11.6. The truncation error of the BTCS method is $O(\Delta t) + O(\Delta x^2)$. For a constant value of d, $\Delta t = d\,\Delta x^2/\alpha$. Thus, as Δx is successively halved, Δt is quartered. Consequently, both the $O(\Delta t)$ term and the $O(\Delta x^2)$ term should decrease by a

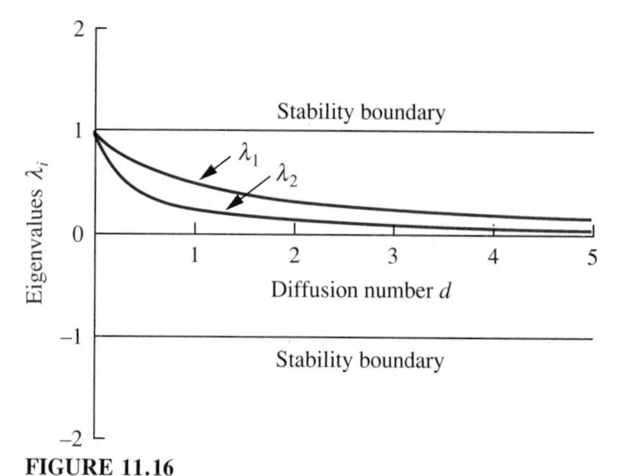

FIGURE 11.16
Eigenvalues of the BTCS approximation of the diffusion equation.

factor of approximately four as Δx is halved for a constant value of d. This result is clearly evident from the results presented in Table 11.6.

The backward-time centered-space (BTCS) method has an infinite numerical signal propagation speed. Numerically, information propagates throughout the entire physical space during each time step. The diffusion equation has an infinite physical propagation speed. Consequently, the BTCS method correctly models this feature of the diffusion equation.

When the PDE is nonlinear, the corresponding FDE is nonlinear. Consequently, a system of nonlinear FDEs must be solved. For one-dimensional problems, this situation is the same as described in Section 8.8 for ordinary differential equations, and the solution procedures described there also apply here. When systems of PDEs are considered, a corresponding system of FDEs is obtained at each solution point, and the combined equations at all of the solution points yield block

TABLE 11.6
Parametric Study of $T(0.4, 5.0)$*

	$T(0.4, 5.0)$, C			
Δx, cm	$d = 0.5$	$d = 1.0$	$d = 2.5$	$d = 5.0$
0.1	48.38102	49.00885	50.74168	53.11624
	1.25552	1.88300	3.61618	5.99074
0.05	47.43605	47.59478	48.06648	48.83200
	0.31055	0.46928	0.94098	1.70650
0.025	47.20293	47.24260	47.36143	47.55874
	0.07743	0.11710	0.23593	0.43324
0.0125	47.14484	47.15476	47.18449	47.23402
	0.01934	0.02926	0.05899	0.10852

* Errors are listed below the solution values.

tridiagonal systems of FDEs. A procedure for solving block tridiagonal systems is presented in Section 1.5. For multidimensional physical spaces, banded matrices result. Such problems are frequently solved by alternating-direction implicit (ADI) methods or approximate-factorization implicit (AFI) methods, as described by Peaceman and Rachford (1955) and Douglas (1962). The solution of nonlinear equations and multidimensional problems is discussed in Section 11.8. The solution of a coupled system of several nonlinear multidimensional PDEs by an implicit finite difference method is indeed a formidable task.

In summary, the backward-time centered-space approximation of the diffusion equation is implicit, two-level, single-step, $O(\Delta t)+O(\Delta x^2)$, unconditionally stable, and convergent. Consequently, the time step size is chosen based on accuracy requirements, not stability requirements.

11.6 THE CRANK–NICOLSON METHOD

The backward-time centered-space (BTCS) approximation of the diffusion equation $\bar{f}_t = \alpha \bar{f}_{xx}$ presented in Section 11.5 has a major advantage over explicit methods: it is unconditionally stable. It is an implicit, two-level, single-step method. The finite difference approximation of the spatial derivative is second-order. However, the finite difference approximation of the time derivative is only first-order. Using a second-order finite difference approximation of the time derivative would be an obvious improvement.

Crank and Nicolson (1947) proposed approximating the partial derivative $\bar{f}_t$ at grid point $(i, n + \frac{1}{2})$ by the second-order centered-difference approximation [Eq. (10.59)] and the partial derivative $\bar{f}_{xx}$ by the average value

$$\bar{f}_{xx}|_i^{n+1/2} = \frac{1}{2}(\bar{f}_{xx}|_i^{n+1} + \bar{f}_{xx}|_i^n) \tag{11.33}$$

The order of this approximation is expected to be $O(\Delta t^2)$, but that must be proven from the MDE. The partial derivatives $\bar{f}_{xx}$ at time levels n and $n + 1$ are approximated by the second-order centered-difference approximations [Eq. (10.69b) and (10.70b)]. The finite difference stencil is illustrated in Fig. 11.17. The resulting finite difference approximation of the one-dimensional diffusion equation is

$$\frac{f_i^{n+1} - f_i^n}{\Delta t} = \alpha \frac{1}{2}\left(\frac{f_{i+1}^{n+1} - 2f_i^{n+1} + f_{i-1}^{n+1}}{\Delta x^2} + \frac{f_{i+1}^n - 2f_i^n + f_{i-1}^n}{\Delta x^2}\right) \tag{11.34}$$

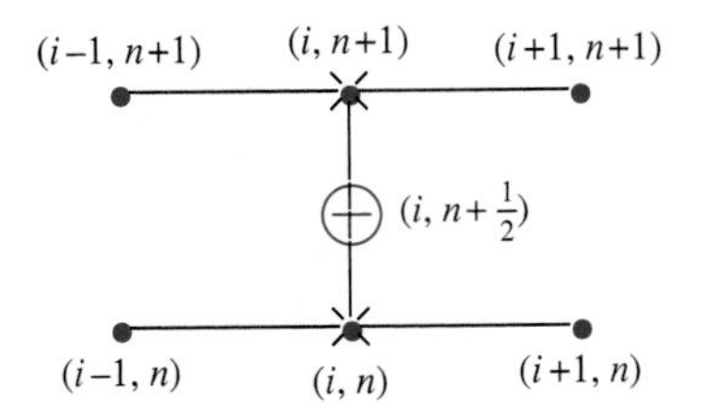

FIGURE 11.17
Crank–Nicolson method stencil.

Rearranging Eq. (11.34) yields the finite difference equation

$$\boxed{-df_{i-1}^{n+1} + 2(1+d)f_i^{n+1} - df_{i+1}^{n+1} = df_{i-1}^n + 2(1-d)f_i^n + df_{i+1}^n} \tag{11.35}$$

where $d = \alpha\,\Delta t/\Delta x^2$ is the diffusion number.

The first form of the modified differential equation (MDE) obtained by writing Taylor series for $f(x,t)$ about point $(i, n+\frac{1}{2})$ is

$$\begin{aligned} f_t = \alpha f_{xx} - \frac{1}{24} f_{ttt}\,\Delta t^2 + \cdots + \frac{1}{8}\alpha\, f_{xxtt}\,\Delta t^2 \\ + \frac{1}{12}\alpha\, f_{xxxx}\,\Delta x^2 + \frac{1}{360}\alpha\, f_{xxxxxx}\,\Delta x^4 + \cdots \end{aligned} \tag{11.36}$$

and the second form of the MDE is

$$f_t = \alpha f_{xx} + \left(\frac{1}{12}\alpha\,\Delta x^2\right) f_{xxxx} + \left(\frac{1}{12}\alpha^3\,\Delta t^2 + \frac{1}{360}\alpha\,\Delta x^4\right) f_{xxxxxx} + \cdots \tag{11.37}$$

As $\Delta t \to 0$ and $\Delta x \to 0$, all the truncation error terms go to zero, and Eq. (11.36) approaches $f_t = \alpha f_{xx}$. Consequently, Eq. (11.35) is consistent with the diffusion equation. From Eq. (11.37), the FDE is $O(\Delta t^2) + O(\Delta x^2)$. From Eq. (11.37), implicit numerical diffusion is present, but implicit numerical dispersion is not. The amplification factor G is

$$G = \frac{1 - d(1 - \cos\theta)}{1 + d(1 - \cos\theta)} \tag{11.38}$$

The term $(1 - \cos\theta) \geq 0$ for all values of $\theta = k\,\Delta x$. Consequently $|G| \leq 1$ for all positive values of d, and Eq. (11.35) is unconditionally stable. The Crank–Nicolson approximation of the diffusion equation is consistent and unconditionally stable. Consequently, by the Lax equivalence theorem, the Crank–Nicolson approximation of the diffusion equation is convergent.

Now consider the solution of the unsteady one-dimensional diffusion equation by the Crank–Nicolson method. The finite difference grid for advancing the solution from time level n to time level $n+1$ is illustrated in Fig. 11.13. For Dirichlet boundary conditions (i.e., the value of the function is specified at the boundaries), the finite difference equation must be applied only at the interior points. Equation (11.35) applies directly at points 3 to $imax - 2$. At points 2 and $imax - 1$, Eq. (11.35) is modified by transferring the known values $\bar{f}(0,t)$ and $\bar{f}(L,t)$ to the right-hand side of the equation. The following set of simultaneous linear equations is obtained:

$$\begin{aligned} 2(1+d)f_2^{n+1} - df_3^{n+1} &= b_2 \\ -df_2^{n+1} + 2(1+d)f_3^{n+1} - df_4^{n+1} &= b_3 \\ -df_3^{n+1} + 2(1+d)f_4^{n+1} - df_5^{n+1} &= b_4 \\ &\vdots \\ -df_{imax-2}^{n+1} + 2(1+d)f_{imax-1}^{n+1} &= b_{imax-1} \end{aligned} \tag{11.39}$$

where the nonhomogeneous terms b_i are given by

$$\begin{aligned}
b_2 &= d\overline{f}(0, t^n) + 2(1-d)f_2^n + df_3^n + d\overline{f}(0, t^{n+1}) \\
b_3 &= df_2^n + 2(1-d)f_3^n + df_4^n \\
b_4 &= df_3^n + 2(1-d)f_4^n + df_5^n \\
&\vdots \\
b_{imax-1} &= df_{imax-2}^n + 2(1-d)f_{imax-1}^n + d\overline{f}(L, t^n) + d\overline{f}(L, t^{n+1})
\end{aligned} \tag{11.40}$$

Equation (11.39) comprises a tridiagonal system of linear equations, which is very similar to the system of equations developed in Section 11.5 for the backward-time centered-space (BTCS) method. Consequently, the present system of equations also can be solved by the Thomas algorithm, as discussed in Section 11.5.

Like the backward-time centered-space (BTCS) method, the Crank–Nicolson method is unconditionally stable. Consequently, the solution at a given time level can be reached with much less computational effort by taking large time steps. The time step is limited only by accuracy requirements.

Example 11.4. Solution by the Crank–Nicolson method. We will solve the heat conduction problem described in Section 11.1 by the Crank–Nicolson method with $\Delta x = 0.1$ cm. Let $\Delta t = 0.5$ s, so $d = 0.5$. The numerical solution is presented in Fig. 11.18. As expected, the results are more accurate than the corresponding results presented in Fig. 11.14 for the BTCS method.

The numerical solution at $t = 10.0$ s, obtained with $\Delta t = 1.0$, 2.5, 5.0, and 10.0 s, for which $d = 1.0$, 2.5, 5.0, and 10.0, respectively, is presented in Fig. 11.19. These

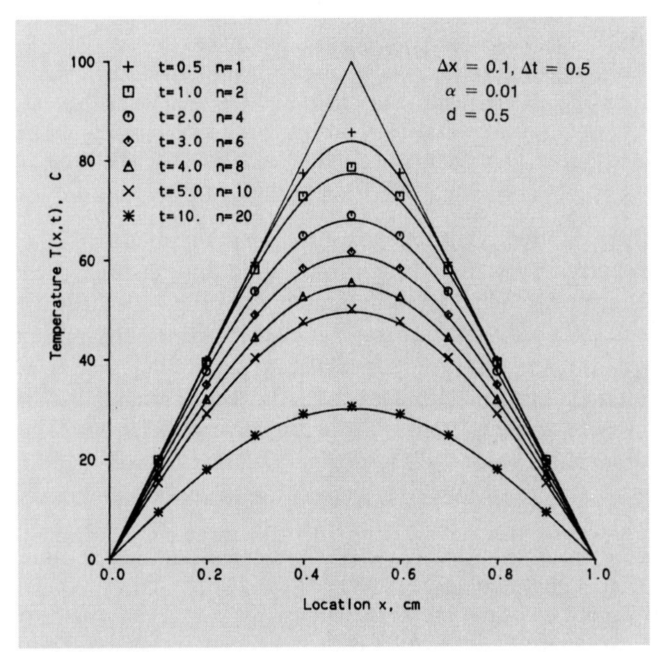

FIGURE 11.18
Solution by the Crank–Nicolson method with $d = 0.5$.

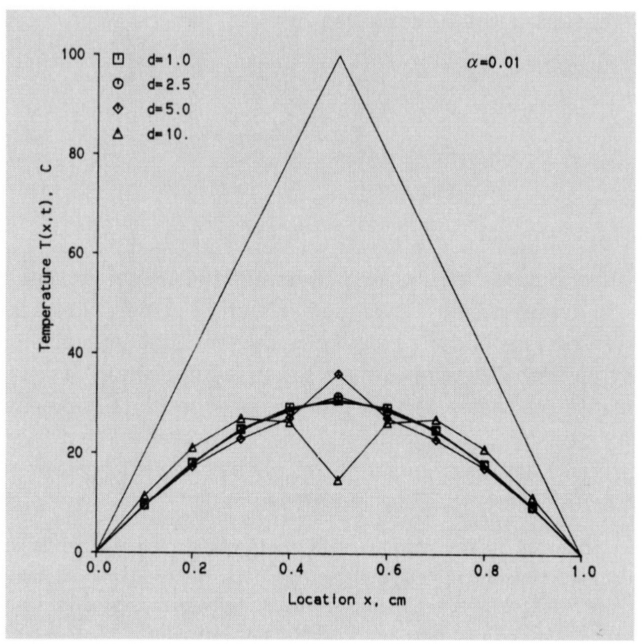

FIGURE 11.19
Solution at $t = 10.0$ s by the Crank–Nicolson method.

results clearly demonstrate the unconditional stability of the Crank–Nicolson method. However, an overshoot and oscillation exists in the numerical solution for all values of d considered in Fig. 11.19. These oscillations are not due to an instability. They are an inherent feature of the Crank–Nicolson method when the diffusion number becomes large. The source of these oscillations can be determined by examining the eigenvalues of the coefficient matrix for the complete system of linear equations, Eq. (11.39). The results presented in Fig. 11.19 suggest that values of the diffusion number d much greater than 1.0 lead to a serious loss of accuracy in the transient solution.

A matrix method stability analysis of the FTCS approximation of the diffusion equation is presented in Example 10.14 for a finite difference grid with two interior points. The resulting eigenvalues are presented in Fig. 10.18. Performing a similar analysis for the Crank–Nicolson method gives the results presented in Fig. 11.20. These results show that the eigenvalues are in the range $-1 \le \lambda_i \le 1$, which demonstrates unconditional stability. As the diffusion number d increases, however, the eigenvalues decrease and eventually become negative. The presence of negative eigenvalues causes the numerical solution to overshoot and oscillate about the exact solution. However, these oscillations are stable, because $-1 \le \lambda_i$.

The final results presented for the Crank–Nicolson method are those of a parametric study in which the value of $T(0.4, 5.0)$ is calculated using values of $\Delta x = 0.1$, 0.05, 0.025, and 0.0125 cm, for values of $d = 0.5$, 1.0, 2.0, and 5.0. The value of Δt for each solution is determined by the specified values of Δx and d. The exact solution is $\overline{T}(0.4, 5, 0) = 47.12550$ C. The results

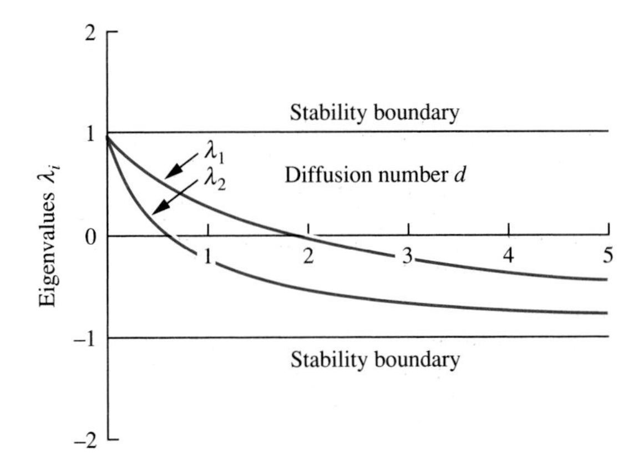

FIGURE 11.20
Eigenvalues of the Crank–Nicolson approximation of the diffusion equation.

are presented in Table 11.7. The truncation error of the Crank–Nicolson method is $O(\Delta t^2)+O(\Delta x^2)$. For a given value of d, $\Delta t = d\,\Delta x^2/\alpha$. Thus, as Δx is successively halved, Δt is quartered. Consequently, the $O(\Delta t^2)$ term should decrease by a factor of approximately 16 and the $O(\Delta x^2)$ term should decrease by a factor of approximately four as Δx is halved for a constant value of d. The results presented in Table 11.7 show that the total error decreases by a factor of approximately four, indicating that the $O(\Delta x^2)$ term is the dominant error term.

The Crank–Nicolson method has an infinite numerical signal propagation speed. Numerically, information propagates throughout the entire physical space during each time step. The diffusion equation has an infinite physical propagation speed. Consequently, the Crank–Nicolson method correctly models this feature of the diffusion equation.

The implicit Crank–Nicolson method can be used to solve nonlinear PDEs, systems of PDEs, and multidimensional PDEs. The techniques and problems are the same as those discussed at the end of Section 11.5 for the BTCS method and in Section 11.8.

TABLE 11.7
Parametric Study of $T(0.4, 5.0)$*

	$T(0.4, 5.0)$, C			
Δx, cm	$d = 0.5$	$d = 1.0$	$d = 2.5$	$d = 5.0$
0.1	47.72690	47.70475	46.15112	47.92356
	0.60140	0.57925	−0.97438	0.79806
0.05	47.27620	47.27443	47.28311	47.01556
	0.15070	0.14893	0.15761	−0.10994
0.025	47.16319	47.16308	47.16232	47.15837
	0.03769	0.03758	0.03682	0.03287
0.0125	47.12492	47.13491	47.13487	47.13470
	0.00942	0.00941	0.00937	0.00920

* Errors are listed below the solution values.

In summary, the Crank–Nicolson approximation of the diffusion equation is implicit, two-level, single-step, $O(\Delta t^2) + O(\Delta x^2)$, unconditionally stable, and convergent. Consequently, the time step size is chosen based on accuracy requirements, not stability requirements.

11.7 DERIVATIVE BOUNDARY CONDITIONS

All the finite difference solutions to the unsteady one-dimensional diffusion equation discussed thus far have been for Dirichlet boundary conditions, that is, the values of the function are specified on the boundaries. In this section, several procedures for implementing derivative, or Neumann, boundary conditions are presented.

The general features of a derivative boundary condition can be illustrated by considering a modification of the heat conduction problem presented in Section 11.1, in which the thickness of the plate is $L = 0.5$ cm and the boundary condition on the right side of the plate is

$$T_x(0.5, t) = 0.0 \tag{11.41}$$

The initial condition, $T(x, 0.0)$, and the boundary condition of the left side, $T(0.0, t)$, are the same as in the original problem. This problem is identical to the original problem, due to the symmetry of the initial condition and the boundary conditions. The exact solution is given by Eq. (11.6), tabulated in Table 11.1, and illustrated in Fig. 11.21. The solution smoothly approaches the asymptotic steady state solution $T(x, \infty) = 0.0$.

In this section, we will solve this problem numerically using the forward-time centered-space (FTCS) method at the interior points, combined with the

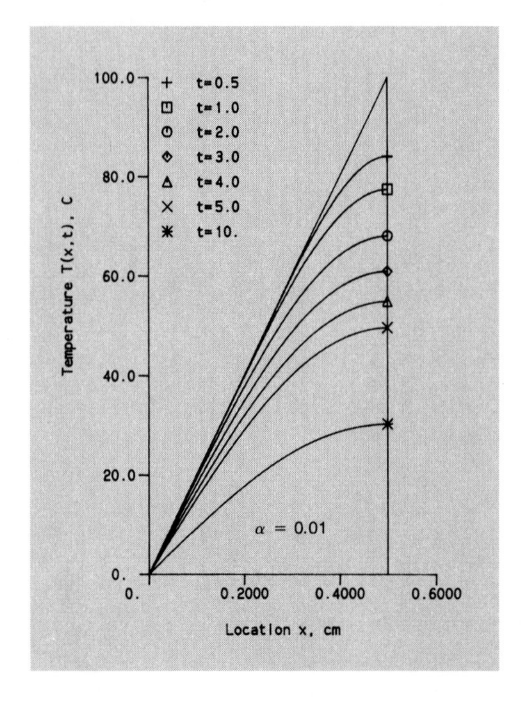

FIGURE 11.21
Exact solution with a derivative BC.

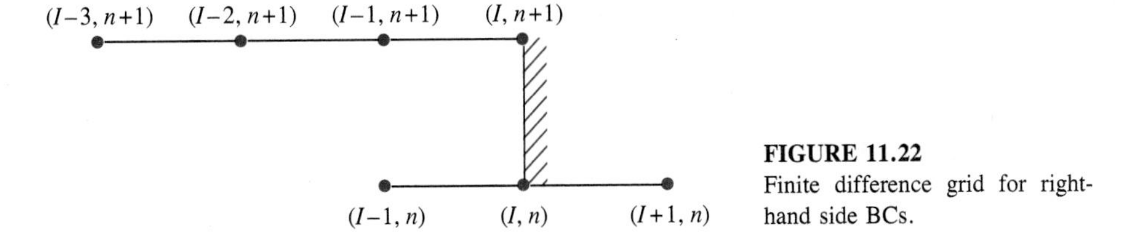

FIGURE 11.22
Finite difference grid for right-hand side BCs.

following two approaches for implementing the derivative boundary condition:

1. Application of the interior point FDE at the boundary point
2. Extrapolation of the interior point solution to the boundary point

In both cases, careful attention will be given to the order of the truncation error of the finite difference approximation to the partial differential equation and to the order of the discretization error of the corresponding finite difference equation.

The implementation of a derivative boundary condition does not depend on whether the problem is an equilibrium problem or a propagation problem, nor does the number of space dimensions alter the procedure. Consequently, the procedures presented in Section 8.6 for implementing a derivative boundary condition for one-dimensional equilibrium problems can be applied directly to one-dimensional propagation problems. Consequently, those results are applied in this section without derivation. The finite difference grid for implementing right-hand side boundary conditions is illustrated in Fig. 11.22.

Interior Point FDE at the Boundary

First, let us apply the FTCS finite difference equation (FDE) at grid point I on the right-hand boundary, as illustrated in Fig. 11.22. The FDE is [see Eq. (11.7)];

$$f_I^{n+1} = f_I^n + d\left(f_{I-1}^n - 2f_I^n + f_{I+1}^n\right) \tag{11.42}$$

Grid point $I+1$ is outside of the solution domain, so f_{I+1}^n is not defined. However, a value for f_{I+1}^n can be determined from the boundary condition on the right-hand boundary, $\bar{f}_x|_I^n$ = known.

The finite difference approximation employed in Eq. (11.42) for the space derivative $\bar{f}_{xx}$ is second-order. It is desirable to match this truncation error by using a second-order finite difference approximation for the derivative boundary condition $\bar{f}_x|_I^n$ = known. Thus, from Eq. (10.64b),

$$\bar{f}_x|_I^n = \frac{\bar{f}_{I+1}^n - \bar{f}_{I-1}^n}{2\Delta x} + O(\Delta x^2) \tag{11.43}$$

Dropping the truncation error and solving Eq. (11.43) for f_{I+1}^n gives

$$f_{I+1}^n = f_{I-1}^n + 2\bar{f}_x|_I^n\,\Delta x \tag{11.44}$$

Substituting this result into Eq. (11.42) yields

$$f_I^{n+1} = f_I^n + d\left(f_{I-1}^n - 2f_I^n + (f_{I-1}^n + 2\bar{f}_x|_I^n\,\Delta x)\right) \tag{11.45}$$

Rearranging Eq. (11.45) gives the FDE applicable at the right-hand boundary:

$$f_I^{n+1} = f_I^n + 2d(f_{I-1}^n - f_I^n + \bar{f}_x|_I^n \Delta x) \tag{11.46}$$

Equation (11.46) must be examined for consistency and stability. Consider the present example, where $\bar{f}_x|_I^n = 0$. The first form of the modified differential equation (MDE) corresponding to Eq. (11.46) is

$$f_t = \alpha f_{xx} - \frac{1}{2} f_{tt} \Delta t - \frac{1}{3} f_{xxx} \Delta x + \frac{1}{12} f_{xxxx} \Delta x^2 + \cdots \tag{11.47}$$

and the second form of the MDE is

$$f_t = \alpha f_{xx} - \frac{1}{3} \Delta x\, f_{xxx} + \left(\frac{1}{12} \Delta x^2 - \frac{1}{2} \alpha^2 \Delta t \right) f_{xxxx} + \cdots \tag{11.48}$$

As $\Delta x \to 0$ and $\Delta t \to 0$, all the truncation error terms go to zero, and Eq. (11.47) approaches $f_t = \alpha f_{xx}$. Consequently, Eq. (11.46) is consistent with the diffusion equation. The FDE is $O(\Delta t) + O(\Delta x)$. Both even and odd spatial derivatives are present in the truncation error, so both implicit numerical diffusion and dispersion are present in the FDE. A matrix method stability analysis yields the stability criterion $d \leq \frac{1}{2}$.

Before applying Eq. (11.46) in a numerical example, let us compare the order of Eq. (11.46), which is $O(\Delta t) + O(\Delta x)$, with the order of the FDE that applies at the interior points, Eq. (11.42). As shown in Section 11.2 [see Eq. (11.9)], Eq. (11.42) is $O(\Delta t) + O(\Delta x^2)$. Thus, Eq. (11.46) is one order lower in Δx than Eq. (11.42). This discrepancy in order arises as a consequence of the manner in which the boundary condition is implemented. Even though the truncation error of the finite difference approximation (FDA) of $\bar{f}_x$ at the boundary is the same order as the truncation error of the FDA of $\bar{f}_{xx}$ in the partial differential equation, when Eq. (11.44) is substituted into Eq. (11.42), the error is one order lower. This mismatch in the orders always occurs when the orders of the partial derivatives being approximated are different (i.e., $\bar{f}_{xx}$ and $\bar{f}_x$ in the present case). This may or may not be acceptable, depending on the problem. For example, if the solution is well-behaved near the boundary and the gradients are small, this mismatch in the orders may not significantly affect the accuracy of the overall solution. This is the case in the present example, because $\bar{f}_x = 0.0$ at the right-hand boundary. In other cases where the solution is less well-behaved near the boundary and the gradients there are large, this mismatch in the orders may cause a significant loss of accuracy.

Example 11.5. Solution with a derivative BC using the PDE. We will work the example problem with $\Delta x = 0.1$ cm and $\Delta t = 0.5$ s, so $d = 0.5$, using Eq. (11.46) at the right-hand boundary. The results are presented in Fig. 11.23*a*. The numerical solution is a good approximation of the exact solution. These results are comparable to the results presented in Fig. 11.6.

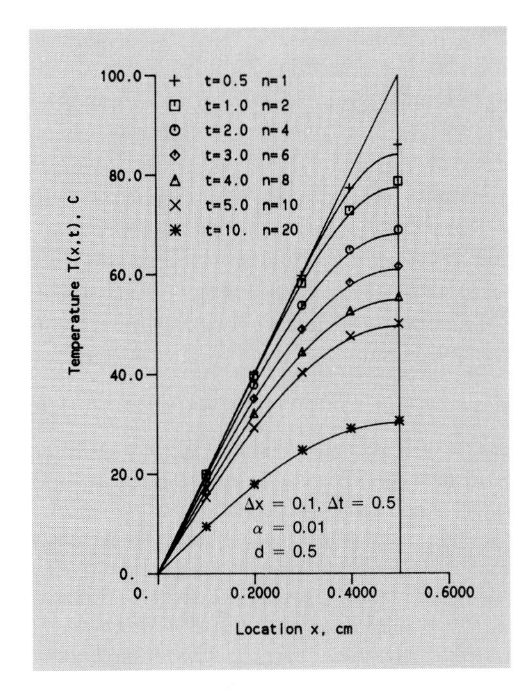

FIGURE 11.23a
Solution with a derivative BC: (*a*) PDE at the boundary.

Extrapolation

Next, let us consider a procedure for implementing a derivative boundary condition by extrapolating the solution at the boundary point from the solution at the adjacent interior points. The finite difference grid is illustrated in Fig. 11.22. The solution is first computed at all of the interior points at time level $n + 1$. A Newton backward-difference interpolating polynomial with base point at location I is then fitted to the data at time level $n+1$, differentiated, and solved for the derivative at the boundary point. The known derivative boundary condition is then substituted into that equation, which is then solved for the function at the boundary point at time level $n + 1$, f_I^{n+1}.

This procedure is presented in Section 8.6 for a one-dimensional equilibrium problem in terms of the variable $y(x)$. The results obtained there apply here directly with y_i replaced by f_i^{n+1}. Recall Eqs. (8.83), (8.85), and (8.87):

$$f_I^{n+1} = f_{I-1}^{n+1} + \Delta x\, \overline{f}_x|_I^{n+1}, \qquad \Delta x\, O(\Delta x) \quad (11.49)$$

$$f_I^{n+1} = \frac{1}{3}(4f_{I-1}^{n+1} - f_{I-2}^{n+1} + 2\Delta x\, \overline{f}_x|_I^{n+1}), \qquad \Delta x\, O(\Delta x^2) \quad (11.50)$$

$$f_I^{n+1} = \frac{1}{11}(18f_{I-1}^{n+1} - 9f_{I-2}^{n+1} + 2f_{I-3}^{n+1} + 6\Delta x\, \overline{f}_x|_I^{n+1}), \qquad \Delta x\, O(\Delta x^3) \quad (11.51)$$

The first form of the modified differential equation corresponding to Eq. (11.49) is

$$f_t = \alpha f_{xx} + \frac{3}{2}\alpha f_{xx} - \frac{1}{2}f_{tt}\,\Delta t + \cdots \quad (11.52)$$

The term $(3\alpha/2)\overline{f}_{xx}$ does not go to zero as $\Delta t \to 0$ and $\Delta x \to 0$. Consequently, Eq. (11.49) is not consistent with the diffusion equation. In fact, Eq. (11.49) models the diffusion equation with 150 percent additional diffusion. Conducting a consistency analysis of Eq. (11.50) shows that it is consistent with the diffusion equation and $O(\Delta t) + O(\Delta x)$. The order of Eq. (11.50) is one order lower in Δx than the order of Eq. (11.42). This same discrepancy in orders occurred with Eq. (11.46). As discussed for that equation, this may or may not be acceptable, depending on the problem being solved. Performing a matrix method stability analysis shows that Eq. (11.50) is stable if $d \leq \frac{1}{2}$. Conducting a consistency analysis of Eq. (11.51) shows that it is consistent with the diffusion equation and $O(\Delta t) + O(\Delta x^2)$. Performing a matrix method stability analysis shows that Eq. (11.51) is stable if $d \leq \frac{1}{2}$.

Example 11.6. Solution with a derivative BC by extrapolation. We will work the example problem using the extrapolation method. The results are presented in Figs. 11.23*b* to 11.23*d*. For linear extrapolation, Fig. 11.23*b* shows that, although the solution is not completely unrealistic, the solution is not a good approximation of the exact solution. This is not surprising, since Eq. (11.49) is not consistent with the diffusion equation. For quadratic extrapolation, Fig. 11.23*c* shows that the results are not quite as good as the results presented in Fig. 11.23*a* obtained by using the PDE at the boundary, but they are considerably better than the results presented in Fig. 11.23*b* for the linearly extrapolated boundary condition. The results presented in Fig. 11.23*d* for cubic extrapolation are somewhat better than the results obtained with quadratic extrapolation and comparable to the results presented in Fig. 11.23*a*.

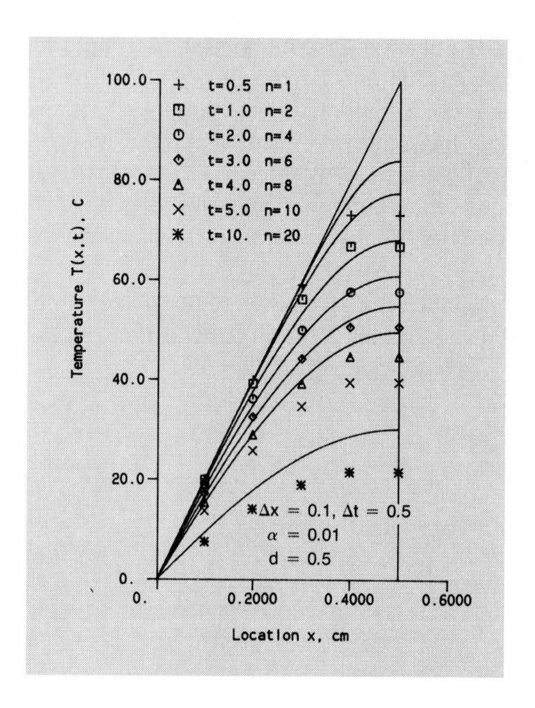

FIGURE 11.23*b*
Solution with a derivative BC: (*b*) Linear extrapolation.

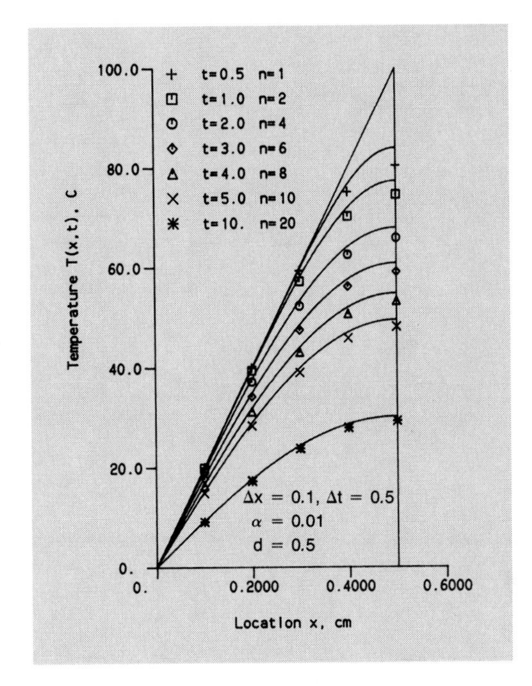

FIGURE 11.23*c*
Solution with a derivative BC: (*c*) Quadratic extrapolation.

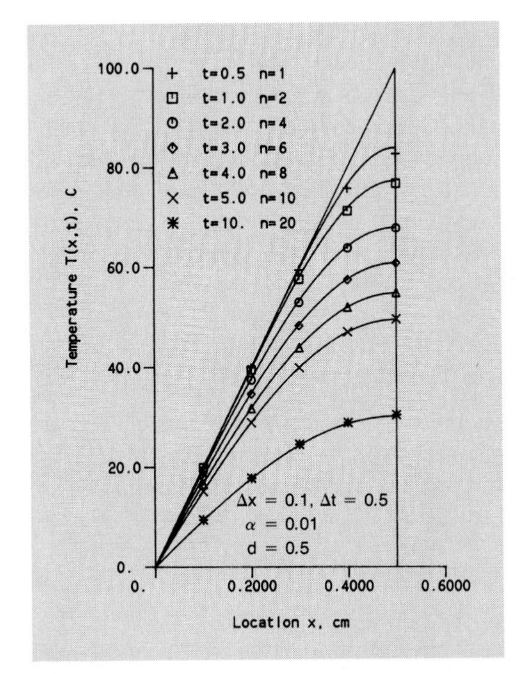

FIGURE 11.23*d*
Solution with a derivative BC: (*d*) Cubic extrapolation.

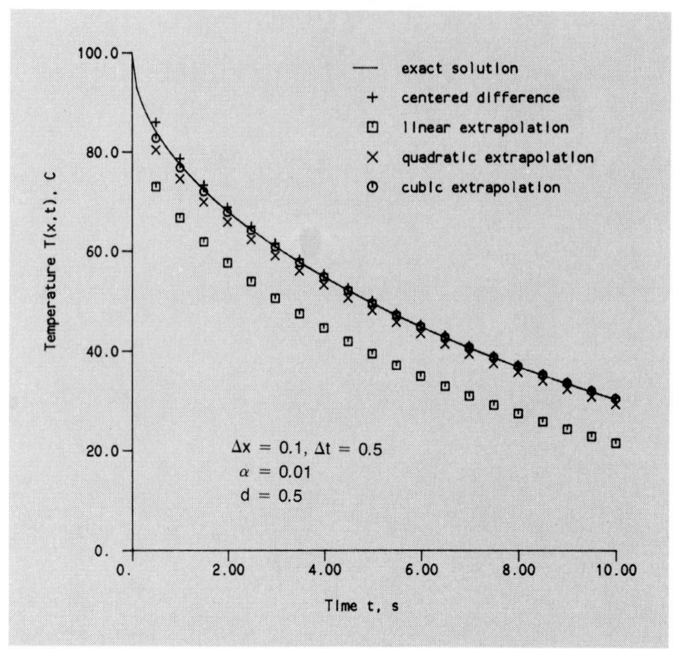

FIGURE 11.24
Solution at the right-hand side.

As a final illustration of the methods presented in this section, Fig. 11.24 presents the solution at the right-hand boundary as a function of time for the exact solution and the numerical solution obtained with the four boundary condition methods applied at the right-hand boundary. The solutions with the centered difference approximation and the cubic extrapolation are both quite good. The solution with quadratic extrapolation is reasonably good, although somewhat less accurate than the other two solutions. The solution with linear extrapolation, while following the general trends, is unacceptable.

11.8 NONLINEAR EQUATIONS AND MULTIDIMENSIONAL PROBLEMS

All the finite difference equations and examples presented so far in this chapter are for the linear one-dimensional diffusion equation. Some of the problems that arise for nonlinear partial differential equations and for multidimensional problems are discussed in this section.

Nonlinear PDEs

Consider the nonlinear one-dimensional convection–diffusion equation:

$$\boxed{\bar{f}_t + u(\bar{f})\bar{f}_x = \alpha(\bar{f})\bar{f}_{xx}} \tag{11.53}$$

where the convection velocity u and the diffusion coefficient α depend on $\bar{f}$. The FTCS approximation of Eq. (11.53) is

$$\frac{f_i^{n+1} - f_i^n}{\Delta t} + u_i^n \frac{f_{i+1}^n - f_{i-1}^n}{2\Delta x} = \alpha_i^n \frac{f_{i+1}^n - 2f_i^n + f_{i-1}^n}{\Delta x^2} \tag{11.54}$$

The nonlinear coefficients are simply evaluated at the base point (i, n) where f_i^n, and hence u_i^n and α_i^n, are known. The FDE is linear and explicit, so the nonlinear coefficients cause no numerical complications. The solution f_i^{n+1} can be determined directly from Eq. (11.54). This type of result is typical of all explicit finite difference approximations.

The BTCS approximation of Eq. (11.53) is

$$\frac{f_i^{n+1} - f_i^n}{\Delta t} + u_i^{n+1} \frac{f_{i+1}^{n+1} - f_{i-1}^{n+1}}{2\Delta x} = \alpha_i^{n+1} \frac{f_{i+1}^{n+1} - 2f_i^{n+1} + f_{i-1}^{n+1}}{\Delta x^2} \tag{11.55}$$

The nonlinear coefficients present a serious numerical problem. The coefficients u_i^{n+1} and α_i^{n+1} depend on f_i^{n+1}, which is unknown. Equation (11.55), when applied at every point in the finite difference grid, yields a coupled system of nonlinear finite difference equations. The nonlinear system of FDEs can be solved by simply lagging the nonlinear coefficients (i.e., letting $u_i^{n+1} = u_i^n$ and $\alpha_i^{n+1} = \alpha_i^n$), by iteration, by Newton's method, or by time linearization. Iteration and Newton's method are discussed in Section 8.8 for nonlinear one-dimensional boundary-value problems. Time linearization is presented in Section 7.11 for nonlinear one-dimensional initial-value problems. The Taylor series for $\bar{f}_i^{n+1}$ with base point (i, n) is

$$\bar{f}_i^{n+1} = \bar{f}_i^n + \bar{f}_t|_i^n \Delta t + O(\Delta t^2) \tag{11.56}$$

The derivative $\bar{f}_t|_i^n$ is obtained from the PDE, which is evaluated at grid point (i, n) using the same spatial finite difference approximations used to derive the implicit FDE. Values of u_i^{n+1} and α_i^{n+1} can be evaluated for the value of f_i^{n+1} obtained from Eq. (11.56). Time linearization requires a considerable amount of additional work. It also introduces additional truncation errors that depend on Δt, which reduces the accuracy and generally restricts the time step, thus reducing the advantage of unconditional stability associated with implicit finite difference equations.

Multidimensional Problems

Consider the two-dimensional diffusion equation:

$$\boxed{\bar{f}_t = \alpha(\bar{f}_{xx} + \bar{f}_{yy})} \tag{11.57}$$

The FTCS approximation of Eq. (11.57) is

$$\frac{f_{i,j}^{n+1} - f_{i,j}^{n}}{\Delta t} = \alpha \left(\frac{f_{i+1,j}^{n} - 2f_{i,j}^{n} + f_{i-1,j}^{n}}{\Delta x^2} + \frac{f_{i,j+1}^{n} - 2f_{i,j}^{n} + f_{i,j-1}^{n}}{\Delta y^2} \right) \tag{11.58}$$

Equation (11.58) can be solved directly to yield $f_{i,j}^{n+1}$. No additional numerical complications arise because of the second spatial derivative. For the three-dimensional diffusion equation, the additional derivative $\overline{f}_{zz}$ is present in the PDE. Its finite difference approximation is simply added to Eq. (11.58) without further complications. This type of result is typical of all explicit finite difference approximations.

The BTCS approximation of Eq. (11.57) is

$$\frac{f_{i,j}^{n+1} - f_{i,j}^{n}}{\Delta t} = \alpha \left(\frac{f_{i+1,j}^{n+1} - 2f_{i,j}^{n+1} + f_{i-1,j}^{n+1}}{\Delta x^2} + \frac{f_{i,j+1}^{n+1} - 2f_{i,j}^{n+1} + f_{i,j-1}^{n+1}}{\Delta y^2} \right) \tag{11.59}$$

Applying Eq. (11.59) at every point in a two-dimensional finite difference grid yields a banded pentadiagonal matrix, which requires a large amount of computational effort. Successive overrelaxation (SOR) methods can be applied for two-dimensional problems, but even that approach becomes almost prohibitive for three-dimensional problems. Alternating-direction implicit (ADI) methods [Peaceman and Rachford (1955) and Douglas (1962)] and approximate-factorization implicit (AFI) methods can be used to reduce the banded matrices to two (or three for three-dimensional problems) systems of tridiagonal matrices, which can be solved successively by the Thomas algorithm (see Section 1.5).

Another problem that arises in multidimensional problems is that the boundaries of the physical domain $D(x, y)$ or $D(x, y, z)$ do not fall on the coordinate lines of a Cartesian coordinate system. In that case, the physical space must be transformed to a body-fitted uniform orthogonal computational space $D(\xi, \eta)$ or $D(\xi, \eta, \phi)$ in which the boundaries of the physical space fall on the boundaries of the computational space. This process is discussed in Chapter 13.

ALTERNATING-DIRECTION IMPLICIT (ADI) METHOD. The alternating-direction implicit (ADI) approach consists of solving the PDE in two steps. In the first time step, the spatial derivatives in one direction, say y, are evaluated at the known time level n and the other spatial derivatives, say x, are evaluated at the unknown time level $n + 1$. On the next time step, the process is reversed. Consider the two-dimensional diffusion equation, Eq. (11.57). For the first step, the semi-discrete (i.e., time discretization only) finite difference approximation yields

$$\frac{f_{i,j}^{n+1} - f_{i,j}^{n}}{\Delta t} = f_{xx}\big|_{i,j}^{n+1} + f_{yy}\big|_{i,j}^{n} \tag{11.60}$$

For the second step,

$$\frac{f_{i,j}^{n+2} - f_{i,j}^{n+1}}{\Delta t} = f_{xx}\big|_{i,j}^{n+1} + f_{yy}\big|_{i,j}^{n+2} \tag{11.61}$$

If the spatial derivatives in Eqs. (11.60) and (11.61) are replaced by three-point second-order centered-difference approximations, Eqs. (11.60) and (11.61) both yield a tridiagonal system of FDEs, which can be solved by the Thomas algorithm (see Section 1.5). Ferziger (1981) shows that the alternating-direction implicit method is consistent, $O(\Delta t^2) + O(\Delta x^2) + O(\Delta y^2)$, and unconditionally stable.

Alternating-direction implicit procedures can also be applied to three-dimensional problems, in which case a third permutation of Eqs. (11.60) and (11.61) involving the z-direction derivatives is required. A direct extension of the procedure presented above does not work. A modification that does work in three dimensions is presented by Douglas (1962) and Douglas and Gunn (1964).

The ADI method must be treated carefully at the $n + 1$ time step at the boundaries. No problem arises for constant BCs. However, for time-dependent BCs, Eq. (11.60), which is $O(\Delta t)$, yields less accurate solutions than Eq. (11.61), which is $O(\Delta t^2)$. When accurate BCs are specified, the errors in the solution at the boundaries at time steps $n + 1$ and $n + 2$ are of different order, which introduces additional errors into the solution. Ferziger (1981) discusses techniques for minimizing this problem.

APPROXIMATE-FACTORIZATION IMPLICIT (AFI) METHOD. The approximate-factorization implicit (AFI) approach can be illustrated for the BTCS approximation of the two-dimensional diffusion equation, Eq. (11.57), by expressing it in the semi-discrete form

$$\frac{f_i^{n+1} - f_i^n}{\Delta t} = \alpha\left(\frac{\partial^2}{\partial x^2} + \frac{\partial^2}{\partial y^2}\right) f_{i,j}^{n+1} \tag{11.62}$$

Collecting terms yields the two-dimensional operator

$$\left(1 - \alpha\,\Delta t\left(\frac{\partial^2}{\partial x^2} + \frac{\partial^2}{\partial y^2}\right)\right) f_{i,j}^{n+1} = f_{i,j}^n \tag{11.63}$$

Equation (11.63) can be approximated by the product of two one-dimensional operators:

$$\left(1 - \alpha\,\Delta t\frac{\partial^2}{\partial x^2}\right)\left(1 - \alpha\,\Delta t\frac{\partial^2}{\partial y^2}\right) f_{i,j}^{n+1} = f_{i,j}^n \tag{11.64}$$

Equation (11.64) can be solved in two steps:

$$\left(1 - \alpha\,\Delta t\frac{\partial^2}{\partial y^2}\right) f_{i,j}^{*} = f_{i,j}^n \tag{11.65a}$$

$$\left(1 - \alpha\,\Delta t\frac{\partial^2}{\partial x^2}\right) f_{i,j}^{n+1} = f_{i,j}^{*} \tag{11.65b}$$

If the spatial derivatives in Eqs. (11.65*a*) and (11.65*b*) are replaced by three-point second-order centered-difference approximations, Eqs. (11.65*a*) and (11.65*b*) both yield a tridiagonal system of FDEs, which can be solved by the Thomas algorithm (see Section 1.5).

Multiplying the two operators in Eq. (11.64) yields the single operator

$$\left(1 - \alpha\,\Delta t\left(\frac{\partial^2}{\partial x^2} + \frac{\partial^2}{\partial y^2}\right) + \alpha^2\,\Delta t^2 \frac{\partial^2}{\partial x^2}\frac{\partial^2}{\partial y^2}\right) f_{i,j}^{n+1} = f_{i,j}^{n} \tag{11.66}$$

The $O(\Delta t^2)$ term is not present in the original finite difference equation, Eq. (11.63). Thus, the factorization has introduced a local $O(\Delta t^2)$ error term into the solution. For this reason, this approach is called an *approximate*-factorization implicit method. The local error of the BTCS approximation is $O(\Delta t^2)$, so the approximate factorization preserves the order of the BTCS approximation.

Approximate factorization can be applied to three-dimensional problems, in which case a third one-dimensional operator is added to Eq. (11.64), with a corresponding third step in Eq. (11.65).

SPLITTING METHODS. The alternating-direction implicit method and the approximate-factorization implicit method are examples of a more general class of methods, called *splitting methods*. The idea of splitting methods is to factor a differential operator whose corresponding FDEs are difficult to solve into the product of differential operators whose corresponding FDEs are easier to solve.

To illustrate the similarity of ADI methods and AFI methods, let us approximate the two-dimensional diffusion equation, Eq. (11.57), in two ways: by the conventional Crank–Nicolson approach and by the ADI approach. The ADI approach can be shown to be equivalent to the approximate factorization of the Crank–Nicolson approach.

Consider the semi-discrete Crank–Nicolson approximation of the two-dimensional diffusion equation, Eq. (11.57), for a time step of $2\Delta t$ from time level n to time level $n + 2$:

$$f^{n+2} - f^{n} = \frac{\alpha(2\Delta t)}{2}\Big(\big(f_{xx}|^{n+2} + f_{yy}|^{n+2}\big) + \big(f_{xx}|^{n} + f_{yy}|^{n}\big)\Big) \tag{11.67}$$

Equation (11.67) can be arranged as follows:

$$\left(1 - \alpha\,\Delta t\left(\frac{\partial^2}{\partial x^2} + \frac{\partial^2}{\partial y^2}\right)\right) f^{n+2} = \left(1 + \alpha\,\Delta t\left(\frac{\partial^2}{\partial x^2} + \frac{\partial^2}{\partial y^2}\right)\right) f^{n} \tag{11.68}$$

Next recall the semi-discrete ADI approximations of the two-dimensional diffusion equation, Eqs. (11.60) and (11.61), written in the form

$$\left(1 - \alpha\,\Delta t \frac{\partial^2}{\partial x^2}\right) f^{n+1} = \left(1 + \alpha\,\Delta t \frac{\partial^2}{\partial y^2}\right) f^{n} \tag{11.69}$$

$$\left(1 - \alpha\,\Delta t \frac{\partial^2}{\partial x^2}\right) f^{n+2} = \left(1 + \alpha\,\Delta t \frac{\partial^2}{\partial x^2}\right) f^{n+1} \tag{11.70}$$

Assuming that all these linear operators are commutative, Eq. (11.69) can be solved for f^{n+1}, which can be substituted into Eq. (11.70) to yield the single operator

$$\left(1 - \alpha\,\Delta t\frac{\partial^2}{\partial x^2}\right)\left(1 - \alpha\,\Delta t\frac{\partial^2}{\partial y^2}\right)f^{n+2} = \left(1 + \alpha\,\Delta t\frac{\partial^2}{\partial x^2}\right)\left(1 + \alpha\,\Delta t\frac{\partial^2}{\partial y^2}\right)f^{n} \tag{11.71}$$

Expanding Eq. (11.71) gives

$$\left(1 - \alpha\,\Delta t\left(\frac{\partial^2}{\partial x^2} + \frac{\partial^2}{\partial y^2}\right) + \alpha^2\,\Delta t^2\frac{\partial^2}{\partial x^2}\frac{\partial^2}{\partial y^2}\right)f^{n+2}$$
$$= \left(1 + \alpha\,\Delta t\left(\frac{\partial^2}{\partial x^2} + \frac{\partial^2}{\partial y^2}\right) + \alpha^2\,\Delta t^2\frac{\partial^2}{\partial x^2}\frac{\partial^2}{\partial y^2}\right)f^{n} \tag{11.72}$$

Equation (11.72) is identical to the result obtained by the Crank–Nicolson approximation, Eq. (11.67), except for the term

$$\alpha\,\Delta t^2\left(\frac{\partial^2}{\partial x^2} + \frac{\partial^2}{\partial y^2}\right)(f^{n+2} - f^n) = 2\alpha\,\Delta t^3\left(\frac{\partial^2}{\partial x^2} + \frac{\partial^2}{\partial y^2}\right)\frac{\partial f}{\partial t} \tag{11.73}$$

where $\partial f/\partial t \approx (f^{n+2} - f^n)/2\Delta t$. Equation (11.73) is $O(\Delta t^3)$, which is consistent with the local truncation error of the Crank–Nicolson method. Consequently, the ADI splitting specified by Eqs. (11.60) and (11.61) is comparable to the Crank–Nicolson approximation, but tridiagonal matrices must be solved rather than banded pentadiagonal matrices. A considerable reduction in computational effort is achieved. An even more significant reduction is obtained for three-dimensional problems.

Equation (11.71) can be related to the AFI method by writing it as a two-step method:

$$\left(1 - \alpha\,\Delta t\frac{\partial^2}{\partial y^2}\right)f^{*} = \left(1 + \alpha\,\Delta t\left(\frac{\partial^2}{\partial x^2} + \frac{\partial^2}{\partial y^2}\right)\right)f^{n} \tag{11.74}$$

$$\left(1 - \alpha\,\Delta t\frac{\partial^2}{\partial y^2}\right)f^{n+2} = f^{*} \tag{11.75}$$

The results presented in this section illustrate the interrelationships between standard implicit multidimensional FDAs, the ADI method, and the AFI method. Splitting methods such as the ADI and AFI methods yield large savings in computational effort when solving multidimensional problems by implicit methods.

11.9 ASYMPTOTIC STEADY STATE SOLUTIONS

The solution of steady equilibrium problems and mixed elliptic/parabolic or mixed elliptic/hyperbolic problems as the asymptotic solution in time of appropriate unsteady propagation problems is discussed in Section 10.10. An example of that technique is presented in this section, using the unsteady diffusion equation to obtain solutions of the steady diffusion equation.

Consider the steady diffusion equation:

$$\hat{f}_{xx} = 0 \tag{11.76}$$

The solution to Eq. (11.76) is the function $\hat{f}(x)$, which must satisfy two boundary conditions. The appropriate unsteady propagation problem for solving Eq. (11.76) is the unsteady diffusion equation

$$\bar{f}_t = \alpha \bar{f}_{xx} \tag{11.77}$$

The solution to Eq. (11.77) is the function $\bar{f}(x, t)$, which must satisfy an initial condition, $\bar{f}(x, 0.0) = F(x)$, and two boundary conditions. If the boundary conditions for $\bar{f}(x, t)$ are the same as the boundary conditions for $\hat{f}(x)$, then

$$\hat{f}(x) = \lim_{t \to \infty} \bar{f}(x, t) = \bar{f}(x, \infty) \tag{11.78}$$

As long as the solution converges, the particular choice for the initial condition should not affect the steady state solution.

The following problem is considered in this section to illustrate the solution of steady equilibrium problems as the asymptotic solution of unsteady propagation problems. A porous plate of thickness $L = 1.0$ cm is cooled by a fluid flowing through the porous material, as illustrated in Fig. 11.25. This problem is governed by the steady convection–diffusion equation:

$$u\hat{f}_x = \alpha \hat{f}_{xx} \tag{11.79}$$

where u is the convection velocity (cm/s) and α is the thermal diffusivity (cm^2/s). The temperature on the two faces of the plate are $\hat{T}(0.0) = 0$ C and $\hat{T}(1.0) = 100$ C. The exact solution to this problem is

$$\hat{T}(x) = 100\frac{e^{(Px/L)} - 1}{e^P - 1} \tag{11.80}$$

where $P = (uL/\alpha)$ is the Peclet number. The solution for $P = 10$ is tabulated in Table 11.8 and presented in Fig. 11.26, corresponding to $t = 0.0$.

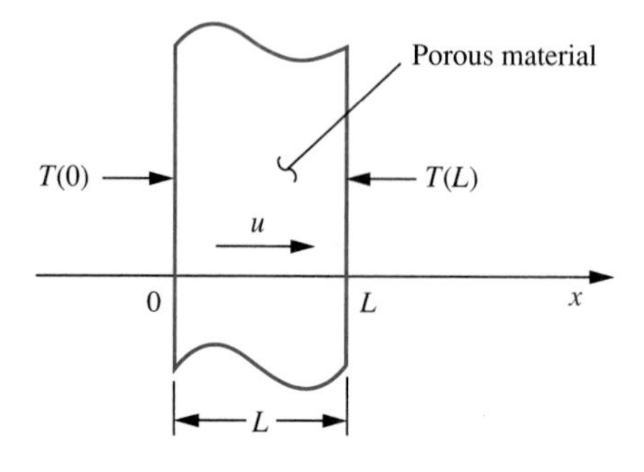

FIGURE 11.25
Heat transfer in a porous plate.

TABLE 11.8
Exact solution of the heat transfer problem

	Temperature $\overline{T}(x, t)$, C							
t, s	$x = 0.0$	$x = 0.2$	$x = 0.4$	$x = 0.6$	$x = 0.7$	$x = 0.8$	$x = 0.9$	$x = 1.0$
0.0	0.00	0.03	0.24	1.83	4.97	13.53	36.79	100.00
0.5	0.00	0.05	0.41	3.02	8.18	21.67	51.86	100.00
1.0	0.00	0.09	0.67	4.89	12.56	29.42	59.40	100.00
1.5	0.00	0.14	1.09	7.33	17.08	35.47	64.09	100.00
2.0	0.00	0.24	1.72	10.03	21.26	40.22	67.39	100.00
2.5	0.00	0.89	3.54	12.77	24.98	44.07	69.90	100.00
5.0	0.00	2.09	8.29	24.57	38.32	56.06	77.10	100.00
10.0	0.00	7.72	19.72	39.20	52.11	66.88	83.07	100.00
50.0	0.00	19.76	39.60	59.60	69.66	79.76	89.87	100.00
∞	0.00	20.00	40.00	60.00	70.00	80.00	90.00	100.00

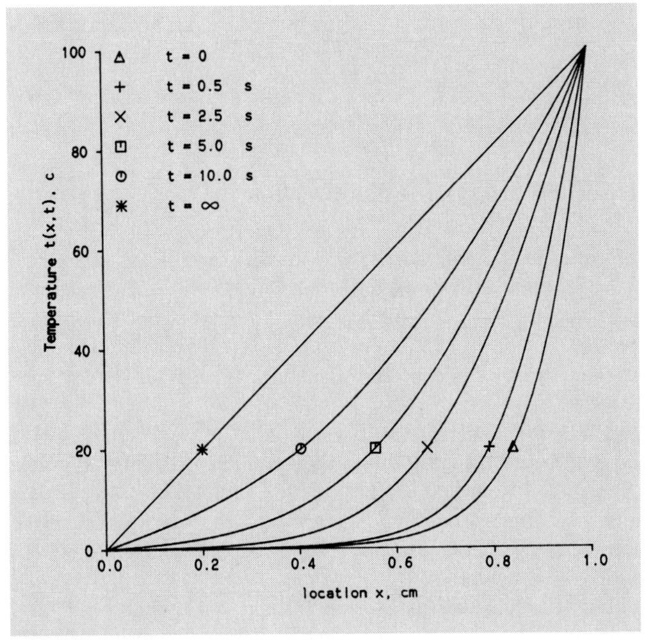

FIGURE 11.26
Exact solution of the heat transfer problem.

At time $t = 0$, the fluid flow is stopped, and the temperature distribution changes, due to pure heat conduction, which is governed by the diffusion equation $\bar{f}_t = \alpha \bar{f}_{xx}$. The exact solution to this problem is

$$\begin{aligned}\bar{T}(x,t) = 100\Bigg(\frac{x}{L} &+ 2\sum_{m=1}^{\infty}(-1)^m \frac{1}{m\pi}\sin\left(\frac{m\pi x}{L}\right)e^{-\lambda_m t} \\ &+ \frac{2}{e^P - 1}\sum_{m=1}^{\infty}\left[\frac{m\pi}{P^2 + (m\pi)^2}\left(1 - (-1)^m e^P\right)\right. \\ &\left. + \frac{1}{m\pi}\left((-1)^m - 1\right)\sin\left(\frac{m\pi x}{L}\right)e^{-\lambda_m t}\right]\Bigg)\end{aligned} \tag{11.81}$$

where $\lambda_m = (m^2\pi^2\alpha/L^2)$. The exact solution at selected values of time for $P = 10$ and $\alpha = 0.01$ cm^2/s is tabulated in Table 11.8 and illustrated in Fig. 11.26. The temperature distribution smoothly approaches the asymptotic steady state solution

$$\bar{T}(x,\infty) = 100\frac{x}{L} \tag{11.82}$$

which is the exact solution of the steady diffusion equation $\hat{T}_{xx} = 0$.

Example 11.7. Asymptotic steady state solutions. We will solve this unsteady heat conduction problem for the asymptotic steady state solution with $\Delta x = 0.1$ cm by several numerical methods. First, consider the FTCS method with $\Delta t = 0.5$ s, for which $d = 0.5$. The results are presented in Fig. 11.27. The agreement between the numerical solution and the exact solution is excellent. The asymptotic steady state solution is obtained after 100 time steps.

Next consider the DuFort–Frankel method, which is an unconditionally stable explicit method, with $\Delta t = 5.0$ s, which is 10 times larger than the maximum allowable time step for the FTCS method. The results are presented in Fig. 11.28. The transient solution is obviously totally incorrect. The solution overshoots, then comes back to the steady state solution. The correct asymptotic steady state solution is attained, however, after approximately 50 time steps.

Next consider the BTCS method, which is unconditionally stable, with $\Delta t = 10.0$ s, for which $d = 10.0$, which is 20 times larger than the maximum allowable time step for the FTCS method. The results are presented in Fig. 11.29. The numerical transient solution lags the exact transient solution rather badly. However, the asymptotic steady state solution is attained after approximately 10 time steps. Figure 11.30 presents the solution by the BTCS method for $\Delta t = 100.0$ s, for which $d = 100.0$. The asymptotic steady state solution is attained in two time steps. The asymptotic steady state solution is attained in one time step for values of $\Delta t \geq 1000.0$ s, for which $d \geq 1000.0$.

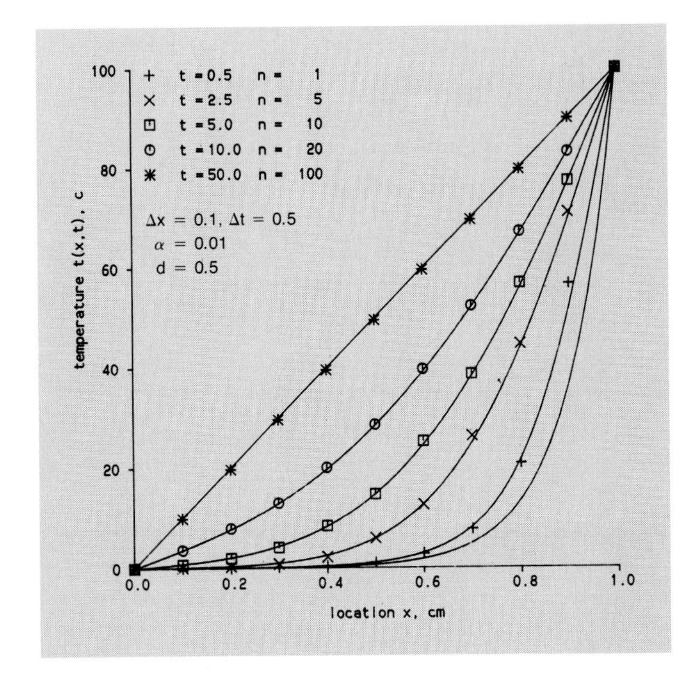

FIGURE 11.27
Solution by the FTCS method with $d = 0.5$.

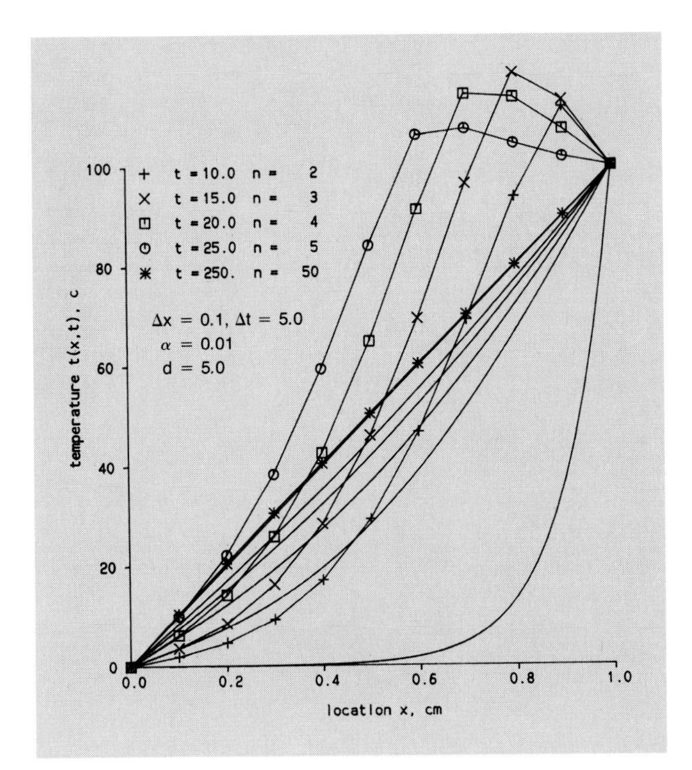

FIGURE 11.28
Solution by the DuFort–Frankel method with $d = 5.0$.

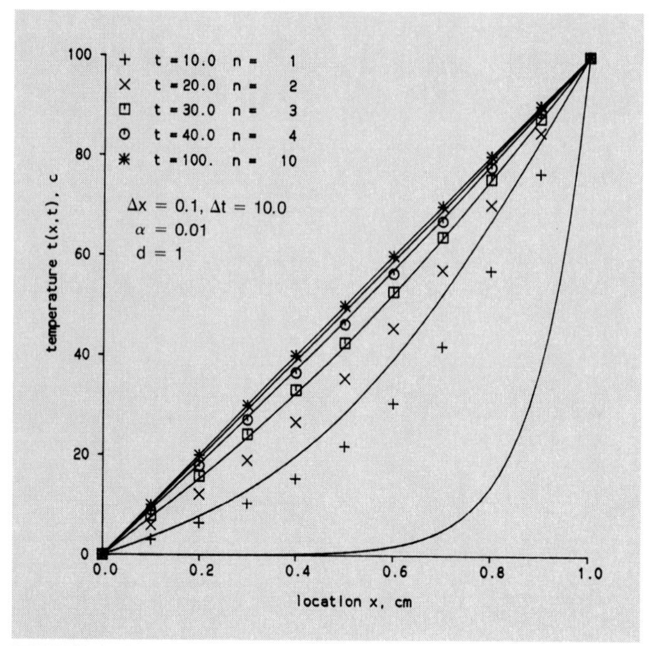

FIGURE 11.29
Solution by the BTCS method with $d = 10.0$.

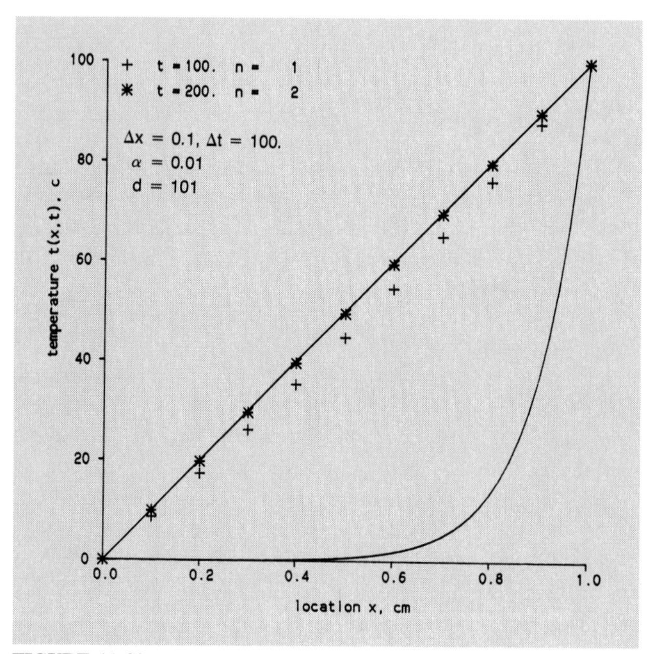

FIGURE 11.30
Solution by the BTCS method with $d = 100.0$.

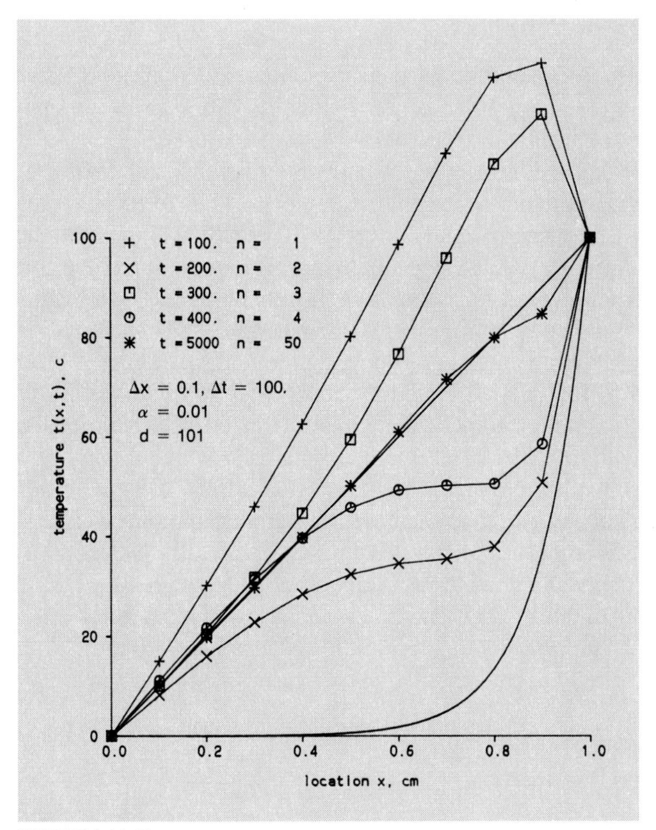

FIGURE 11.31
Solution by the Crank–Nicolson method with $d = 100.0$.

Figure 11.31 presents the solution by the Crank–Nicolson method for $\Delta t = 100.0$ s, for which $d = 100.0$. The transient solution overshoots and oscillates about the steady state solution. The asymptotic steady state solution has not been attained even after 50 time steps. The situation becomes worse for larger values of d. Consequently, the Crank–Nicolson method is not recommended for solving steady equilibrium problems as the asymptotic steady state solution of unsteady propagation problems.

In summary, steady equilibrium problems, mixed elliptic/parabolic problems, and mixed elliptic/hyperbolic problems can be solved as the asymptotic steady state solution of an appropriate unsteady propagation problem. For linear problems, the asymptotic steady state solution can be attained in one or two steps by the BTCS method, which is the recommended method for such problems. For nonlinear problems, the BTCS method becomes quite time-consuming. For multidimensional problems, the ADI method can be used. The asymptotic steady state approach is a powerful procedure for solving difficult equilibrium problems and mixed equilibrium/propagation problems.

SUMMARY

The numerical solution of parabolic partial differential equations by finite difference methods is discussed in this chapter. Parabolic PDEs govern propagation problems, which have an infinite information propagation speed. They are solved numerically by marching methods. The unsteady one-dimensional diffusion equation, $\bar{f}_t = \alpha \bar{f}_{xx}$, is considered as the model parabolic PDE in this chapter.

Explicit finite difference methods, as typified by the FTCS method, are conditionally stable and require a relatively small step size in the marching direction to satisfy stability criteria. Implicit methods, as typified by the BTCS method, are unconditionally stable. The marching step size is restricted by accuracy requirements, not stability requirements. For accurate solutions of transient problems, the marching step size for implicit methods cannot be very much larger than the stable step size for explicit methods. Asymptotic steady state solutions can be obtained very efficiently by the BTCS method with a large marching step size.

Nonlinear partial differential equations can be solved directly by explicit methods. When solved by implicit methods, systems of nonlinear FDEs must be solved. Multidimensional problems can be solved directly by explicit methods. When solved by implicit methods, large banded systems of FDEs result. Alternating-direction implicit (ADI) methods and approximate-factorization implicit (AFI) methods can be used to solve multidimensional problems.

PROBLEMS

Section 11.1 Introduction

1. Consider the unsteady one-dimensional diffusion equation $\bar{f}_t = \alpha \bar{f}_{xx}$. Classify this PDE. Determine the characteristic curves. Discuss the significance of these results as regards domain of dependence, range of influence, signal propagation speed, auxiliary conditions, and numerical solution procedures.
2. Develop the exact solution of the heat conduction problem presented in Section 11.1, Eq. (11.6).
3. By hand, calculate the exact solution for $T(0.5, 10.0)$.
4. Write a computer program to evaluate the exact solution of the heat conduction problem. Use the program to reproduce Table 11.1.

Section 11.2 The Forward-Time Centered-Space Method

5. Derive the FTCS approximation of the unsteady one-dimensional diffusion equation, Eq. (11.7), including the leading truncation error terms in Δt and Δx.
6. Derive the first, second, and approximate second forms of the MDE corresponding to Eq. (11.7). Analyze consistency, order, and implicit numerical diffusion and dispersion.
7. Perform a von Neumann stability analysis of Eq. (11.7).
8. Perform a matrix method stability analysis of the FTCS method, Eq. (11.7), for (*a*) two interior points and (*b*) three interior points.

9. By hand calculation, determine the solution of the example heat conduction problem by the FTCS method at $t = 0.5$ s for $\Delta x = 0.1$ cm and $\Delta t = 0.1$ s.
10. By hand calculation, derive the results presented in Figs. 11.7 and 11.8.
11. Write a computer program to implement the numerical solution of the example heat conduction problem by the FTCS method. Use the program to reproduce Tables 11.2 and 11.3. Compare the results with the exact solution presented in Table 11.1.
12. Use the program developed in Problem 11 to reproduce Fig. 11.6. Compare the results with the exact solution presented in Table 11.1. Repeat the calculations for $\Delta x = 0.05$ cm and $\Delta t = 0.125$ s. Compare the errors and the ratios of the errors for the two solutions at $t = 5.0$ s.

Section 11.3 The Richardson (Leapfrog) Method

13. Derive the Richardson (leapfrog) approximation of the unsteady one-dimensional diffusion equation, Eq. (11.14), including the leading truncation error terms in Δt and Δx.
14. Perform a von Neumann stability analysis of Eq. (11.14).

Section 11.4 The DuFort–Frankel Method

15. Derive the DuFort–Frankel approximation of the unsteady one-dimensional diffusion equation, Eq. (11.19), including the leading truncation error terms in Δt and Δx.
16. Derive the first and approximate second forms of the MDE corresponding to Eq. (11.19). Analyze consistency, order, and implicit numerical diffusion and dispersion.
17. Perform a von Neumann stability analysis of Eq. (11.19). Analyze the three cases which depend on the sign of the term $(1 - 4d^2 \sin^2 \theta)$.
18. Perform a matrix method stability analysis of the DuFort–Frankel method, Eq. (11.19), for (*a*) two interior points and (*b*) three interior points.
19. By hand, calculate the results presented in Fig. 11.11 for $d = 2.5$ and 5.0.

Section 11.5 The Backward-Time Centered-Space Method

20. Derive the BTCS approximation of the unsteady one-dimensional diffusion equation, Eq. (11.26), including the leading truncation error terms in Δt and Δx.
21. Derive the first and approximate second forms of the MDE corresponding to Eq. (11.26). Analyze consistency, order, and implicit numerical diffusion and dispersion.
22. Perform a von Neumann stability analysis of Eq. (11.26).
23. Perform a matrix method stability analysis of the BTCS method, Eq. (11.26), for two interior points.
24. By hand calculation, determine the solution of the example heat conduction problem by the BTCS method at $t = 0.5$ s for $\Delta x = 0.1$ cm and $\Delta t = 0.5$ s.
25. Write a computer program to implement the numerical solution of the example heat conduction problem by the BTCS method. Use the program to reproduce the results presented in Figs. 11.14 and 11.15. Compare the results with the exact solution presented in Table 11.1.

26. Use the program developed in Problem 25 and repeat the calculations for $\Delta x = 0.05$ cm. Compare the errors and the ratios of the errors for the two solutions at $t = 10.0$ s.

Section 11.6 The Crank–Nicolson Method

27. Derive the Crank–Nicolson approximation of the unsteady one-dimensional diffusion equation, Eq. (11.35), including the leading truncation error terms in Δt and Δx.
28. Derive the first and approximate second forms of the MDE corresponding to Eq. (11.35). Analyze consistency, order, and implicit numerical diffusion and dispersion.
29. Perform a von Neumann stability analysis of Eq. (11.35).
30. Perform a matrix method stability analysis of the Crank–Nicolson method, Eq. (11.35), for two interior points.
31. By hand calculation, determine the solution of the example heat conduction problem by the Crank–Nicolson method at $t = 0.5$ s for $\Delta x = 0.1$ cm and $\Delta t = 0.5$ s.
32. Write a computer program to implement the numerical solution of the example heat conduction problem by the Crank–Nicolson method. Use the program to reproduce the results presented in Figs. 11.18 and 11.19. Compare the results with the exact solution presented in Table 11.1.
33. Use the program developed in Problem 32 and repeat the calculations for $\Delta x = 0.05$ cm. Compare the errors and the ratios of the errors for the two solutions at $t = 10.0$ s.

Section 11.7 Derivative Boundary Conditions

34. Derive Eq. (11.46).
35. By hand calculation using Eq. (11.46) at the boundary point, determine the solution of the example heat conduction problem presented in Section 11.7 at $t = 2.5$ s for $\Delta x = 0.1$ cm and $\Delta t = 0.5$ s using the FTCS method.
36. Derive Eqs. (11.49), (11.50), and (11.51).
37. Work Problem 35 using Eqs. (11.49), (11.50), and (11.51).
38. Modify the computer program written in Problem 11 to incorporate the four derivative boundary condition procedures on the right-hand boundary. Check out the program by reproducing Figs. 11.23*a* to 11.23*d*.

Section 11.8 Nonlinear Equations and Multidimensional Problems

39. Consider the following nonlinear parabolic PDE for the generic dependent variable $f(x, y)$, which serves as a model equation in fluid mechanics:

$$f f_x = \alpha f_{yy} \tag{P11.39}$$

where $f(x, 0) = f_1$, $f(x, Y) = f_2$, and $f(0, y) = F(y)$. (*a*) Derive the FTCS approximation of Eq. (P11.39). (*b*) Perform a von Neumann stability analysis of the linearized FDE. (*c*) Derive the first and approximate second forms of the MDE corresponding to the linearized FDE. Investigate consistency and order. (*d*) Discuss a strategy for solving this problem numerically.
40. Work Problem 39 using the BTCS method. Discuss a strategy for solving this problem numerically (*a*) using linearization, and (*b*) using Newton's method.

41. Equation (P11.39) can be written as

$$(f^2/2)_x = \alpha f_{yy} \tag{P11.41}$$

Work problem 39*a* for this form of the PDE. (*b*) Repeat Problem 40 for this form of the PDE.

42. Write a computer program to solve Problem 39 numerically for $f_1 = f_2 = 0$, $Y = 1.0$, $\alpha = 1.0$, and $F(y) = 200y$ for $0 \le y \le 0.5$ and $200(1-y)$ for $0.5 \le y \le 1.0$. March from $x = 0$ to $x = 10.0$.

43. Consider the unsteady two-dimensional diffusion equation:

$$\bar{f}_t = \alpha(\bar{f}_{xx} + \bar{f}_{yy}) \tag{P11.43}$$

(*a*) Derive the FTCS approximation of Eq. (P11.43), including the leading truncation error terms in Δt, Δx, and Δy. (*b*) Derive the first and approximate second forms of the MDE. Analyze consistency, order, and implicit numerical diffusion and dispersion. (*c*) Perform a von Neumann stability analysis of the FDE.

44. Work Problem 43 using the BTCS method.

Section 11.9 Asymptotic Steady State Solutions

45. Consider steady heat transfer in a rod with an insulated end, as discussed in Section 8.6. The steady boundary-value problem is specified by:

$$\hat{T}_{xx} - \alpha^2(\hat{T} - T_a) = 0, \quad \hat{T}(0) = T_1 \text{ and } \hat{T}_x(L) = 0 \tag{P11.45a}$$

where $\alpha^2 = hP/kA$, which is defined in Section 8.6. The exact solution for $T_1 = 100$, $\alpha = 2$, and $L = 1$ is given by Eq. (8.70) and illustrated in Fig. 8.9. This steady state problem can be solved as the asymptotic solution in time of the following unsteady problem:

$$\beta\bar{T}_t = \bar{T}_{xx} - \alpha^2(\bar{T} - T_a), \quad \bar{T}(0) = T_1 \text{ and } \bar{T}_x(L) = 0 \tag{P11.45b}$$

with the initial temperature distribution $\bar{T}(x,0) = F(x)$, where $\beta = \rho C/k$, ρ is the density of the rod (kg/m^3), C is the specific heat (J/kg-K), and k is the thermal conductivity (J/s-m-K). Equation (P11.45*b*) can be derived by combining the analyses presented in Sections II.5 and II.6. (*a*) Derive Eq. (P11.45*b*). (*b*) Develop the FTCS approximation of Eq. (P11.45*b*). (*c*) Let $\hat{T}(0) = 100$, $\hat{T}_x(1) = 0$, $T_a = 0$, $L = 1$, $\alpha = 2$, $\beta = 10$, and the initial temperature distribution $\bar{T}(x,0) = 100(1-x)$. Solve for the steady state solution by solving Eq. (P11.45*b*) by the FTCS method with $\Delta x = 0.1$ cm and $\Delta t = 0.1$ s. Compare the results with the exact solution presented in Table 8.9. (*d*) Develop the BTCS approximation of Eq. (P11.45*b*). (*e*) Repeat Part (*c*) using the BTCS method. Try large values of Δt to reach the steady state as rapidly as possible.

CHAPTER 12

HYPERBOLIC PARTIAL DIFFERENTIAL EQUATIONS

The Convection Equation

Contents

Example

12.1 INTRODUCTION

The general features of *hyperbolic* partial differential equations (PDEs) are discussed in Section III.7. In that section it is shown that hyperbolic PDEs govern propagation problems, which are initial–boundary-value problems in open domains. Consequently, hyperbolic PDEs are solved numerically by marching methods.

From a characteristic analysis, it is shown in Section III.7 that problems governed by hyperbolic PDEs have a finite signal propagation speed $c = dx/dt$. As a result, the solution at a given point P at time level n depends on the solution only within a finite domain of dependence in the solution domain at times preceding time level n. Likewise, the solution at a given point P at time level n influences the solution only within a finite range of influence in the solution domain at times after time level n. These general features of hyperbolic PDEs are illustrated in Fig. 12.1.

The basic properties of finite difference methods for solving propagation problems are discussed in Chapter 10. A finite difference grid must be superimposed on the continuous solution domain, and finite difference approximations to the individual exact partial derivatives appearing in the partial differential equation must be chosen. The resulting finite difference equation (FDE) must be analyzed

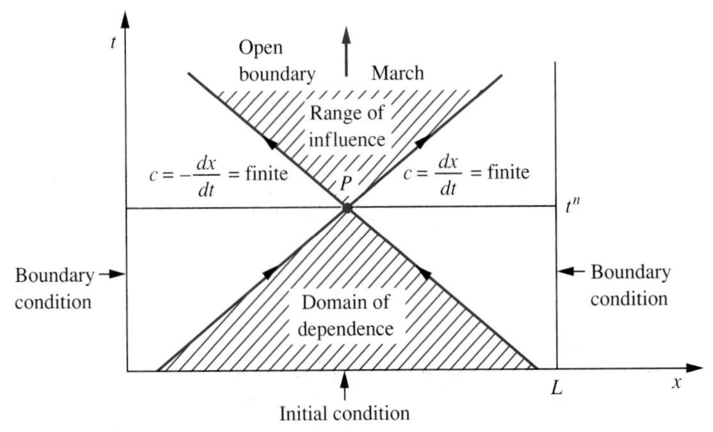

FIGURE 12.1
Domain of dependence and range of influence for a hyperbolic PDE.

for consistency, order, stability, and convergence. The effects of implicit numerical diffusion and dispersion must be considered. All these properties are discussed in Chapter 10.

The present chapter is devoted to the numerical solution of the unsteady one-dimensional hyperbolic convection equation:

$$\boxed{\bar{f}_t + u\bar{f}_x = 0} \tag{12.1}$$

It is shown in Section III.7 that the convection equation has real characteristic curves, the *pathlines*.

The numerical solution of Eq. (12.1) by several methods is presented in this chapter. For each method, the modified differential equation (MDE) is presented; consistency and order are investigated; the amplification factor G obtained from a von Neumann stability analysis is presented and stability is analyzed; convergence is investigated; and the presence or absence of implicit numerical diffusion and dispersion is determined.

The convection equation models a wave traveling in one direction. Thus, the convection equation models the essential features of the more complex wave motion governed by the wave equation, in which waves travel in all directions. The general features of the numerical solution of the convection equation also apply to the numerical solution of the wave equation. Consequently, this chapter is devoted to the numerical solution of the convection equation to gain insight into the numerical solution of more complicated hyperbolic PDEs, such as the wave equation.

The solution to Eq. (12.1) is the function $\bar{f}(x, t)$. This function must satisfy an initial condition at time $t = 0$, $\bar{f}(x, 0) = F(x)$. Since Eq. (12.1) is first-order in space, only one boundary condition can be applied. In effect, this boundary condition is analogous to an initial condition in space. Consequently, both the time coordinate and the space coordinate have a specified initial value and an unspecified open final value.

The exact solution of the convection equation, Eq. (12.1), is given by

$$\bar{f}(x, t) = F(x - ut) \tag{12.2}$$

which can be proven by substitution into Eq. (12.1). The significance of Eq. (12.2) is illustrated as follows. Consider the arbitrary initial property distribution

$$\bar{f}(x, t) = \bar{f}(x, 0) = F(x) \tag{12.3a}$$

At any later time t,

$$\bar{f}(x, t) = F(x - ut) \tag{12.3b}$$

These two property distributions are identical, except that $F(x - ut)$ is translated to the right by the distance ut. Consequently, the entire initial property distribution

$F(x)$ is convected to the right, without changes in magnitude or shape, at the convection velocity u.

The convection equation applies to problems in such areas as fluid mechanics and convection heat transfer. The convection equation governing convection heat transfer is considered in this chapter in order to illustrate numerical methods for solving the convection equation. In this case, Eq. (12.1) becomes

$$T_t + uT_x = 0 \tag{12.4}$$

where T is the temperature (C) and u is the convection velocity (cm/s). The solution to Eq. (12.2) is the function $T(x, t)$. This function must satisfy an initial condition at time $t = 0$, $T(x, 0) = F(x)$, and a boundary condition at $x = X$, $T(X, t) = G(t)$.

The following simple problem is considered in this chapter in order to illustrate the behavior of several numerical integration methods applied to the convection equation. A constant-area tube having an infinite length is filled with a stationary fluid having a very low thermal conductivity, so that heat diffusion is negligible. In the range $0.0 \le x \le 1.0$, the fluid has the initial temperature distribution given by

$$T(x, 0) = 200x, \qquad 0.0 \le x \le 0.5 \tag{12.5a}$$

$$T(x, 0) = 200(1 - x), \qquad 0.5 \le x \le 1.0 \tag{12.5b}$$

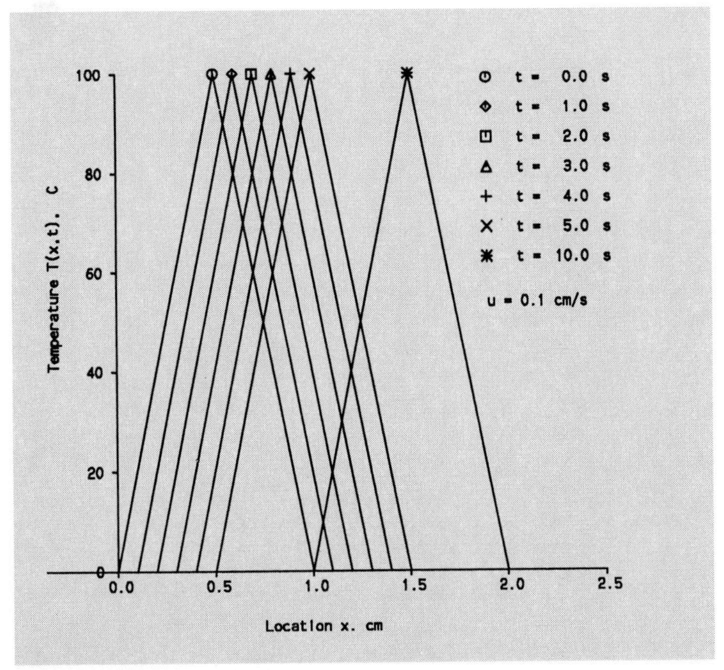

FIGURE 12.2
Exact solution of the convection problem.

The initial temperature is zero everywhere outside of this range. This initial temperature distribution is illustrated by the curve labeled $t = 0.0$ in Fig. 12.2. At time $t = 0.0$, the fluid is instantaneously given the velocity $u = 0.1$ cm/s to the right. The temperature distribution $T(x, t)$ in the tube is required. For the present problem, the temperature distribution specified by Eq. (12.5) simply moves to the right at the speed $u = 0.1$ cm/s. The exact solutions for several values of time are presented in Fig. 12.2. Note that the discontinuity in slope at the peak of the temperature distribution is preserved during convection.

12.2 THE METHOD OF CHARACTERISTICS

The concept of *characteristics* of partial differential equations is introduced in Section III.3. Characteristics are $(n-1)$-dimensional hypersurfaces in n-dimensional hyperspace (where n is the number of independent variables in the problem) that have some very special features. In two-dimensional space, which is the case considered here (i.e., physical space x and time t), characteristics are lines (curved, in general) in the solution domain $D(x, t)$ along which information propagates. If a partial differential equation possesses real characteristics, then information propagates along the characteristics. The presence of characteristics has a significant impact on the solution of a partial differential equation (by both analytical and numerical methods).

The procedure for determining the characteristics of a single first-order PDE is presented in Section III.3. Let us apply that procedure to the convection equation:

$$\bar{f}_t + u\bar{f}_x = 0 \tag{12.6}$$

Differentiating the function $\bar{f}(x, t)$ yields

$$d\bar{f} = \bar{f}_x dx + \bar{f}_t dt \tag{12.7}$$

In matrix form, Eqs. (12.6) and (12.7) can be written as

$$\begin{bmatrix} 1 & u \\ dt & dx \end{bmatrix} \begin{bmatrix} \bar{f}_t \\ \bar{f}_x \end{bmatrix} = \begin{bmatrix} 0 \\ d\bar{f} \end{bmatrix} \tag{12.8}$$

The characteristics of Eq. (12.6) are determined by setting the determinant of the coefficient matrix of Eq. (12.8) equal to zero. This gives

$$\boxed{\frac{dx}{dt} = u} \tag{12.9}$$

Equation (12.9) is the characteristic equation (i.e., the differential equation that specifies the characteristic curves) corresponding to the unsteady one-dimensional convection equation.

The compatibility equation that is valid along the characteristic curves is determined by first rearranging Eq. (12.7) into the form

$$\frac{d\bar{f}}{dt} = \bar{f}_t + \frac{dx}{dt}\bar{f}_x \tag{12.10a}$$

Along the characteristic curves, $dx/dt = u$, and Eq. (12.10a) becomes

$$\frac{d\bar{f}}{dt} = \bar{f}_t + u\bar{f}_x \tag{12.10b}$$

Substituting Eq. (12.6) into Eq. (12.10a) yields

$$\boxed{\frac{d\bar{f}}{dt} = 0} \tag{12.11}$$

Equation (12.11) is the *compatibility equation,* which specifies the behavior of the dependent variable $\bar{f}(x, t)$ along, and only along, the characteristic curves.

For the linear convection equation (i.e., u = constant), Eq. (12.9) can be integrated to yield the straight line

$$\boxed{x = x_0 + ut} \tag{12.12}$$

and Eq. (12.11) can be integrated to give

$$\boxed{\bar{f} = \text{constant}} \tag{12.13}$$

Consequently, the value $\bar{f}_0 = \bar{f}(x_0, 0)$ propagates along the characteristic line $x = x_0 + ut$ unchanged in magnitude. In effect, the entire initial property distribution $\bar{f}(x, 0) = F(x)$ propagates unchanged in shape in the positive x direction with the velocity u. This result is the exact solution for Eq. (12.6) [see Eq. (12.2)].

When u is not constant, the characteristic curves are given by

$$\boxed{x = x_0 + \int u\, dt} \tag{12.14}$$

In many cases, the convection velocity u depends on the property being convected, in this case the variable $\bar{f}(x, t)$. In such cases, Eq. (12.14) may require numerical integration.

Frequently a nonhomogeneous term is present in the convection equation. For example,

$$\bar{f}_t + u\bar{f}_x = F(x, t, \bar{f}) \tag{12.15}$$

In this case, the compatibility equation, Eq. (12.11), becomes

$$\frac{d\bar{f}}{dt} = F(x, t, \bar{f}) \tag{12.16}$$

Integrating Eq. (12.16) yields

$$\boxed{\bar{f}(x, t) = \bar{f}(x_0, 0) + \int F(x, t, \bar{f})\, dt} \tag{12.17}$$

which may also require numerical integration. In general, Eqs. (12.14) and (12.17) are coupled, so they must be integrated simultaneously.

The concept of characteristics, presented in this section, identifies special curves in the solution domain, called characteristic curves, along which the governing partial differential equation becomes a total differential equation, called the compatibility equation. Characteristics are the paths of propagation of information in the physical space.

The presence of characteristics must be accounted for in the numerical solution of hyperbolic PDEs. The characteristics can be used directly to solve the PDEs by numerically constructing the characteristic curves and numerically integrating the compatibility equation along the characteristic curves, as in Eqs. (12.14) and (12.17). Such a procedure is called the *numerical method of characteristics* and is presented in Section 12.11.

Hyperbolic PDEs can also be solved numerically by replacing both the time and space derivatives by finite difference approximations on a fixed finite difference grid, as done in Chapter 11 for parabolic PDEs. In that case, the characteristic curves govern the allowable step size in time and determine the allowable boundary conditions. That approach is developed in this chapter in Sections 12.3 to 12.10, 12.12, and 12.13.

12.3 THE FORWARD-TIME CENTERED-SPACE METHOD

The most straightforward finite difference method for solving hyperbolic partial differential equations would appear to be the forward-time centered-space (FTCS) method. The FTCS method is applied to the diffusion equation in Section 11.2. It is shown there that the FTCS approximation of the diffusion equation is conditionally stable (i.e., $d = \alpha\,\Delta t/\Delta x^2 \le \frac{1}{2}$). However, when applied to the convection equation $\bar{f}_t + u\bar{f}_x = 0$, the FTCS method is unconditionally unstable.

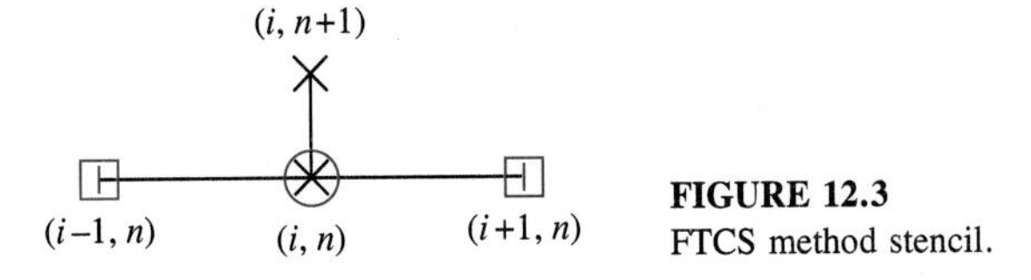

FIGURE 12.3
FTCS method stencil.

Introducing the first-order forward-difference approximation for $\bar{f}_t$ [Eq. (10.54)] and the second-order centered-difference approximation for $\bar{f}_x$ [Eq. (10.64*b*)] into the convection equation yields

$$\frac{f_i^{n+1} - f_i^n}{\Delta t} + u\frac{f_{i+1}^n - f_{i-1}^n}{2\Delta x} = 0 \tag{12.18}$$

Solving Eq. (12.18) for f_i^{n+1} gives the FTCS approximation of the convection equation:

$$\boxed{f_i^{n+1} = f_i^n - \frac{c}{2}(f_{i+1}^n - f_{i-1}^n)} \tag{12.19}$$

where $c = u\Delta t/\Delta x$ is the convection number. The corresponding finite difference stencil is illustrated in Fig. 12.3.

The first form of the modified differential equation (MDE) is

$$f_t + uf_x = -\frac{1}{2}f_{tt}\,\Delta t - \frac{1}{6}f_{ttt}\,\Delta t^2 - \cdots - \frac{1}{6}uf_{xxx}\,\Delta x^2 - \cdots \tag{12.20}$$

and the second form of the MDE is

$$f_t + uf_x = -\frac{1}{2}u^2\,\Delta t f_{xx} + \left(-\frac{1}{3}u^3\,\Delta t^2 - \frac{1}{6}u\,\Delta x^2\right)f_{xxx} + \cdots \tag{12.21}$$

As $\Delta t \to 0$ and $\Delta x \to 0$, Eq. (12.20) approaches $f_t + uf_x = 0$, which is the convection equation. Consequently, Eq. (12.19) is a consistent approximation of that equation. From Eq. (12.21), the FDE is $O(\Delta t) + O(\Delta x^2)$. The amplification factor G corresponding to Eq. (12.19) is

$$G = 1 - Ic\sin\theta \tag{12.22}$$

The magnitude of G is

$$|G| = (1 + c^2\sin^2\theta)^{1/2} \tag{12.23}$$

which is greater than unity for $c > 0$. Consequently, Eq. (12.19) is unconditionally unstable.

Example 12.1. Solution by the FTCS method. To illustrate the unstable behavior of the FTCS method applied to the convection equation, the solution to the convection problem presented in Section 12.1 is presented in Fig. 12.4 for $\Delta x = 0.1$ cm with $\Delta t = 0.5$ s, for which $c = u\Delta t/\Delta x = (0.1)(0.5)/0.1 = 0.5$. The solution is presented

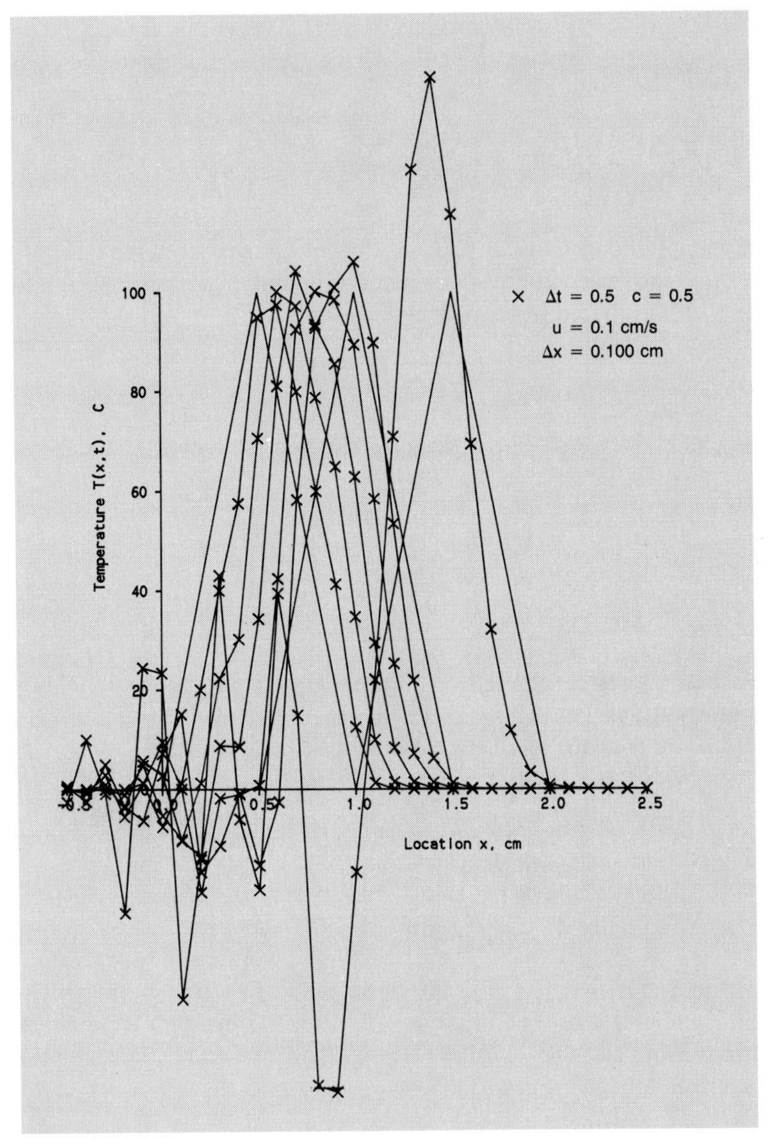

FIGURE 12.4
Solution by the FTCS method.

at times from 1.0 to 5.0 s and 10.0 s. The amplitude of the solution increases as the wave propagates to the right. Solutions for larger values of c are not shown, because they are totally unrealistic. All the other examples in this chapter are solved with $\Delta x = 0.05$ cm and $\Delta t = 0.25$ s. For the FTCS method, that combination, for which $c = 0.5$ as in the present example, goes unstable more rapidly, so the results could not be illustrated in the figure.

In summary, the FTCS approximation of the convection equation is unconditionally unstable. Consequently, it is unsuitable for solving convection problems.

12.4 THE LAX METHOD

Lax (1954) proposed a modification to the FTCS method for the convection equation that yields a conditionally stable method. In that modification, the value f_i^n in the finite difference approximation of $\overline{f}_t|_i^n$ [see Eq. (12.18)] is approximated by $(f_{i+1}^n + f_{i-1}^n)/2$. The resulting finite difference equation is

$$f_i^{n+1} = \frac{1}{2}(f_{i+1}^n + f_{i-1}^n) - \frac{c}{2}(f_{i+1}^n - f_{i-1}^n) \tag{12.24}$$

Equation (12.24) is the Lax approximation of the convection equation. The corresponding finite difference stencil is illustrated in Fig. 12.5. Equation (12.24) is identical to the first method-of-characteristics approximation of the linear convection equation presented in Section 12.11 [see Eq. (12.85)].

The first form of the modified differential equation (MDE) is

$$f_t + uf_x = -\frac{1}{2}f_{tt}\,\Delta t - \frac{1}{6}f_{ttt}\,\Delta t^2 - \cdots - \frac{1}{6}uf_{xxx}\,\Delta x^2 - \cdots + \frac{1}{2}f_{xx}\,\frac{\Delta x^2}{\Delta t} + \cdots \tag{12.25}$$

and the second form of the MDE is

$$f_t + uf_x = \frac{1}{2}\left(\frac{\Delta x^2}{\Delta t} - u^2\,\Delta t\right)f_{xx} + \frac{1}{3}(u\,\Delta x^2 - u^3\,\Delta t^2)f_{xxx} + \cdots \tag{12.26}$$

As $\Delta t \to 0$ and $\Delta x \to 0$, the first three terms on the right-hand side of Eq. (12.25) go to zero. However, the fourth term does not go to zero. In fact, that term becomes indeterminate. Consequently, Eq. (12.24) is not a consistent approximation of the convection equation. However, if the ratio $\Delta x/\Delta t$ is held constant as $\Delta t \to 0$ and $\Delta x \to 0$, for example at the value $\beta = \Delta x/\Delta t$, then Eq. (12.25) approaches the equation

$$f_t + uf_x = \frac{1}{2}(\beta\,\Delta x - u^2\,\Delta t)f_{xx} \tag{12.27}$$

which is the parabolic convection–diffusion equation. Substituting the convection

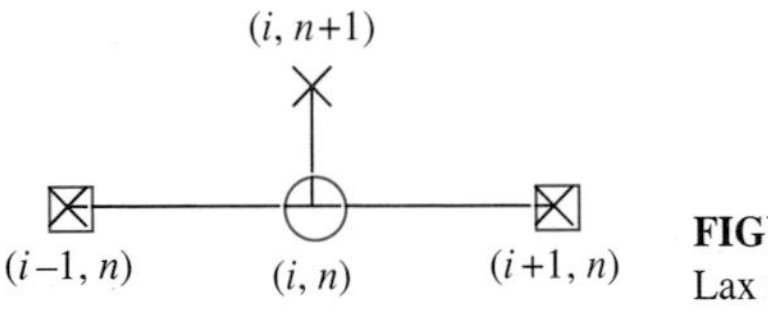

FIGURE 12.5
Lax method stencil.

number $c = u\Delta t/\Delta x$ into Eq. (12.27) yields

$$f_t + uf_x = \frac{1}{2}\left(\frac{1}{c}u\,\Delta x - u^2\,\Delta t\right) f_{xx} \tag{12.28}$$

which can be written as

$$f_t + uf_x = \frac{1}{2}u\,\Delta x\left(\frac{1}{c} - c\right) f_{xx} \tag{12.29}$$

Equation (12.29) can be interpreted as the convection–diffusion equation

$$f_t + uf_x = \alpha_n f_{xx} \tag{12.30}$$

where the numerical diffusion coefficient α_n is

$$\alpha_n = \frac{1}{2}u\,\Delta x\left(\frac{1}{c} - c\right) \tag{12.31}$$

For large values of β (i.e., large values of Δx or small values of Δt), the numerical solution of the convection equation behaves more like the solution of the convection–diffusion equation than like the solution of the convection equation. In fact, for $\Delta t = 0$ (i.e., $c = 0$), no convection will occur, but the initial data will be diffused by the numerical diffusion in Eq. (12.24). As $c \to 1$, $\alpha_n \to 0$, and the implicit numerical diffusion vanishes. Implicit numerical diffusion is discussed more thoroughly in Section 12.5.

The conditional stability of the Lax method is somewhat surprising, since the Lax method appears to be only a minor variation of the FTCS method, which is unconditionally unstable when applied to the convection equation. Obviously, some major effect has occurred. What has happened is that the Lax method has introduced implicit numerical diffusion into the finite difference equation. This implicit numerical diffusion acts like real physical diffusion and adds sufficient diffusion to the FTCS method to make it conditionally stable.

From Eq. (12.26), it is seen that the Lax approximation of the convection equation is $O(\Delta t) + O(\Delta x^2) + O(\Delta x^2/\Delta t)$. As seen in Eq. (12.26), both even and odd space derivatives are present in the truncation error. Hence, implicit numerical diffusion and dispersion are both present in the method. From a von Neumann stability analysis,

$$G = \cos\theta - Ic\sin\theta \tag{12.32}$$

The magnitude of G is

$$|G| = (\cos^2\theta + c^2\sin^2\theta)^{1/2} = \left(1 - \sin^2\theta(1 - c^2)\right)^{1/2}$$

Since $\sin^2\theta \geq 0$ for all values of $\theta = (k\,\Delta x)$, $|G| \leq 1$ if

$$\boxed{c = \frac{u\,\Delta t}{\Delta x} \leq 1} \tag{12.33}$$

Thus, the Lax approximation of the convection equation is conditionally stable. Equation (12.33) is the celebrated Courant–Friedrichs–Lewy (1928) stability criterion, commonly called the *CFL stability criterion*. In essence, Eq. (12.33) states that the numerical speed of propagation, $u_n = \Delta x / \Delta t$, must be greater than or equal to the physical speed of propagation, u. The Lax approximation of the convection equation may behave in a numerically consistent manner if $\Delta x / \Delta t$ is held constant. It is conditionally stable. Consequently, by the Lax equivalence theorem, it may behave as a convergent approximation of the convection equation.

Example 12.2. Solution by the Lax method. We will solve the convection problem presented in Section 12.1, using Eq. (12.24) for $\Delta x = 0.05$ cm, for $\Delta t = 0.05$, 0.25, 0.45, and 0.5 s. For $u = 0.1$ cm/s and $\Delta x = 0.05$ cm, $c = u\,\Delta t / \Delta x = (0.1)\,\Delta t/(0.05) = 2\,\Delta t$. Thus, the numerical value of Δt is half the numerical value of c for this choice of physical properties. The results are presented in Fig. 12.6 at times from 1.0 to 5.0 s for $c = 0.5$, and at 10.0 s for $c = 0.1$, 0.5, 0.9, and 1.0. The solution at every other grid point is denoted by the symbols.

Several important features are illustrated in Fig. 12.6. When $c = 1$, the numerical solution is identical to the exact solution, for the linear convection equation. This is not true for the nonlinear convection equation. When $c = 0.5$, the amplitude of the solution is severely damped as the wave propagates, and the peak of the wave is rounded. The general shape of the solution is maintained, but the leading and trailing edges of the wave are quite smeared out. These effects are due to implicit numerical diffusion and dispersion. The result at $t = 10.0$ s for $c = 0.1$ is completely smeared out. The

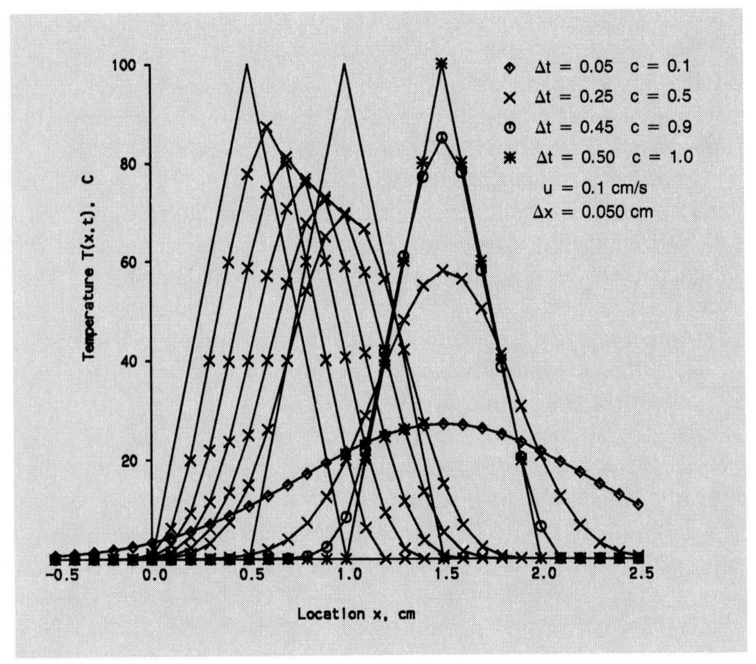

FIGURE 12.6
Solution by the Lax method.

numerical solution does not even resemble the general shape of the exact solution. These effects are the result of the implicit numerical diffusion that is present in the Lax method. In effect, the initial data distribution is being both convected and diffused, and the effect of diffusion increases as the time step is decreased. The solution for $c = 0.9$ is much closer to the exact solution, except at the peak, which is severely damped. The presence of large amounts of implicit numerical diffusion at small values of the convection number c is a serious problem with the Lax method.

The explicit Lax method can be used in a straightforward manner to solve nonlinear PDEs, systems of PDEs, and multidimensional problems, as discussed in Section 12.14.

In summary, the Lax approximation of the convection equation is explicit, two-level, single-step, $O(\Delta t) + O(\Delta x^2) + O(\Delta x^2/\Delta t)$, and conditionally stable. Excessive implicit numerical diffusion is present, which makes the Lax method a poor choice for solving the convection equation.

12.5 NUMERICAL DIFFUSION

The presence of diffusion in a physical process acts to diffuse, or smear out, nonuniformities in the physical property distribution. Real physical diffusion (mass diffusion, momentum diffusion, heat diffusion, i.e., conduction, neutron diffusion, etc.) is governed by a diffusion mechanism of the form αf_{xx}, where α is the diffusion coefficient, which is always positive.

As discussed in Section 10.6, the actual partial differential equation that is solved by a finite difference approximation of an exact partial differential equation is called the modified differential equation (MDE) and differs from the exact PDE by the presence of the truncation error terms. As discussed in Section 10.8, all truncation error terms containing an even spatial derivative contribute to implicit numerical diffusion. This type of diffusion is called *numerical diffusion* to differentiate it from real physical diffusion. It is called *implicit* numerical diffusion because it is implicit in the finite difference equation. If the leading even spatial derivative in the truncation error is f_{xx}, then the implicit numerical diffusion competes directly with the real physical diffusion in the numerical solution.

Truncation errors are always present in the finite difference approximation of a PDE. In most cases, even spatial derivatives are present, and implicit numerical diffusion occurs. Many finite difference approximations of the first spatial derivative $\bar{f}_x$ yield a leading truncation error term containing f_{xxxx}. Even though this term is diffusive, it does not compete directly with the real physical diffusion $\alpha \bar{f}_{xx}$. However, many finite difference approximations of the first time derivative $\bar{f}_t$ yield a leading truncation error term containing f_{xx}, which competes directly with the real physical diffusion $\alpha \bar{f}_{xx}$. As a general rule, second-order approximations of $\bar{f}_t$ do not yield an f_{xx} term in the truncation error, but first-order approximations of $\bar{f}_t$ do yield an f_{xx} term in the truncation error. Inconsistent finite difference approximations, such as the Lax method [see Section 12.4], frequently introduce an f_{xx} term in the truncation error.

When second-order implicit numerical diffusion is present in an FDE, the numerical solution will be diffused erroneously. Consequently, when developing or using finite difference methods to solve a PDE, care must be taken to reduce or eliminate the effects of implicit numerical diffusion.

As shown in Section 12.4, the Lax approximation of the convection equation $\bar{f}_t + u\bar{f}_x = 0$ is actually modeling the partial differential equation [see Eq. (12.29)]

$$f_t + uf_x = \frac{1}{2}u\,\Delta x\left(\frac{1}{c} - c\right)f_{xx} \tag{12.34}$$

which can be written as

$$f_t + uf_x = \alpha_n f_{xx} \tag{12.35}$$

where α_n is a numerical diffusion coefficient. Consequently, Eq. (12.35) models the convection–diffusion equation with implicit numerical diffusion. The implicit numerical diffusion coefficient α_n is given by

$$\alpha_n = \frac{1}{2}u\,\Delta x\left(\frac{1}{c} - c\right) \tag{12.36}$$

As $c \to 1.0$, the implicit numerical diffusion goes to zero. However, as $c \to 0$, the implicit numerical diffusion grows without bound and eventually dominates the solution.

Numerical solutions of nonlinear PDEs frequently contain large nonphysical oscillations, due to the omission of some diffusion mechanism in the physical model or the inability of the finite grid spacing to resolve small-scale diffusion effects. In such cases, it is common practice to introduce a diffusion term into the PDE explicitly to smooth the numerical oscillations. This form of numerical diffusion is called *explicit* numerical diffusion to distinguish it from the implicit numerical diffusion introduced by the truncation error of the finite difference approximation of the convection term.

Many models of explicit numerical diffusion have been suggested in the literature. Most of these models take one of the following forms:

$$\alpha_n f_{xx} \tag{12.37}$$

$$\alpha_n f_{xxxx} \tag{12.38}$$

$$\alpha_n f_{xx} + \beta_n f_{xxxx} \tag{12.39}$$

$$\alpha_n f_{xx} f_{xx} \tag{12.40}$$

Equations (12.37) to (12.40) are called second-order explicit numerical diffusion, fourth-order explicit numerical diffusion, combined second- and fourth-order explicit numerical diffusion, and product-fourth-order explicit numerical diffusion, respectively. The explicit numerical diffusion coefficients α_n and β_n may be constants, functions of the grid spacings Δt and Δx, or functions of the dependent variable $f(x, t)$ or some of its derivatives.

In summary, implicit numerical diffusion arises because of the presence of even spatial derivatives in the truncation error. Care must be taken to minimize its effect on numerical solutions. Explicit numerical diffusion is a form of numerical diffusion introduced explicitly into the PDE to smooth nonphysical numerical oscillations. Considerable care is required in the use of explicit numerical diffusion.

12.6 UPWIND METHODS

It is shown in the method-of-characteristics analysis of the convection equation presented in Section 12.2 that information propagates along the characteristic curves specified by $dx/dt = u$ [see Eq. (12.9)]. Thus, information propagates from either the left or the right side of the solution point, depending on whether $u > 0$ or $u < 0$, respectively. This type of information propagation is referred to as *upwind* propagation, since the information comes from the direction from which the convection velocity comes, that is, the upwind direction. Finite difference methods that account for the upwind influence are called *upwind* methods. One such method is presented in this section for the linear convection equation.

The simplest procedure for developing an upwind finite difference equation is to replace the time derivative $\overline{f}_t|_i^n$ by the first-order forward-difference approximation at grid point (i, n) [Eq. (10.54)] and to replace the space derivative $\overline{f}_x|_i^n$ by the first-order one-sided-difference approximation in the upstream direction [i.e., Eq. (10.63*b*) if $u > 0$ and Eq. (10.62*b*) if $u < 0$]. The finite difference stencil is presented in Fig. 12.7 for $u > 0$. The finite difference approximation is

$$\frac{f_i^{n+1} - f_i^n}{\Delta t} + u\frac{f_i^n - f_{i-1}^n}{\Delta x} = 0 \tag{12.41}$$

The truncation error is $O(\Delta t) + O(\Delta x)$. Solving for f_i^{n+1} yields

$$\boxed{f_i^{n+1} = f_i^n - c(f_i^n - f_{i-1}^n)} \tag{12.42}$$

Equation (12.42) is identical to the second method-of-characteristics approximation of the linear convection equation, presented in Section 12.11 [see Eq. (12.88)].

The first form of the modified differential equation (MDE) is

$$f_t + uf_x = -\frac{1}{2}f_{tt}\,\Delta t - \frac{1}{6}f_{ttt}\,\Delta t^2 - \cdots + \frac{1}{2}uf_{xx}\,\Delta x - \frac{1}{6}uf_{xxx}\,\Delta x^2 + \cdots \tag{12.43}$$

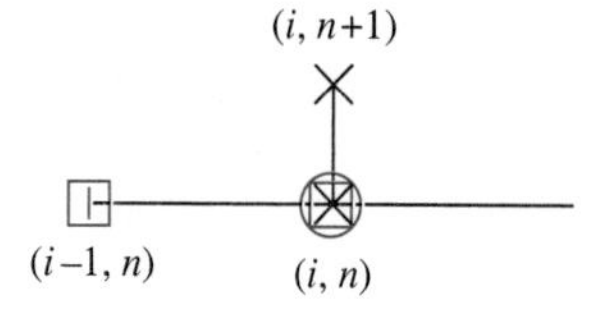

FIGURE 12.7
First-order upwind method stencil.

and the second form of the MDE is

$$f_t + u f_x = \left(\frac{1}{2}u\,\Delta x - \frac{1}{2}u^2\,\Delta t\right) f_{xx} + \left(-\frac{1}{3}u^3\,\Delta t^2 + \frac{1}{2}u^2\,\Delta x\,\Delta t - \frac{1}{6}u\,\Delta x^2\right) f_{xxx} + \cdots \tag{12.44}$$

As $\Delta t \to 0$ and $\Delta x \to 0$, Eq. (12.43) approaches $f_t + u f_x = 0$. Consequently, Eq. (12.42) is consistent with the convection equation. From Eq. (12.44), the FDE is $O(\Delta t) + O(\Delta x)$. From Eq. (12.44), implicit numerical diffusion and dispersion are both present, except when $c = 1.0$. In that case, the truncation errors are all zero, and the FDE matches the PDE exactly. The amplification factor G is given by

$$G = (1 - c) + c\cos\theta - Ic\sin\theta \tag{12.45}$$

Equation (12.45) is the equation of a circle in the complex plane, as illustrated in Fig. 12.8. The center of the circle is at $(1 - c, 0)$, and its radius is c. For stability, $|G| \leq 1$, which requires the circle to be within the unit circle. This is guaranteed if

$$\boxed{c = \frac{u\,\Delta t}{\Delta x} \leq 1} \tag{12.46}$$

Equation (12.46) is the CFL stability criterion. Consequently, the first-order upwind approximation of the convection equation is conditionally stable. It is also consistent. Consequently, by the Lax equivalence theorem, it is a convergent approximation of the convection equation.

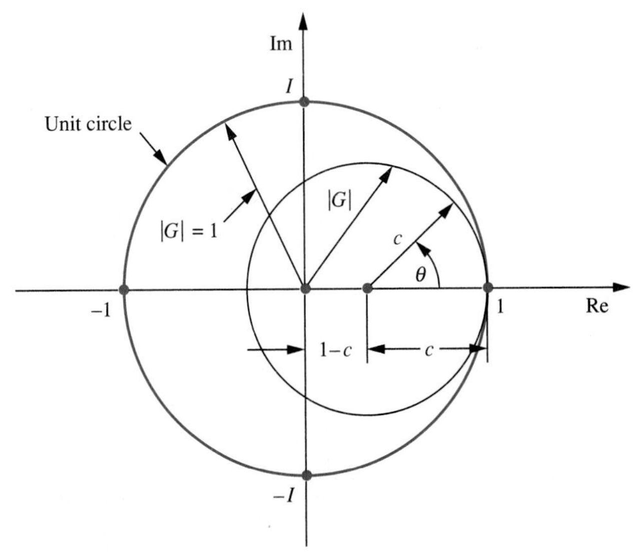

FIGURE 12.8
Locus of the amplification factor G for the first-order upwind method.

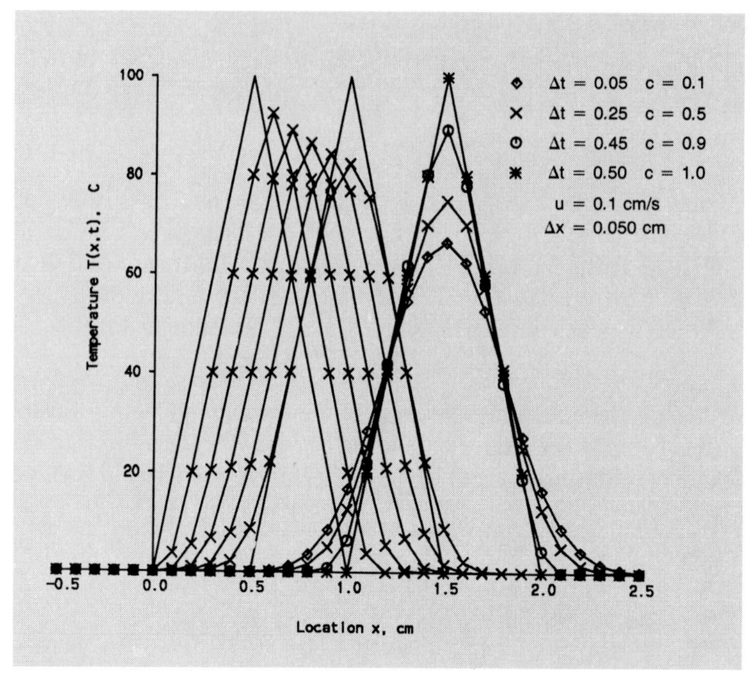

FIGURE 12.9
Solution by the first-order upwind method.

Example 12.3. Solution by the first-order upwind method. As an example of the first-order upwind method, we will solve the convection problem presented in Section 12.1, using Eq. (12.42) for $\Delta x = 0.05$ cm. The results are presented in Fig. 12.9 at times from 1.0 to 5.0 s for $c = 0.5$, and at 10.0 s for $c = 0.1$, 0.5, 0.9, and 1.0.

Several important features are illustrated in Fig. 12.9. When $c = 1.0$, the numerical solution is identical to the exact solution, for the linear convection equation. This is not true for the nonlinear convection equation. When $c = 0.5$, the amplitude of the solution is damped as the wave moves to the right, and the sharp peak becomes rounded. These effects, which are due to implicit numerical diffusion, are discussed more fully in Section 12.5. The results at $t = 10.0$ s for $c = 0.1$, 0.5, 0.9, and 1.0 show that the amount of implicit numerical diffusion depends on the convection number c. The large errors associated with the implicit numerical diffusion make the first-order upwind method a poor choice for solving the convection equation.

The explicit first-order upwind method can be used in a straightforward manner to solve nonlinear PDEs, systems of PDEs, and multidimensional problems, as discussed in Section 12.14.

In summary, the first-order upwind method applied to the convection equation is explicit, two-level, single-step, $O(\Delta t) + O(\Delta x)$, conditionally stable, and convergent. However, it introduces significant amounts of implicit numerical diffusion into the solution. Consequently, it is not a very accurate method for solving convection problems. Second-order upwind methods can be developed to give more accurate solutions of convection problems.

12.7 THE LEAPFROG METHOD

The Lax method developed in Section 12.4 and the first-order upwind method developed in Section 12.6 have several desirable features. Both methods are explicit, two-level, single-step methods. However, both methods introduce a large amount of implicit numerical diffusion when the convection number is less than 1.0. Both methods are only first-order accurate in time, and the first-order upwind method is only first-order accurate in space. In spite of these disadvantages, both of these methods are useful in certain applications. However, it is obvious that methods with less implicit numerical diffusion, second-order accuracy in time, and second-order accuracy in space, are desirable. One such method, the leapfrog method, is presented in this section.

Recall the unsteady one-dimensional convection equation $\bar{f}_t + u\bar{f}_x = 0$. Replace the exact partial derivative $\bar{f}_t|_i^n$ by the second-order centered-difference approximation [Eq. (10.61b)] and the exact partial derivative $\bar{f}_x|_i^n$ by the second-order centered-difference approximation [Eq. (10.64*b*)]. The corresponding finite difference stencil is presented in Fig. 12.10. The resulting finite difference approximation of the convection equation is

$$\frac{f_i^{n+1} - f_i^{n-1}}{2\Delta t} + u\frac{f_{i+1}^n - f_{i-1}^n}{2\Delta x} = 0 \tag{12.47}$$

Solving for f_i^{n+1} yields

$$\boxed{f_i^{n+1} = f_i^{n-1} - c(f_{i+1}^n - f_{i-1}^n)} \tag{12.48}$$

where $c = u\Delta t/\Delta x$ is the convection number.

The leapfrog method appears to be a significant improvement over the Lax and first-order upwind methods, because of the increased accuracy of the finite difference approximation of $\bar{f}_t$. The addition of a third time level to a finite difference method has two potential disadvantages: all three time levels may have to be stored in the computer, thus increasing the storage requirements by 50 percent; and a special starting procedure is required to advance the solution from time level 0 to time level 1. The additional time level is not a problem in the

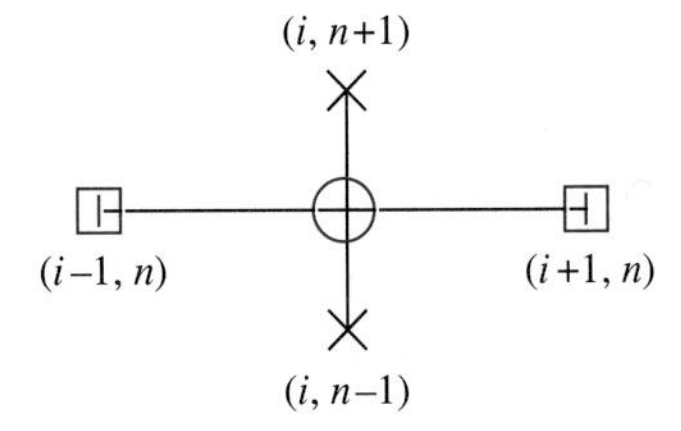

FIGURE 12.10
Leapfrog method stencil.

leapfrog method, because f_i^{n+1} can be stored in place of f_i^{n-1}, so only two levels of computer storage are required. The starting problem can be solved by using a two-level method to calculate the solution at time level 1.

The first form of the modified differential equation (MDE) is

$$f_t + u f_x = -\frac{1}{6} f_{ttt}\,\Delta t^2 - \frac{1}{120} f_{ttttt}\,\Delta t^4 - \cdots - \frac{1}{6} u f_{xxx}\,\Delta x^2 - \frac{1}{120} f_{xxxxx}\,\Delta x^4 - \cdots \tag{12.49}$$

and the second form of the MDE is

$$f_t + u f_x = \left(\frac{1}{6} u^3\,\Delta t^2 - \frac{1}{6} u\,\Delta x^2\right) f_{xxx} + \left(-\frac{3}{40} u^5\,\Delta t^4 + \frac{1}{12} u^3\,\Delta x^2\,\Delta t^2 - \frac{1}{120} u\,\Delta x^4\right) f_{xxxxx} + \cdots \tag{12.50}$$

As $\Delta t \to 0$ and $\Delta x \to 0$, Eq. (12.49) approaches $f_t + u f_x = 0$. Therefore, Eq. (12.48) is a consistent approximation of the convection equation. From Eq. (12.50), the FDE is $O(\Delta t^2) + O(\Delta x^2)$. From Eq. (12.50), there are no even spatial derivatives in the truncation error, so there is no implicit numerical diffusion. Implicit numerical dispersion, however, is present, except when $c = 1.0$. In that case, the truncation errors are zero, and the FDE matches the PDE exactly (for the linear convection equation only). The amplification factor G is given by

$$G^2 + I\,(2c \sin\theta)\,G - 1 = 0 \tag{12.51}$$

Solving Eq. (12.51) by the quadratic formula yields

$$G = \pm\sqrt{1 - c^2 \sin^2\theta} - I c \sin\theta \tag{12.52}$$

When $c^2 \sin^2\theta > 1$, which requires $c > 1$, the square root term is imaginary, and

$$G = I\left(-c \sin\theta \pm \sqrt{c^2 \sin^2\theta - 1}\right) \tag{12.53}$$

Equation (12.53) shows that $|G| > 1$, thus the method is unstable. When $c^2 \sin^2\theta \le 1$, which for generality requires that $c \le 1$, Eq. (12.52) yields

$$|G| = (1 - c^2 \sin^2\theta + c^2 \sin^2\theta)^{1/2} = 1 \tag{12.54}$$

Equation (12.54) shows that the leapfrog method is marginally stable (i.e., $|G| = 1$) for all values of $c \le 1$. This is a desirable result, because it means that there is no implicit numerical diffusion in the method. This result is also apparent from Eq. (12.50), which contains no even spatial derivatives in the truncation error. Consequently, the leapfrog approximation of the convection equation is stable if

$$c = \frac{u\,\Delta t}{\Delta x} \le 1 \tag{12.55}$$

The leapfrog approximation of the convection equation is consistent and conditionally stable. Consequently, by the Lax equivalence theorem, it is a convergent approximation of the convection equation.

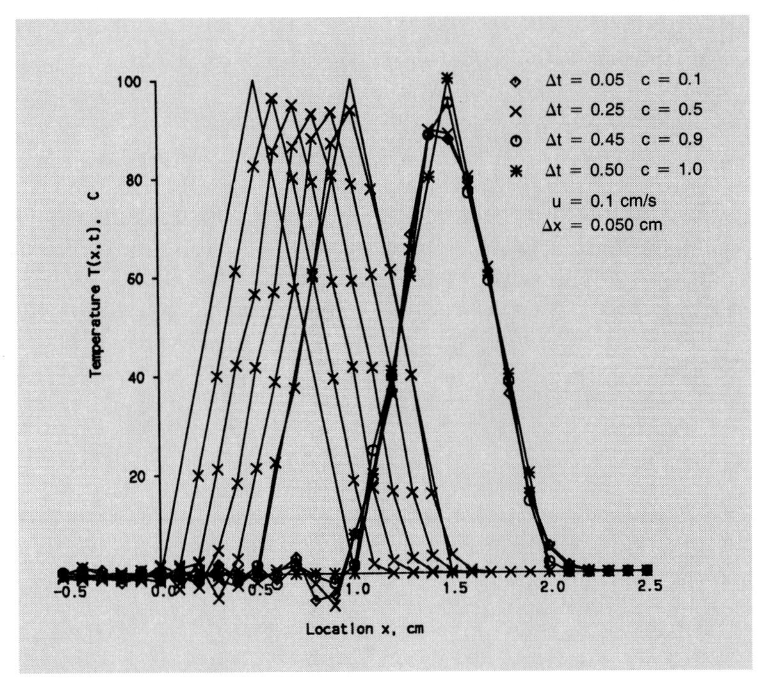

FIGURE 12.11
Solution by the leapfrog method.

Example 12.4. Solution by the leapfrog method. We will solve the convection problem presented in Section 12.1, using Eq. (12.48) with $\Delta x = 0.05$ cm. The results are presented in Fig. 12.11 at times from 1.0 to 5.0 s for $c = 0.5$, and at 10.0 s for $c = 0.1$, 0.5, 0.9, and 1.0. The first step in each case is the exact solution presented in Section 12.1.

Figure 12.11 illustrates several important features of the leapfrog method. When $c = 1.0$, the numerical solution is identical to the exact solution, for the linear convection equation. This is not true for the nonlinear convection equation. For $c < 1.0$, the amplitude of the solution is rounded slightly as the wave moves to the right. The results at $t = 10.0$ s for $c = 0.1, 0.5, 0.9$, and 1.0 show that the numerical signal propagation speed does not have much effect on the magnitude of the solution. However, the numerical solution lags the exact solution slightly, with the amount of lag increasing as the numerical signal propagation speed (i.e., the convection number) decreases. The results presented in Fig. 12.11 suggest that the leapfrog method is a fair method for solving the convection equation.

The explicit leapfrog method can be used in a straightforward manner to solve nonlinear PDEs, systems of PDEs, and multidimensional problems, as discussed in Section 12.14.

In summary, the leapfrog method applied to the convection equation is explicit, single-step, three-level, $O(\Delta t^2)+O(\Delta x^2)$, conditionally stable, and convergent. In some problems, the leapfrog method exhibits an odd–even decoupling, in which the errors at every other time level grow somewhat independently of the errors at the other set of every other time levels. Consequently, the leapfrog method is not a popular method for solving convection equations.

12.8 THE LAX–WENDROFF ONE-STEP METHOD

The Lax–Wendroff (1960) one-step method is a very popular explicit finite difference method. For the linear convection equation, the Lax–Wendroff one-step method is identical to the Leith (1965) method and the method presented by Noh and Protter (1963). For the unsteady one-dimensional convection equation $\bar{f}_t + u\bar{f}_x = 0$, the function to be determined is $\bar{f}(x, t)$. Expanding $\bar{f}(x, t)$ in a Taylor series in time gives

$$\bar{f}_i^{n+1} = \bar{f}_i^n + \bar{f}_t|_i^n \, \Delta t + \frac{1}{2}\bar{f}_{tt}|_i^n \, \Delta t^2 + O(\Delta t^3) \tag{12.56}$$

The derivative $\bar{f}_t$ is determined directly from the partial differential equation:

$$\bar{f}_t = -u\bar{f}_x \tag{12.57}$$

The derivative $\bar{f}_{tt}$ is determined by differentiating the partial differential equation with respect to time. Thus,

$$\bar{f}_{tt} = (\bar{f}_t)_t = (-u\bar{f}_x)_t = -u(\bar{f}_t)_x = -u(-u\bar{f}_x)_x = u^2\bar{f}_{xx} \tag{12.58}$$

Substituting Eqs. (12.57) and (12.58) into Eq. (12.56) yields

$$\bar{f}_i^{n+1} = \bar{f}_i^n - u\bar{f}_x|_i^n \, \Delta t + \frac{1}{2}u^2\bar{f}_{xx}|_i^n \, \Delta t^2 + O(\Delta t^3) \tag{12.59}$$

Approximating the two spatial derivatives by second-order centered-difference approximations [Eqs. (10.64*b*) and (10.69*b*), respectively] gives

$$f_i^{n+1} = f_i^n - u\left(\frac{f_{i+1}^n - f_{i-1}^n}{2\Delta x}\right)\Delta t + \frac{1}{2}u^2\left(\frac{f_{i+1}^n - 2f_i^n + f_{i-1}^n}{\Delta x^2}\right)\Delta t^2 \tag{12.60}$$

Introducing the convection number $c = u\Delta t/\Delta x$ yields

$$f_i^{n+1} = f_i^n - \frac{c}{2}(f_{i+1}^n - f_{i-1}^n) + \frac{c^2}{2}(f_{i+1}^n - 2f_i^n + f_{i-1}^n) \tag{12.61}$$

Equation (12.61) is the Lax–Wendroff one-step approximation of the linear convection equation. The corresponding finite difference stencil is presented in Fig. 12.12. Equation (12.61) is identical to the third method-of-characteristics approximation of the linear convection equation presented in Section 12.11 [see Eq. (12.92)].

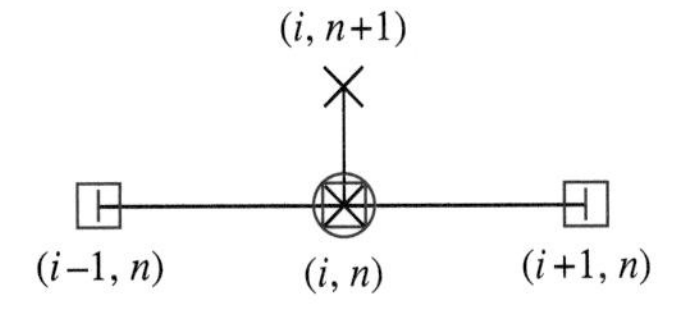

FIGURE 12.12
Lax–Wendroff one-step method stencil.

The first form of the modified differential equation (MDE) is

$$f_t + uf_x = -\frac{1}{2}f_{tt}\,\Delta t - \frac{1}{6}f_{ttt}\,\Delta t^2 - \frac{1}{24}f_{tttt}\,\Delta t^3 - \cdots - \frac{1}{6}uf_{xxx}\,\Delta x^2 - \cdots$$
$$+ \frac{1}{2}u^2 f_{xx}\,\Delta t + \frac{1}{24}u^2 f_{xxxx}\,\Delta x^2\,\Delta t + \cdots \tag{12.62}$$

and the second form of the MDE is

$$f_t + uf_x = \left(-\frac{1}{6}u\,\Delta x^2 + \frac{1}{6}u^3\,\Delta t^2\right)f_{xxx} + \left(-\frac{1}{8}u^2\,\Delta x^2\,\Delta t + \frac{1}{8}u^4\,\Delta t^3\right)f_{xxxx} + \cdots \tag{12.63}$$

As $\Delta t \to 0$ and $\Delta x \to 0$, Eq. (12.62) approaches $f_t + uf_x$. Consequently, Eq. (12.61) is a consistent approximation of the convection equation. Equation (12.62) suggests that the FDE is $O(\Delta t) + O(\Delta x^2)$. However, as shown by Eq. (12.63), the $O(\Delta t)$ terms cancel exactly, and the FDE is $O(\Delta t^2) + O(\Delta x^2)$. For this FDE, the second form of the MDE is required to determine the true order of the approximation. Because the leading truncation error term in Eq. (12.63) contains an odd space derivative, the FDE is predominately dispersive. Higher-order even derivatives do appear, so the FDE has some implicit numerical diffusion. When the convection number c is unity, all the truncation errors are zero, and the exact solution is obtained (for the linear convection equation only). The amplification factor G is given by

$$G = \left((1 - c^2) + c^2\cos\theta\right) - I c\sin\theta \tag{12.64}$$

Equation (12.64) represents an ellipse in the complex plane, as illustrated in Fig. 12.13. The center of the ellipse is at $(1 - c^2, 0)$ and the length of the axes of the ellipse are c and c^2. For stability, $|G| \le 1$, which requires that the ellipse lie on or within the unit circle. From Fig. 12.13, three conditions are obvious. The axes c and c^2 must both be less than or equal to unity. In addition, at point (1,0), the curvature of the ellipse must be greater than the curvature of the unit circle. With some further analysis, it can be shown that this condition is satisfied if $c \le 1$. All three necessary conditions are satisfied by the single sufficient condition

$$\boxed{c = \frac{u\,\Delta t}{\Delta x} \le 1} \tag{12.65}$$

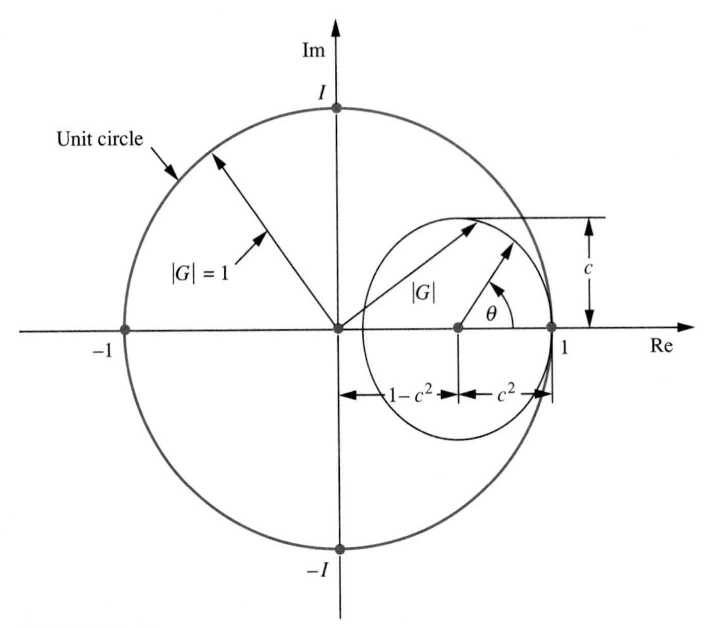

FIGURE 12.13
Locus of the amplification factor G for the Lax–Wendroff one-step method.

Consequently, the method is conditionally stable. The Lax–Wendroff one-step approximation of the convection equation is consistent and conditionally stable. Consequently, by the Lax equivalence theorem, it is a convergent finite difference approximation of the convection equation.

Example 12.5. Solution by the Lax–Wendroff one-step method. We wil solve the convection problem presented in Section 12.1, using Eq. (12.61) for $\Delta x = 0.05$ cm. The results are presented in Fig. 12.14 at times from 1.0 to 5.0 s for $c = 0.5$, and at 10.0 s for $c = 0.1, 0.5, 0.9$, and 1.0.

Figure 12.14 illustrates several important features of Eq. (12.61). When $c = 1.0$, the numerical solution is identical to the exact solution, for the linear convection equation. That is not the case for the nonlinear convection equation. When $c = 0.5$, the amplitude of the solution is damped slightly, and the sharp peak becomes rounded. However, the wave shape is maintained quite well. That is not the case for the FTCS method and the first-order upwind method, which are illustrated in Figs. 12.6 and 12.9. The results at $t = 10.0$ s, for $c = 0.1, 0.5$, and 0.9, are all reasonable approximations of the exact solution. There is some decrease in the numerical convection velocity. Slight *wiggles* appear in the trailing portion of the wave, due to implicit numerical dispersion. Such wiggles are a common feature of second-order finite difference approximations of the time derivative in convection problems. Overall, the Lax–Wendroff one-step method yields a good solution to the linear convection equation.

The Lax–Wendroff one-step method is an efficient and accurate method for solving the linear convection equation. For nonlinear PDEs and systems of PDEs, however, the method becomes quite complicated. The complications arise in the

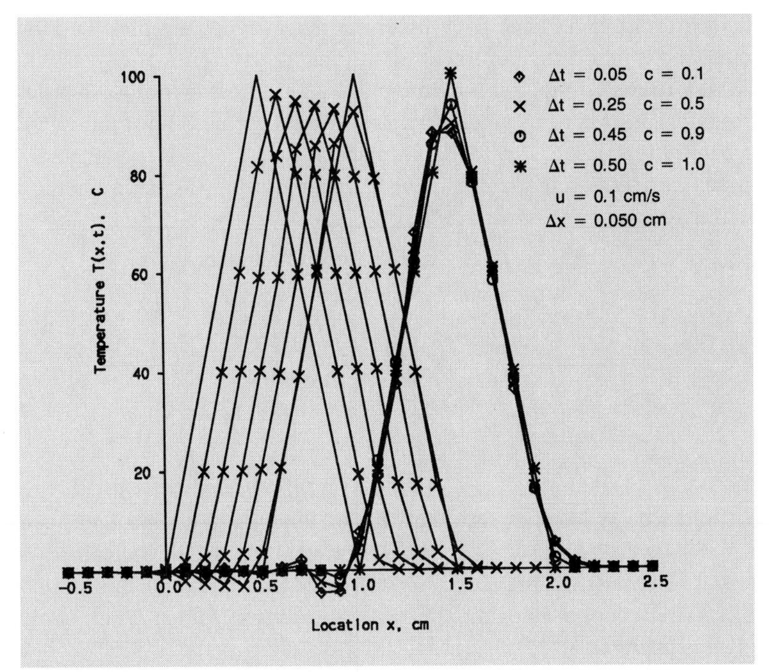

FIGURE 12.14
Solution by the Lax–Wendroff one-step method.

replacement of the second-order time derivative $\overline{f}_{tt}$ in terms of space derivatives by differentiating the governing partial differential equation. The simple result obtained in Eq. (12.58) no longer applies. Consequently, the Lax–Wendroff one-step method is not used very often. More efficient methods, such as the Lax–Wendroff two-step methods presented in Section 12.9 and the MacCormack method presented in Section 12.10, are generally used for nonlinear equations and systems of equations. These methods have the same general features as the Lax–Wendroff one-step method, but they are considerably less complicated for nonlinear PDEs, and thus considerably more efficient.

In summary, the Lax–Wendroff one-step method applied to the convection equation is explicit, two-level, single-step, $O(\Delta t^2)+O(\Delta x^2)$, conditionally stable, and convergent. The method is quite complicated for nonlinear PDEs, systems of PDEs, and two- and three-dimensional physical spaces.

12.9 LAX–WENDROFF TWO-STEP METHODS

The Lax–Wendroff (1960) one-step method presented in Section 12.8 has many desirable features when applied to the linear convection equation. However, when applied to a nonlinear PDE or a system of PDEs, the method becomes considerably more complicated. Richtmyer (1963) presented a three-level two-step method that is equivalent to the Lax–Wendroff one-step method for the linear convection equation. The first step uses the Lax (1954) method to obtain provisional values at the second time level, and the second step uses the leapfrog method to obtain final values at the third time level. The Richtmyer method is much simpler than the Lax–Wendroff one-step method for nonlinear equations and systems of equations. Quite commonly, any two-step method which can be interpreted as a second-order Taylor series in time is referred to as a *two-step Lax–Wendroff* method or a method of the *Lax–Wendroff type*.

For the linear convection equation $\bar{f}_t + u\bar{f}_x = 0$, the two-step method proposed by Richtmyer (1963) is

$$f_i^{n+1} = \frac{1}{2}(f_{i+1}^n + f_{i-1}^n) - \frac{c}{2}(f_{i+1}^n - f_{i-1}^n) \tag{12.66}$$

$$f_i^{n+2} = f_i^n - c(f_{i+1}^{n+1} - f_{i-1}^{n+1}) \tag{12.67}$$

where Eq. (12.66) is the Lax method [Eq. (12.24)] applied from time level n to time level $n + 1$ and Eq. (12.67) is the leapfrog method [Eq. (12.48)] applied from time level $n + 1$ to time level $n + 2$. The first step [i.e., the Lax method] is a provisional step. The results of this step are used only to implement the second step. The results of the second step are the desired solution values. The finite difference stencil is illustrated in Fig. 12.15.

Equations (12.66) and (12.67) comprise a Lax–Wendroff type two-step method for the linear convection equation. This Lax–Wendroff two-step method is an explicit, three-level, two-step, $O(\Delta t^2) + O(\Delta x^2)$, finite difference method. The third time level is not a problem, because the value of f_i^{n+2} can be stored in place of f_i^n, so only two levels of computer storage are required.

Equations (12.66) and (12.67) do not look anything like the Lax–Wendroff one-step method [i.e., Eq. (12.61)]. However, substituting Eq. (12.66) applied at grid points $(i-1)$ and $(i+1)$ into Eq. (12.67) gives Eq. (12.61) [for a time step of $2\Delta t$ and a space increment of $2\Delta x$]. Consequently, the two methods are equivalent for the linear convection equation. For nonlinear PDEs or systems of PDEs, the two methods, while similar in behavior, are not identical.

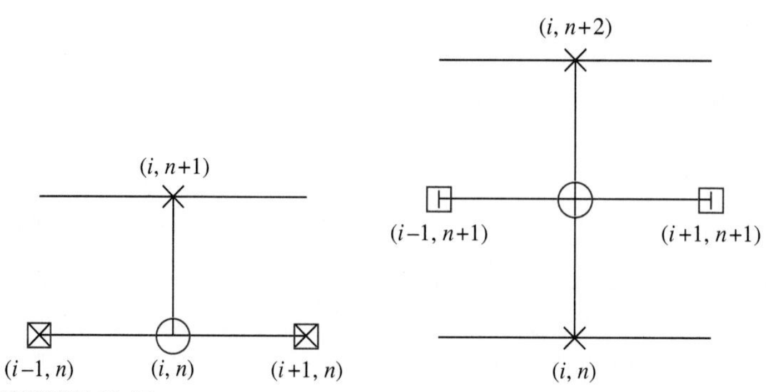

FIGURE 12.15
Lax–Wendroff (Richtmyer) two-step method stencil.

Since the Lax–Wendroff two-step method proposed by Richtmyer is equivalent to the Lax–Wendroff one-step method for the linear convection equation, it follows that the consistency and stability analyses are identical. Thus, as demonstrated in Section 12.8, the method is consistent with the convection equation, $O(\Delta t^2) + O(\Delta x^2)$, conditionally stable ($c = u\,\Delta t/\Delta x \le 1$), and convergent.

Example 12.6. Solution by the Lax–Wendroff (Richtmyer) two-step method. We will solve the convection problem presented in Section 12.1, using Eqs. (12.66) and (12.67) for $\Delta x = 0.05$ cm. The results are presented in Fig. 12.16 at times from 1.0 to 5.0 s for $c = 0.5$, and at 10.0 s for $c = 0.1, 0.5, 0.9$, and 1.0. The general features of the numerical solution are similar to those presented in Fig. 12.14 for the Lax–Wendroff one-step method. The implicit numerical diffusion and dispersion are more severe, however, because the Lax–Wendroff two-step method is equivalent to the Lax–Wendroff one-step method with a time step of $2\Delta t$ and a spatial grid size of $2\Delta x$. In fact, applying the Lax–Wendroff two-step method with $\Delta x = 0.025$ cm, with a corresponding halving of Δt, yields the same results as presented in Fig. 12.14.

Numerous other two-step methods have been proposed. Only one of them is mentioned here. Burstein (1967) modified the Richtmyer method by applying it over half-mesh spacings $\Delta x/2$ and $\Delta t/2$. The corresponding finite difference

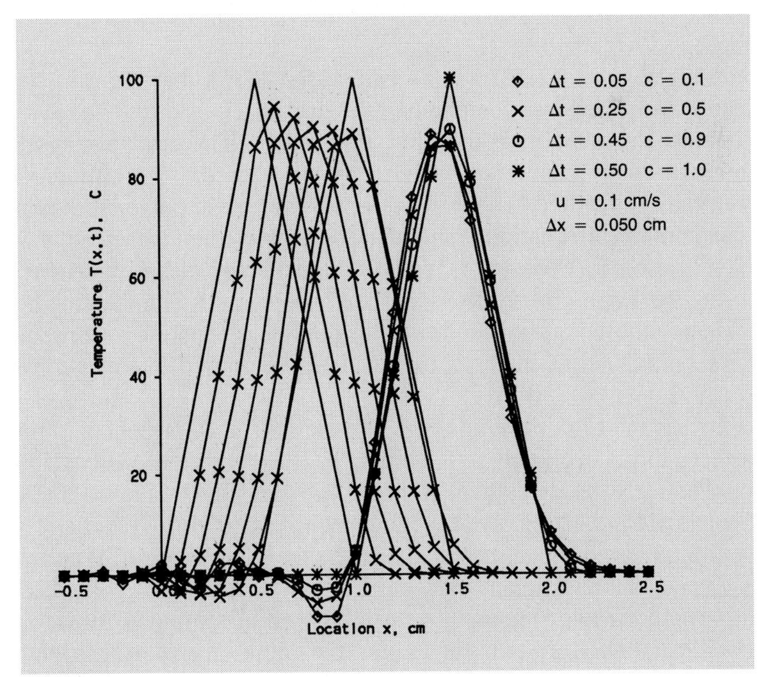

FIGURE 12.16
Solution by the Lax–Wendroff (Richtmyer) two-step method.

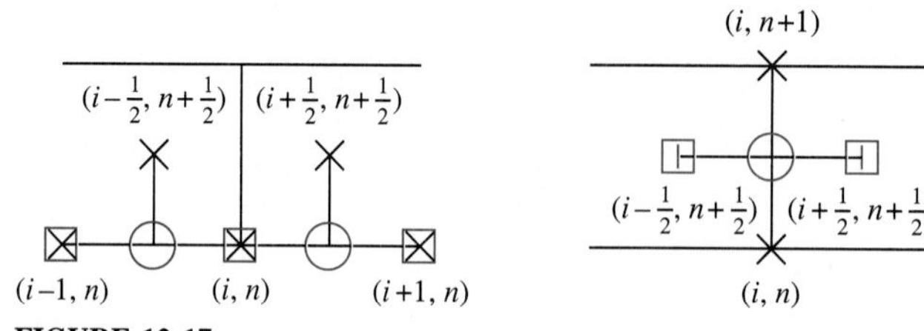

FIGURE 12.17
Burstein method stencil.

stencil is illustrated in Fig. 12.17. In that case, Eqs. (12.66) and (12.67) become

$$f_{i+1/2}^{n+1/2} = \frac{1}{2}(f_{i+1}^n + f_i^n) - \frac{c}{2}(f_{i+1}^n - f_i^n) \tag{12.68}$$

$$f_{i-1/2}^{n+1/2} = \frac{1}{2}(f_i^n + f_{i-1}^n) - \frac{c}{2}(f_i^n - f_{i-1}^n) \tag{12.69}$$

$$f_i^{n+1} = f_i^n - c\left(f_{i+1/2}^{n+1/2} - f_{i-1/2}^{n+1/2}\right) \tag{12.70}$$

For the linear convection equation, the Burstein method is equivalent to the Richtmyer method at interior points away from the boundaries, but difficulties arise at the boundaries at the half-mesh locations. Difficulties arise for nonlinear PDEs, because the function values are not defined at the half-mesh locations. Consequently, half-mesh methods like the Burstein method are not as popular as full-mesh methods.

Comparing Figures 12.12, 12.15, and 12.17 shows that the grid spacings for the Richtmyer method must be one-half the grid spacings of the Lax–Wendroff method to obtain the solution at the same grid points. The grid spacings for the Burstein method are the same as the grid spacings of the Lax–Wendroff one-step method, but the method has problems at the half-mesh points with boundary conditions and nonlinear equations. The MacCormack method presented in Section 12.10, which is also a Lax–Wendroff type two-step method, achieves second-order accuracy using the same grid spacings as the Lax–Wendroff one-step method and has no problems with boundary conditions or nonlinear equations. Consequently, the Richtmyer and Burstein methods are not frequently used to solve convection problems.

In summary, the Lax–Wendroff type two-step methods presented in this section are explicit, three-level, two-step, $O(\Delta t^2) + O(\Delta x^2)$, conditionally stable, and convergent. The methods are equivalent to the Lax–Wendroff one-step method for the linear convection equation. However, for nonlinear PDEs, systems of PDEs, and two- and three-dimensional physical spaces, the Lax–Wendroff type two-step methods are much more efficient than the Lax–Wendroff one-step method. The explicit Lax–Wendroff two-step methods can be used in a straightforward manner to solve nonlinear PDEs, systems of PDEs, and multidimensional problems, as discussed in Section 12.14.

12.10 THE MACCORMACK METHOD

MacCormack (1969) proposed a two-step predictor–corrector finite difference method of the Lax–Wendroff type. The MacCormack method uses the same grid spacings as the Lax–Wendroff (1960) one-step method, thus eliminating the requirement of more grid points associated with the Richtmyer (1963) method and the requirement of boundary conditions at half-mesh points associated with the Burstein (1967) method. The MacCormack method can solve linear partial differential equations, nonlinear PDEs, and systems of PDEs with equal ease, whereas the Lax–Wendroff one-step method becomes quite complicated for nonlinear PDEs and systems of PDEs. Consequently, the MacCormack method is a widely used method.

The basis of the Lax–Wendroff one-step method (see Section 12.8) is the second-order Taylor series given in Eq. (12.56), where $\bar{f}_t$ is determined directly from the PDE and $\bar{f}_{tt}$ is determined by differentiating the PDE with respect to time. An alternate approach for evaluating $\bar{f}_{tt}|_i^n$ employs a first-order forward-time Taylor series for $\bar{f}_t|_i^{n+1}$ about grid point (i, n). Thus,

$$\bar{f}_t|_i^{n+1} = \bar{f}_t|_i^n + \bar{f}_{tt}|_i^n\,\Delta t + O(\Delta t^2) \tag{12.71}$$

Solving Eq. (12.71) for $\bar{f}_{tt}|_i^n$ yields

$$\bar{f}_{tt}|_i^n = \frac{\bar{f}_t|_i^{n+1} - \bar{f}_t|_i^n}{\Delta t} + O(\Delta t) \tag{12.72}$$

Substituting Eq. (12.72) into Eq. (12.56) gives

$$\bar{f}_i^{n+1} = \bar{f}_i^n + \frac{1}{2}\left(\bar{f}_t|_i^n + \bar{f}_t|_i^{n+1}\right)\Delta t + O(\Delta t^3) \tag{12.73}$$

Equation (12.73) can be solved for f_i^{n+1} by determining $\bar{f}_t|_i^n$ and $\bar{f}_t|_i^{n+1}$ from the PDE and dropping the truncation error terms. This gives

$$f_i^{n+1} = f_i^n - \frac{1}{2}\left(u\bar{f}_x|_i^n + u\bar{f}_x|_i^{n+1}\right)\Delta t \tag{12.74}$$

Replacing $\bar{f}_x|_i^n$ and $\bar{f}_x|_i^{n+1}$ by second-order centered-difference approximations yields an $O(\Delta t^3) + O(\Delta x^2)$ FDE, which has $O(\Delta t^2)$ global order. This replacement yields an implicit FDE, which is difficult to solve for nonlinear PDEs. Consequently, a predictor-corrector approach is used to solve Eq. (12.74). MacCormack proposed a two-step method that calculates provisional values of $\overline{f_i^{n+1}}$, using first-order forward-difference approximations of $\bar{f}_t|_i^n$ and $\bar{f}_x|_i^n$, to give

$$\boxed{f_i^{\overline{n+1}} = f_i^n - c\,(f_{i+1}^n - f_i^n)} \tag{12.75}$$

where $c = u\,\Delta t/\Delta x$ is the convection number. In the second and final step,

Eq. (12.74) is solved by evaluating $f_x|_i^n$ using the first-order forward-difference approximation for $\overline{f}_x|_i^n$ and evaluating $f_x|_i^{n+1}$ using the first-order backward-difference approximation based on the provisional values of $f^{\overline{n+1}}$. Equation (12.74) becomes

$$f_i^{n+1} = f_i^n - \frac{1}{2}\left(c\left(f_{i+1}^n - f_i^n\right) + c\left(f_i^{\overline{n+1}} - f_{i-1}^{\overline{n+1}}\right)\right) \tag{12.76}$$

Rearranging Eq. (12.76) and introducing Eq. (12.75) yields a computationally more efficient form of the corrector equation:

$$\boxed{f_i^{n+1} = \frac{1}{2}\left(f_i^n + f_i^{\overline{n+1}} - c\left(f_i^{\overline{n+1}} - f_{i+1}^{\overline{n-1}}\right)\right)} \tag{12.77}$$

Equations (12.75) and (12.77) comprise the MacCormack approximation of the linear convection equation. The finite difference stencils are presented in Fig. 12.18.

Equation (12.75) employs a forward-difference approximation of $\overline{f}_x|_i^n$, and Eq. (12.76) employs a backward-difference approximation of $\overline{f}_x|_i^{n+1}$. This differencing can be reversed. Either way, there is a slight bias in the solution, due to the one-sided differences. If desired, this bias can be reduced by alternating the direction of the predictor and corrector spatial differences from one time level to the next.

The properties of the MacCormack method are not readily apparent from Eqs. (12.75) and (12.77). The time averaging of the space derivatives in the corrector, Eq. (12.76), suggests that the method may be $O(\Delta t^2)$. Since both space derivatives are one-sided first-order differences, it would appear that the overall method is $O(\Delta x)$. However, a very fortuitous cancellation of the $O(\Delta x)$ truncation error terms occurs, and the MacCormack method is $O(\Delta x^2)$.

Equations (12.75) and (12.77) do not look anything like the Lax–Wendroff one-step method [i.e., Eq. (12.61)]. However, substituting Eq. (12.75), applied at grid points (i, n) and $(i-1, n)$, into Eq. (12.77) gives Eq. (12.61). Consequently, the two methods are identical for the linear convection equation. For nonlinear

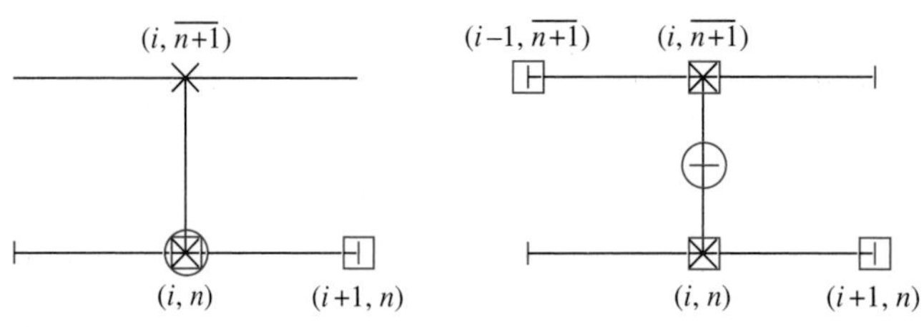

FIGURE 12.18
MacCormack method stencil.

PDEs or systems of PDEs, the two methods, while similar in behavior, are not identical.

Since the MacCormack method is identical to the Lax–Wendroff one-step method, for the linear convection equation, it follows that the consistency and stability analyses are identical. Thus, as demonstrated in Section 12.8, the method is consistent with the convection equation, $O(\Delta t^2) + O(\Delta x^2)$, conditionally stable (i.e., $c = u\Delta t/\Delta x \leq 1$), and convergent.

Example 12.7. Solution by the MacCormack method. The MacCormack approximation of the linear convection equation is identical to the Lax–Wendroff one-step approximation of the linear convection equation. Consequently, the results presented in Example 12.5 also apply to the MacCormack method. The MacCormack method is an excellent method for solving convection problems.

When the partial differential equation being solved is nonlinear (i.e., the coefficient of $\bar{f}_x$ depends on $\bar{f}$), the coefficient is simply evaluated at grid point (i, n) for the predictor and at grid point $(i, \overline{n+1})$ for the corrector. When solving systems of PDEs, Eqs. (12.75) and (12.77) are simply applied to every PDE in the system. The MacCormack method extends directly to two- and three-dimensional physical spaces simply by adding on the appropriate one-sided finite difference approximations to the y and z space derivatives. The stability boundaries are more restrictive in those cases. The MacCormack method also can be used to solve the parabolic convection–diffusion equation. In view of these features of the MacCormack method, it is a very popular method for solving both parabolic and hyperbolic PDEs.

In summary, the MacCormack approximation of the convection equation is explicit, two-level, two-step, $O(\Delta t^2) + O(\Delta x^2)$, conditionally stable, and convergent. The method is identical to the Lax–Wendroff one-step method for the linear convection equation. However, for nonlinear equations, systems of equations, and two- and three-dimensional physical spaces, the MacCormack method is much more efficient than the Lax–Wendroff one-step method.

12.11 THE NUMERICAL METHOD OF CHARACTERISTICS

The method of characteristics, presented in Section 12.2, is essentially a coordinate transformation that transforms the governing partial differential equation from physical coordinates (i.e., x and t) to characteristic coordinates (i.e., position along the characteristic curves). The governing partial differential equation can be replaced by the equivalent set of the corresponding characteristic equation and the applicable compatibility equation. The characteristic coordinate system is constructed by integrating the characteristic equation, and the distribution of the dependent variable along the characteristic curves is determined by integrating the compatibility equation along the characteristic curves. When the characteristic equation and the compatibility equation are coupled or nonlinear, numerical integration is required.

For the linear convection equation, $\bar{f}_t + u\bar{f}_x = 0$, as shown in Section 12.2, the characteristic equation is [see Eq. (12.9)]

$$\frac{dx}{dt} = u \tag{12.78}$$

and the corresponding compatibility equation is [see Eq. (12.11)]

$$\frac{d\bar{f}}{dt} = 0 \tag{12.79}$$

Two different methods can be employed for constructing the characteristic coordinate system. The *direct marching* method follows a discrete identifiable characteristic curve from its origin on the initial data surface to the final extent of its range of interest, as illustrated in Fig. 12.19*a*. The *inverse marching* method employs a prespecified grid in the region of interest, and constructs a local characteristic coordinate system at each prespecified grid point, as illustrated in Fig. 12.19*b*.

The direct marching method has several advantages. Primarily, information is propagated along continuous characteristic curves. No interpolation is needed to obtain the data required to advance the solution along a characteristic curve. These advantages result in very accurate numerical solutions. However, the direct marching method has several disadvantages. The step sizes along the various characteristic curves may be different, especially if more than one first-order partial differential equation is involved or if the partial differential equation is nonlinear. This causes the solution to be obtained at different values of time on each characteristic curve. The characteristic curves may coalesce or spread apart in a nonlinear problem, resulting in a highly nonuniform finite difference grid. In problems involving systems of PDEs in more than two independent variables, the direct marching method cannot be employed.

The inverse marching method has several advantages. The most important advantage is the use of a regular prespecified grid. The solution is obtained at the same values of time on all of the characteristic curves. However, the inverse marching method has two major disadvantages. First, the time step must be the same at all grid points. This is a serious disadvantage in nonlinear problems, where the convection speed may vary greatly over the region of interest. The second major disadvantage is that the rearward projected characteristic curves do not intersect the known solution surface at the prespecified grid points. Consequently, the initial data at the points of intersection of the rearward projected characteristic curves and the previous solution surface must be determined by interpolation, which takes computational effort and introduces interpolation errors into the initial data.

In most unsteady applications, the advantages of the regular prespecified grid associated with the inverse marching method outweigh the disadvantages of the method, and it is preferred over the direct marching method. Consequently, the inverse marching method is employed in the numerical method of characteristics developed in the remainder of this section.

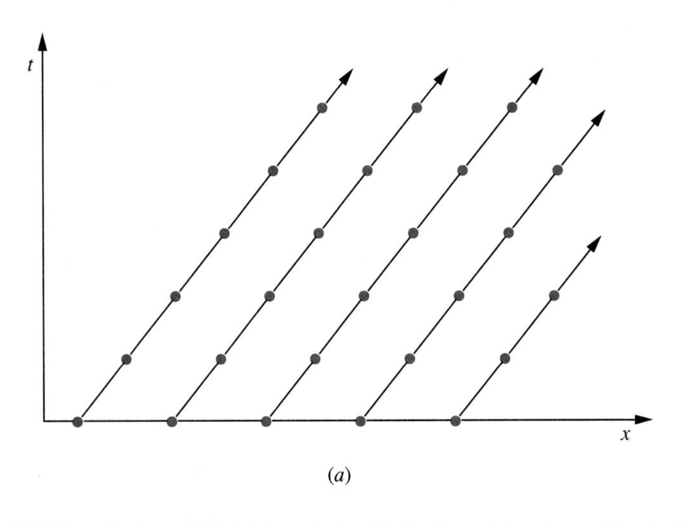

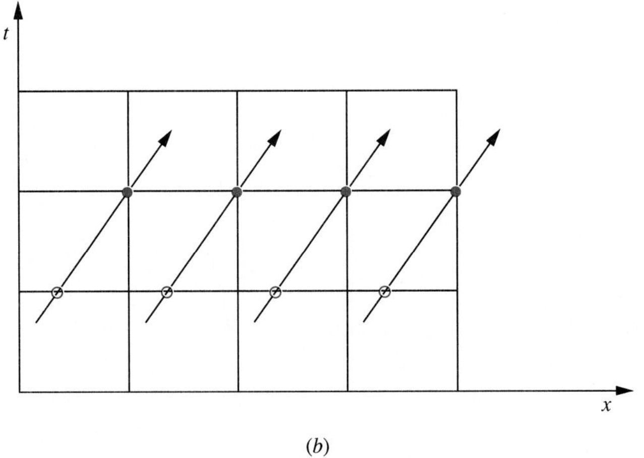

FIGURE 12.19
Characteristic networks: (*a*) direct marching method; (*b*) inverse marching method.

Figure 12.20 illustrates the computational network at a prespecified grid point in the inverse marching method. Point $(i, n + 1)$ is the solution point. The characteristic curve passing through the solution point is projected rearward until it intersects time level n at point a. For the linear convection equation, Eq. (12.78) yields

$$\boxed{(x_i - x_a) = u(t^{n+1} - t^n) = u\,\Delta t} \qquad (12.80)$$

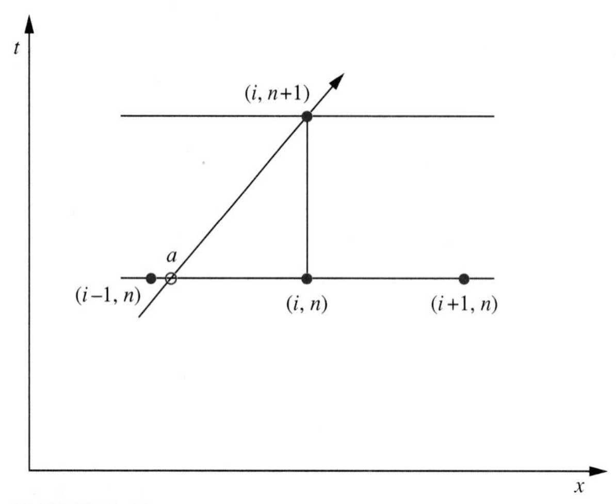

FIGURE 12.20
Computational network for the inverse marching method.

and Eq. (12.79) gives

$$\boxed{f_i^{n+1} = f_a} \tag{12.81}$$

At this point, an interpolating polynomial must be fitted to the initial data at time level n to evaluate f_a. The value of x_a determined from Eq. (12.80) is substituted into the interpolating polynomial to determine f_a, which, by Eq. (12.81), is equal to f_i^{n+1}. Several choices exist for fitting the interpolating polynomial. The three most common choices for fitting the interpolating polynomial are:

1. Linear interpolation using points $(i-1, n)$ and $(i+1, n)$
2. Linear interpolation using points $(i-1, n)$ and (i, n)
3. Quadratic interpolation using points $(i-1, n)$, (i, n), and $(i+1, n)$

All three choices are illustrated in the following discussion.

FIRST MOC ALGORITHM. First, consider linear interpolation using grid points $(i-1, n)$ and $(i+1, n)$. Thus,

$$\frac{f_{i+1}^n - f_a}{f_{i+1}^n - f_{i-1}^n} = \frac{x_{i+1} - x_a}{x_{i+1} - x_{i-1}} = \frac{\Delta x + (x_i - x_a)}{2\Delta x} \tag{12.82}$$

Substituting Eq. (12.80) into Eq. (12.82) gives

$$\frac{f_{i+1}^n - f_a}{f_{i+1}^n - f_{i-1}^n} = \frac{\Delta x + u\,\Delta t}{2\Delta x} = \frac{1}{2}\left(1 + \frac{u\,\Delta t}{\Delta x}\right) = \frac{1}{2}(1 + c) \tag{12.83}$$

where $c = u\Delta t/\Delta x$ is the convection number. Solving Eq. (12.83) for f_a yields

$$f_a = f_{i+1}^n - \frac{1}{2}(1 + c)\left(f_{i+1}^n - f_{i-1}^n\right) \tag{12.84}$$

Rearranging Eq. (12.84) and substituting into Eq. (12.81) yields

$$\boxed{f_i^{n+1} = \frac{1}{2}(f_{i+1}^n + f_{i-1}^n) - \frac{c}{2}(f_{i+1}^n - f_{i-1}^n)} \tag{12.85}$$

Equation (12.85) is the first method-of-characteristics approximation of the linear convection equation. For the linear convection equation, Eq. (12.85) is identical to the Lax method [Eq. (12.24)], which is discussed in Section 12.4.

When one solves linear PDEs, the finite difference equations approximating the characteristic equation and the compatibility equation, along with the interpolating polynomial used to determine the initial data, can usually be combined to yield a single finite difference equation, such as Eq. (12.85). In such cases, consistency, order, stability, convergence, and implicit numerical diffusion and dispersion can be investigated directly, as discussed in Chapter 10. When the PDE is nonlinear, the characteristic and compatibility equations must be integrated numerically, as illustrated by Eqs. (12.14) and (12.17). In such cases, it can be extremely tedious to combine the corresponding FDEs and the interpolating polynomial to obtain a single FDE.

SECOND MOC ALGORITHM. Next, consider linear interpolation using points $(i-1, n)$ and (i, n). Thus,

$$\frac{f_i^n - f_a}{f_i^n - f_{i-1}^n} = \frac{x_i - x_a}{x_i - x_{i-1}} \tag{12.86}$$

Substituting Eq. (12.80) into Eq. (12.86) gives

$$\frac{f_i^n - f_a}{f_i^n - f_{i-1}^n} = \frac{u\,\Delta t}{\Delta x} = c \tag{12.87}$$

Solving Eq. (12.87) for f_a and substituting the result into Eq. (12.81) yields

$$\boxed{f_i^{n+1} = f_i^n - c(f_i^n - f_{i-1}^n)} \tag{12.88}$$

Equation (12.88) is the second method-of-characteristics approximation of the linear convection equation. For the linear convection equation, Eq. (12.88) is identical to the first-order upwind method [see Eq. (12.42)], which is discussed in Section 12.6.

THIRD MOC ALGORITHM. Finally, consider quadratic interpolation using grid points $(i-1, n)$, (i, n), and $(i+1, n)$. Thus,

$$f(x) = a + bx + cx^2 \tag{12.89}$$

Fitting Eq. (12.89) to the three grid points, with $x = 0$ at grid point (i, n) and $x = \pm\Delta x$ at grid points $(i \pm 1, n)$, gives

$$f(x) = f_i^n + \frac{f_{i+1}^n - f_{i-1}^n}{2\Delta x}x + \frac{f_{i+1}^n - 2f_i^n + f_{i-1}^n}{2\Delta x^2}x^2 \tag{12.90}$$

From Eq. (12.80), for $x_i = 0$,

$$x_a = x_i - u\,\Delta t = -c\,\Delta x \tag{12.91}$$

Substituting Eq. (12.91) into Eq. (12.90) to determine f_a and substituting that result into Eq. (12.81) yields

$$\boxed{f_i^{n+1} = f_i^n - \frac{c}{2}(f_{i+1}^n - f_{i-1}^n) + \frac{c^2}{2}(f_{i+1}^n - 2f_i^n + f_{i-1}^n)} \tag{12.92}$$

Equation (12.92) is the third method-of-characteristics approximation of the linear convection equation. For the linear convection equation, Eq. (12.92) is identical to the Lax–Wendroff one-step method [Eq. (12.61)], which is presented in Section 12.8, and the MacCormack method, which is presented in Section 12.10.

The results presented in the foregoing discussion are all for the linear homogeneous convection equation. In that case, the differential equation for the characteristic curves, Eq. (12.78), and the corresponding compatibility equation, Eq. (12.79), can be integrated exactly. The results can be combined with an interpolating polynomial for $f(x)$ at time level n to yield a single finite difference equation. Equations (12.85), (12.88), and (12.92) are the results of such combinations.

Finite difference equations such as Eqs. (12.85), (12.88), and (12.92) mask the basic features of the numerical method of characteristics. In essence, the method of characteristics is a coordinate transformation that transforms the governing partial differential equation from physical coordinates (i.e., x and t) to characteristic coordinates (i.e., position along the characteristic curves). In the numerical method of characteristics, the characteristic coordinate system is first constructed by numerically integrating the characteristic equation. The distribution of the dependent variable along the characteristic curves is then determined by numerically integrating the compatibility equation along the characteristic curves. When the inverse marching method illustrated in Figure 12.19*b* is employed, a third step, interpolation in the initial data surface, is required.

In the general case for the nonlinear nonhomogeneous convection equation, each of these three steps must be performed explicitly. These three steps can be combined into a simple single finite difference equation only for the linear homogeneous convection equation. Example 12.8 illustrates the numerical method of characteristics for a nonlinear hyperbolic PDE.

Example 12.8. Numerical method of characteristics for a nonlinear PDE. Consider the nonlinear convection equation

$$\bar{f}_t + u\bar{f}_x = F \tag{12.93}$$

where the convection velocity, $u = u(\bar{f})$, and the source term, $F = F(t, x, \bar{f})$, both depend on the property being convected. For this case, the characteristic equation is [see Eq. (12.9)]

$$\frac{dx}{dt} = u(\bar{f}) \tag{12.94}$$

and the compatibility equation is [see Eq. (12.16)]

$$\frac{d\bar{f}}{dt} = F(t, x, \bar{f}) \tag{12.95}$$

Equations (12.94) and (12.95) comprise a coupled set of nonlinear ordinary differential equations. Their solution generally must be obtained numerically.

The classical numerical integration method employed in the numerical method of characteristics is the modified Euler method, which is a two-step predictor–corrector method (see Section 7.5). Consider the finite difference grid illustrated in Fig. 12.20. The solution of Eq. (12.94) for the predictor is

$$(x_i^{n+1} - x_a) = u(f_a)\,\Delta t \tag{12.96}$$

Equation (12.96) cannot be solved for x_a until f_a is known. Consequently, an iterative procedure is required to solve Eq. (12.96). For example, f_a could be approximated by f_i^n, $u(f_a)$ can then be calculated, and x_a can be determined. The value of $f_a = f(x_a)$ can then be approximated by fitting an interpolating polynomial to the initial data and interpolating. The value of u_a can then be recalculated for this value of f_a, and the above process can be repeated to obtain new values of x_a and f_a. This procedure can be repeated once, twice, or a specified number of times, or until some convergence criterion is satisfied. The solution of Eq. (12.95) for the predictor is

$$f_i^{\overline{n+1}} = f_a + F(t, x_a, f_a)\,\Delta t \tag{12.97}$$

where the superscript $\overline{n+1}$ denotes the predictor solution. This completes the predictor.

The solution of Eq. (12.94) for the corrector is

$$(x_i^{n+1} - x_a) = [u(f)]_{\text{average}}\,\Delta t \tag{12.98}$$

where the term $[u(f)]_{\text{average}}$ can be determined in either of two ways. In the first way, $u(f)$ is calculated at points a and $(i, \overline{n+1})$, using the results of the predictor calculations, and the two values are averaged. In the second way, f is calculated at points a and $(i, \overline{n+1})$ and averaged, and $u(f_{\text{average}})$ is calculated. In either case, x_a can be relocated. This, of course, changes the value of f_a and u_a, and the process can be iterated as described for the predictor. The solution of Eq. (12.95) for the corrector is then

$$f_i^{n+1} = f_a + [F(t, x, f)]_{\text{average}}\,\Delta t \tag{12.99}$$

where the term $[F(f)]_{\text{average}}$ can be determined in either of the two ways presented for solving Eq. (12.98). This completes the corrector.

The corrector steps for Eqs. (12.98) and (12.99) both can be iterated using the value f_i^{n+1} determined in Eq. (12.99). Repetitive iteration is generally not as worthwhile as reducing the grid spacing, especially in a second-order method.

A good understanding of the method of characteristics is essential to the development of finite difference methods for solving hyperbolic partial differential equations. Physical paths of propagation of information through the solution domain are present. Proper account of these paths of propagation must be taken in order to obtain physically correct numerical solutions of hyperbolic partial differential equations.

12.12 THE BACKWARD-TIME CENTERED-SPACE METHOD

The method of characteristics, the Lax method, the upwind method, the leapfrog method, and the Lax–Wendroff type methods are all examples of explicit finite difference methods. In explicit methods, the finite difference approximations to the individual exact partial derivatives in the partial differential equation are evaluated at a grid point at the known time level. Consequently, the solution at a point at the next time level can be expressed explicitly in terms of the solution at known grid points. Explicit finite difference methods have many desirable features. Foremost among these for hyperbolic PDEs is that explicit methods have a finite numerical signal propagation speed, which gives rise to finite numerical domains of dependence and ranges of influence. Hyperbolic PDEs have a finite physical propagation speed, which gives rise to finite physical domains of dependence and ranges of influence. Consequently, explicit finite difference methods closely match the physical propagation properties of hyperbolic PDEs.

However, explicit methods share one undesirable feature: they are only conditionally stable. Consequently, the allowable time step is usually quite small, and the amount of computational effort required to obtain the solution of some problems is immense. A procedure for avoiding the time step limitation would obviously be desirable. Implicit finite difference methods furnish such a procedure. Implicit finite difference methods are unconditionally stable. There is no limit on the allowable time step required to achieve a stable solution. There is, of course, some practical limit on the time step required to maintain the truncation errors within reasonable limits, but this is not a stability consideration; it is an accuracy consideration.

Implicit methods do have some disadvantages, however. The foremost disadvantage is that the solution at a point at the solution time level depends on the solutions at neighboring points at the solution time level, which are also unknown. Consequently, the solution is implied in terms of other unknown solutions, systems of equations must be solved to obtain the solution at each time level, and the numerical signal propagation speed is infinite. Additional complexities arise when the partial differential equations are nonlinear. This gives rise to nonlinear finite difference equations, which must be solved by some manner of linearization, iteration, or both. However, the major disadvantage is the infinite numerical signal propagation speed, which gives rise to infinite domains of dependence and ranges of influence. This obviously violates the finite domains of dependence and ranges of influence associated with hyperbolic PDEs.

In spite of these disadvantages, the advantage of unconditional stability makes implicit finite difference methods attractive. Consequently, the backward-time centered-space (BTCS) method is presented in this section.

In this section, we will solve the unsteady one-dimensional convection equation by the backward-time centered-space (BTCS) method. This method is also called the *fully implicit* method. The finite difference equation (FDE) which approximates the partial differential equation is obtained by replacing the exact partial derivative $\bar{f}_t$ with the first-order backward-difference approximation [Eq. (10.57*b*)] and the exact partial derivative $\bar{f}_x$ with the second-order centered-space approximation [Eq. (10.64*b*)]. The finite difference stencil is presented in Fig. 12.21. The resulting finite difference approximation of the convection equation is

$$\frac{f_i^{n+1} - f_i^n}{\Delta t} + u\frac{f_{i+1}^{n+1} - f_{i-1}^{n+1}}{2\Delta x} = 0 \tag{12.100}$$

Rearranging Eq. (12.100) yields

$$\boxed{-\frac{c}{2}f_{i-1}^{n+1} + f_i^{n+1} + \frac{c}{2}f_{i+1}^{n+1} = f_i^n} \tag{12.101}$$

where $c = u\Delta t/\Delta x$ is the convection number.

Equation (12.101) cannot be solved explicitly for f_i^{n+1}, because the two unknown neighboring values f_{i-1}^{n+1} and f_{i+1}^{n+1} also appear in the equation. The value of f_i^{n+1} is implied in Eq. (12.101), however. Finite difference equations in which the unknown value of f_i^{n+1} is implied in terms of its unknown neighbors, rather than being explicitly given in terms of known initial values, are called implicit equations.

The first form of the modified differential equation (MDE) is

$$f_t + uf_x = \frac{1}{2}f_{tt}\,\Delta t - \frac{1}{6}f_{ttt}\,\Delta t^2 - \cdots - \frac{1}{6}uf_{xxx}\,\Delta x^2 - \frac{1}{120}uf_{xxxxx}\,\Delta x^4 - \cdots \tag{12.102}$$

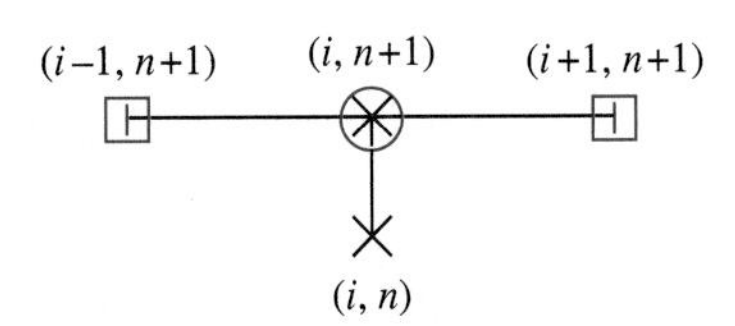

FIGURE 12.21
BTCS method stencil.

and the second form of the MDE is

$$f_t + uf_x = \frac{1}{2}u^2\,\Delta t f_{xx} + \left(-\frac{1}{6}u\,\Delta x^2 - \frac{1}{3}u^3\,\Delta t^2\right) f_{xxx} + \cdots \tag{12.103}$$

As $\Delta t \to 0$ and $\Delta x \to 0$, the truncation error terms go to zero, and Eq. (12.102) approaches $f_t + uf_x = 0$. Consequently, Eq. (12.101) is consistent with the convection equation. From Eq. (12.103), the FDE is $O(\Delta t) + O(\Delta x^2)$. From Eq. (12.103), it is apparent that both implicit numerical diffusion and dispersion are present. The amplification factor G is given by

$$G = \frac{1}{1 + Ic\sin\theta} \tag{12.104}$$

Since $|1 + Ic\sin\theta| > 1$ for all values of θ and all values of c, the BTCS method is unconditionally stable when applied to the convection equation. The BTCS method applied to the convection equation is consistent and unconditionally stable. Consequently, by the Lax equivalence theorem, it is a convergent finite difference approximation of the convection equation.

Consider now the solution of the unsteady one-dimensional convection equation by the BTCS method. The finite difference grid for advancing the solution from time level n to time level $n + 1$ is illustrated in Fig. 12.22. There is an obvious problem with the boundary conditions. The first-order convection equation can have only one boundary condition. Implicit finite difference methods require two boundary conditions, due to the infinite numerical signal propagation speed. This is an obvious inconsistency. As demonstrated in Section 12.1, the solution to the one-dimensional convection equation is a single wave propagating either to the right or to the left with the convection speed u. Consequently, information propagates in only one direction, and the solution domain must be open in that direction. There is no physical mechanism to reflect a wave in the other direction. This open boundary can be simulated in an implicit finite difference method by

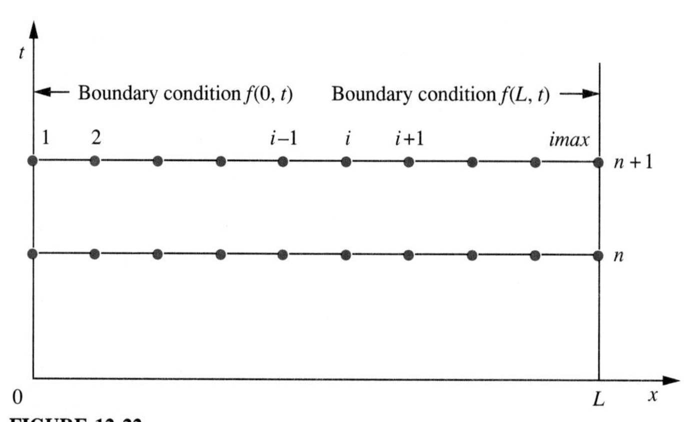

FIGURE 12.22
Finite difference grid for implicit methods.

placing the open boundary at a large distance from the region of interest and applying the initial condition at that location as a boundary condition.

Equation (12.101) applies directly at points 3 to $imax - 2$ in Fig. 12.22. At points 2 and $imax - 1$, Eq. (12.101) is modified by transferring the known values $\bar{f}(0, t)$ and $\bar{f}(L, t)$ to the right-hand side of the equation. The following set of simultaneous linear equations is obtained:

$$
\begin{aligned}
f_2^{n+1} + \frac{c}{2} f_3^{n+1} &= b_2 \\
-\frac{c}{2} f_2^{n+1} + f_3^{n+1} + \frac{c}{2} f_4^{n+1} &= b_3 \\
-\frac{c}{2} f_3^{n+1} + f_4^{n+1} + \frac{c}{2} f_5^{n+1} &= b_4 \\
&\vdots \\
-\frac{c}{2} f_{imax-2}^{n+1} + f_{imax-1}^{n+1} &= b_{imax-1}
\end{aligned}
\tag{12.105}
$$

where the nonhomogeneous terms b_i are given by

$$
\begin{aligned}
b_2 &= f_2^n + \frac{c}{2}\bar{f}(0, t^{n+1}) \\
b_3 &= f_3^n \\
b_4 &= f_4^n \\
&\vdots \\
b_{imax-1} &= f_{imax-1}^n - \frac{c}{2}\bar{f}(L, t^{n+1})
\end{aligned}
\tag{12.106}
$$

Equation (12.105) is a tridiagonal system of linear equations. That system of equations may be written as

$$
\mathbf{A}\mathbf{f}^{n+1} = \mathbf{b} \tag{12.107}
$$

where $\mathbf{A}$ is the $(imax - 2) \times (imax - 2)$ coefficient matrix, $\mathbf{f}^{n+1}$ is the $(imax - 2) \times 1$ solution column vector, and $\mathbf{b}$ is the $(imax - 2) \times 1$ column vector of nonhomogeneous terms. Equation (12.107) can be solved very efficiently by the Thomas algorithm presented in Section 1.5. Since the coefficient matrix $\mathbf{A}$ does not change from one time level to the next, **LU** decomposition can be employed with the Thomas algorithm to reduce the computational effort even further. As shown in Section 1.5, once the **LU** decomposition has been performed, the number of multiplications and divisions required to solve a tridiagonal system of linear equations by the Thomas algorithm is $3n$, where $n = (imax - 2)$ is the number of equations.

Example 12.9. Solution by the BTCS method. We will solve the convection problem, presented in Section 12.1, by the BTCS method for $\Delta x = 0.05$ cm. For this initial-value problem, numerical boundaries are located 100 grid points to the left and right of the initial triangular wave, that is, at $x = -5.0$ cm and 6.0 cm, respectively. The results

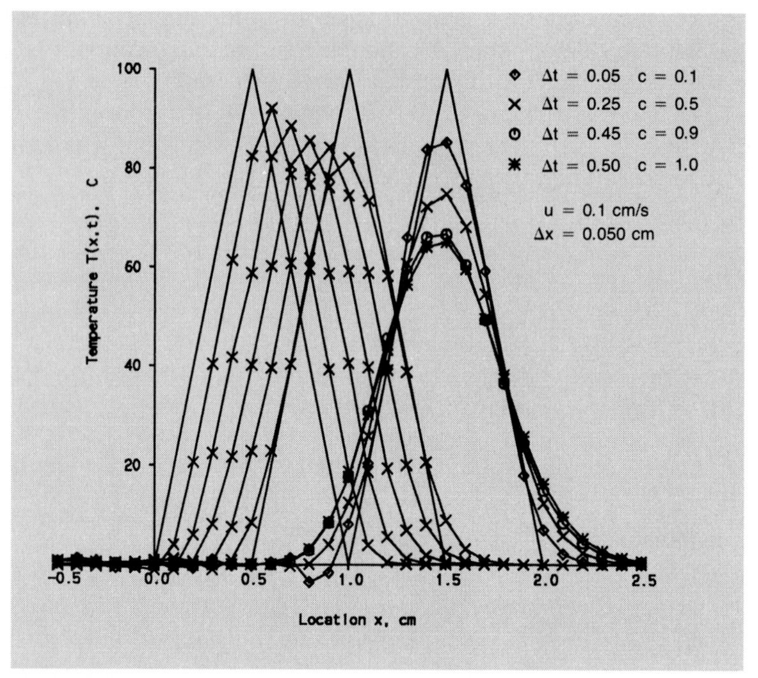

FIGURE 12.23
Solution by the BTCS method.

are presented in Fig. 12.23 at times from 1.0 to 5.0 s for $c = 0.5$, and at 10.0 s for $c = 0.1$, 0.5, 0.9, and 1.0, and in Fig. 12.24 at 10.0 s for $c = 0.1$, 0.5, 0.9, 1.0, 2.5, 5.0, and 10.0.

Several important features of the BTCS method applied to the convection equation are illustrated in Figs. 12.23 and 12.24. For $c = 0.5$, the solution is severely damped as the wave propagates, and the peak of the wave is rounded. These effects are due to implicit numerical diffusion and dispersion. At $t = 10.0$ s, the best solutions are obtained for the smallest values of c. For the larger values of c (i.e., $c \geq 5.0$), the solutions barely resemble the true solution. These results demonstrate that the method is indeed stable for $c > 1$, but that the quality of the solution is very poor. The peaks in the solutions at $t = 10.0$ s for the different values of c are lagging further and further behind the peak in the exact solution, which demonstrates that the numerical signal propagation speed is less than the physical signal propagation speed. This effect is due to implicit numerical dispersion. Overall, the BTCS method applied to the convection equation yields rather poor results.

The BTCS method is $O(\Delta t)$. An $O(\Delta t^2)$ implicit FDE can be developed using the Crank–Nicolson approach presented in Section 11.6 for the diffusion equation. The procedure is straightforward. The major use of implicit methods for solving hyperbolic problems is to obtain the asymptotic steady state solution of mixed elliptic/hyperbolic problems. As pointed out in Section 11.9, the BTCS method is preferred over the Crank–Nicolson method for obtaining asymptotic steady state solutions. Consequently the Crank–Nicolson method is not developed for the convection equation.

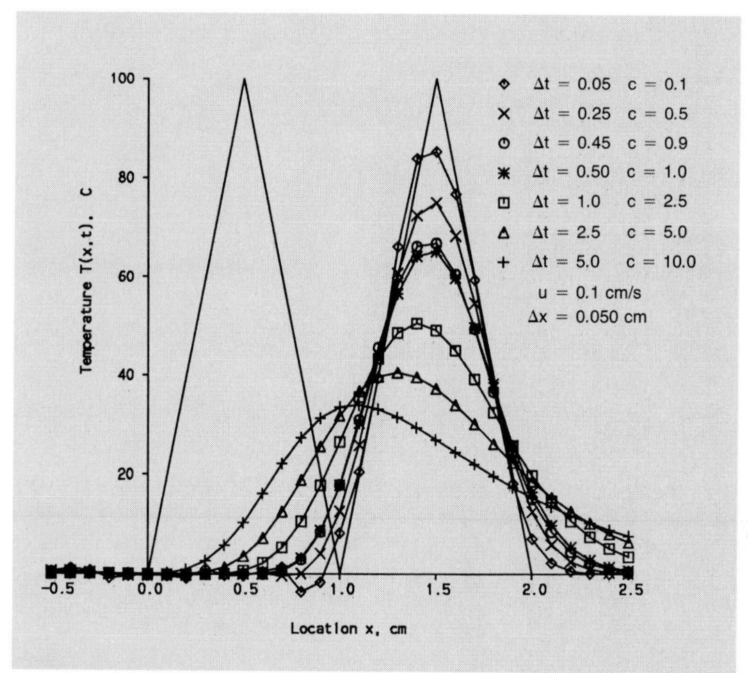

FIGURE 12.24
Solution at $t = 10.0$ s by the BTCS method.

The implicit BTCS method becomes considerably more complicated when applied to nonlinear PDEs, systems of PDEs, and multidimensional problems. A discussion of these problems is presented in Section 12.14.

In summary, the BTCS approximation of the convection equation is implicit, two-level, single-step, $O(\Delta t) + O(\Delta x^2)$, unconditionally stable, and convergent. The implicit nature of the method yields a set of finite difference equations, which must be solved simultaneously. For one-dimensional problems, that can be accomplished by the Thomas algorithm. The infinite numerical signal propagation speed does not correctly model the finite physical signal propagation speed. The BTCS approximation of the convection equation yields poor results, except for very small values of the convection number, for which explicit methods are usually more efficient.

12.13 THE HOPSCOTCH METHOD

The hopscotch method is an interesting combination of the forward-time centered-space (FTCS) method and the backward-time centered-space (BTCS) method. Gourlay (1970) presents a detailed discussion of the hopscotch method. It is generally used in two- and three-dimensional problems. The hopscotch method is applied to the one-dimensional convection equation in this section.

The basic idea of the hopscotch method is to make two sweeps through the solution domain at each time step. On the first sweep, the explicit FTCS method

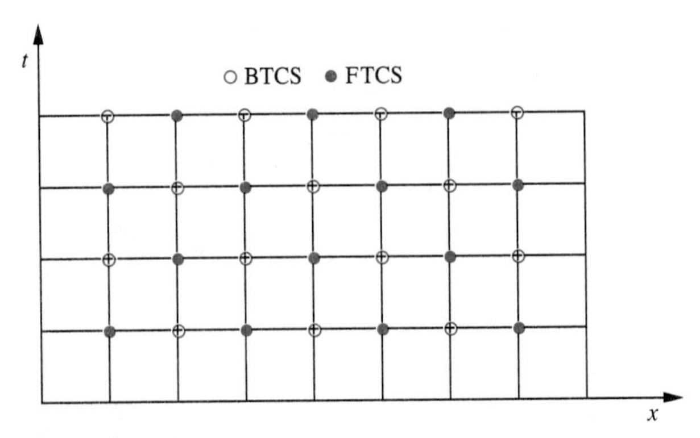

FIGURE 12.25
Hopscotch method sweep pattern.

is applied at every other grid point, as illustrated in Fig. 12.25. From Eq. (12.19),

$$f_i^{n+1} = f_i^n - \frac{c}{2}(f_{i+1}^n - f_{i-1}^n) \tag{12.108}$$

On the second sweep, the implicit BTCS method is applied at the remaining grid points, as illustrated in Fig. 12.25. From Eq. (12.101),

$$-\frac{c}{2}f_{i-1}^{n+1} + f_i^{n+1} + \frac{c}{2}f_{i+1}^{n+1} = f_i^n \tag{12.109}$$

Equation (12.109) appears to be implicit, but the values of $f_{i\pm1}^{n+1}$ are known from the first sweep through the grid with the explicit FTCS method. Consequently, Eq. (12.109) can be solved explicitly for f_i^{n+1} to give

$$f_i^{n+1} = f_i^n - \frac{c}{2}(f_{i+1}^{n+1} - f_{i-1}^{n+1}) \tag{12.110}$$

Equation (12.108) can be replaced by the simpler equation

$$f_i^{n+2} = 2f_i^{n+1} - f_i^n \tag{12.111}$$

which further increases the efficiency of the method. Equation (12.108) must be used on the first time step, but Eq. (12.111) can be used at all subsequent time steps.

The pattern of explicit points and implicit points is alternated at each time level, as illustrated in Fig. 12.25. The name *hopscotch* arises from the alternating sweep pattern.

The hopscotch concept can be developed using the Lax method at the explicit points instead of the FTCS method.

The hopscotch method applied to the convection equation is consistent, $O(\Delta t) + O(\Delta x^2)$, and conditionally stable ($c = u\,\Delta t/\Delta x \le 1$). It is equally applicable to nonlinear PDEs and systems of PDEs. Some problems may arise with more complicated boundary conditions for the implicit points. Since both Eqs. (12.108) [or equivalently, Eq. (12.111)] and (12.110) can be solved explicitly, no system of equations must be solved.

Example 12.10. Solution by the hopscotch method. We will solve the convection problem, presented in Section 12.1, by the hopscotch method for $\Delta x = 0.05$ cm. Due to the discontinuity in the slope of the initial data at $x = 0.5$, a slightly more accurate solution is obtained if the BTCS method is used at this point on the first time step. The numerical boundary conditions are treated as described in Section 12.12 for the BTCS method. The results are presented in Fig. 12.26 at times from 1.0 to 5.0 s for $c = 0.5$, and at 10.0 s for $c = 0.1$, 0.5, 0.9, and 1.0.

Several important features of the hopscotch method applied to the convection equation are illustrated in Fig. 12.26. For $c = 0.5$, the solution is slightly damped as the wave propagates. At $t = 10.0$ s, the solutions for all values of c are comparable. Overall, the hopscotch method applied to the convection equation gives reasonably good results.

Extending the explicit hopscotch method to solve nonlinear PDEs complicates the solution, since the nonlinear coefficients are unknown at the base point

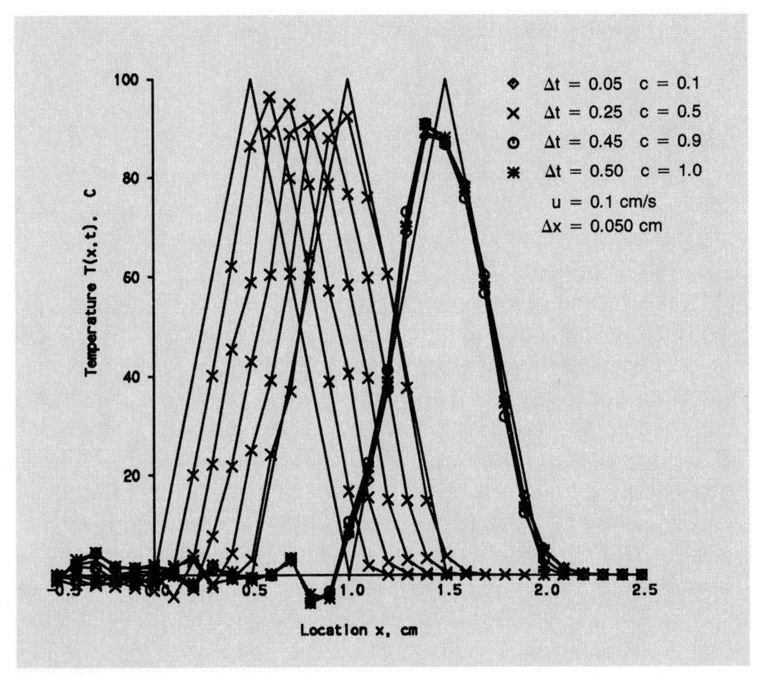

FIGURE 12.26
Solution by the hopscotch method.

for the BTCS method. Extension to systems of PDEs and multidimensional PDEs is straightforward, as discussed in Section 12.14.

In summary, the hopscotch approximation of the convection equation is explicit, two-level, two-sweep single-step, $O(\Delta t) + O(\Delta x^2)$, conditionally stable, and convergent. The hopscotch method is a reasonably good method for solving convection problems.

12.14 NONLINEAR EQUATIONS AND MULTIDIMENSIONAL PROBLEMS

The finite difference equations and examples presented in this chapter are for the linear one-dimensional convection equation. In each section in this chapter, a brief paragraph is presented discussing the suitability of the method for solving nonlinear equations and multidimensional problems. The additional complexities associated with solving nonlinear equations and multidimensional problems are discussed in considerable detail in Section 11.8 for the parabolic diffusion equation. The problems and solutions discussed there apply directly to finite difference methods for solving the convection equation.

Generally speaking, explicit methods can be extended directly to solve nonlinear equations or multidimensional convection problems. Implicit methods, on the other hand, yield nonlinear FDEs when applied to nonlinear PDEs. Methods for solving nonlinear FDEs are discussed in Section 11.8. When applied to multidimensional problems, implicit methods result in large banded systems of FDEs. Methods for solving these problems, such as alternating-direction implicit (ADI) methods and approximate-factorization implicit (AFI) methods, are also discussed in Section 11.8.

SUMMARY

The numerical solution of hyperbolic partial differential equations by finite difference methods is discussed in this chapter. Hyperbolic PDEs govern propagation problems, which have a finite information propagation speed. They are solved numerically by marching methods.

Explicit finite difference methods, as typified by the Lax–Wendroff type methods, are conditionally stable and require a relatively small step size in the marching direction to satisfy stability criteria. Implicit methods, as typified by the BTCS method, are unconditionally stable. The marching step size is restricted by accuracy requirements, not stability requirements. For accurate solutions of transient problems, the marching step size for implicit methods cannot be very much larger than the stable step size for explicit methods. Asymptotic steady state solutions can be obtained very efficiently by the BTCS method with a large marching step size.

Nonlinear partial differential equations can be solved directly by explicit methods. When solved by implicit methods, systems of nonlinear FDEs must be solved. Multidimensional problems can be solved directly by explicit methods. When they are solved by implicit methods, large banded systems of FDEs result. Alternating-direction implicit (ADI) methods and approximate-factorization implicit (AFI) methods can be used to solve multidimensional problems.

PROBLEMS

Section 12.1 Introduction

1. Consider the unsteady one-dimensional convection equation $\bar{f}_t + u\bar{f}_x = 0$. Classify this PDE. Determine the characteristic curves. Discuss the significance of these results as regards domain of dependence, range of influence, signal propagation speed, auxiliary conditions, and numerical solution procedures.
2. Develop the exact solution for the convection problem presented in Section 12.1, Eq. (12.3*b*), and discuss its significance.

Section 12.2 The Method of Characteristics

3. Develop the method-of-characteristics analysis of the linear convection equation presented in Section 12.2. Discuss the effects of nonlinearities on the results.

Section 12.3 The Forward-Time Centered-Space Method

4. Derive the FTCS approximation of the unsteady one-dimensional convection equation, Eq. (12.19), including the leading truncation error terms in Δt and Δx.
5. Perform a von Neumann stability analysis of Eq. (12.19).
6. By hand calculation, solve the problem presented in Example 12.1 by the FTCS method with $\Delta x = 0.1$ cm and $\Delta t = 1.0$ s for $t = 2.0$ s.

Section 12.4 The Lax Method

7. Derive the Lax approximation of the unsteady one-dimensional convection equation, Eq. (12.24), including the leading truncation error terms in Δt and Δx.
8. Derive the first and approximate second forms of the MDE corresponding to Eq. (12.24). Analyze consistency, order, and implicit numerical diffusion and dispersion.
9. Perform a von Neumann stability analysis of Eq. (12.24).
10. By hand calculation, determine the solution of the example convection problem by the Lax method at $t = 1.0$ s for $\Delta x = 0.1$ cm and $\Delta t = 0.5$ s. Compare the results with the exact solution.
11. Write a computer program to implement the solution of the example convection problem by the Lax method. Use the program to solve the example convection problem with $\Delta x = 0.1$ cm and $\Delta t = 0.5$ s for $t = 10.0$ s. Compare the results with the exact solution.
12. Use the program developed in Problem 11 to reproduce the results presented in Fig. 12.6. Compare the errors with the errors in Problem 11 at several selected locations and times.

Section 12.6 Upwind Methods

13. Derive the first-order upwind approximation of the unsteady one-dimensional convection equation for $u > 0$, Eq. (12.42), including the leading truncation error terms in Δt and Δx.
14. Derive the first and approximate second forms of the MDE corresponding to Eq. (12.42). Analyze consistency, order, and implicit numerical diffusion and dispersion.

15. Perform a von Neumann stability analysis of Eq. (12.42).

16. By hand calculation, determine the solution of the example convection problem by the first-order upwind method at $t = 1.0$ s for $\Delta x = 0.1$ cm and $\Delta t = 0.5$ s. Compare the results with the exact solution.

17. Write a computer program to implement the solution of the example convection problem by the first-order upwind method. Use the program to solve the example convection problem with $\Delta x = 0.1$ cm and $\Delta t = 0.5$ s for $t = 10.0$ s. Compare the results with the exact solution.

18. Use the program developed in Problem 17 to reproduce the results presented in Fig. 12.9. Compare the errors with the errors in Problem 17 at several selected locations and times.

19. An $O(\Delta x^2)$ upwind approximation can be developed by using a second-order backward-difference approximation for $\overline{f}_x$. (*a*) Derive the FDE, including the leading truncation error terms in Δt and Δx. (*b*) Perform a von Neumann stability analysis of this FDE.

20. An $O(\Delta x^3)$ upwind approximation of the unsteady one-dimensional convection equation can be developed by the third-order nonsymmetrical upwind-biased-difference approximation for $\overline{f}_x$ proposed by Leonard (1978), Eq. (14.40). (*a*) Derive this FDE, including the leading truncation error terms in Δt and Δx. (*b*) Perform a von Neumann stability analysis of the FDE.

Section 12.7 The Leapfrog Method

21. Derive the leapfrog approximation of the unsteady one-dimensional convection equation, Eq. (12.48), including the leading truncation error terms in Δt and Δx.

22. Derive the first and approximate second forms of the MDE corresponding to Eq. (12.48). Analyze consistency, order, and implicit numerical diffusion and dispersion.

23. Perform a von Neumann stability analysis of Eq. (12.48).

24. By hand calculation, determine the solution of the example convection problem by the leapfrog method at $t = 1.0$ s for $\Delta x = 0.1$ cm and $\Delta t = 0.5$ s. Use the exact solution at $t = 0.5$ s for the first time step. Compare the results with the exact solution.

25. Write a computer program to implement the solution of the example convection problem by the leapfrog method. Use the program to solve the example convection problem with $\Delta x = 0.1$ cm and $\Delta t = 0.5$ s for $t = 10.0$ s. Compare the results with the exact solution.

26. Use the program developed in Problem 25 to reproduce the results presented in Fig. 12.11. Compare the errors with the errors in Problem 25 at several locations and times.

Section 12.8 The Lax–Wendroff One-Step Method

27. Derive the Lax–Wendroff (1960) one-step approximation of the unsteady one-dimensional convection equation, Eq. (12.61), including the leading truncation error terms in Δt and Δx.

28. Derive the first, second, and approximate second forms of the MDE corresponding to Eq. (12.61). Analyze consistency, order, and implicit numerical diffusion and dispersion.

29. Perform a von Neumann stability analysis of Eq. (12.61).

30. By hand calculation, determine the solution of the example convection problem by the Lax–Wendroff one-step method at $t = 1.0$ s for $\Delta x = 0.1$ cm and $\Delta t = 0.5$ s. Compare the results with the exact solution.

31. Write a computer program to implement the solution of the example convection problem by the Lax–Wendroff one-step method. Use the program to solve the example convection problem with $\Delta x = 0.1$ cm and $\Delta t = 0.5$ s for $t = 10.0$ s. Compare the results with the exact solution.

32. Use the program developed in Problem 31 to reproduce the results presented in Fig. 12.14. Compare the errors with the errors in Problem 31 at several locations and times.

Section 12.9 Lax–Wendroff Two-Step Methods

33. Derive the Lax–Wendroff (Richtmyer, 1963) two-step approximation of the unsteady one-dimensional convection equation, Eqs. (12.66) and (12.67), including the leading truncation error terms in Δt and Δx. Show that, for the linear convection equation, the two-step method is equivalent to the Lax–Wendroff one-step method for $2\Delta t$ and $2\Delta x$.

34. By hand calculation, determine the solution of the example convection problem by the Lax–Wendroff (Richtmyer) two-step method at $t = 1.0$ s for $\Delta x = 0.1$ cm and $\Delta t = 0.5$ s. Compare the results with the exact solution.

35. Write a computer program to implement the solution of the example convection problem by the Lax–Wendroff (Richtmyer) two-step method. Use the program to solve the example convection problem with $\Delta x = 0.1$ cm and $\Delta t = 0.5$ s for $t = 10.0$ s. Compare the results with the exact solution.

36. Use the program developed in Problem 35 to reproduce the results presented in Fig. 12.16. Compare the errors with the errors in Problem 35 at several locations and times.

Section 12.10 The MacCormack Method

37. Develop the MacCormack approximation of the unsteady one-dimensional convection equation, Eqs. (12.75) and (12.77), including the leading truncation error terms. Show that, for the linear convection equation, the two-step method is identical to the Lax–Wendroff one-step method.

38. By hand calculation, determine the solution of the example convection problem by the MacCormack method at $t = 1.0$ s for $\Delta x = 0.1$ cm and $\Delta t = 0.5$ s. Compare the results with the results of Problem 30. Compare the results with the exact solution.

39. Write a computer program to implement the solution of the example convection problem by the MacCormack method. Use the program to reproduce the results presented in Fig. 12.14.

Section 12.11 The Numerical Method of Characteristics

40. Develop the first method-of-characteristics algorithm. Work Problem 10 by this method. Compare the results with the results of Problem 10.

41. Develop the second method-of-characteristics algorithm. Work Problem 16 by this method. Compare the results with the results of Problem 16.

42. Develop the third method-of-characteristics algorithm. Work Problem 30 by this method. Compare the results with the results of Problem 30.

43. Develop a numerical procedure to solve the unsteady one-dimensional nonlinear convection equation $\bar{f}_t + \bar{f}\bar{f}_x = 0$ by the third method-of-characteristics algorithm.

Section 12.12 The Backward-Time Centered-Space Method

44. Derive the BTCS approximation of the unsteady one-dimensional convection equation, Eq. (12.101), including the leading truncation error terms in Δt and Δx.
45. Derive the first and approximate second forms of the MDE corresponding to Eq. (12.101). Analyze consistency, order, and implicit numerical diffusion and dispersion.
46. Perform a von Neumann stability analysis of Eq. (12.101).
47. By hand calculation, determine the solution of the example convection problem by the BTCS method at $t = 1.0$ s for $\Delta x = 0.25$ cm and $\Delta t = 1.0$ s. Apply the initial conditions as boundary conditions at $x = -0.5$ and 1.5 cm. Compare the results with the exact solution.
48. Write a computer program to implement the solution of the example convection problem by the BTCS method. Use the program to solve the example convection problem with $\Delta x = 0.1$ cm and $\Delta t = 1.0$ s for $t = 10.0$ s. Compare the results with the exact solution.
49. Use the program developed in Problem 48 to reproduce the results presented in Figs. 12.23 and 12.24. Compare the errors with the errors in Problem 48 at several locations and times.

Section 12.13 The Hopscotch Method

50. Derive the hopscotch approximation of the unsteady one-dimensional convection equation, Eqs. (12.108) and (12.110), including the leading truncation error terms in Δt and Δx.
51. Derive Eq. (12.111).
52. By hand calculation, determine the solution of the example convection problem by the hopscotch method at $t = 1.0$ s for $\Delta x = 0.1$ cm and $\Delta t = 0.5$ s. Compare the results with the exact solution.
53. Write a computer program to implement the solution of the example convection problem by the hopscotch method. Use the program to solve the example convection problem with $\Delta x = 0.1$ cm and $\Delta t = 0.5$ s for $t = 10.0$ s. Compare the results with the exact solution.
54. Use the program developed in Problem 53 to reproduce the results presented in Fig. 12.26. Compare the errors with the errors in Problem 53 at several locations and times.

Section 12.14 Nonlinear Equations and Multidimensional Problems

55. Consider the following hyperbolic PDE for the generic dependent variable $\bar{f}(x, t)$, which serves as a model equation in fluid dynamics:

$$\bar{f}_t + \bar{f}\bar{f}_x = 0 \tag{P12.55}$$

where $\bar{f}(x, 0) = F(x)$. (*a*) Develop the Lax approximation of Eq. (P12.55). (*b*) Discuss a strategy for solving this problem numerically.

56. Solve Problem 55 by the MacCormack method.

57. Solve Problem 55 by the BTCS method. (*a*) Discuss a strategy for solving this problem numerically by linearization and iteration. (*b*) Discuss a strategy for solving this problem by Newton's method.

58. Equation (1) can be written as

$$\bar{f}_t + \left(\frac{1}{2}\bar{f}^2\right)_x = 0 \tag{P12.58}$$

which is the conservation form of the nonlinear PDE. (*a*) Repeat Problem 55 for Eq. (P12.58). (*b*) Repeat Problem 56 for Eq. (P12.58). (*c*) Repeat Problem 57 for Eq. (P12.58).

59. Equation (P12.58) can be written in the form

$$Q_t + E_x = 0 \tag{P12.59a}$$

where $Q = \bar{f}$ and $E = (\bar{f}^2/2)$. Solving Eq. (P12.59*a*) by the BTCS method yields the nonlinear FDE

$$Q_i^{n+1} - Q_i^n + \frac{\Delta t}{2\Delta x}\left(E_{i+1}^{n+1} - E_{i-1}^{n+1}\right) = 0 \tag{P12.59b}$$

which is a nonlinear FDE. Equation (P12.59*b*) can be time linearized as follows:

$$E^{n+1} = E^n + \frac{\partial E}{\partial Q}\Big|^n \left(Q^{n+1} - Q^n\right) = E^n + A^n\left(Q^{n+1} - Q_n\right) \tag{P12.59c}$$

where $A^n = (\partial E/\partial Q)^n$. Combining Eqs. (P12.59*b*) and (P12.59*c*) and letting $\Delta Q = (Q^{n+1} - Q^n)$ yields the delta form of the FDE, which is linear in ΔQ:

$$\Delta Q_i + \frac{\Delta t}{2\Delta x}(A_{i+1}^n\,\Delta Q_{i+1} - A_{i-1}^n\,\Delta Q_{i-1}) = -\frac{\Delta t}{2\Delta x}(E_{i+1}^n - E_{i-1}^n) \tag{P12.59d}$$

Apply this procedure to develop a strategy for solving Eq. (P12.58).

60. Write a computer program to solve Problem 55 numerically for $F(x) = 200x$ for $0 \le x \le 0.5$ and $200(1 - x)$ for $0.5 \le x \le 1.0$. March from $t = 0$ to $t = 10.0$ s with $\Delta x = 0.1$ cm and $\Delta t = 0.5$ s.

61. Solve Problem 60 using the MacCormack method developed in Problem 56.

62. Solve Problem 60 using the BTCS method developed in Problem 59.

63. Consider the unsteady two-dimensional convection equation

$$\bar{f}_t + u\bar{f}_x + u\bar{f}_y = 0 \tag{P12.63}$$

(*a*) Derive the Lax–Wendroff one-step approximation of Eq. (P12.63), including the leading truncation error terms in Δt, Δx, and Δy. (*b*) Derive the first and approximate second forms of the MDE. Analyze consistency, order, and implicit numerical diffusion and dispersion. (*c*) Perform a von Neumann stability analysis of the FDE.

64. Work Problem 63 by the BTCS method.

CHAPTER 13

COORDINATE TRANSFORMATIONS AND GRID GENERATION

Section

Examples

13.1 INTRODUCTION

The governing differential equations of engineering and science are generally derived and expressed in a Cartesian (i.e., rectangular) coordinate system. All the examples considered in Chapters 7 to 12 are expressed in Cartesian coordinates.

Finite difference methods for solving differential equations require that the continuous physical space be discretized into a uniform orthogonal computational

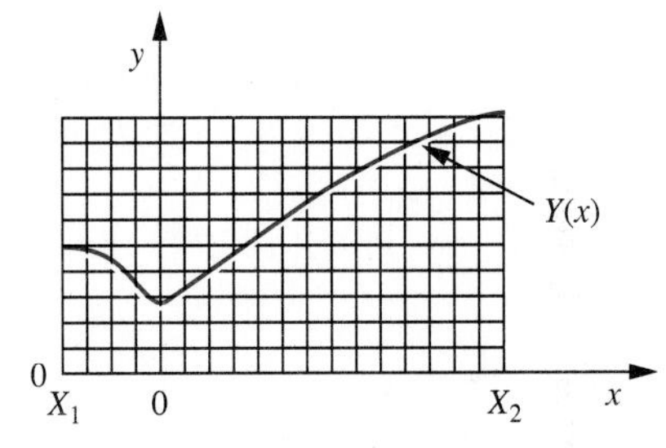

FIGURE 13.1
Physical space and a Cartesian grid.

space. However, the application of boundary conditions requires that the boundaries of the physical space fall on coordinate lines (surfaces) of the coordinate system. Accurate resolution of the solution requires that grid points be clustered in regions of large gradients. Economy requires that grid points be spread out in regions of small gradients. These requirements are generally incompatible with a Cartesian coordinate system.

As an example, consider the physical space illustrated in Fig. 13.1, which is bounded by the four boundaries $x = X_1$, $x = X_2$, $y = 0$, and $y = Y(x)$, in which the function $f(x, y)$ is governed by a partial differential equation. Assume that the x gradient (i.e., f_x) is much larger near $x = 0$ than at any other location. Superimposing a uniform orthogonal Cartesian grid on the physical space, as illustrated in Fig. 13.1, leads to the following problems:

1. The upper boundary of the physical space (i.e., the $y = Y(x)$ boundary) does not fall on a coordinate line (i.e., a line of constant y), so the application of boundary conditions (BCs) is difficult.
2. The grid spacings adjacent to the upper boundary are not uniform, so centered-difference finite difference approximations (FDAs) are not second-order.
3. In view of the large values of f_x near $x = 0$, the uniform grid spacing in the x direction (i.e., Δx) is either too large near $x = 0$ or too small away from $x = 0$.

The first and third problems listed above can be eliminated by using the body-fitted clustered grid illustrated in Fig. 13.2*a*. However, the grid spacings Δx and Δy are

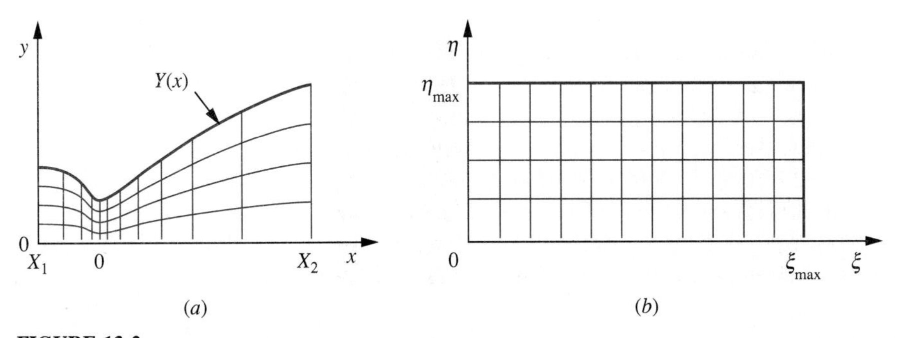

FIGURE 13.2
Body-fitted coordinate system: (*a*) physical space; (*b*) computational space.

both nonuniform everywhere, and the grid is not orthogonal. This problem can be eliminated by transforming the nonuniform nonorthogonal physical space illustrated in Fig. 13.2*a* into the uniform orthogonal computational space illustrated in Fig. 13.2*b*.

The transformation relating the physical space and the computational space is specified by the *direct* transformation:

$$\xi = \xi(x, y) \qquad \text{and} \qquad \eta = \eta(x, y) \tag{13.1}$$

The transformation from computational space to physical space is specified by the *inverse* transformation:

$$x = x(\xi, \eta) \qquad \text{and} \qquad y = y(\xi, \eta) \tag{13.2}$$

The determination of the coordinate transformation is called *grid generation*.

Once the coordinate transformation has been determined, the differential equations must be transformed from physical space xy to computational space $\xi\eta$. For example, consider the first-order PDE

$$a\frac{\partial f}{\partial x} + b\frac{\partial f}{\partial y} = c \tag{13.3}$$

Equation (13.3) is transformed from physical space xy to computational space $\xi\eta$ by applying the chain rule for partial derivatives. Thus,

$$\frac{\partial f}{\partial x} = \frac{\partial f}{\partial \xi}\frac{\partial \xi}{\partial x} + \frac{\partial f}{\partial \eta}\frac{\partial \eta}{\partial x} = \xi_x\frac{\partial f}{\partial \xi} + \eta_x\frac{\partial f}{\partial \eta} \tag{13.4a}$$

$$\frac{\partial f}{\partial y} = \frac{\partial f}{\partial \xi}\frac{\partial \xi}{\partial y} + \frac{\partial f}{\partial \eta}\frac{\partial \eta}{\partial y} = \xi_y\frac{\partial f}{\partial \xi} + \eta_y\frac{\partial f}{\partial \eta} \tag{13.4b}$$

where the derivatives ξ_x, ξ_y, η_x, and η_y are the *metrics* of the direct transformation. Substituting Eq. (13.4) into Eq. (13.3) yields the transformed PDE. Thus,

$$(a\xi_x + b\xi_y)f_\xi + (a\eta_x + b\eta_y)f_\eta = c \tag{13.5}$$

Equation (13.5) is solved in the uniform orthogonal computational space $\xi\eta$ using second-order centered-difference finite difference approximations (FDAs).

The advantages of transforming the differential equations to a body-fitted uniform orthogonal computational space are as follows:

1. The boundaries of the physical space fall on coordinate lines of the computational space, so BCs can be implemented accurately and easily.

2. The finite difference approximations of the exact partial derivatives are obtained on a uniform orthogonal grid.
3. Grid points can be clustered in regions of large gradients and spread out in regions of small gradients.

The most significant disadvantage is that the transformed PDEs are more complicated, so the resulting finite difference equations (FDEs) are also more complicated.

Two classical coordinate transformations are presented in Section 13.2. The generalized coordinate transformation is developed in Section 13.3. An introduction to grid generation is presented in Section 13.4. Algebraic grid generation is introduced in Section 13.5, and grid generation using differential equations is discussed in Section 13.6. The use of coordinate transformations and grid generation is essential to the solution of differential equations in complicated physical spaces by finite difference methods.

13.2 CLASSICAL COORDINATE SYSTEMS

Two of the most important coordinate systems besides the Cartesian coordinate system are the cylindrical and spherical coordinate systems. Many physical problems possess cylindrical symmetry or spherical symmetry. In such cases, the governing differential equations should be solved in those coordinate systems. Those two coordinate systems are presented in this section.

Cylindrical Coordinate System

The relationship between Cartesian and cylindrical coordinates is illustrated in Fig. 13.3. The inverse transformation is specified by

$$x = r\cos\theta, \qquad y = r\sin\theta, \qquad \text{and} \qquad z = z \tag{13.6}$$

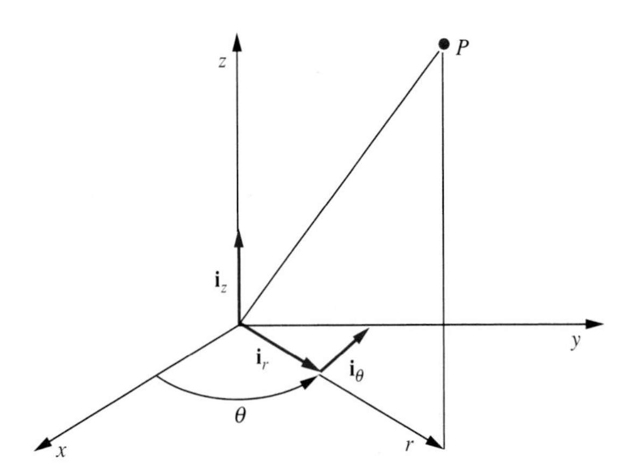

FIGURE 13.3
Cylindrical coordinate system.

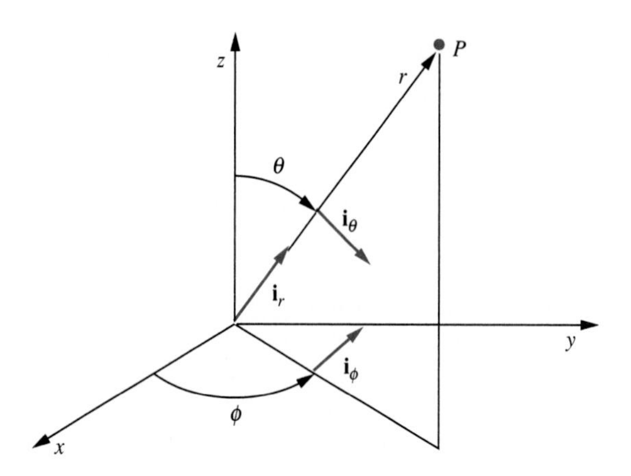

FIGURE 13.4
Spherical coordinate system.

The vector derivative operator ∇f is given by

$$\nabla f = \mathbf{i}_r f_r + \mathbf{i}_\theta \frac{1}{r} f_\theta + \mathbf{i}_z f_z \tag{13.7}$$

where $\mathbf{i}_r$, $\mathbf{i}_\theta$, and $\mathbf{i}_z$ are unit vectors in the r, θ, and z directions, respectively. The vector Laplacian operator $\nabla^2 f$ is given by

$$\nabla^2 f = f_{rr} + \frac{1}{r} f_r + \frac{1}{r^2} f_{\theta\theta} + f_{zz} \tag{13.8}$$

Spherical Coordinate System

The relationship between Cartesian and spherical coordinates is illustrated in Fig. 13.4. The inverse transformation is specified by

$$x = r \sin\theta \cos\phi, \quad y = r \sin\theta \sin\phi, \qquad \text{and} \qquad z = r\cos\theta \tag{13.9}$$

The vector derivative operator ∇f is given by

$$\nabla f = \mathbf{i}_r f_r + \mathbf{i}_\theta \frac{1}{r} f_\theta + \mathbf{i}_\phi \frac{1}{r \sin\theta} f_\phi \tag{13.10}$$

where $\mathbf{i}_r$, $\mathbf{i}_\theta$, and $\mathbf{i}_\phi$ are unit vectors in the r, θ, and ϕ directions, respectively. The vector Laplacian operator $\nabla^2 f$ is given by

$$\nabla^2 f = f_{rr} + \frac{2}{r} f_r + \frac{1}{r^2} f_{\theta\theta} + \frac{1}{r^2 \tan\theta} f_\theta + \frac{1}{r^2 \sin^2\theta} f_{\phi\phi} \tag{13.11}$$

13.3 GENERALIZED COORDINATE TRANSFORMATIONS

Consider a nonuniform nonorthogonal physical space $xyzt$ which is to be transformed to a uniform orthogonal computational space $\xi\eta\phi\tau$ by the direct transformation:

$$\boxed{\begin{aligned} \xi &= \xi(x, y, z, t), & \eta &= \eta(x, y, z, t), \\ \phi &= \phi(x, y, z, t), & \text{and} \quad \tau &= t \end{aligned}} \tag{13.12}$$

Consider the generic dependent variable $f(x, y, z, t)$. Applying the chain rule for partial derivatives yields:

$$\frac{\partial f}{\partial x} = \frac{\partial f}{\partial \xi}\frac{\partial \xi}{\partial x} + \frac{\partial f}{\partial \eta}\frac{\partial \eta}{\partial x} + \frac{\partial f}{\partial \phi}\frac{\partial \phi}{\partial x} + \frac{\partial f}{\partial \tau}\frac{\partial \tau}{\partial x} = \xi_x \frac{\partial f}{\partial \xi} + \eta_x \frac{\partial f}{\partial \eta} + \phi_x \frac{\partial f}{\partial \phi} \tag{13.13a}$$

$$\frac{\partial f}{\partial y} = \frac{\partial f}{\partial \xi}\frac{\partial \xi}{\partial y} + \frac{\partial f}{\partial \eta}\frac{\partial \eta}{\partial y} + \frac{\partial f}{\partial \phi}\frac{\partial \phi}{\partial y} + \frac{\partial f}{\partial \tau}\frac{\partial \tau}{\partial y} = \xi_y \frac{\partial f}{\partial \xi} + \eta_y \frac{\partial f}{\partial \eta} + \phi_y \frac{\partial f}{\partial \phi} \tag{13.13b}$$

$$\frac{\partial f}{\partial z} = \frac{\partial f}{\partial \xi}\frac{\partial \xi}{\partial z} + \frac{\partial f}{\partial \eta}\frac{\partial \eta}{\partial z} + \frac{\partial f}{\partial \phi}\frac{\partial \phi}{\partial z} + \frac{\partial f}{\partial \tau}\frac{\partial \tau}{\partial z} = \xi_z \frac{\partial f}{\partial \xi} + \eta_z \frac{\partial f}{\partial \eta} + \phi_z \frac{\partial f}{\partial \phi} \tag{13.13c}$$

$$\frac{\partial f}{\partial t} = \frac{\partial f}{\partial \xi}\frac{\partial \xi}{\partial t} + \frac{\partial f}{\partial \eta}\frac{\partial \eta}{\partial t} + \frac{\partial f}{\partial \phi}\frac{\partial \phi}{\partial t} + \frac{\partial f}{\partial \tau}\frac{\partial \tau}{\partial t} = \xi_t \frac{\partial f}{\partial \xi} + \eta_t \frac{\partial f}{\partial \eta} + \phi_t \frac{\partial f}{\partial \phi} + \frac{\partial f}{\partial \tau} \tag{13.13d}$$

where $\tau_x = \tau_y = \tau_z = 0$ and $\tau_t = 1$. The derivatives ξ_x, ξ_y, ξ_z, ξ_t, η_x, and so on are the metrics of the direct transformation.

If the metrics of the direct transformation are known [i.e., Eq. (13.12) is known], then the differential equations can be transformed to computational space using Eq. (13.13). In most cases, the direct transformation specified by Eq. (13.12) is not known. The inverse transformation from computational space $\xi\eta\phi\tau$ to physical space $xyzt$ is usually known:

$$\boxed{\begin{aligned} x &= x(\xi, \eta, \phi, \tau), & y &= y(\xi, \eta, \phi, \tau), \\ z &= z(\xi, \eta, \phi, \tau), & \text{and} \quad t &= \tau \end{aligned}} \tag{13.14}$$

The metrics of the inverse transformation (i.e., x_ξ, x_η, x_ϕ, x_τ, y_ξ, etc.) can be determined from Eq. (13.14). The metrics of the direct transformation (i.e., ξ_x, ξ_y, ξ_z, ξ_t, η_x, etc.) must be expressed in terms of the metrics of the inverse transformation.

Differentiating Eq. (13.14) gives

$$dx = x_\xi d\xi + x_\eta d\eta + x_\phi d\phi + x_\tau d\tau \tag{13.15a}$$

$$dy = y_\xi d\xi + y_\eta d\eta + y_\phi d\phi + y_\tau d\tau \tag{13.15b}$$

$$dz = z_\xi d\xi + z_\eta d\eta + z_\phi d\phi + z_\tau d\tau \tag{13.15c}$$

$$dt = d\tau \tag{13.15d}$$

Writing Eq. (13.15) in matrix form yields

$$\begin{bmatrix} x_\xi & x_\eta & x_\phi & x_\tau \\ y_\xi & y_\eta & y_\phi & y_\tau \\ z_\xi & z_\eta & z_\phi & z_\tau \\ 0 & 0 & 0 & 1 \end{bmatrix} \begin{bmatrix} d\xi \\ d\eta \\ d\phi \\ d\tau \end{bmatrix} = \begin{bmatrix} dx \\ dy \\ dz \\ dt \end{bmatrix} \tag{13.16}$$

Solving for $d\xi$ by Cramer's rule yields

$$d\xi = \frac{\begin{vmatrix} dx & x_\eta & x_\phi & x_\tau \\ dy & y_\eta & y_\phi & y_\tau \\ dz & z_\eta & z_\phi & z_\tau \\ dt & 0 & 0 & 1 \end{vmatrix}}{\begin{vmatrix} x_\xi & x_\eta & x_\phi & x_\tau \\ y_\xi & y_\eta & y_\phi & y_\tau \\ z_\xi & z_\eta & z_\phi & z_\tau \\ 0 & 0 & 0 & 1 \end{vmatrix}} \tag{13.17}$$

The denominator of Eq. (13.17) is the Jacobian determinant of the inverse transformation, denoted by I:

$$I = \frac{\partial(x, y, z)}{\partial(\xi, \eta, \phi)} = \begin{vmatrix} x_\xi & x_\eta & x_\phi \\ y_\xi & y_\eta & y_\phi \\ z_\xi & z_\eta & z_\phi \end{vmatrix} \tag{13.18a}$$

$$I = x_\xi (y_\eta z_\phi - y_\phi z_\eta) - x_\eta (y_\xi z_\phi - y_\phi z_\xi) + x_\phi (y_\xi z_\eta - y_\eta z_\xi) \tag{13.18b}$$

Solving Eq. (13.17) for $d\xi$ yields

$$d\xi = \frac{1}{I} \begin{vmatrix} dx & x_\eta & x_\phi \\ dy & y_\eta & y_\phi \\ dz & z_\eta & z_\phi \end{vmatrix} - \frac{dt}{I} \begin{vmatrix} x_\eta & x_\phi & x_\tau \\ y_\eta & y_\phi & y_\tau \\ z_\eta & z_\phi & z_\tau \end{vmatrix} \tag{13.19}$$

Solving Eq. (13.19) for ξ_x by solving for $d\xi/dx$ and letting $dy = dz = dt = 0$ gives

$$\xi_x = \frac{y_\eta z_\phi - y_\phi z_\eta}{I} \tag{13.20a}$$

In a similar manner,

$$\xi_y = -\frac{x_\eta z_\phi - x_\phi z_\eta}{I} \tag{13.20b}$$

$$\xi_z = \frac{x_\eta y_\phi - x_\phi y_\eta}{I} \tag{13.20c}$$

$$\xi_t = -\frac{1}{I}(x_\eta y_\phi z_\tau + x_\phi y_\tau z_\eta + x_\tau y_\eta z_\phi - x_\eta y_\tau z_\phi - x_\phi y_\eta z_\tau - x_\tau y_\phi z_\eta) \tag{13.21}$$

Solving Eq. (13.16) for $d\eta$ and $d\phi$ and evaluating the metrics in a similar manner yields:

$$\eta_x = -\frac{y_\xi z_\phi - y_\phi z_\xi}{I} \tag{13.22a}$$

$$\eta_y = \frac{x_\xi z_\phi - x_\phi z_\xi}{I} \tag{13.22b}$$

$$\eta_z = -\frac{x_\xi y_\phi - x_\phi y_\xi}{I} \tag{13.22c}$$

$$\eta_t = \frac{1}{I}(x_\xi y_\phi z_\tau + x_\phi y_\tau z_\xi + x_\tau y_\xi z_\phi - x_\xi y_\tau z_\phi - x_\phi y_\xi z_\tau - x_\tau y_\phi z_\xi) \tag{13.23}$$

$$\phi_x = \frac{y_\xi z_\eta - y_\eta z_\xi}{I} \tag{13.24a}$$

$$\phi_y = -\frac{x_\xi z_\eta - x_\eta z_\xi}{I} \tag{13.24b}$$

$$\phi_z = \frac{x_\xi y_\eta - x_\eta y_\xi}{I} \tag{13.24c}$$

$$\phi_t = -\frac{1}{I}(x_\xi y_\eta z_\tau + x_\eta y_\tau z_\xi + x_\tau y_\xi z_\eta - x_\xi y_\tau z_\eta - x_\eta y_\xi z_\tau - x_\tau y_\eta z_\xi) \tag{13.25}$$

When the grid is stationary (i.e., not changing with time), $\xi_t = \eta_t = \phi_t = 0$.

Equations (13.20), (13.22), and (13.24) are frequently expressed in terms of the Jacobian determinant J of the direct transformation, Eq. (13.12). Thus,

$$J = \frac{\partial(\xi, \eta, \phi)}{\partial(x, y, z)} \tag{13.26}$$

Differentiating Eq. (13.12) and writing the result in matrix form, as done for Eq. (13.14) to obtain (13.16), gives

$$\begin{bmatrix} \xi_x & \xi_y & \xi_z & \xi_t \\ \eta_x & \eta_y & \eta_z & \eta_t \\ \phi_x & \phi_y & \phi_z & \phi_t \\ 0 & 0 & 0 & 1 \end{bmatrix} \begin{bmatrix} dx \\ dy \\ dz \\ dt \end{bmatrix} = \begin{bmatrix} d\xi \\ d\eta \\ d\phi \\ d\tau \end{bmatrix} \tag{13.27}$$

Comparing Eqs. (13.16) and (13.27) shows that

$$\begin{bmatrix} \xi_x & \xi_y & \xi_z & \xi_t \\ \eta_x & \eta_y & \eta_z & \eta_t \\ \phi_x & \phi_y & \phi_z & \phi_t \\ 0 & 0 & 0 & 1 \end{bmatrix} = \begin{bmatrix} x_\xi & x_\eta & x_\phi & x_\tau \\ y_\xi & y_\eta & y_\phi & y_\tau \\ z_\xi & z_\eta & z_\phi & z_\tau \\ 0 & 0 & 0 & 1 \end{bmatrix}^{-1} \tag{13.28}$$

which shows that

$$J = \frac{1}{I} \tag{13.29}$$

Thus, Eqs. (13.20) to (13.25) can be written as $\xi_x = J(y_\eta z_\phi - y_\phi z_\eta)$, and so forth.

13.4 GRID GENERATION

Grid generation is the process of determining the coordinate transformation that maps the body-fitted nonuniform nonorthogonal physical space $xyzt$ into the transformed uniform orthogonal computational space $\xi\eta\phi\tau$. The book edited by Thompson (1982) and the book by Thompson et al. (1985) present a comprehensive introduction to the methods of grid generation.

The coordinate transformation must satisfy several requirements. The following list includes the most common requirements.

1. The grid in the transformed computational space must be uniform and orthogonal.
2. The transformation must be one-to-one.
3. The transformation must be nonsingular. That is, the Jacobian determinants I and J both must be nonzero.
4. The transformation must yield a body-fitted grid.
5. Grid points must be closely spaced in regions of large gradients and widely spaced in regions of small gradients.
6. The transformation must be smooth so that the transformation metrics are continuous.
7. The maximum and minimum values of the transformed coordinates must occur on the boundaries of the physical space.
8. Coordinate lines (or surfaces) of the same family must not cross.
9. Complete control of the spacing of points on the boundaries of the physical space must be possible.
10. Reasonable control of the spacing of points within the physical space must be possible.
11. The transformation must be applicable to both two- and three-dimensional physical spaces.

Several additional characteristics of coordinate transformations are desirable. Several of the more common additional characteristics are listed below.

1. Coordinate lines (or surfaces) of different families should not be too skewed with respect to each other.
2. In some cases, the ability to specify the grid spacing in the physical space adjacent to the boundaries is required.
3. In some cases, the ability to specify the angle of intersection of coordinate lines (or surfaces) with the boundaries is required.
4. The grid generation method should be efficient and straightforward to use.

Grid generation in one space dimension is straightforward. The two boundaries (i.e., end points) of the physical space must be specified, and the problem reduces to determining the grid spacing in one dimension. Several simple algebraic methods for one-dimensional grid generation are presented in Section 13.5. One-dimensional grid generation is important in itself for use in one-dimensional problems. It is also important in two-dimensional grid generation, where the boundaries of the two-dimensional space are one-dimensional spaces.

Just as the boundaries of two-dimensional spaces are one-dimensional spaces, the boundaries of three-dimensional spaces are two-dimensional spaces. Grid generation within two- and three-dimensional spaces is considerably more complicated than one-dimensional grid generation.

There are two basic steps in grid generation:

1. Specification of the boundary point distribution
2. Determination of the interior point distribution

There are three general methods of grid generation:

1. Conformal mapping
2. Algebraic methods
3. Differential equation methods

Conformal mapping is based on complex variable theory, which is limited to two dimensions. Consequently, that method is not as general as the other methods and will not be considered further.

Algebraic methods and differential equation methods can be applied to both two- and three-dimensional spaces. Consequently, they are the methods of choice. Algebraic methods are introduced Section 13.5 and differential equation methods are introduced in Section 13.6.

13.5 ALGEBRAIC GRID GENERATION

Algebraic grid generation involves the generation of a body-fitted coordinate transformation using algebraic equations. For example

$$\xi = a + bx + cx^2 \tag{13.30}$$

is a one-dimensional algebraic transformation from physical space x to transformed space ξ. As noted in Section 13.4, one-dimensional transformations are important both for one-dimensional spaces and for generating the point distributions along the boundaries of two-dimensional spaces. Four one-dimensional algebraic transformations, three two-dimensional algebraic transformations, and two three-dimensional algebraic transformations are illustrated in Section 13.5.

One-Dimensional Algebraic Transformations

Numerous one-dimensional algebraic transformations can be generated using simple functions, for example

1. Polynomials
2. Trigonometric functions
3. Logarithmic functions
4. Geometric progressions

Some general features of one-dimensional transformations are illustrated in Fig. 13.5. Figure 13.5*a* illustrates the situation where grid points are to be clustered about the center of the physical space, whereas Fig. 13.5*b* illustrates the case where grid points are to be clustered adjacent to the boundaries of the physical space. The left or right portion of either distribution can be used alone. The four simple functions listed above are illustrated in Example 13.1 by developing the right portion of the transformation illustrated in Fig. 13.5*a*.

The range of values of the transformed variable ξ is arbitrary. The most common ranges are $0 \leq \bar{\xi} \leq 1$ and $1 \leq \xi \leq \xi_{\max}$, where ξ is an integer. The

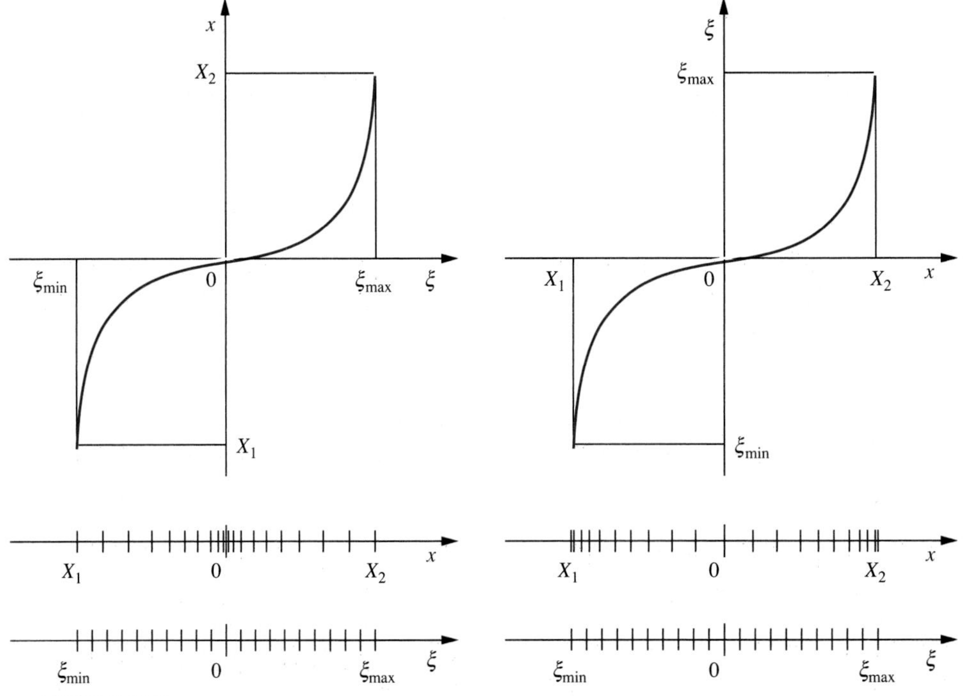

FIGURE 13.5
General features of one-dimensional transformations: (*a*) clustering at $x = 0$; (*b*) clustering at X_1 and X_2.

transformed variables $\bar{\xi}$ and ξ are related as follows:

$$\bar{\xi} = \frac{\xi - 1}{\xi_{\max} - 1} \quad (0 \le \bar{\xi} \le 1, 1 \le \xi \le \xi_{\max}) \tag{13.31}$$

Integer values such as ξ are preferred, since the integer values of ξ can correspond to the integer index variables in a computer program, and the increment $\Delta\xi$, which appears in finite difference approximations, is 1.0. The transformed variables $\bar{\xi}$ and ξ are used in the transformations presented in this section.

POLYNOMIALS. Consider the general polynomial

$$\boxed{x = a + b\bar{\xi} + c\bar{\xi}^2 + d\bar{\xi}^3 + \cdots} \tag{13.32}$$

Differentiating Eq. (13.32) and solving for $\bar{\xi}_x$ yields the transformation metric $\bar{\xi}_x$:

$$\boxed{\bar{\xi}_x = \frac{1}{b + 2c\bar{\xi} + 3d\bar{\xi}^2 + \cdots}} \tag{13.33}$$

The coefficients a, b, c, and so on are determined by applying boundary conditions and constraints, such as

$$x = X_1 \rightarrow \bar{\xi} = 0 \quad \text{and} \quad \xi = 1 \tag{13.34a}$$

$$x = X_2 \rightarrow \bar{\xi} = 1 \quad \text{and} \quad \xi = \xi_{\max} \tag{13.34b}$$

$$x = X_i \rightarrow \bar{\xi} = \bar{\xi}_i \quad \text{and} \quad \xi = \xi_i \tag{13.34c}$$

$$x_\xi = x_{\xi i} \rightarrow \bar{\xi} = \bar{\xi}|_i \quad \text{and} \quad \xi = \xi_i \tag{13.34d}$$

Equations (13.34*a*) and (13.34*b*) specify the boundaries of the transformation. Equation (13.34*c*) can be used to specify the location of interior points, thus controlling the distribution of points within the physical space. Equation (13.34*d*) can be used to specify the value of the metric x_ξ at a specified point. Sufficient constraints must be specified to permit evaluation of all the coefficients in Eq. (13.32).

TRIGONOMETRIC FUNCTIONS. Consider the trigonometric function

$$\boxed{\xi = a + b\tan^{-1} cx, \qquad (1 \le \xi \le \xi_{\max})} \tag{13.35}$$

Differentiating Eq. (13.35) yields

$$\boxed{\xi_x = \frac{bc}{1 + (cx)^2}} \tag{13.36}$$

Equation (13.36) requires the inverse transformation $x(\xi)$:

$$x = \frac{1}{c}\tan\big((\xi - a)/b\big) \tag{13.37}$$

The coefficients a, b, and c are obtained by applying boundary conditions and constraints, such as Eq. (13.34).

LOGARITHMIC FUNCTIONS. Roberts (1971) suggested the use of logarithmic functions for boundary-layer-type fluid flows. Based on that suggestion, Anderson et al. (1984) proposed the following transformation:

$$\boxed{\bar{\xi} = 1 - \frac{\ln\Big(\big((\beta + 1) - (x/L)\big)/\big((\beta - 1) + (x/L)\big)\Big)}{\ln\big((\beta + 1)/(\beta - 1)\big)}} \tag{13.38}$$

where $0 \le x \le L$ and $1 \le \beta \le \infty$. Grid points are clustered near $x = 0$ as $\beta \to 1$. Differentiating Eq. (13.38) yields

$$\boxed{\bar{\xi}_x = \frac{2\beta}{L\Big(\beta^2 - (1 - (x/L))^2\Big)\ln\Big((\beta + 1)/(\beta - 1)\Big)}} \tag{13.39}$$

Equation (13.39) requires the inverse transformation $x(\xi)$:

$$x = L\,\frac{(\beta + 1) - (\beta - 1)\Big(\big((\beta + 1)/(\beta - 1)\big)^{(1-\bar{\xi})}\Big)}{\big((\beta + 1)/(\beta - 1)\big)^{(1-\bar{\xi})} + 1} \tag{13.40}$$

The parameter β is chosen to achieve the desired clustering near $x = 0$.

GEOMETRIC PROGRESSIONS. As a final example of a one-dimensional algebraic transformation, consider geometric progressions, in which each spatial increment is a fixed multiple of the previous spatial increment:

$$\boxed{\Delta x_i = (x_{i+1} - x_i) = r\,\Delta x_{i-1} = r\,(x_i - x_{i-1})} \tag{13.41}$$

where r is the ratio of successive increments. Let L be the total size of the physical space, $a = \Delta x_0 = (x_1 - x_0)$ be the first increment, and $l = \Delta x_{n-1} = (x_n - x_{n-1})$ be the final increment, where n is the number of terms in the progression (i.e., the number of spatial increments). From the properties of geometric progressions,

$$l = ar^{n-1} \tag{13.42a}$$

$$L = a\frac{r^n - 1}{r - 1} \tag{13.42b}$$

Once L and n are specified, r can be chosen to give a specified value of a or l. Then the inverse transformation $x(\xi)$ can be determined by applying Eq. (13.41).

The above procedure yields $x(\xi)$, and thus $\xi(x)$, as a set of discrete values. The evaluation of the transformation metric ξ_x must be accomplished numerically by, for example, using the second-order centered-difference finite difference approximation given by Eq. (5.94):

$$\xi_x|_i = \frac{1}{x_\xi|_i} = \frac{1}{(x_{i+1} - x_{i-1})/2\Delta\xi} \tag{13.43}$$

At the left and right boundaries, one-sided finite difference approximations are required. These are given by Eqs. (5.95) and (5.96), respectively.

Example 13.1. One-dimensional algebraic transformations. We will illustrate the one-dimensional algebraic transformations presented in this section by transforming the physical space $0 \le x \le 1$ to the transformed space $1 \le \xi \le 11$. Thus, the boundary conditions are

$$x = 0.0 \quad \rightarrow \quad \bar{\xi} = 0 \quad \text{and} \quad \xi = 1 \tag{13.44a}$$

$$x = 1.0 \quad \rightarrow \quad \bar{\xi} = 1 \quad \text{and} \quad \xi = 11 \tag{13.44b}$$

Let the first increment be 0.02. Thus,

$$x = 0.02 \quad \rightarrow \quad \bar{\xi} = 0.1 \quad \text{and} \quad \xi = 2 \tag{13.44c}$$

For transformations having a fourth degree of freedom, let the final increment be 0.20. Thus,

$$x = 0.8 \quad \rightarrow \quad \bar{\xi} = 0.9 \quad \text{and} \quad \xi = 10 \tag{13.44d}$$

TABLE 13.1
One-dimensional transformations $x(\xi)$

ξ	$\bar{\xi}$	$P_2(\xi)$	$P_3(\xi)$	$\tan^{-1}(x)$	**ln(x)**	**Geometric**
1	0.0	0.000000	0.000000	0.000000	0.000000	0.000000
2	0.1	0.020000	0.020000	0.020000	0.020000	0.020000
3	0.2	0.057778	0.053333	0.040851	0.048651	0.046645
4	0.3	0.113333	0.094917	0.063553	0.089256	0.082141
5	0.4	0.186667	0.150667	0.089473	0.145939	0.129432
6	0.5	0.277778	0.250000	0.120718	0.223410	0.192433
7	0.6	0.386667	0.353333	0.160945	0.326294	0.276365
8	0.7	0.513333	0.478333	0.217365	0.457835	0.388183
9	0.8	0.657778	0.626667	0.306789	0.618079	0.537149
10	0.9	0.820000	0.800000	0.480141	0.802186	0.735608
11	1.0	1.000000	1.000000	1.000000	1.000000	1.000000

Quadratic Polynomial. Substituting Eqs. (13.44a) to (13.44c) into Eq. (13.32), solving for a to c, and substituting the results into Eqs. (13.32) and (13.33) gives

$$x = 0.111111\,\bar{\xi} + 0.888889\,\bar{\xi}^2 \tag{13.45a}$$

$$\xi_x = (\xi_{\max} - 1)\,\bar{\xi}_x = \frac{10}{0.111111 + 2(0.888889)\,\bar{\xi}} \tag{13.45b}$$

The transformation specified by Eq. (13.45a) is tabulated in Table 13.1 and illustrated in Fig. 13.6. The transformation metric specified by Eq. (13.45b) is tabulated in Table 13.2 and illustrated in Fig. 13.7.

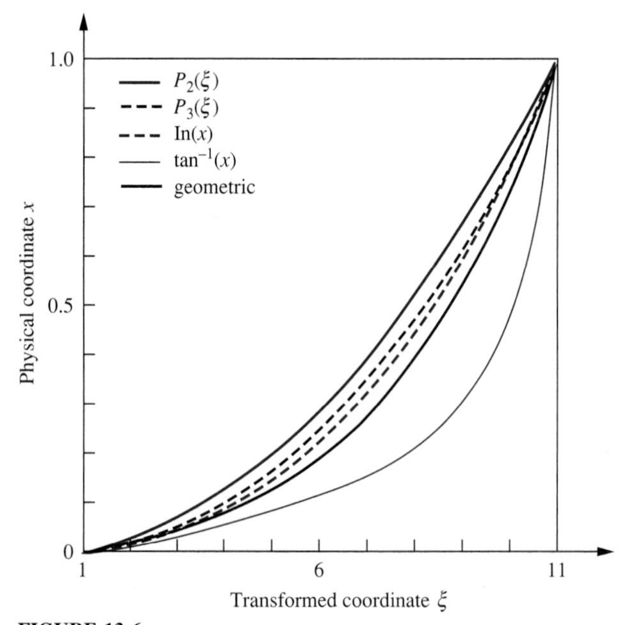

FIGURE 13.6
One-dimensional transformations $x(\xi)$.

TABLE 13.2
One-dimensional transformation metrics $\xi_x(\xi)$

ξ	$\overline{\xi}$	$P_2(\xi)$	$P_3(\xi)$	$\tan^{-1}(x)$	**ln(x)**	**Geometric**
1	0.0	90.0000	72.0000	50.3451	60.3452	59.9604
2	0.1	34.6154	37.8947	49.3182	41.9387	42.8774
3	0.2	21.4286	24.6575	46.3214	29.4055	32.1846
4	0.3	15.5172	17.7340	41.5991	20.8794	24.1584
5	0.4	12.1622	13.5339	35.5366	15.0906	18.1338
6	0.5	10.0000	10.7463	28.6285	11.1772	13.6116
7	0.6	8.4906	8.7805	21.4385	8.5563	10.2171
8	0.7	7.3770	7.3320	14.5531	6.8377	7.6692
9	0.8	6.5217	6.2284	8.5342	5.7656	5.7566
10	0.9	5.8442	5.3651	3.8727	5.1801	4.3210
11	1.0	5.2941	4.6753	0.9490	4.9942	3.3629

Cubic Polynomial. Substituting Eqs. (13.44a) to (13.44d) into Eq. (13.32), solving for a to d, and substituting the results into Eqs. (13.32) and (13.33) yields

$$x = 0.138889\,\overline{\xi} + 0.583333\,\overline{\xi}^{\,2} + 0.277778\,\overline{\xi}^{\,3} \tag{13.46a}$$

$$\xi_x = (\xi_{\max} - 1)\,\overline{\xi}_x = \frac{10}{0.138889 + 2(0.583333)\,\overline{\xi} + 3(0.277778)\,\overline{\xi}^{\,2}} \tag{13.46b}$$

The results are tabulated in Tables 13.1 and 13.2 and illustrated in Figs. 13.6 and 13.7.

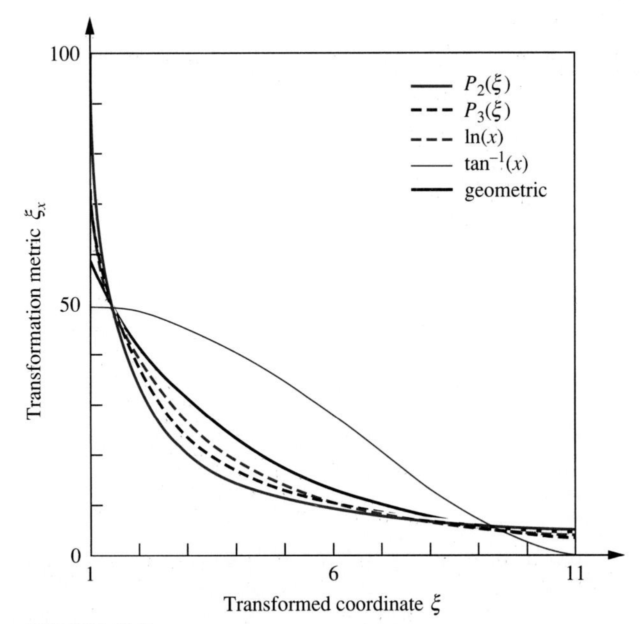

FIGURE 13.7
One-dimensional transformation metrics $\xi_x(\xi)$.

Trigonometric Function. Substituting Eqs. (13.44a) to (13.44c) into Eq. (13.35) yields $a = 1$, $b = 10/\tan^{-1} c$, and

$$f(c) = \tan^{-1} c - 10 \tan^{-1}(0.02c) = 0 \tag{13.47}$$

Solving Eq. (13.47) by the secant method yields $c = 7.214808$. Substituting a to c into Eqs. (13.35) to (13.37) yields

$$\xi = 1 + 0.121790 \tan^{-1}(7.214808x) \tag{13.48a}$$

$$\xi_x = \frac{0.878688}{1 + (7.214808x)^2} \tag{13.48b}$$

$$x = \frac{1}{7.214808} \tan\big((\xi - 1)/0.121790\big) \tag{13.48c}$$

The results are tabulated in Tables 13.1 and 13.2 and illustrated in Figs. 13.6 and 13.7.

Logarithmic Function. Substituting Eqs. (13.44a) to (13.44c) into Eq. (13.38) yields the nonlinear function

$$f(\beta) = 0.9\ln\left(\frac{\beta + 1}{\beta - 1}\right) - \ln\left(\frac{\beta + 0.98}{\beta - 0.98}\right) = 0 \tag{13.49}$$

Solving Eq. (13.49) by the secant method gives $\beta = 1.044139$. Equations (13.40) and (13.39) become

$$x = 1.0\,\frac{2.044139 - 0.044139\big((46.310919)^{(1-\bar{\xi})}\big)}{(46.310919)^{(1-\bar{\xi})} + 1} \tag{13.50a}$$

$$\xi_x = \frac{20.882789}{1.0\big(1.090227 - (1 - x)^2\big)3.835378} \tag{13.50b}$$

The results are tabulated in Tables 13.1 and 13.2 and illustrated in Figs. 13.6 and 13.7.

Geometric Progression. Substituting Eqs. (13.44a) to (13.44c) into Eq. (13.42b) yields the nonlinear function

$$f(r) = r^{10} - 50r + 49 = 0 \tag{13.51}$$

Solving Eq. (13.51) by Newton's method yields $r = 1.332232$. Equation (13.41) becomes

$$\Delta x_i = 1.332232\Delta x_{i-1} \qquad (i = 2, \ldots, 10) \tag{13.52}$$

where $\Delta x_1 = 0.02$. Values of $x(\xi)$ are tabulated in Table 13.1 and illustrated in Fig. 13.6. Values of ξ_x are computed from Eqs. (13.43), (5.95), and (5.96). These results are tabulated in Table 13.2 and illustrated in Fig. 13.7.

Summary. The results presented in Figs. 13.6 and 13.7 show that the polynomial, logarithmic, and geometric progression transformations yield similar results. The tangent transformation produces a more packed grid near $x = 0$. All the transformations are subject to the constraint that the first increment is 0.02. Varying this value yields families of transformations. All these functions are suitable for one-dimensional transformations.

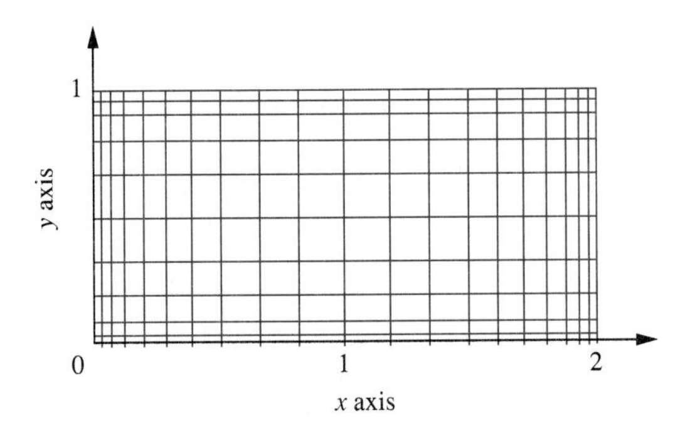

FIGURE 13.8
Orthogonal one-dimensional transformations.

Two-Dimensional Algebraic Transformations

Two-dimensional algebraic transformations can be developed for some geometries. The following three examples are presented in this section:

1. Orthogonal one-dimensional transformations
2. Normalizing transformation
3. Connection functions

ORTHOGONAL ONE-DIMENSIONAL TRANSFORMATIONS. An extremely simple two-dimensional transformation can be constructed by applying two orthogonal one-dimensional transformations in the special case where the physical space is rectangular and grid point clustering is required. Figure 13.8 illustrates such a transformation. The $x \rightarrow \xi$ transformation and the $y \rightarrow \eta$ transformation are independent and noninteracting. The transformations illustrated in Fig. 13.8 are both quadratic polynomials.

NORMALIZING TRANSFORMATION. When the physical space is not rectangular, a more general transformation is required. Consider the physical space illustrated in Fig. 13.9. The x coordinate can be transformed by any one-dimensional transformation, if desired. The x coordinate in Fig. 13.9 is not transformed. It is simply discretized into equally spaced points. The y coordinate is then discretized

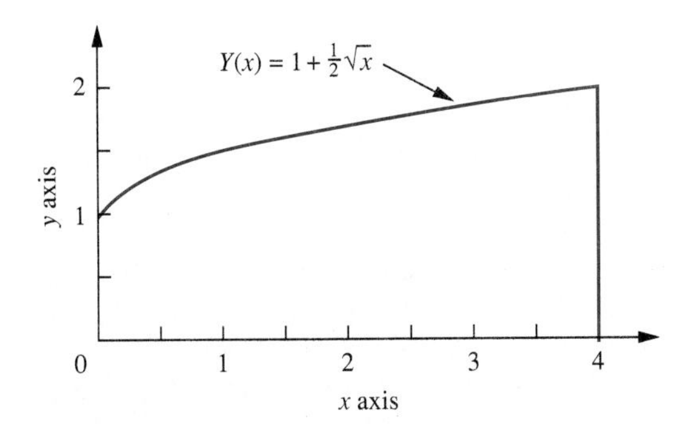

FIGURE 13.9
Physical domain.

TABLE 13.3
Normalizing transformation

	ξ										
	1	**3**	**5**	**7**	**9**	**11**	**13**	**15**	**17**	**19**	**21**
η						x					
11	0.000	0.400	0.800	1.200	1.600	2.000	2.400	2.800	3.200	3.600	4.000
9	0.000	0.400	0.800	1.200	1.600	2.000	2.400	2.800	3.200	3.600	4.000
7	0.000	0.400	0.800	1.200	1.600	2.000	2.400	2.800	3.200	3.600	4.000
5	0.000	0.400	0.800	1.200	1.600	2.000	2.400	2.800	3.200	3.600	4.000
3	0.000	0.400	0.800	1.200	1.600	2.000	2.400	2.800	3.200	3.600	4.000
1	0.000	0.400	0.800	1.200	1.600	2.000	2.400	2.800	3.200	3.600	4.000
						y					
11	1.000	1.316	1.447	1.548	1.632	1.707	1.775	1.837	1.894	1.949	2.000
9	0.800	1.053	1.158	1.238	1.306	1.366	1.420	1.469	1.516	1.559	1.600
7	0.600	0.790	0.868	0.929	0.979	1.024	1.065	1.102	1.137	1.169	1.200
5	0.400	0.526	0.579	0.619	0.653	0.683	0.710	0.735	0.758	0.779	0.800
3	0.200	0.263	0.289	0.310	0.326	0.341	0.355	0.367	0.379	0.390	0.400
1	0.000	0.000	0.000	0.000	0.000	0.000	0.000	0.000	0.000	0.000	0.000

into equally spaced points at each x location by the normalizing transformation

$$\overline{\eta} = \frac{y}{Y(x)} \qquad (0 \leq \overline{\eta} \leq 1) \tag{13.53}$$

where $Y(x)$ is the upper boundary. Equation (13.53) can be stretched by the stretching transformation

$$\eta = 1 + (\eta_{max} - 1)\overline{\eta} \quad (1 \leq \eta \leq \eta_{max}) \tag{13.54}$$

The transformation metrics are given by

$$\xi_x = 1 \qquad \text{and} \qquad \xi_y = 0 \tag{13.55a}$$

$$\overline{\eta}_x = y\frac{Y'(x)}{(Y(x))^2} \qquad \text{and} \qquad \overline{\eta}_y = \frac{1}{Y(x)} \tag{13.55b}$$

Applying the normalizing transformation with $\xi_{max} = 21$ and $\eta_{max} = 11$ to the physical space illustrated in Fig. 13.9, with Δx = constant, yields the results presented in Table 13.3. To conserve space, only every other grid point is tabulated. The results of the complete transformation are illustrated in Fig. 13.10.

CONNECTION FUNCTIONS. As an example of the application of connection functions, consider the two-dimensional annular flow passage illustrated in Fig. 13.11, which was transformed to a uniform orthogonal computational space by Wang and Hoffman (1986). The boundaries of the physical space consist of the two solid

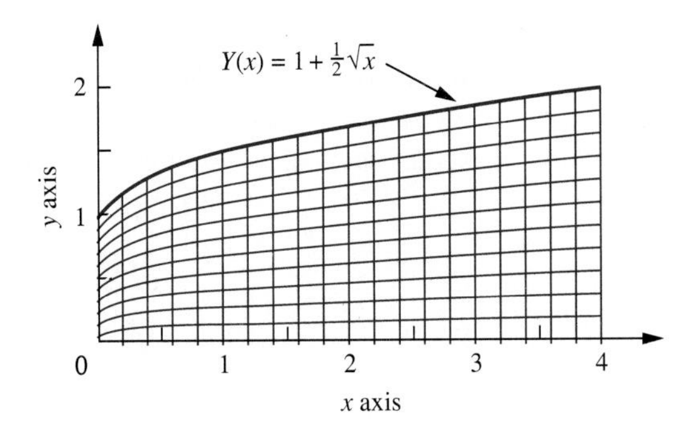

FIGURE 13.10
Normalizing transformation.

boundaries specified by the wall contour and the centerbody contour, denoted by the subscripts w and c, respectively, and the two vertical lines across the inlet and exit boundaries, denoted by the subscripts i and e, respectfully. A *middleline* through the physical space, denoted by the subscript m, is also used in the grid generation process. The middleline is defined by

$$y_m(x) = \frac{1}{2}\big(y_w(x) + y_c(x)\big) \tag{13.56a}$$

Due to the presence of large gradients near the minimum point on the wall (denoted as point wt) and the maximum point on the centerbody (denoted as point ct) it is desired to cluster grid lines in the neighborhood of these two points. Since points wt and ct do not occur at the same x location, two independent boundary point distributions are required to obtain the desired clustering. A corresponding point, mt, on the middleline is defined by

$$x_{mt} = \frac{1}{2}(x_{wt} + x_{ct}) \tag{13.56b}$$

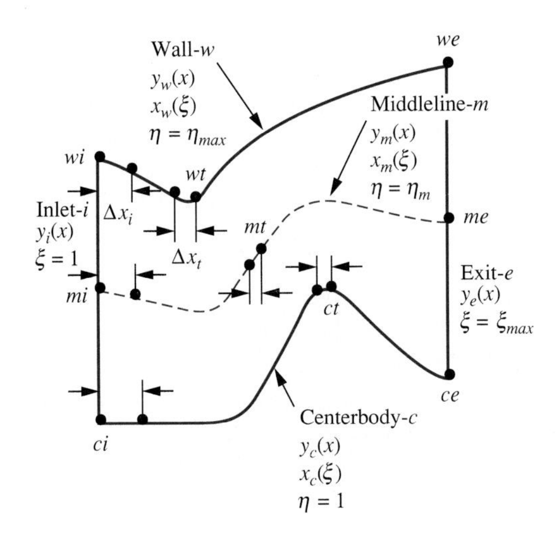

FIGURE 13.11
Physical domain.

Once the boundary point distributions are specified, the interior point distribution is determined by interpolating the boundary point distributions into the interior of the physical space using connection functions.

A total of six cubic polynomials were fitted to the wall, middleline, and centerbody:

$$x(\bar{\xi}) = a + b\bar{\xi} + c\bar{\xi}^2 + d\bar{\xi}^3 \qquad (0 \le \bar{\xi} \le 1) \tag{13.57}$$

The first three cubic polynomials, from the inlet i to point t, satisfied the following four constraints: $x_i \to \bar{\xi} = 0$; $x_t \to \bar{\xi} = 1$; $\Delta x_i / \Delta x_t = R$ (where $R > 1$); and $d^2x/d\bar{\xi}^2 = 0$ at point t so that $x(\bar{\xi})$ has an inflection point at point t. The second three polynomials, from point t to the exit e, satisfied the following four constraints: $x_t \to \bar{\xi} = 0$; $x_e \to \bar{\xi} = 1$; the slopes $dx/d\bar{\xi}$ of the first and second cubics are equal at point t, and $d^2x/d\bar{\xi}^2 = 0$ at point t. Substituting these constraints into Eq. (13.57) yields expressions for the coefficients a to d for each of the six cubic polynomials. Those expressions are presented by Wang and Hoffman.

The connection function between the three boundaries can be expressed as

$$x = x(\bar{\xi}, \bar{\eta}) \qquad \text{and} \qquad y = y(\bar{\xi}, \bar{\eta}) \tag{13.58}$$

where $y_c(x) \to \bar{\eta} = 0$, $y_m(x) \to \bar{\eta}_m$, and $y_w(x) \to \bar{\eta} = 1$. Wang and Hoffman (1986) employed quadratic connection functions. That is,

$$x = x_0(\bar{\xi}) + x_1(\bar{\xi})\bar{\eta} + x_2(\bar{\xi})\bar{\eta}^2 \tag{13.59a}$$

$$y = y_0(\bar{\xi}) + y_1(\bar{\xi})\bar{\eta} + y_2(\bar{\xi})\bar{\eta}^2 \tag{13.59b}$$

The functions $x_0(\bar{\xi})$, $x_1(\bar{\xi})$, and so on are determined by requiring Eq. (13.59) to satisfy the grid point distributions along the boundaries of the physical space. That is,

$$x_w = x_w(\bar{\xi}), \qquad x_m = x_m(\bar{\xi}), \qquad \text{and} \qquad x_c = x_c(\bar{\xi}) \tag{13.60a}$$

$$y_w = y_w(\bar{\xi}), \qquad y_m = y_m(\bar{\xi}), \qquad \text{and} \qquad y_c = y_c(\bar{\xi}) \tag{13.60b}$$

If only two boundaries are used, only the coefficients of the linear terms in Eq. (13.59) can be determined. Using the middleline defined by Eq. (13.56) permits the determination of the coefficients of the quadratic terms in Eq. (13.59). The specific forms of the six coefficient functions $x(\bar{\xi})$ and $y(\bar{\xi})$ in Eq. (13.59) are presented by Wang and Hoffman. An example of this grid generation method is illustrated in Fig. 13.12.

Three-Dimensional Algebraic Transformations

Devising algebraic transformations for three-dimensional domains is quite challenging. Two approaches are discussed in this section:

1. Stacked two-dimensional transformations
2. Superelliptical boundaries

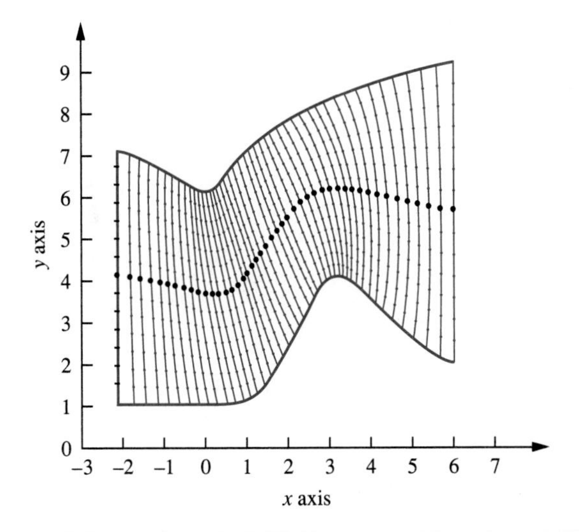

FIGURE 13.12
Grid point distribution.

STACKED TWO-DIMENSIONAL TRANSFORMATIONS. In situations where one family of the bounding surfaces is flat or cylindrical, a series of two-dimensional transformations can be stacked from one bounding surface to the other. The two-dimensional transformations can be either algebraically or numerically generated. The transformation metrics in the stacked direction must be evaluated numerically. This approach can be used for any shape domain that has parallel bounding walls, such as that illustrated in Fig. 13.13. A series of two-dimensional transformations in xz planes is simply stacked together in the y direction. If desired, a one-dimensional transformation can be used in the y direction to space the stacked two-dimensional transformations. This approach has been used for turbomachinery cascades, where blade-to-blade transformations are stacked in the radial direction.

SUPERELLIPTICAL BOUNDARIES. When a portion of the bounding surface of the physical space can be specified by an analytical function, it may be possible to develop a three-dimensional algebraic transformation. An example is the family of superelliptical flow passages studied by Marcum and Hoffman (1988). Three

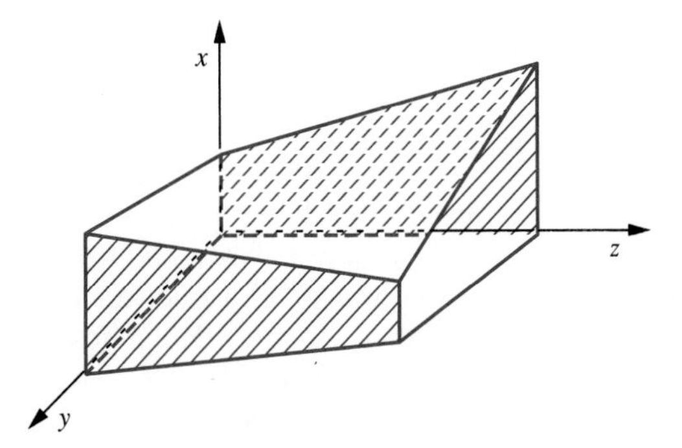

FIGURE 13.13
Stacked two-dimensional algebraic transformations.

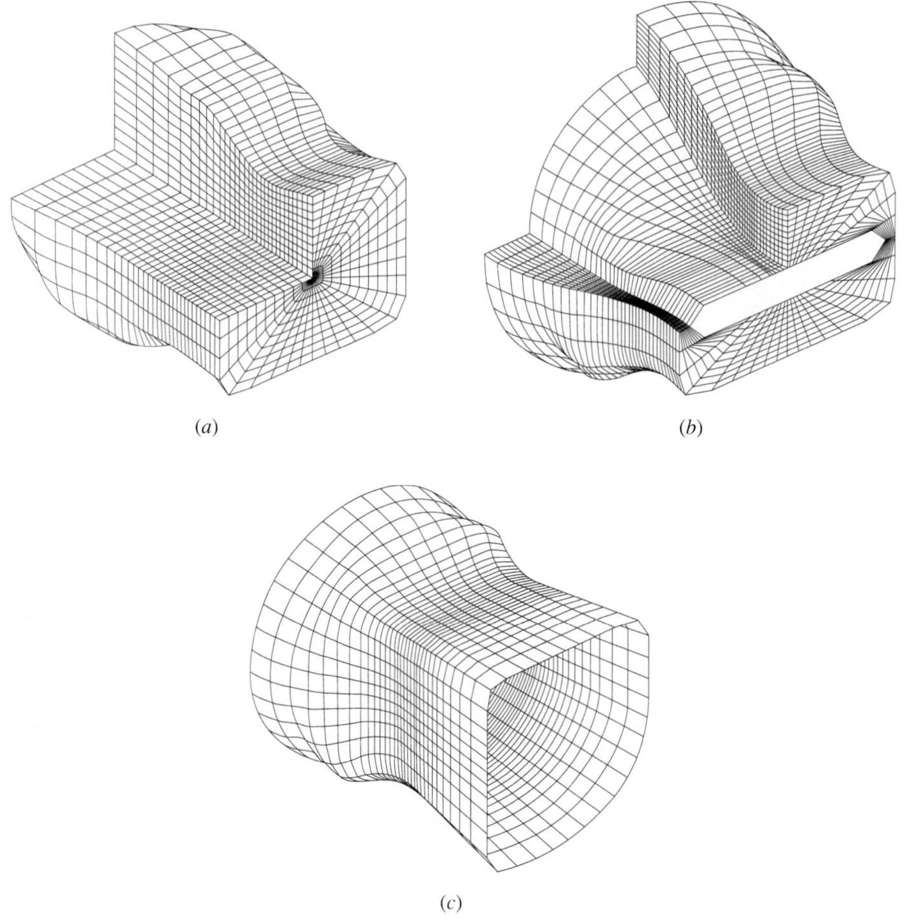

FIGURE 13.14
Superelliptical transformations: (*a*) symmetric; (*b*) centerbody; (*c*) asymmetric.

examples are presented in Fig. 13.14. The wall and centerbody (if present) in each quadrant are specified by the superelliptical function:

$$\left(\frac{R(x,\theta)\cos\theta}{A(x)}\right)^{E(x)} + \left(\frac{R(x,\theta)\sin\theta}{B(x)}\right)^{E(x)} = 1 \tag{13.61}$$

where $R(x,\theta)$ is the wall or centerbody radius, $A(x)$ is the radius in the $\theta = 0$ and π coordinate planes, $B(x)$ is the radius in the $\theta = \pi/2$ and $3\pi/2$ coordinate planes, and $E(x)$ is the superelliptical exponent, which has the range $E(x) \geq 2$. All four quadrants may have the same contour, as illustrated in Figs. 13.14*a* and 13.14*b*, or all four quadrants can have different contours, as illustrated in Fig. 13.14*c*. The grid in the physical space consists of planes perpendicular to the axial direction, meridional planes (i.e., planes at constant values of θ passing through the axis of the flow passage), and surfaces that are parallel to the wall and centerbody surfaces in transformed space. A one-dimensional transformation is used in the axial direction to pack planes near the minimum cross-sectional area, where the flowfield gradients are largest. The trigonometric transformation specified by Eqs. (13.35) to (13.37) was employed in Fig. 13.14. At each axial location on each meridional plane, the normalizing transformation specified by Eqs. (13.53) and (13.54) was used. Thus,

$$\eta(x, r, \theta) = 1 + (\eta_{\max} - 1)\left(\frac{r - R_c(x, \theta)}{R_w(x, \theta) - R_c(x, \theta)}\right) \quad (1 \leq \eta \leq \eta_{\max}) \tag{13.62}$$

where $R_c(x, \theta)$ and $R_w(x, \theta)$ are the centerbody and wall contours, respectively. The trigonometric transformation specified by Eqs. (13.35) to (13.37) can be employed in the meridional (i.e., θ) direction to cluster meridional planes in the corners of the flow passage. That was not done in the results presented in Fig. 13.14.

13.6 GRID GENERATION USING DIFFERENTIAL EQUATIONS

Grid generation using differential equations involves the generation of a body-fitted coordinate transformation using differential equations. Although one-, two-, and three-dimensional transformations can be developed using differential equations, suitable one-dimensional transformations usually can be found using algebraic methods, so differential equation methods are more relevant to two- and three-dimensional transformations. The review by Thompson et al. (1982), the book edited by Thompson (1982), and the book by Thompson et al. (1985) present a thorough introduction to grid generation using partial differential equations.

The problem can be stated as follows. Determine the coordinate transformation

$$\xi = \xi(x, y, z), \qquad \eta = \eta(x, y, z), \qquad \text{and} \qquad \phi = \phi(x, y, z) \tag{13.63}$$

that satisfies the boundary point distributions

$$\xi = F(x, y, z), \qquad \eta = G(x, y, z), \qquad \text{and} \qquad \phi = H(x, y, z) \tag{13.64}$$

where the three functions specified in Eq. (13.63) satisfy some differential equation.

Grid generation using differential equations involves the following two steps:

1. Determine the grid point distribution on the boundaries of the physical space. For two-dimensional spaces, the boundaries are one-dimensional spaces. The required one-dimensional grid point distributions can be obtained by algebraic methods. For three-dimensional spaces, the boundaries are two-dimensional spaces. The required two-dimensional grid point distributions can be obtained either by algebraic methods or by a two-dimensional differential equation method.

2. Assume that the interior grid point distribution is specified by a differential equation that satisfies the grid point distributions specified on the boundaries and yields an acceptable interior grid point distribution.

Any of the three classical types of partial differential equation (i.e., elliptic, parabolic, or hyperbolic) can be used as the governing grid generation differential equation. The list of requirements that coordinate transformations must satisfy, which is presented in Section 13.4, suggests the use of an elliptic differential equation as the governing differential equation. For example, closed domains, continuous functions and derivatives, and maximum and minimum function values on the boundaries are features of the solution of elliptic PDEs. Consequently, the majority of grid generation by differential equations is based on elliptic PDEs as generating functions. Nevertheless, some success has been obtained using parabolic and hyperbolic PDEs as generating functions.

The most common elliptic PDE used for grid generation is the Poisson equation:

$$\nabla^2\xi = P(\xi, \eta, \phi), \qquad \nabla^2\eta = Q(\xi, \eta, \phi), \qquad \text{and} \qquad \nabla^2\phi = R(\xi, \eta, \phi) \tag{13.65}$$

with boundary conditions specified by Eq. (13.64), where the nonhomogeneous terms $P(\xi, \eta, \phi)$, and so on are used to control the distribution of points within the physical space. Solving Eq. (13.65) yields the direct transformation, Eq. (13.63). Unfortunately, a problem arises in the numerical solution of Eq. (13.65). The uniform orthogonal transformed grid $\xi\eta\phi$ is known, but the nonuniform nonorthogonal physical grid xyz is not known. In fact, the object of the grid generation process is to determine the grid in the xyz space. Consequently, Eq. (13.65) cannot be solved directly. The inverse transformation

$$x = x(\xi, \eta, \phi), \qquad y = y(\xi, \eta, \phi), \qquad \text{and} \qquad z = z(\xi, \eta, \phi) \tag{13.66}$$

must be solved for. Thus, the roles of the independent variables (i.e., x, y, and z) and the dependent variables (i.e., ξ, η, and ϕ) in Eq. (13.65) must be interchanged in the generating elliptic PDEs. This interchange does not change the classification of the PDEs.

Two-Dimensional Grid Generation

For simplicity, consider a steady two-dimensional grid generation problem:

$$\nabla^2\xi = \xi_{xx} + \xi_{yy} = P(\xi, \eta) \tag{13.67a}$$

$$\nabla^2\eta = \eta_{xx} + \eta_{yy} = Q(\xi, \eta) \tag{13.67b}$$

From the chain rule for partial derivatives of the generic function $f(x, y)$:

$$f_x = f_\xi \xi_x + f_\eta \eta_x \qquad (13.68a)$$

$$f_y = f_\xi \xi_y + f_\eta \eta_y \qquad (13.68b)$$

In a similar manner, second derivatives are given by

$$f_{xx} = (f_x)_x = (f_\xi \xi_x)_x + (f_\eta \eta_x)_x \qquad (13.69a)$$

$$f_{xx} = f_\xi \xi_{xx} + \xi_x (f_{\xi\xi} \xi_x + f_{\xi\eta} \eta_x) + f_\eta \eta_{xx} + \eta_x (f_{\eta\xi} \xi_x + f_{\eta\eta} \eta_x) \qquad (13.69b)$$

$$f_{yy} = f_\xi \xi_{yy} + \xi_y (f_{\xi\xi} \xi_y + f_{\xi\eta} \eta_y) + f_\eta \eta_{yy} + \eta_y (f_{\eta\xi} \xi_y + f_{\eta\eta} \eta_y) \qquad (13.69c)$$

Adding Eqs. (13.69*b*) and (13.69*c*) gives

$$\nabla^2 f = f_{xx} + f_{yy} = \left(\xi_x^2 + \xi_y^2\right) f_{\xi\xi} + 2(\xi_x \eta_x + \xi_y \eta_y) f_{\xi\eta} + \left(\eta_x^2 + \eta_y^2\right) f_{\eta\eta} + \nabla^2 \xi f_\xi + \nabla^2 \eta f_\eta \qquad (13.70)$$

Let $f = x$ in Eq. (13.70). Then $\nabla^2 x = x_{xx} + x_{yy} = 0$, and Eq. (13.70) becomes

$$\left(\xi_x^2 + \xi_y^2\right) x_{\xi\xi} + 2(\xi_x \eta_x + \xi_y \eta_y) x_{\xi\eta} + \left(\eta_x^2 + \eta_y^2\right) x_{\eta\eta} = -(P x_\xi + Q x_\eta) \qquad (13.71)$$

where $\nabla^2 \xi = P$ and $\nabla^2 \eta = Q$ from Eqs. (13.67*a*) and (13.67*b*), respectively. Recall the relationships between the metric coefficients of the direct and inverse transformations, Eqs. (13.20) to (13.25). For the two-dimensional case, $z_\xi = z_\eta = 0$, $z_\phi = 1$, and

$$\xi_x = J y_\eta \quad \text{and} \quad \xi_y = -J x_\eta \qquad (13.72)$$

$$\eta_x = -J y_\xi \quad \text{and} \quad \eta_y = J x_\xi \qquad (13.73)$$

$$I = \frac{1}{J} = x_\xi y_\eta - x_\eta y_\xi \qquad (13.74)$$

Substituting these results into Eq. (13.71) and simplifying gives

$$\left(x_\eta^2 + y_\eta^2\right) x_{\xi\xi} - 2(x_\xi x_\eta + y_\xi y_\eta) x_{\xi\eta} + \left(x_\xi^2 + y_\xi^2\right) x_{\eta\eta} = -I^2 (P x_\xi + Q x_\eta) \qquad (13.75)$$

Equation (13.75) can be written in the condensed form

$$\boxed{\alpha x_{\xi\xi} - 2\beta x_{\xi\eta} + \gamma x_{\eta\eta} = -I^2 (P x_\xi + Q x_\eta)} \qquad (13.76)$$

Repeating the steps in Eqs. (13.71) to (13.76) with $f = y$ yields

$$\boxed{\alpha y_{\xi\xi} - 2\beta y_{\xi\eta} + \gamma y_{\eta\eta} = -I^2 (P y_\xi + Q y_\eta)} \qquad (13.77)$$

In Eqs. (13.76) and (13.77),

$$\alpha = x_\eta^2 + y_\eta^2, \qquad \beta = (x_\xi x_\eta + y_\xi y_\eta), \qquad \text{and} \qquad \gamma = x_\xi^2 + y_\xi^2 \tag{13.78}$$

The boundary conditions for Eqs. (13.76) and (13.77) are

$$\boxed{x = F(\xi, \eta) \qquad \text{and} \qquad y = G(\xi, \eta)} \tag{13.79}$$

Equations (13.76) and (13.77) comprise a system of two quasilinear (i.e., linear in the highest order derivatives) elliptic PDEs with Dirichlet BCs. Equations (13.76) and (13.77) are considerably more complicated than Eqs. (13.67*a*) and (13.67*b*). However, Eqs. (13.76) and (13.77) apply in the known uniform orthogonal transformed space $\xi\eta$, whereas Eqs. (13.67*a*) and (13.67*b*) apply in the unknown nonuniform nonorthogonal physical space xy.

Writing Eq. (13.76) in finite difference form using second-order centered difference approximations of the exact partial derivatives yields the following FDE:

$$\begin{aligned}\alpha_{i,j}\frac{x_{i+1,j} - 2x_{i,j} + x_{i-1,j}}{\Delta\xi^2} &- 2\beta_{i,j}\frac{x_{i+1,j+1} - x_{i-1,j+1} - x_{i+1,j-1} + x_{i-1,j-1}}{4\Delta\xi\Delta\eta} \\ &+ \gamma_{i,j}\frac{x_{i,j+1} - 2x_{i,j} + x_{i,j-1}}{\Delta\eta^2} \\ &= -I_{i,j}^2\left(\frac{x_{i+1,j} - x_{i-1,j}}{2\Delta\xi}P_{i,j} + \frac{x_{i,j+1} - x_{i,j-1}}{2\Delta\eta}Q_{i,j}\right)\end{aligned} \tag{13.80}$$

where the finite difference approximations of α, β, γ, and I are

$$\alpha_{i,j} = (x_\eta|_{i,j})^2 + (y_\eta|_{i,j})^2 \tag{13.81}$$

$$\beta_{i,j} = (x_\xi|_{i,j})(x_\eta|_{i,j}) + (y_\xi|_{i,j})(y_\eta|_{i,j}) \tag{13.82}$$

$$\gamma_{i,j} = (x_\xi|_{i,j})^2 + (y_\xi|_{i,j})^2 \tag{13.83}$$

$$I = (x_\xi|_{i,j})(y_\eta|_{i,j}) - (x_\eta|_{i,j})(y_\xi|_{i,j}) \tag{13.84}$$

and the finite difference approximations of x_ξ, x_η, y_ξ, and y_η are

$$x_\xi|_{i,j} = \frac{x_{i+1,j} - x_{i-1,j}}{2\Delta\xi} \qquad \text{and} \qquad x_\eta|_{i,j} = \frac{x_{i,j+1} - x_{i,j-1}}{2\Delta\eta} \tag{13.85}$$

$$y_\xi|_{i,j} = \frac{y_{i+1,j} - y_{i-1,j}}{2\Delta\xi} \qquad \text{and} \qquad y_\eta|_{i,j} = \frac{y_{i,j+1} - y_{i,j-1}}{2\Delta\eta} \tag{13.86}$$

Multiplying Eq. (13.80) by $\Delta\xi^2$ and collecting terms yields

$$x_{i-1,j-1}\left(-\frac{\beta_{i,j}}{2}\frac{\Delta\xi}{\Delta\eta}\right)+x_{i-1,j}\left(\alpha_{i,j}-I_{i,j}^2P_{i,j}\frac{\Delta\xi}{2}\right)+x_{i-1,j+1}\left(\frac{\beta_{i,j}}{2}\frac{\Delta\xi}{\Delta\eta}\right)$$
$$+x_{i,j-1}\left(\gamma_{i,j}\frac{\Delta\xi^2}{\Delta\eta^2}-I_{i,j}^2Q_{i,j}\frac{\Delta\xi^2}{2\Delta\eta}\right)-2x_{i,j}\left(\alpha_{i,j}+\gamma_{i,j}\frac{\Delta\xi^2}{\Delta\eta^2}\right)$$
$$+x_{i,j+1}\left(\gamma_{i,j}\frac{\Delta\xi^2}{\Delta\eta^2}+I_{i,j}^2Q_{i,j}\frac{\Delta\xi^2}{2\Delta\eta}\right)+x_{i+1,j-1}\left(\frac{\beta_{i,j}}{2}\frac{\Delta\xi}{\Delta\eta}\right)$$
$$+x_{i+1,j}\left(\alpha_{i,j}+I_{i,j}^2P_{i,j}\frac{\Delta\xi}{2}\right)+x_{i+1,j+1}\left(-\frac{\beta_{i,j}}{2}\frac{\Delta\xi}{\Delta\eta}\right)=0 \qquad (13.87)$$

The finite difference approximation of Eq. (13.77) yields a FDE similar to Eq. (13.80), with x replaced by y. When $\Delta\xi = \Delta\eta = 1$, Eq. (13.87) and its counterpart for $y(\xi, \eta)$ simplify considerably.

Equation (13.87) and its counterpart for $y(\xi, \eta)$ can be solved by iteration as follows:

1. Prescribe a uniform orthogonal rectangular grid on the $\xi\eta$ plane, as illustrated in Fig. 13.15.
2. Specify the distributions of $x = F(\xi, \eta)$ and $y = G(\xi, \eta)$ on the boundaries of the rectangular $\xi\eta$ space.
3. Choose an initial approximation, $x^{(0)}(\xi, \eta)$ and $y^{(0)}(\xi, \eta)$, for the interior point distribution.
4. Evaluate α, β, γ, and I based on the initial approximation $x^{(0)}(\xi, \eta)$ and $y^{(0)}(\xi, \eta)$ or on a subsequent approximation $x^{(k)}(\xi, \eta)$ and $y^{(k)}(\xi, \eta)$.
5. Solve the linearized system of FDEs, Eq. (13.89) and its counterpart for $y(\xi, \eta)$, by an SOR method (point SOR, line SOR, or alternating-direction line SOR).
6. Periodically update the coefficients as the solution proceeds, typically by underrelaxation, and repeat Step 5.
7. Repeat Steps 5 and 6 to convergence.

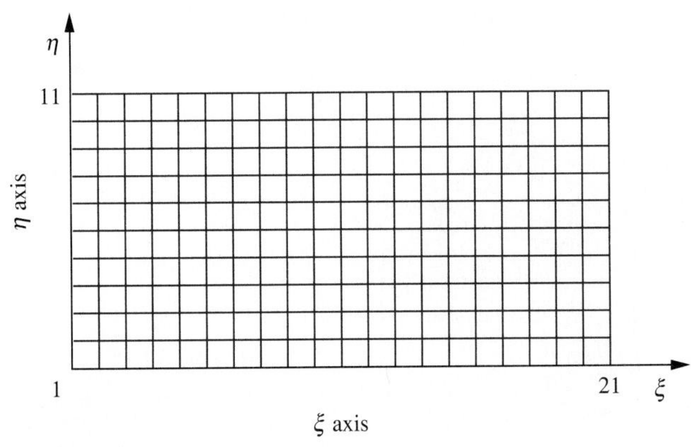

FIGURE 13.15
Computational space.

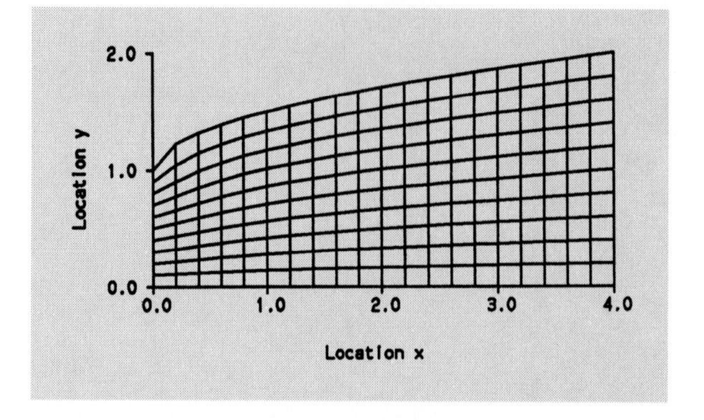

FIGURE 13.16
Grid generation using the Laplace equation with uniform boundary point distribution.

Example 13.2. Grid generation using the Laplace equation. To illustrate grid generation using elliptic PDEs, we will develop a grid for the two-dimensional domain illustrated in Fig. 13.9 using Eqs. (13.76) and (13.77). Let the left- and right-hand boundaries be discretized into 10 equally spaced increments in y. Let the top and bottom boundaries be discretized into 21 equally spaced increments in x. Let $P(\xi, \eta) = Q(\xi, \eta) = 0$. The computational space is illustrated in Fig. 13.15.

Use the normalizing transformation presented in Table 13.3 and illustrated in Fig. 13.10 as the initial approximation for $x^{(0)}(\boldsymbol{\xi}, \boldsymbol{\eta})$ and $y^{(0)}(\boldsymbol{\xi}, \boldsymbol{\eta})$. Solve the linearized system of FDEs by the SOR method presented in Section 1.8, using the over-relaxation factor ω_{opt} given by Eq. (9.72), which for a 21×11 grid gives $\omega_{\text{opt}} = 1.60565794$. Update the coefficients after each SOR pass, and use the full updated values on the next SOR pass.

The solution required 24 iterations to converge to $|\Delta x_{\max}|$ and $|\Delta y_{\max}|$ both less than 0.000001. The results are illustrated in Fig. 13.16. Comparing the results presented in Figs. 13.10 and 13.16 shows that the grid generated by the Laplace equations is almost identical to the grid generated by the normalizing transformation. The ξ lines are vertical in this case, since the x values on the upper and lower boundaries are identical.

To improve the grid, cluster the points on the top boundary near $x = 0$ using the algebraic quadratic transformation given by Eq. (13.32), with $x_2 = 0.1$. When this was computed, the solution required 29 iterations to converge. The results are illustrated in Fig. 13.17. The clustering at $x = 0$ on the top boundary has improved the grid point distribution in the top left-hand portion of the physical domain.

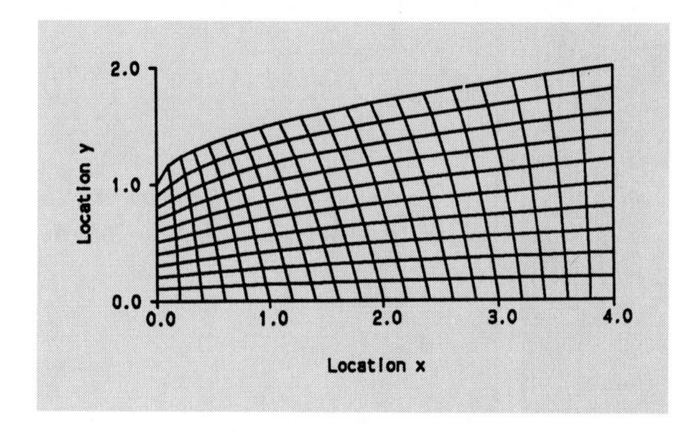

FIGURE 13.17
Grid generation using the Laplace equation with clustered top boundary.

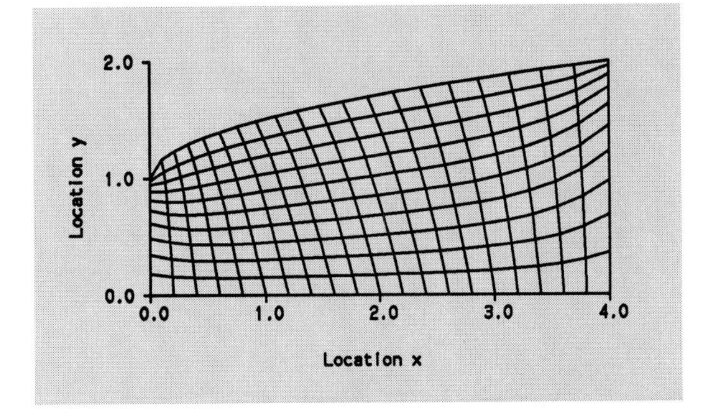

FIGURE 13.18
Grid generation using the Laplace equation with clustered left, right, and top boundaries.

Finally, consider the situation in which it is desired to cluster complete grid lines adjacent to the top boundary. One possible mechanism for accomplishing this goal is to cluster the grid points on the left and right boundaries adjacent to the top boundary. This can be accomplished by applying the algebraic quadratic transformation given by Eq. (13.32) on both boundaries. On the left boundary, let $x_{10} = 0.98$, and on the right boundary, let $x_{10} = 1.96$. The initial approximation for the interior grid point distribution was obtained by linear interpolation along the ξ lines between the upper and lower boundaries. The solution required 33 iterations to converge. The results are illustrated in Fig. 13.18. The effects of clustering the points on the left and right boundaries adjacent to the top boundary do not penetrate very far into the interior of the physical domain. Some more direct form of interior grid point distribution control is required. Such control can be obtained by using the Poisson equation as the generating elliptic PDE.

The poor grid distribution adjacent to the top boundary illustrated in Fig. 13.18 demonstrates the need for direct control of the interior grid point distribution. This can be accomplished by using the Poisson equation, Eq. (13.67), as the generating elliptic PDE, where the nonhomogeneous terms $P(\xi, \eta)$ and $Q(\xi, \eta)$ are used to achieve the desired interior grid point distribution. This procedure is introduced in the following subsection. The finite difference equations approximating Eq. (13.67), that is Eq. (13.87) and its counterpart for $y(\xi, \eta)$, include the nonhomogeneous terms $P(\xi, \eta)$ and $Q(\xi, \eta)$.

Interior Grid Point Control

The Poisson equations used for grid generation are given by Eq. (13.67). The finite difference forms of these equations are given by Eq. (13.87) and its counterpart for $y(\xi, \eta)$. Specific functional forms must be chosen for $P(\xi, \eta)$ and $Q(\xi, \eta)$ to achieve the desired interior grid point distribution. Numerous approaches have been taken to this problem. The book by Thompson et al. (1985) presents a general approach. Thomas and Middlecoff (1980), Steger and Sorenson (1979), and Hilgenstock (1988) present specific methods for clustering grid lines adjacent to a boundary. Basic features of these methods are discussed in this section.

The general effects of the nonhomogeneous terms $P(\xi, \eta)$ and $Q(\xi, \eta)$ on the interior grid point distribution can be illustrated by considering the square physical space xy illustrated in Fig. 13.19a and the corresponding transformed

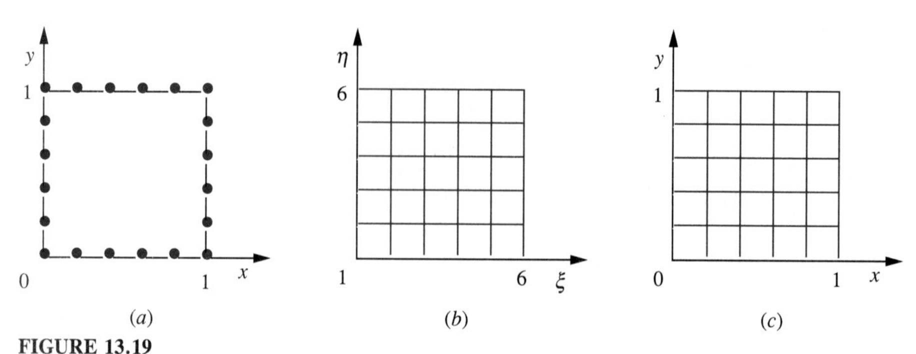

FIGURE 13.19
Square domain: (*a*) physical space; (*b*) transformed space; (*c*) Laplace grid.

space $\xi\eta$ illustrated in Fig. 13.19*b*. Let each boundary of the physical space be discretized into five equal increments, as illustrated in Fig. 13.19*a*. Using the Laplace equation as a grid generator yields the grid illustrated in Fig. 13.19*c*. Using the Poisson equation as a grid generator yields the grids illustrated in Fig. 13.20. In all four cases, the values of P and Q are constant over the entire grid. As illustrated in Figures 13.20*a* and 13.20*b*, positive values of P cause ξ lines to move in the positive x direction, and negative values of P cause ξ lines to move in the negative x direction. Nonzero values of P have no effect on η lines. Figures 13.20*c* and 13.20*d* show that Q has analogous effects on η lines and no effects on ξ lines.

The results presented in Fig. 13.20 illustrate the effects of P and Q on interior grid points. Consider a grid point adjacent to a top boundary, as illustrated in Fig. 13.21. The boundary point itself is fixed. Nonzero values of P tend to move the interior point right or left, thus influencing the angle of intersection of the ξ line with the boundary. Nonzero values of Q tend to move the interior point up or down, thus influencing the spacing of the η lines adjacent to the boundary. Similar results can be developed for left, right, and bottom boundaries. Consequently, the angle of intersection of interior grid lines with the boundaries and the spacing of interior grid lines adjacent to the boundaries can be controlled by the choices for $P(\xi, \eta)$ and $Q(\xi, \eta)$.

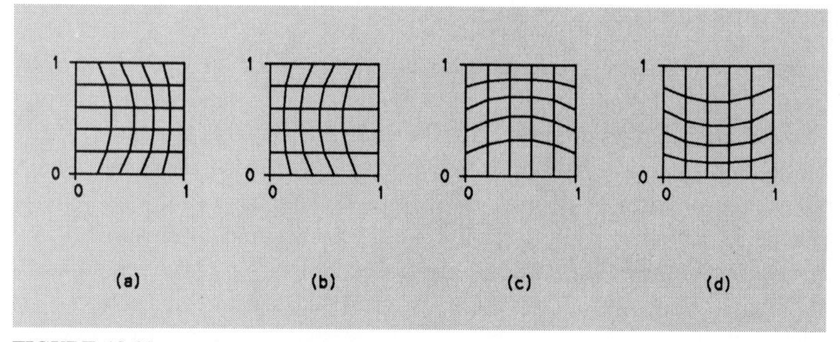

FIGURE 13.20
Effects of P and Q on the interior grid: (*a*) $P = +10$, $Q = 0$; (*b*) $P = -10$, $Q = 0$; (*c*) $P = 0$, $Q = +10$; (*d*) $P = 0$, $Q = -10$.

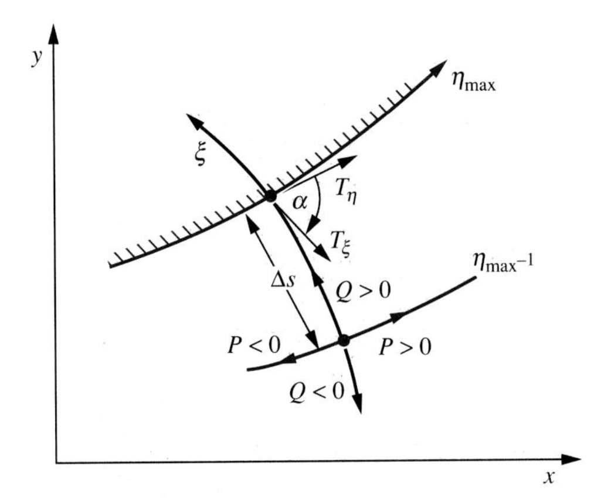

FIGURE 13.21
Effect of P and Q adjacent to a top boundary.

The general approach for interior grid point control has two steps:

1. Specification of $P(\xi, \eta)$ and $Q(\xi, \eta)$ on the boundaries to achieve the desired effects at the boundaries.
2. Extrapolation of the boundary values of $P(\xi, \eta)$ and $Q(\xi, \eta)$ into the interior of the domain to achieve the desired effects in the interior.

Several techniques for implementing these two steps are presented in the following discussion.

First, consider the specification of $P(\xi, \eta)$ and $Q(\xi, \eta)$ on the boundaries. The method developed by Thomas and Middlecoff (1980) consists of determining the values of P and Q on the boundaries by imposing the following two constraints:

1. The transverse coordinate lines at the boundaries are locally straight, that is, their curvature is zero.
2. The transverse coordinate lines at the boundaries are orthogonal to the boundaries.

The methods developed by Steger and Sorenson (1979) and Hilgenstock (1988) consist of determining the values of P and Q on the boundaries by imposing the following two constraints:

1. The spacing in the physical space along the transverse coordinate line between the boundary coordinate line and the first interior coordinate line is specified a priori.
2. The angle of intersection of the transverse coordinate lines with the boundary coordinate line is specified a priori.

Thomas and Middlecoff (1980) and Steger and Sorenson (1979) both considered the limiting forms of Eq. (13.67) on the boundaries and imposed their constraints on those results to determine the values of $P(\xi, \eta)$ and $Q(\xi, \eta)$ on the boundaries.

Hilgenstock (1988) implemented his constraints directly by an iterative approach, which is discussed later in this section.

After the values of $P(\xi, \eta)$ and $Q(\xi, \eta)$ are determined on the boundaries by any method, they must be extrapolated into the interior of the domain. Several approaches to achieve this result have been used. Three of the more common procedures are as follows:

1. Linearly extrapolate the boundary values of P and Q into the interior.
2. Exponentially extrapolate the boundary values of P and Q into the interior. This procedure is illustrated in Example 13.3.
3. Solve Laplace equations for P and Q (i.e., $\nabla^2 P = 0$ and $\nabla^2 Q = 0$) to determine the values of P and Q in the interior.

Any method for determining the boundary values of P and Q can be used in conjunction with any method for extrapolating the boundary values into the interior.

None of the procedures presented above is completely foolproof. They all require considerable trial and error to achieve an acceptable grid point distribution with an acceptable amount of effort. Nevertheless, such methods have proven to be quite effective, and they are in widespread use. To illustrate these concepts, the method presented by Hilgenstock (1988) is developed in the following paragraphs for controlling the grid adjacent to the top boundary of a two-dimensional space.

As illustrated in Fig. 13.21, the nonhomogeneous terms $P(\xi, \eta)$ and $Q(\xi, \eta)$ influence the location of grid points adjacent to the top boundary. $P(\xi, \eta)$ influences the inclination of the ξ lines and $Q(\xi, \eta)$ influences the mesh spacing in the η direction. Consequently, values of $P(\xi, \eta)$ and $Q(\xi, \eta)$ can be chosen to achieve the required inclination and spacing, respectively. However, the required values of $P(\xi, \eta)$ and $Q(\xi, \eta)$ are unknown initially, so they must be determined iteratively as suggested by Hilgenstock. Thus,

$$P^{n+1} = P^n + \Delta P^n \tag{13.88a}$$

$$Q^{n+1} = Q^n + \Delta Q^n \tag{13.88b}$$

where n denotes the iteration level. The initial values of $P(\xi, \eta)$ and $Q(\xi, \eta)$ can be set to zero. Alternately, Eq. (13.87) and its counterpart for $y(\xi, \eta)$ can be solved for the values of $P(\xi, \eta)$ and $Q(\xi, \eta)$ corresponding to the initial grid distribution. In the present example, $P(\xi, \eta)$ and $Q(\xi, \eta)$ are set to zero initially.

The angle of intersection between a ξ line and the top boundary, which is the η line corresponding to $\eta_{\max}$, can be determined from the vector dot product of the tangent vector to the ξ line (i.e., $\mathbf{T}_\xi$) and the tangent vector to the η-line (i.e., $\mathbf{T}_\eta$) at the boundary. Thus

$$\mathbf{T}_\xi \cdot \mathbf{T}_\eta = |\mathbf{T}_\xi|\,|\mathbf{T}_\eta| \cos\alpha \tag{13.89}$$

Solving Eq. (13.89) for the angle α yields

$$\alpha = \cos^{-1}\left(\frac{\mathbf{T}_\xi \cdot \mathbf{T}_\eta}{|\mathbf{T}_\xi|\,|\mathbf{T}_\eta|}\right) \tag{13.90}$$

Let $\alpha*$ be the desired angle of intersection. Then the required correction ΔP^n to P^n is

$$\Delta P^n = +\tan^{-1}\left(\frac{\alpha^n - \alpha*}{\alpha*}\right) \tag{13.91}$$

As illustrated in Fig. 13.21, increasing P decreases α and vice versa. Thus, if $(\alpha^n - \alpha*) > 0$, α must be decreased, which requires an increase in P. This accounts for the plus sign in Eq. (13.91). The $\tan^{-1}$ function has no geometrical meaning. It is used simply to bound the value of ΔP^n. In the limit as n increases, $(\alpha^n - \alpha*) \to 0$, and $\Delta P^n \to 0$.

The tangent vectors $\mathbf{T}_\xi$ and $\mathbf{T}_\eta$ must be determined numerically from the grid point locations. The finite difference grid for evaluating $\mathbf{T}_\xi$ and $\mathbf{T}_\eta$ on a top boundary is illustrated in Fig. 13.22. The vector $\mathbf{T}_\xi$ is given by

$$\mathbf{T}_\xi = \frac{(x_{i,j-1} - x_{i,j})}{\Delta s}\mathbf{i} + \frac{(y_{i,j-1} - y_{i,j})}{\Delta s}\mathbf{j} \tag{13.92}$$

where Δs is given by Eq. (13.96). The vector $\mathbf{T}_\eta$ is given by

$$\mathbf{T}_\eta = \frac{dx}{dt}\mathbf{i} + \frac{dy}{dt}\mathbf{j} \tag{13.93}$$

where dx/dt and dy/dt are the rates of change of x and y, respectively, along the direction t, which is tangent to the boundary. Evaluating dx/dt and dy/dt numerically yields

$$\frac{dx}{dt} = \left(\frac{1}{\Delta t_+ + \Delta t_-}\right)\left(\left(\frac{\Delta t_-}{\Delta t_+}\right)(x_{i+1,j} - x_{i,j}) + \left(\frac{\Delta t_+}{\Delta t_-}\right)(x_{i,j} - x_{i-1,j})\right) \tag{13.94a}$$

$$\frac{dy}{dt} = \left(\frac{1}{\Delta t_+ + \Delta t_-}\right)\left(\left(\frac{\Delta t_-}{\Delta t_+}\right)(y_{i+1,j} - y_{i,j}) + \left(\frac{\Delta t_+}{\Delta t_-}\right)(y_{i,j} - y_{i-1,j})\right) \tag{13.94b}$$

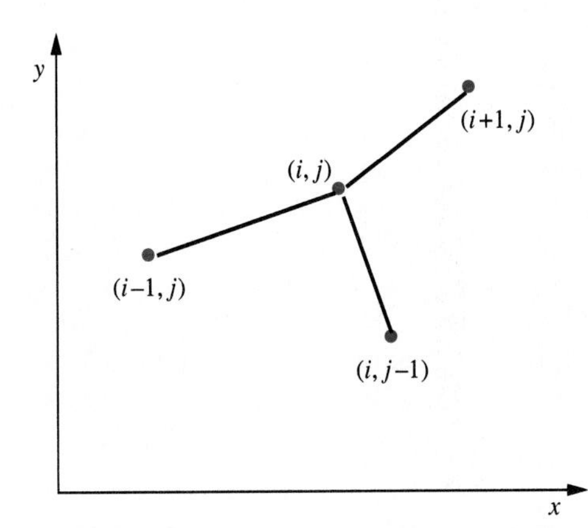

FIGURE 13.22
Finite difference grid.

TABLE 13.4
Signs of corrections ΔP^n and ΔQ^n on boundaries

	Sign of correction	
Boundary	ΔP^n	ΔQ^n
Left	$-$	$-$
Right	$+$	$+$
Top	$+$	$+$
Bottom	$-$	$-$

where

$$\Delta t_+ = \left((x_{i+1,j} - x_{i,j})^2 + (y_{i+1,j} - y_{i,j})^2\right)^{1/2} \tag{13.95a}$$

$$\Delta t_- = \left((x_{i,j} - x_{i-1,j})^2 + (y_{i,j} - y_{i-1,j})^2\right)^{1/2} \tag{13.95b}$$

Equations (13.94) and (13.95) are obtained by centered-difference finite difference approximations in the nonuniform xy grid. Similar expressions can be developed for left, right, and bottom boundaries.

The spacing Δs between the boundary point and the first interior point on a ξ line is given by

$$\Delta s = \left((x_{i,j-1} - x_{i,j})^2 + (y_{i,j-1} - y_{i,j})^2\right)^{1/2} \tag{13.96}$$

Let Δs^* be the desired spacing. Then the required correction ΔQ^n to Q^n is

$$\Delta Q^n = +\tan^{-1}\left(\frac{\Delta s^n - \Delta s^*}{\Delta s^*}\right) \tag{13.97}$$

As illustrated in Fig. 13.21, increasing Q decreases Δs and vice versa. Thus, if $(\Delta s^n - \Delta s^*) > 0$, Δs must be decreased, which requires an increase in Q. This accounts for the plus sign in Eq. (13.97). In the limit as n increases, $(\Delta s^n - \Delta s^*) \to 0$, and $\Delta Q^n \to 0$.

Either or both of the corrections, ΔP^n and ΔQ^n, can be overrelaxed or underrelaxed if required.

The signs of the corrections ΔP^n and ΔQ^n, + in Eq. (13.90) and + in Eq. (13.97), depend on the type of boundary, that is, top or bottom. On left and right boundaries, angle control is governed by Q and spatial increment control is governed by P. Thus, Eq. (13.91) would specify ΔQ^n instead of ΔP^n, and Eq. (13.97) would specify ΔP^n instead of ΔQ^n. Table 13.4 presents the signs of the corrections for these four types of boundaries.

After the increments ΔP^n and ΔQ^n have been determined on the boundaries, P^{n+1} and Q^{n+1} on the boundaries can be determined from Eq. (13.88). Values of P and Q inside the domain are determined by exponentially extrapolating the boundary values into the interior by the following extrapolation formulas:

$$P(\xi, \eta) = P(\xi, 1)e^{-a(\eta-1)/(\eta_{\max}-1)} + P(\xi, \eta_{\max})e^{-b(\eta_{\max}-\eta)/(\eta_{\max}-1)} \tag{13.98a}$$

$$Q(\xi, \eta) = Q(\xi, 1)e^{-c(\eta-1)/(\eta_{\max}-1)} + Q(\xi, \eta_{\max})e^{-d(\eta_{\max}-\eta)/(\eta_{\max}-1)} \tag{13.98b}$$

where the first terms represent boundary control on the bottom boundary and the second terms represent boundary control on the top boundary. Either boundary or both boundaries can be subjected to boundary control. Analogous extrapolation formulas apply for left and right boundary control. If top or bottom boundary control is used in conjunction with left or right boundary control, their effects must be averaged. Large values of the exponential coefficients in Eqs. (13.98) result in rapid decay, whereas small values result in slow decay.

All the results presented in this example can be extended directly to three-dimensional spaces.

Example 13.3. Grid generation using the Poisson equation. Recall the grid generation problem presented in Example 13.2. As illustrated in Fig. 13.18, boundary point clustering on the left and right boundaries did not penetrate into the interior of the domain along the top boundary. We will use the interior grid point control procedure presented by Hilgenstock (1988) to control the grid line spacing adjacent to the top boundary and to force the ξ lines to be perpendicular to the top boundary.

Consider the boundary point distributions employed in Fig. 13.18, which are discussed in Example 13.2. Grid points on the top boundary are clustered near $x = 0$, and grid points on the left and right boundaries are clustered near the top boundary. Let the initial approximation of the interior grid point distribution be determined by quadratic packing along straight lines joining corresponding ξ values on the top and bottom boundaries. Specify the desired angle of intersection of the ξ-lines with the top boundary to be 90°, that is, perpendicular intersections. Define Δs^* adjacent to the top boundary to be the same as the values obtained for the initial grid. Let the exponential decay coefficients in Eq. (13.98) be $b = 10.0$ and $d = 10.0$. Let the convergence tolerance for Δx and Δy be 0.0001.

The solution converged after 193 iterations. The results are illustrated in Fig. 13.23. Comparing Figs. 13.18 and 13.23 illustrates the improved interior grid point distribution obtainable using the Poisson equation for interior grid point control.

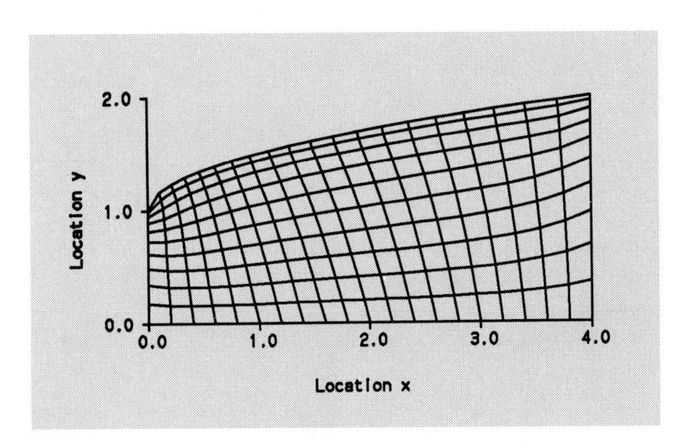

FIGURE 13.23
Grid generation using the Poisson equation with top boundary control.

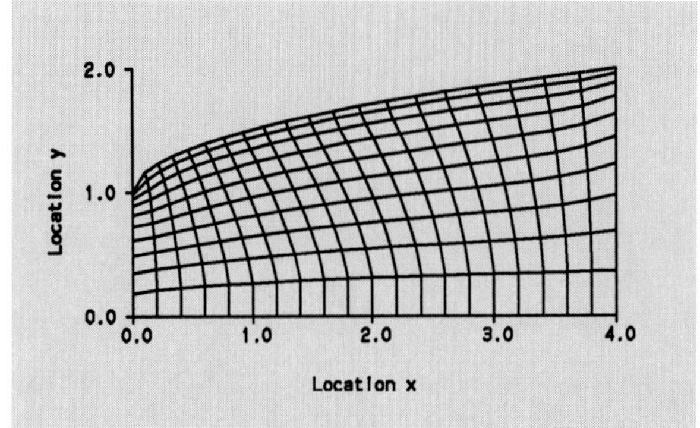

FIGURE 13.24
Grid generation using the Poisson equation with top and bottom boundary control.

Although the results presented in Fig. 13.23 are quite good along the top boundary, the angle of intersection of ξ lines with the bottom boundary is a bit skewed. To correct this problem, we also use interior grid control on the bottom boundary in the same manner as done on the top boundary. Let the exponential decay coefficients be $a = 5.0$, $b = 10.0$, $c = 1.0$, and $d = 10.0$. The solution converged after 207 iterations; the results are illustrated in Fig. 13.24. Comparing Figs. 13.18, 13.23, and 13.24 illustrates the effectiveness of the Poisson equation for interior grid point control.

Three-Dimensional Grid Generation

Steady two-dimensional grid generation using the Poisson equation is discussed and illustrated in the preceeding two subsections. That approach can be extended directly to three dimensions. The results of that extension are presented in this section without derivation.

Equations (13.76) and (13.77) become

$$\alpha_{11}x_{\xi\xi}+\alpha_{12}x_{\xi\eta}+\alpha_{13}x_{\xi\phi}+\alpha_{22}x_{\eta\eta}+\alpha_{23}x_{\eta\phi}+\alpha_{33}x_{\phi\phi} = -I^2(Px_\xi + Qx_\eta + Rx_\phi) \tag{13.99}$$

$$\alpha_{11}y_{\xi\xi}+\alpha_{12}y_{\xi\eta}+\alpha_{13}y_{\xi\phi}+\alpha_{22}y_{\eta\eta}+\alpha_{23}y_{\eta\phi}+\alpha_{33}y_{\phi\phi} = -I^2(Py_\xi + Qy_\eta + Ry_\phi) \tag{13.100}$$

$$\alpha_{11}z_{\xi\xi}+\alpha_{12}z_{\xi\eta}+\alpha_{13}z_{\xi\phi}+\alpha_{22}z_{\eta\eta}+\alpha_{23}z_{\eta\phi}+\alpha_{33}z_{\phi\phi} = -I^2(Pz_\xi + Qz_\eta + Rz_\phi) \tag{13.101}$$

where the coefficients α_{jk} are given by

$$\alpha_{jk} = \sum_{m=1}^{3} \beta_{mj}\beta_{mk} \qquad (j, k = 1, 2, 3) \tag{13.102}$$

$$\alpha_{11} = \beta_{11}^2 + \beta_{21}^2 + \beta_{31}^2 \tag{13.103a}$$

$$\alpha_{12} = \beta_{11}\beta_{12} + \beta_{21}\beta_{22} + \beta_{31}\beta_{32} \tag{13.103b}$$

$$\alpha_{13} = \beta_{11}\beta_{13} + \beta_{21}\beta_{23} + \beta_{31}\beta_{33} \tag{13.103c}$$

$$\alpha_{22} = \beta_{12}^2 + \beta_{22}^2 + \beta_{32}^2 \tag{13.103d}$$

$$\alpha_{23} = \beta_{12}\beta_{13} + \beta_{22}\beta_{23} + \beta_{32}\beta_{33} \tag{13.103e}$$

$$\alpha_{33} = \beta_{13}^2 + \beta_{23}^2 + \beta_{33}^2 \tag{13.103f}$$

and β_{ij} are given by

$$\beta_{ij} = I\frac{\partial u_j}{\partial x_i} \tag{13.104}$$

where u_j $(j = 1, 2, 3)$ corresponds to ξ, η, and ϕ, respectively, and $x_i(i = 1, 2, 3)$ corresponds to x, y, and z, respectively:

$$\beta_{11} = I\xi_x = y_\eta z_\phi - y_\phi z_\eta \tag{13.105a}$$

$$\beta_{12} = I\eta_x = y_\phi z_\xi - y_\xi z_\phi \tag{13.105b}$$

$$\beta_{13} = I\phi_x = y_\xi z_\eta - y_\eta z_\xi \tag{13.105c}$$

$$\beta_{21} = I\xi_y = x_\phi z_\eta - x_\eta z_\phi \tag{13.105d}$$

$$\beta_{22} = I\eta_y = x_\xi z_\phi - x_\phi z_\xi \tag{13.105e}$$

$$\beta_{23} = I\phi_y = x_\eta z_\xi - x_\xi z_\eta \tag{13.105f}$$

$$\beta_{31} = I\xi_z = x_\eta y_\phi - x_\phi y_\eta \tag{13.105g}$$

$$\beta_{32} = I\eta_z = x_\phi y_\xi - x_\xi y_\phi \tag{13.105h}$$

$$\beta_{33} = I\phi_z = x_\xi y_\eta - x_\eta y_\xi \tag{13.105i}$$

Equations (13.99) to (13.101) are solved by the procedure presented in Example 13.2 for solving the two-dimensional equations.

SUMMARY

Finite difference methods for solving differential equations require that the physical space be transformed to a body-fitted uniform orthogonal computational space. The process of determining the appropriate coordinate transformation is called grid generation. Grid generation to achieve a suitable body-fitted coordinate system is an essential part of the numerical solution of differential equations by finite difference methods.

Grid generation can be accomplished by algebraic methods or differential equation methods. One-dimensional transformations are nearly always determined by algebraic methods. Two- and three-dimensional algebraic transformations can be derived for some simple geometrics. In general, two- and three-dimensional transformations are developed using differential equation methods.

Several one-dimensional algebraic transformations are presented in this chapter. These transformations are adequate for most one-dimensional problems. Examples of two- and three-dimensional algebraic transformations are presented. The general concepts of grid generation using elliptic partial differential equations are presented. A two-dimensional example is presented to illustrate the procedure.

PROBLEMS

Section 13.1 Introduction

1. Transform the unsteady two-dimensional linear convection equation $\bar{f}_t + u\bar{f}_x + v\bar{f}_y = 0$ from xy space to $\xi\eta$ space.
2. Work Problem 1 for the two-dimensional Poisson equation $\bar{f}_{xx} + \bar{f}_{yy} = F(x, y)$.
3. Work Problem 1 for the unsteady two-dimensional diffusion equation $\bar{f}_t = \alpha(\bar{f}_{xx} + \bar{f}_{yy})$.
4. Work Problem 1 for the unsteady two-dimensional convection-diffusion equation $\bar{f}_t + u\bar{f}_x + v\bar{f}_y = \alpha(\bar{f}_{xx} + \bar{f}_{yy})$.

Section 13.3 Generalized Coordinate Transformations

5. Verify Eq. (13.18).
6. Verify Eqs. (13.20) to (13.25).
7. Verify Eq. (13.29).

Section 13.5 Algebraic Grid Generation

8. Work Example 13.1 for the following conditions: $x = 0 \to \bar{\xi} = 0$ and $\xi = 1$, $x = 1.0 \to \bar{\xi} = 1$ and $\xi = 11$, $x = 0.01 \to \bar{\xi} = 0.1$ and $\xi = 2$, and $x = 0.8 \to \bar{\xi} = 0.9$ and $\xi = 10$.
9. Work Example 13.1 for the following conditions: $x = 0 \to \bar{\xi} = 0$ and $\xi = 1$, $x = 1.0 \to \bar{\xi} = 1$ and $\xi = 11$, $x = 0.25 \to \bar{\xi} = 0.1$ and $\xi = 2$, and $x = 0.99 \to \bar{\xi} = 0.9$ and $\xi = 10$.
10. Consider a two-dimensional xy space bounded on the left and right by vertical lines at $x = 0$ and $x = 4$, on the top by $y = 1 + \sqrt{x}/2$, and on the bottom by $y = 0.0$. Consider the transformed space $1 \le \xi \le 9$ and $1 \le \eta \le 5$. Let Δx be uniform on the top and bottom boundaries. Develop the normalizing transformation for this xy space. Present the results for x, y, ξ_x, ξ_y, η_x, η_y, and I in the format illustrated in Table 13.3. Plot the grid in xy space.
11. Work Problem 10 with the bottom boundary $y = 0.5 - \sqrt{x}/4$.
12. Work Problem 10 with the right boundary $y = x - 2$.
13. Work Problem 10 with the left boundary $y = 1 - x$ and the right boundary $y = x - 2$.

14. Consider a two-dimensional xy space bounded on the left and right by vertical lines at $x = 0$ and $y = 4$, on the top by $y = 1 + \sqrt{x}/2$, and on the bottom by $y = 0.5 - \sqrt{x}/4$. Consider the transformation to $\xi\eta$ space with $1 \leq \xi \leq 9$ and $1 \leq \eta \leq 5$. Cluster points on the top boundary using a quadratic transformation so that $x = 0.1 \rightarrow \xi = 2$. Let Δx be uniform on the lower boundary. Develop a normalizing transformation for this problem. Present the results for x, y, ξ_x, ξ_y, η_x, η_y, and I in the format illustrated in Table 13.3. Plot the grid in xy space.
15. For the xy space described in Problem 14, construct a middleline using Eq. (13.56a). Apply a quadratic transformation on the middleline with $x = 1.5 \rightarrow \xi = 5$. Apply a quadratic connection function to determine the coordinate transformation. Present the same results requested in Problem 14. Plot the grid in xy space.

Section 13.6 Grid Generation Using Differential Equations

16. Verify Eqs. (13.76) and (13.77).
17. Consider the xy space described in Problem 10. Using the results of the normalizing transformation developed in that problem as an initial approximation, make two passes through the elliptic grid generation procedure based on the Laplace equation. Use Gauss–Seidel iteration. (a) Don't update coefficients between passes. (b) Do update coefficients between passes.
18. Write a computer program to implement the grid generation procedure based on the Laplace equation. Let the boundary point distributions be input data. Use the SOR method to solve the difference equations. Let all interior x and y values be zero initially. Update the nonlinear coefficients after each pass through the SOR procedure. Iterate until $|\Delta x_{\max}|$ and $|\Delta y_{\max}|$ change by less than the tolerance ϵ. Use the program to work Problem 17 with $\epsilon = 0.0001$.
19. Use the program developed in Problem 18 to reproduce the results that are presented in Fig. 13.16.
20. Use the program developed in Problem 18 to reproduce the results that are presented in Fig. 13.17.
21. Use the program developed in Problem 18 to reproduce the results that are presented in Fig. 13.18.
22. Work Problem 19 with the bottom boundary changed from $y = 0$ to $y = 0.5 - \sqrt{x}/4$, with Δx = constant on the bottom boundary.
23. Work Problem 20 with the bottom boundary changed from $y = 0$ to $y = 0.5 - \sqrt{x}/4$, with Δx = constant on the bottom boundary.
24. Work Problem 21 with the bottom boundary changed from $y = 0$ to $y = 0.5 - \sqrt{x}/4$, with Δx = constant on the bottom boundary.
25. Consider the unit square $0 \leq x \leq 1$ and $0 \leq y \leq 1$. Let Δx and Δy be uniform on the boundaries. Let $1 \leq \xi \leq 3$ and $1 \leq \eta \leq 3$. Use the grid generation procedure based on the Poisson equation to solve for $x(2, 2)$ and $y(2, 2)$ for *(a)* $P = Q = 0$, *(b)* $P = 10$ and $Q = 0$, *(c)* $P = -10$ and $Q = 0$, *(d)* $P = 0$ and $Q = 10$, *(e)* $P = 0$ and $Q = -10$, *(f)* $P = 10$ and $Q = 10$, and *(g)* $P = -10$ and $Q = -10$.
26. Modify the computer program developed in Problem 18 to solve the Poisson equation with constant P and Q as the generating elliptic PDE. Using this program, work Problem 25.
27. Using the program developed in Problem 26, reproduce the results presented in Fig. 13.20.

28. Modify the program developed in Problem 26 to implement the Hilgenstock method (Hilgenstock, 1988) of interior grid point control adjacent to the top boundary. Use the program to reproduce the results presented in Fig. 13.23.

29. Modify the program developed in Problem 28 to include grid point control adjacent to the bottom boundary. Use the program to reproduce the results presented in Fig. 13.24.

30. Work Problem 28 with the bottom boundary changed from $y = 0$ to $y = 0.5 - \sqrt{x}/4$, with Δx = constant on the bottom boundary.

31. Work Problem 29 with the bottom boundary described in Problem 30.

CHAPTER 14

PARABOLIC PARTIAL DIFFERENTIAL EQUATIONS

The Convection–Diffusion Equation

Section

Example

14.1 INTRODUCTION

The general features of parabolic partial differential equations (PDEs) are discussed in Section III.6. An introduction to the numerical solution of parabolic PDEs is presented in Chapter 11, which is devoted to the solution of the diffusion equation. Those sections should be reviewed before the present chapter is studied.

As discussed in Section 11.1, two of the more common parabolic PDEs are the diffusion equation and the convection–diffusion equation, presented below for the generic dependent variable $\bar{f}(x, t)$:

$$\bar{f}_t = \alpha \bar{f}_{xx} \tag{14.1}$$

$$\bar{f}_t + u\bar{f}_x = \alpha \bar{f}_{xx} \tag{14.2}$$

where α is the diffusion coefficient and u is the convection velocity. Since the classification of a PDE is determined by the coefficients of its highest-order derivatives, the presence of the first-order convection term $u\bar{f}_x$ in the convection–diffusion equation does not affect its classification. The diffusion equation and the convection–diffusion equation are both parabolic PDEs. However, the presence of the first-order convection term has a major influence on the numerical solution procedure.

Chapter 11 is devoted to the numerical solution of the diffusion equation, Eq. (14.1). Most of the concepts, techniques, and conclusions presented in Chapter 11 for solving the diffusion equation are directly applicable, sometimes with very minor modifications, to solving the convection–diffusion equation. Consequently, Chapter 11 should be studied before the present chapter, which is devoted to the numerical solution of the convection–diffusion equation, Eq. (14.2), is studied.

The finite difference grids and finite difference approximations presented in Section 10.4 are used to solve the convection–diffusion equation. The concepts of consistency, order, stability, and convergence presented in Section 10.6 are directly applicable to the convection–diffusion equation. In essence, Chapter 10 should be considered as the first part of the present chapter. Chapter 14 is, thus, a direct continuation of Chapters 10 and 11 to solve the convection–diffusion equation.

The solution to Eq. (14.2) is the function $\bar{f}(x, t)$. This function must satisfy an initial condition at $t = 0$, $\bar{f}(x, 0) = F(x)$. The time coordinate has an unspecified (i.e., open) final value. Equation (14.2) is second-order in the space coordinate x. Consequently, two boundary conditions (BCs) are required. These BCs may be of the Dirichlet type (i.e., specified values of $\bar{f}$), the Neumann type (i.e., specified values of $\bar{f}_x$), or the mixed type (i.e., specified combinations of $\bar{f}$ and $\bar{f}_x$). The space coordinate x must be a closed physical domain.

The convection–diffusion equation applies to problems in such areas as mass transport, momentum transport, energy transport, and neutron transport. Most people have some physical feeling for heat transfer, due to its presence in our everyday life. Consequently, the convection–diffusion equation governing heat transfer in a porous plate is used in this chapter to demonstrate numerical methods for solving the convection–diffusion equation. That equation is presented in Section III.8, Eq. (III.108), which is repeated below:

$$T_t + \mathbf{V} \cdot \nabla T = \alpha \nabla^2 T \tag{14.3}$$

where T is the temperature (C), $\mathbf{V}$ is the vector convection velocity (cm/s), and α is the thermal diffusivity (cm^2/s). For unsteady one-dimensional heat transfer, Eq. (14.3) becomes

$$T_t + uT_x = \alpha T_{xx} \tag{14.4}$$

The solution to Eq. (14.4) is the function $T(x, t)$. This function must satisfy an initial condition at time $t = 0$, $T(x, 0) = F(x)$, and a set of boundary conditions at $x = 0$ and $x = L$. The boundary conditions may be of the Dirichlet type, the Neumann type, or the mixed type.

To illustrate the behavior of several numerical integration methods applied to the convection–diffusion equation, the following simple problem will be considered in this chapter: A porous plate of thickness $L = 1.0$ cm is cooled by a fluid flowing through the porous material, as illustrated in Fig. 14.1. The thermal con-

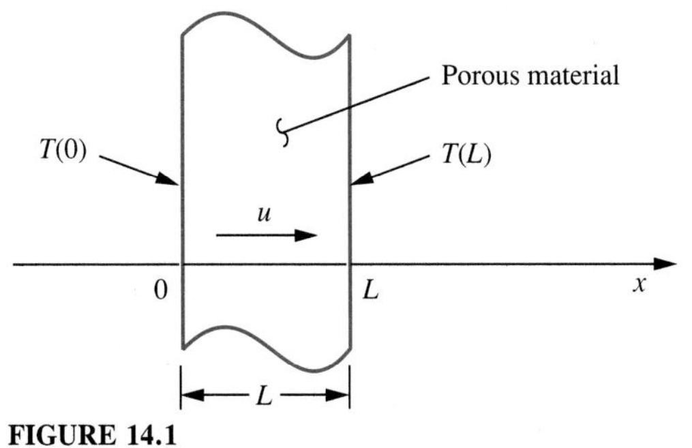

FIGURE 14.1
Heat transfer in a porous plate.

ductivity of the porous material is small compared to the thermal conductivity of the fluid, so that heat conduction through the porous material itself is negligible compared to heat transfer through the fluid by convection and conduction (i.e., diffusion). The temperatures on the two faces of the plate are

$$T(0, t) = 0 \text{ C} \qquad \text{and} \qquad T(L, t) = 100 \text{ C} \tag{14.5}$$

The initial fluid velocity is zero, so the initial temperature distribution is the pure conduction distribution:

$$T(x, 0) = 100x/L, \qquad 0 \leq x \leq L \tag{14.6}$$

This initial temperature distribution is illustrated by the top curve in Fig. 14.2. At time $t = 0$, the fluid in the plate is instantaneously given a constant velocity u to the right. The temperature distribution $T(x, t)$ in the fluid is required.

The exact solution to this problem is obtained by replacing the original problem with two auxiliary problems. Both problems satisfy Eq. (14.4). For the first problem, $T(x, 0) = 0$, $T(0, t) = 0$, and $T(L, t) = 100$. For the second problem, $T(x, 0)$ is given by Eq. (14.6), $T(0, t) = 0$, and $T(L, t) = 0$. Since Eq. (14.4) is linear, the solution to the original problem is the sum of the solutions to the two auxiliary problems. The exact solution to each of the two auxiliary problems is obtained by assuming a product solution of the form $T(x, t) = X(x)\tilde{T}(t)$, separating variables, integrating the resulting two ordinary differential equations, applying the boundary conditions at $x = 0$ and $x = L$, and superimposing an

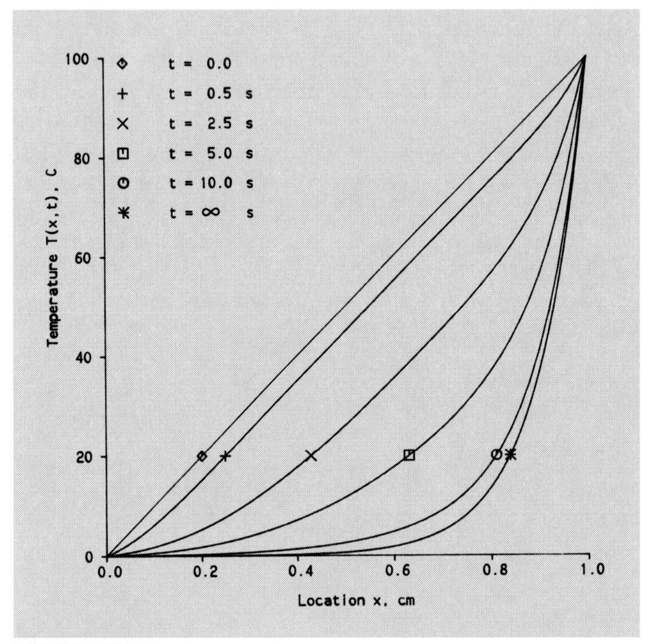

FIGURE 14.2
Exact transient solution for $P = 10$.

infinite number of solutions to obtain the general solution. The coefficients of the general solution are chosen to satisfy the initial condition at $t = 0$. The final result is

$$T(x, t) = 100\left(\frac{\exp(Px/L) - 1}{\exp(P) - 1} + \frac{4\pi \exp(Px/2L) \sinh(P/2)}{\exp(P) - 1} \sum_{m=1}^{\infty} A_m + 2\pi \exp(Px/2L) \sum_{m=1}^{\infty} B_m\right) \tag{14.7}$$

where P is the *Peclet number*

$$P = \frac{uL}{\alpha} \tag{14.8}$$

The coefficients A_m and B_m are given by

$$A_m = (-1)^m \frac{m}{\beta_m} \sin\left(\frac{m\pi x}{L}\right) e^{-\lambda_m t} \tag{14.9}$$

$$B_m = \left((-1)^{m+1} \frac{m}{\beta_m}\left(1 + \frac{P}{\beta_m}\right) e^{-P/2} + \frac{mP}{\beta_m^2}\right) \sin\left(\frac{m\pi x}{L}\right) e^{-\lambda_m t} \tag{14.10}$$

where

$$\beta_m = \left(\frac{P}{2}\right)^2 + (m\pi)^2 \tag{14.11}$$

$$\lambda_m = \frac{u^2}{4\alpha} + \frac{m^2\pi^2\alpha}{L^2} = \frac{\alpha\beta_m}{L^2} \tag{14.12}$$

The exact transient solution at selected values of time for $L = 1.0$ cm, $u = 0.1$ cm/s, and $\alpha = 0.01$ cm^2/s, for which the Peclet number $P = 10$, is tabulated in Table 14.1 and illustrated in Fig. 14.2. As expected, heat flows out of the faces of the plate to the surroundings by diffusion, and heat is carried out of the plate by convection. The temperature distribution smoothly approaches the asymptotic steady state solution

$$T(x, \infty) = 100\frac{\exp(Px/L) - 1}{\exp(P) - 1} \tag{14.13}$$

TABLE 14.1
Exact transient solution for $P = 10$

	Temperature $T(x, t)$, C							
t, s	$x = 0.0$	$x = 0.2$	$x = 0.4$	$x = 0.6$	$x = 0.7$	$x = 0.8$	$x = 0.9$	$x = 1.0$
0.0	0.00	20.00	40.00	60.00	70.00	80.00	90.00	100.00
0.5	0.00	15.14	35.00	55.00	65.00	75.02	85.43	100.00
1.0	0.00	11.36	30.05	50.00	60.02	70.18	81.57	100.00
1.5	0.00	8.67	25.39	45.02	55.07	65.50	77.99	100.00
2.0	0.00	6.72	21.25	40.14	50.18	60.91	74.55	100.00
2.5	0.00	5.29	17.71	35.46	45.41	56.43	71.20	100.00
5.0	0.00	1.80	7.13	17.74	25.64	36.78	56.13	100.00
10.0	0.00	0.30	1.38	4.81	9.09	18.39	40.96	100.00
50.00	0.00	0.03	0.24	1.83	4.97	13.53	36.79	100.00
∞	0.00	0.03	0.24	1.83	4.97	13.53	36.79	100.00

In this chapter, numerical methods for solving the unsteady convection–diffusion equation are illustrated by solving the unsteady heat transfer problem just described. As noted in the previous paragraph, the solution of the unsteady problem approaches the asymptotic steady state solution as time increases. That fact can be used to obtain the solution of steady state problems as the asymptotic solution in time of an appropriate unsteady problem. That approach to solving steady state problems is discussed in Section 10.10. Exact steady state solutions, for several values of the Peclet number P, are tabulated in Table 14.2 and illustrated in Fig. 14.3.

14.2 THE FORWARD-TIME CENTERED-SPACE METHOD

In this section the convection–diffusion equation $\bar{f}_t + u\bar{f}_x = \alpha\bar{f}_{xx}$ is solved numerically by the forward-time centered-space (FTCS) method. The base point for the finite difference approximations (FDAs) of the individual exact partial derivatives is grid point (i, n). The partial derivative $\bar{f}_t$ is replaced by the first-order forward-difference FDA [see Eq. (10.54)], the partial derivative $\bar{f}_x$ is replaced

TABLE 14.2
Exact steady state solutions for several values of P

	Temperature $T(x, \infty)$, C							
P	$x = 0.0$	$x = 0.2$	$x = 0.4$	$x = 0.6$	$x = 0.7$	$x = 0.8$	$x = 0.9$	$x = 1.0$
0	0.00	20.00	40.00	60.00	70.00	80.00	90.00	100.00
1	0.00	12.89	28.62	47.85	59.00	71.32	84.95	100.00
2	0.00	7.70	19.18	36.31	47.82	61.87	79.04	100.00
5	0.00	1.17	4.33	12.95	21.79	36.36	60.39	100.00
10	0.00	0.03	0.24	1.83	4.97	13.52	36.79	100.00
20	0.00	0.00	0.00	0.03	0.25	1.83	13.53	100.00
50	0.00	0.00	0.00	0.00	0.00	0.00	0.67	100.00

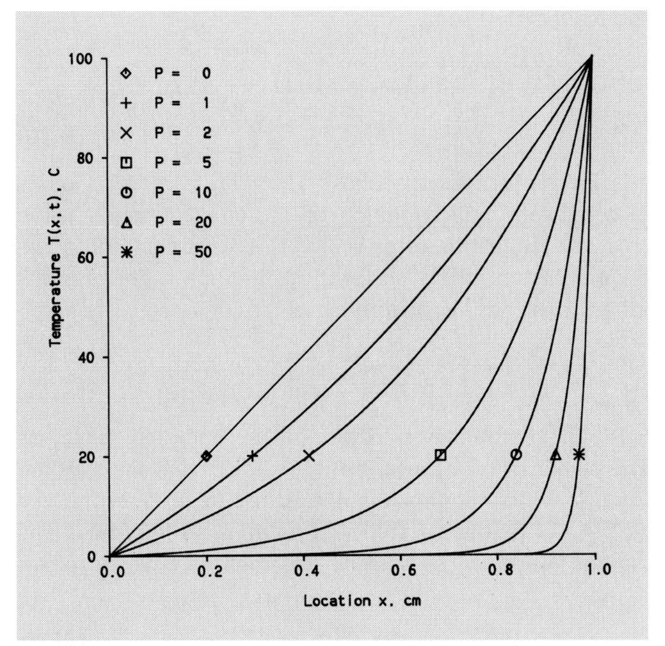

FIGURE 14.3
Exact steady state solutions for several values of P.

by the second-order centered-difference FDA [see Eq. (10.64*b*)], and the partial derivative $\overline{f}_{xx}$ is replaced by the second-order centered-difference FDA [see Eq. (10.69*b*)]. The corresponding finite difference stencil is illustrated in Fig. 14.4. The resulting finite difference equation (FDE) is

$$f_i^{n+1} = f_i^n - \frac{c}{2}(f_{i+1}^n - f_{i-1}^n) + d(f_{i+1}^n - 2f_i^n + f_{i-1}^n) \tag{14.14}$$

where $c = u\,\Delta t/\Delta x$ is the convection number and $d = \alpha\,\Delta t/\Delta x^2$ is the diffusion number.

The first form of the modified differential equation (MDE) is

$$f_t + uf_x = \alpha f_{xx} - \frac{1}{2}f_{tt}\,\Delta t - \frac{1}{6}f_{ttt}\,\Delta t^2 - \cdots - \frac{1}{6}uf_{xxx}\,\Delta x^2 - \cdots + \frac{1}{12}\alpha f_{xxxx}\,\Delta x^4 + \cdots \tag{14.15}$$

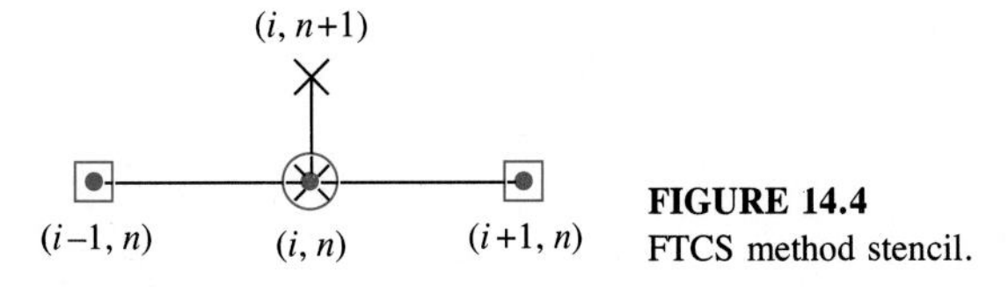

FIGURE 14.4
FTCS method stencil.

and the second form of the MDE is

$$f_t + uf_x = \alpha f_{xx} + \left(-\frac{1}{2}u^2\,\Delta t\right)f_{xx} + \left(-\frac{1}{6}u\,\Delta x^2 + u\alpha\,\Delta t - \frac{1}{3}u^3\,\Delta t^2\right)f_{xxx} + \cdots \tag{14.16}$$

As $\Delta t \to 0$ and $\Delta x \to 0$, Eq. (14.15) approaches $f_t + uf_x = \alpha f_{xx}$. Consequently, Eq. (14.14) is a consistent approximation of the convection–diffusion equation. From Eq. (14.16), the truncation error is $O(\Delta t) + O(\Delta x^2)$. Both even and odd spatial derivatives are present in Eq. (14.16), so implicit numerical diffusion and dispersion both are present. The amplification factor G corresponding to Eq. (14.14) is

$$G = (1 - 2d) + 2d\cos\theta - I\,c\sin\theta \tag{14.17}$$

For $-\infty \leq \theta \leq \infty$, Eq. (14.17) represents an ellipse in the complex plane, as illustrated in Fig. 14.5. The center of the ellipse is at $(1 - 2d, 0)$ and the axes are $2d$ and c. For stability, $|G| \leq 1$, which requires that the ellipse lie on or within the unit circle $|G| = 1$. From Fig. 14.5, three stability conditions are obvious. The real and imaginary axes of the ellipse must both be less than or equal to unity. From curves a and b,

$$c \leq 1 \qquad \text{and} \qquad 2d \leq 1 \tag{14.18}$$

In addition, at point $(1, 0)$ the curvature of the ellipse must be greater than the curvature of the unit circle. This condition is satisfied if

$$c^2 \leq 2d \tag{14.19}$$

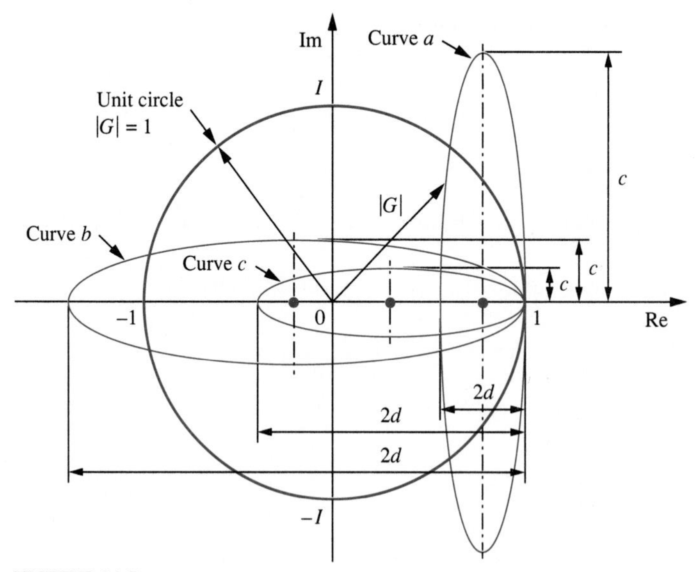

FIGURE 14.5
Locus of the amplification factor G for the FTCS method.

which, with $2d \le 1$, includes the condition $c \le 1$. Thus, the stability criteria for the FTCS approximation of the convection–diffusion equation are

$$\boxed{c^2 \le 2d \le 1} \tag{14.20}$$

Consequently, the method is conditionally stable. Curve c in Fig. 14.5 illustrates a stable condition. The FTCS approximation of the convection–diffusion equation is consistent and conditionally stable. Consequently, by the Lax equivalence theorem, it is a convergent approximation of that equation.

Example 14.1. Solution by the FTCS method. We will solve the convection–diffusion problem presented in Section 14.1 using Eq. (14.14) with $\Delta x = 0.1$ cm. The exact solution at selected times is presented in Table 14.1. The numerical solution for $\Delta t = 0.5$ s, for which $c = u\,\Delta t/\Delta x = (0.1)(0.5)/(0.1) = 0.5$ and $d = \alpha\,\Delta t/\Delta x^2 = (0.01)(0.5)/(0.1)^2 = 0.5$, and the corresponding errors are presented in Table 14.3. Those results are illustrated in Fig. 14.6.

From Fig. 14.6, it is apparent that the numerical solution is a reasonable approximation of the exact solution. The errors presented in Table 14.3 support this observation. Compare these results with the solution of the diffusion equation presented in Example 11.1 and illustrated in Fig. 11.6. It is apparent that the solution of the convection–diffusion equation has larger errors than the solution of the diffusion equation. These larger errors are a direct consequence of the presence of the convection term $u\bar{f}_x$. As the solution progresses in time, the numerical solution smoothly approaches the steady state solution.

TABLE 14.3
Numerical solution and errors* for $c = d = 0.5$

	Temperature T, C							
t, s	$x = 0.0$	$x = 0.2$	$x = 0.4$	$x = 0.6$	$x = 0.7$	$x = 0.8$	$x = 0.9$	$x = 1.0$
0.0	0.00	20.00	40.00	60.00	70.00	80.00	90.00	100.0
0.5	0.00	15.00	35.00	55.00	65.00	75.00	85.00	100.0
		−0.14	0.00	0.00	0.00	−0.02	−0.43	
1.0	0.00	10.00	30.00	50.00	60.00	70.00	81.25	100.0
		−1.36	−0.05	0.00	−0.02	−0.18	−0.32	
1.5	0.00	7.81	25.00	45.00	55.00	65.31	77.50	100.0
		−0.86	−0.39	−0.02	−0.07	−0.19	−0.49	
2.0	0.00	5.63	20.00	40.00	50.08	60.63	73.98	100.0
		−1.09	−1.25	−0.14	−0.10	−0.28	−0.57	
2.5	0.00	4.49	16.58	35.02	45.16	56.05	70.47	100.0
		−0.80	−1.13	−0.44	−0.25	−0.38	−0.73	
5.0	0.00	1.32	5.80	15.76	23.73	34.48	53.85	100.0
		−0.48	−1.33	−1.98	−1.91	−2.30	−2.28	
10.0	0.00	0.18	0.90	3.47	7.00	15.14	37.04	100.0
		−0.12	−0.48	−1.34	−2.09	−3.25	−3.92	
50.0	0.00	0.01	0.14	1.23	3.70	11.11	33.33	100.0
		−0.02	−0.10	−0.60	−1.27	−2.42	−3.46	

* Errors are listed below the solution values.

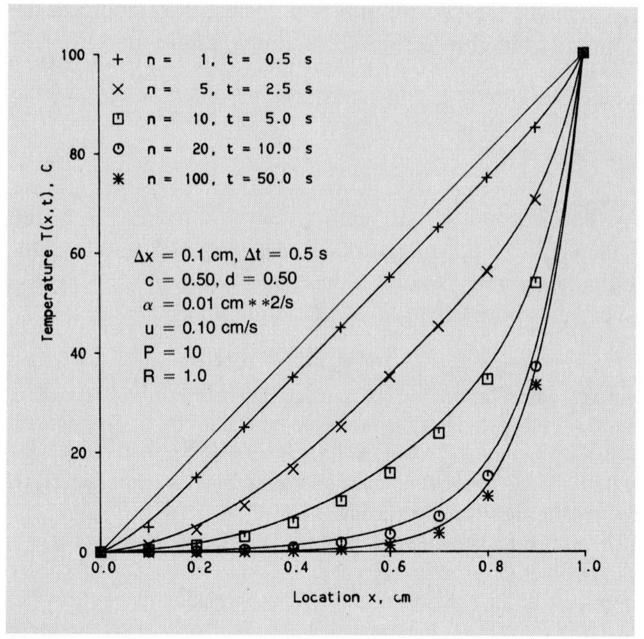

FIGURE 14.6
Transient solution by the FTCS method for $P = 10$.

As discussed in Section 10.10, the solution of the steady state convection–diffusion equation can be obtained as the asymptotic solution in time of an appropriate unsteady problem having the same boundary conditions. This approach is illustrated in Fig. 14.6, where the numerical solution at $t = 50$ s (100 time steps) has reached an asymptotic limit that is a good approximation of the steady state solution. Figure 14.7 presents asymptotic steady state solutions obtained by the FTCS method for values of the Peclet number $P = 1$, 2, 5, 10, 20, and 50, corresponding to $u = 0.01$, 0.02, 0.05, 0.1, 0.2, and 0.5 cm/s, respectively. For small values of the Peclet number (i.e., $P \le 5$), the numerical solutions are an excellent approximation of the exact solutions. For moderate values of the Peclet number (i.e., $5 \le P \le 10$), the numerical solutions are a reasonable approximation of the exact solutions. However, for $P = 20$, the numerical solution is a very poor approximation. For $P = 50$, the numerical solution exhibits a spatial oscillation that violates physical reality. This spatial oscillation is not an instability; it is an overshoot. For this example, the Peclet number $P = 20$ is apparently the boundary between physically correct results for $P < 20$ and physically incorrect results for $P > 20$. The culprit in this behavior is the *cell Peclet number* $R = u\,\Delta x/\alpha$, which is discussed in the following paragraphs.

The cause of the spatial oscillation in the steady state solution for values of the Peclet number greater than 20 can be determined by considering the leading truncation error term in the second form of the MDE, Eq. (14.16):

$$-\frac{1}{2}u^2\,\Delta t\, f_{xx} \tag{14.21}$$

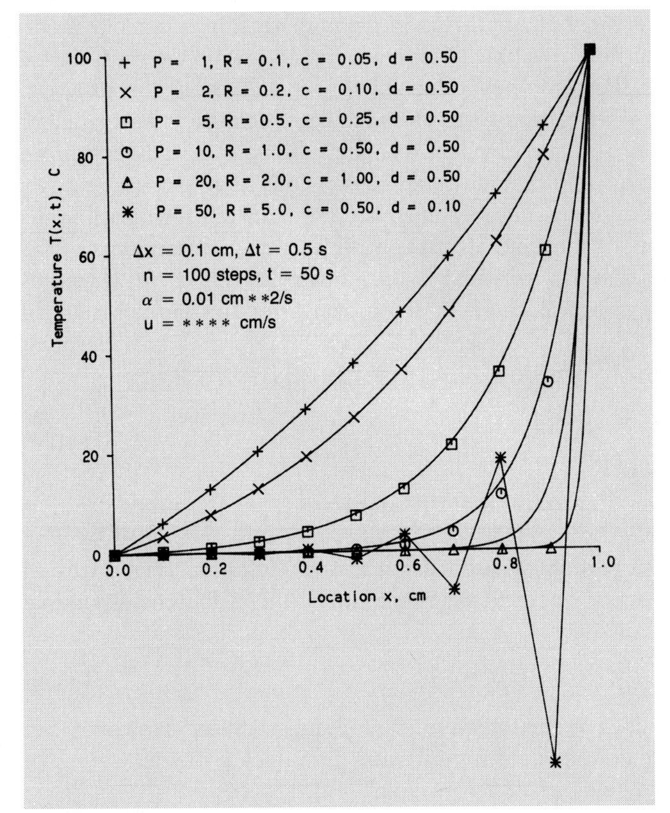

FIGURE 14.7
Steady-state solutions by the FTCS method.

This term is an implicit numerical diffusion term (see Section 10.9), which arises because of the finite difference approximation of the convection term $u\overline{f}_x$. When solving the convection–diffusion equation, which has real physical diffusion (i.e., $\alpha\overline{f}_{xx}$), by the FTCS method, the presence of implicit numerical diffusion reduces the effect of the real physical diffusion. The first two terms on the right-hand side of Eq. (14.16) can be combined as follows:

$$\alpha f_{xx} - \frac{1}{2}u^2\,\Delta t f_{xx} = \left(1 - \frac{1}{2}\frac{u^2\,\Delta t}{\alpha}\right)\alpha f_{xx} = \left(1 - \frac{1}{2}cR\right)\alpha f_{xx} \tag{14.22}$$

where $c = u\,\Delta t/\Delta x$ is the convection number and $R = u\Delta x/\alpha$ is the *cell Peclet (*or *Reynolds)* number:

$$\boxed{R = \frac{u\,\Delta x}{\alpha}} \tag{14.23}$$

The name *cell Peclet number* originated in the numerical heat transfer literature. In the computational fluid dynamics literature, the comparable term is called the *cell Reynolds* number. For specified values of u and α, R varies directly with the physical grid size Δx. The primary effect of the cell Peclet/Reynolds number is to decrease the effect of the real physical diffusion. This is an accuracy problem, not a stability problem. Numerous references in the literature erroneously state that the cell Peclet/Reynolds number must be less than 2.0 for stability. As pointed out by Thompson, Webb, and Hoffman (1985), this incorrect conclusion results from an incorrect stability analysis. Even though the cell Peclet/Reynolds number is not a stability criterion, it has a significant effect on the accuracy of the numerical solution.

The implicit numerical diffusion in Eq. (14.22) is given by

$$-\frac{1}{2}cR\alpha f_{xx} \tag{14.24}$$

which is always negative. Real physical diffusion $\alpha \overline{f}_{xx}$, on the other hand, is always positive. As shown by the heuristic stability analysis developed by Hirt (1968), the combination of real physical diffusion and implicit numerical diffusion must be positive to achieve a stable FDE. From Eq. (14.22), the corresponding stability criterion is

$$cR \leq 2 \tag{14.25}$$

If $c = 1$, Eq. (14.25) does indeed require $R \leq 2$ for stability. However, for $c \leq 1$, Eq. (14.25) is the correct stability criterion. Introducing the definitions of c and R into Eq. (14.25) yields $c^2 \leq 2d$, which is Eq. (14.19).

The effect of the cell Peclet/Reynolds number on the behavior of the finite difference equation can be illustrated by rewriting Eq. (14.14) as follows:

$$f_i^{n+1} = \left(\frac{1}{2}c + d\right)f_{i-1}^n + (1 - 2d)f_i^n + \left(-\frac{1}{2}c + d\right)f_{i+1}^n \tag{14.26}$$

The convection number c can be rearranged as

$$c = \frac{u\,\Delta t}{\Delta x} = \left(\frac{u\,\Delta t}{\Delta x}\right)\left(\frac{\Delta x}{\Delta x}\right)\left(\frac{\alpha}{\alpha}\right) = \left(\frac{\alpha\,\Delta t}{\Delta x^2}\right)\left(\frac{u\,\Delta x}{\alpha}\right) = dR \tag{14.27}$$

Substituting Eq. (14.27) into Eq. (14.26) gives

$$f_i^{n+1} = \frac{1}{2d}(2 + R)f_{i-1}^n + (1 - 2d)f_i^n + \frac{1}{2}d(2 - R)f_{i+1}^n \tag{14.28}$$

When the cell Peclet/Reynolds number $R > 2$, the coefficient of f_{i+1}^n is negative. Thus, the contribution to f_i^{n+1} from f_{i+1}^n is negative, which is physically incorrect. However, this is an *overshoot* problem, not a stability problem. Consequently, the cell Peclet/Reynolds number criterion

$$R \leq 2 \tag{14.29}$$

must be satisfied to obtain physically correct solutions without overshoot.

For the results presented in Figs. 14.6 and 14.7, $\Delta x = 0.1$ cm. Thus,

$$R = \frac{u\,\Delta x}{\alpha} = \frac{uL}{\alpha}\frac{\Delta x}{L} = 0.1P \tag{14.30}$$

Consequently, for $P < 20, R < 2$, and physically correct solutions are obtained. The case $P = 20$, for which $R = 2$, is the limiting value of Eq. (14.29). For $P > 20, R > 2$, and the solutions are physically incorrect, even though they are stable. This effect is responsible for the incorrect solution for $P = 50$ in Fig. 14.7.

The effect of the spatial grid size Δx on the cell Peclet/Reynolds number R is illustrated in Fig. 14.8 for $P = 20$. For $\Delta x = 0.0714$ cm ($imax = 15$), $R = 1.43$, and the numerical solution is a reasonable approximation of the exact solution. For $\Delta x = 0.1$ cm ($imax = 11$), $R = 2$, and the limiting solution is obtained. For $\Delta x = 0.1667$ cm ($imax = 7$), $R = 3.33$, and the solution is physically incorrect.

As a final demonstration of the influence of the cell Peclet/Reynolds number, numerical solutions for $P = 20$ with $\Delta x = 0.025$ cm are presented in Fig. 14.9. The value of $\Delta t = 0.025$ s. For this value of Δx, the values of the cell Peclet/Reynolds numbers are only one-fourth as large as when $\Delta x = 0.1$. The solutions are extremely accurate for Peclet numbers up to 20, and the solution for

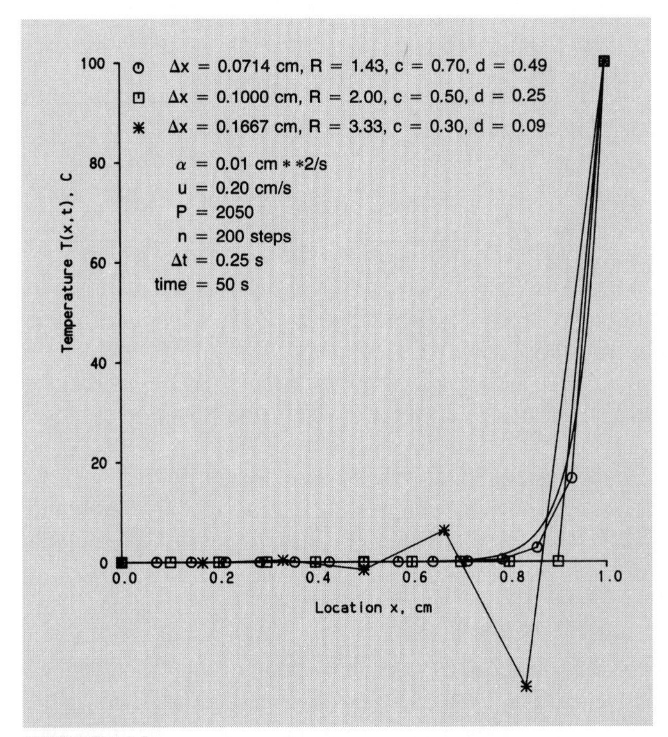

FIGURE 14.8
Steady-state solutions by the FTCS method for $P = 20$.

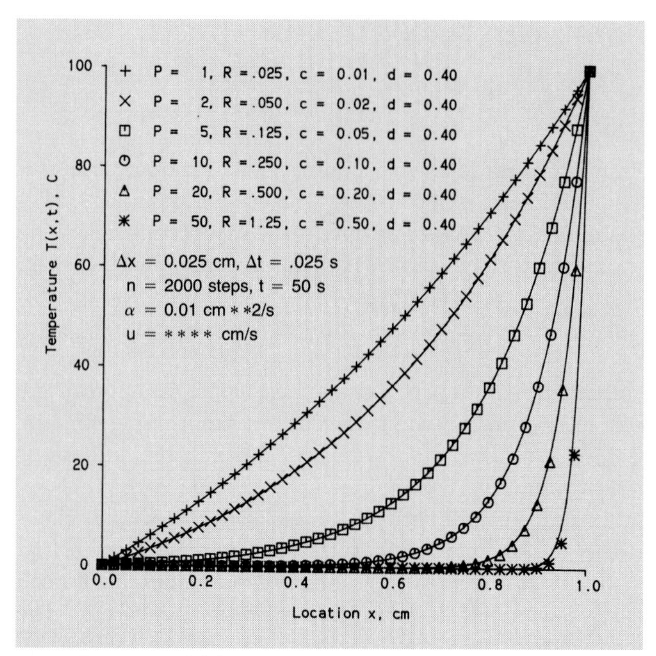

FIGURE 14.9
Steady-state solutions by the FTCS method with $\Delta x = 0.025$.

$P = 50$ is reasonably accurate. Comparing Figs. 14.7 and 14.9 illustrates both the increased accuracy due to the smaller spatial grid spacing and the effect of the smaller cell Peclet number at larger values of the physical Peclet number.

The stability criterion $2d \leq 1$ imposes a serious limitation on the practicality of the FTCS approximation of the convection–diffusion equation. As Δx is decreased to improve accuracy, Δt must decrease as the square of Δx, for $d = \alpha\, \Delta t/\Delta x^2 =$ constant. Thus, if Δx is halved, for example, four times as many time steps are required to reach a given time level, and twice as much work is required for each time step since twice as many physical grid points are involved. Thus, the computational effort increases by a factor of *eight*. Consequently, the FTCS approximation of the convection–diffusion equation is not a very efficient method.

The FTCS method can be applied directly to solve nonlinear PDEs, systems of PDEs, and multidimensional problems. A brief discussion of these problems is presented in Section 14.13. The stability limits for multidimensional problems is usually more restrictive.

In summary, the forward-time centered-space (FTCS) approximation of the convection–diffusion equation is explicit, two-level, single-step, $O(\Delta t)+O(\Delta x^2)$, conditionally stable, and convergent. It gives reasonably good results when applied to the convection–diffusion equation. Like most explicit methods applied to the convection–diffusion equation, it is somewhat inefficient, because the time step varies as the square of the spatial grid size.

14.3 THE LAX AND RICHARDSON (LEAPFROG) METHODS

The forward-time centered-space (FTCS) method applied to the convection equation is unconditionally unstable (see Section 12.3). Lax (1954) introduced a modification to the FTCS approximation of the convection equation that makes it conditionally stable (see Section 12.4). Consequently, it might seem that applying the Lax method to the convection term in the convection–diffusion equation could be useful. Unfortunately, that procedure yields an unconditionally unstable finite difference equation. Consequently, that method is not considered further.

The Richardson (1910) (leapfrog) method is applied to the diffusion equation in Section 11.3, where it is shown that the resulting finite difference equation is unconditionally unstable. In Section 12.7, the leapfrog method is applied to the convection equation, where it is found to be marginally stable (i.e., $|G| = 1.0$). Consequently, it would seem that applying the leapfrog method to the convection–diffusion equation would be unconditionally unstable. That is indeed the case. Consequently, that method is not considered further.

14.4 UPWIND METHODS

The first-order upwind method is applied to the convection equation in Section 12.6. The basic concept behind upwind methods is that exact convection derivatives should be approximated by one-sided finite difference approximations in the upwind direction (i.e., the direction from which the velocity comes). The simplest upwind method for approximating the convection–diffusion equation $\bar{f}_t + u\bar{f}_x = \alpha\bar{f}_{xx}$ is obtained by modifying the forward-time centered-space (FTCS) approximation of the convection–diffusion equation, employing a first-order one-sided (i.e., upwind) finite difference approximation for the convection term instead of a centered finite difference approximation. For $u > 0$, the resulting FDE is

$$\boxed{f_i^{n+1} = f_i^n - c(f_i^n - f_{i-1}^n) + d(f_{i+1}^n - 2f_i^n + f_{i-1}^n)} \tag{14.31}$$

where $c = u\,\Delta t/\Delta x$ is the convection number and $d = \alpha\,\Delta t/\Delta x^2$ is the diffusion number. The corresponding finite difference stencil is presented in Fig. 14.10.

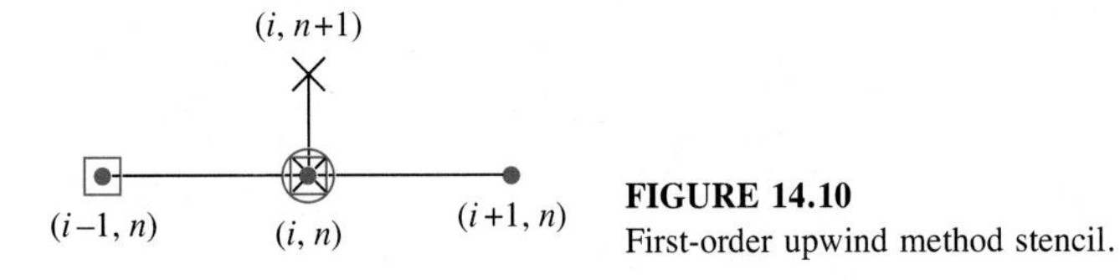

FIGURE 14.10
First-order upwind method stencil.

The first form of the modified differential equation (MDE) is

$$f_t + uf_x = \alpha f_{xx} - \frac{1}{2} f_{tt}\,\Delta t - \frac{1}{6} f_{ttt}\,\Delta t^2 - \cdots$$
$$+ \frac{1}{2} u f_{xx}\,\Delta x - \frac{1}{6} u f_{xxx}\,\Delta x^2 + \cdots + \frac{1}{12} \alpha f_{xxxx}\,\Delta x^2 + \cdots \tag{14.32}$$

and the second form of the MDE is

$$f_t + uf_x = \alpha f_{xx} + \left(\frac{1}{2} u\,\Delta x - \frac{1}{2} u^2\,\Delta t\right) f_{xx}$$
$$+ \left(-\frac{1}{3} u^3\,\Delta t^2 + u\alpha\,\Delta t + \frac{1}{2} u^2\,\Delta t\,\Delta x - \frac{1}{6} u\,\Delta x^2\right) f_{xxx} + \cdots \tag{14.33}$$

As $\Delta t \to 0$ and $\Delta x \to 0$, Eq. (14.32) approaches $f_t + uf_x = \alpha f_{xx}$. Consequently, Eq. (14.31) is a consistent approximation of the convection–diffusion equation. From Eq. (14.33), the truncation error is $O(\Delta t) + O(\Delta x)$. Both even and odd spatial derivatives are present in Eq. (14.33), so implicit numerical diffusion and dispersion both are present. The amplification factor G corresponding to Eq. (14.31) is

$$G = \big(1 - (c + 2d)\big) + (c + 2d)\cos\theta - I c \sin\theta \tag{14.34}$$

For $-\infty \le \theta \le \infty$, Eq. (14.34) represents an ellipse in the complex plane with its center at $[1 - (c + 2d), 0]$ on the real axis and with axes of $(c + 2d)$ and c. By analogy to the results presented in Section 14.2 for the forward-time centered-space (FTCS) method, where $(c + 2d)$ in Eq. (14.34) corresponds to $2d$ in Eq. (14.17), the stability criteria corresponding to Eq. (14.34) are

$$\boxed{c^2 \le (c + 2d) \le 1} \tag{14.35}$$

Consequently, the method is conditionally stable. The first-order upwind approximation of the convection–diffusion equation is consistent and conditionally stable. Consequently, by the Lax equivalence theorem, it is a convergent approximation of that equation.

Example 14.2. Solution by the first-order upwind method. Now we will solve the convection–diffusion problem presented in Section 14.1 using Eq. (14.31), with $\Delta x = 0.1$ cm. The transient solution for $\Delta t = 0.25$ s, for which $c = d = 0.25$ and $(c+2d) = 0.75$, is presented in Fig. 14.11. It is obvious from these results that the numerical solution is predicting the general features of the exact solution. However, the errors are rather large. The numerical solution lags the exact solution rather severely as time progresses. The asymptotic steady state solution also lags the exact steady state solution rather badly. These results are considerably less accurate than the results presented in Fig. 14.6, which were obtained by the FTCS method.

Fig. 14.12 presents asymptotic steady state solutions for several values of the Peclet number P. For small values of the Peclet number ($P \le 1$), the numerical solutions

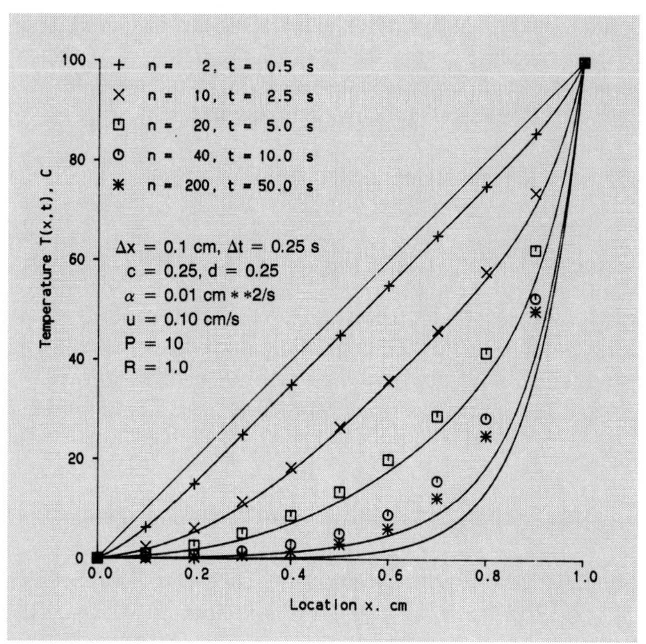

FIGURE 14.11
Transient solution by the first-order upwind method for $P = 10$.

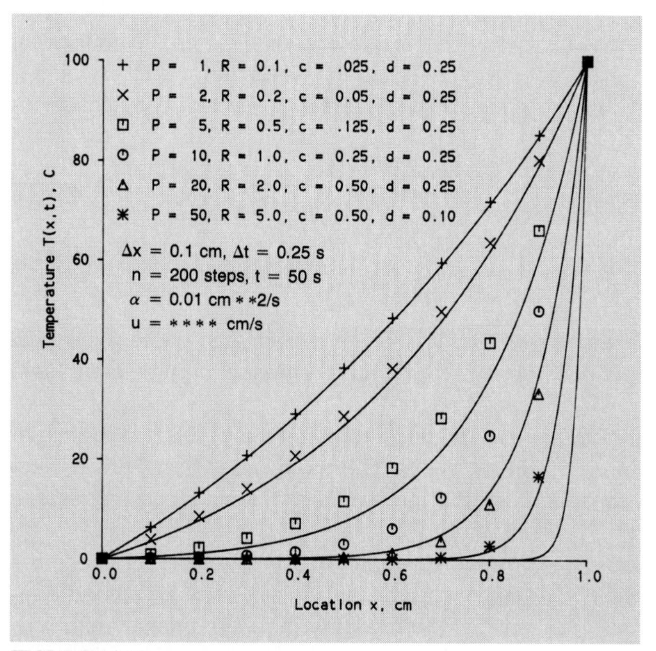

FIGURE 14.12
Steady-state solutions by the first-order upwind method.

are a good approximation of the exact solutions. The asymptotic steady state solutions lag the exact steady state solutions more and more as the Peclet number increases. The culprit in this behavior is the implicit numerical diffusion introduced into the finite difference equation by the first-order one-sided approximation of the convection term $u\overline{f}_x$.

From Eq. (14.33), the implicit numerical diffusion is

$$\left(\frac{1}{2}u\,\Delta x - \frac{1}{2}u^2\,\Delta t\right)f_{xx} = \frac{1}{2}u\,\Delta x(1-c)f_{xx} \tag{14.36}$$

When $c = 1.0$, the implicit numerical diffusion is zero. For any other value of $c < 1.0$ (which is required for stability), the implicit numerical diffusion is positive. Consequently, it adds to the effect of the real physical diffusion $\alpha\overline{f}_{xx}$. The real physical diffusion and the implicit numerical diffusion can be combined to give

$$\left(\left(1 - \frac{1}{2}cR\right) + \frac{1}{2}R\right)\alpha f_{xx} \tag{14.37}$$

where $R = u\,\Delta x/\alpha$ is the cell Peclet/Reynolds number. The terms in the inner parentheses in Eq. (14.37) are the same as the combined real physical diffusion and implicit numerical diffusion for the FTCS method [see Eq. (14.22)]. The other term in Eq. (14.37) increases the implicit numerical diffusion above that of the FTCS method. In fact, when $R = 2$, the amount of additional implicit numerical diffusion is equal to the magnitude of the real physical diffusion. From Eq. (14.37), it is clear that the magnitude of the implicit numerical diffusion depends on the cell Peclet/Reynolds number, and that the effect of implicit numerical diffusion can be greater than the effect of the real physical diffusion.

For the results presented in Fig. 14.11, $R = u\,\Delta x/\alpha = (0.1)(0.1)/(0.01) = 1.0$, for which Eq. (14.37) gives

$$\left(\left(1 - \frac{1}{2}(0.25)(1)\right) + \frac{1}{2}(1)\right)\alpha f_{xx} = 1.375\,\alpha f_{xx} \tag{14.38}$$

Consequently, the effective diffusion is 37.5 percent larger than the real physical diffusion. This effect is responsible for the lagging solution presented in Figs. 14.11 and 14.12.

Application of explicit upwind methods to nonlinear PDEs, systems of PDEs, and multidimensional problems is straightforward, as discussed in Section 14.13. The stability limits for multidimensional problems are usually more restrictive.

In summary, the first-order upwind approximation of the convection–diffusion equation is explicit, two-level, single-step, $O(\Delta t) + O(\Delta x)$, conditionally stable, and convergent. For cell Peclet/Reynolds numbers greater than 1.0, it introduces significant amounts of implicit numerical diffusion into the solution. Consequently, it is not a very good method for solving convection–diffusion problems.

14.5 THE LEONARD METHOD

The first-order upwind method presented in Section 14.4 has an $O(\Delta x)$ truncation error and a significant amount of implicit numerical diffusion. Leonard (1978) proposed a modification to the first-order upwind method that has an $O(\Delta x^3)$ truncation error for the finite difference approximation (FDA) of the convection term $u\bar{f}_x$. This modification changes the overall order of the FDE to $O(\Delta x^2)$ and significantly reduces the implicit numerical diffusion present in the first-order upwind method. The Leonard method is presented in this section.

The base point for the FDAs of the individual exact partial derivatives in the convection–diffusion equation $\bar{f}_t + u\bar{f}_x = \alpha\bar{f}_{xx}$ is grid point (i, n). The partial derivative $\bar{f}_t$ is replaced by the first-order forward-difference FDA [see Eq. (11.54)], and the partial derivative $\bar{f}_{xx}$ is replaced by the second-order centered-difference FDA [see Eq. (11.69b)]. The partial derivative $\bar{f}_x$ is replaced by the third-order upwind-biased FDA obtained by combining Taylor series expansions for $\bar{f}(x, t)$ at points $(i + 1, n)$, (i, n), $(i - 1, n)$, and $(i-2, n)$ to eliminate both the second and third derivative terms. The finite difference stencil for the Leonard method is presented in Fig. 14.13. The resulting FDA is

$$\bar{f}_x|_i^n = \frac{2\bar{f}_{i+1}^n + 3\bar{f}_i^n - 6\bar{f}_{i-1}^n + \bar{f}_{i-2}^n}{6\Delta x} + O(\Delta x^3) \tag{14.39}$$

which can be rearranged into the form

$$\bar{f}_x|_i^n = \frac{\bar{f}_{i+1}^n - \bar{f}_{i-1}^n}{2\Delta x} - \frac{\bar{f}_{i+1}^n - 3\bar{f}_i^n + 3\bar{f}_{i-1}^n - \bar{f}_{i-2}^n}{6\Delta x} + O(\Delta x^3) \tag{14.40}$$

Introducing the FDAs into the convection–diffusion equation and dropping the truncation error terms gives

$$\boxed{\begin{aligned} f_i^{n+1} = f_i^n - \frac{c}{2}\Big((f_{i+1}^n - f_{i-1}^n) - \frac{1}{3}(f_{i+1}^n - 3f_i^n + 3f_{i-1}^n - f_{i-2}^n)\Big) \\ +d(f_{i+1}^n - 2f_i^n + f_{i-1}^n) \end{aligned}} \tag{14.41}$$

where $c = u\,\Delta t/\Delta x$ is the convection number and $d = \alpha\,\Delta t/\Delta x^2$ is the diffusion number.

A problem arises with the application of Eq. (14.41) at the point immediately adjacent to an upstream boundary. Two upstream points are required and only one upstream point, the boundary point itself, exists. Consequently, the solution at the

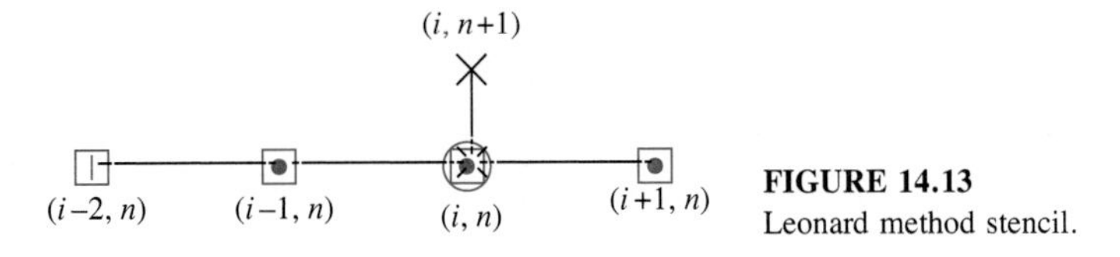

FIGURE 14.13
Leonard method stencil.

point adjacent to an upstream boundary must be obtained by some other method, such as the first-order upwind method.

The first form of the modified differential equation (MDE) is

$$f_t + uf_x = \alpha f_{xx} - \frac{1}{2} f_{tt}\,\Delta t - \frac{1}{6} f_{ttt}\,\Delta t^2 - \frac{1}{24} f_{tttt}\,\Delta t^3 - \cdots$$
$$- \frac{1}{12} u f_{xxxx}\,\Delta x^3 + \cdots \frac{1}{12} \alpha f_{xxxx}\,\Delta x^2 + \cdots \qquad (14.42)$$

and the second form of the MDE is

$$f_t + uf_x = \alpha f_{xx} + \left(-\frac{1}{2}u^2\,\Delta t\right) f_{xx} + \left(u\alpha\,\Delta t - \frac{1}{3}u^3\,\Delta t^2\right) f_{xxx}$$
$$+ \left(-\frac{1}{2}\alpha^2\,\Delta t + u^2\alpha\,\Delta t^2 - \frac{1}{4}u^4\,\Delta t^3 + \frac{1}{12}\alpha\,\Delta x^2 - \frac{1}{12}u\,\Delta x^3\right) f_{xxxx} + \ldots \qquad (14.43)$$

As $\Delta t \to 0$ and $\Delta x \to 0$, Eq. (14.42) approaches $f_t + uf_x = \alpha f_{xx}$. Consequently, Eq. (14.41) is a consistent approximation of the convection–diffusion equation. From Eq. (14.43), the FDE is $O(\Delta t) + O(\Delta x^2)$. Both even and odd spatial derivatives appear in Eq. (14.43), so implicit numerical diffusion and dispersion are both present. The amplification factor G corresponding to Eq. (14.41) is

$$G = \left(1 - \frac{c}{2} - 2d + \left(\frac{2}{3}c + 2d\right)\cos\theta - \frac{c}{6}\cos 2\theta\right) + I\left(-\frac{4}{3}c\sin\theta + \frac{c}{6}\sin 2\theta\right) \qquad (14.44)$$

The complexity of Eq. (14.44) precludes an exact solution for the stability criteria. However, the stability criteria can be determined numerically by systematically choosing combinations of c and d and, for each combination, varying $\theta = k\,\Delta x$ through a period of 2π to determine the corresponding values of $|G|$. The locus of combinations of c and d that give $|G| = 1$ can be plotted, as illustrated in Fig. 14.14, to separate stable and unstable combinations of c and d. As illustrated in Fig. 14.14, the Leonard method is conditionally stable. However, the stable region illustrated in Fig. 14.14 is smaller than the stable regions for most explicit methods. The stable regions for the FTCS method [see Eq. (14.20)] and the first-order upwind method [see Eq. (14.35)] are illustrated for comparison. The Leonard approximation of the convection–diffusion equation is consistent and conditionally stable. Consequently, by the Lax equivalence theorem, it is a convergent approximation of that equation.

Example 14.3. Solution by the Leonard method. Now we will solve the convection–diffusion problem presented in Section 14.1 using Eq. (14.41) with $\Delta x = 0.1$ cm. The Leonard method requires that the solution at the point adjacent to the upstream boundary be determined by some other method. In this example, where the exact solution is known, the solution at that point is specified as the exact solution. The transient solution for $\Delta t = 0.25$ s, for which $c = d = 0.25$, is presented in Fig. 14.15. These results are an excellent approximation of the exact transient solution. They are considerably better than the results presented in Fig. 14.11 for the first-order upwind method.

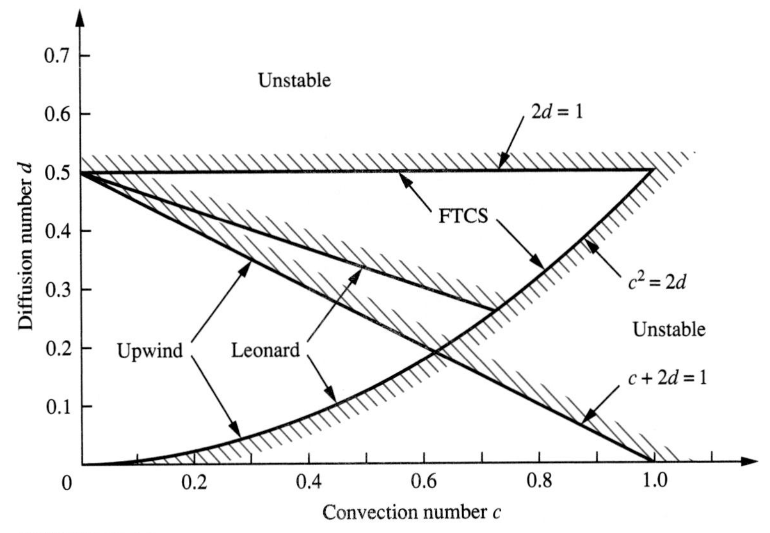

FIGURE 14.14
Stability diagram for the Leonard method.

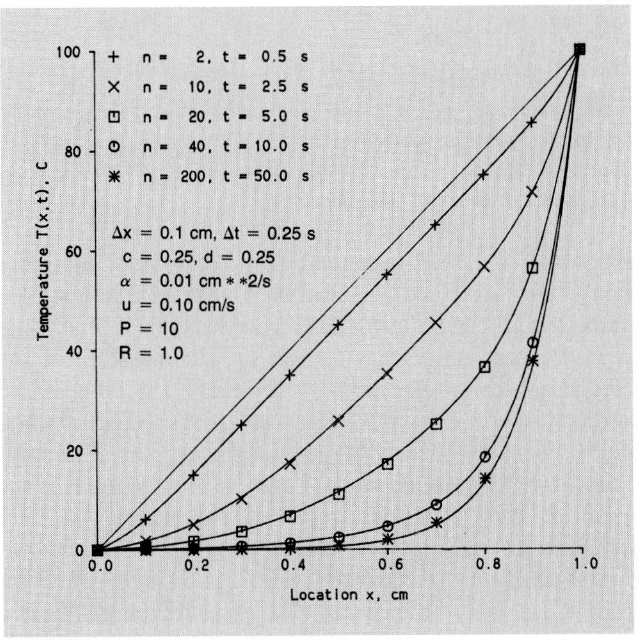

FIGURE 14.15
Transient solution by the Leonard method for $P = 10$.

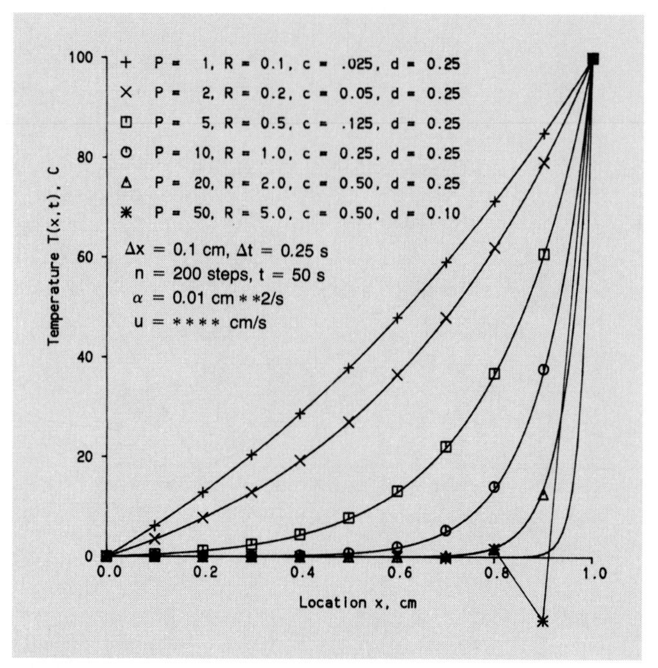

FIGURE 14.16
Steady-state solutions by the Leonard method.

Fig. 14.16 presents asymptotic steady state solutions for several values of the Peclet number P. For values of the Peclet number up to approximately 20, the numerical solutions are an excellent approximation of the exact solutions. For larger values of the Peclet number, physically incorrect behavior is obtained.

Two of the major objectives of the Leonard method are to increase the order of the approximation of the convection term $u\overline{f}_x$, which it does, and to decrease the amount of implicit numerical diffusion introduced into the FDE by the finite difference approximation of the convection term. From the second form of the MDE, Eq. (14.43), the second-order implicit numerical diffusion is found to be the same as the second-order implicit numerical diffusion of the FTCS method [see Eq. (14.16)], which is negative instead of positive as for the first-order upwind method [see Eq. (14.36)]. Consequently, the Leonard method reduces the excessive implicit numerical diffusion of the first-order upwind method.

Application of the explicit Leonard method to nonlinear PDEs, systems of PDEs, and multidimensional problems is straightforward, as discussed in Section 14.13. The stability limits for multidimensional problems are generally more restrictive.

In summary, the Leonard approximation of the convection–diffusion equation is explicit, two-level, single-step, $O(\Delta t) + O(\Delta x^2)$, conditionally stable, and convergent. A separate procedure is required to calculate the solution at the point adjacent to the upstream boundary. The Leonard method gives good results when applied to the convection–diffusion equation.

14.6 THE DUFORT–FRANKEL METHOD

As pointed out in Section 14.3, the Richardson (leapfrog) approximation of the convection–diffusion equation is unconditionally unstable. As demonstrated in Section 11.3, the Richardson (leapfrog) approximation of the diffusion equation is also unconditionally unstable. DuFort and Frankel (1953) proposed a modification of the Richardson method that yields an unconditionally stable explicit finite difference equation (FDE) when applied to the diffusion equation, as shown in Section 11.4. In that modification, the central grid point value f_i^n in the second-order centered-difference approximation of $\overline{f}_{xx}$ is replaced by the approximation $f_i^n = (f_i^{n+1} + f_i^{n-1})/2$. Applying the same idea to the convection–diffusion equation gives

$$\frac{f_i^{n+1} - f_i^{n-1}}{2\Delta t} + u\frac{f_{i+1}^n - f_{i-1}^n}{2\Delta x} = \alpha\frac{f_{i+1}^n - (f_i^{n+1} + f_i^{n-1}) + f_{i-1}^n}{\Delta x^2} \tag{14.45}$$

Solving Eq. (14.45) for f_i^{n+1} yields

$$\boxed{(1 + 2d)f_i^{n+1} = -c(f_{i+1}^n - f_{i-1}^n) + (1 - 2d)f_i^{n-1} + 2d(f_{i+1}^n + f_{i-1}^n)} \tag{14.46}$$

where $c = u\,\Delta t/\Delta x$ is the convection number and $d = \alpha\,\Delta t/\Delta x^2$ is the diffusion number. The corresponding finite difference stencil is presented in Fig. 14.17. The DuFort–Frankel method is a three-level method. Consequently, it cannot be used for the first time step. A separate starting method, such as the FTCS method, is required.

The first form of the modified differential equation (MDE) is

$$f_t + uf_x = \alpha f_{xx} - \alpha\frac{\Delta t^2}{\Delta x^2}f_{tt} - \frac{1}{6}f_{ttt}\,\Delta t^2 + \cdots - \frac{1}{6}uf_{xxx}\,\Delta x^2 - \cdots + \frac{1}{12}\alpha f_{xxxx}\,\Delta x^2 + \cdots \tag{14.47}$$

and the second form of the MDE is

$$f_t + uf_x = \alpha f_{xx} - \left(u^2\alpha\frac{\Delta t^2}{\Delta x^2}\right)f_{xx} + \left(\frac{1}{6}u^3\,\Delta t^2 - \frac{1}{6}u\,\Delta x^2 + 2u\alpha^2\frac{\Delta t^2}{\Delta x^2} - 2u^3\alpha^2\frac{\Delta t^4}{\Delta x^4}\right)f_{xxx} + \cdots \tag{14.48}$$

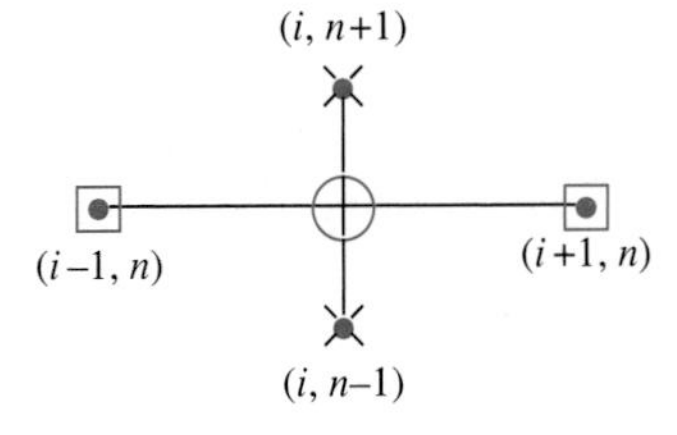

FIGURE 14.17
DuFort–Frankel method stencil.

As $\Delta t \rightarrow 0$ and $\Delta x \rightarrow 0$, the terms $\Delta t^2/\Delta x^2$, and so forth in Eq. (14.47) do not go to zero. In fact they are indeterminate. Consequently, Eq. (14.46) is not a consistent approximation of the convection–diffusion equation. However, if the ratio $(\Delta t/\Delta x)^2$ is held constant as $\Delta t \rightarrow 0$ and $\Delta x \rightarrow 0$, at the value $\beta = (\Delta t/\Delta x)^2$ for example, then Eq. (14.47) approaches the equation

$$f_t + u f_x = \alpha f_{xx} - \alpha \beta f_{tt} \tag{14.49}$$

which is a hyperbolic PDE. In spite of this inconsistency, useful results can be obtained with the DuFort–Frankel method for small values of Δt if not too many time steps are taken. From Eq. (14.48), it is seen that the DuFort–Frankel approximation of the convection–diffusion equation is $O(\Delta t^2) + O(\Delta x^2) + O(\Delta t^2/\Delta x^2)$. Both even and odd spatial derivatives appear in Eq. (14.48), so implicit numerical diffusion and dispersion are both present. The amplification factor G is given by

$$(1 + 2d)G^2 + (-4d \cos\theta + I2c \sin\theta)G - (1 - 2d) = 0 \tag{14.50}$$

Further analysis of Eq. (14.50) shows that there is no restriction on the diffusion number d and that the only stability criterion is $c \leq 1$.

Example 14.4. Solution by the DuFort–Frankel method. We will solve the convection–diffusion problem presented in Section 14.1, using Eq. (14.46) with $\Delta x = 0.1$ cm. The DuFort–Frankel method requires a separate starting method for the first time step. In this example, where the exact solution is known, it is used for the first time step. The transient solution for $\Delta t = 0.5$ s, for which $c = d = 0.5$, is presented in Fig. 14.18. These results are a reasonable approximation of the exact solution.

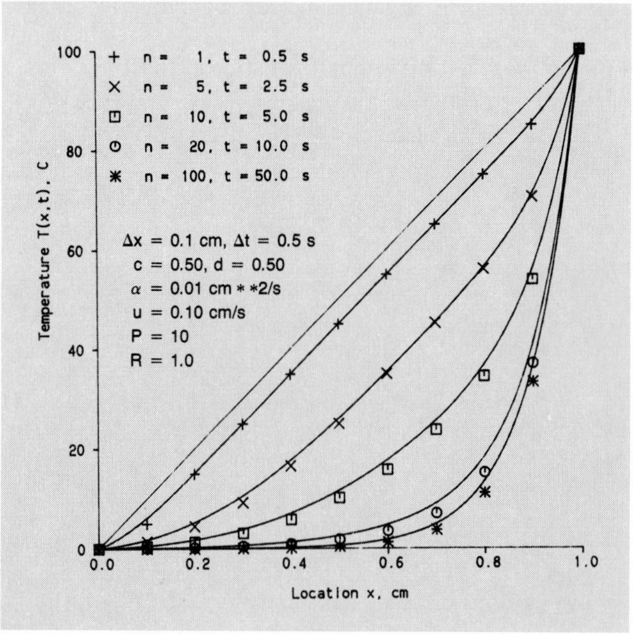

FIGURE 14.18
Transient solution by the DuFort–Frankel method for $P = 10$.

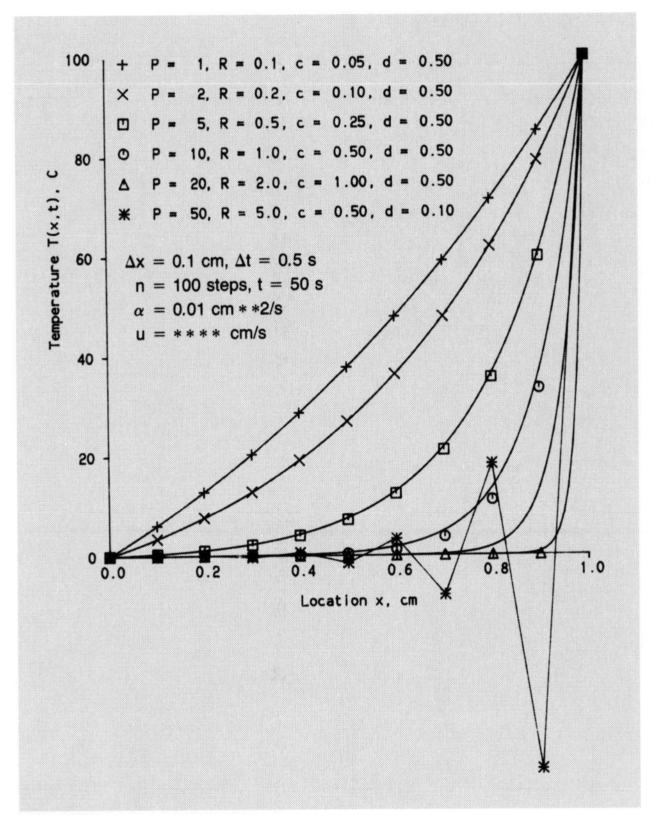

FIGURE 14.19
Steady-state solutions by the DuFort–Frankel method.

Fig. 14.19 presents asymptotic steady state solutions, for $c = d = 0.5$, for several values of the Peclet number P. For values of the cell Peclet number R less than 2.0 (i.e., $P < 20$), the numerical solutions are quite accurate. However, for values of $R > 2$ (i.e., $P > 20$), physically incorrect behavior is obtained.

One advantage of the DuFort–Frankel approximation of the convection–diffusion equation is that there is no stability limitation on the diffusion number d. Figure 14.20 presents the numerical solution for $P = 5.0$ for $\Delta t = 2.0$ s, for which $c = 1.0$ and $d = 2.0$. Although the solution is stable, the transient solution is not very accurate. The problem here is similar to the problem discussed in Section 11.4 for the DuFort–Frankel approximation of the diffusion equation. That is, even though there is no stability limitation on the diffusion number d, the diffusion number cannot be much larger than the stability limitation $d \le \frac{1}{2}$ associated with the FTCS approximation of the convection–diffusion equation if accurate results are to be obtained. The asymptotic steady state solution, however, is still quite accurate.

The explicit DuFort–Frankel method can be applied in a straightforward manner to solve nonlinear PDEs, systems of PDEs, and multidimensional problems, as discussed in Section 14.13.

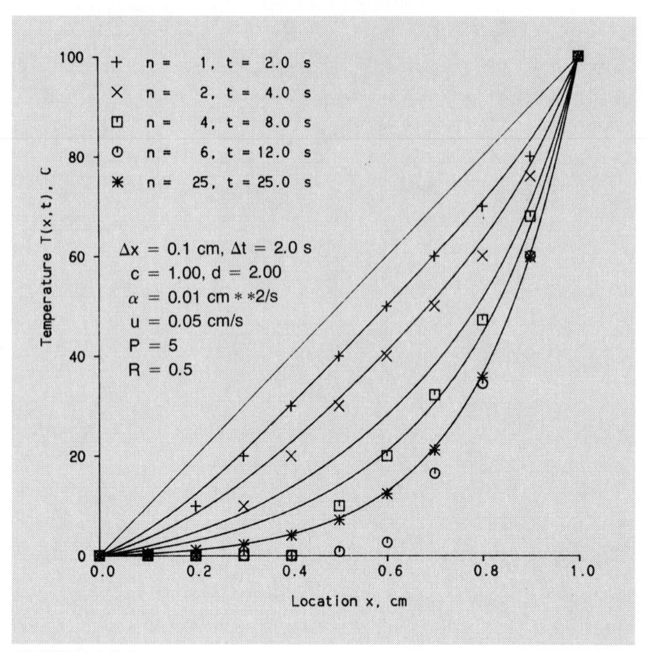

FIGURE 14.20
Transient solution by the DuFort–Frankel method for $P = 5$ with $d = 2.0$.

In summary, the DuFort–Frankel approximation of the convection–diffusion equation is explicit, three-level, single-step, $O(\Delta t^2) + O(\Delta x^2) + O(\Delta t^2/\Delta x^2)$, and conditionally stable (i.e., no condition on d, but $c \leq 1$). However, large values of d result in inaccurate solutions. A starting method is required to obtain the solution for the first time step.

14.7 LAX–WENDROFF TYPE METHODS

Lax–Wendroff type methods, in the most general sense, are methods that can be interpreted as a second-order forward-time Taylor series. That is, for the function $\bar{f}(x, t)$,

$$\bar{f}_i^{n+1} = \bar{f}_i^n + \bar{f}_t|_i^n \, \Delta t + \frac{1}{2}\bar{f}_{tt}|_i^n \, \Delta t^2 + O(\Delta t^3) \tag{14.51}$$

Several Lax–Wendroff type methods have been developed, depending on the procedure used to evaluate $\bar{f}_{tt}|_i^n$. Several of these methods are discussed in this section. None of the methods discussed in this section are very popular for solving the convection–diffusion equation, so no numerical results are presented.

The Lax–Wendroff (1960) one-step method, presented in Section 12.8 for the convection equation, evaluates $\overline{f}_t|_i^n$ directly from the partial differential equation and $\overline{f}_{tt}|_i^n$ by differentiating the PDE with respect to time. As discussed in Section 12.8, the Lax–Wendroff one-step method becomes quite complicated when applied to nonlinear PDEs. It becomes even more complicated when second-order spatial derivatives are present. Consequently, it is not often used to solve the convection–diffusion equation.

The Adams-Bashforth (1883) method evaluates $\overline{f}_{tt}|_i^n$ from a second-order backward-time Taylor series expansion for $\overline{f}_t|_i^{n-1}$ about grid point (i, n). Substituting that result into Eq. (14.51) gives

$$\overline{f}_i^{n+1} = \overline{f}_i^n + \frac{3}{2}\overline{f}_t|_i^n \,\Delta t - \frac{1}{2}\overline{f}_t|_i^{n-1}\,\Delta t^2 + O(\Delta t^3) \tag{14.52}$$

Equation (14.52) is unconditionally unstable when applied to the convection equation. However, the method is conditionally stable when applied to the convection–diffusion equation by evaluating the diffusion term by the second-order centered-difference approximation at grid point (i, n). Thus,

$$\begin{aligned} f_i^{n+1} = f_i^n &- \frac{3}{4}c(f_{i+1}^n - f_{i-1}^n) + \frac{1}{4}c(f_{i+1}^{n-1} - f_{i-1}^{n-1}) \\ &+ d(f_{i+1}^n - 2f_i^n + f_{i-1}^n) \end{aligned} \tag{14.53}$$

The Adams-Bashforth approximation of the convection–diffusion equation is explicit, three level, single step, $O(\Delta t^2) + O(\Delta x^2)$, and conditionally stable.

Several two-step Lax–Wendroff type methods for the convection equation are presented in Section 12.9 [the Richtmyer (1963) and Burstein (1967) methods] and in Section 12.10 [the MacCormack (1969) method]. The Richtmyer and Burstein methods are three-level two-step methods. The first step in the Richtmyer method is the Lax method applied at grid point (i, n) to obtain a provisional result at grid point $(i, n+1)$, followed by the leapfrog method applied at grid point $(i, n+1)$ to obtain the final solution at grid point $(i, n+2)$. The Burstein method is similar, but it applies at half-mesh points. Both of these Lax–Wendroff type two-step methods are unconditionally unstable because of the time centering of the diffusion term (see Section 14.3). The MacCormack method yields very good results when applied to the convection–diffusion equation. Section 14.8 is devoted to the MacCormack method.

Two additional methods for solving the convection–diffusion equation are presented below to illustrate the variety of explicit methods that have been devised.

The first is the Brailovskaya (1965) method, which is a two-level two-step method. The first step uses the forward-time centered-space (FTCS) method to obtain provisional values at time level $\overline{n+1}$. The second step evaluates the convection term at time level $n+1$ and the diffusion term at time level n. Thus, the second step is

$$f_i^{n+1} = f_i^n - \frac{c}{2}\left(f_{i+1}^{\overline{n+1}} - f_{i-1}^{\overline{n+1}}\right) + d\left(f_{i+1}^n - 2f_i^n + f_{i-1}^n\right) \tag{14.54}$$

A von Neumann stability analysis shows that $c \leq 1$ and $d \leq \frac{1}{4}$ for stability. The Brailovskaya approximation of the convection–diffusion equation is explicit, two-level, two-step, $O(\Delta t) + O(\Delta x^2)$, and conditionally stable.

Allen and Cheng (1970) proposed a variation of the Brailovskaya method that eliminates the diffusion limit on the time step. For the first step, the function value f_i^n in the finite difference approximation (FDA) of the diffusion term $\overline{f}_{xx}$ is replaced by $f_i^{\overline{n+1}}$. Thus,

$$\frac{f_i^{\overline{n+1}} - f_i^n}{\Delta t} = -u\frac{f_{i+1}^n - f_{i-1}^n}{2\Delta x} + \alpha\frac{f_{i+1}^n - 2f_i^{\overline{n+1}} + f_{i-1}^n}{\Delta x^2} \tag{14.55}$$

Solving Eq. (14.55) for $f_i^{\overline{n+1}}$ gives

$$(1+2d)f_i^{\overline{n+1}} = f_i^n - \frac{c}{2}\left(f_{i+1}^n - f_{i-1}^n\right) + d\left(f_{i+1}^n + f_{i-1}^n\right) \tag{14.56}$$

For the second step, the FDA of the diffusion term $\overline{f}_{xx}$ is centered at grid point $(i, n+1)$, but the function value f_i^{n+1} is replaced by f_i^{n+1}. Thus,

$$\frac{f_i^{n+1} - f_i^n}{\Delta t} = -u\frac{f_{i+1}^{\overline{n+1}} - f_{i-1}^{\overline{n+1}}}{2\Delta x} + \alpha\frac{f_{i+1}^{\overline{n+1}} - 2f_i^{n+1} + f_{i-1}^{\overline{n+1}}}{\Delta x^2} \tag{14.57}$$

Solving Eq. (14.57) for f_i^{n+1} gives

$$(1+2d)f_i^{n+1} = f_i^n - \frac{c}{2}\left(f_{i+1}^{\overline{n+1}} - f_{i-1}^{\overline{n+1}}\right) + d\left(f_{i+1}^{\overline{n+1}} + f_{i-1}^{\overline{n+1}}\right) \tag{14.58}$$

A von Neumann stability analysis shows that $c \leq 1$ for stability, with no restrictions on the diffusion number d. The Allen-Cheng approximation of the convection–diffusion equation is explicit, two-level, two-step, $O(\Delta t) + O(\Delta x^2)$, and conditionally stable.

14.8 THE MACCORMACK METHOD

The MacCormack (1969) method is applied to the convection equation in Section 12.10. As discussed there, the MacCormack method is based on the second-order forward-time Taylor series:

$$\bar{f}_i^{n+1} = \bar{f}_i^n + \bar{f}_t|_i^n \,\Delta t + \frac{1}{2}\bar{f}_{tt}|_i^n \,\Delta t^2 + O(\Delta t^3) \tag{14.59}$$

where $\bar{f}_t|_i^n$ is determined directly from the PDE and $\bar{f}_{tt}|_i^n$ is determined from a second-order forward-time Taylor series expansion for $\bar{f}_t|_i^{n+1}$ about grid point (i,n). The result [see Eq. (12.73)] is

$$\bar{f}_i^{n+1} = \bar{f}_i^n + \frac{1}{2}(\bar{f}_t|_i^n + \bar{f}_t|_i^{n+1})\Delta t + O(\Delta t^3) \tag{14.60}$$

Equation (14.60) can be solved for f_i^{n+1} by dropping the truncation error terms and replacing $\bar{f}_t|_i^n$ and $\bar{f}_t|_i^{n+1}$ in terms of spatial derivatives from the PDE. A two-step predictor-corrector approach is required to evaluate f_i^{n+1} explicitly. In the first step, $\bar{f}_x|_i^n$ is approximated by the first-order forward-difference approximation. These results are used to determine the provisional values $f_i^{\overline{n+1}}$. In the second step, Eq. (14.60) is solved by evaluating $f_x|_i^n$ as done for the predictor and $f_x|_i^{\overline{n+1}}$ using the first-order backward-difference approximation based on the provisional values of $f^{\overline{n+1}}$.

The MacCormack method is applied to the convection–diffusion equation by first rewriting it in the form

$$\bar{f}_t = (-u\bar{f} + \alpha\bar{f}_x)_x \tag{14.61}$$

In this form, u and α can both be variable, so the method applies directly to nonlinear PDEs. For the first (predictor or provisional) step

$$\boxed{f_i^{\overline{n+1}} = f_i^n + \left(-\frac{(uf)_{i+1}^n - (uf)_i^n}{\Delta x} + \frac{(\alpha f_x)_{i+1}^n - (\alpha f_x)_i^n}{\Delta x}\right)\Delta t} \tag{14.62}$$

where

$$(\alpha f_x)_{i+1}^n = \alpha_{i+1}^n \frac{f_{i+1}^n - f_i^n}{\Delta x} \quad \text{and} \quad (\alpha f_x)_i^n = \alpha_i^n \frac{f_i^n - f_{i-1}^n}{\Delta x} \tag{14.63}$$

The finite difference stencil for the first step is illustrated in Figure 14.21a. For the linear case, where u and α are constant, Eq. (14.62) reduces to

$$\boxed{f_i^{\overline{n+1}} = f_i^n - c(f_{i+1}^n - f_i^n) + d(f_{i+1}^n - 2f_i^n + f_{i-1}^n)} \tag{14.64}$$

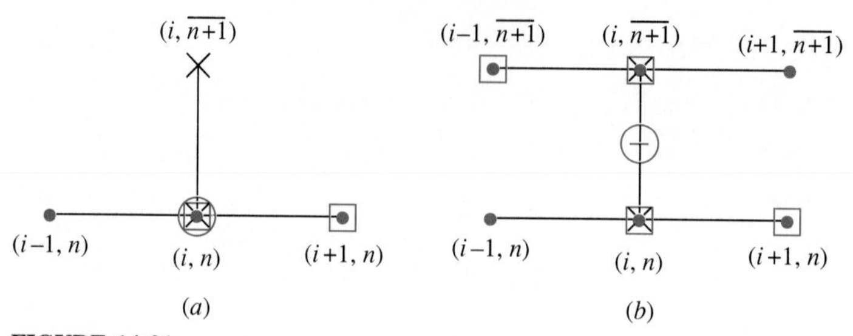

FIGURE 14.21
MacCormack method stencil. (a) Predictor. (b) Corrector.

For the second (corrector or final) step

$$f_i^{n+1} = f_i^n + \frac{1}{2}\left(-\frac{(uf)_{i+1}^n - (uf)_i^n}{\Delta x} - \frac{(uf)_i^{\overline{n+1}} - (uf)_{i-1}^{\overline{n+1}}}{\Delta x} + \frac{(\alpha f_x)_{i+1}^n - (\alpha f_x)_i^n}{\Delta x} + \frac{(\alpha f_x)_i^{\overline{n+1}} - (\alpha f_x)_{i-1}^{\overline{n+1}}}{\Delta x}\right)\Delta t \tag{14.65}$$

where

$$(\alpha f_x)_i^{\overline{n+1}} = \alpha_i^{\overline{n+1}} \frac{f_{i+1}^{\overline{n+1}} - f_i^{\overline{n+1}}}{\Delta x} \quad \text{and} \quad (\alpha f_x)_{i-1}^{\overline{n+1}} = \alpha_{i-1}^{\overline{n+1}} \frac{f_i^{\overline{n+1}} - f_{i-1}^{\overline{n+1}}}{\Delta x} \tag{14.66}$$

The finite difference stencil for the second step is illustrated in Fig. 14.21*b*. Combining Eqs. (14.62) and (14.65) yields the computationally more efficient result

$$f_i^{n+1} = \frac{1}{2}\left(f_i^n + f_i^{\overline{n+1}} + \left(-\frac{(uf)_i^{\overline{n+1}} - (uf)_{i-1}^{\overline{n+1}}}{\Delta x} + \frac{(\alpha f_x)_i^{\overline{n+1}} - (\alpha f_x)_{i-1}^{\overline{n+1}}}{\Delta x}\right)\Delta t\right) \tag{14.67}$$

For the linear case, where u and α are constant, Eq. (14.67) reduces to

$$f_i^{n+1} = \frac{1}{2}\left(f_i^n + f_i^{\overline{n+1}} - c\left(f_i^{\overline{n+1}} - f_{i-1}^{\overline{n+1}}\right) + d\left(f_{i+1}^{\overline{n+1}} - 2f_i^{\overline{n+1}} + f_{i-1}^{\overline{n+1}}\right)\right) \tag{14.68}$$

Equation (14.62) [or Eq. (14.64)] combined with Eq. (14.67) [or Eq. (14.68)] comprises the MacCormack approximation of the convection–diffusion equation. Equations (14.62) and (14.64) employ forward-difference approximations and Eqs. (14.67) and (14.68) employ backward-difference approximations. This differencing can be reversed. Either way, there is a slight bias in the solution due to the one-sided differences. If desired, this bias can be reduced somewhat by alternating the direction of the predictor and corrector differences from one time level to the next.

Accuracy, order, stability, and consistency analyses of the two-step MacCormack approximation of the nonlinear convection–diffusion equation are not available. However, for the linear convection–diffusion equation, Eqs. (14.64) and (14.68) can be combined to yield the single-step equation

$$\boxed{f_i^{n+1} = Af_{i-2}^n + Bf_{i-1}^n + Cf_i^n + Df_{i+1}^n + Ef_{i+2}^n} \tag{14.69}$$

where

$$A = \frac{1}{2}cd + \frac{1}{2}d^2 \tag{14.70a}$$

$$B = \frac{1}{2}c + d - cd + \frac{1}{2}c^2 - 2d^2 \tag{14.70b}$$

$$C = 1 - 2d - c^2 + 3d^2 \tag{14.70c}$$

$$D = -\frac{1}{2}c + d + cd + \frac{1}{2}c^2 - 2d^2 \tag{14.70d}$$

$$E = -\frac{1}{2}cd + \frac{1}{2}d^2 \tag{14.70e}$$

The first form of the modified differential equation (MDE) is

$$\begin{aligned} f_t + uf_x &= \alpha f_{xx} - \frac{1}{2}f_{tt}\,\Delta t - \frac{1}{6}f_{ttt}\,\Delta t^2 - \frac{1}{24}f_{tttt}\,\Delta t^3 + \cdots + \frac{1}{2}u^2 f_{xx}\,\Delta t \\ &+ \left(-\frac{1}{6}u\,\Delta x^2 - u\alpha\,\Delta t\right)f_{xxx} + \left(\frac{1}{2}\alpha^2\Delta t + \frac{1}{24}u^2\,\Delta x^2\,\Delta t + \frac{1}{12}\alpha\,\Delta x^2\right)f_{xxxx} + \cdots \end{aligned} \tag{14.71}$$

and the second form of the MDE is

$$\begin{aligned} f_t + uf_x &= \alpha f_{xx} + \left(-\frac{1}{6}u\,\Delta x^2 + \frac{1}{6}u^3\,\Delta t^2\right)f_{xxx} \\ &+ \left(\frac{1}{12}\alpha\,\Delta x^2 - \frac{1}{8}u^2\,\Delta x^2\,\Delta t - \frac{1}{2}u^2\alpha\,\Delta t^2 + \frac{1}{8}u^4\,\Delta t^3\right)f_{xxxx} + \cdots \end{aligned} \tag{14.72}$$

As $\Delta t \to 0$ and $\Delta x \to 0$, the truncation error terms in Eq. (14.71) go to zero, and Eq. (14.71) approaches $f_t + uf_x = \alpha f_{xx}$. Consequently, Eq. (14.69) is a consistent approximation of the convection–diffusion equation. From Eq. (14.72), the FDE is $O(\Delta t^2) + O(\Delta x^2)$. The leading truncation error term in Eq. (14.72) contains f_{xxx}. Consequently, the FDE is predominately dispersive. Higher-order even derivatives are present, so the FDE also has implicit numerical diffusion. The amplification factor G is

$$G = \big(C + (B + D)\cos\theta + (A + E)\cos 2\theta\big) + I\big((D - B)\sin\theta + (E - A)\sin 2\theta\big) \tag{14.73}$$

Equation (14.73) is too complicated to yield simple exact stability criteria. Alternatively, $|G|$ can be evaluated numerically for all combinations of c and d over a range of values of c and d, for $0 \le \theta \le 2\pi$. The locus of combinations of c and d that give $|G| = 1$ can be plotted, as illustrated in Fig. 14.22, to separate stable and unstable combinations of c and d. As illustrated in Fig. 14.22, the MacCormack method is conditionally stable. The stable regions for the FTCS method and the first-order upwind method are illustrated for comparison. The stable region is almost the entire rectangle within the limits $c \le 0.9$ and $d \le 1/2$. Consequently, Eq. (14.69) is conditionally stable. The MacCormack approximation of the linear convection–diffusion equation is consistent and conditionally stable; consequently, by the Lax equivalence theorem, it is a convergent finite difference approximation of the convection–diffusion equation.

Example 14.5. Solution by the MacCormack method. We will solve the convection–diffusion problem presented in Section 14.1, using Eqs. (14.64) and (14.68) with $\Delta x =$

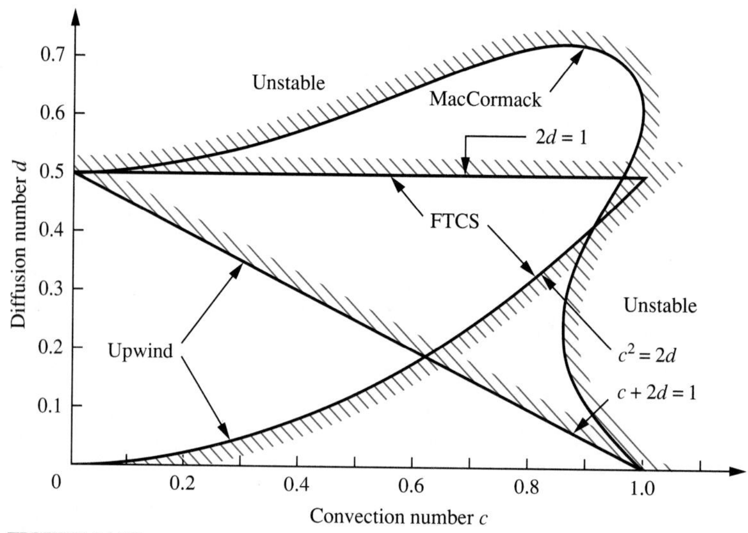

FIGURE 14.22
Stability diagram for the MacCormack method.

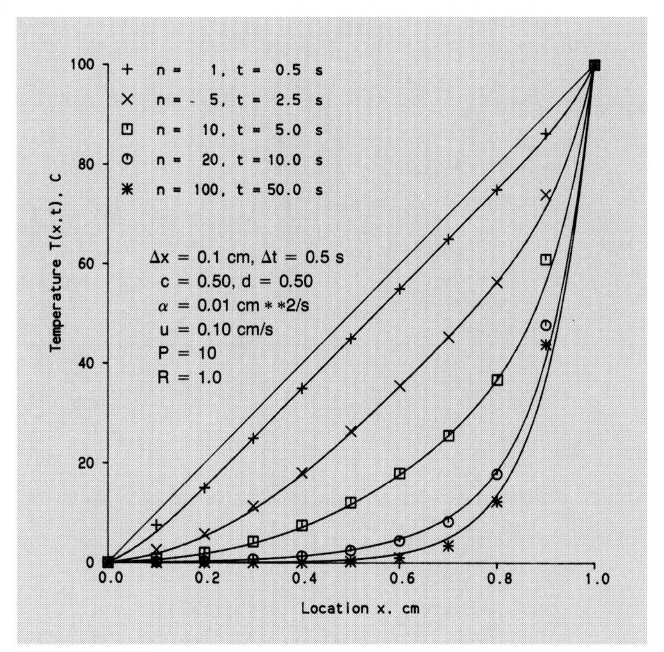

FIGURE 14.23
Transient solution by the MacCormack method for $P = 10$.

0.1 cm. The numerical solution of the transient problem with $\Delta t = 0.5$ s, for which $c = d = 0.5$, is presented in Fig. 14.23. These results are a very good approximation of the exact transient solution.

Figure 14.24 presents asymptotic steady state solutions for several values of the Peclet number P. As found for most explicit methods, physically correct solutions are obtained for values of the cell Peclet number R less than 2.0, and physically incorrect solutions are obtained for larger values of R.

As demonstrated in Example 14.5, the MacCormack method is an efficient and accurate method for solving the linear convection–diffusion equation. The method is equally efficient and accurate for solving the nonlinear convection–diffusion equation. When systems of PDEs are involved, the method is simply applied to every PDE in the system. The MacCormack method extends directly to two- and three-dimensional physical spaces simply by adding on the appropriate one-sided finite difference approximations to the y and z space derivatives. The stability boundaries are smaller for two- and three-dimensional physical spaces. In view of these attributes, the MacCormack method is very popular for solving convection–diffusion problems.

In summary, the MacCormack approximation of the convection–diffusion equation is explicit, two-level, two-step, $O(\Delta t^2) + O(\Delta x^2)$, conditionally stable, and convergent. It is an excellent method for solving convection–diffusion problems.

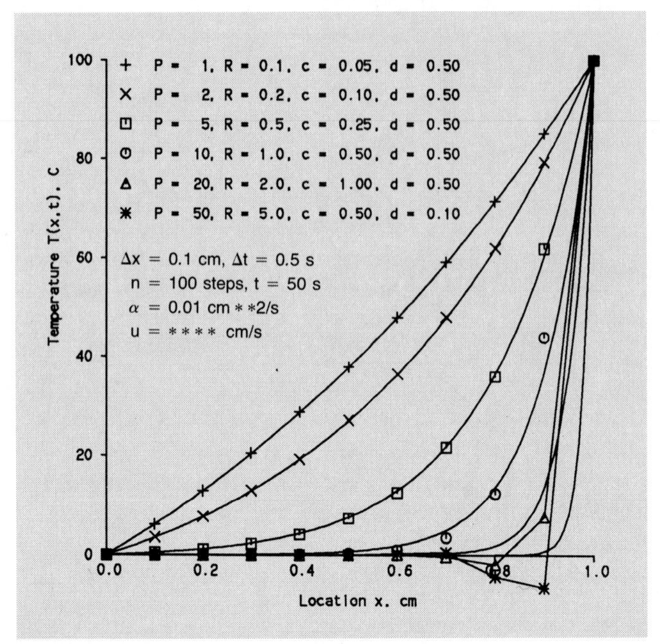

FIGURE 14.24
Steady-state solutions by the MacCormack method.

14.9 THE BACKWARD-TIME CENTERED-SPACE METHOD

The backward-time centered-space (BTCS) method is applied to the diffusion equation in Section 11.5 and to the convection equation in Section 12.12. In this section, the BTCS method is applied to the convection–diffusion equation $\bar{f}_t + u\bar{f}_x = \alpha\bar{f}_{xx}$. The base point for the finite difference approximation of the individual exact partial derivatives is grid point $(i, n+1)$. The finite difference stencil is illustrated in Fig. 14.25. The resulting finite difference approximation is

$$\frac{f_i^{n+1} - f_i^n}{\Delta t} + u\frac{f_{i+1}^{n+1} - f_{i-1}^{n+1}}{2\Delta x} = \alpha\frac{f_{i+1}^{n+1} - 2f_i^{n+1} + f_{i-1}^{n+1}}{\Delta x^2} \tag{14.74}$$

Rearranging Eq. (14.74) yields

$$-\left(\frac{1}{2}c + d\right)f_{i-1}^{n+1} + (1 + 2d)f_i^{n+1} + \left(\frac{1}{2}c - d\right)f_{i+1}^{n+1} = f_i^n \tag{14.75}$$

where $c = u\,\Delta t/\Delta x$ is the convection number and $d = \alpha\,\Delta t/\Delta x^2$ is the diffusion number. Equation (14.75) cannot be solved explicitly for f_i^{n+1}, because

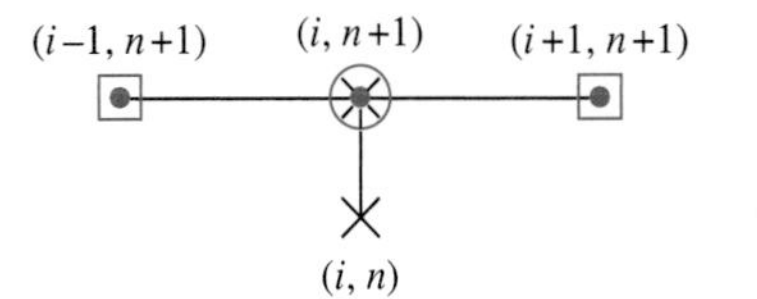

FIGURE 14.25
BTCS method stencil.

the two unknown neighboring values f_{i-1}^{n+1} and f_{i+1}^{n+1} also appear in the equation. Consequently, an implicit system of finite difference equations results.

The first form of the modified differential equation (MDE) is

$$f_t + uf_x = \alpha f_{xx} + \frac{1}{2} f_{tt}\,\Delta t - \frac{1}{6} f_{ttt}\,\Delta t^2 + \cdots - \frac{1}{6} u f_{xxx}\,\Delta x^2 + \cdots + \frac{1}{12}\alpha f_{xxxx}\,\Delta x^2 + \cdots \tag{14.76}$$

and the second form of the MDE is

$$f_t + uf_x = \alpha f_{xx} + \left(\frac{1}{2}u^2\,\Delta t\right) f_{xx} + \left(-u\alpha\,\Delta t - \frac{1}{3}u^3\,\Delta t^2 - \frac{1}{6}u\,\Delta x^2\right) f_{xxx} + \cdots \tag{14.77}$$

As $\Delta t \to 0$ and $\Delta x \to 0$, Eq. (14.76) approaches $f_t + uf_x = \alpha f_{xx}$. Consequently, Eq. (14.75) is a consistent approximation of the convection–diffusion equation. From Eq. (14.77), the truncation error is $O(\Delta t) + O(\Delta x^2)$. Both even and odd spatial derivatives appear in Eq. (14.77), so implicit numerical diffusion and dispersion are both present. The amplification factor G is

$$G = \frac{1}{1 + 2d(1 - \cos\theta) + Ic\sin\theta} \tag{14.78}$$

The term $(1 - \cos\theta) \geq 0$ for all values of $\theta = k\Delta x$. Consequently, $|G| \leq 1$ for all values of c and d, and Eq. (14.75) is unconditionally stable. The BTCS approximation of the convection–diffusion equation is consistent and unconditionally stable. Consequently, by the Lax equivalence theorem, it is a convergent approximation of that equation.

Consider now the solution of the convection–diffusion equation by the BTCS method. As discussed in Section 11.5 for the diffusion equation, a tridiagonal system of equations results when Eq. (14.75) is applied at every grid point. That system of equations can be solved by the Thomas algorithm (see Section 1.5). For the linear convection–diffusion equation, **LU** decomposition can be used.

Example 14.6. Solution by the BTCS method. We will solve the convection–diffusion problem presented in Section 14.1, using Eq. (14.75) with $\Delta x = 0.1$ cm. The transient solution for $\Delta t = 0.5$ s, for which $c = d = 0.5$, is presented in Fig. 14.26. These results are a reasonable approximation of the exact transient solution.

The asymptotic steady state solutions for several values of the Peclet number P are presented in Fig. 14.27. For $R < 2.0$, physically correct results are obtained. However,

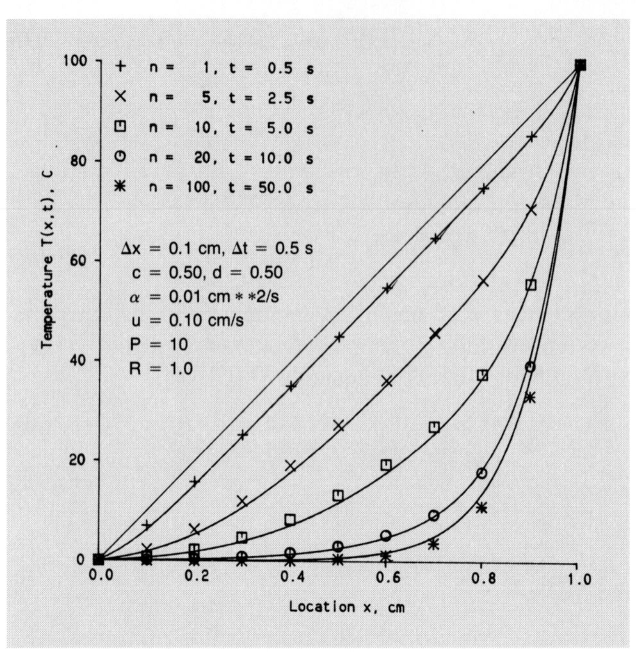

FIGURE 14.26
Transient solution by the BTCS method for $P = 10$.

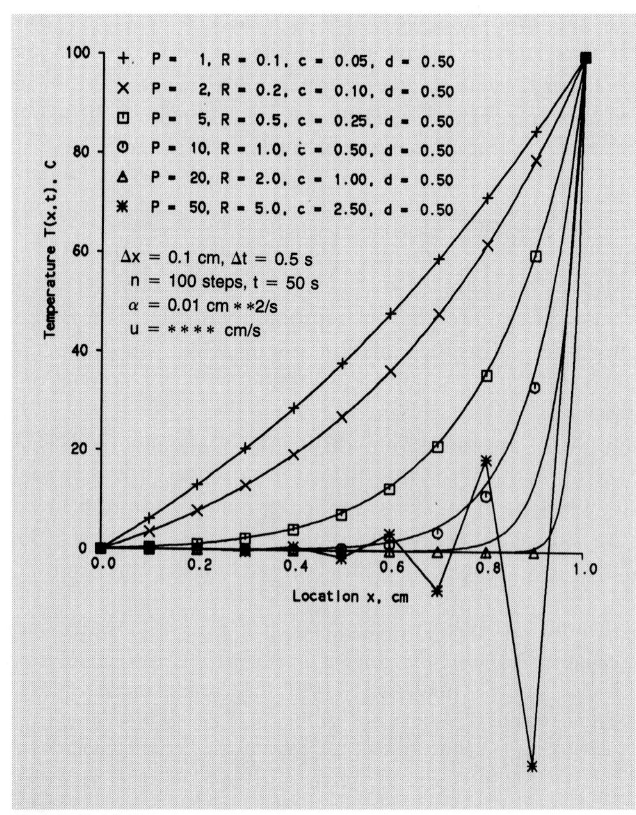

FIGURE 14.27
Steady-state solutions by the BTCS method.

for $R > 2$, the results are physically incorrect. This asymptotic steady state behavior is identical to the behavior of several of the explicit methods. In fact, at the asymptotic steady state limit, the finite difference approximations of the spatial derivatives are the same in several of the methods considered so far, except for the first-order upwind method, the Leonard method, and the MacCormack method.

As shown by Eq. (14.78), Eq. (14.75) is unconditionally stable. Consequently, large time steps can be taken to reduce the computational effort, if the accuracy is acceptable. Fig. 14.28 presents the transient solution for $\Delta t = 5.0$ s, for which $c = d = 5.0$. These results demonstrate the unconditional stability of the method. However, the numerical solution lags the exact transient solution considerably. If the decreased accuracy associated with the larger time step is acceptable, then the solution can be obtained with considerably less computational effort. However, the results presented in Fig. 14.28 suggest that values of c and d much larger than 1.0 lead to serious decreases in accuracy.

The asymptotic steady state solution presented in Fig. 14.28 is obtained in only 10 time steps. This solution required only 10 percent of the computational effort required to obtain the asymptotic steady state solution presented in Fig. 14.26, with no loss of accuracy. This example demonstrates one of the most important uses of implicit methods: the ability to obtain asymptotic steady state solutions with much less computational effort than required by explicit methods. In fact, the asymptotic steady state solution can be reached in one or two steps for extremely large values of Δt. This increased speed is reduced somewhat for nonlinear PDEs, which require iteration, linearization, or both to solve the system of nonlinear FDEs.

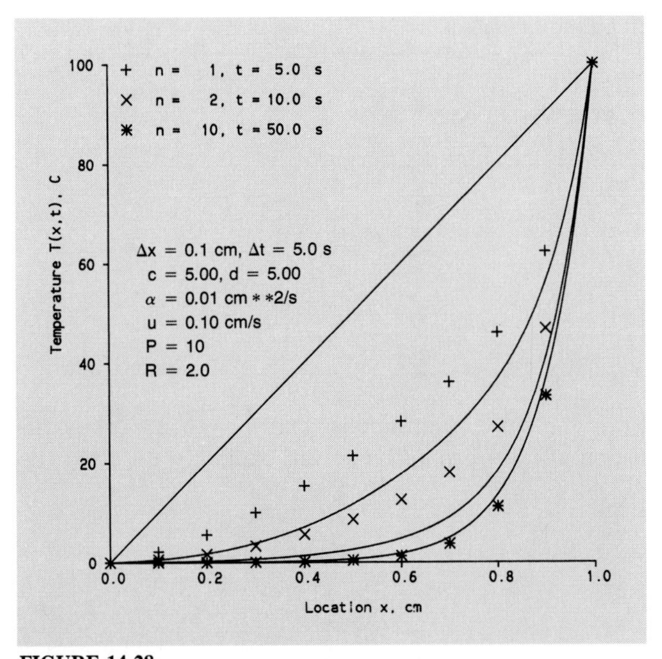

FIGURE 14.28
Transient solution by the BTCS method for $P = 10$ with $c = 5.0$ and $d = 5.0$.

The implicit BTCS method becomes considerably more complicated when applied to nonlinear PDEs, systems of PDEs, and multidimensional problems. A brief introduction to these problems is presented in Section 14.13.

In summary, the BTCS approximation of the convection–diffusion equation is implicit, two-level, single-step, $O(\Delta t) + O(\Delta x^2)$, unconditionally stable, and convergent. The implicit nature of the method yields a set of finite difference equations, which must be solved simultaneously. For one-dimensional problems, that can be accomplished by the Thomas algorithm. The BTCS approximation of the convection–diffusion equation yields reasonable transient solutions for modest values of the convection and diffusion numbers and good asymptotic steady state solutions for large values of Δt.

14.10 THE CRANK–NICOLSON METHOD

The Crank–Nicolson (1947) method is applied to the diffusion equation in Section 11.6. In this section, the Crank–Nicolson concept is applied to the convection–diffusion equation $\bar{f}_t + u\bar{f}_x = \alpha\bar{f}_{xx}$. The base point for the finite difference approximations of the individual exact partial derivatives is grid point $(i, n + 1/2)$. The finite difference stencil is presented in Fig. 14.29. The resulting finite difference approximation is

$$\frac{f_i^{n+1} - f_i^n}{\Delta t} = \frac{1}{2}\left(-u\frac{f_{i+1}^n - f_{i-1}^n}{2\Delta x} - u\frac{f_{i+1}^{n+1} - f_{i-1}^{n+1}}{2\Delta x}\right)$$
$$+\frac{1}{2}\left(\alpha\frac{f_{i+1}^n - 2f_i^n + f_{i-1}^n}{\Delta x^2} + \alpha\frac{f_{i+1}^{n+1} - 2f_i^{n+1} + f_{i-1}^{n+1}}{\Delta x^2}\right) \tag{14.79}$$

Rearranging Eq. (14.79) gives

$$-\left(\frac{1}{2}c + d\right)f_{i-1}^{n+1} + 2(1 + d)f_i^{n+1} + \left(\frac{1}{2}c - d\right)f_{i+1}^{n+1}$$
$$= \left(\frac{1}{2}c + d\right)f_{i-1}^n + 2(1 - d)f_i^n - \left(\frac{1}{2}c - d\right)f_{i+1}^n \tag{14.80}$$

where $c = u\,\Delta t/\Delta x$ is the convection number and $d = \alpha\,\Delta t/\Delta x^2$ is the diffusion number. Equation (14.80) cannot be solved explicitly for f_i^{n+1}, because

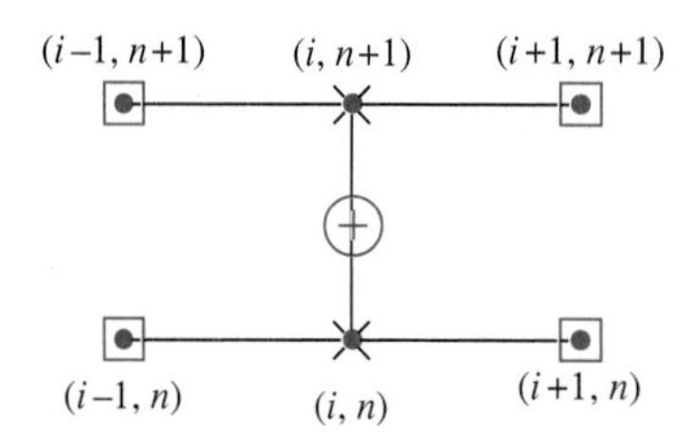

FIGURE 14.29
Crank–Nicolson method stencil.

the two unknown neighboring values f_{i-1}^{n+1} and f_{i+1}^{n+1} also appear in the equation. Consequently, an implicit system of finite difference equations results.

The first form of the modified differential equation (MDE) is

$$f_t + uf_x = \alpha f_{xx} - \frac{1}{24} f_{ttt}\,\Delta t^2 - \cdots - \frac{1}{6} u f_{xxx}\,\Delta x^2 - \cdots - \frac{1}{8} u f_{xtt}\,\Delta t^2 + \cdots + \frac{1}{12}\alpha f_{xxxx}\,\Delta x^2 + \frac{1}{8}\alpha f_{xxtt}\,\Delta t^2 + \cdots \quad (14.81)$$

and the second form of the MDE is

$$f_t + uf_x = \alpha f_{xx} + \left(-\frac{1}{12}u^3\,\Delta t^2 - \frac{1}{6}u\,\Delta x^2\right) f_{xxx} + \left(\frac{1}{4}u^2\alpha\,\Delta t^2 + \frac{1}{12}\alpha\,\Delta x^2\right) f_{xxxx} + \cdots \quad (14.82)$$

As $\Delta t \to 0$ and $\Delta x \to 0$, Eq. (14.81) approaches $f_t + uf_x = \alpha f_{xx}$. Consequently, Eq. (14.80) is a consistent approximation of the convection–diffusion equation. From Eq. (14.82), the truncation error is $O(\Delta t^2) + O(\Delta x^2)$. Both even and odd spatial derivatives appear in Eq. (14.82), so implicit numerical diffusion and dispersion are both present. The amplification factor G is

$$G = \frac{1 - d(1 - \cos\theta) - I(c/2)\sin\theta}{1 + d(1 - \cos\theta) + I(c/2)\sin\theta} \quad (14.83)$$

The term $(1 - \cos\theta) \geq 0$ for all values of $\theta = k\,\Delta x$. Consequently, the real part of the numerator is less than or equal to the real part of the denominator, so the magnitude of the numerator is less than or equal to the magnitude of the denominator. Consequently, $|G| \leq 1$ for all positive values of c and d, and Eq. (14.80) is unconditionally stable. The Crank–Nicolson approximation of the convection–diffusion equation is consistent and unconditionally stable; consequently, by the Lax equivalence theorem, it is a convergent approximation of that equation.

As discussed in Section 11.5 for the diffusion equation, a system of finite difference equations must be solved. That system of equations can be solved by the Thomas algorithm (see Section 1.5). For the linear convection–diffusion equation, **LU** decomposition can be used.

Example 14.7. Solution by the Crank–Nicolson method. We will solve the convection–diffusion problem presented in Section 14.1, using Eq. (14.80) with $\Delta x = 0.1$ cm. The transient solution for $\Delta t = 0.5$ s, for which $c = d = 0.5$, is presented in Fig. 14.30. These results are a good approximation of the exact solution. The asymptotic steady state solutions presented in Fig. 14.31 are identical to the results obtained by the BTCS method, which are presented in Fig. 14.27.

Fig. 14.32 presents the numerical solution for $\Delta t = 5.0$ s, for which $c = d = 5.0$. These results are stable, and the asymptotic steady state solution is the same as for the smaller time step. However, the transient solution is not very good. The results presented in Fig. 14.32 suggest that values of c and d much larger than 1.0 lead to serious decreases in the accuracy of transient solutions.

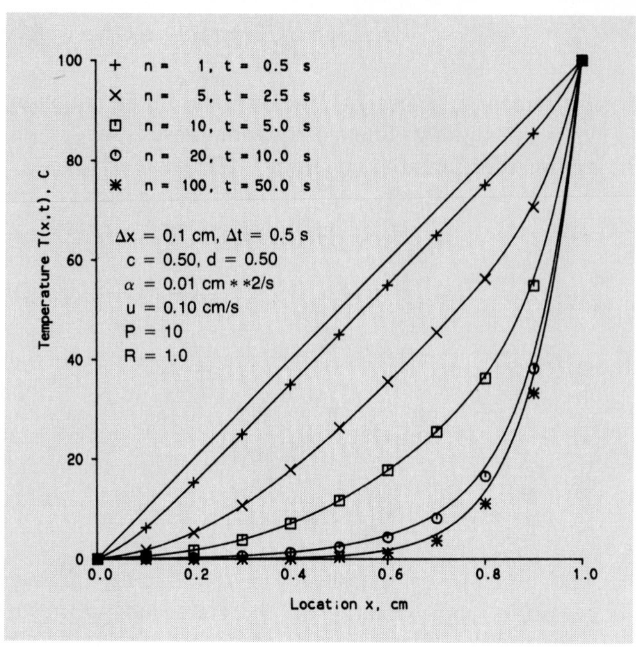

FIGURE 14.30
Transient solution by the Crank–Nicolson method for $P = 10$.

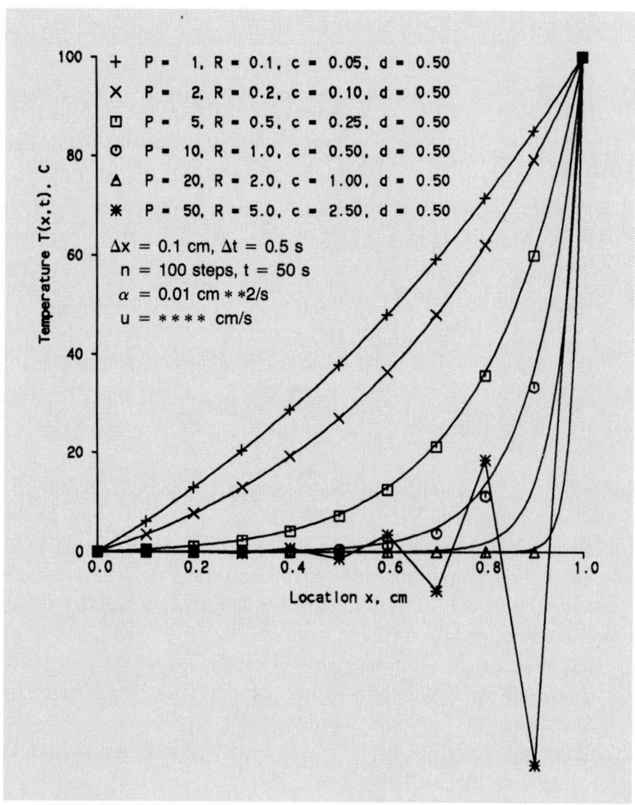

FIGURE 14.31
Steady-state solutions by the Crank–Nicolson method.

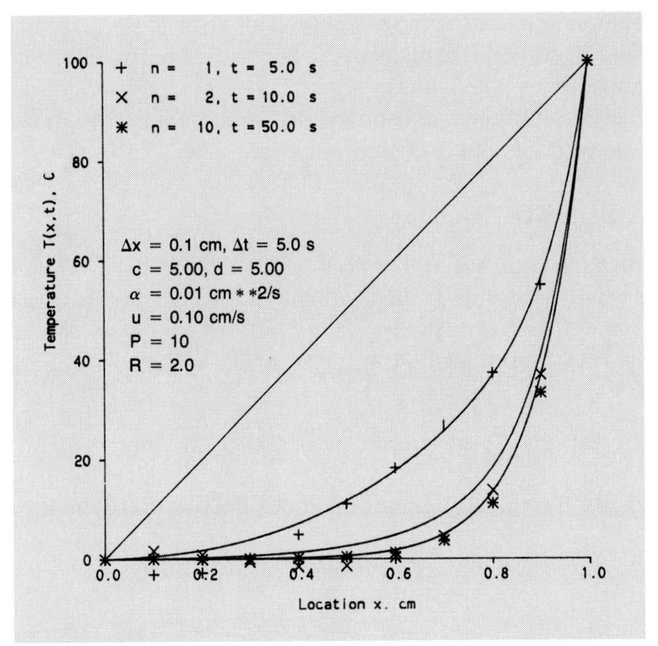

FIGURE 14.32
Transient solution by the Crank–Nicolson method for $P = 10$ with $c = 5.0$ and $d = 5.0$.

The results presented in Fig. 14.28 using the BTCS method with a large time step behave quite differently from the results presented in Fig. 14.32. Neither method gives accurate transient solutions for large time steps. Both methods give accurate asymptotic steady state solutions using large time steps. However, the BTCS method approaches the asymptotic steady state solution smoothly as Δt is increased to large values, whereas the Crank–Nicolson method overshoots the steady state solution for large values of Δt and approaches the asymptotic steady state solution in a damped oscillatory manner. These different behaviors occur because the eigenvalues of the BTCS amplification matrix are always positive (and less than 1.0), whereas the eigenvalues of the Crank–Nicolson amplification matrix are negative (but greater than -1.0) for large values of Δt. Basically, the presence of the finite difference approximations of the spatial derivatives at time level n, included in the Crank–Nicolson method to achieve second-order time accuracy, impede the approach to the asymptotic steady state solution, which does not depend on any initial data. Consequently, when solving steady state problems as the asymptotic solution in time of an appropriate unsteady problem, fully implicit methods, such as the BTCS method, should be employed.

The Crank–Nicolson method becomes considerably more complicated when applied to nonlinear PDEs, systems of PDEs, and multidimensional PDEs. A brief introduction to these problems is presented in Section 14.13.

In summary, the Crank–Nicolson approximation of the convection–diffusion equation is implicit, two-level, single-step, $O(\Delta t^2)+O(\Delta x^2)$, unconditionally stable, and convergent. The implicit nature of the method yields a set of finite difference equations, which must be solved simultaneously. For one-dimensional problems, that can be accomplished by the Thomas algorithm. The Crank–Nicolson approximation of the convection–diffusion equation yields good transient solutions for modest values of the convection and diffusion numbers.

14.11 THE KELLER BOX METHOD

The Keller (1970) box method is an $O(\Delta t^2) + O(\Delta x^2)$ method that allows the physical grid spacing to be nonuniform. In this section, the Keller box method is applied to the convection–diffusion equation $\bar{f}_t + u\bar{f}_x = \alpha\bar{f}_{xx}$, which can be written as the following pair of first-order PDEs:

$$\bar{f}_x = \bar{g} \tag{14.84}$$

$$\bar{f}_t + u\bar{f}_x = \alpha\bar{g}_x \tag{14.85}$$

The finite difference stencils for the Keller box method are illustrated in Fig. 14.33.

Equation (14.84) is approximated at grid point $(i - \frac{1}{2}, n + 1)$ as

$$f_i^{n+1} - f_{i-1}^{n+1} = g_{i-1/2}^{n+1}\,\Delta x_i = \frac{\Delta x_i}{2}(g_i^{n+1} + g_{i-1}^{n+1}) \tag{14.86}$$

where the second-order centered-difference approximation is used for the derivative, $\bar{g}_{i-1/2}^{n+1}$ is evaluated as an average between $(i, n+1)$ and $(i-1, n+1)$, and $\Delta x_i = (x_i - x_{i-1})$. Equation (14.85) is approximated at grid point $(i - \frac{1}{2}, n + \frac{1}{2})$ as

$$(f_i^{n+1} + f_{i-1}^{n+1}) - (f_i^n + f_{i-1}^n) + \frac{u\,\Delta t}{\Delta x_i}\Big((f_i^{n+1} + f_i^n) - (f_{i-1}^{n+1} + f_{i-1}^n)\Big)$$
$$= \frac{\alpha\,\Delta t}{\Delta x_i}\Big((g_i^{n+1} + g_i^n) - (g_{i-1}^{n+1} + g_{i-1}^n)\Big) \tag{14.87}$$

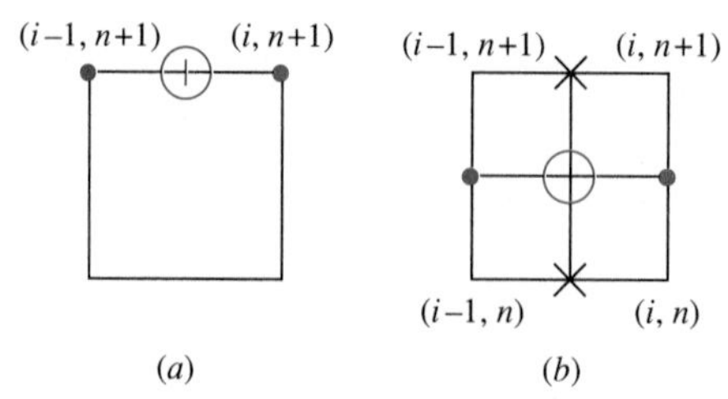

FIGURE 14.33
Keller box method stencils. (a) Eq. 14.84. (b) Eq. (14.85).

where second-order centered-difference approximations are used for the derivatives and all function values at midintervals are evaluated as appropriate averages.

Now consider the solution of the unsteady one-dimensional convection–diffusion equation by the Keller box method. The finite difference grid for advancing the solution from time level n to time level $n+1$ is illustrated in Fig. 14.33. Equations (14.86) and (14.87), when applied to the $(imax-1)$ spatial intervals, yield a coupled set of linear algebraic equations for f^{n+1} and g^{n+1}. Each equation contains two variables (i.e., f and g) at two mesh points. The matrix equation for this set of finite difference equations has the block tridiagonal structure discussed in Section 1.5, where the blocks are 2×2 matrices. Some care is required with the first and last set of equations which correspond to the first and last grid increments, respectively, because f_1^{n+1} and f_{imax}^{n+1} are specified by the boundary conditions, whereas g_1^{n+1} and g_{imax}^{n+1} are both unknown. This system of equations can be solved very efficiently by the block tridiagonal algorithm presented in Section 1.5. Note that Δx_i can vary from point to point. The variable grid size capability is the major advantage of the Keller box method. The method is well suited for the use of extrapolation, thus yielding higher-order results with a relatively simple algorithm.

For a uniform grid (i.e., $\Delta x_i = \Delta x$) and a single simple PDE such as the one-dimensional convection–diffusion equation, the system of coupled finite difference equations [i.e., Eqs. (14.86) and (14.87)] can be combined to yield a single FDE. First, apply Eq. (14.86) at spatial location $i+1$ by replacing all values of i with $i+1$, subtract that result from Eq. (14.86), and apply that result at time level n by replacing all values of n with $n+1$. Then apply Eq. (14.87) at spatial location $i+1$ by replacing all values of i with $i+1$, and add the result to Eq. (14.87). Combining the result of the first step with the result of the second step yields the single FDE

$$\boxed{\begin{aligned}&(1+c-2d)f_{i+1}^{n+1} + 2(1+2d)f_i^{n+1} + (1-c-2d)f_{i-1}^{n+1}\\ &= (1-c+2d)f_{i+1}^{n} + 2(1-2d)f_i^{n} + (1+c+2d)f_{i-1}^{n}\end{aligned}} \tag{14.88}$$

where $c = u\,\Delta t/\Delta x$ is the convection number and $d = \alpha\,\Delta t/\Delta x^2$ is the diffusion number. Equation (14.88) is the Keller box approximation of the linear convection–diffusion equation for uniform Δx.

The first form of the modified differential equation (MDE) is

$$\begin{aligned}f_t + uf_x &= \alpha f_{xx} - \frac{1}{24}f_{ttt}\,\Delta t^2 - \cdots - \frac{1}{6}uf_{xxx}\,\Delta x^2 - \frac{1}{8}uf_{xtt}\,\Delta t^2 + \cdots\\ &\quad + \frac{1}{12}\alpha f_{xxxx}\,\Delta x^2 + \frac{1}{8}\alpha f_{xxtt}\,\Delta t^2 + \cdots - \frac{1}{4}f_{xxt}\,\Delta x^2 + \cdots\end{aligned} \tag{14.89}$$

and the second form of the MDE is

$$f_t + uf_x = \alpha f_{xx} + \left(-\frac{1}{12}u^3\,\Delta t^2 + \frac{1}{12}u\,\Delta x^2\right)f_{xxx} + \left(\frac{1}{4}u^2\alpha\,\Delta t^2 - \frac{1}{6}\alpha\,\Delta x^2\right)f_{xxxx} + \cdots \tag{14.90}$$

As $\Delta t \to 0$ and $\Delta x \to 0$, Eq. (14.89) approaches $f_t + uf_x = \alpha f_{xx}$. Consequently, Eq. (14.88) is a consistent approximation of the convection–diffusion equation. From Eq. (14.90), the truncation error is $O(\Delta t^2) + O(\Delta x^2)$. Both even and odd spatial derivatives appear in Eq. (14.90), so implicit numerical diffusion and dispersion are both present. The amplification factor G is

$$G = \frac{(1 + \cos\theta) - 2d(1 - \cos\theta) - Ic\sin\theta}{(1 + \cos\theta) + 2d(1 - \cos\theta) + Ic\sin\theta} \tag{14.91}$$

The term $(1 - \cos\theta) \geq 0$ for all values of $\theta = k\Delta x$. Consequently, the real part of the numerator is less than or equal to the real part of the denominator, so the magnitude of the numerator is less than or equal to the magnitude of the denominator. Consequently, $|G| \leq 1$ for all positive values of c and d, and Eq. (14.88) is unconditionally stable. Thus, by the Lax equivalence theorem, Eq. (14.88) is a convergent approximation of the convection–diffusion equation.

Example 14.8. Solution by the Keller box method. We will solve the convection–diffusion problem presented in Section 14.1, using Eq. (14.88) with $\Delta x = 0.1$ cm. The transient solution for $\Delta t = 0.5$ s, for which $c = d = 0.5$, is presented in Fig. 14.34. These results are similar to the results obtained by the Crank–Nicolson method, which are presented in Fig. 14.30. Fig. 14.35 presents the asymptotic steady state solutions. These results and the conclusions drawn from them are the same as presented in Example 14.7 for the Crank–Nicolson method.

The Keller box method becomes considerably more complicated when applied to nonlinear PDEs, systems of PDEs, and multidimensional PDEs. A brief introduction to these problems is presented in Section 14.13.

In summary, the Keller box approximation of the convection–diffusion equation is implicit, two-level, single-step, $O(\Delta t^2) + O(\Delta x^2)$, unconditionally stable, and convergent. The major advantage of the method is that the physical grid spacing can be nonuniform. Due to the implicit nature of the finite difference equations, a system of FDEs must be solved simultaneously, by the Thomas algorithm for example. The Keller box approximation of the convection–diffusion equation yields good transient solutions for modest values of the convection and diffusion numbers.

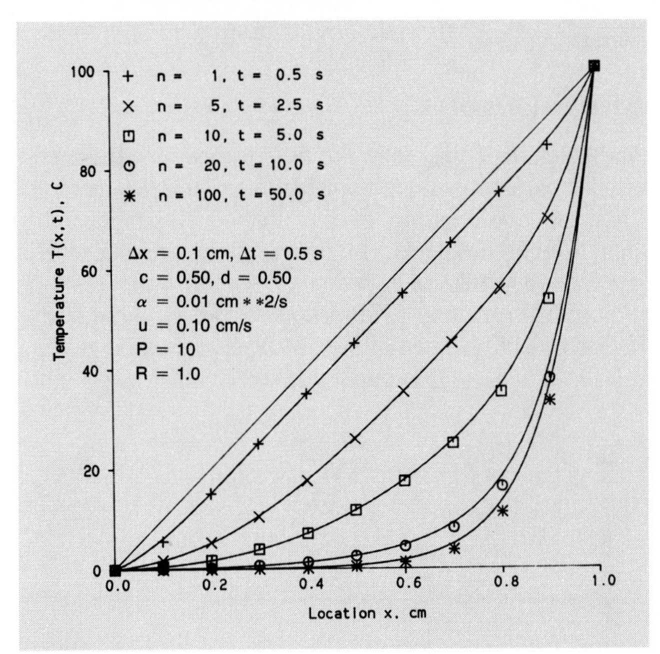

FIGURE 14.34
Transient solution by the Keller box method for $P = 10$.

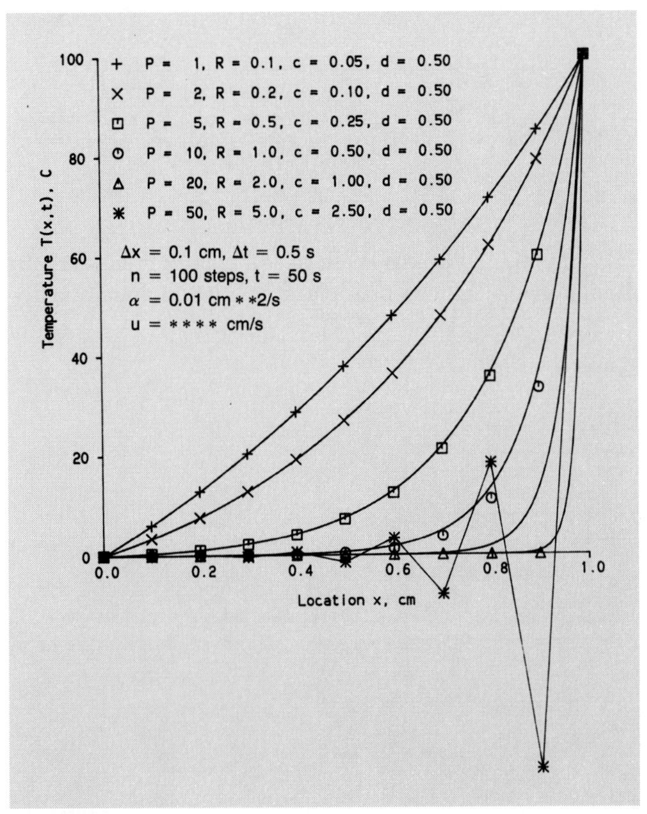

FIGURE 14.35
Steady-state solutions by the Keller box method.

14.12 THE HOPSCOTCH METHOD

The hopscotch method is an interesting combination of the forward-time centered-space (FTCS) method and the backward-time centered-space (BTCS) method. Gourlay (1970) presents a detailed discussion of the method. It is generally used in two- and three-dimensional problems. In this section, the hopscotch method is applied to the convection–diffusion equation $\bar{f}_t + u\bar{f}_x = \alpha\bar{f}_{xx}$.

The basic idea of the hopscotch method is to make two sweeps through the solution domain at each time step, as illustrated in Fig. 14.36. On the first sweep, the explicit FTCS method [see Eq. (14.14)] is applied at every other grid point. Thus,

$$f_i^{n+1} = f_i^n - \frac{c}{2}(f_{i+1}^n - f_{i-1}^n) + d(f_{i+1}^n - 2f_i^n + f_{i-1}^n) \tag{14.92}$$

On the second sweep, the implicit BTCS method [see Eq. (14.75)] is applied at the remaining points. Equation (14.75) appears to be implicit, but the values of $f_{i\pm1}^{n+1}$ are known from the first sweep through the grid with the explicit FTCS method. Consequently, Eq. (14.75) can be solved explicitly for f_i^{n+1} to give

$$(1 + 2d)f_i^{n+1} = f_i^n + \left(\frac{1}{2}c + d\right)f_{i-1}^{n+1} - \left(\frac{1}{2}c - d\right)f_{i+1}^{n+1} \tag{14.93}$$

The pattern of explicit points and implicit points is alternated at each time level, as illustrated in Fig. 14.36. Equation (14.92) can be replaced by the computationally

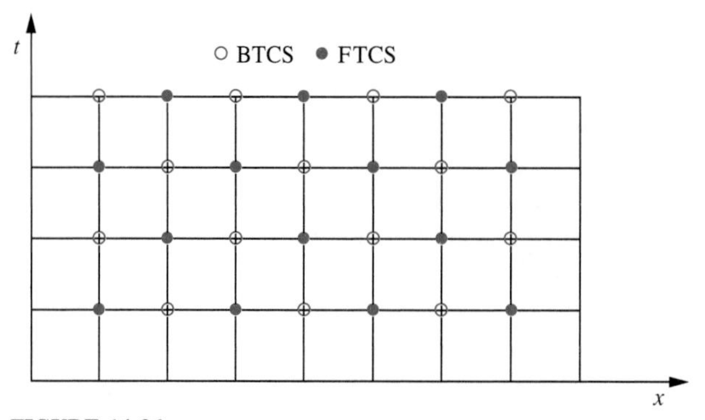

FIGURE 14.36
Hopscotch method sweep pattern.

simpler equivalent equation

$$f_i^{n+2} = 2f_i^{n+1} - f_i^n \tag{14.94}$$

which further increases the efficiency of the method. Equation (14.92) must be used on the first time step, but Eq. (14.94) can be used at all subsequent time steps.

The hopscotch method, applied to the convection–diffusion equation, is consistent, $O(\Delta t) + O(\Delta x^2)$, and conditionally stable (i.e., $c \le 1$). There is no stability restriction on the diffusion number d.

Example 14.9. Solution by the hopscotch method. We will solve the convection–diffusion problem presented in Section 14.1, for $\Delta x = 0.1$ cm, using the hopscotch method. The BTCS method is used at odd values of i on the first time step. The transient solution for $\Delta t = 0.5$ s, for which $c = d = 0.5$, is presented in Fig. 14.37. The asymptotic steady state solutions are presented in Fig. 14.38. These results are a reasonable approximation of the exact solution.

Extending the explicit hopscotch method to solve nonlinear PDEs complicates the solution, since the nonlinear coefficients are unknown at the base point

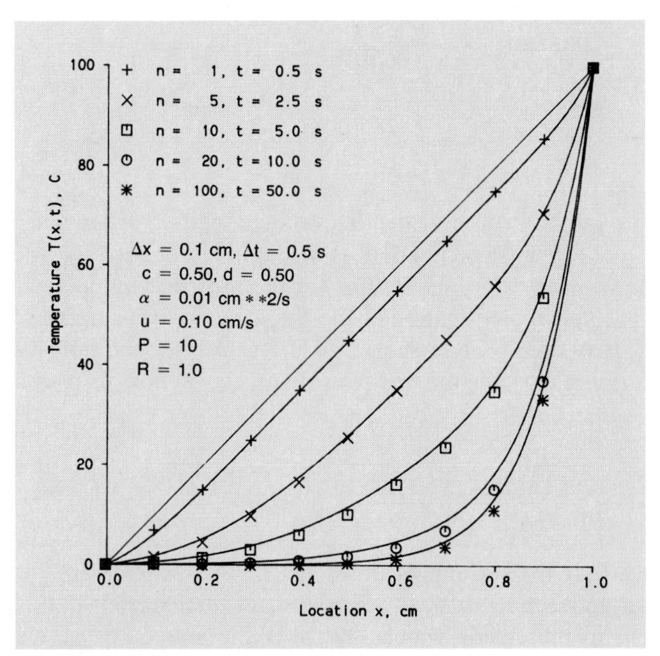

FIGURE 14.37
Transient solution by the hopscotch method for P = 10.

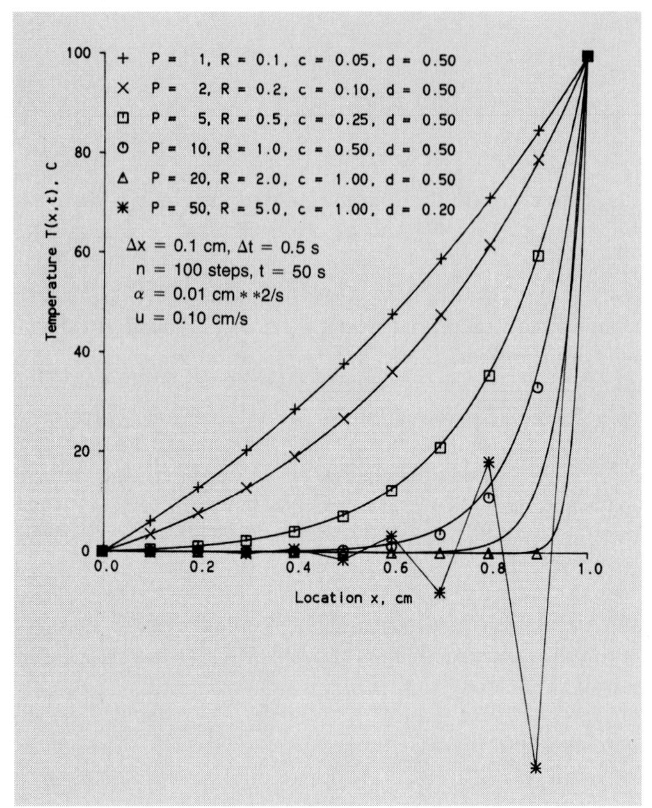

FIGURE 14.38
Steady-state solutions by the hopscotch method.

for the BTCS method. The method can be extended in a straightforward manner to systems of PDEs and multidimensional PDEs, as discussed in Section 14.13. Some problems may arise with boundary conditions for the implicit points.

In summary, the hopscotch approximation of the convection–diffusion equation is explicit, two-level, two-sweep single-step, $O(\Delta t) + O(\Delta x^2)$, conditionally stable, and convergent. It is a reasonable method for solving convection–diffusion problems.

14.13 NONLINEAR EQUATIONS AND MULTIDIMENSIONAL PROBLEMS

The finite difference equations and examples presented in this chapter are for the linear one-dimensional convection–diffusion equation. In each section in this chapter, a brief paragraph is presented, which discusses the suitability of the method for solving nonlinear equations and multidimensional problems. The additional complexities associated with solving nonlinear equations and multidimensional problems are discussed in considerable detail in Section 11.8 for the parabolic diffusion equation. The techniques discussed there apply directly to finite difference methods for solving the convection–diffusion equation.

Generally speaking, explicit methods can be extended directly to solve nonlinear and multidimensional convection–diffusion problems. Implicit methods, on the other hand, yield systems of nonlinear FDEs when applied to nonlinear PDEs. Methods for solving systems of nonlinear FDEs are discussed in Section 11.8. When applied to multidimensional problems, implicit methods result in large banded systems of FDEs. Methods for solving such problems are also discussed in Section 11.8.

SUMMARY

The numerical solution of the parabolic convection–diffusion equation by finite difference methods is discussed in this chapter. Explicit finite difference methods, as typified by the FTCS method, are conditionally stable and require a relatively small step size in the marching direction to satisfy stability criteria. Accurate solutions of transient problems can be obtained by explicit methods. Implicit methods, as typified by the BTCS method, are unconditionally stable. The marching step size is restricted by accuracy requirements, not stability requirements. For accurate solutions of transient problems, the marching step size for implicit methods cannot be very much larger than the stable step size for explicit methods. Asymptotic steady state solutions, on the other hand, can be obtained very efficiently by the BTCS method with a large marching step size.

Nonlinear partial differential equations can be solved directly by explicit methods. When nonlinear PDEs are solved by implicit methods, systems of nonlinear FDEs result and must be solved. Multidimensional problems can be solved directly by explicit methods. When solved by implicit methods, large banded systems of FDEs result. Alternating-direction implicit (ADI) methods and approximate-factorization implicit (AFI) methods, which are discussed in Section 11.8, can be used to solve multidimensional problems.

PROBLEMS

Section 14.1 Introduction

1. Consider the unsteady one-dimensional convection–diffusion equation $\bar{f}_t + u\bar{f}_x = \alpha\bar{f}_{xx}$. Classify this PDE. Determine the characteristic curves. Discuss the significance of these results as regards domain of dependence, range of influence, signal propagation speed, auxiliary conditions, and numerical solution procedures.
2. Develop the exact solution for the heat transfer problem presented in Section 14.1, Eqs. (14.7) and (14.13).
3. By hand calculation, evaluate the exact solution of the heat transfer problem for $P = 10$ for $T(0.8, 5.0)$ and $T(0.8, \infty)$.
4. Write a computer program to evaluate the exact solution of the heat transfer problem. Use the program to reproduce Tables 14.1 and 14.2.

Section 14.2 The Forward-Time Centered-Space Method

5. Derive the FTCS approximation of the unsteady one-dimensional convection–diffusion equation, Eq. (14.14), including the leading truncation error terms in Δt and Δx.
6. Derive the first and approximate second forms of the MDE corresponding to Eq. (14.14). Analyze consistency, order, and implicit numerical diffusion and dispersion.
7. Perform a von Neumann stability analysis of Eq. (14.14).
8. By hand calculation, determine the solution of the example heat transfer problem for $P = 10$ at $t = 1.0$ s by the FTCS method for $\Delta x = 0.1$ cm and $\Delta t = 0.5$ s. Compare the results with the exact solution in Table 14.1.
9. Write a computer program to implement the numerical solution of the example heat transfer problem by the FTCS method. Use the program to reproduce the results presented in Fig. 14.6.
10. Use the program developed in Problem 9 to reproduce the results presented in Fig. 14.7.
11. Use the program developed in Problem 9 to reproduce the results presented in Fig. 14.8.
12. Use the program developed in Problem 9 to reproduce the results presented in Fig. 14.9.

Section 14.3 The Lax and Richardson (Leapfrog) Methods

13. Derive the Lax approximation of the unsteady one-dimensional convection–diffusion equation, including the leading truncation error terms in Δt and Δx.
14. Perform a von Neumann stability analysis of the Lax FDE.
15. Derive the Richardson (leapfrog) approximation of the unsteady one-dimensional convection–diffusion equation, including the leading truncation error terms in Δt and Δx.
16. Perform a von Neumann stability analysis of the Richardson (leapfrog) FDE.

Section 14.4 Upwind Methods

17. Derive the first-order upwind approximation of the unsteady one-dimensional convection–diffusion equation for $u > 0$, Eq. (14.31), including the leading truncation error terms in Δt and Δx.
18. Derive the first and approximate second forms of the MDE corresponding to Eq. (14.31). Analyze consistency, order, and implicit numerical diffusion and dispersion.
19. Perform a von Neumann stability analysis of Eq. (14.31).
20. By hand calculation, determine the solution of the example heat transfer problem for $P = 10$ at $t = 0.5$ s by the first-order upwind method for $\Delta x = 0.1$ cm and $\Delta t = 0.25$ s.
21. Write a computer program to implement the numerical solution of the example heat transfer problem by the first-order upwind method. Use the program for $\Delta x = 0.1$ cm and $\Delta t = 0.25$ s to reproduce the results presented in Figs. 14.11 and 14.12.
22. An $O(\Delta x^2)$ upwind approximation of the unsteady one-dimensional convection–diffusion equation can be developed by using a second-order backward-difference approximation for $\bar{f}_x$. (*a*) Derive the FDE, including the leading truncation error terms in Δt and Δx. (*b*) Derive the first and approximate second forms of the corresponding MDE. Analyze consistency and order. (*c*) Perform a von Neumann stability analysis of this FDE to determine the amplification factor G. Analyze G as described in Section 14.5.

Section 14.5 The Leonard Method

23. Derive the Leonard approximation of the unsteady one-dimensional convection–diffusion equation, Eq. (14.41), including the leading truncation error terms in Δt and Δx.
24. Derive the first and approximate second forms of the MDE corresponding to Eq. (14.41). Analyze consistency, order, and implicit numerical diffusion and dispersion.
25. Perform a von Neumann stability analysis of Eq. (14.41) to determine the amplification factor G. Analyze G as described in Section 14.5.
26. By hand calculation, determine the solution of the example heat transfer problem for $P = 10$ at $t = 1.0$ s by the Leonard method for $\Delta x = 0.1$ cm and $\Delta t = 0.25$ s.
27. Write a computer program to implement the numerical solution of the example heat transfer problem by the Leonard method. Use the program to reproduce the results presented in Figs. 14.15 and 14.16. Use the exact solution at $x = 0.1$ cm.

Section 14.6 The DuFort–Frankel Method

28. Derive the DuFort–Frankel approximation of the unsteady one-dimensional convection–diffusion equation, Eq. (14.46), including the leading truncation error terms in Δt and Δx.
29. Derive the first and approximate second forms of the MDE corresponding to Eq. (14.46). Analyze consistency, order, and implicit numerical diffusion and dispersion.
30. Perform a von Neumann stability analysis of Eq. (14.46) to determine the amplification factor G.
31. By hand calculation, determine the solution of the example heat transfer problem for $P = 10$ at $t = 1.0$ s by the DuFort–Frankel method for $\Delta x = 0.1$ cm and $\Delta t = 0.5$ s.
32. Write a computer program to implement the numerical solution of the example heat transfer problem by the DuFort–Frankel method. Use the program to reproduce the results presented in Figs. 14.18 and 14.19.

Section 14.7 Lax–Wendroff Type Methods

33. Derive the Adams–Bashforth approximation of the unsteady one-dimensional convection–diffusion equation, including the leading truncation error terms in Δt and Δx.
34. Derive the first and approximate second forms of the MDE corresponding to the FDE developed in Problem 33. Analyze consistency, order, and implicit numerical diffusion and dispersion.
35. Work Problem 34 for the Brailovskaya FDE, Eq. (14.54).
36. Work Problem 34 for the Allen–Cheng FDE, Eq. (14.56).

Section 14.8 The MacCormack Method

37. Develop the MacCormack approximation of the unsteady one-dimensional convection–diffusion equation, Eqs. (14.62), (14.64), (14.67), and (14.68), including the leading truncation error terms. Combine the two-step FDEs to obtain the single step FDE, Eq. (14.69), for the linear case.
38. Derive the first and approximate second forms of the MDE corresponding to Eq. (14.69). Analyze consistency, order, and implicit numerical diffusion and dispersion.

39. Perform a von Neumann stability analysis of Eq. (14.69). (*a*) Derive the amplification factor G. (*b*) Analyze G numerically to obtain the results presented in Fig. 14.22.

40. By hand calculation, determine the solution of the example heat transfer problem for $P = 10$ at $t = 1.0$ s by the MacCormack method for $\Delta x = 0.1$ cm and $\Delta t = 0.5$ s.

41. Write a computer program to implement the numerical solution of the example heat transfer problem by the MacCormack method. Use the program to reproduce the results presented in Figs. 14.23 and 14.24.

42. Use the program developed in Problem 41 to solve Problem 41 for $\Delta x = 0.05$ cm and $\Delta t = 0.125$ s. Compare the errors and the ratios of the errors for the two solutions at $t = 5.0$ s.

43. Work Problem 37 using a backward predictor and a forward corrector.

44. Derive the first and approximate second forms of the MDE corresponding to the FDE developed in Problem 43. Analyze consistency, order, and implicit numerical diffusion and dispersion.

45. Work Problem 40 using the FDEs developed in Problem 43.

46. Work Problem 41 using the FDEs developed in Problem 43.

47. Work Problem 42 using the program developed in Problem 46.

Section 14.9 The Backward-Time Centered-Space Method

48. Derive the BTCS approximation of the unsteady one-dimensional convection–diffusion equation, Eq. (14.75), including the leading truncation error terms in Δt and Δx.

49. Derive the first and approximate second forms of the MDE corresponding to Eq. (14.75). Analyze consistency, order, and implicit numerical diffusion and dispersion.

50. Perform a von Neumann stability analysis of Eq. (14.75).

51. By hand calculation, determine the solution of the example heat transfer problem for $P = 10$ at $t = 1.0$ s with $\Delta x = 0.1$ cm and $\Delta t = 1.0$ s.

52. By hand calculation, estimate the asymptotic steady state solution of the example heat transfer problem for $P = 10$ with $\Delta x = 0.1$ cm by letting $\Delta t = 1000.0$ s.

53. Write a computer program to implement the numerical solution of the example heat transfer problem by the BTCS method. Use the program to reproduce the results presented in Figs. 14.26 and 14.27.

54. Use the program developed in Problem 53 to solve Problem 53 for $\Delta x = 0.05$ cm and $\Delta t = 0.25$ s. Compare the errors and the ratios of the errors for the two solutions at $t = 5.0$ s.

55. Use the program developed in Problem 53 to reproduce the results presented in Fig. 14.27. Use large values of Δt to reach the asymptotic steady state solution as rapidly as possible.

Section 14.10 The Crank–Nicolson Method

56. Derive the Crank–Nicolson approximation of the unsteady one-dimensional convection–diffusion equation, Eq. (14.80), including the leading truncation error terms in Δt and Δx.

57. Derive the first and approximate second forms of the MDE corresponding to Eq. (14.80). Analyze consistency, order, and implicit numerical diffusion and dispersion.

58. Perform a von Neumann stability analysis of Eq. (14.80).

59. By hand calculation, determine the solution of the example heat transfer problem for $P = 10$ at $t = 1.0$ s with $\Delta x = 1.0$ cm and $\Delta t = 1.0$ s.

60. Write a computer program to implement the numerical solution of the example heat transfer problem by the Crank–Nicolson method. Use the program to reproduce the results presented in Figs. 14.29 and 14.30.

61. Use the program developed in Problem 60 to solve Problem 60 for $\Delta x = 0.05$ cm and $\Delta t = 0.25$ s. Compare the errors and the ratios of the errors for the two solutions at $t = 5.0$ s.

62. Use the program developed in Problem 60 to reproduce the results presented in Fig. 14.30. Use large values of Δt to reach the asymptotic steady state solution as rapidly as possible.

Section 14.11 The Keller Box Method

63. Derive the Keller box approximation of the unsteady one-dimensional convection–diffusion equation, Eqs. (14.86) and (14.87), including the leading truncation error terms in Δt and Δx.

64. For $\Delta x =$ constant, derive Eq. (14.88).

65. Derive the first and approximate second forms of the MDE corresponding to Eq. (14.88). Analyze consistency, order, and implicit numerical diffusion and dispersion.

66. Perform a von Neumann stability analysis of Eq. (14.88).

67. By hand calculation using Eqs. (14.86) and (14.87), determine the solution of the example heat transfer problem for $P = 10$ at $t = 1.0$ s with $\Delta x = 0.1$ cm and $\Delta t = 1.0$ s.

68. Use the geometric coordinate transformation presented in Table 13.1 (by a mirror image reflection) to develop a packed grid near $x = 1.0$ cm. Repeat Problem 67 for this grid.

69. Write a computer program to implement the numerical solution of the example heat transfer problem by the Keller box method. Use the program to reproduce the results presented in Figs. 14.34 and 14.35.

70. Use the program developed in Problem 69 to solve Problem 69 for $\Delta x = 0.05$ cm and $\Delta t = 0.25$ s. Compare the errors and the ratios of the errors for the two solutions at $t = 5.0$ s.

Section 14.12 The Hopscotch Method

71. Derive the hopscotch approximation of the unsteady one-dimensional convection–diffusion equation, Eqs. (14.92) and (14.93), including the leading truncation error terms in Δt and Δx.

72. Derive Eq. (14.94).

73. By hand calculation, determine the solution of the example heat transfer problem for $P = 10$ at $t = 1.0$ s by the hopscotch method for $\Delta x = 0.1$ cm and $\Delta t = 0.5$ s.

74. Write a computer program to implement the numerical solution of the example heat transfer problem by the hopscotch method. Use the program to reproduce the results presented in Figs. 14.37 and 14.38.

75. Use the program developed in Problem 74 to solve Problem 74 for $\Delta x = 0.05$ cm and $\Delta t = 0.125$ s. Compare the errors and the ratios of the errors for the two solutions at $t = 5.0$ s.

Section 14.13 Nonlinear Equations and Multidimensional Problems

Problems 39 to 44 in Chapter 11 and Problems 55 to 64 in Chapter 12 illustrate the problems that arise due to nonlinear equations and multidimensional problems. Those problems can be used to demonstrate these effects for the convection–diffusion equation.

76. Derive the FTCS approximation of the unsteady two-dimensional convection–diffusion equation $\bar{f}_t + u\bar{f}_x + v\bar{f}_y = \alpha(\bar{f}_{xx} + \bar{f}_{yy})$.

77. Derive the MDE for the FDE derived in Problem 76.

78. Derive the amplification factor G for the FDE derived in Problem 76.

79. Work Problem 76 using the BTCS method.

80. Derive the MDE for the FDE derived in Problem 79.

81. Derive the amplification factor G for the FDE derived in Problem 79.

CHAPTER

15

HYPERBOLIC PARTIAL DIFFERENTIAL EQUATIONS

The Wave Equation

Section

Example

15.1 INTRODUCTION

The general features of hyperbolic partial differential equations (PDEs) are discussed in Section III.7. An introduction to the numerical solution of hyperbolic PDEs is presented in Section 12.1. Those sections should be reviewed before the present chapter is studied.

Two of the more common hyperbolic PDEs are the convection equation and the wave equation, presented below for the generic dependent variable $\bar{f}(x, t)$:

$$\bar{f}_t + u\bar{f}_x = 0 \tag{15.1}$$

$$\bar{f}_{tt} = a^2\bar{f}_{xx} \tag{15.2}$$

where u is the convection velocity and a is the wave propagation speed. Equation (15.2) is equivalent to the following set of two coupled first-order convection equations:

$$\bar{f}_t + a\bar{g}_x = 0 \tag{15.3}$$

$$\bar{g}_t + a\bar{f}_x = 0 \tag{15.4}$$

Equations (15.3) and (15.4) suggest that the wave equation can be solved by the same methods that are employed to solve the simpler convection equation.

Chapter 12 is devoted to the numerical solution of the convection equation, Eq. (15.1). Most of the concepts, techniques, and conclusions presented in Chapter 12 for solving the convection equation are directly applicable, sometimes with very minor modifications, to solving the wave equation. Consequently, Chapter

12 should be studied before one studies the present chapter, which is devoted to the numerical solution of the wave equation, Eq. (15.2), expressed as a coupled set of convection equations, Eqs. (15.3) and (15.4).

The finite difference grids and finite difference approximations presented in Section 10.4 are used to solve the wave equation. The concepts of consistency, order, stability, and convergence presented in Section 10.6 are directly applicable to the wave equation. In essence, Chapter 10 should be considered as the first part of the present chapter. Chapter 15 is, therefore, a direct continuation of Chapters 10 and 12 to solve the wave equation.

The solution to Eqs. (15.3) and (15.4) consists of the two functions $\bar{f}(x, t)$ and $\bar{g}(x, t)$. These functions must satisfy initial conditions at $t = 0$,

$$\bar{f}(x, 0) = F(x) \qquad \text{and} \qquad \bar{g}(x, 0) = G(x) \tag{15.5}$$

and a set of boundary conditions at $x = 0$ and $x = L$. The boundary conditions may be of the Dirichlet type (i.e., specified $\bar{f}$ and $\bar{g}$), the Neumann type (i.e., specified derivatives of $\bar{f}$ and $\bar{g}$), or the mixed type (i.e., specified combinations of $\bar{f}$ and $\bar{g}$ and the derivatives of $\bar{f}$ and $\bar{g}$).

As discussed in Section 12.1, the exact solution of a single convection equation, for example, Eq. (15.1), is given by

$$\bar{f}(x, t) = F(x - ut) \tag{15.6}$$

which can be demonstrated by direct substitution. Equation (15.6) defines a right-traveling wave, which propagates (i.e., convects) the initial condition to the right at the speed u, unchanged in magnitude and shape.

The exact solution of the wave equation, Eq. (15.2), is given by

$$\bar{f}(x, t) = \mathcal{F}(x - at) + \mathcal{G}(x + at) \tag{15.7}$$

which can be demonstrated by direct substitution. Equation (15.7) represents the superposition of a right-traveling wave, $\mathcal{F}(x - at)$, and a left-traveling wave, $\mathcal{G}(x + at)$, which propagate information to the right and left, respectively, at the wave propagation speed a, unchanged in magnitude and shape. The second-order wave equation requires two initial conditions:

$$\bar{f}(x, 0) = \phi(x) \qquad \text{and} \qquad \bar{f}_t(x, 0) = \theta(x) \tag{15.8}$$

Substituting Eq. (15.8) into Eq. (15.7) gives

$$\phi(x) = \mathcal{F}(x) + \mathcal{G}(x) \tag{15.9}$$

$$\theta(x) = -a\mathcal{F}'(x) + a\mathcal{G}'(x) \tag{15.10}$$

where the prime $'$ denotes ordinary differentiation with respect to the arguments of $\mathcal{F}$ and $\mathcal{G}$. Integrating Eq. (15.10) yields

$$-\mathcal{F}(x) + \mathcal{G}(x) = \frac{1}{a}\int_{x_0}^{x} \theta(\xi)\, d\xi \tag{15.11}$$

where x_0 is a reference location and ξ is a dummy variable. Combining Eqs.

(15.9) and (15.11) gives

$$\mathcal{F}(x) = \frac{1}{2}\left(\phi(x) - \frac{1}{a}\int_{x_0}^{x} \theta(\xi)\, d\xi\right) \qquad \text{and} \qquad \mathcal{G}(x) = \frac{1}{2}\left(\phi(x) + \frac{1}{a}\int_{x_0}^{x} \theta(\xi)\, d\xi\right) \tag{15.12}$$

Substituting Eq. (15.12) into Eq. (15.7) and combining the integrals yields

$$\bar{f}(x, t) = \frac{1}{2}\left(\phi(x - at) + \phi(x + at) + \frac{1}{2a}\int_{x-at}^{x+at} \theta(\xi)\, d\xi\right) \tag{15.13}$$

Equation (15.13) is the exact solution of the wave equation. It is generally called the *d'Alembert solution*.

The wave equation applies to problems of vibrating systems, such as vibrating strings and acoustic fields. Most people have some physical feeling for acoustics, due to its presence in our everyday life. Consequently, the wave equation governing acoustic fields is considered in this chapter to demonstrate numerical methods for solving the wave equation. That equation is presented in Section III.7, Eq. (III.91), which is repeated below:

$$P_{tt} = a^2 P_{xx} \tag{15.14}$$

where P is the acoustic pressure perturbation (N/m^2 = Pascals = Pa) and a is the speed of sound (m/s). The superscript $'$ on P and the subscript 0 on a have been dropped for clarity. Equation (15.14) requires two initial conditions, $P(x, 0)$ and $P_t(x, 0)$. As shown in Section III.7, Eq. (15.14) is obtained by combining Eqs. (III.89) and (III.90), which are repeated below:

$$\rho u_t + P_x = 0 \tag{15.15a}$$

$$P_t + \rho a^2 u_x = 0 \tag{15.15b}$$

where ρ is the density (kg/m^3) and u is the acoustic velocity perturbation (m/s).

The following simple problem is considered in this chapter to illustrate the behavior of several numerical integration methods applied to the wave equation. An infinitely long duct, illustrated in Fig. 15.1, is filled with a stagnant compressible fluid for which the density $\rho = 1.0$ kg/m^3 and the acoustic wave velocity $a = 1000$ m/s. The fluid is initially at rest, $u(x, 0) = 0.0$, and has an initial acoustic pressure distribution given by

$$P(x, 0) = 200(x - 1), \qquad 1.0 \le x \le 1.5 \tag{15.16a}$$

$$P(x, 0) = 200(2 - x), \qquad 1.5 \le x \le 2.0 \tag{15.16b}$$

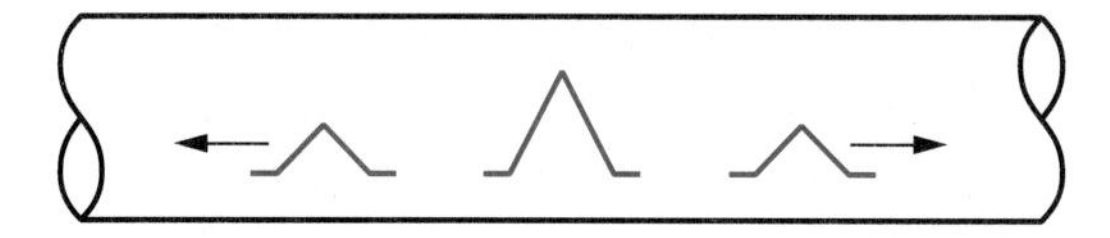

FIGURE 15.1
Acoustic wave propagation in an infinite duct.

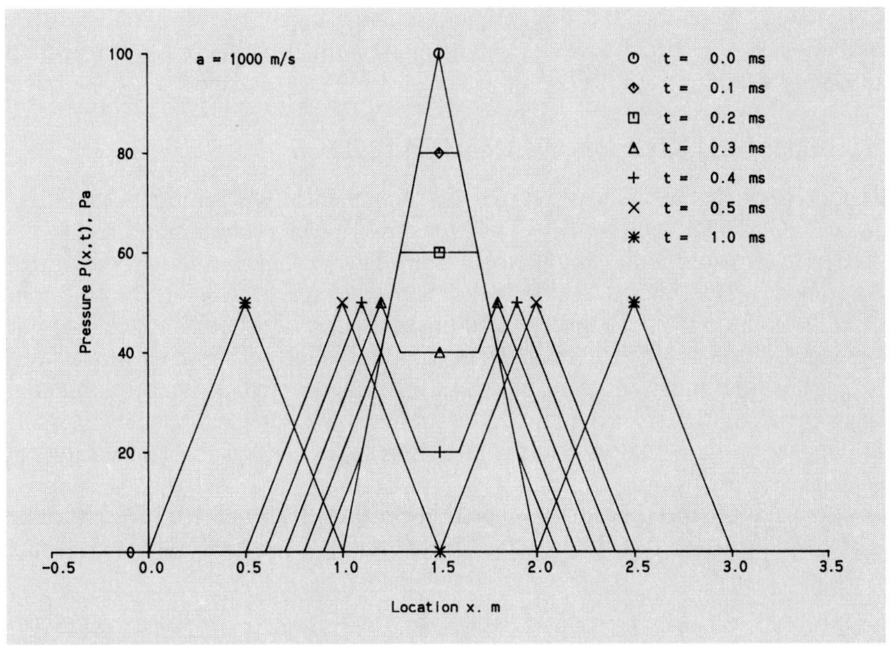

FIGURE 15.2
Exact solution of the acoustics problem.

where P is measured in Pa (i.e., N/m^2) and x is measured in m. This initial pressure distribution appears as the central tall peak in Fig. 15.2. For an infinitely long duct, there are no boundary conditions (except, of course, at infinity, which is not of interest in the present problem). The pressure distribution $P(x, t)$ is required.

For the acoustics problem discussed above, combining Eq. (15.15*b*) and the initial condition $u(x, 0) = 0.0$ shows that $P_t(x, 0) = 0$, so that $\theta(x) = 0$. Combining Eqs. (15.7) and (15.13) shows that

$$\mathcal{F}(x - at) + \mathcal{G}(x + at) = \frac{1}{2}\big(\phi(x - at) + \phi(x + at)\big) \tag{15.17}$$

Equation (15.17) must hold for all combinations of x and t. Thus

$$\mathcal{F}(x - at) = \frac{1}{2}\phi(x - at) \qquad \text{and} \qquad \mathcal{G}(x + at) = \frac{1}{2}\phi(x + at) \tag{15.18}$$

Equation (15.18) shows that at $t = 0$, $\mathcal{F}(x) = \phi(x)/2$ and $\mathcal{G}(x) = \phi(x)/2$. Thus, the exact solution of the acoustics problem consists of the superposition of two identical traveling waves, each having one-half the amplitude of the initial wave. One wave propagates to the right and one wave propagates to the left, both with the wave propagation speed a. Essentially, the initial distribution, which is the superposition of two identical waves, simply decomposes into the two individual waves. The exact solution for several values of time t (in ms) is presented in Fig. 15.2. Note that the discontinuities in the slope of the initial pressure distribution at $x = 1.0$, 1.5, and 2.0 m are preserved during the wave propagation process.

15.2 THE METHOD OF CHARACTERISTICS

The concept of characteristics of partial differential equations is introduced in Section III.3. Characteristics are $(n-1)$-dimensional hypersurfaces in n-dimensional hyperspace (where n is the number of independent variables in the problem) that have some very special features. In two-dimensional space, which is the case considered here (i.e., physical space x and time t), characteristics are lines (curved, in general) in the solution domain $D(x, t)$ along which information propagates. If a partial differential equation possesses real characteristics, then information propagates along the characteristics. The presence of characteristics has a significant impact on the solution of a partial differential equation (by both analytical and numerical methods).

Let us apply the concepts presented in Sections III.3 and III.7 to determine the characteristics of the system of two convection equations [Eqs. (15.3) and (15.4)]:

$$\bar{f}_t + a\bar{g}_x = 0 \tag{15.19}$$

$$\bar{g}_t + a\bar{f}_x = 0 \tag{15.20}$$

Applying the chain rule to the continuous functions $\bar{f}(x, t)$ and $\bar{g}(x, t)$ yields

$$d\bar{f} = \bar{f}_t\,dt + \bar{f}_x\,dx \qquad \text{and} \qquad d\bar{g} = \bar{g}_t\,dt + \bar{g}_x\,dx \tag{15.21}$$

Writing Eqs. (15.19) to (15.21) in matrix form yields

$$\begin{bmatrix} 1 & 0 & 0 & a \\ 0 & a & 1 & 0 \\ dt & dx & 0 & 0 \\ 0 & 0 & dt & dx \end{bmatrix} \begin{bmatrix} \bar{f}_t \\ \bar{f}_x \\ \bar{g}_t \\ \bar{g}_x \end{bmatrix} = \begin{bmatrix} 0 \\ 0 \\ d\bar{f} \\ d\bar{g} \end{bmatrix} \tag{15.22}$$

The characteristics of Eqs. (15.19) and (15.20) are determined by setting the determinant of the coefficient matrix of Eq. (15.22) equal to zero. This gives the characteristic equation

$$(1)\left(-(dx)^2\right) + dt(a^2\,dt) = 0 \tag{15.23}$$

Solving Eq. (15.23) for dx/dt gives

$$\boxed{\frac{dx}{dt} = \pm a} \tag{15.24}$$

Equation (15.24) shows that there are two distinct real roots associated with the characteristic equation. The physical speed of propagation of information, c, along the characteristic curves is

$$c = \frac{dx}{dt} = \pm a \tag{15.25}$$

Consequently, information propagates in both the positive and negative x directions at the wave speed a.

The compatibility equation that is valid along the characteristic curves is obtained as follows. Consider the generic dependent variable $\bar{f}(x, t)$. The total differential of $\bar{f}(x, t)$ is given by

$$d\bar{f} = \bar{f}_t\, dt + \bar{f}_x\, dx = \left(\bar{f}_t + \frac{dx}{dt}\bar{f}_x\right) dt \tag{15.26}$$

Along the characteristic curves, the physical signal propagation speed $dx/dt = \pm a$. Consequently, along the characteristic curves, Eq. (15.26) becomes

$$\frac{d\bar{f}}{dt} = (\bar{f}_t \pm a\bar{f}_x) \tag{15.27}$$

A similar expression can be derived for $d\bar{g}/dt$.

Equations (15.19) and (15.20) can be put into the form of Eq. (15.27) by adding Eq. (15.20) to Eq. (15.19) to give

$$(\bar{f}_t + a\bar{f}_x) + (\bar{g}_t + a\bar{g}_x) = 0 \tag{15.28a}$$

and subtracting Eq. (15.20) from Eq. (15.19) to give

$$(\bar{f}_t - a\bar{f}_x) - (\bar{g}_t - a\bar{g}_x) = 0 \tag{15.28b}$$

Comparing Eqs. (15.27) and (15.28) shows that the terms in parentheses in Eq. (15.28) are simply $d\bar{f}/dt$ and $d\bar{g}/dt$ along the characteristic curves. Consequently, Eq. (15.28) can be written as

$$d\bar{f} + d\bar{g} = 0 \quad \text{along} \quad \frac{dx}{dt} = +a \tag{15.29a}$$

$$d\bar{f} - d\bar{g} = 0 \quad \text{along} \quad \frac{dx}{dt} = -a \tag{15.29b}$$

Equations (15.29) are the compatibility equations corresponding to Eqs. (15.19) and (15.20).

For the linear wave equation represented by the pair of coupled first-order convection equations, the characteristic equation, Eq. (15.24), can be integrated to give

$$x = x_0 \pm a(t - t_0) \tag{15.30}$$

and the compatibility equations, Eq. (15.29), can be integrated to yield

$$\bar{f} + \bar{g} = \bar{f}_0 + \bar{g}_0 = R_+ \quad \text{along} \quad \frac{dx}{dt} = +a \tag{15.31a}$$

$$\bar{f} - \bar{g} = \bar{f}_0 - \bar{g}_0 = R_- \quad \text{along} \quad \frac{dx}{dt} = -a \tag{15.31b}$$

where x_0 is the initial location of the characteristic curve at time t_0, $\bar{f}_0$ and $\bar{g}_0$ are the values of $\bar{f}(x, t_0)$ and $\bar{g}(x, t_0)$ at that location, and the constants of integration R_+ and R_- are called *Riemann invariants*.

For the single linear convection equation considered in Section 12.2, only one family of characteristic curves exists (i.e., right-running waves), and the dependent variable is constant along each characteristic curve of that family. For the linear wave equation, two families of characteristic curves exist (i.e., right-running and left-running waves), and the Riemann invariants R_+ and R_- are constant along each characteristic curve of the appropriate family. Essentially, two waves are propagating, one in the $+x$ direction and one in the $-x$ direction. Each wave carries with it a particular value of R_+ or R_-, respectively. The values of $\bar{f}$ and $\bar{g}$ at any point can be determined from the values of the Reimann invariants R_+ and R_- at that point by solving Eqs. (15.31a) and (15.31b) simultaneously.

In the nonlinear case, where the wave speed a is not constant, the characteristic curves are given by

$$x = x_0 \pm \int a\, dt \tag{15.32}$$

In many cases, the speed of propagation a depends on one or more of the properties being propagated, that is, $\bar{f}(x, t)$ and $\bar{g}(x, t)$. In such cases, Eq. (15.32) may require numerical integration.

Frequently a nonhomogeneous term is present in the convection equations. In that case, Eqs. (15.19) and (15.20) become

$$\bar{f}_t + a\bar{g}_x = \bar{F}(x, t, \bar{f}, \bar{g}) \tag{15.33a}$$

$$\bar{g}_t + a\bar{f}_x = \bar{G}(x, t, \bar{f}, \bar{g}) \tag{15.33b}$$

and Eq. (15.29) becomes

$$d\bar{f} + d\bar{g} = (\bar{F} + \bar{G})\, dt \quad \text{along} \quad \frac{dx}{dt} = +a \tag{15.34a}$$

$$d\bar{f} - d\bar{g} = (\bar{F} - \bar{G})\, dt \quad \text{along} \quad \frac{dx}{dt} = -a \tag{15.34b}$$

Integrating Eq. (15.34) yields

$$\bar{f} + \bar{g} = \bar{f}_0 + \bar{g}_0 + \int (\bar{F} + \bar{G})\, dt \qquad \text{along } \frac{dx}{dt} = +a \tag{15.35a}$$

$$\bar{f} - \bar{g} = \bar{f}_0 - \bar{g}_0 + \int (\bar{F} - \bar{G})\, dt \qquad \text{along } \frac{dx}{dt} = -a \tag{15.35b}$$

which may also require numerical integration. In general, Eqs. (15.32) and (15.35) are coupled, so they must be solved simultaneously.

The concept of characteristics presented in this section identifies special curves in the solution domain, called characteristic curves, along which linear combinations of the governing partial differential equations become total differential equations, called compatibility equations. Characteristics are the paths of propagation of information in the physical space. The presence of characteristics must be accounted for in the numerical solution of hyperbolic PDEs. They can be used directly to solve the PDEs by numerically constructing the characteristic curves and numerically integrating the compatibility equation along the characteristic curves. Such a procedure, called the *numerical method of characteristics*, is presented in Section 15.10.

Hyperbolic PDEs can also be solved numerically by replacing both the time and space derivatives by finite difference approximations on a fixed finite difference grid, as done in Chapter 12 for the convection equation. In that case, the characteristic curves govern the allowable step size in time and determine the allowable boundary conditions. Such procedures are presented in Sections 15.3 to 15.9 and 15.11 to 15.14.

15.3 THE FORWARD-TIME CENTERED-SPACE METHOD

The most straightforward finite difference method for solving hyperbolic partial differential equations would appear to be the forward-time centered-space (FTCS) method. The FTCS method is applied to the convection equation in Section 12.3, where it is shown that it is unconditionally unstable. The FTCS approximation of the wave equation is also unstable, as shown in the following analysis.

Recall the pair of first-order convection equations that are equivalent to the wave equation [Eqs. (15.3) and (15.4)]:

$$\bar{f}_t + a\bar{g}_x = 0 \tag{15.36}$$

$$\bar{g}_t + a\bar{f}_x = 0 \tag{15.37}$$

Introducing the first-order forward-difference approximation [Eq. (10.54)] for $\bar{f}_t$ and $\bar{g}_t$ and the second-order centered-difference approximation [Eq. (10.64*b*)] for

$\overline{f}_x$ and $\overline{g}_x$ and solving for f_i^{n+1} and g_i^{n+1} yields

$$f_i^{n+1} = f_i^n - \frac{c}{2}(g_{i+1}^n - g_{i-1}^n) \tag{15.38}$$

$$g_i^{n+1} = g_i^n - \frac{c}{2}(f_{i+1}^n - f_{i-1}^n) \tag{15.39}$$

where $c = a\Delta t/\Delta x$ is the convection number.

A von Neumann stability analysis must consider Eqs. (15.38) and (15.39) simultaneously, because they are coupled. This is accomplished by substituting the Fourier components of both $f(x, t)$ and $g(x, t)$ into Eqs. (15.38) and (15.39). Thus,

$$f_i^{n+1} = f_i^n - \frac{c}{2}(g_i^n e^{I\theta} - g_i^n e^{-I\theta}) \tag{15.40}$$

$$g_i^{n+1} = g_i^n - \frac{c}{2}(f_i^n e^{I\theta} - f_i^n e^{-I\theta}) \tag{15.41}$$

Substituting the relationships between the exponential functions and the sine and cosine functions, then rearranging, gives

$$f_i^{n+1} = f_i^n - g_i^n Ic\sin\theta \tag{15.42}$$

$$g_i^{n+1} = g_i^n - f_i^n Ic\sin\theta \tag{15.43}$$

Writing Eqs. (15.42) and (15.43) in matrix form yields

$$\begin{bmatrix} f_i^{n+1} \\ g_i^{n+1} \end{bmatrix} = \begin{bmatrix} 1 & -Ic\sin\theta \\ -Ic\sin\theta & 1 \end{bmatrix} \begin{bmatrix} f_i^n \\ g_i^n \end{bmatrix} \tag{15.44a}$$

which can be written as

$$\mathbf{F}^{n+1} = \mathbf{G}\mathbf{F}^n \tag{15.44b}$$

where $\mathbf{F}^{\mathrm{T}} = (f_i \ g_i)$ and $\mathbf{G}$ is the amplification matrix

$$\mathbf{G} = \begin{bmatrix} 1 & -Ic\sin\theta \\ -Ic\sin\theta & 1 \end{bmatrix} \tag{15.45}$$

For Eqs. (15.38) and (15.39) to be stable, the eigenvalues λ of the amplification matrix $\mathbf{G}$ must be ≤ 1.0. Solving for the eigenvalues gives

$$\begin{vmatrix} (1-\lambda) & -Ic\sin\theta \\ -Ic\sin\theta & (1-\lambda) \end{vmatrix} = 0 \tag{15.46}$$

which gives

$$(1-\lambda)^2 + c^2\sin^2\theta = 0 \tag{15.47}$$

Solving Eq. (15.47) for λ yields

$$\lambda = 1 \pm Ic \sin\theta \tag{15.48}$$

The magnitude of λ is

$$|\lambda| = (1 + c^2 \sin^2\theta)^{1/2} \tag{13.49}$$

which is greater than unity for $c > 0$. Consequently, Eqs. (15.38) and (15.39) are unconditionally unstable.

Example 15.1. Solution by the FTCS method. To illustrate the unstable behavior of the FTCS method applied to the pair of convection equations that correspond to the wave equation, we try to solve the acoustics problem presented in Section 15.1. Applying the FTCS method to Eq. (15.15) yields

$$u_i^{n+1} = u_i^n - \frac{1}{2}\left(\frac{\Delta t}{\rho\,\Delta x}\right)(P_{i+1}^n - P_{i-1}^n) \tag{15.50}$$

$$P_i^{n+1} = P_i^n - \frac{1}{2}\left(\frac{\rho a^2 \Delta t}{\Delta x}\right)(u_{i+1}^n - u_{i-1}^n) \tag{15.51}$$

Considerable care must be devoted to the units of the physical variables to ensure that the pair of FDEs is consistent. Let u, Δx, and Δt be measured in units of mm/s, m, and ms, respectively. Recall that $\rho = 1.0\ \text{kg/m}^3$ and a $= 1000$ m/s. Equation (15.50) with units explicitly included becomes

$$u_i^{n+1}\left(\frac{\text{m}}{1000\ \text{s}}\right) = u_i^n\left(\frac{\text{m}}{1000\ \text{s}}\right) - \frac{1}{2}\left(\frac{\Delta t\ \text{s}}{1000}\right)\left(\frac{\text{m}^3}{1.0\ \text{kg}}\right)\left(\frac{1}{\Delta x\ \text{m}}\right)(P_{i+1}^n - P_{i-1}^n)\left(\frac{\text{N}}{\text{m}^2}\right)\left(\frac{\text{kg-m}}{\text{N-s}^2}\right) \tag{15.52}$$

Gathering all the units together yields

$$u_i^{n+1} = u_i^n - \frac{1}{2}\frac{\Delta t}{\Delta x}\left[\left(\frac{1000\ \text{s}}{\text{m}}\right)\left(\frac{\text{s}}{1000}\right)\left(\frac{\text{m}^3}{\text{kg}}\right)\left(\frac{1}{\text{m}}\right)\left(\frac{\text{N}}{\text{m}^2}\right)\left(\frac{\text{kg-m}}{\text{N-s}^2}\right)\right](P_{i+1}^n - P_{i-1}^n) \tag{15.53}$$

The terms involving the units combine to unity. Thus, Eq. (15.53) becomes

$$u_i^{n+1} = u_i^n - \frac{c}{2}(P_{i+1}^n - P_{i-1}^n) \tag{15.54}$$

where $c = \Delta t/\Delta x$. Equation (15.51) with units becomes

$$P_i^{n+1}\left(\frac{\text{N}}{\text{m}^2}\right) = P_i^n\left(\frac{\text{N}}{\text{m}^2}\right) - \frac{1}{2}\left(\frac{1.0\ \text{kg}}{\text{m}^3}\right)\left(\frac{1000\ \text{m}}{\text{s}}\right)^2\left(\frac{\Delta t\ \text{s}}{1000}\right)\left(\frac{1}{\Delta \text{x m}}\right)(u_{i+1}^n - u_{i-1}^n)\left(\frac{\text{m}}{\text{s}}\right)\left(\frac{\text{N-s}^2}{\text{kg-m}}\right) \tag{15.55}$$

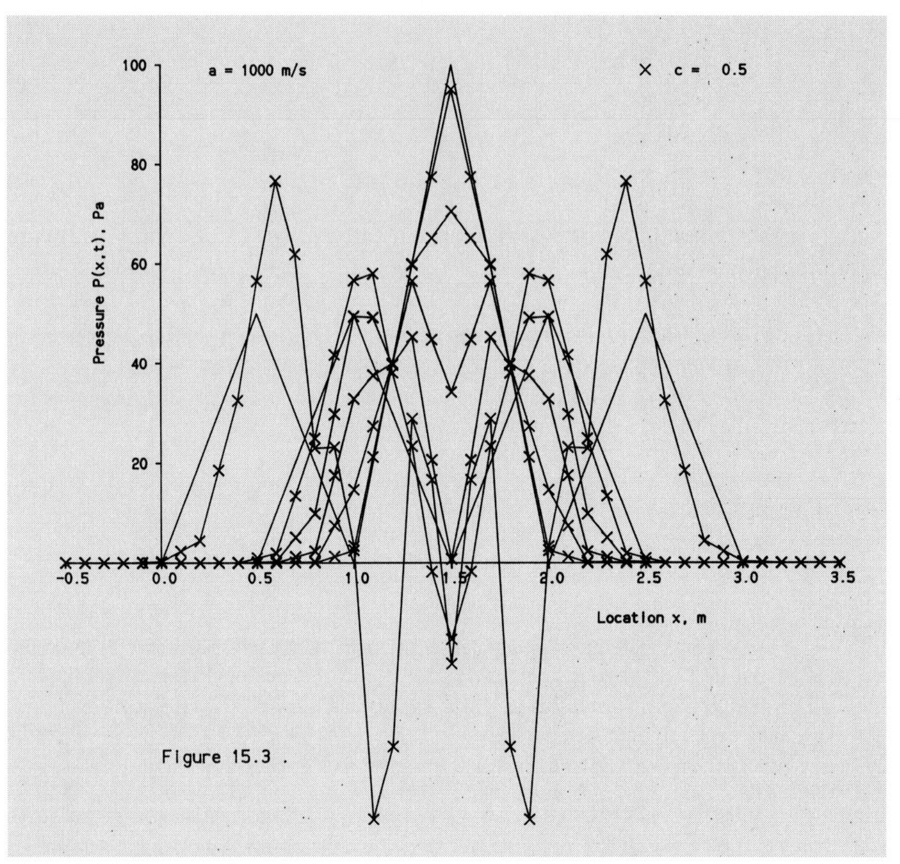

FIGURE 15.3
Solution by the FTCS method.

Gathering all the units together yields

$$P_i^{n+1} = P_i^n - \frac{1}{2}\frac{\Delta t}{\Delta x}\left[\left(\frac{\text{m}^2}{\text{N}}\right)\left(\frac{\text{kg}}{\text{m}^3}\right)\left(\frac{1000\text{ m}}{\text{s}}\right)^2\left(\frac{\text{s}}{1000}\right)\left(\frac{1}{\text{m}}\right)\left(\frac{\text{N-s}^2}{\text{kg-m}}\right)\right](u_{i+1}^n - u_{i-1}^n) \quad (15.56)$$

The terms involving the units combine to unity. Thus, Eq. (15.56) becomes

$$P_i^{n+1} = P_i^n - \frac{c}{2}(u_{i+1}^n - u_{i-1}^n) \quad (15.57)$$

where $c = \Delta t/\Delta x$.

Now let $\Delta x = 0.05$ m and $\Delta t = 0.025$ ms. For this case, $c = \Delta t/\Delta x = 0.025/0.05 = 0.5$. The results are presented in Fig. 15.3 at $t = 0.1$, 0.2, 0.3, 0.4, 0.5, and 1.0 ms, corresponding to $n = 2$, 4, 6, 8, 10, and 20 time steps, respectively. The amplitude of the solution increases as the wave propagates, which is clearly unstable behavior. The solution increases much more rapidly for larger values of the time step Δt.

In summary, the FTCS approximation of the wave equation is unstable. Consequently, it is unsuitable for solving that equation. In fact, the FTCS approximation is unconditionally unstable for all hyperbolic PDEs.

15.4 THE LAX METHOD

Lax (1954) proposed a modification to the FTCS method for the convection equation that yields a conditionally stable method. That modification is presented in Section 12.4. In that modification, the value f_i^n in the finite difference approximation of $\overline{f}_t|_i^n$ is approximated by $(f_{i+1}^n + f_{i-1}^n)/2$. Making that same approximation for f_i^n and g_i^n in Eqs. (15.38) and (15.39) yields the Lax approximation of the coupled convection equations that correspond to the wave equation:

$$f_i^{n+1} = \frac{1}{2}(f_{i+1}^n + f_{i-1}^n) - \frac{c}{2}(g_{i+1}^n - g_{i-1}^n) \tag{15.58}$$

$$g_i^{n+1} = \frac{1}{2}(g_{i+1}^n + g_{i-1}^n) - \frac{c}{2}(f_{i+1}^n - f_{i-1}^n) \tag{15.59}$$

Equations (15.58) and (15.59) are identical to the first method-of-characteristics approximation of the linear wave equation [see Eqs. (15.132) and (15.133) in Section 15.10].

The first form of the modified differential equation (MDE) corresponding to Eq. (15.58) is

$$\begin{aligned} f_t + a g_x = & -\frac{1}{2} f_{tt}\,\Delta t - \frac{1}{6} f_{ttt}\,\Delta t^2 - \cdots \\ & - \frac{1}{6} a g_{xxx}\,\Delta x^2 - \cdots + \frac{1}{2} f_{xx}\,\frac{\Delta x^2}{\Delta t} + \cdots \end{aligned} \tag{15.60}$$

and the second form of the MDE is

$$f_t + a g_x = \frac{1}{2}\left(\frac{\Delta x^2}{\Delta t} - a^2\,\Delta t\right) f_{xx} + \frac{1}{3}(a\,\Delta x^2 - a^3\,\Delta t^2) g_{xxx} + \cdots \tag{15.61}$$

As $\Delta t \to 0$ and $\Delta x \to 0$, the first three terms on the right-hand side of Eq. (15.60) go to zero. The fourth term, however, becomes indeterminate. Consequently, Eq. (15.58) is not a consistent approximation of Eq. (15.3). As discussed in Section 12.4, Eq. (15.61) approaches the parabolic PDE

$$f_t + a g_x = \frac{1}{2}\left(\frac{\Delta x^2}{\Delta t} - a^2\,\Delta t\right) f_{xx} = \alpha_n f_{xx} \tag{15.62}$$

where $\alpha_n f_{xx}$ is implicit numerical diffusion. For large values of Δx or small values of Δt, the numerical solution of Eqs. (15.58) and (15.59) behaves more like the solution of the convection–diffusion equation than like the solution of the wave equation. From Eq. (15.61), it is seen that Eq. (15.58) is $O(\Delta t) + O(\Delta x^2) + O(\Delta x^2/\Delta t)$. As seen in Eq. (15.61), both even and odd space derivatives are present in the truncation error. Hence, implicit numerical diffusion and dispersion are both present in the FDE. The leading truncation error term contains f_{xx}. Consequently, the truncation error is predominately diffusive. Similar results and conclusions apply to Eq. (15.59).

A von Neumann stability analysis must consider Eqs. (15.58) and (15.59) simultaneously, because they are coupled. This is accomplished by substituting the Fourier components of both $f(x, t)$ and $g(x, t)$ into Eqs. (15.58) and (15.59), and proceeding as in Section 15.3. The amplification matrix $\mathbf{G}$ is

$$\mathbf{G} = \begin{bmatrix} \cos\theta & -Ic\sin\theta \\ -Ic\sin\theta & \cos\theta \end{bmatrix} \tag{15.63}$$

For Eqs. (15.58) and (15.59) to be stable, the eigenvalues of the amplification matrix $\mathbf{G}$ must be ≤ 1.0. Thus,

$$\begin{vmatrix} [\cos\theta - \lambda] & -Ic\sin\theta \\ -Ic\sin\theta & [\cos\theta - \lambda] \end{vmatrix} = 0 \tag{15.64}$$

Solving Eq. (15.64) yields

$$[\cos\theta - \lambda]^2 + c^2\sin^2\theta = 0 \tag{15.65}$$

Solving for λ gives

$$\lambda = \cos\theta \pm Ic\sin\theta \tag{15.66}$$

The magnitude of λ is

$$|\lambda| = (\cos^2\theta + c^2\sin^2\theta)^{1/2} = \left(1 - \sin^2\theta(1 - c^2)\right)^{1/2} \tag{15.67}$$

Since $\sin^2\theta \geq 0$ for all values of $\theta = k\,\Delta x$, $|\lambda|$ will be less than unity if

$$\boxed{c = \frac{a\,\Delta t}{\Delta x} \leq 1} \tag{15.68}$$

where c is the convection number based on the wave propagation speed a. Equation (15.68) is the CFL stability criterion developed by Courant et al. (1928). Consequently, the Lax approximation of the wave equation is conditionally stable.

The Lax approximation of the wave equation may behave in a numerically consistent way if $\Delta x/\Delta t$ is constant. It is conditionally stable. Consequently, by the Lax equivalence theorem, it may behave as a convergent approximation of the wave equation.

The conditional stability of the Lax method is somewhat surprising, since the Lax method appears to be only a minor modification of the FTCS method, which is unconditionally unstable when applied to the wave equation. As discussed in Section 12.4 for the convection equation, the Lax method has introduced implicit numerical diffusion, which is discussed in Section 12.5, into the finite difference equation. This implicit numerical diffusion acts like real physical diffusion and adds sufficient diffusion to the FTCS method to make it conditionally stable.

Example 15.2. Solution by the Lax method. We will solve the acoustics problem presented in Section 15.1 by the Lax method, for $\Delta x = 0.05$ cm. The units used in the FDEs and the definition of the convection number, $c = \Delta t/\Delta x$, are the same as presented in Example 15.1. The results are presented in Fig. 15.4 at times from 0.1 to 0.5 ms for $c = 0.5$, corresponding to $\Delta t = 0.025$ ms, and at $t = 1.0$ ms for $c = 0.1$, 0.5, 0.9, and 1.0, corresponding to $\Delta t = 0.005$, 0.025, 0.045, and 0.05 ms, respectively. As illustrated in Fig. 15.4, the wave shape is rounded and damped. For small values of Δt (i.e., small values of c), the solution is completely smeared out. These effects are the result of the implicit numerical diffusion that is present in the Lax method. In effect, the initial data distribution is being both convected and diffused, and the effect of diffusion increases as the time step is decreased. The presence of large numerical diffusion at small values of c is a serious problem with the Lax method.

The Lax method can be applied in a straightforward manner to solve nonlinear PDEs, systems of PDEs, and multidimensional problems, as discussed in Section 15.16. The stability limit is more restrictive in the latter case.

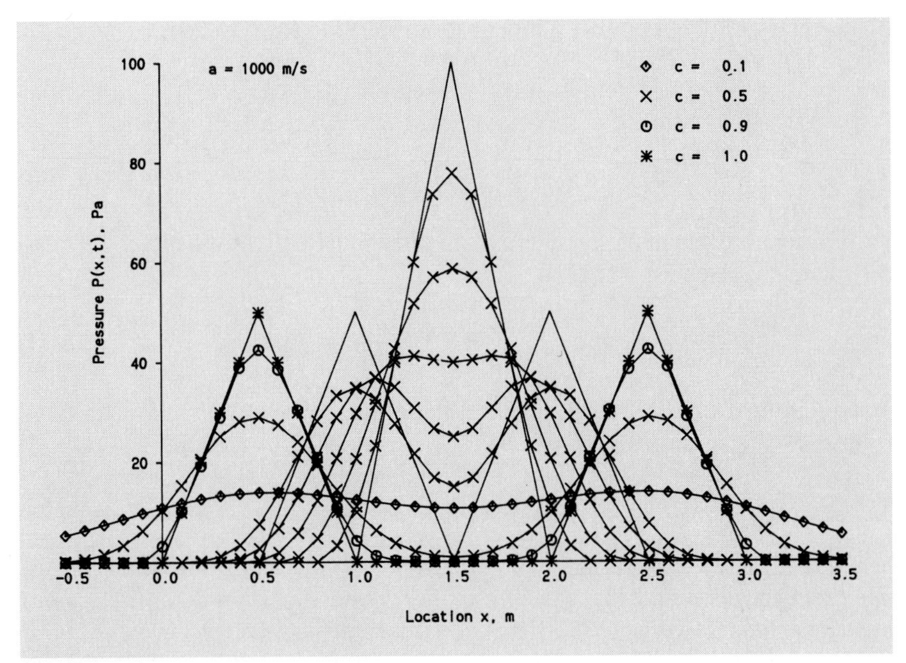

FIGURE 15.4
Solution by the Lax method.

In summary, the Lax approximation of the wave equation is explicit, single-step, two-level, $O(\Delta t) + O(\Delta x^2) + O(\Delta x^2/\Delta t)$, and conditionally stable. Excessive implicit numerical diffusion is present, which makes the Lax method a poor choice for solving coupled convection equations and the wave equation.

15.5 UPWIND METHODS

It is shown in the method of characteristics analysis of the wave equation presented in Section 15.2 that information propagates along the characteristic curves specified by $dx/dt = \pm a$ [see Eq. (15.24)]. Thus, information propagates from both the left and the right side of the solution point, corresponding to $+a$ and $-a$, respectively. This type of information propagation is referred to as upwind propagation, since the information comes from the direction from which the wave velocity comes, that is, the upwind direction. Finite difference methods that account for the upwind influence are called upwind methods. The first-order upwind method is presented in this section for the linear wave equation.

The upwind direction is not readily apparent in the pair of first-order PDEs that represent the wave equation. However, when these equations are placed in characteristic form, the upwind direction becomes apparent. As shown in Section 15.2, the characteristic curves corresponding to the wave equation are [see Eq. (15.24)]

$$\frac{dx}{dt} = \pm a \tag{15.69}$$

and the corresponding compatibility equations are [see Eq. (15.29)]

$$d\bar{f} + d\bar{g} = 0 \qquad \text{along} \quad \frac{dx}{dt} = +a \tag{15.70a}$$

$$d\bar{f} - d\bar{g} = 0 \qquad \text{along} \quad \frac{dx}{dt} = -a \tag{15.70b}$$

The total differentials $d\bar{f}$ and $d\bar{g}$ are directional derivatives along the characteristic curves [see Eq. (15.27)]. Thus,

$$\frac{d\bar{f}}{dt} = \bar{f}_t \pm a\bar{f}_x \qquad \text{and} \qquad \frac{d\bar{g}}{dt} = \bar{g}_t \pm a\bar{g}_x \tag{15.71}$$

Substituting Eqs. (15.71) into Eqs. (15.70) yields

$$(\bar{f}_t + a\bar{f}_{x^-}) + (\bar{g}_t + a\bar{g}_{x^-}) = 0 \tag{15.72}$$

$$(\bar{f}_t - a\bar{f}_{x^+}) - (\bar{g}_t - a\bar{g}_{x^+}) = 0 \tag{15.73}$$

where Eq. (15.72) applies along $dx/dt = +a$ (i.e., along the characteristic curve from the left) and Eq. (15.73) applies along $dx/dt = -a$ (i.e., along the characteristic curve from the right). Consequently, $\bar{f}_x$ and $\bar{g}_x$ in Eq. (15.72) should be approximated as one-sided differences from the left (i.e., from the $-x$ direction), and $\bar{f}_x$ and $\bar{g}_x$ in Eq. (15.73) should be approximated as one-sided differences from the right (i.e., from the $+x$ direction). This is indicated by attaching the superscript minus $(-)$ to the space derivatives in Eq. (15.72) and the superscript plus $(+)$ to the space derivatives in Eq. (15.73). Solving Eqs. (15.72) and (15.73) simultaneously for $\overline{f}_t$ and $\overline{g}_t$ yields

$$\overline{f}_t + \frac{a}{2}(\overline{f}_{x^-} - \overline{f}_{x^+}) + \frac{a}{2}(\overline{g}_{x^-} + \overline{g}_{x^+}) = 0 \tag{15.74}$$

$$\overline{g}_t + \frac{a}{2}(\overline{g}_{x^-} - \overline{g}_{x^+}) + \frac{a}{2}(\overline{f}_{x^-} + \overline{f}_{x^+}) = 0 \tag{15.75}$$

Equations (15.74) and (15.75) are in a form suitable for developing upwind finite difference approximations.

The simplest procedure for developing an upwind finite difference approximation is to replace the time derivatives $\overline{f}_t|_i^n$ and $\overline{g}_t|_i^n$ by the first-order forward-difference approximation at grid point (i, n) [Eq. (10.54)] and to replace the space derivatives $\overline{f}_x|_i^n$ and $\overline{g}_x|_i^n$ by first-order one-sided-differences in the upwind direction [i.e., Eq. (10.63*b*) for $\overline{f}_{x^-}$ and $\overline{g}_{x^-}$ and Eq. (10.62*b*) for $\overline{f}_{x^+}$ and $\overline{g}_{x^+}$]. For Eq. (15.74), this yields

$$f_i^{n+1} = f_i^n - \frac{c}{2}[(g_i^n - g_{i-1}^n) + (g_{i+1}^n - g_i^n)] - \frac{c}{2}[(f_i^n - f_{i-1}^n) - (f_{i+1}^n - f_i^n)] \tag{15.76}$$

which can be rearranged as

$$f_i^{n+1} = f_i^n - \frac{c}{2}(g_{i+1}^n - g_{i-1}^n) + \frac{c}{2}(f_{i+1}^n - 2f_i^n + f_{i-1}^n) \tag{15.77}$$

In a similar manner, Eq. (15.75) yields

$$g_i^{n+1} = g_i^n - \frac{c}{2}(f_{i+1}^n - f_{i-1}^n) + \frac{c}{2}(g_{i+1}^n - 2g_i^n + g_{i-1}^n) \tag{15.78}$$

Equations (15.77) and (15.78) are identical to the second method-of-characteristics approximation of the linear wave equation developed in Section 15.10 [see Eqs. (15.138) and (15.139)].

The first form of the MDE corresponding to Eq. (15.77) is

$$f_t + a g_x = -\frac{1}{2}f_{tt}\,\Delta t - \frac{1}{6}f_{ttt}\,\Delta t^2 - \cdots - \frac{1}{2}a f_{xx}\,\Delta x - \cdots - \frac{1}{6}a g_{xxx}\,\Delta x^2 - \cdots \tag{15.79}$$

and the second form of the MDE is

$$f_t + a g_x = \frac{1}{2}\left(-a\,\Delta x - a^2\,\Delta t\right) f_{xx} + \left(-\frac{1}{6} a\,\Delta x^2 - \frac{1}{2} a^2\,\Delta t\,\Delta x - \frac{1}{3} a^3\,\Delta t^2\right) g_{xxx} + \cdots \tag{15.80}$$

As $\Delta t \to 0$ and $\Delta x \to 0$, the truncation error terms in Eq. (15.79) go to zero, and Eq. (15.79) approaches $f_t + a g_x = 0$. Consequently, Eq. (15.77) is a consistent approximation of Eq. (15.3). From Eq. (15.80), the FDE is $O(\Delta t) + O(\Delta x)$. From Eq. (15.80), implicit numerical diffusion and dispersion are both present. The FDE is predominately diffusive, because the leading truncation error term contains f_{xx}. Similar results and conclusions apply to Eq. (15.78). The von Neumann stability analysis of Eqs. (15.77) and (15.78) proceeds in the same manner as the analysis of Eqs. (15.38) and (15.39). The result is

$$\lambda = (1 - c) + c\cos\theta - I c \sin\theta \tag{15.81}$$

Equation (15.81) is the equation of a circle in the complex plane with center at $(1 - c, 0)$ and radius c. For stability, $|\lambda| \le 1$. This is guaranteed if the convection number $c = a\Delta t/\Delta x \le 1$. Similar results and conclusions apply to Eq. (15.78). The first-order upwind approximation of the wave equation is consistent and conditionally stable; consequently, by the Lax equivalence theorem, it is a consistent approximation of that equation.

Example 15.3. Solution by the first-order upwind method. Now we will solve the acoustics problem presented in Section 15.1 by the first-order upwind method for $\Delta x = 0.05$ m. The units used in the FDEs and the definition of the convection number, $c = \Delta t/\Delta x$, are the same as presented in Example 15.1. The results are presented in Fig. 15.5 at times from 0.1 to 0.5 ms for $c = 0.5$, corresponding to $\Delta t = 0.025$ ms, and at $t = 1.0$ ms for $c = 0.1$, 0.5, 0.9, and 1.0, corresponding to $\Delta t = 0.005$, 0.025, 0.045, and 0.05 ms, respectively. As illustrated in the figure, the waves becomes rounded and damped as they propagate. For small values of Δt (i.e., small values of c), the damping is quite severe. These effects are due to the implicit numerical diffusion present in the first-order upwind method. At large values of c, the effects of the implicit numerical diffusion are considerably reduced. Enough numerical diffusion is present to make the first-order upwind method a poor choice for solving the wave equation.

Explicit upwind methods can be used to solve nonlinear PDEs, systems of PDEs, and multidimensional problems, as discussed in Section 15.16. The stability limit is more restrictive for multidimensional problems.

In summary, the first-order upwind approximation of the wave equation is explicit, two-level, single-step, $O(\Delta t) + O(\Delta x)$, conditionally stable, and convergent. However, it introduces significant amounts of implicit numerical diffusion into the solution. Consequently, it is not a very accurate method for solving convection equations or the wave equation. Second-order upwind methods can be developed, which give more accurate solutions of convection problems.

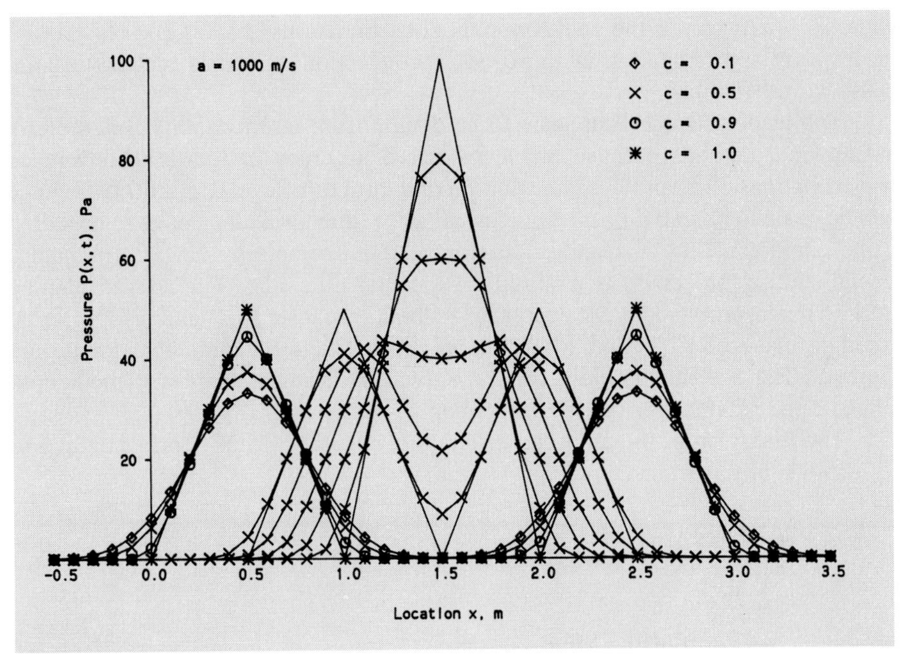

FIGURE 15.5
Solution by the first-order upwind method.

15.6 THE LEAPFROG METHOD

The Lax method developed in Section 15.4 and the upwind method developed in Section 15.5 have several desirable features. Both of them are explicit, two-level, single-step methods. However, they both introduce a significant amount of implicit numerical diffusion when the convection number is less than 1.0. Both of them are only first-order accurate in time, and the first-order upwind method is only first-order accurate in space. In spite of these disadvantages, these methods are useful in certain applications. However, it is obvious that methods with less implicit numerical diffusion, second-order accuracy in time, and second-order accuracy in space are desirable. One such method, the *leapfrog* method, is presented in this section.

Recall the pair of convection equations, $\overline{f}_t + a\overline{g}_x = 0$ and $\overline{g}_t + a\overline{f}_x = 0$, that correspond to the wave equation. Replacing the exact partial derivatives $\overline{f}_t|_i^n$ and $\overline{g}_t|_i^n$ by the second-order centered-difference approximation [Eq. (10.61)], replacing the exact partial derivatives $\overline{f}_x|_i^n$ and $\overline{g}_x|_i^n$ by the second-order centered-difference approximation [Eq. (11.64*b*)], then solving for f_i^{n+1} and g_i^{n+1}, gives

$$f_i^{n+1} = f_i^{n-1} - c(g_{i+1}^n - g_{i-1}^n) \tag{15.82}$$

$$g_i^{n+1} = g_i^{n-1} - c(f_{i+1}^n - f_{i-1}^n) \tag{15.83}$$

where $c = a\Delta t/\Delta x$ is the convection number. Equations (15.82) and (15.83) are the leapfrog approximation of the coupled convection equations that correspond to the wave equation.

The leapfrog method appears to be a significant improvement over the Lax and upwind methods because of the increased accuracy of the finite difference approximations of $\bar{f}_t$ and $\bar{g}_t$. The addition of a third time level to a finite difference method has two potential disadvantages: all three time levels may have to be stored in the computer, thus increasing the storage requirements by 50 percent, and a special starting procedure is required for the first time step. The additional time level is not a problem in the leapfrog method, because f_i^{n+1} and g_i^{n+1} can be stored in place of f_i^{n-1} and g_i^{n-1}, so only two levels of computer storage are required. The starting problem can be solved by using a two-level method to calculate the solution for the first time step.

The first form of the modified differential equation (MDE) corresponding to Eq. (15.82) is

$$f_t + a g_x = -\frac{1}{6} f_{ttt}\,\Delta t^2 - \frac{1}{120} f_{ttttt}\,\Delta t^4 - \cdots - \frac{1}{6} a g_{xxx}\,\Delta x^2 - \frac{1}{120} a g_{xxxxx}\,\Delta x^4 - \cdots \tag{15.84}$$

and the second form of the MDE is

$$f_t + a g_x = -\frac{1}{6}\left(a^3\,\Delta t^2 - a\,\Delta x^2\right) g_{xxx} + \left(-\frac{3}{40} a^5\,\Delta t^4 + \frac{1}{12} a^3\,\Delta t^2\,\Delta x^2 - \frac{1}{120} a\,\Delta x^4\right) g_{xxxxx} + \cdots \tag{15.85}$$

As $\Delta t \to 0$ and $\Delta x \to 0$, the truncation error terms go to zero, and Eq. (15.84) approaches $f_t + a g_x = 0$. Therefore, Eq. (15.82) is a consistent approximation of $\bar{f}_t + a\bar{g}_x = 0$. From Eq. (15.85), the FDE is $O(\Delta t^2) + O(\Delta x^2)$. From Eq. (15.85), there are no even spatial derivatives in the truncation error, so there is no numerical diffusion. Implicit numerical dispersion, however, is present, except when $c = 1.0$. In that case, the truncation errors are zero, and the FDE matches the PDE exactly (for the linear wave equation only). Similar results hold for Eq. (15.83).

The amplification factor G is given by

$$G^2 + I\,(2c\sin\theta)\,G - 1 = 0 \tag{15.86}$$

Solving Eq. (15.86) by the quadratic formula yields

$$G = \pm\sqrt{1 - c^2\sin^2\theta} - Ic\sin\theta \tag{15.87}$$

When $c^2\sin^2\theta > 1$, which occurs when $c > 1$, the square root term is imaginary, and

$$G = I\left(-c\sin\theta \pm \sqrt{c^2\sin^2\theta - 1}\right) \tag{15.88}$$

Equation (15.88) shows that $|G| > 1$, thus the method is unstable. When $c^2 \sin^2\theta \le 1$, which occurs when $c \le 1$, Eq. (15.87) yields

$$|G| = (1 - c^2 \sin^2\theta + c^2 \sin^2\theta)^{1/2} = 1 \tag{15.89}$$

Equation (15.89) shows that the leapfrog method is marginally stable (i.e., $|G| = 1$) for all values of $c \le 1$. This is a desirable result, because it shows that there is no implicit numerical diffusion in the method. This conclusion is also obtained from Eq. (15.85), which contains no even derivatives in the truncation error. Consequently, the leapfrog approximation of the wave equation is stable if

$$c = \frac{a\,\Delta t}{\Delta x} \le 1 \tag{15.90}$$

The leapfrog approximation of the wave equation is consistent and conditionally stable. Consequently, by the Lax equivalence theorem, it is a convergent approximation of the wave equation.

Example 15.4. Solution by the leapfrog method. We will solve the acoustics problem presented in Section 15.1, using Eqs. (15.82) and (15.83) with $\Delta x = 0.05$m. The units used in the FDEs and the definition of the convection number, $c = \Delta t/\Delta x$, are the same as presented in Example 15.1. The results are presented in Fig. 15.6 at times from 0.1 to 0.5 ms for $c = 0.5$, corresponding to $\Delta t = 0.025$ ms, and at 1.0 ms for $c = 0.1$, 0.5, 0.9, and 1.0, corresponding to $\Delta t = 0.005$, 0.025, 0.045, and 0.05 ms, respectively. The exact solution presented in Section 15.1 was used for the first step in each case.

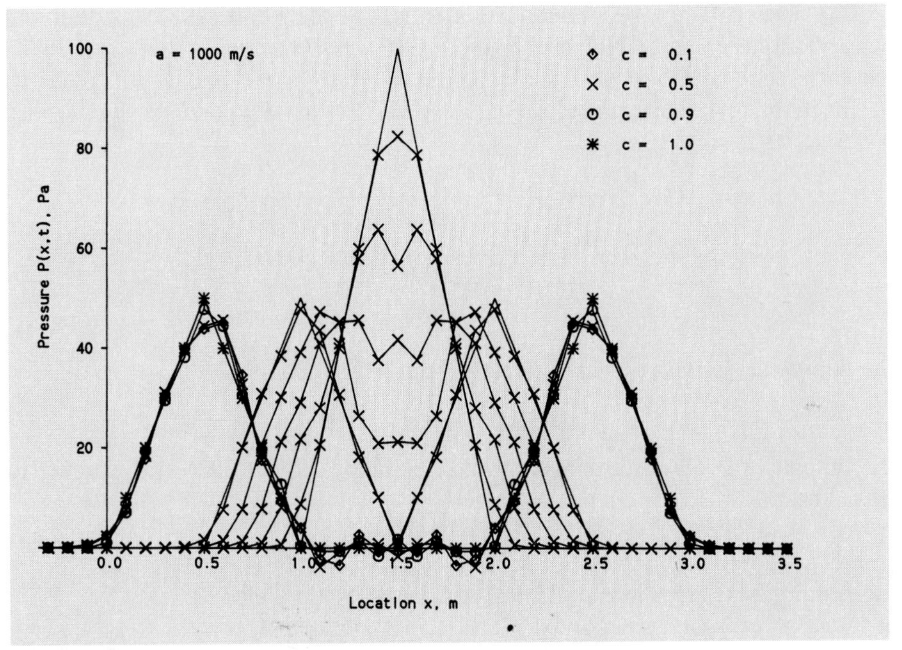

FIGURE 15.6
Solution by the leapfrog method.

Figure 15.6 illustrates several important features of the leapfrog method. When $c = 1.0$, the numerical solution is identical to the exact solution, for the linear wave equation. This is not true for nonlinear PDEs. For $c < 1.0$, the amplitude of the solution is damped slightly as the waves propagate. The results at $t = 1.0$ ms for $c = 0.1$, 0.5, 0.9, and 1.0 show that the numerical solution lags the exact solution slightly, with the amount of lag increasing as the numerical signal propagation speed (i.e., the convection number) decreases. The results presented in Fig. 15.6 suggest that the leapfrog method is a good method for solving the wave equation. However, the error behavior on alternate time steps can grow in opposite directions, which can lead to a poor solution. Consequently, the leapfrog method is not a popular method for solving coupled convection equations or the wave equation.

The explicit leapfrog method can be applied in a straightforward manner to solve nonlinear PDEs, systems of PDEs, and multidimensional problems, as discussed in Section 15.16.

In summary, the leapfrog method applied to the wave equation is explicit, single-step, three-level, $O(\Delta t^2)+O(\Delta x^2)$, conditionally stable, and convergent. It is not a popular method for solving convection problems due to its error behavior in some problems.

15.7 THE LAX–WENDROFF ONE-STEP METHOD

The one-step method developed by Lax and Wendroff (1960) is a very popular $O(\Delta t^2) + O(\Delta x^2)$ explicit finite difference method. For the linear wave equation, the Lax–Wendroff one-step method is identical to the Leith (1965) method and the method presented by Noh and Protter (1963). For the pair of first-order PDEs that correspond to the linear wave equation, $\bar{f}_t + a\bar{g}_x = 0$ and $\bar{g}_t + a\bar{f}_x = 0$, the functions to be determined are $\bar{f}(x, t)$ and $\bar{g}(x, t)$. Expanding $\bar{f}(x, t)$ in a Taylor series in time gives

$$\bar{f}_i^{n+1} = \bar{f}_i^n + \bar{f}_t|_i^n \Delta t + \frac{1}{2}\bar{f}_{tt}|_i^n \Delta t^2 + O(\Delta t^3) \tag{15.91}$$

The derivative $\bar{f}_t$ is determined directly from the PDE:

$$\bar{f}_t = -a\bar{g}_x \tag{15.92}$$

The derivative $\bar{f}_{tt}$ is determined by differentiating Eq. (15.92) with respect to time. Thus,

$$\bar{f}_{tt} = (\bar{f}_t)_t = (-a\bar{g}_x)_t = -a(\bar{g}_t)_x = -a(-a\bar{f}_x)_x = a^2\bar{f}_{xx} \tag{15.93}$$

Substituting Eqs. (15.92) and (15.93) into Eq. (15.91) yields

$$\bar{f}_i^{n+1} = \bar{f}_i^n - a\bar{g}_x|_i^n \Delta t + \frac{1}{2}a^2\bar{f}_{xx}|_i^n \Delta t^2 + O(\Delta t^3) \tag{15.94}$$

Approximating the two space derivatives by second-order centered-difference approximations [Eqs. (10.64*b*) and (10.69*b*), respectively] gives

$$f_i^{n+1} = f_i^n - \frac{a\,\Delta t}{2\Delta x}(g_{i+1}^n - g_{i-1}^n) + \frac{a^2\,\Delta t^2}{2\Delta x^2}(f_{i+1}^n - 2f_i^n + f_{i-1}^n) \tag{15.95}$$

Introducing the convection number $c = a\,\Delta t/\Delta x$ yields

$$\boxed{f_i^{n+1} = f_i^n - \frac{c}{2}(g_{i+1}^n - g_{i-1}^n) + \frac{c^2}{2}(f_{i+1}^n - 2f_i^n + f_{i-1}^n)} \tag{15.96}$$

Performing the same steps for the function $\overline{g}(x, t)$ yields

$$\boxed{g_i^{n+1} = g_i^n - \frac{c}{2}(f_{i+1}^n - f_{i-1}^n) + \frac{c^2}{2}(g_{i+1}^n - 2g_i^n + g_{i-1}^n)} \tag{15.97}$$

Equations (15.96) and (15.97) are the Lax–Wendroff one-step approximation of the coupled convection equations that correspond to the linear wave equation.

The first form of the MDE corresponding to Eq. (15.96) is

$$\begin{aligned} f_t + ag_x = & -\frac{1}{2}f_{tt}\,\Delta t - \frac{1}{6}f_{ttt}\,\Delta t^2 - \frac{1}{24}f_{tttt}\,\Delta t^3 - \cdots \\ & - \frac{1}{6}ag_{xxx}\,\Delta x^2 - \cdots + \frac{1}{2}a^2 f_{xx}\,\Delta t + \frac{1}{24}a^2 f_{xxxx}\,\Delta t\,\Delta x^2 + \cdots \end{aligned} \tag{15.98}$$

and the second form of the MDE is

$$f_t + ag_x = \frac{1}{6}(a^3\,\Delta t^2 - a\,\Delta x^2)\,g_{xxx} + \frac{1}{8}(a^4\,\Delta t^3 - a^2\,\Delta t\,\Delta x^2)\,f_{xxxx} + \cdots \tag{15.99}$$

As $\Delta t \to 0$ and $\Delta x \to 0$, the truncation error terms in Eq. (15.98) go to zero, and Eq. (15.98) approaches $f_t + ag_x$. Consequently, (15.96) is consistent with $\overline{f}_t + a\overline{g}_x = 0$. From Eq. (15.99), the FDE is $O(\Delta t^2) + O(\Delta x^2)$. From Eq. (15.99), implicit numerical diffusion and dispersion are both present. The FDE is predominantly dispersive, because the leading truncation error term contains f_{xxx}. Similar results and conclusions apply to Eqs. (15.97). The von Neumann stability analysis of Eqs. (15.96) and (15.97) proceeds in the same manner as the analysis of Eqs. (15.38) and (15.39). The result is

$$\lambda = \left[(1 - c^2) + c^2\cos\theta\right] - I\,c\sin\theta \tag{15.100}$$

Equation (15.100) respresents an ellipse in the complex plane with center at

$(1 - c^2, 0)$ and axes c and c^2. For stability, $|\lambda| \leq 1$. This is guaranteed if the convection number $c = a\Delta t/\Delta x \leq 1$ [see Eq. (12.64) in Section 12.8]. The Lax–Wendroff one-step approximation of the wave equation is consistent and conditionally stable. Consequently, by the Lax equivalence theorem, it is a consistent approximation of that equation.

Example 15.5. Solution by the Lax-Wendroff one-step method. Now we will solve the acoustics problem presented in Section 15.1 by the Lax–Wendroff one-step method, with $\Delta x = 0.05$ m. The units used in the FDEs and the definition of the convection number, $c = \Delta t/\Delta x$, are the same as presented in Example 15.1. The results are presented in Fig. 15.7 at times from 0.1 to 0.5 ms for $c = 0.5$, corresponding to $\Delta t = 0.025$ ms, and at $t = 1.0$ ms for $c = 0.1$, 0.5, 0.9, and 1.0, corresponding to $\Delta t = 0.005$, 0.025, 0.045, and 0.05 ms, respectively.

When $c = 1.0$, the numerical solution is identical to the exact solution, for the linear wave equation. This is not true for nonlinear PDEs. For the other three values of c, the solutions are all quite good. As c decreases, the numerical solution lags the exact solution slightly due to implicit numerical dispersion. The peak of the wave is slightly rounded. Overall, the Lax–Wendroff one-step method gives excellent results for convection problems.

As demonstrated in Example 15.5, the Lax–Wendroff one-step method is an efficient and accurate method for solving the linear wave equation. For nonlinear PDEs and systems of PDEs, however, the method becomes quite complicated.

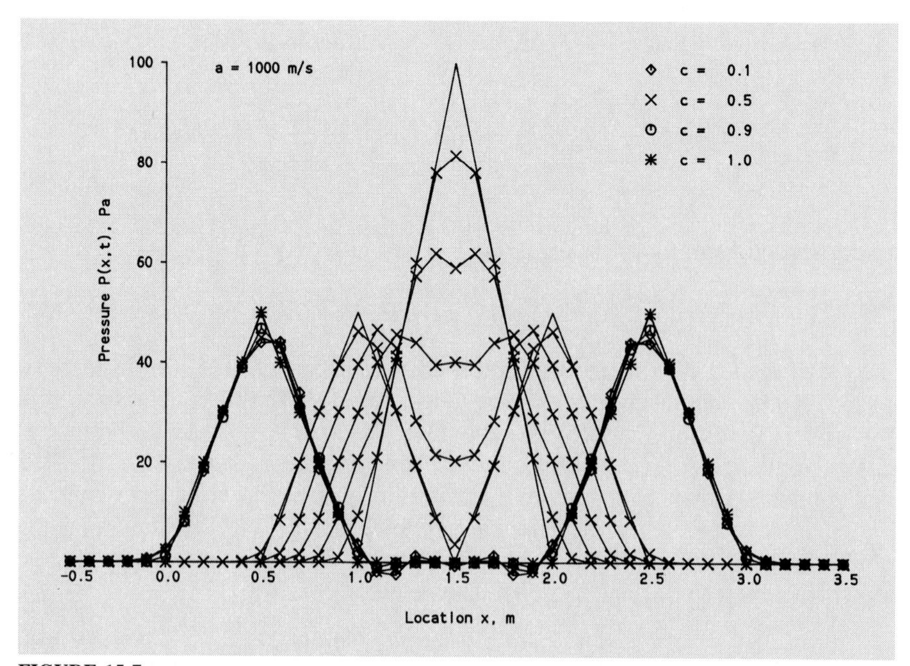

FIGURE 15.7
Solution by the Lax–Wendroff one-step method.

The complications arise in the replacement of the second-order time derivatives $\bar{f}_{tt}$ and $\bar{g}_{tt}$ in terms of space derivatives by differentiating the governing partial differential equations. The simple result obtained in Eq. (15.93) no longer applies. Consequently, the Lax–Wendroff one-step method is not used very often. More efficient methods, such as the Lax–Wendroff two-step methods presented in Section 15.8 and the MacCormack method presented in Section 15.9, are generally used for nonlinear equations and systems of equations. These methods have the same general features as the Lax-Wendroff one-step method, but they are considerably less complex for nonlinear PDEs, and thus considerably more efficient.

In summary, the Lax–Wendroff one-step method applied to the coupled convection equations and the wave equation is explicit, single-step, two-level, $O(\Delta t^2)+O(\Delta x^2)$, conditionally stable, and convergent. The method is quite complicated for nonlinear PDEs, systems of PDEs, and two- and three-dimensional problems.

15.8 LAX–WENDROFF TWO-STEP METHODS

The Lax–Wendroff one-step method presented in Section 15.7 has many desirable features when applied to the linear wave equation. However, when applied to nonlinear PDEs or a system of PDEs, the method becomes considerably more complicated. Richtmyer (1963) presented a two-step three-level method that is equivalent to the Lax–Wendroff one-step method for the linear wave equation. The first step uses the Lax method to obtain provisional values at the second time level; the second step uses the leapfrog method to obtain final values at the third time level. The Richtmyer method is much simpler than the Lax–Wendroff one-step method for nonlinear equations and systems of equations. Any two-step method that can be interpreted as a second-order Taylor series in time is commonly referred to as a two-step Lax–Wendroff method or a method of the Lax–Wendroff type.

For the pair of linear convection equations, $\bar{f}_t + a\bar{g}_x = 0$ and $\bar{g}_t + a\bar{f}_x = 0$, which corresponds to the linear wave equation, the two-step method proposed by Richtmyer is

$$f_i^{n+1} = \frac{1}{2}(f_{i+1}^n + f_{i-1}^n) - \frac{c}{2}(g_{i+1}^n - g_{i-1}^n) \tag{15.101}$$

$$g_i^{n+1} = \frac{1}{2}(g_{i+1}^n + g_{i-1}^n) - \frac{c}{2}(f_{i+1}^n - f_{i-1}^n) \tag{15.102}$$

$$f_i^{n+2} = f_i^n - c(g_{i+1}^{n+1} - g_{i-1}^{n+1}) \tag{15.103}$$

$$g_i^{n+2} = g_i^n - c(f_{i+1}^{n+1} - f_{i-1}^{n+1}) \tag{15.104}$$

where Eqs. (15.101) and (15.102) are the Lax method [Eqs. (15.58) and (15.59)] applied from time level n to time level $n + 1$, and Eqs. (15.103) and (15.104) are the leapfrog method [Eqs. (15.82) and (15.83)] applied from time level $n + 1$ to time level $n + 2$. The first step [i.e., the Lax method] is a provisional step. The results of this step are used only to implement the second step. The results of the second step are the desired solution values.

Equations (15.101) to (15.104) comprise a Lax–Wendroff two-step method for the coupled convection equations that correspond to the linear wave equation. This Lax–Wendroff two-step method is an explicit, three-level, two-step, $O(\Delta t^2)+O(\Delta x^2)$, finite difference method. The third time level is not a problem, because the values of f_i^{n+2} and g_i^{n+2} can be stored in place of f_i^n and g_i^n, so only two levels of computer storage are required.

Equations (15.101) to (15.104) do not look anything like the Lax–Wendroff one-step method [i.e., Eqs. (15.96) and (15.97)]. However, substituting Eqs. (15.101) and (15.102) into Eqs. (15.103) and (15.104) gives Eqs. (15.96) and (15.97) (for a time step of $2\Delta t$ and a spatial increment of $2\Delta x$). Consequently, the two methods are equivalent for the linear wave equation. For nonlinear PDEs and systems of PDEs, the two methods, while similar in behavior, are not equivalent.

Since the Lax–Wendroff two-step method is equivalent to the Lax-Wendroff one-step method for the linear convection equation, it follows that the consistency and stability analyses are identical. Thus, as demonstrated in Section 15.7, the method is consistent with the wave equation, conditionally stable ($c = a\,\Delta t/\Delta x \le 1$), and convergent.

Example 15.6. Solution by the Lax–Wendroff two-step method. We will solve the acoustics problem presented in Section 15.1 for $\Delta x = 0.05$ m. The units used in the FDEs and the definition of the convection number, $c = \Delta t/\Delta x$, are the same as presented in Example 15.1. The results are presented in Fig. 15.8 at times from 0.1 to 0.5 ms for $c = 0.5$, corresponding to $\Delta t = 0.025$ ms, and at 1.0 ms for $c = 0.1$, 0.5, 0.9, and 1.0, corresponding to $\Delta t = 0.005$, 0.025, 0.045, and 0.05 ms, respectively.

The general features of the numerical solution are similar to those presented in Figure 15.7 for the Lax–Wendroff one-step method. The numerical dispersion is more severe because the Lax–Wendroff two-step method is equivalent to the Lax–Wendroff one-step method with a time step of $2\Delta t$ and a spatial grid increment of $2\Delta x$. In fact, applying the Lax–Wendroff two-step method with $\Delta x = 0.025$ m yields the same results as presented in Fig. 15.7.

Numerous other two-step methods based on a second-order Taylor series in time have been proposed. The Burstein (1967) method uses half-mesh spacings $\Delta x/2$ and $\Delta t/2$. The corresponding finite difference stencil is illustrated in Figure 12.17. The Burstein method is applied to the convection equation in Section 12.9. The MacCormack (1969) method, which is also a Lax–Wendroff type two-step method, achieves second-order accuracy using the same grid spacings as the Lax–Wendroff one-step method and has no problems with boundary conditions or nonlinear equations. Consequently, the Richtmyer and Burstein methods are not

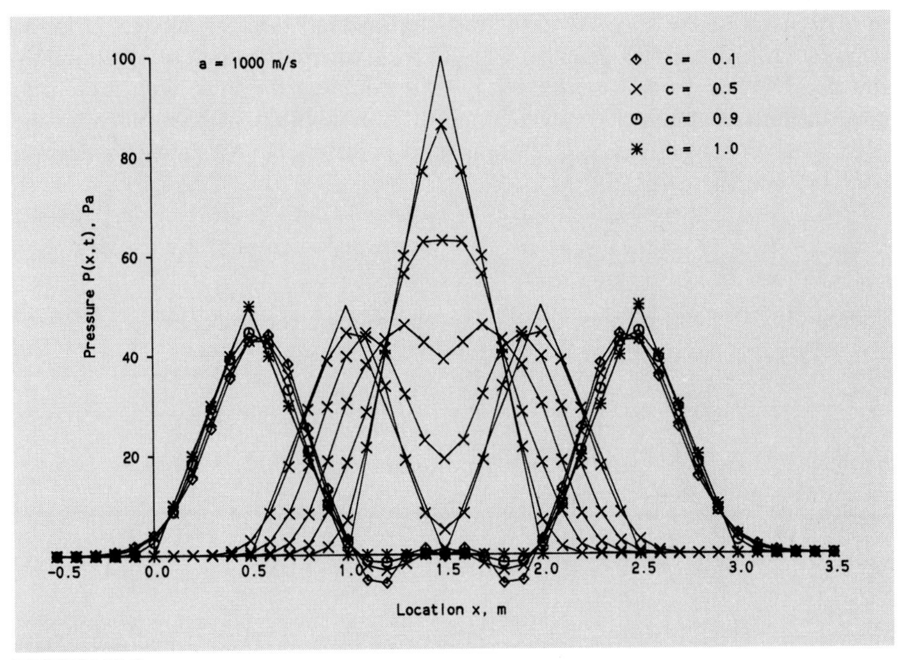

FIGURE 15.8
Solution by the Lax–Wendroff (Richtmyer) two-step method.

frequently used to solve wave propagation problems. The MacCormack method is presented in Section 15.9.

In summary, the Lax–Wendroff (Richtmyer) two-step method presented in this section is explicit, three-level, two-step, $O(\Delta t^2) + O(\Delta x^2)$, conditionally stable, and convergent. The method is identical to the Lax–Wendroff one-step method for the coupled linear convection equations and linear wave equation. However, for nonlinear PDEs, systems of PDEs, and two- and three-dimensional problems, Lax–Wendroff two-step methods are much more efficient than the Lax–Wendroff one-step method.

15.9 THE MACCORMACK METHOD

MacCormack (1969) proposed a two-step predictor–corrector finite difference method of the Lax–Wendroff type. The MacCormack method uses the same finite difference grid as the Lax–Wendroff one-step method, thus eliminating the requirement of more grid points associated with the Richtmyer (1963) method and the requirement of boundary conditions at half-mesh points associated with the Burstein (1967) method. The MacCormack method can solve linear partial differential equations, nonlinear PDEs, and systems of PDEs with equal ease. Recall that the Lax–Wendroff one-step method becomes quite complicated for nonlinear PDEs and systems of PDEs. Consequently, the MacCormack method is a widely used method.

The basis of the Lax–Wendroff one-step method (see Section 15.7) is the second-order Taylor series given in Eq. (15.91), where $\overline{f}_t$ is determined directly from the PDE and $\overline{f}_{tt}$ is determined by differentiating the PDE with respect to time. An alternate approach for evaluating $\overline{f}_{tt}|_i^n$ employs a first-order forward-time Taylor series expansion for $\overline{f}_t|_i^{n+1}$ about grid point (i, n). As shown in Section 10.10 [Eq. (10.73)], this gives

$$\overline{f}_i^{n+1} = \overline{f}_i^n + \frac{1}{2}(\overline{f}_t|_i^n + \overline{f}_t|_i^{n+1})\,\Delta t + O(\Delta t^3) \tag{15.105}$$

Equation (15.105) can be solved for f_i^{n+1} by dropping the truncation error terms and determining $\overline{f}_t|_i^n$ and $\overline{f}_t|_i^{n+1}$ from the PDE. This gives

$$f_i^{n+1} = f_i^n - \frac{1}{2}(ag_x|_i^n + ag_x|_i^{n+1})\,\Delta t \tag{15.106}$$

Performing similar steps for $\overline{g}(x, t)$ yields

$$g_i^{n+1} = g_i^n - \frac{1}{2}(af_x|_i^n + af_x|_i^{n+1})\,\Delta t \tag{15.107}$$

However, $f_x|_i^{n+1}$ and $g_x|_i^{n+1}$ involve unknown values of $f(x, t)$ and $g(x, t)$ at time level $n + 1$.

The MacCormack method is a two-step method that predicts provisional values of f_i^{n+1} and g_i^{n+1} using first-order forward-difference approximations of $\overline{f}_t|_i^n$, $\overline{f}_x|_i^n$, $\overline{g}_t|_i^n$, and $\overline{g}_x|_i^n$ to give

$$f_i^{\overline{n+1}} = f_i^n - c(g_{i+1}^n - g_i^n) \tag{15.108}$$

$$g_i^{\overline{n+1}} = g_i^n - c(f_{i+1}^n - f_i^n) \tag{15.109}$$

where the superscript $\overline{n+1}$ denotes provisional values and $c = a\,\Delta t/\Delta x$ is the convection number. In the second and final step, Eqs. (15.106) and (15.107) are solved by evaluating $f_x|_i^n$ and $g_x|_i^n$ using first-order forward-difference approximations, as in the predictor step, and evaluating $f_x|_i^{n+1}$ and $g_x|_i^{n+1}$ using first-order backward-difference approximations based on the provisional values of $f^{\overline{n+1}}$ and $g^{\overline{n+1}}$. Equations (15.106) and (15.107) become

$$f_i^{n+1} = f_i^n - \frac{1}{2}\left[c\,(g_{i+1}^n - g_i^n) + c\left(g_i^{\overline{n+1}} - g_{i-1}^{\overline{n+1}}\right)\right] \tag{15.110}$$

$$g_i^{n+1} = g_i^n - \frac{1}{2}\left[c\,(f_{i+1}^n - f_i^n) + c\left(f_i^{\overline{n+1}} - f_{i-1}^{\overline{n+1}}\right)\right] \tag{15.111}$$

Rearranging Eqs. (15.110) and (15.111) and introducing Eqs. (15.108) and (15.109) yields the computationally more efficient forms of the corrector equations:

$$f_i^{n+1} = \frac{1}{2}\left[f_i^n + \overline{f_i^{n+1}} - c\left(\overline{g_i^{n+1}} - \overline{g_{i-1}^{n+1}}\right)\right] \tag{15.112}$$

$$g_i^{n+1} = \frac{1}{2}\left[g_i^n + \overline{g_i^{n+1}} - c\left(\overline{f_i^{n+1}} - \overline{f_{i-1}^{n+1}}\right)\right] \tag{15.113}$$

Equations (15.108), (15.109), (15.112), and (15.113) comprise the MacCormack approximation of the coupled convection equations that correspond to the wave equation. The corresponding finite difference stencils are presented in Fig. 12.18.

Equations (15.108) and (15.109) employ forward-difference approximations of the spatial derivatives, and Eqs. (15.112) and (15.113) employ backward-difference approximations. This differencing can be reversed. Either way, there is a slight bias in the solution due to the one-sided differences. If desired, this bias can be reduced somewhat by alternating the direction of the predictor and corrector differences from one time level to the next.

The properties of the MacCormack method are not readily apparent from Eqs. (15.108), (15.109), (15.112), and (15.113). The time averaging of the space derivatives in the corrector step suggests that the method may be $O(\Delta t^2)$. Since both space derivatives are one-sided differences, it would appear that the corrector might be $O(\Delta x)$. However, a very fortuitous cancellation of the $O(\Delta x)$ truncation error terms occurs, and the MacCormack method is $O(\Delta x^2)$.

Equations (15.108), (15.109), (15.112), and (15.113) do not look anything like the Lax–Wendroff one-step method [i.e., Eqs. (15.96) and (15.97)]. However, substituting Eqs. (15.108) and (15.109), applied at grid points (i, n) and $(i-1, n)$, into Eqs. (15.112) and (15.113) gives Eqs. (15.96) and (15.97). Consequently, the two methods are identical for the coupled linear convection equations that correspond to the linear wave equation. For nonlinear PDEs and systems of PDEs, the two methods, while similar in behavior, are not identical.

Since the MacCormack method is identical to the Lax–Wendroff one-step method, for linear equations, it follows that the consistency and stability analyses are identical. Thus, as demonstrated in Section 15.7, the method is consistent with the coupled convection equations, $O(\Delta t^2) + O(\Delta x^2)$, conditionally stable $[c = (a\Delta t/\Delta x) \leq 1)]$, and convergent.

Example 15.7. Solution by the MacCormack method. The MacCormack finite difference approximation of the coupled convection equations that correspond to the linear wave equation is identical to the Lax–Wendroff one-step approximation of those equation. Consequently, the results presented in Example 15.5 also apply to the MacCormack method. The MacCormack method is an excellent method for solving convection and wave propagation problems.

When the partial differential equation being solved is nonlinear (i.e., the coefficient of $\bar{f}_x$ depends on $\bar{f}$), the coefficient is simply evaluated at grid point (i, n) for the predictor and at grid point $(i, \overline{n+1})$ for the corrector. When solving systems of PDEs, the predictor and corrector steps are simply applied to every PDE in the system. The MacCormack method extends directly to two- and three-dimensional physical spaces simply by adding on the appropriate one-sided finite difference approximations to the y and z space derivatives. The stability limit, however, is more restrictive for multidimensional problems. In view of these features of the MacCormack method, it is a very popular method for solving both parabolic and hyperbolic PDEs.

In summary, the MacCormack approximation of the coupled convection equations that correspond to the linear wave equation is explicit, two-level, two-step, $O(\Delta t^2) + O(\Delta x^2)$, conditionally stable, and convergent. The method is identical to the Lax–Wendroff one-step method for linear equations. However, for nonlinear equations, systems of equations, and two- and three-dimensional problems, the MacCormack method is much more efficient than the Lax–Wendroff one-step method.

15.10 THE NUMERICAL METHOD OF CHARACTERISTICS

The numerical method of characteristics (MOC) is introduced in the first six paragraphs of Section 12.11. Those paragraphs should be reviewed before studying this section. The present section extends the concepts presented in Section 12.11 for a single convection equation to the wave equation, as represented by a pair of coupled convection equations. The inverse marching method illustrated in Fig. 15.9 is used to solve the pair of coupled convection equations.

The system of convection equations under consideration is specified by Eqs. (15.3) and (15.4):

$$\bar{f}_t + a\bar{g}_x = 0 \qquad (15.114)$$

$$\bar{g}_t + a\bar{f}_x = 0 \qquad (15.115)$$

As shown in Section 15.2, the corresponding characteristic curves are given by [see Eq. (15.30)]:

$$x = x_0 \pm a(t - t_0) \qquad (15.116)$$

and the corresponding compatibility equations are [see Eq. (15.31)]

$$\bar{f} \pm \bar{g} = \bar{f}_0 \pm \bar{g}_0 \qquad (15.117)$$

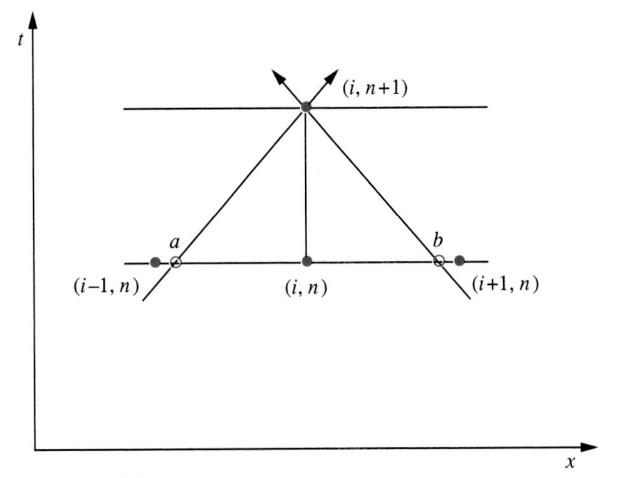

FIGURE 15.9
Computational network for the numerical MOC.

Figure 15.9 illustrates the computational network at a prespecified grid point in the inverse marching method. Point $(i, n+1)$ is the solution point. The two characteristic curves passing through the solution point are projected rearward until they intersect the initial-value line at points a and b. For the linear wave equation, Eq. (15.116) yields

$$(x_i - x_a) = a(t^{n+1} - t^n) = a\,\Delta t \tag{15.118}$$

$$(x_i - x_b) = -a(t^{n+1} - t^n) = -a\,\Delta t \tag{15.119}$$

and Eq. (15.117) gives

$$f_i^{n+1} + g_i^{n+1} = f_a + g_a \tag{15.120}$$

$$f_i^{n+1} - g_i^{n+1} = f_b - g_b \tag{15.121}$$

Adding and subtracting Eqs. (15.120) and (15.121) gives

$$f_i^{n+1} = \frac{1}{2}\left[(f_a + f_b) + (g_a - g_b)\right] \tag{15.122}$$

$$g_i^{n+1} = \frac{1}{2}\left[(g_a + g_b) + (f_a - f_b)\right] \tag{15.123}$$

The method of characteristics can be applied to solve the acoustics problem presented in Section 15.1. The governing equations, Eqs. (15.15), are:

$$\rho \overline{u}_t + \overline{P}_x = 0 \tag{15.124}$$

$$\overline{P}_t + \rho a^2 \overline{u}_x = 0 \tag{15.125}$$

where $\overline{P}$ and $\overline{u}$ are the acoustic pressure and velocity, respectively. Equations (15.124) and (15.125) can be solved by Eqs. (15.122) and (15.123) by letting $f = P$ and $g = \rho a^2 u$. Thus,

$$P_i^{n+1} = \frac{1}{2}\left[(P_a + P_b) + \rho a^2(u_a - u_b)\right] \tag{15.126}$$

$$u_i^{n+1} = \frac{1}{2}\left[(u_a + u_b) + \frac{1}{\rho a^2}(P_a - P_b)\right] \tag{15.127}$$

At this point, interpolating polynomials must be fitted to the initial data at time level n to determine the properties at points a and b. The values of x_a and x_b, determined from Eqs. (15.118) and (15.119), respectively, are substituted into the interpolating polynomials to determine f_a, f_b, g_a, and g_b, which are substituted into Eqs. (15.122) and (15.123) to determine f_i^{n+1} and g_i^{n+1}. Several choices exist for fitting the interpolating polynomial. As discussed in Section 12.11, the three most common choices are:

1. Linear interpolation using points $(i-1, n)$ and $(i+1, n)$
2. Linear interpolation using the two nearest points
3. Quadratic interpolation using points $(i-1, n)$, (i, n), and $(i+1, n)$

All three choices are presented in Section 12.11 for f_a. Similar expressions can be developed for f_b, g_a, and g_b.

First MOC Algorithm

First, consider linear interpolation using points $(i-1, n)$ and $(i+1, n)$. As shown in Section 12.11 [see Eq. (12.85)], this gives

$$f_a = \frac{1}{2}(f_{i+1}^n + f_{i-1}^n) - \frac{c}{2}(f_{i+1}^n - f_{i-1}^n) \tag{15.128}$$

$$g_a = \frac{1}{2}(g_{i+1}^n + g_{i-1}^n) - \frac{c}{2}(g_{i+1}^n - g_{i-1}^n) \tag{15.129}$$

where $c = a\Delta t/\Delta x$ is the convection number. In a similar manner,

$$f_b = \frac{1}{2}(f_{i+1}^n + f_{i-1}^n) + \frac{c}{2}(f_{i+1}^n - f_{i-1}^n) \tag{15.130}$$

$$g_b = \frac{1}{2}(g_{i+1}^n + g_{i-1}^n) + \frac{c}{2}(g_{i+1}^n - g_{i-1}^n) \tag{15.131}$$

Substituting the values of f_a, f_b, g_a, and g_b determined from Eqs. (15.128) to (15.131) into Eqs. (15.122) and (15.123) yields f_i^{n+1} and g_i^{n+1}. This procedure is the first method-of-characteristics approximation of the wave equation.

When solving linear PDEs, the finite difference equations approximating the characteristic equations and the compatibility equations, along with the interpolating polynomials used to determine the initial data, can be combined to yield a single finite difference equation for each dependent variable. In such cases, consistency, order, stability, convergence, and implicit numerical diffusion and dispersion can be investigated directly, as discussed in Chapter 10. When the PDE is nonlinear, the characteristic and compatibility equations must be integrated numerically, as illustrated by Eqs. (15.32) and (15.35). In such cases, it can be extremely tedious to combine the corresponding FDEs and the interpolating polynomials to obtain a single FDE.

Explicitly substituting Eqs. (15.128) to (15.131) into Eqs. (15.122) and (15.123) yields

$$f_i^{n+1} = \frac{1}{2}(f_{i+1}^n + f_{i-1}^n) - \frac{c}{2}(g_{i+1}^n - g_{i-1}^n) \tag{15.132}$$

$$g_i^{n+1} = \frac{1}{2}(g_{i+1}^n + g_{i-1}^n) - \frac{c}{2}(f_{i+1}^n - f_{i-1}^n) \tag{15.133}$$

Equations (15.132) and (15.133) are the explicit forms of the FDEs for the first method-of-characteristics approximation of the coupled convection equations that correspond to the linear wave equation. Equations (15.132) and (15.133) are identical to the Lax approximation of those equations [see Eqs. (15.58) and (15.59)], which is presented in Section 15.4. The consistency, order, stability, convergence, and implicit numerical diffusion and dispersion of Eqs. (15.132) and (15.133) are discussed in Section 15.4. The numerical solution of the example acoustics problem is presented in Example 15.2.

Second MOC Algorithm

Next, consider linear interpolation at point a using grid points $(i-1, n)$ and (i, n) and linear interpolation at point b using grid points (i, n) and $(i+1, n)$.

As shown in Section 12.11 [see Eq. (12.88)], this gives

$$f_a = f_i^n - c(f_i^n - f_{i-1}^n) \tag{15.134}$$

$$g_a = g_i^n - c(g_i^n - g_{i-1}^n) \tag{15.135}$$

In a similar manner, f_b and g_b are given by

$$f_b = f_i^n + c(f_{i+1}^n - f_i^n) \tag{15.136}$$

$$g_b = g_i^n + c(g_{i+1}^n - g_i^n) \tag{15.137}$$

Substituting Eqs. (15.134) to (15.137) into Eqs. (15.122) and (15.123) yields f_i^{n+1} and g_i^{n+1}. This procedure is the second method-of-characteristics approximation of the coupled convection equations that correspond to the wave equation.

Explicitly substituting Eqs. (15.134) to (15.137) into Eqs. (15.122) and (15.123) yields

$$f_i^{n+1} = f_i^n - \frac{c}{2}(g_{i+1}^n - g_{i-1}^n) + \frac{c}{2}(f_{i+1}^n - 2f_i^n + f_{i-1}^n) \tag{15.138}$$

$$g_i^{n+1} = g_i^n - \frac{c}{2}(f_{i+1}^n - f_{i-1}^n) + \frac{c}{2}(g_{i+1}^n - 2g_i^n + g_{i-1}^n) \tag{15.139}$$

Equations (15.138) and (15.139) are the explicit forms of the FDEs for the second method-of-characteristics approximation of the coupled convection equations that correspond to the linear wave equation. Equations (15.138) and (15.139) are identical to the first-order upwind approximation of those equations [see Eqs (15.77) and (15.78)], which is presented in Section 15.5.

The consistency, order, stability, convergence, and implicit numerical diffusion and dispersion of Eqs. (15.138) and (15.139) are discussed in Section 15.5. The numerical solution of the example acoustics problem is presented in Example 15.3.

Third MOC Algorithm

Finally, let us consider quadratic interpolation at both points a and b using grid points $(i-1, n)$, (i, n), and $(i+1, n)$. As shown in Section 12.11 [see Eq. (12.92)], this gives

$$f_a = f_i^n - \frac{c}{2}(f_{i+1}^n - f_{i-1}^n) + \frac{c^2}{2}(f_{i+1}^n - 2f_i^n + f_{i-1}^n) \tag{15.140}$$

$$g_a = g_i^n - \frac{c}{2}(g_{i+1}^n - g_{i-1}^n) + \frac{c^2}{2}(g_{i+1}^n - 2g_i^n + g_{i-1}^n) \tag{15.141}$$

In a similar manner, it can be shown that

$$f_b = f_i^n + \frac{c}{2}(f_{i+1}^n - f_{i-1}^n) + \frac{c^2}{2}(f_{i+1}^n - 2f_i^n + f_{i-1}^n) \tag{15.142}$$

$$g_b = g_i^n + \frac{c}{2}(g_{i+1}^n - g_{i-1}^n) + \frac{c^2}{2}(g_{i+1}^n - 2g_i^n + g_{i-1}^n) \tag{15.143}$$

Substituting the above results into Eqs. (15.122) and (15.123) yields f_i^{n+1} and g_i^{n+1}. This procedure is the third method-of-characteristics approximation of the coupled convection equations that correspond to the wave equation.

Explicitly substituting Eqs. (15.140) to (15.143) into Eqs. (15.122) and (15.123) yields

$$f_i^{n+1} = f_i^n - \frac{c}{2}(g_{i+1}^n - g_{i-1}^n) + \frac{c^2}{2}(f_{i+1}^n - 2f_i^n + f_{i-1}^n) \tag{15.144}$$

$$g_i^{n+1} = g_i^n - \frac{c}{2}(f_{i+1}^n - f_{i-1}^n) + \frac{c^2}{2}(g_{i+1}^n - 2g_i^n + g_{i-1}^n) \tag{15.145}$$

Equations (15.144) and (15.145) are the explicit forms of the FDEs for the third method-of-characteristics approximation of the coupled convection equations that correspond to the linear wave equation. These equations are identical to the Lax–Wendroff one-step approximation of those equations [see Eqs. (15.96) and (15.97)], which is presented in Section 15.7. The consistency, order, stability, convergence, and implicit numerical diffusion and dispersion of Eqs. (15.144) and (15.145) are discussed in Section 15.7. The numerical solution of the example acoustics problem is presented in Example 15.5.

The results presented in this section are all for the coupled convection equations that correspond to the linear homogeneous wave equation. In that case, the differential equation for the characteristic curves, Eq. (15.24), and the corresponding compatibility equation, Eq. (15.29), can be integrated exactly. The results are Eqs. (15.30) and (15.31), respectively. Equations (15.30) and (15.31) can be combined with interpolating polynomials for $f(x)$ and $g(x)$ at time level n to yield a single finite difference equation for each dependent variable. Equations (15.132) and (15.133), (15.138) and (15.139), and (15.144) and (15.145) are the results of such combinations.

Finite difference equations such as these mask the essential features of the numerical method of characteristics. In essence, the method of characteristics is a coordinate transformation that transforms the governing partial differential equations from physical coordinates (e.g., x and t) to characteristic coordinates (i.e., position along the characteristic curves). In the numerical method of characteristics, the characteristic coordinate system is first constructed by numerically integrating the characteristic equations. The distribution of the dependent variables along the characteristic curves is determined next, by numerically integrating the compatibility equations along the characteristic curves. When the inverse marching method illustrated in Fig. 15.9 is employed, a third step, interpolation in the initial-data surface, is required.

In the general case for nonlinear nonhomogeneous hyperbolic PDEs, each of these three steps must be performed explicitly. Only for linear PDEs can these three steps be combined into a simple single finite difference equation for each dependent variable.

An introduction to the numerical method of characteristics for nonlinear hyperbolic PDEs is presented in Example 12.8. A similar procedure can be developed for a coupled system of two or more nonlinear hyperbolic PDEs.

A good understanding of the method of characteristics is essential to the development of finite difference methods for solving hyperbolic partial differential equations. Physical paths of propagation of information through the solution domain are present. To obtain physically correct numerical solutions of hyperbolic partial differential equations, proper account of these paths of propagation must be taken.

15.11 THE FLUX-VECTOR-SPLITTING METHOD

As shown in Section 15.2, the coupled system of two convection equations that corresponds to the linear wave equation, like all hyperbolic PDEs, has preferred paths of information propagation: the two characteristic curves $dx/dt = +a$ and $dx/dt = -a$. Information comes from both the left and the right at every point.

The numerical method of characteristics presented in Section 15.10 is basically a coordinate transformation from xt space to characteristic space. The paths of information propagation—the characteristics—become the independent variables, and the numerical paths of propagation match the physical paths of propagation exactly. Unfortunately, the characteristic curves must be constructed numerically, which is a formidable task in steady three-dimensional problems and unsteady two- and three-dimensional problems. Examples of such procedures are presented by Vadyak, Hoffman, and Bishop (1984), Wang and Hoffman (1988), and Marcum and Hoffman (1985), respectively.

When the spatial derivatives are approximated by *centered* finite difference approximations, the preferred paths of information propagation are ignored. Upwind methods that are based on a method-of-characteristics analysis of the PDEs to identify the upwind direction associated with each spatial derivative yield finite difference methods that account for the proper direction of signal propagation, as illustrated in Sections 15.5 and 15.10. That approach becomes quite complicated for nonlinear PDEs, large systems of PDEs, and multidimensional problems. The *flux-vector-splitting* method presented by Steger and Warming (1981) is a systematic approach for accomplishing the identification of the direction of information propagation of each spatial derivative without resorting to a complicated method-of-characteristics analysis. The Steger-Warming flux-vector-splitting method is applied to the coupled system of convection equations that correspond to the wave equation in this section.

Consider the coupled system of linear convection equations:

$$\bar{f}_t + a\bar{g}_x = 0 \tag{15.146}$$

$$\bar{g}_t + a\bar{f}_x + 0 \tag{15.147}$$

Equations (15.146) and (15.147) can be written in the so-called conservation form

$$\frac{\partial \mathbf{Q}}{\partial t} + \frac{\partial \mathbf{E}}{\partial x} = \mathbf{0} \tag{15.148}$$

where $\mathbf{Q}$ is the 2×1 solution vector and $\mathbf{E}$ is the 2×1 flux vector:

$$\mathbf{Q} = \begin{bmatrix} \bar{f} \\ \bar{g} \end{bmatrix} \quad \text{and} \quad \mathbf{E} = \begin{bmatrix} a\bar{g} \\ a\bar{f} \end{bmatrix} \tag{15.149}$$

Equation (15.148) can be written in the form:

$$\boxed{\frac{\partial \mathbf{Q}}{\partial t} + \mathbf{A}\frac{\partial \mathbf{Q}}{\partial x} = 0} \tag{15.150}$$

where $\mathbf{A}$ is the Jacobian matrix

$$\mathbf{A} = \frac{\partial \mathbf{E}}{\partial \mathbf{Q}} = \frac{\partial(a\bar{g}, a\bar{f})}{\partial(\bar{f}, \bar{g})} = \begin{bmatrix} 0 & a \\ a & 0 \end{bmatrix} \tag{15.151}$$

The matrix $\mathbf{A}$ can be diagonalized as follows:

$$\boxed{\mathbf{A} = \mathbf{S}\mathbf{\Lambda}\mathbf{S}^{-1}} \tag{14.152}$$

where $\mathbf{\Lambda}$ is the diagonal matrix of eigenvalues, $\mathbf{S}$ is the corresponding matrix of eigenvectors, and $\mathbf{S}^{-1}$ is the inverse of $\mathbf{S}$.

The eigenvalues of $\mathbf{A}$, determined from $\det(\mathbf{A} - \lambda\mathbf{I}) = 0$, are $\lambda = \pm a$. The positive eigenvalue $\lambda = +a$ corresponds to information being propagated to the right, which comes from the left. The negative eigenvalue $\lambda = -a$ corresponds to information being propagated to the left, which comes from the right. Thus, the eigenvalue matrix Λ is

$$\mathbf{\Lambda} = \begin{bmatrix} a & 0 \\ 0 & -a \end{bmatrix} \tag{15.153}$$

The eigenvalue matrix $\mathbf{\Lambda}$ can be split into two matrices containing only positive and only negative eigenvalues:

$$\mathbf{\Lambda} = \mathbf{\Lambda}^+ + \mathbf{\Lambda}^- = \begin{bmatrix} a & 0 \\ 0 & 0 \end{bmatrix} + \begin{bmatrix} 0 & 0 \\ 0 & -a \end{bmatrix} \tag{15.154}$$

The eigenvectors of $\mathbf{A}$, determined from $(\mathbf{A} - \lambda\mathbf{I})\mathbf{x} = 0$, are

$$\mathbf{S} = \begin{bmatrix} 1 & -1 \\ 1 & 1 \end{bmatrix} \tag{15.155}$$

The inverse of $\mathbf{S}$ is

$$\mathbf{S}^{-1} = \frac{1}{2}\begin{bmatrix} 1 & 1 \\ -1 & 1 \end{bmatrix} \tag{15.156}$$

The Jacobian matrix $\mathbf{A}$ can be split as follows:

$$\mathbf{A} = \mathbf{S\Lambda S}^{-1} = \mathbf{S}(\mathbf{\Lambda}^+ + \mathbf{\Lambda}^-)\mathbf{S}^{-1} = \mathbf{S\Lambda}^+\mathbf{S}^{-1} + \mathbf{S\Lambda}^-\mathbf{S}^{-1} = \mathbf{A}^+ + \mathbf{A}^- \tag{15.157}$$

where

$$\mathbf{A}^+ = \mathbf{S\Lambda}^+\mathbf{S}^{-1} = \begin{bmatrix} 1 & -1 \\ 1 & 1 \end{bmatrix}\begin{bmatrix} a & 0 \\ 0 & 0 \end{bmatrix}\frac{1}{2}\begin{bmatrix} 1 & 1 \\ -1 & 1 \end{bmatrix} = \frac{1}{2}\begin{bmatrix} a & a \\ a & a \end{bmatrix} \tag{15.158a}$$

$$\mathbf{A}^- = \mathbf{S\Lambda}^-\mathbf{S}^{-1} = \begin{bmatrix} 1 & -1 \\ 1 & 1 \end{bmatrix}\begin{bmatrix} 0 & 0 \\ 0 & -a \end{bmatrix}\frac{1}{2}\begin{bmatrix} 1 & 1 \\ -1 & 1 \end{bmatrix} = \frac{1}{2}\begin{bmatrix} -a & a \\ a & -a \end{bmatrix} \tag{15.158b}$$

For homogeneous functions, $\mathbf{E} = \mathbf{AQ}$. Thus, the flux vector $\mathbf{E}$ can be split as follows:

$$\mathbf{E} = \mathbf{AQ} = (\mathbf{A}^+ + \mathbf{A}^-)\mathbf{Q} = \mathbf{A}^+\mathbf{Q} + \mathbf{A}^-\mathbf{Q} = \mathbf{E}^+ + \mathbf{E}^- \tag{15.159}$$

where

$$\mathbf{E}^+ = \mathbf{A}^+\mathbf{Q} = \frac{1}{2}\begin{bmatrix} a & a \\ a & a \end{bmatrix}\begin{bmatrix} \bar{f} \\ \bar{g} \end{bmatrix} = \frac{a}{2}\begin{bmatrix} (\bar{f} + \bar{g}) \\ (\bar{f} + \bar{g}) \end{bmatrix} \tag{15.160a}$$

$$\mathbf{E}^- = \mathbf{A}^-\mathbf{Q} = \frac{1}{2}\begin{bmatrix} -a & a \\ a & -a \end{bmatrix}\begin{bmatrix} \bar{f} \\ \bar{g} \end{bmatrix} = \frac{a}{2}\begin{bmatrix} -(\bar{f} - \bar{g}) \\ (\bar{f} - \bar{g}) \end{bmatrix} \tag{15.160b}$$

Thus, Eq. (15.148) can be written as:

$$\boxed{\frac{\partial \mathbf{Q}}{\partial t} + \frac{\partial \mathbf{E}^+}{\partial x} + \frac{\partial \mathbf{E}^-}{\partial x} = 0} \tag{15.161}$$

Substituting Eq. (15.160) into Eq. (15.161) verifies that Eq. (15.161) is identical to Eq. (15.148). Equation (15.161) is the flux-vector-split form of the partial differential equations.

The simplest procedure for approximating Eq. (15.161) is to replace the time derivative $\partial \mathbf{Q}/\partial t$ by the first-order forward-difference approximation at grid point (i, n) [Eq. (10.54)], the space derivative $\partial \mathbf{E}^+/\partial x$ by the first-order backward-difference approximation [Eq. (10.63*b*)], and the space derivative $\partial \mathbf{E}^-/\partial x$ by the first-order forward-difference approximation [Eq. (10.62*b*)]. This yields

$$\mathbf{Q}_i^{n+1} = \mathbf{Q}_i^n - \frac{\Delta t}{\Delta x}\left(\mathbf{E}^+|_i^n - \mathbf{E}^+|_{i-1}^n\right) - \frac{\Delta t}{\Delta x}\left(\mathbf{E}^-|_{i+1}^n - \mathbf{E}^-|_i^n\right) \tag{15.162}$$

Substituting $\mathbf{Q}$ and $\mathbf{E}$ into Eq. (15.162) yields the first-order upwind results presented in Section 15.5 [see Eqs. (15.77) and (15.78)]. Consequently, the flux-vector-splitting method presented by Steger and Warming yields the same results obtained by a method-of-characteristics splitting. Thus, the consistency, order, stability, and convergence analysis are the same as those presented in Section 15.5. For the coupled system of two linear convection equations, the two procedures are comparable in complexity of formulation. However, for nonlinear PDEs and multidimensional problems, the Steger–Warming flux-vector-splitting method is more straightforward than the method of characteristics.

Example 15.8. Solution by the flux-vector-splitting method. The Steger–Warming flux-vector-splitting method yields the same finite difference equations as the first-order upwind method presented in Section 15.5. Consequently, the solution to the acoustics problem presented in Section 15.1 by the flux-vector-splitting method is identical to the solution by the first-order upwind method, which is presented in Example 15.3.

In summary, the flux-vector-splitting method yields a form of the PDE that can be solved by upwind methods that account for the directions of information propagation. First-order upwind methods introduce significant amounts of implicit numerical diffusion into the solution, as illustrated in Example 15.3. Second-order upwind methods can be developed to give more accurate solutions of convection problems.

15.12 THE BACKWARD-TIME CENTERED-SPACE METHOD

The method of characteristics, the Lax method, the first-order upwind method, the leapfrog method, the Lax–Wendroff type methods, and the flux-vector-splitting methods are all explicit finite difference methods. Explicit methods share one undesirable feature: they are only conditionally stable. Consequently, the allowable time step is usually quite small, and the amount of computational effort required to obtain the solution to some problems is immense. On the other hand, *implicit* finite difference methods, in which the unknown value of the solution at a point is implied in terms of its unknown neighbors rather than being explicitly given in terms of known initial values, are unconditionally stable. There is no limit on the allowable time step required to achieve a stable solution. There is, of course, a practical limit on the time step required to maintain the truncation errors within reasonable limits, but this is not a stability consideration: it is an accuracy consideration. The relative advantages and disadvantages of explicit and implicit finite difference methods are discussed in the introductory paragraphs of Section 12.12.

In this section, we will solve the pair of first-order PDEs, $\bar{f}_t + a\bar{g}_x = 0$ and $\bar{g}_t + a\bar{f}_x = 0$, which correspond to the linear wave equation, by the backward-time centered-space (BTCS) method. This method is also called the fully implicit method. The finite difference equations (FDEs) that approximate the partial differential equations are obtained by replacing the exact partial derivatives $\bar{f}_t$ and $\bar{g}_t$ by the first-order backward-difference approximation [Eq. (10.57)] and the exact partial derivatives $\bar{f}_x$ and $\bar{g}_x$ by the second-order centered-space approximation [Eq. (10.65b)]. The resulting finite difference equations are

$$-\frac{c}{2}g_{i-1}^{n+1} + f_i^{n+1} + \frac{c}{2}g_{i+1}^{n+1} = f_i^n \tag{15.163}$$

$$-\frac{c}{2}f_{i-1}^{n+1} + g_i^{n+1} + \frac{c}{2}f_{i+1}^{n+1} = g_i^n \tag{15.164}$$

where $c = a\Delta t/\Delta x$ is the convection number.

Equation (15.163) cannot be solved explicitly for f_i^{n+1}, because the two unknown neighboring values g_{i-1}^{n+1} and g_{i+1}^{n+1} also appear in the equation. Likewise, Eq. (15.164) cannot be solved explicitly for g_i^{n+1}, because the two unknown neighboring values f_{i-1}^{n+1} and f_{i+1}^{n+1} also appear in the equation. The values of f_i^{n+1} and g_i^{n+1} are implied in Eqs. (15.163) and (15.164), however. Therefore, the BTCS method is an implicit method.

The first form of the modified differential equation (MDE) corresponding to Eq. (15.163), obtained by writing Taylor series for $f(x, t)$ and $g(x, t)$ about point $(i, n+1)$, is

$$f_t + ag_x = \frac{1}{2}f_{tt}\,\Delta t - \frac{1}{6}f_{ttt}\,\Delta t^2 + \cdots - \frac{1}{6}ag_{xxx}\,\Delta x^2 + \cdots \tag{15.165}$$

and the second form of the MDE is

$$f_t + ag_x = \frac{1}{2}a^2\,\Delta t f_{xx} + \left(-\frac{1}{3}a^3\,\Delta t^2 - \frac{1}{6}a\,\Delta x^2\right)g_{xxx} - \cdots \tag{15.166}$$

As $\Delta t \to 0$ and $\Delta x \to 0$, the truncation error terms go to zero, and Eq. (15.165) approaches $f_t + ag_x = 0$. Consequently, Eq. (15.163) is consistent with the PDE $\bar{f}_t + a\bar{g}_x = 0$. From Eq. (15.166), the FDE is $O(\Delta t) + O(\Delta x^2)$. From Eq. (15.166), it is apparent that both implicit numerical diffusion and dispersion are present. Similar conclusions apply to Eq. (15.164). Applying the von Neumann stability analysis to Eqs. (15.163) and (15.164) yields

$$\begin{bmatrix} 1 & Ic\sin\theta \\ Ic\sin\theta & 1 \end{bmatrix} \begin{bmatrix} f_i^{n+1} \\ g_i^{n+1} \end{bmatrix} = \begin{bmatrix} f_i^n \\ g_i^n \end{bmatrix} \tag{15.167}$$

which can be written as

$$\mathbf{A}\mathbf{F}^{n+1} = \mathbf{F}^n \tag{15.168}$$

where $\mathbf{F}^{\mathrm{T}} = (f_i \ g_i)$. Solving for $\mathbf{F}^{n+1}$ gives

$$\mathbf{F}^{n+1} = \mathbf{A}^{-1}\mathbf{F}^n = \mathbf{G}\mathbf{F}^n \tag{15.169}$$

The eigenvalues of the amplification matrix $\mathbf{G} = \mathbf{A}^{-1}$ are the reciprocals of the eigenvalues of the matrix $\mathbf{A}$. Thus,

$$\lambda = \frac{1}{1 \pm Ic\sin\theta} \tag{15.170}$$

Since $|1 \pm Ic\sin\theta| \geq 1$ for all values of $\theta = k\,\Delta x$ and c, the BTCS method is unconditionally stable when applied to the wave equation. The BTCS method applied to the wave equation is consistent and unconditionally stable; consequently, by the Lax equivalence theorem, it is a convergent finite difference approximation of that equation.

Consider now the solution by the BTCS method of the two coupled linear convection equations that correspond to the linear wave equation. The finite difference grid for advancing the solution from time level n to time level $n + 1$ is illustrated in Fig. 15.10. Equations (15.163) and (15.164) apply directly at points 3 to $imax - 2$ in Fig. 15.10. At points 2 and $imax - 1$, the FDEs are modified by transferring the known values $\overline{f}(0, t)$, $\overline{f}(L, t)$, $\overline{g}(0, t)$, and $\overline{g}(L, t)$ to the right-hand side of the equations. The following set of simultaneous linear equations is

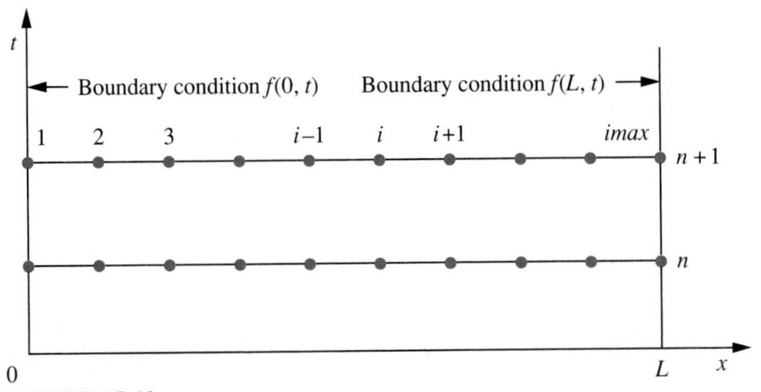

FIGURE 15.10
Finite difference grid for implicit methods.

obtained:

$$
\begin{aligned}
f_2^{n+1} + \frac{c}{2} g_3^{n+1} &= a_2 \\
g_2^{n+1} + \frac{c}{2} f_3^{n+1} &= b_2 \\
-\frac{c}{2} g_2^{n+1} + f_3^{n+1} + \frac{c}{2} g_4^{n+1} &= a_3 \\
-\frac{c}{2} f_2^{n+1} + g_3^{n+1} + \frac{c}{2} f_4^{n+1} &= b_3 \\
&\vdots \\
-\frac{c}{2} g_{imax-2}^{n+1} + f_{imax-1}^{n+1} &= a_{imax-1} \\
-\frac{c}{2} f_{imax-2}^{n+1} + g_{imax-1}^{n+1} &= b_{imax-1}
\end{aligned}
\tag{15.171}
$$

where the nonhomogeneous terms a_i and b_i are given by

$$
\begin{aligned}
a_2 &= f_2^n + \frac{c}{2}\overline{g}(0, t^{n+1}) \\
b_2 &= g_2 + \frac{c}{2}\overline{f}(0, t^{n+1}) \\
a_3 &= f_3^n \\
b_3 &= g_3^n \\
&\vdots \\
a_{imax-1} &= f_{imax-1}^n - \frac{c}{2}\overline{g}(L, t^{n+1}) \\
b_{imax-1} &= g_{imax-1}^n - \frac{c}{2}\overline{f}(L, t^{n+1})
\end{aligned}
\tag{15.172}
$$

Equation (15.171) is a 2×2 block tridiagonal system of linear equations. That system of equations may be written as

$$
\mathbf{A}\mathbf{x} = \mathbf{c} \tag{15.173}
$$

where

$$
\mathbf{A} = \begin{bmatrix}
\mathbf{D} & \mathbf{U} & \mathbf{0} & \mathbf{0} & \cdots & \mathbf{0} & \mathbf{0} & \mathbf{0} \\
\mathbf{L} & \mathbf{D} & \mathbf{U} & \mathbf{0} & \cdots & \mathbf{0} & \mathbf{0} & \mathbf{0} \\
\mathbf{0} & \mathbf{L} & \mathbf{D} & \mathbf{U} & \cdots & \mathbf{0} & \mathbf{0} & \mathbf{0} \\
\vdots & \vdots & \vdots & \vdots & \ddots & \vdots & \vdots & \vdots \\
\mathbf{0} & \mathbf{0} & \mathbf{0} & \mathbf{0} & \cdots & \mathbf{L} & \mathbf{D} & \mathbf{U} \\
\mathbf{0} & \mathbf{0} & \mathbf{0} & \mathbf{0} & \cdots & \mathbf{0} & \mathbf{L} & \mathbf{D}
\end{bmatrix} \tag{15.174}
$$

$$\mathbf{L} = \begin{bmatrix} 0 & -\frac{c}{2} \\ -\frac{c}{2} & 0 \end{bmatrix}, \qquad \mathbf{D} = \begin{bmatrix} 1 & 0 \\ 0 & 1 \end{bmatrix}, \qquad \mathbf{U} = \begin{bmatrix} 0 & \frac{c}{2} \\ \frac{c}{2} & 0 \end{bmatrix} \tag{15.175}$$

$$\mathbf{x} = \begin{bmatrix} X_2 \\ X_3 \\ \vdots \\ X_{imax-1} \end{bmatrix}, \qquad \mathbf{c} = \begin{bmatrix} C_2 \\ C_3 \\ \vdots \\ C_{imax-1} \end{bmatrix} \tag{15.176}$$

$$X_i = \begin{bmatrix} f_i \\ g_i \end{bmatrix} \quad \text{and} \quad C_i = \begin{bmatrix} a_i \\ b_i \end{bmatrix} \tag{15.177}$$

Equation (15.173) can be solved efficiently by the block tridiagonal algorithm discussed in Section 1.5.

Because of the special structure of Eqs. (15.163) and (15.164), they can be decoupled into two tridiagonal sets of equations, each of which can be solved by the Thomas algorithm. This is accomplished by applying Eq. (15.163) at grid points 2, 4, 6, . . . , $imax - 1$ and Eq. (15.164) at grid points 3, 5, 7, . . . , $imax - 2$. This procedure requires that $imax$ be an odd number. Thus, Eqs. (15.163) and (15.164) yield

$$\begin{aligned}
f_2^{n+1} + \frac{c}{2} g_3^n &= b_2 \\
-\frac{c}{2} f_2^{n+1} + g_3^{n+1} + \frac{c}{2} f_4^{n+1} &= b_3 \\
-\frac{c}{2} g_3^{n+1} + f_4^{n+1} + \frac{c}{2} g_5^{n+1} &= b_4 \\
&\vdots \\
-\frac{c}{2} g_{imax-2}^{n+1} + f_{imax-1}^{n+1} &= b_{imax-1}
\end{aligned} \tag{15.178}$$

where the nonhomogeneous terms b_i are given by

$$\begin{aligned}
b_2 &= f_2^n + \frac{c}{2}\overline{g}(0, t^{n+1}) \\
b_3 &= g_3^n \\
b_4 &= f_4^n \\
&\vdots \\
b_{imax-1} &= f_{imax-1}^n - \frac{c}{2}\overline{g}(L, t^{n+1})
\end{aligned} \tag{15.179}$$

Equation (15.178) can be solved for f_2^{n+1}, g_3^{n+1}, f_4^{n+1}, g_5^{n+1}, and so on, using the Thomas algorithm. A similar set of equations can be developed for g_2^{n+1}, f_3^{n+1}, g_4^{n+1}, f_5^{n+1}, and so forth.

Example 15.9. Solution by the BTCS method. We will solve the acoustics problem presented in Section 15.1 by the BTCS method for $\Delta x = 0.05$ m. The units used in the FDEs and the definition of the convection number, $c = \Delta t/\Delta x$, are the same as presented in Example 15.1. The boundary conditions required by the implicit finite difference method are placed at $x = -9.0$ and 12.0 m (i.e., 200 grid points to the left and right of the extent of the initial pressure distribution). The results are presented in Fig. 15.11 at times from 0.1 to 0.5 ms for $c = 0.5$, corresponding to $\Delta t = 0.025$ ms, at 1.0 ms for $c = 0.1$, 0.5, 0.9 and 1.0, corresponding to $\Delta t = 0.005$, 0.025, 0.045, and 0.05 ms, respectively, and in Fig. 15.12 at 1.0 ms for $c = 1.0$, 2.5, 5.0, and 10.0, corresponding to $\Delta t = 0.05$, 0.125, 0.25, and 0.5 ms, respectively.

Several important features of the BTCS method applied to the wave equation are illustrated in Figs. 15.11 and 15.12. For $c = 0.5$, the solution is severely damped as the waves propagate. The peaks of the waves are rounded. These effects are due to implicit numerical diffusion and dispersion. At $t = 1.0$ ms, the best solutions are obtained for the smallest values of c. For the larger values of c (i.e., $c \geq 5.0$), the solutions barely resemble the exact solution. These results demonstrate that the method is indeed stable for $c > 1.0$, but that the quality of the solution is very poor. The peaks in the solution at $t = 1.0$ ms for the different values of c are lagging further and further behind the peaks in the exact solution, which demonstrates that the numerical signal propagation

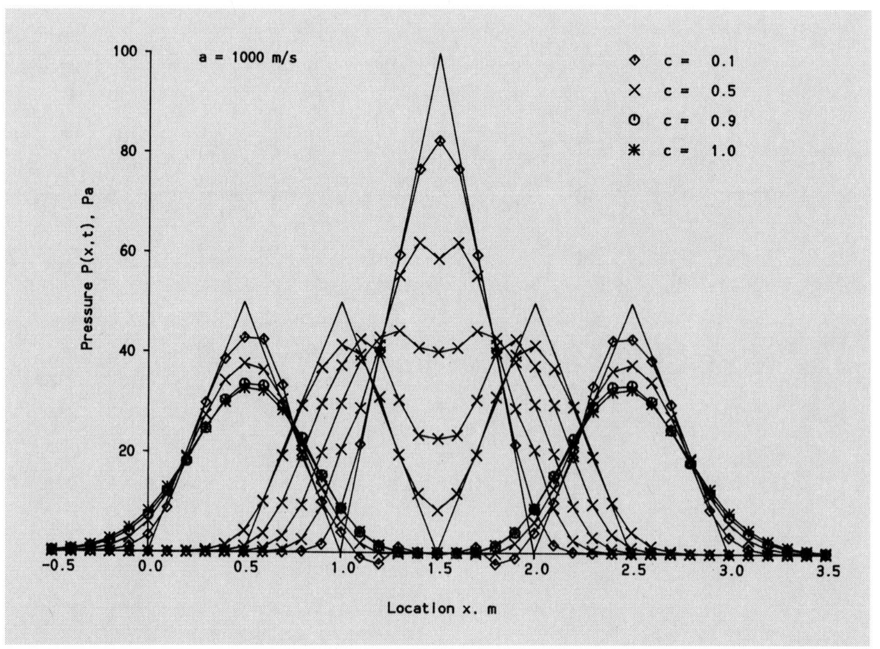

FIGURE 15.11
Solution by the BTCS method.

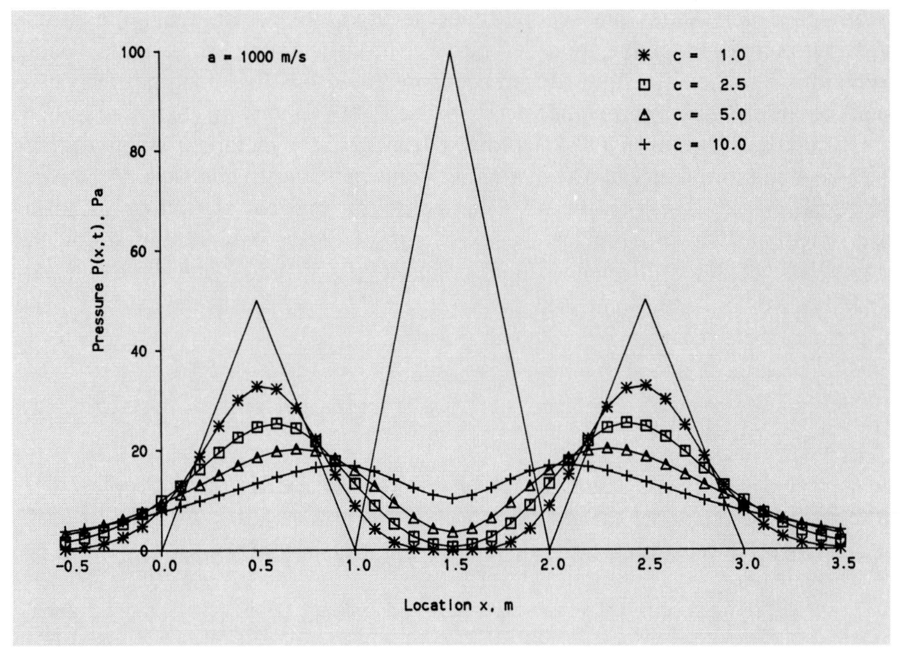

FIGURE 15.12
Solution at t = 1.0 ms by the BTCS method.

speed is less than the physical signal propagation speed. This effect is due to numerical dispersion. Overall, the BTCS method applied to the wave equation yields rather poor results.

The BTCS method becomes considerably more complicated when applied to nonlinear PDEs, systems of PDEs, and multidimensional PDEs. The procedure and the problems are discussed in Section 15.16.

In summary, the BTCS approximation of the wave equation is implicit, single-step, two-level, $O(\Delta t) + O(\Delta x^2)$, unconditionally stable, and convergent. The implicit nature of the method yields a set of finite difference equations, which must be solved simultaneously. For one-dimensional problems, that can be accomplished by a block tridiagonal algorithm. The infinite numerical signal propagation speed does not correctly model the finite physical signal propagation speed. The BTCS approximation of the wave equation yields poor results, except for very small values of the convection number c, for which explicit methods are usually more efficient.

15.13 THE CRANK–NICOLSON METHOD

The backward-time centered-space (BTCS) method developed in Section 15.12 has a major advantage over explicit methods: it is unconditionally stable. It is an implicit, two-level, single-step method. The finite difference approximations of the space derivatives are second-order accurate. However, the finite difference approximations of the time derivatives are only first-order accurate. Using a second-order accurate finite difference approximation for the time derivative would be an obvious improvement.

Crank and Nicolson (1947) proposed an $O(\Delta t^2)$ method for solving the diffusion equation. Let's apply that same concept to solve the pair of convection equations, $\overline{f}_t + a\overline{g}_x = 0$ and $\overline{g}_t + a\overline{f}_x = 0$, that correspond to the linear wave equation. We will replace the exact partial derivatives $\overline{f}_t$ and $\overline{g}_t$ by the second-order centered-difference approximation [Eq. (10.59)] and the exact partial derivatives $\overline{f}_x$ and $\overline{g}_x$ at grid point $(i, n + 1/2)$ by the averages of $\overline{f}_x$ and $\overline{g}_x$ at time levels n and $n + 1$. Thus,

$$\overline{f}_x|_i^{n+1/2} = \frac{1}{2}(\overline{f}_x|_i^{n+1} + \overline{f}_x|_i^n) \quad \text{and} \quad \overline{g}_x|_i^{n+1/2} = \frac{1}{2}(\overline{g}_x|_i^{n+1} + \overline{g}_x|_i^n) \tag{15.180}$$

The partial derivatives $\overline{f}_x$ and $\overline{g}_x$ at time levels n and $n + 1$ are replaced by the second-order centered-difference approximations [Eqs. (10.64*b*) and (10.65*b*), respectively]. The resulting finite difference approximation of $\overline{f}_t + a\overline{g}_x = 0$ is

$$\frac{f_i^{n+1} - f_i^n}{\Delta t} + a\frac{1}{2}\left(\frac{g_{i+1}^{n+1} - g_{i-1}^{n+1}}{2\Delta x} + \frac{g_{i+1}^n - g_{i-1}^n}{2\Delta x}\right) = 0 \tag{15.181}$$

A similar finite difference approximation can be developed for $\overline{g}_t + a\overline{f}_x = 0$. Rearranging the two FDEs yields

$$-\frac{c}{4}g_{i-1}^{n+1} + f_i^{n+1} + \frac{c}{4}g_{i+1}^{n+1} = \frac{c}{4}g_{i-1}^n + f_i^n - \frac{c}{4}g_{i+1}^n \tag{15.182}$$

$$-\frac{c}{4}f_{i-1}^{n+1} + g_i^{n+1} + \frac{c}{4}f_{i+1}^{n+1} = \frac{c}{4}f_{i-1}^n + g_i^n - \frac{c}{4}f_{i+1}^n \tag{15.183}$$

where $c = a\,\Delta t/\Delta x$ is the convection number.

The first form of the modified equation (MDE) corresponding to Eq. (15.182), obtained by writing Taylor series for $f(x, t)$ and $g(x, t)$ about point $(i, n + \frac{1}{2})$, is

$$f_t + ag_x = -\frac{1}{24}f_{ttt}\,\Delta t^2 - \frac{1}{3840}f_{ttttt}\,\Delta t^4 - \cdots - \frac{1}{8}ag_{ttx}\,\Delta t^2 - \frac{1}{48}a\,\Delta t^2\,\Delta x^2 g_{ttxxx}$$
$$- \frac{1}{384}a\,\Delta t^4 g_{ttttx} - \frac{1}{6}a\,\Delta x^2 g_{xxx} - \frac{1}{120}a\,\Delta x^4 g_{xxxxx} - \cdots \tag{15.184}$$

and the second form of the MDE is

$$f_t + a g_x = \left(-\frac{1}{12}a^3\,\Delta t^2 - \frac{1}{6}a\,\Delta x^2\right)g_{xxx}$$
$$+\left(-\frac{1}{80}a^5\,\Delta t^4 - \frac{1}{24}a^3\,\Delta t^2\,\Delta x^2 - \frac{1}{120}a\,\Delta x^4\right)g_{xxxxx} + \cdots \tag{15.185}$$

As $\Delta t \to 0$ and $\Delta x \to 0$, the truncation error terms go to zero and Eq. (15.184) approaches $f_t + a g_x = 0$. Consequently Eq. (15.182) is a consistent approximation of $\overline{f}_t + a\overline{g}_x = 0$. The truncation error is $O(\Delta t^2) + O(\Delta x^2)$. Only odd spatial derivatives appear in Eq. (15.185), so implicit numerical dispersion is present, but there is no implicit numerical diffusion. The eigenvalues of the amplification matrix corresponding to Eqs. (15.182) and (15.183) are

$$\lambda = \frac{1 \pm I(c/2)\sin\theta}{1 \pm I(c/2)\sin\theta} \tag{15.186}$$

Equation (15.186) shows that $|\lambda| = 1$ for all values of c and $\theta = k\,\Delta x$. Consequently, the Crank–Nicolson method is unconditionally stable when applied to the wave equation. The result $|\lambda| = 1$ shows that the method has no implicit numerical diffusion, which is also demonstrated by Eq. (15.185). The Crank–Nicolson approximation of the wave equation is consistent and unconditionally stable; consequently, by the Lax equivalence theorem, it is a convergent finite difference approximation of that equation.

Now consider the solution of the wave equation by the Crank–Nicolson method. The finite difference grid for advancing the solution from time level n to time level $n+1$ is presented in Figure 15.10. Equations (15.182) and (15.183) apply directly at points 3 to $imax - 3$. At points 2 and $imax - 1$, the FDEs are modified by transferring the known values $\overline{f}(0, t)$, $\overline{f}(L, t)$, $\overline{g}(0, t)$, and $\overline{g}(L, t)$ to the right-hand side of the equations. The following set of simultaneous linear equations is obtained:

$$\begin{aligned}
f_2^{n+1} + \frac{c}{4}g_3^{n+1} &= a_2 \\
g_2^{n+1} + \frac{c}{4}f_3^{n+1} &= b_2 \\
-\frac{c}{4}g_2^{n+1} + f_3^{n+1} + \frac{c}{4}g_4^{n+1} &= a_3 \\
-\frac{c}{4}f_2^{n+1} + g_3^{n+1} + \frac{c}{4}f_4^{n+1} &= b_3 \\
&\vdots \\
-\frac{c}{4}g_{imax-2}^{n+1} + f_{imax-1}^{n+1} &= a_{imax-1} \\
-\frac{c}{4}f_{imax-2}^{n+1} + g_{imax-1}^{n+1} &= b_{imax-1}
\end{aligned} \tag{15.187}$$

where the nonhomogeneous terms a_i and b_i are given by

$$a_2 = \frac{c}{4}g(0, t^n) + f_2^n - \frac{c}{4}g_3^n + \frac{c}{4}\overline{g}(0, t^{n+1})$$

$$b_2 = \frac{c}{4}f(0, t^n) + g_2^n - \frac{c}{4}f_3^n + \frac{c}{4}\overline{f}(0, t^{n+1})$$

$$a_3 = \frac{c}{4}g_2^n + f_3^n - \frac{c}{4}g_4^n$$

$$b_3 = \frac{c}{4}f_2^n + g_3^n - \frac{c}{4}f_4^n$$

$$\vdots$$

$$a_{imax-1} = \frac{c}{4}g_{imax-2}^n + f_{imax-1}^n - \frac{c}{4}g(L, t^n) - \frac{c}{4}\overline{g}(L, t^{n+1})$$

$$b_{imax-1} = \frac{c}{4}f_{imax-2}^n + g_{imax-1}^n - \frac{c}{4}f(L, t^n) - \frac{c}{4}\overline{f}(L, t^{n+1}) \qquad (15.188)$$

Equation (15.187) is a 2×2 block tridiagonal system of linear equations. This system of equations is very similar to the system of equations developed in Section 15.12 for the backward-time centered-space (BTCS) method. Consequently, the present system of equations can be solved by the procedures discussed in Section 15.12. Equation (15.187) can be uncoupled into two tridiagonal sets of equations, similar to Eq. (15.178).

Like the backward-time centered-space method, the Crank–Nicolson method is unconditionally stable. Consequently, the solution at a given time level can be reached with much less computational effort by taking large time steps. The time step is limited only by accuracy requirements.

Example 15.10. Solution by the Crank–Nicolson method. We will solve the acoustics problem presented in Section 15.1 by the Crank–Nicolson method for $\Delta x = 0.05$ m. The units used in the FDEs and the definition of the convection number, $c = \Delta t/\Delta x$, are the same as presented in Example 15.1. The boundary conditions are treated as described for the BTCS method in Example 15.9. The results are presented in Fig. 15.13 at times from 0.1 to 0.5 ms for $c = 0.5$, corresponding to $\Delta t = 0.025$ ms, at 1.0 ms for $c = 0.1$, 0.5, 0.9, and 1.0, corresponding to $\Delta t = 0.005$, 0.025, 0.045, and 0.05 ms, respectively, and in Fig. 15.14 at 1.0 ms for $c = 1.0$, 2.5, 5.0, and 10.0, corresponding to $\Delta t = 0.05$, 0.125, 0.25, and 0.5 ms, respectively.

Several important features of the Crank–Nicolson method applied to the wave equation are illustrated in Figs. 15.13 and 15.14. For $c = 0.5$, the solution is slightly damped as the wave propagates. The peak of the wave is rounded. At $t = 1.0$ ms, the best solutions are obtained for small values of c. For the larger values of c (i.e., $c \geq 2.0$), the numerical solution lags the exact solution severely, which demonstrates that the numerical signal propagation speed is less than the physical signal propagation speed. This effect is due to the numerical dispersion present in the method. Overall, the Crank–Nicolson method applied to the wave equation gives good results for $c \leq 1.0$, but does not perform very well for $c \geq 2.0$.

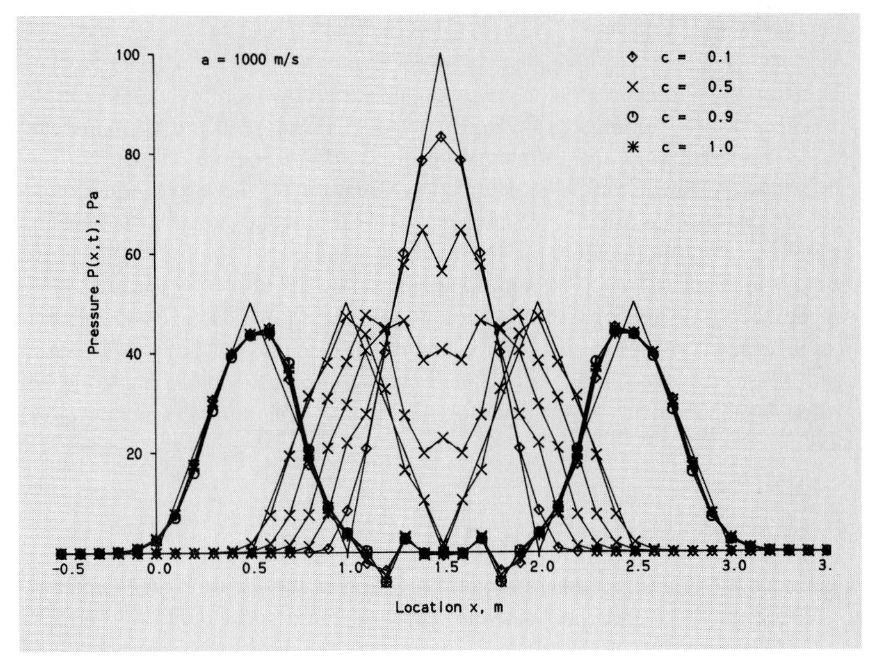

FIGURE 15.13
Solution by the Crank–Nicolson method.

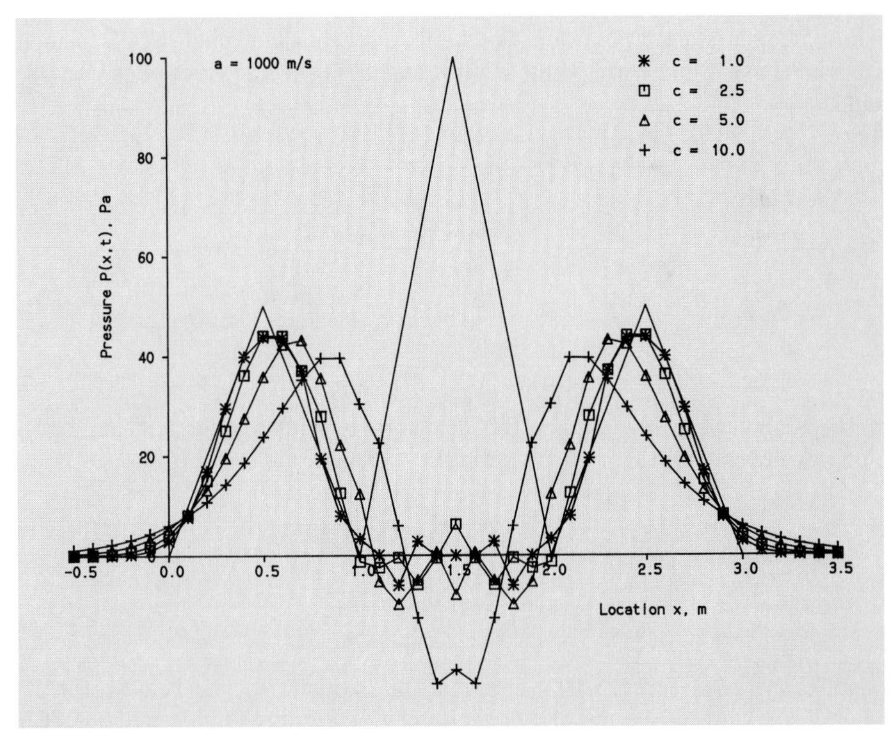

FIGURE 15.14
Solution at $t = 1.0$ ms by the Crank–Nicolson method.

The implicit Crank–Nicolson method becomes considerably more complicated when applied to nonlinear PDEs, systems of PDEs, and multidimensional problems. The techniques and problems are discussed in Section 15.16.

In summary, the Crank–Nicolson approximation of the wave equation is implicit, single-step, two-level, $O(\Delta t^2) + O(\Delta x^2)$, unconditionally stable, and convergent. The implicit nature of the method yields a set of finite difference equations, which must be solved simultaneously. For one-dimensional problems, this can be accomplished by a block tridiagonal algorithm. The infinite numerical signal propagation speed does not correctly model the finite physical signal propagation speed. The Crank–Nicolson method does not yield very good results when applied to the wave equation for convection numbers greater than about 2.0.

15.14 THE HOPSCOTCH METHOD

The hopscotch method is an interesting combination of the forward-time centered-space (FTCS) method and the backward-time centered-space (BTCS) method. Gourlay (1970) presents a detailed discussion of the hopscotch method. It is generally used in two- and three-dimensional problems. The hopscotch method is applied to the one-dimensional wave equation in this section.

The basic idea of the hopscotch method is to make two sweeps through the solution domain at each time step. On the first sweep, the explicit FTCS method is applied at every other grid point, as illustrated in Fig. 12.25. From Eqs. (15.38) and (15.39),

$$f_i^{n+1} = f_i^n - \frac{c}{2}\left(g_{i+1}^n - g_{i-1}^n\right) \tag{15.189}$$

$$g_i^{n+1} = g_i^n - \frac{c}{2}\left(f_{i+1}^n - f_{i-1}^n\right) \tag{15.190}$$

On the second sweep, the implicit BTCS method is applied at the remaining grid points, as illustrated in Fig. 12.25. From Eqs. (15.163) and (15.164),

$$-\frac{c}{2}g_{i-1}^{n+1} + f_i^{n+1} + \frac{c}{2}g_{i+1}^{n+1} = f_i^n \tag{15.191}$$

$$-\frac{c}{2}f_{i-1}^{n+1} + g_i^{n+1} + \frac{c}{2}f_{i+1}^{n+1} = g_i^n \tag{15.192}$$

Equations (15.191) and (15.192) appear to be implicit, but the values of $f_{i\pm1}^{n+1}$ and $g_{i\pm1}^{n+1}$ are known from the first sweep through the grid with the explicit FTCS method. Consequently, Eqs. (15.191) and (15.192) can be solved explicitly for

f_i^{n+1} and g_i^{n+1} to give

$$f_i^{n+1} = f_i^n - \frac{c}{2}(g_{i+1}^{n+1} - g_{i-1}^{n+1}) \tag{15.193}$$

$$g_i^{n+1} = g_i^n - \frac{c}{2}(f_{i+1}^{n+1} - f_{i-1}^{n+1}) \tag{15.194}$$

The pattern of explicit points and implicit points is alternated at each time level, as illustrated in Figure 12.25. The name *hopscotch* arises from the alternating sweep pattern. As illustrated in Section 12.13 for the convection equation, Eqs. (15.189) and (15.190) can be replaced by the simpler equations

$$f_i^{n+2} = 2f_i^{n+1} - f_i^n \tag{15.195}$$

$$g_i^{n+2} = 2g_i^{n+1} - g_i^n \tag{15.196}$$

which further increases the efficiency of the method. Equations (15.189) and (15.190) must be used on the first time step, but Eqs. (15.195) and (15.196) can be used at all subsequent time steps.

The hopscotch concept can be developed using the Lax method at the explicit points instead of the FTCS method.

The hopscotch approximation of the coupled convection equations that correspond to the wave equation is consistent, $O(\Delta t) + O(\Delta x^2)$, and conditionally stable ($c = a\Delta t/\Delta x) \leq 1$). It is equally applicable to nonlinear PDEs, systems of PDEs, and multidimensional problems. Some problems may arise with more complicated boundary conditions for the implicit points. Since all the FDEs can be solved explicitly, no system of equations needs to be solved.

Example 15.11. Solution by the hopscotch method. Let us solve the acoustics problem presented in Section 15.1 by the hopscotch method for $\Delta x = 0.05$ m. The units used in the FDEs and the definition of the convection number, $c = \Delta t/\Delta x$, are the same as presented in Example 15.1. Due to the discontinuity in the slope of the initial data at $x = 0.5$, a slightly more accurate solution is obtained if the BTCS method is used at this point on the first time step. The boundary conditions are treated as described in Example 15.9. The results are presented in Figure 15.15 at times from 0.1 to 0.5 ms for $c = 0.5$, corresponding to $\Delta t = 0.025$ ms, and at 1.0 ms for $c = 0.1$, 0.5, 0.9, and 1.0, corresponding to $\Delta t = 0.005$, 0.025, 0.045, and 0.05 ms, respectively.

Several important features of the hopscotch method applied to the wave equation are illustrated in Fig. 15.15. For $c = 0.5$, the solution is slightly damped as the wave propagates. At $t = 1.0$ ms, the solutions for all values of c are comparable. Overall, the hopscotch method applied to the wave equation gives good results.

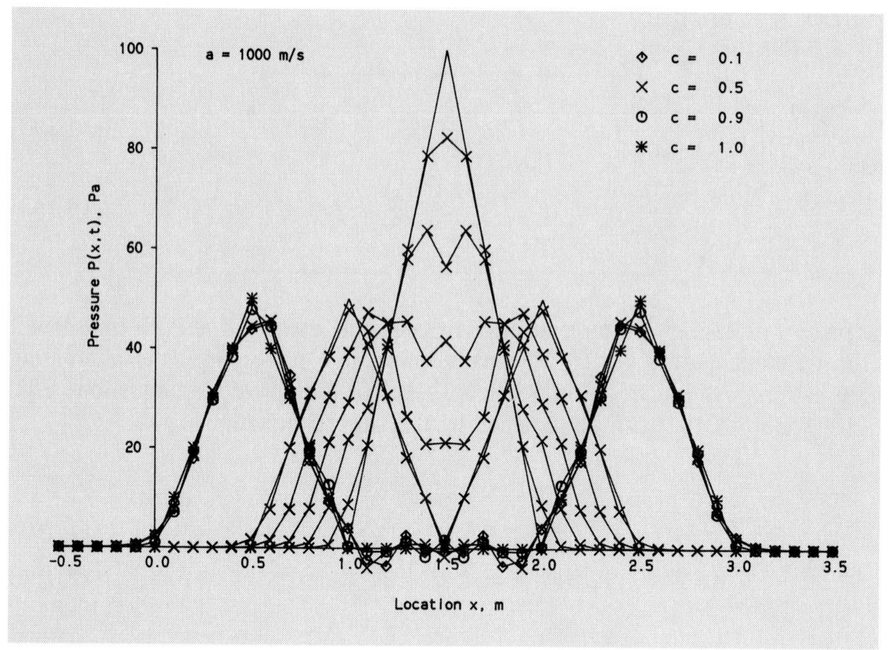

FIGURE 15.15
Solution by the hopscotch method.

The explicit hopscotch method can be extended in a straightforward manner to solve systems of PDEs and multidimensional problems, as discussed in Section 15.16. The solution of nonlinear PDEs is more complicated, since the nonlinear coefficients are not known at the base point in the BTCS method.

In summary, the hopscotch approximation of the wave equation is explicit, two-sweep single-step, two-level, $O(\Delta t) + O(\Delta x^2)$, conditionally stable, and convergent. It is a fairly good method for solving wave propagation problems.

15.15 BOUNDARY CONDITIONS

All of the examples presented so far consider an initial-value problem only. The two waves traveling to the left and right will travel forever unless a boundary is encountered. Many types of boundary conditions arise in convection problems. In some problems, such as fluid dynamics, the numerical implementation of convection boundary conditions is quite complicated. Consider the pair of coupled convection equations that correspond to the wave equation:

$$\bar{f}_t + a\bar{g}_x = 0 \tag{15.197}$$

$$\bar{g}_t + a\bar{f}_x = 0 \tag{15.198}$$

Two types of convection boundary conditions (BCs) are illustrated in this section for Eqs. (15.197) and (15.198): (a) $\bar{f} = 0$, and (b) $\bar{g} = 0$. These BCs are illustrated in Example 15.12 for the acoustics problem presented in Section 15.1.

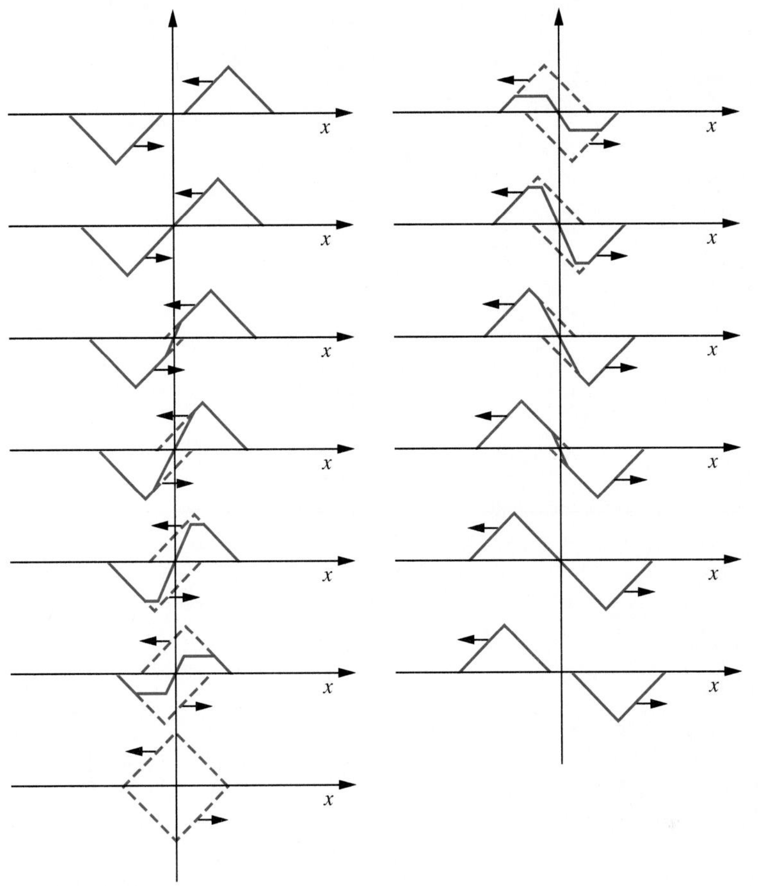

FIGURE 15.16
Wave cancellation.

For linear PDEs, solutions can be superimposed. Consider a semi-infinite domain extending from $x = 0$ to ∞, in which a wave is traveling to the left, with a boundary condition (BC) specified at $x = 0$. Imagine a second semi-infinite domain extending from $x = -\infty$ to 0, in which a wave is traveling to the right. The initial conditions for the second domain are specified so that at the location of the BC at $x = 0$, the right-running wave from the imaginary domain and the left-running wave from the real domain superimpose to satisfy the BC.

To illustrate this procedure, consider a left-traveling wave carrying a triangular property distribution toward a boundary at $x = 0$, as illustrated in Fig. 15.16. Consider a wave cancellation boundary condition, in which the real wave and an imaginary image wave from the left cancel. An imaginary right-traveling image wave is created so that the two waves arrive at the boundary $x = 0$ at the same time and cancel each other as they cross, as illustrated in Fig. 15.16. After the waves cross, the imaginary right-traveling image wave becomes a real

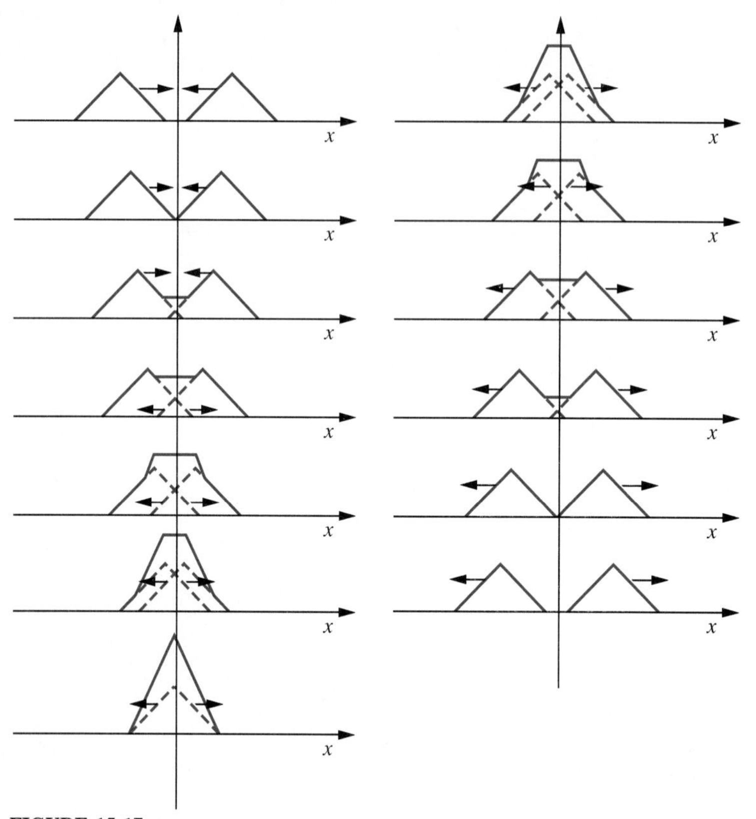

FIGURE 15.17
Wave addition.

right-traveling wave resulting from the interaction of the original left-traveling wave with the boundary.

Next, consider a right-traveling wave carrying a triangular property distribution in the domain from $x = -\infty$ to 0 toward a boundary at $x = 0$, as illustrated in Figure 15.17. Consider a wave addition boundary condition in which the real wave and an imaginary image wave add together. An imaginary left-traveling image wave is created so that the two waves arrive at the boundary $x = 0$ at the same time and add together as they cross, as illustrated in Fig. 15.17. After the waves cross, the imaginary left-traveling image wave becomes a real left-traveling wave resulting from the interaction of the original right-traveling wave with the boundary.

Finally, consider wave propagation in a finite domain. To illustrate the concepts, consider a finite domain with a wave cancellation boundary condition at $x = 0$, a wave addition boundary condition at $x = 3$, and an initial triangular property distribution from $x = 1$ to $x = 2$, as illustrated by the first line in Fig. 15.18. As discussed in Section 15.1, the initial property distribution actually consists of two half-size triangular waves of opposite families, one traveling to

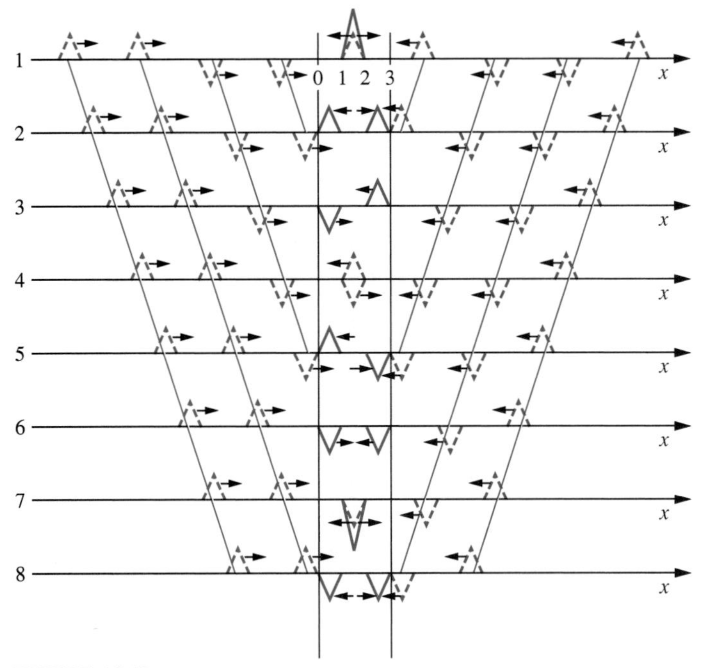

FIGURE 15.18
Wave propagation in a finite domain.

the left and one traveling to the right. The second and third lines in Fig. 15.18 correspond to the single wave interactions illustrated in Figs. 15.16 and 15.17. The reflected waves travel across the solution domain in lines 4 and 5 and arrive at the opposite boundaries from which they were created. More imaginary image waves must be created to enforce the BCs as these waves interact with the boundaries, as illustrated in lines 5 and 6 of Fig. 15.18. In line 7, the reflected waves superimpose to create a mirror image of the initial property distribution. These wave reflection and interaction processes continue indefinitely.

Now let us consider the acoustics problem presented in Section 15.1 with boundary conditions. At $x = 0$, let the left end of the duct be open to the atmosphere, where $P(0, t) = 0$. At $x = 3$, let the right end of the duct be solid and perfectly reflecting, so $u(3, t) = 0$. Recall the governing PDEs of the acoustic problem, Eq. (15.15):

$$\rho u_t + P_x = 0 \tag{15.199}$$

$$P_t + \rho a^2 u_x = 0 \tag{15.200}$$

At $x = 0$, $P(0, t) = 0$, so $P_t(0, t) = 0$. Thus, Eq. (15.200) shows that $u_x(0, t) = 0$, so $u(x < 0, t) = u(x > 0, t)$. From Fig. 15.16, during the wave cancellation process, $P_x(0, t) =$ constant and positive, so $P(x < 0, t) = -P(x > 0, t)$. At $x = 3$, $u(3, t) = 0$, so $u_t(3.0, t) = 0$. Thus, Eq. (15.199) shows that $P_x(3, t) = 0$, so $P(x < 3, t) = P(x > 3, t)$. During the wave addi-

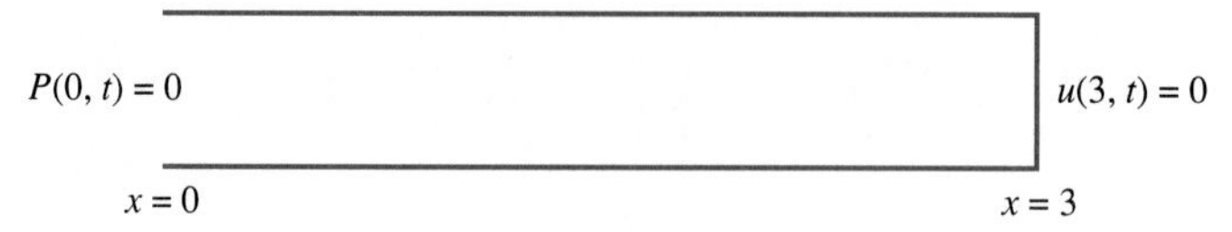

FIGURE 15.19
Acoustic wave propagation in a finite duct.

tion process for $P(3, t)$, the velocity $u(3, t)$ is undergoing a wave cancellation process similar to that illustrated in Figure 15.16. Consequently, $u_x(3, t)$ = constant and negative, so $u(x > 3, t) = -u(x < 3, t)$. In summary, the boundary conditions for the acoustics problem presented in Section 15.1 are

$$P(0, t) = 0 \qquad u(3, t) = 0 \tag{15.201}$$

$$P(x < 0, t) = -P(x > 0, t) \qquad u(x > 3, t) = -u(x < 3, t) \tag{15.202}$$

$$u(x < 0, t) = u(x > 0, t) \qquad P(x < 3, t) = P(x > 3, t) \tag{15.203}$$

This analysis illustrates the complexity of boundary conditions for systems of convection equations, and the necessity to understand the ramifications of the characteristics of the PDEs.

Example 15.12. Solution with boundary conditions. Let us solve the acoustics problem presented in Section 15.1 with an open end at $x = 0$ and a closed end at $x = 3$ m, as illustrated in Fig. 15.19. The triangular initial condition is specified in Section 15.1, Eq. (15.16), and the boundary conditions are specified by Eqs. (15.201) to (15.203). We will use the Lax–Wendroff-one-step method presented in Section 15.7 to solve the PDEs. The units used in the FDEs and the definition of the convection number, $c = \Delta t/\Delta x$, are the same as presented in Example 15.1. For these choices of units, Eqs. (15.199) and (15.200) effectively correspond to

$$u_t + P_x = 0 \tag{15.204}$$

$$P_t + u_x = 0 \tag{15.205}$$

Thus, Eqs. (15.96) and (15.97) can be applied directly by letting $f = P$, $g = u$, and $c = \Delta t/\Delta x$, to yield

$$P_i^{n+1} = P_i^n - \frac{c}{2}(u_{i+1}^n - u_{i-1}^n) + \frac{c^2}{2}(P_{i+1}^n - 2P_i^n + P_{i-1}^n) \tag{15.206}$$

$$u_i^{n+1} = u_i^n - \frac{c}{2}(P_{i+1}^n - P_{i-1}^n) + \frac{c^2}{2}(u_{i+1}^n - 2u_i^n + u_{i-1}^n) \tag{15.207}$$

Let $i = 0$ to I, so $i = 0$ corresponds to the open boundary at $x = 0$ and $i = I$ corresponds to the closed boundary at $x = 3$, as illustrated in Figure 15.20.

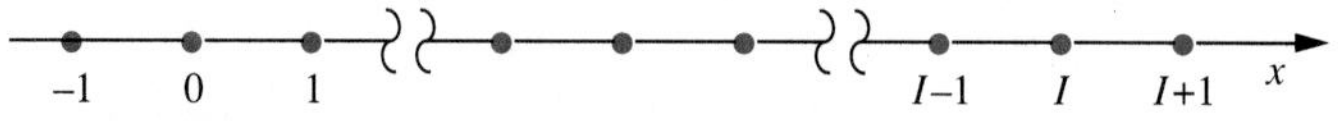

−1 0 1 $I-1$ I $I+1$ x

FIGURE 15.20
Finite difference grid at the boundaries.

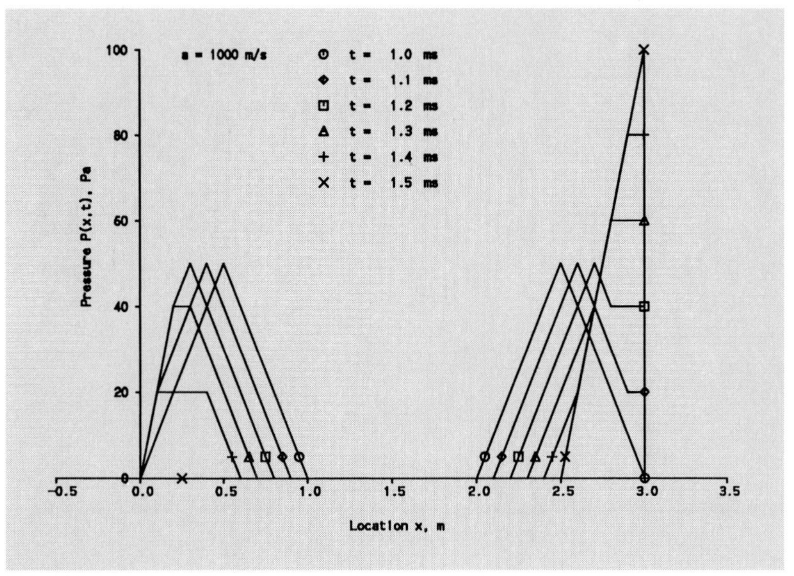

FIGURE 15.21
Exact solution for the incident wave.

At $i = 0$, substituting Eqs. (15.201) to (15.203) into Eqs. (15.206) and (15.207) gives

$$0 = 0 - \frac{c}{2}(u_1^n - u_1^n) + \frac{c^2}{2}\Big(P_1^n - 2(0) + (-P_1^n)\Big) \tag{15.208}$$

$$u_0^{n+1} = u_0^n - \frac{c}{2}\Big(P_1^n - (-P_1^n)\Big) + \frac{c^2}{2}(u_1^n - 2u_0^n + u_1^n) \tag{15.209}$$

Equation (15.208) is satisfied identically. Equation (15.209) yields

$$\boxed{u_0^{n+1} = u_0^n - cP_1^n + c^2(u_1^n - u_0^n)} \tag{15.210}$$

At $i = I$, substituting Eqs. (15.201) to (15.203) into Eqs. (15.206) and (15.207) gives

$$P_I^{n+1} = P_I^n - \frac{c}{2}\Big((-u_{I-1}^n) - u_{I-1}^n\Big) + \frac{c^2}{2}(P_{I-1}^n - 2P_I^n + P_{I-1}^n) \tag{15.211}$$

$$0 = 0 - \frac{c}{2}(P_{I-1}^n - P_{I-1}^n) + \frac{c^2}{2}\Big((-u_{I-1}^n) - 2(0) + u_{I-1}^n\Big) \tag{15.212}$$

Equation (15.212) is satisfied identically. Equation (15.211) yields

$$\boxed{P_I^{n+1} = P_I^n + cu_{I-1}^n + c^2(P_{I-1}^n - P_I^n)} \tag{15.213}$$

The exact solution for the incident wave is presented in Fig. 15.21, and the exact solution for the reflected wave is presented in Fig. 15.22.

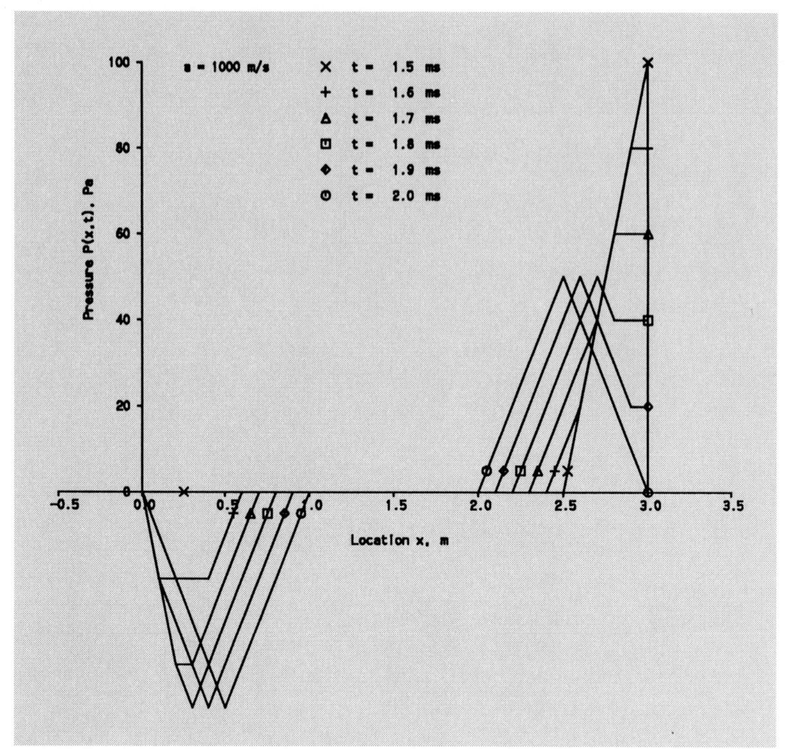

FIGURE 15.22
Exact solution for the reflected wave.

For the numerical solution, let $\Delta x = 0.05$ m and $\Delta t = 0.025$ ms, so $c = \Delta t/\Delta x = 0.025/0.05 = 0.5$. The results for the incident wave are presented in Fig. 15.23 at $t = 1.0$, 1.1, 1.2, 1.3, 1.4 and 1.5 ms, corresponding to $n = 40$, 44, 48, 52, 56, and 60 time steps, respectively. The results for the reflected wave are presented in Fig. 15.24 at $t = 1.5$, 1.6, 1.7, 1.8, 1.9, and 2.0 ms, corresponding to 60, 64, 68, 72, 76, and 80 time steps, respectively.

For both waves, the peaks of the waves are rounded, but the wave speeds and the general shapes of the waves are predicted quite well. More accurate results can be obtained by taking larger time steps to increase the convection number c closer to unity, and by decreasing the size of the physical grid increment Δx. For $c = 1.0$, the exact solution is obtained for the linear problem. That is not the case for nonlinear convection problems. Overall, Lax–Wendroff type methods give good results for convection problems.

The results presented in this section for implementing boundary conditions for systems of convection equations illustrate the complexity of such problems. In general, insufficient BCs are specified directly for all the variables at all the boundaries. Consequently, additional information must be obtained from the governing PDEs and the physics of the problem. The complexity increases for large systems of PDEs, nonlinear PDEs, and multidimensional problems.

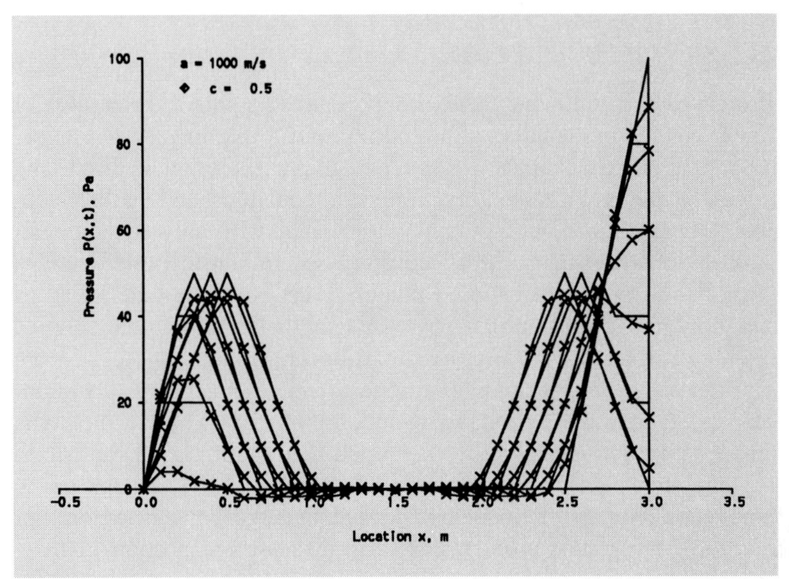

FIGURE 15.23
Solution for the incident wave using the Lax–Wendroff one-step method.

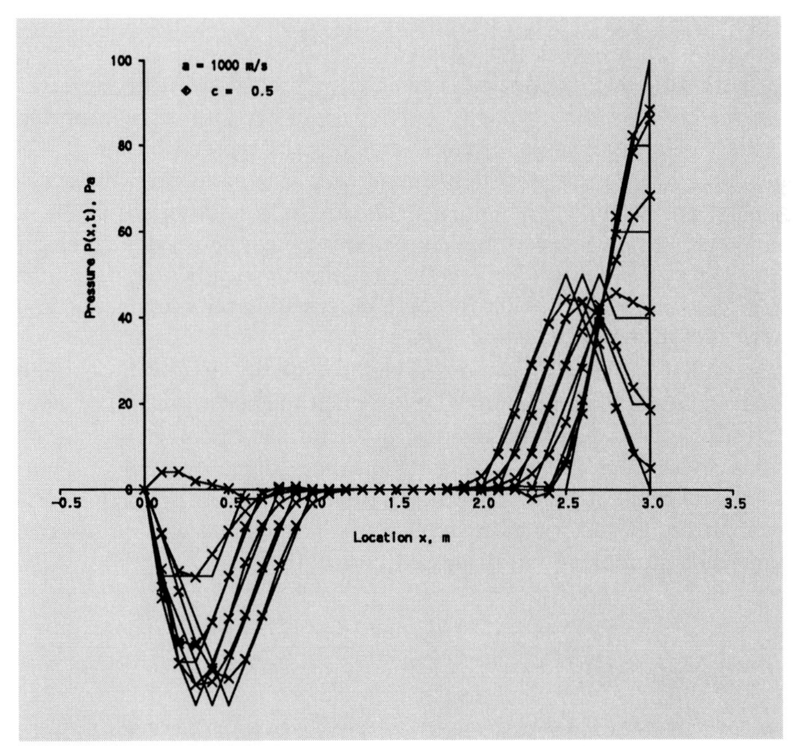

FIGURE 15.24
Solution for the reflected wave using the Lax–Wendroff one-step method.

15.16 NONLINEAR EQUATIONS AND MULTIDIMENSIONAL PROBLEMS

The finite difference equations and examples presented in this chapter are for the coupled linear convection equations that correspond to the linear wave equation. In each section in this chapter, a brief paragraph is presented discussing the suitability of the method for solving nonlinear equations and multidimensional problems. The additional complexities associated with solving nonlinear equations and multidimensional problems are discussed in considerable detail in Section 11.8 for the parabolic diffusion equation. The problems and solutions discussed there apply directly to finite difference methods for solving the coupled linear convection equations that correspond to the linear wave equation.

Generally speaking, explicit methods can be extended directly to solve nonlinear equations and/or multidimensional convection problems. Implicit methods, on the other hand, yield nonlinear FDEs when applied to nonlinear PDEs. Methods for solving nonlinear FDEs are discussed in Section 11.8. When applied to multidimensional problems, implicit methods result in large banded systems of FDEs. Methods for solving such problems are also discussed in Section 11.8.

SUMMARY

The numerical solution of a coupled system of two hyperbolic linear convection equations, which correspond to the hyperbolic linear wave equation, by finite difference methods is discussed in this chapter.

Explicit finite difference methods, as typified by Lax–Wendroff type methods, are conditionally stable and require a relatively small step size in the marching direction to satisfy stability criteria. Implicit methods, as typified by the BTCS method, are unconditionally stable. The marching step size is restricted by accuracy requirements, not stability requirements. For accurate solutions of transient problems, the marching step size for implicit methods cannot be very much larger than the stable step size for explicit methods. Asymptotic steady state solutions can be obtained very efficiently by the BTCS method with a large marching step size.

Nonlinear partial differential equations can be solved directly by explicit methods. When nonlinear PDEs are solved by implicit methods, systems of nonlinear FDEs must be solved. Multidimensional problems can be solved directly by explicit methods. When multidimensional problems are solved by implicit methods, large banded systems of FDEs results. Alternating-direction implicit (ADI) methods and approximate-factorization implicit (AFI) methods can be used to solve multidimensional problems, as discussed in Section 11.8.

PROBLEMS

Section 15.1 Introduction

1. Consider the set of two coupled unsteady one-dimensional convection equations:

$$\bar{f}_t + a\bar{g}_x = 0 \quad \text{and} \quad \bar{g}_t + a\bar{f}_x = 0 \tag{P15.1}$$

Classify this set of PDEs. Determine the characteristic curves. Discuss the significance of these results as regards domain of dependence, range of influence, signal propagation speed, and numerical solution procedures.

2. Develop the exact solution for the acoustics problem presented in Section 15.1 and discuss its significance.

Section 15.2 The Method of Characteristics

3. Develop the method-of-characteristics analysis of the two coupled unsteady one-dimensional convection equations presented in Section 15.2. Discuss the effects of nonlinearities on the results.

Section 15.3 The Forward-Time Centered-Space Method

4. Derive the FTCS approximation of the coupled convection equations, Eqs. (15.38) and (15.39), including the leading truncation error terms in Δt and Δx.
5. Perform a von Neumann stability analysis of Eqs. (15.38) and (15.39).
6. By hand calculation, solve the example acoustics problem presented in Example 15.1 at $t = 0.1$ ms by the FTCS method with $\Delta x = 0.5$ m and $\Delta t = .05$ ms. Compare the results with the exact solution.

Section 15.4 The Lax Method

7. Derive the Lax approximation of the coupled convection equations, Eqs. (15.58) and (15.59), including the leading truncation error terms in Δt and Δx.
8. Derive the first and approximate second forms of the MDE corresponding to Eq. (15.58). Analyze consistency, order, and implicit numerical diffusion and dispersion.
9. Perform a von Neumann stability analysis of Eqs. (15.58) and (15.59).
10. By hand calculation, determine the solution of the example acoustics problem at $t = 0.1$ ms by the Lax method with $\Delta x = 0.1$ m and $\Delta t = 0.05$ ms. Compare the results with the exact solution.
11. Write a computer program to implement the solution of the example acoustics problem by the Lax method. Use the program to reproduce the results presented in Fig. 15.4.
12. Use the program developed in Problem 11 to solve the example acoustics problem with $\Delta x = 0.1$ m and $\Delta t = 0.05$ ms. Compare the errors with the errors in Problem 11.

Section 15.5 Upwind Methods

13. Derive the first-order upwind approximation of the coupled convection equations, Eqs. (15.77) and (15.78), including the leading truncation error terms in Δt and Δx.
14. Derive the first and approximate second forms of the MDE corresponding to Eq. (15.77). Analyze consistency, order, and implicit numerical diffusion and dispersion.
15. Perform a von Neumann stability analysis of Eqs. (15.77) and (15.78).
16. By hand calculation, determine the solution of the example acoustics problem at $t = 0.1$ ms by the first-order upwind method with $\Delta x = 0.1$ m and $\Delta t = 0.05$ ms. Compare the results with the exact solution.

17. Write a computer program to implement the solution of the example acoustics problem by the first-order upwind method. Use the program to reproduce the results presented in Fig. 15.5.
18. Use the program developed in Problem 17 to solve the example acoustics problem with $\Delta x = 0.1$ m and $\Delta t = 0.05$ ms. Compare the errors with the errors in Problem 17.

Section 15.6 The Leapfrog Method

19. Derive the leapfrog approximation of the convection equations, Eqs. (15.82) and (15.83), including the leading truncation error terms in Δt and Δx.
20. Derive the first and approximate second forms of the MDE corresponding to Eq. (15.82). Analyze consistency, order, and implicit numerical diffusion and dispersion.
21. Perform a von Neumann stability analysis of Eqs. (15.82) and (15.83).
22. By hand calculation, determine the solution of the example acoustics problem at $t = 0.1$ ms by the leapfrog method with $\Delta x = 0.1$ m and $\Delta t = 0.05$ ms. Use the exact solution for the first time step. Compare the results with the exact solution.
23. Write a computer program to implement the solution of the example acoustics problem by the leapfrog method. Use the program to reproduce the results presented in Fig. 15.6.
24. Use the program developed in Problem 23 to solve the example acoustics problem with $\Delta x = 0.1$ m and $\Delta t = 0.05$ ms. Compare the errors with the errors in Problem 23.

Section 15.7 The Lax–Wendroff One-Step Method

25. Derive the Lax–Wendroff one-step approximation of the coupled convection equations, Eq. (15.96) and (15.97), including the leading truncation error terms in Δt and Δx.
26. Derive the first and approximate second forms of the MDE corresponding to Eq. (15.96). Analyze consistency, order, and implicit numerical diffusion and dispersion.
27. Perform a von Neumann stability analysis of Eqs. (15.96) and (15.97).
28. By hand calculation, determine the solution of the example acoustics problem at $t = 0.1$ ms by the Lax–Wendroff one-step method with $\Delta x = 0.1$ m and $\Delta t = 0.05$ ms. Compare the results with the exact solution.
29. Write a computer program to implement the solution of the example acoustics problem by the Lax–Wendroff one-step method. Use the program to reproduce the results presented in Fig. 15.7.
30. Use the program developed in Problem 29 to solve the example acoustics problem with $\Delta x = 0.1$ m and $\Delta t = 0.05$ ms. Compare the errors with the errors in Problem 29.

Section 15.8 Lax–Wendroff Two-Step Methods

31. Derive the Lax–Wendroff [Richtmyer (1963)] two-step approximation of the coupled convection equations, Eqs. (15.101) to (15.104), including the leading truncation error terms in Δt and Δx. Show that, for the linear convection equations, the two-step method is equivalent to the Lax–Wendroff one-step method for $2\Delta t$ and $2\Delta x$.
32. By hand calculation, determine the solution of the example acoustics problem at $t = 0.1$ ms by the Lax–Wendroff (Richtmyer) two-step method with $\Delta x = 0.1$ m and $\Delta t = 0.05$ ms. Compare the results with the exact solution.
33. Write a computer program to implement the solution of the example acoustics problem by the Lax–Wendroff (Richtmyer) one-step method. Use the program to reproduce the results presented in Fig. 15.8.

34. Use the program developed in Problem 33 to solve the example acoustics problem with $\Delta x = 0.1$ m and $\Delta t = 0.05$ ms. Compare the errors with the errors in Problem 33.

Section 15.9 The MacCormack Method

35. Develop the MacCormack approximation of the coupled convection equations, Eqs. (15.108) to (15.111), including the leading truncation error terms. Show that, for the linear convection equations, the two-step method is identical to the Lax–Wendroff one-step method.

36. By hand calculation, determine the solution of the example acoustics problem at $t = 0.1$ ms by the MacCormack method with $\Delta x = 0.1$ m and $\Delta t = 0.05$ ms. Compare the results with the exact solution.

37. Write a computer program to implement the solution of the example acoustics problem by the MacCormack method. Use the program to reproduce the results presented in Fig. 15.7.

Section 15.10 The Numerical Method of Characteristics

38. Develop the first method-of-characteristics algorithm for the coupled convection equations. By hand calculation, determine the solution of the example acoustics problem at $t = 0.1$ ms with $\Delta x = 0.1$ m and $\Delta t = 0.05$ ms. Compare the results with the exact solution.

39. Develop the second method-of-characteristics algorithm for the coupled convection equations. Work Problem 38 by this method.

40. Develop the third method-of-characteristics algorithm for the coupled convection equations. Work Problem 38 by this method.

41. Develop a numerical procedure to solve the unsteady one-dimensional coupled nonlinear convection equations $\overline{f}_t + \overline{f}\,\overline{g}_x = 0$ and $\overline{g}_t + \overline{g}\,\overline{f}_x = 0$ by the third method of characteristics algorithm.

Section 15.11 The Flux-Vector-Splitting Method

42. Develop the flux-vector-splitting approximation of the PDE $Q_t + E_x = 0$, Eq. (15.161).

43. Show that substituting Eq. (15.149) into Eq. (15.162) yields Eqs. (15.77) and (15.78).

44. By hand calculation, determine the solution of the example acoustics problem at $t = 0.1$ ms by the flux-vector-splitting method with $\Delta x = 0.1$ m and $\Delta t = 0.05$ ms. Compare the results with the exact solution.

45. Write a computer program to implement the solution of the example acoustics problem by the flux-vector-splitting method. Use the program to reproduce the results presented in Fig. 15.5.

46. Use the program developed in Problem 45 to solve the example acoustics problem with $\Delta x = 0.1$ m and $\Delta t = 0.05$ ms. Compare the errors with the errors in Problem 45.

Section 15.12 The Backward-Time Centered-Space Method

47. Derive the BTCS approximation of the coupled convection equations, Eqs. (15.163) and (15.164), including the leading truncation error terms in Δt and Δx.

48. Derive the first and approximate second forms of the MDE corresponding to Eq. (15.163). Analyze consistency, order, and implicit numerical diffusion and dispersion.

49. Perform a von Neumann stability analysis of Eqs. (15.163) and (15.164).

50. By hand calculation, determine the solution of the example acoustics problem at $t = 0.25$ ms by the BTCS method with $\Delta x = 0.25$ m and $\Delta t = 0.25$ ms. Apply the initial conditions as boundary conditions at $x = 0.5$ and 2.5 m. Compare the results with the exact solution.

51. Write a computer program to implement the solution of the example acoustics problem by the BTCS method. Use the program to reproduce the results presented in Figs. 15.11 and 15.12.

52. Use the program developed in Problem 51 to solve the example acoustics problem with $\Delta x = 0.1$ m and $\Delta t = 0.1$ ms. Compare the errors with the errors in Problem 51.

Section 15.13 The Crank–Nicolson Method

53. Derive the Crank–Nicolson approximation of the coupled convection equations, Eqs. (15.182) and (15.183), including the leading truncation error terms in Δt and Δx.

54. Derive the first and approximate second forms of the MDE corresponding to Eq. (15.182). Analyze consistency, order, and implicit numerical diffusion and dispersion.

55. Perform a von Neumann stability analysis of Eqs. (15.182) and (15.183).

56. By hand calculation, determine the solution of the example acoustics problem at $t = 0.25$ ms by the Crank–Nicolson method with $\Delta x = 0.25$ m and $\Delta t = 0.25$ ms. Apply the initial conditions as boundary conditions at $x = 0.5$ and 2.5 m. Compare the results with the exact solution.

57. Write a computer program to implement the solution of the example acoustics problem by the Crank–Nicolson method. Use the program to reproduce the results presented in Figs. 15.13 and 15.14.

58. Use the program developed in Problem 57 to solve the example acoustics problem with $\Delta x = 0.1$ m and $\Delta t = 0.1$ ms. Compare the errors with the errors in Problem 57.

Section 15.14 The Hopscotch Method

59. Derive the hopscotch approximation of the coupled convection equations, Eqs. (15.189), (15.190), (15.193), and (15.194), including the leading truncation error terms in Δt and Δx.

60. Derive Eqs. (15.195) and (15.196).

61. By hand calculation, determine the solution of the example acoustics problem at $t = 0.1$ ms by the hopscotch method with $\Delta x = 0.1$ m and $\Delta t = 0.05$ ms. Compare the results with the exact solution.

62. Write a computer program to implement the solution of the example acoustics problem by the hopscotch method. Use the program to reproduce the results presented in Fig. 15.15.

63. Use the program developed in Problem 62 to solve the example acoustics problem with $\Delta x = 0.1$ m and $\Delta t = 0.05$ ms. Compare the errors with the errors in Problem 62.

Section 15.15 Boundary Conditions

64. Discuss the wave cancellation boundary condition illustrated in Fig. 15.16. Sketch the behavior of a left-traveling upside-down triangular wave at a wave-cancellation boundary.

65. Discuss the wave addition boundary condition illustrated in Fig. 15.17. Sketch the behavior of a right-traveling upside-down triangular wave at a wave addition boundary.

66. Develop the wave pattern illustrated in Fig. 15.18 if the initial triangular wave is upside down.

67. Develop the wave pattern illustrated in Fig. 15.18 if two triangular waves exist of equal amplitude at the initial time. One wave is located from $0 \le x \le 1$ and is traveling to the right. The other wave is located from $2 \le x \le 3$ and is traveling to the left.

68. Work Problem 67 with the first triangular wave upside down.

69. Consider the acoustics problem described in Example 15.12. By hand calculation using the FDEs presented in Section 15.15, calculate the solution for the incident wave at $t = 1.5$ ms for $\Delta x = 0.1$ m and $\Delta t = 0.05$ ms. Start with the exact solution at $t = 1.0$ ms. Assume that the incident wave is the exact solution.

70. Work Problem 69 for the incident wave on the left boundary.

71. Work Problem 69 for the reflected wave on the right boundary, starting with the exact solution at $t = 1.5$ ms, for the solution at $t = 2.0$ ms.

72. Work Problem 69 for the reflected wave on the left boundary, starting with the exact solution at $t = 1.5$ ms, for the solution at $t = 2.0$ ms.

73. Modify the computer program written in Problem 29 to incorporate the wave reflection boundary condition on the right-hand side. Use the program to reproduce the right-hand side results in Figs. 15.23 and 15.24.

74. Modify the computer program written in Problem 29 to incorporate the wave-cancellation boundary condition on the left-hand side. Use the program to reproduce the left-hand side results in Figs. 15.23 and 15.24.

75. Combine Problems 73 and 74 and work the complete problem.

76. Work Problem 73 with a wave-cancellation boundary condition on the right-hand side.

77. Work Problem 74 with a wave-addition boundary condition on the left-hand side.

78. Combine Problems 76 and 77 and work the complete problem.

Section 15.16 Nonlinear Equations and Multidimensional Problems

Problems 39 to 44 in Chapter 11 and Problems 55 to 64 in Chapter 12 illustrate the problems that arise due to nonlinear equations and multidimensional problems. Those problems can be used to demonstrate these effects for coupled convection equations.

79. Consider the unsteady two-dimensional coupled convection equations:

$$\bar{f}_t + u\bar{g}_x + v\bar{g}_y = 0 \qquad \text{and} \qquad g_t + u\bar{f}_x + v\bar{f}_y = 0$$

Develop the MacCormack approximation of these PDEs.

80. Derive the first and approximate second forms of the MDE corresponding to the FDE for f_i^{n+1} developed in Problem 79.

81. Derive the amplification factor G for the FDEs developed in Problem 79.

82. Work Problem 79 by the BTCS method.

83. Derive the first and approximate second forms of the MDE corresponding to the FDE for f_i^{n+1} developed in Problem 82.

84. Derive the amplification factor G for the FDEs developed in Problem 82.

APPENDIX

The Taylor Series

A power series in powers of x is a series of the form

$$\sum_{n=0}^{\infty} a_n x^n = a_0 + a_1 x + a_2 x^2 + \cdots \qquad \text{(A.1)}$$

A power series in powers of $(x - x_0)$ is given by

$$\sum_{n=0}^{\infty} a_n (x - x_0)^n = a_0 + a_1(x - x_0) + a_2(x - x_0)^2 + \cdots \qquad \text{(A.2)}$$

Within its radius of convergence r, any continuous function $f(x)$ can be represented exactly by a power series. Thus,

$$f(x) = \sum_{n=0}^{\infty} a_n (x - x_0)^n \qquad \text{(A.3)}$$

is continuous for $(x_0 - r) < x < (x_0 + r)$.

Taylor Series in One Independent Variable

If the coefficients a_n in Eq. (A.3) are given by the rule

$$a_0 = f(x_0), \quad a_1 = \frac{1}{1!} f'(x_0), \quad a_2 = \frac{1}{2!} f''(x_0), \ldots \qquad \text{(A.4)}$$

then Eq. (A.3) becomes the *Taylor series* of $f(x)$ at $x = x_0$. Thus,

$$f(x) = f(x_0) + \frac{1}{1!}f'(x_0)(x - x_0) + \frac{1}{2!}f''(x_0)(x - x_0)^2 + \cdots \tag{A.5}$$

Equation (A.5) can be written in the simpler form

$$f(x) = f_i + f'\,|_i\,\Delta x + \frac{1}{2}f''|_i\Delta x^2 + \cdots + \frac{1}{n!}f^{(n)}\,|_i\,\Delta x^n + \cdots \tag{A.6}$$

where $f^{(n)} = df^n/dx^n$ and $\Delta x = (x - x_0)$. Equation (A.5) can be written in the compressed form

$$f(x) = \sum_{n=0}^{\infty} \frac{1}{n!} f^{(n)}(x)(x - x_0)^n \tag{A.7}$$

When $x_0 = 0$, the Taylor series is known as the *Maclaurin series*. In that case, Eqs. (A.5) and (A.7) become

$$f(x) = f(0) + f'(0)x + \frac{1}{2}f''(0)x^2 + \cdots \tag{A.8}$$

$$f(x) = \sum_{n=0}^{\infty} \frac{1}{n!} f^{(n)}(0)x^n \tag{A.9}$$

It is, of course, impractical to evaluate an infinite Taylor series term by term. The Taylor series can be written as the finite Taylor series, also known as the *Taylor formula* or *polynomial* with *remainder*, as follows:

$$f(x) = f(x_0) + f'(x_0)(x - x_0) + \frac{1}{2}f''(x_0)(x - x_0)^2 + \cdots + \frac{1}{n!}f^{(n)}(x_0)(x - x_0)^n + R^{n+1} \tag{A.10}$$

where the term R^{n+1} is the remainder term given by

$$R^{n+1} = \frac{1}{(n+1)!} f^{(n+1)}(\xi)(x - x_0)^{n+1} \tag{A.11}$$

where ξ lies between x_0 and x. Equation (A.10) is quite useful in numerical analysis, where an approximation of $f(x)$ is obtained by neglecting the remainder term.

Taylor Series in Two Independent Variables

Power series can also be written for functions of more than one independent variable. For a function of two independent variables, $f(x, y)$, the Taylor series of $f(x, y)$ at (x_0, y_0) is given by

$$f(x,y) = f_0 + \left.\frac{\partial f}{\partial x}\right|_0 (x - x_0) + \left.\frac{\partial F}{\partial y}\right|_0 (y - y_0)$$
$$+ \frac{1}{2!}\left(\left.\frac{\partial^2 f}{\partial x^2}\right|_0 (x - x_0)^2 + 2\left.\frac{\partial^2 f}{\partial x \partial y}\right|_0 (x - x_0)(y - y_0) + \left.\frac{\partial^2 f}{\partial y^2}\right|_0 (y - y_0)\right) + \cdots \tag{A.12}$$

Equation (A.12) can be written in the general form

$$f(x,y) = \sum_{n=0}^{\infty} \frac{1}{n!}\left((x - x_0)\frac{\partial}{\partial x} + (y - y_0)\frac{\partial}{\partial y}\right)^n f(x_0, y_0) \tag{A.13}$$

where the term $(\ldots)^n$ is expanded by the binomial expansion and the resulting expansion operates on the function $f(x, y)$ and is evaluated at (x_0, y_0).

The Taylor formula with remainder for a function of two independent variables is obtained by evaluating the derivatives in the $(n + 1)$st term at the point (x^*, y^*), where (x^*, y^*) lies in the region between points (x_0, y_0) and (x, y).

ANSWERS TO SELECTED PROBLEMS

All of the problems for which answers are given in this section are denoted in the individual chapters by an asterisk appearing before the corresponding problem number.

Chapter 1 Systems of Linear Algebraic Equations

3. (*a*) $\begin{bmatrix} 11 & 20 \\ 21 & 22 \\ 15 & 19 \end{bmatrix}$ (*b*) $\begin{bmatrix} 23 & 39 \\ 5 & -3 \\ 19 & 33 \end{bmatrix}$ (*e*) $\begin{bmatrix} 5 & 13 & 19 \\ 9 & 17 & 19 \\ 6 & 14 & 16 \end{bmatrix}$ (*f*) $\begin{bmatrix} 10 & 26 & 36 \\ 2 & 0 & -4 \\ 8 & 22 & 30 \end{bmatrix}$

(*j*) $\begin{bmatrix} 11 & 11 & 8 \\ 11 & 35 & 20 \\ 8 & 20 & 14 \end{bmatrix}$ (*k*) $\begin{bmatrix} 38 & -1 & 31 \\ -1 & 14 & -2 \\ 31 & -2 & 26 \end{bmatrix}$ (*l*) $\begin{bmatrix} 3 & 7 & 9 \\ 7 & 19 & 25 \\ 9 & 25 & 35 \end{bmatrix}$

8. (*a*) 24, (*c*) Not defined, (*d*) 4

9. (*a*) 24, (*c*) Not defined, (*d*) 4

10. $\mathbf{x}^T = (-1 \quad 2 \quad 1)$

12. $\mathbf{x}^T = (1 \quad 2 \quad 3 \quad 4)$

18. $\mathbf{x}^T = (-1 \quad 2 \quad 1)$

20. $\mathbf{x}^T = (1 \quad 2 \quad 3 \quad 4)$

26. $\mathbf{x}^T = (-1 \quad 2 \quad 1)$

28. $\mathbf{x}^T = (1 \quad 2 \quad 3 \quad 4)$

34.
$$\mathbf{A}^{-1} = \begin{bmatrix} 0.272727 & 0.227273 & 0.863636 \\ 0.363636 & 0.136364 & 0.318182 \\ 0.454545 & 0.045455 & 0.772727 \end{bmatrix} \qquad \mathbf{x} = \begin{bmatrix} -1 \\ 2 \\ 1 \end{bmatrix}$$

36.
$$\mathbf{A}^{-1} = \begin{bmatrix} 164 & -107 & 84 & -13 \\ 14 & -9 & 7 & -1 \\ -127 & 83 & -65 & 10 \\ -49 & 32 & -25 & 4 \end{bmatrix} \qquad \mathbf{x} = \begin{bmatrix} 1 \\ 2 \\ 3 \\ 4 \end{bmatrix}$$

42.
$$\mathbf{LU} = \begin{bmatrix} -2.000000 & 3.000000 & 1.000000 \\ -1.500000 & 8.500000 & -3.500000 \\ -0.500000 & -0.058824 & 1.294118 \end{bmatrix} \qquad \mathbf{x} = \begin{bmatrix} -1 \\ 2 \\ 1 \end{bmatrix}$$

44.
$$\mathbf{LU} = \begin{bmatrix} 1.00 & 3.00 & 2.00 & -1.00 \\ 4.00 & -10.00 & -3.00 & 5.00 \\ 3.00 & 1.20 & -0.40 & 1.00 \\ -1.00 & -0.50 & 6.25 & 0.25 \end{bmatrix} \qquad \mathbf{x} = \begin{bmatrix} 1 \\ 2 \\ 3 \\ 4 \end{bmatrix}$$

50.
$$\mathbf{LU} = \begin{bmatrix} -2.000000 & -1.500000 & -0.500000 \\ 3.000000 & 8.500000 & -0.411765 \\ 1.000000 & -0.500000 & 1.294118 \end{bmatrix} \qquad \mathbf{x} = \begin{bmatrix} -1 \\ 2 \\ 1 \end{bmatrix}$$

52.
$$\mathbf{LU} = \begin{bmatrix} 1.00 & 3.00 & 2.00 & -1.00 \\ 4.00 & -10.00 & 0.30 & -0.50 \\ 3.00 & -12.00 & -0.40 & -2.50 \\ -1.00 & 5.00 & -2.50 & 0.25 \end{bmatrix} \qquad \mathbf{x} = \begin{bmatrix} 1 \\ 2 \\ 3 \\ 4 \end{bmatrix}$$

58. $\mathbf{x}^{\mathrm{T}} = (1 \quad 2 \quad 3 \quad 4)$

63. $k = 10,\ \mathbf{x}^{\mathrm{T}} = (0.805664\ 1.611328\ 2.685547\ 3.759766)$
$k = 75,\ \mathbf{x}^{\mathrm{T}} = (1.000000\ 2.000000\ 3.000000\ 4.000000)$

67. $k = 10,\ \mathbf{x}^{\mathrm{T}} = (1.017937\ 1.976521\ 3.018995\ 3.990502)$
$k = 33,\ \mathbf{x}^{\mathrm{T}} = (1.000001\ 1.999999\ 3.000001\ 3.999999)$

71. $k = 10,\ \mathbf{x}^{\mathrm{T}} = (0.999989\ 1.999969\ 2.999997\ 4.000004)$
$k = 14,\ \mathbf{x}^{\mathrm{T}} = (1.000000\ 2.000000\ 3.000000\ 4.000000)$

Chapter 2 Eigenproblems

9. $k = 6,\ \lambda = 4.506991,\ \mathbf{x}^{\mathrm{T}} = (1.000000\ 0.936741\ 1.285136)$

15. $k = 8,\ \lambda = 6.634524,\ \mathbf{x}^{\mathrm{T}} = (1.000000\ 0.902435\ 1.437475\ 1.647311)$

25. The inverse power method fails when x_1 is the unity component. Let x_2 be the unity component.
$k = 10,\ \lambda_i = -3.505661,\ \lambda = -0.285253,\ \mathbf{x}^{\mathrm{T}} = (-0.578480\ 1.000000\ -0.128294)$
$k = 13,\ \lambda_i = -3.507085,\ \lambda = -0.285142,\ \mathbf{x}^{\mathrm{T}} = (-0.578400\ 1.000000\ -0.128336)$

31. The inverse power method fails when x_1 is the unity component. Let x_3 be the unity component.
$k = 10,\ \lambda_i = -2.439455,\ \lambda = -0.409928,$
$\mathbf{x}^{\mathrm{T}} = (0.861121\ -1.783638\ 1.000000\ -0.213007)$
$k = 16,\ \lambda_i = -2.453820,\ \lambda = -0.407528,$
$\mathbf{x}^{\mathrm{T}} = (0.874804\ -1.800619\ 1.000000\ -0.215314)$

51.
$$\mathbf{A}_s = \begin{bmatrix} 0.2 & 1.0 & 2.0 \\ 2.0 & 0.2 & 1.0 \\ 1.0 & 1.0 & 2.2 \end{bmatrix} \qquad \mathbf{LU} = \begin{bmatrix} 0.200000 & 1.000000 & 2.000000 \\ 10.000000 & -9.800000 & -19.000000 \\ 5.000000 & 0.408163 & -0.044898 \end{bmatrix}$$

$k = 6,\ \lambda_{s,i} = -45.711857,\ \lambda = 0.778124,\ \mathbf{x}^{\mathrm{T}} = (1.000000\ \ 6.792161\ \ -3.507019)$

54.
$$\mathbf{A}_s = \begin{bmatrix} -0.5 & 1.0 & 1.0 & 2.0 \\ 2.0 & -0.5 & 1.0 & 1.0 \\ 3.0 & 2.0 & -0.5 & 2.0 \\ 2.0 & 1.0 & 1.0 & 2.5 \end{bmatrix}$$

$$\mathbf{LU} = \begin{bmatrix} -0.500000 & 1.000000 & 1.000000 & 2.000000 \\ -4.000000 & 3.500000 & 5.000000 & 9.000000 \\ -6.000000 & 2.285714 & -5.928571 & -6.571429 \\ -4.000000 & 1.428571 & 0.361446 & 0.018072 \end{bmatrix}$$

$k = 6,\quad \lambda_{s,i} = 116.776798,\quad \lambda = 1.508563,$
$\mathbf{x}^{\mathrm{T}} = (1.000000e\ 5.046599e\ 5.671066e\ -5.104551)$

$$\mathbf{A}_s = \begin{bmatrix} 1.5 & 1.0 & 1.0 & 2.0 \\ 2.0 & 1.5 & 1.0 & 1.0 \\ 3.0 & 2.0 & 1.5 & 2.0 \\ 2.0 & 1.0 & 1.0 & 4.5 \end{bmatrix}$$

$$\mathbf{LU} = \begin{bmatrix} 1.500000 & 1.000000 & 1.000000 & 2.000000 \\ 1.333333 & 0.166667 & -0.333333 & -1.666667 \\ 2.000000 & 0.000000 & -0.500000 & -2.000000 \\ 1.333333 & -2.000000 & 2.000000 & 2.500000 \end{bmatrix}$$

$k = 15,\quad \lambda_{s,i} = 10.805797,\quad \lambda = -0.407457,$
$\mathbf{x}^{\mathrm{T}} = (1.000000\ -2.058309\ 1.143108\ -0.246128)$

56. $\lambda = \lambda_s^{(10)} + 4.5 = -4.722050 + 4.5 = -0.222050$

$$\mathbf{A}_s = \begin{bmatrix} 1.222050 & 1.000000 & 2.000000 \\ 2.000000 & 1.222050 & 1.000000 \\ 1.000000 & 1.000000 & 3.222050 \end{bmatrix} \quad \mathbf{LU} = \begin{bmatrix} 1.222050 & 1.000000 & 2.000000 \\ 1.636594 & -0.414544 & -2.273188 \\ 0.818297 & -0.438320 & 0.589073 \end{bmatrix}$$

$k = 6,\quad \lambda_{s,i} = -15.849750,\quad \lambda_s = -0.063092,\quad \lambda = \lambda_s - 0.222050$
$\lambda = -0.285142,\quad \mathbf{x}^{\mathrm{T}} = (1.000000\ -1.728895\ 0.221876)$

61. $k = 7,\quad \lambda = 4.507019,\quad \det(\mathbf{D}) = -0.000001$

66. $k = 7,\quad \lambda = -0.285142,\quad \det(\mathbf{D}) = 0.000000$

Chapter 3 Nonlinear Equations

1. (*a*) $i = 13,\quad x = 0.739075,\quad f(x) = 0.00008470$

3. (*a*) $i = 14,\quad x = 0.815613,\quad f(x) = 0.00000434$
(*b*) $i = 14,\quad x = 1.429626,\quad f(x) = 0.00056840$

5. (*a*) $x = \cos(x) = g(x)$
$i = 22,\quad x = 0.739050,\quad g(x) = 0.739050$

8. (*a*) $x = +(\exp(x))^{1/4} = g(x)$
$i = 10,\quad x = 1.429458,\quad g(x) = 1.429557$
(*b*) $x = -(\exp(x))^{1/4}$
$i = 8,\quad x = -0.815585,\quad g(x) = -0.815547$

13. (*a*) $i = 3,\quad x = 0.739085,\quad f(x) = 0.00000000$

14. $i = 5,\quad x = 1.000000,\quad f(x) = 0.00000000$

18. (*a*) $i = 4,\quad x = 0.739085,\quad f(x) = 0.00000000$

19. $i = 7,\quad x = 1.000000,\quad f(x) = 0.00000011$

23. (*a*) $x_0 = 1.5$, $i = 12$, $x = 1.000088$, $f(x) = -0.00000002$
$x_0 = 2.5$, $i = 6$, $x = 3.000000$, $f(x) = 0.00000002$
$x_0 = -3.0$, $i = 17$, $x = 0.999923$, $f(x) = -0.00000001$

24. (*b*) $x_0 = 1.0+I1.0$, $i = 6$, $x = 0.0+I1.0$, $f(x) = 0.00000000+I0.00000000$
$x_0 = 1.0-I1.0$, $i = 6$, $x = 0.0-I1.0$, $f(x) = 0.00000000+I0.00000000$
$x_0 = -3.0+I0.0$, $i = 6$, $x = -2.0+I0.0$, $f(x) = 0.00000000+I0.00000000$

25. $(x_0, y_0) = (1.0, 1.0)$, $i = 6$, $(x, y) = (1.906287$, $y = 0.523977)$,
$f = 0.00000000$, $g = 0.00000000$
$(x_0, y_0) = (0.0, 1.0)$, $i = 6$, $(x, y) = (-0.691051$, $y = 1.625373)$,
$f = 0.00000000$, $g = 0.00000000$

Chapter 4 Polynomial Approximation and Interpolation

1. (*a*) $P_3(1.5) = 4.8750$, (*b*) $P_3'(1.5) = 5.7500$, (*c*) $Q_2(x) = x^2 - 7x + 12$

13. (*a*) $f(2.0) = 5.201650$, Error = 0.201650, Ratio = 4.02
$f(2.0) = 5.050100$, Error = 0.050100
(*b*) $f(2.0) = 5.391433$, Error = 0.391433, Ratio = 3.97
$f(2.0) = 5.098500$, Error = 0.098500

16. (*a*) $P_2(x) = 10.8336 - 18.7510x + 11.4175x^2$, $P_2(0.9) = 3.205875$
(*b*) $P_2(x) = 6.16700 - 6.25075x + 3.08375x^2$, $P_2(0.9) = 3.039163$
(*c*) $P_3(x) = 12.8430 - 29.5865x + 30.1713x^2 - 10.4188x^3$, $P_3(0.9) = 3.049594$
(*d*) $P_3(x) = 9.49900 - 16.5244x + 13.4962x^2 - 3.47083x^3$, $P_3(0.9) = 3.028750$
(*e*) $P_4(x) = 14.5015 - 40.2863x + 54.8364x^2 - 34.7365x^3 + 8.68490x^4$,
$P_4(0.9) = 3.036566$

21. (*a*) 3.205875, (*b*) 3.039163, (*c*) 3.049594, (*d*) 3.028750, (*e*) 3.036566

30. (*a*) 3.205875, (*b*) 3.039163, (*c*) 3.049594, (*d*) 3.028750, (*e*) 3.036566

35. (*a*) 3.205875, (*b*) 3.039163, (*c*) 3.049594, (*d*) 3.028750, (*e*) 3.036566

52. $v(9000, T) = -0.0165440 + 0.0777550 \times 10^{-3}T - 0.0120500 \times 10^{-6}T^2$,
$v(9000, 750) = 0.034994$

$v(10000, T) = -0.0171970 + 0.0740200 \times 10^{-3}T - 0.0128000 \times 10^{-6}T^2$,
$v(10000, 750) = 0.031118$

$v(11000, T) = -0.0172360 + 0.0697700 \times 10^{-3}T - 0.0127000 \times 10^{-6}T^2$,
$v(11000, 750) = 0.027948$

$v(P, 750) = 0.101648 - 0.0105830 \times 10^{-3}P + 0.353000 \times 10^{-9}P^2$,
$v(9500, 750) = 0.032968$

56. $v(P, T) = -7.69900\times10^{-3} + 0.103420\times10^{-3}T - 0.233000\times10^{-6}P - 4.86000\times10^{-9}PT$
$v(9500, 750) = 0.033025$

64. (*b*) 1.673669

74. $C_p(T) = 0.999420 + 0.142900 \times 10^{-3}T$

81. $C_p(T) = 0.853364 + 0.454921 \times 10^{-3}T - 0.228902 \times 10^{-6}T^2 + 0.0729798 \times 10^{-9}T^3 - 0.0113636 \times 10^{-12}T^4$

82. $f = \dfrac{15.915}{\text{Re}^{0.99913}}$

Chapter 5 Numerical Differentiation and Difference Formulas

1. (*a*) $f(x) = -0.0136180 + 2.73190x,$
$f'(1.0) = 2.731900, \quad f''(1.0) = 0.0$
(*b*) $f(x) = 1.375132 - 0.031850x + 1.3750x^2$
$f'(x) = -0.031850 + 2.750x, \quad f'(1.0) = 2.718150$
$f''(x) = 2.750, \quad f''(1.0) = 2.750$
(*c*) $f(x) = 1.031732 + 0.988216667x + 0.3650x^2 + 0.33333333x^3$
$f'(x) = 0.988216667 + 0.7300x + x^2, \quad f' = 2.718216$
$f''(x) = 0.7300 + 2.0x, \quad f''(1.0) = 2.730$

8. (*a*) $f'(1.0) = \dfrac{1}{0.01}\left(0.027319 - \dfrac{1}{2}(0.000275) + \dfrac{1}{3}(0.000002)\right)$

$f'(1.0) = 2.731900,\ 2.718150,\ 2.718217$

$f''(1.0) = \dfrac{1}{(0.01)^2}(0.000275 - 0.000002) = 2.750000,\ 2.730000$

(*b*) $f'(1.0) = \dfrac{1}{0.02}\left(0.054913 - \dfrac{1}{2}(0.001109) + \dfrac{1}{3}(0.000023)\right)$

$f'(1.0) = 2.745650,\ 2.717925,\ 2.718308$

$f''(1.0) = \dfrac{1}{(0.02)^2}(0.001109 - 0.000023) = 2.772500,\ 2.715000$

17. (*b*) $u'(0.0) = \dfrac{1}{1.0}\left(55.56 - \dfrac{1}{2}(-22.23) + \dfrac{1}{3}(0.01)\right)$

$u'(0.0) = 55.56,\ 66.675,\ 66.678$

Chapter 6 Numerical Integration

5. (*a*)

h	I	Error	Ratio
π	15.70796327	−2.00000000	4.66
$\pi/2$	17.27875959	−0.42920368	4.13
$\pi/4$	17.60408217	−0.10388110	4.03
$\pi/8$	17.68219487	−0.02576840	
Exact	17.70796327		

6.

h	I	Error	Ratio
1.6	8.12800000	2.26379084	3.30
0.8	6.54936000	0.68515084	3.60
0.4	6.05468000	0.19047084	3.83
0.2	5.91394000	0.04973084	
Exact	5.86420916		

9. (*a*)

h	I	Error	Ratio
$\pi/2$	17.80235837	0.09439510	20.70
$\pi/4$	17.71252302	0.00455975	16.94
$\pi/8$	17.70823244	0.00026917	16.22
$\pi/16$	17.70797986	0.00001659	
Exact	17.70796327		

13. (*a*)

h	I	Error	Ratio
$\pi/3$	17.74848755	0.04052428	20.16
$\pi/6$	17.70997311	0.00200984	16.84
$\pi/12$	17.70808265	0.00011938	16.20
$\pi/24$	17.70797064	0.00000737	
Exact	17.70796327		

20. (*a*)

h	I	Error	Ratio
$\pi/5$	17.70716636	−0.00079691	84.06
$\pi/10$	17.70795379	−0.00000948	67.71
$\pi/20$	17.70796313	−0.00000014	
Exact	17.70796327		

25. (*a*)

h	$O(h^2)$	$O(h^4)$	$O(h^6)$	$O(h^8)$
π	15.70796327			
$\pi/2$	17.27875959	17.80235837		
$\pi/4$	17.60408217	17.71252302	17.70653400	
$\pi/8$	17.68219487	17.70823244	17.70794640	17.70796882
Exact	17.70796327			

31. (*a*)

h	I	Error	Ratio
π	17.64378284	−0.06418043	21.01
$\pi/2$	17.70490849	−0.00305478	17.00
$\pi/4$	17.70778360	−0.00017967	16.23
$\pi/8$	17.70795220	−0.00001107	
Exact	17.70796327		

32. (*a*)

h	I	Error	Ratio
π	17.70935218	0.00138891	85.52
$\pi/2$	17.70797951	0.00001624	67.67
$\pi/4$	17.70796351	0.00000024	
$\pi/8$	17.70796327	0.00000000	
Exact	17.70796327		

33. (*a*)

h	I	Error	Ratio
π	17.70794750	−0.00001577	315.4
$\pi/2$	17.70796322	−0.00000005	
$\pi/4$	17.70796327	−0.00000000	
Exact	17.70796327		

Chapter 7 One-Dimensional Initial-Value Problems

22. $\Delta t = 0.2$, $y(1.0) = 0.672320$, $E(0.2) = 0.040199$, Ratio $= 2.09$
$\Delta t = 0.1$, $y(1.0) = 0.651322$, $E(0.1) = 0.019201$

23. $\Delta t = 0.2$, $y(1.0) = 0.598122$, $E(0.2) = -0.033998$, Ratio $= 1.92$
$\Delta t = 0.1$, $y(1.0) = 0.614457$, $E(0.1) = -0.017664$

24. $\Delta t = 0.2$, $y(1.0) = 0.629260$, $E(0.2) = -0.002860$, Ratio $= 4.32$
$\Delta t = 0.1$, $y(1.0) = 0.631459$, $E(0.1) = -0.000662$

25. $\Delta t = 0.2$, $y(1.0) = 0.63211476$, $E(0.2) = -0.00000580$, Ratio $= 17.6$
$\Delta t = 0.1$, $y(1.0) = 0.63212023$, $E(0.1) = -0.00000033$

26. $\Delta t = 0.2$, $y(1.0) = 0.63201711$, $E(0.2) = -0.00010345$, Ratio $= 9.83$
$\Delta t = 0.1$, $y(1.0) = 0.63211004$, $E(0.1) = -0.00001052$

27. $\Delta t = 0.2$, $y(1.0) = 0.63213778$, $E(0.2) = 0.00001722$, Ratio $= 14.7$
$\Delta t = 0.1$, $y(1.0) = 0.63212173$, $E(0.1) = 0.00000117$

28. $\Delta t = 0.2$, $y(1.0) = 0.63211820$, $E(0.2) = -0.00000236$, Ratio $= 26.2$
$\Delta t = 0.1$, $y(1.0) = 0.63212047$, $E(0.1) = -0.00000009$

64. $\Delta t = 0.2$, $y(1.0) = 2.102601$, $E(0.2) = -0.345453$, Ratio $= 1.69$
$\Delta t = 0.1$, $y(1.0) = 2.243841$, $E(0.1) = -0.204213$

65. $\Delta t = 0.2$, $y(1.0) = 2.426707$, $E(0.2) = -0.021348$, Ratio $= 3.66$
$\Delta t = 0.1$, $y(1.0) = 2.442230$, $E(0.1) = -0.005825$

66. $\Delta t = 0.2$, $y(1.0) = 2.44802522$, $E(0.2) = -0.00002910$, Ratio $= 35.9$
$\Delta t = 0.1$, $y(1.0) = 2.44805351$, $E(0.1) = -0.00000081$

67. $\Delta t = 0.2$, $y(1.0) = 2.42471257$, $E(0.2) = -0.02334175$, Ratio $= 5.72$
$\Delta t = 0.1$, $y(1.0) = 2.44397647$, $E(0.1) = -0.00407785$

68. $\Delta t = 0.2$, $y(1.0) = 2.44802270$, $E(0.2) = -0.00003162$
$\Delta t = 0.1$, $y(1.0) = 2.44821893$, $E(0.1) = 0.00016461$

69. $\Delta t = 0.2$, $y(1.0) = 2.44835945$, $E(0.2) = 0.00030513$, Ratio = 8.54
$\Delta t = 0.1$, $y(1.0) = 2.44809007$, $E(0.1) = 0.00003575$

92. $\Delta t = 0.20$, $y(1.0) = 2.102601$, $E(0.2) = -0.232621$, Ratio = 2.55
$\Delta t = 0.10$, $y(1.0) = 2.243841$, $E(0.1) = -0.091381$,
$\Delta t = 0.05$, $y(1.0) = 2.335222$, $E(0.05) = 0.0$

93. $\Delta t = 0.20$, $y(1.0) = 2.426707$, $E(0.2) = -0.019843$, Ratio = 4.59
$\Delta t = 0.10$, $y(1.0) = 2.442230$, $E(0.1) = -0.004320$,
$\Delta t = 0.05$, $y(1.0) = 2.446550$, $E(0.05) = 0.0$

94. $\Delta t = 0.20$, $y(1.0) = 2.44802522$, $E(0.2) = -0.00002910$, Ratio = 35.9
$\Delta t = 0.10$, $y(1.0) = 2.44805351$, $E(0.1) = -0.00000081$
$\Delta t = 0.05$, $y(1.0) = 2.44805432$, $E(0.05) = 0.0$

95. $\Delta t = 0.20$, $y(1.0) = 2.42471257$, $E(0.2) = -0.02293328$, Ratio = 6.25
$\Delta t = 0.10$, $y(1.0) = 2.44397647$, $E(0.1) = -0.00366938$,
$\Delta t = 0.05$, $y(1.0) = 2.44764585$, $E(0.05) = 0.0$

96. $\Delta t = 0.20$, $y(1.0) = 2.44802270$, $E(0.2) = -0.00005529$
$\Delta t = 0.10$, $y(1.0) = 2.44821893$, $E(0.1) = 0.00014094$
$\Delta t = 0.05$, $y(1.0) = 2.44807799$, $E(0.05) = 0.0$

97. $\Delta t = 0.20$, $y(1.0) = 2.44835945$, $E(0.2) = 0.00030132$, Ratio = 9.43
$\Delta t = 0.10$, $y(1.0) = 2.44809007$, $E(0.1) = 0.00003194$
$\Delta t = 0.05$, $y(1.0) = 2.44805813$, $E(0.05) = 0.0$

126. $\Delta t = 0.2$, $y(1.0) = 2.00007303$, $E(0.2) = 0.00007303$, Ratio = 26.1
$\Delta t = 0.1$, $y(1.0) = 2.00000281$, $E(0.1) = 0.00000281$

140. (*a*) $\Delta t = 0.2$, $y(1.0) = 0.598122$, $E(0.2) = -0.033998$
$\Delta t = 0.1$, $y(1.0) = 0.614457$, $E(0.1) = -0.017664$
(*b*) $\Delta t = 0.2$, $y(1.0) = 0.598122$, $E(0.2) = -0.033998$
$\Delta t = 0.1$, $y(1.0) = 0.614457$, $E(0.1) = -0.017664$

146. (*a*) $\Delta t = 0.2$, $y(1.0) = 3.039281$, $E(0.2) = 0.591227$, Ratio = 2.13
$\Delta t = 0.1$, $y(1.0) = 2.725422$, $E(0.1) = 0.277367$
(*b*) $\Delta t = 0.2$, $y(1.0) = 3.837679$, $E(0.2) = 1.389625$, Ratio = 4.02
$\Delta t = 0.1$, $y(1.0) = 2.793804$, $E(0.1) = 0.345749$

150. $\Delta t = 0.2$, $y(1.0) = 12.391680$, $z(1.0) = 8.655360$
$\Delta t = 0.1$, $y(1.0) = 15.654961$, $z(1.0) = 10.685748$

151. $\Delta t = 0.2$, $y(1.0) = 19.532354$, $z(1.0) = 13.095753$
$\Delta t = 0.1$, $y(1.0) = 20.735960$, $z(1.0) = 13.840150$

152. $\Delta t = 0.2$, $y(1.0) = 21.25212768$, $z(1.0) = 14.15934151$
$\Delta t = 0.1$, $y(1.0) = 21.27386712$, $z(1.0) = 14.17277742$

186. $\Delta t = 0.01$, $y(0.1) = 2.100000$, $E(0.01) = 0.000000$
$\Delta t = 0.05$, $y(0.1) = 2.109709$, $E(0.05) = 0.009709$

194. $\Delta t = 0.005$, $y(0.1) = 0.366958$, $z(0.1) = 0.000000$
$\Delta t = 0.010$, $y(0.1) = 0.366032$, $z(0.1) = 0.000000$
$\Delta t = 0.020$, $y(0.98) = 0.371602$, $z(0.98) = -1.000000$
$y(1.00) = 0.364170$, $z(1.00) = 1.000000$
$\Delta t = 0.025$, $y(0.975) = 0.372546$, $z(0.975) =$ ******
$y(1.000) = 0.363232$, $z(1.00) =$ ******

199. $\Delta t = 0.0005$, $y(1.0) = 3.619259$, $z(1.0) = -1.809630$
$\Delta t = 0.0010$, $y(1.0) = 3.619169$, $z(1.0) = -1.809584$
$\Delta t = 0.0020$, $y(0.98) = 6.626240$, $z(0.98) = -4.813120$
$y(1.00) = 0.618987$, $z(1.00) = 1.190506$

209. $\Delta t = 0.0005$, $y(1.0) = 0.904815$, $z(1.0) = 0.904815$
$\Delta t = 0.0010$, $y(1.0) = 0.904792$, $z(1.0) = 0.904792$
$\Delta t = 0.0020$, $y(0.98) = -0.093440$, $z(0.98) = 0.906560$
$y(1.00) = 1.904747$, $z(1.00) = 0.904747$

Chapter 8 One-Dimensional Boundary-Value Problems

7.

x	$\bar{y}(x)$	$y(x)$	Error	$y(x)$	Error	$y(x)$	Error
0.00	0.000000	0.000000		0.000000		0.000000	
0.25	1.045057	2.027778	0.982721	1.327386	0.282329	1.162644	0.117587
0.50	1.233303	1.583333	0.350031	1.392072	0.158769	1.304867	0.071564
0.75	1.149746	1.250000	0.100254	1.203698	0.053952	1.175560	0.025815
1.00	1.000000	1.000000		1.000000		1.000000	

8.

x	$\bar{y}(x)$	$y(x)$	Error	$y(x)$	Error	$y(x)$	Error
0.00	0.000000	0.000000		0.000000		0.000000	
0.25	1.045057	0.819554	−0.225503	1.002372	−0.042685	1.036161	−0.008896
0.50	1.233303	1.077398	−0.155905	1.206372	−0.026931	1.227779	−0.005523
0.75	1.149746	1.087621	−0.062125	1.139889	−0.009857	1.147752	−0.001994
1.00	1.000000	1.000000		1.000000		1.000000	

9.

x	$\bar{y}(x)$	$y(x)$	Error	$y(x)$	Error	$y(x)$	Error
0.00	0.000000	0.000000		0.000000			
0.25	1.045057	1.031965	−0.013092	1.044519	−0.000539	1.045030	−0.000027
0.50	1.233303	1.225251	−0.008052	1.232974	−0.000329	1.233286	−0.000017
0.75	1.149746	1.146878	−0.002868	1.149630	−0.000116	1.149740	−0.000006
1.00	1.000000	1.000000		1.000000		1.000000	

40.

x	$\bar{y}(x)$	$y(x)$	Error	$y(x)$	Error	$y(x)$	Error
0.00	0.000000	0.000000		0.000000		0.000000	
0.25	1.045057	1.176150	0.131093	1.072659	0.027601	1.051705	0.006648
0.50	1.233303	1.305085	0.071782	1.249448	0.016146	1.237241	0.003939
0.75	1.149764	1.172518	0.022772	1.155195	0.005431	1.151086	0.001340
1.00	1.000000	1.000000		1.000000		1.000000	

51.

x	$\bar{y}(x)$	$y(x)$	Error
0.00	1.000000	1.000000	
0.25	0.449272	0.444518	−0.004753
0.50	0.263622	0.249256	−0.014366
0.75	0.208528	0.189911	−0.018617
1.00	0.198542	0.179923	−0.018619

57.

x	$\bar{y}(x)$	$y(x)$	Error	$y(x)$	Error
0.00	1.000000	1.000000		1.000000	
0.25	0.449272	0.442720	−0.006551	0.456837	0.007566
0.50	0.263622	0.262284	−0.001338	0.278258	0.014636
0.75	0.208528	0.211022	0.002494	0.225223	0.016695
1.00	0.198542	0.202525	0.003983	0.214211	0.015669

63.

x	$y(x)$	$y'(x)$	$y(x)$	$y'(x)$
0.00	0.000000	2.506447	0.000000	2.532707
0.25	0.446421	0.367691	0.403906	0.568357
0.50	0.497341	−0.106313	0.478689	−0.000161
0.75	0.463610	−0.178353	0.461399	−0.139091
1.00	0.419605	−0.160791	0.424293	−0.151414

71. Solution with $y(5) = 0$ and $y(10) = 0$ for $\Delta x = 0.25$, and with $y(5) = 0$ and $y(10) = 0$ for $\Delta x = 0.125$.

x	$y(x)$	$y(x)$	$y(x)$	$y(x)$
0.00	1.000000	1.000000	1.000000	1.000000
0.25	0.749982	0.750000	0.765603	0.765625
0.50	0.562463	0.562500	0.586138	0.586182
0.75	0.421819	0.421875	0.448727	0.448795
1.00	0.316329	0.316406	0.343513	0.343609

79.

x	$y(x)$	$y(x)$	$y(x)$
0.00	0.000000	0.000000	0.000000
0.25	0.078132	0.371156	0.394922
0.50	0.718639	0.683557	0.708702
0.75	1.385139	0.896736	0.909797
1.00	1.000000	1.000000	1.000000

85.

x	$y(x)$	$y(x)$	$y(x)$
0.00	0.000000	0.000000	0.000000
0.25	0.420275	0.416356	0.415427
0.50	0.735218	0.729755	0.728463
0.75	0.923725	0.919992	0.919107
1.00	1.000000	1.000000	1.000000

91.

x	$\bar{y}(x)$	$y(x)$	Error	$y(x)$	Error
0.00	0.00000000	0.00000000		0.00000000	
0.25	0.18994276	0.18994383	−0.00000108	0.18994377	−0.00000007
0.50	0.43025117	0.43025304	−0.00000127	0.43025296	−0.00000008
0.75	0.70598554	0.70598635	−0.00000081	0.70598630	−0.00000005
1.00	1.00000000	1.00000000		1.00000000	

Chapter 9 Elliptic Partial Differential Equations—The Laplace Equation

10.

$T(x, y)$		x	
y	0.0	5.0	10.0
15.0	100.000000	100.000000	100.000000
10.0	0.000000	26.666667	0.000000
5.0	0.000000	6.666667	0.000000
0.0	0.000000	0.000000	0.000000

12.

$T(x, y)$		x	
y	0.0	5.0	10.0
15.0	0.000000	0.000000	100.000000
10.0	0.000000	33.333333	100.000000
5.0	0.000000	33.333333	100.000000
0.0	0.000000	0.000000	100.000000

14.

$T(x, y)$			x		
y	0.00	0.25	0.50	0.75	1.00
1.00	100.000000	0.000000	0.000000	0.000000	0.000000
0.75	100.000000	50.000000	28.571429	14.285714	0.000000
0.50	100.000000	71.428571	50.000000	28.571429	0.000000
0.25	100.000000	85.714286	71.428571	50.000000	0.000000
0.00	100.000000	100.000000	100.000000	100.000000	100.000000

36.

$T(x, y)$		x	
y	0.0	5.0	10.0
15.0	0.000000	0.000000	0.000000
10.0	0.000000	83.333333	0.000000
5.0	0.000000	83.333333	0.000000
0.0	0.000000	0.000000	0.000000

Chapter 10 Finite Difference Methods for Propagation Problems

25. $$\frac{\bar{f}_i^{n+1} - \bar{f}_i^n}{\Delta t} + \frac{1}{2}\bar{f}_{tt}(\tau)\,\Delta t + u\frac{\bar{f}_{i+1}^{n+1} - \bar{f}_{i-1}^{n+1}}{2\Delta x} - \frac{1}{6}\bar{f}_{xxx}(\xi)\,\Delta x^2 + \cdots = 0$$

$$-\frac{u\,\Delta t}{2\,\Delta x}f_{i-1}^{n+1} + f_i^n + \frac{u\,\Delta t}{2\,\Delta x}f_{i+1}^{n+1} = f_i^n$$

36. $$f_t + uf_x = \frac{1}{2}f_{tt}\,\Delta t - \cdots - \frac{1}{6}uf_{xxx}\,\Delta x^2 - \cdots$$

$$f_t + uf_x = \frac{1}{2}u^2\,\Delta t f_{xx} + \left(-\frac{1}{6}u\,\Delta x^2 - \frac{1}{3}u^3\,\Delta t^2\right)f_{xxx} + \cdots$$

The FDE is consistent and $0(\Delta t) + 0(\Delta x^2)$.

44. $G = 1/(1 + Ic\sin(\theta)$, $|G| \leq 1$ for all values of c. Unconditionally stable.

53. From Problem 36, implicit numerical diffusion and dispersion are both present, and implicit numerical diffusion is dominant.

Chapter 11 Parabolic Partial Differential Equations—The Diffusion Equation

9.

$T(x, t)$				x,cm		
t, s	0.0	0.1	0.2	0.3	0.4	0.5
0.0	0.00	20.00	40.00	60.00	80.00	100.00
0.1	0.00	20.00	40.00	60.00	80.00	96.00
0.2	0.00	20.00	40.00	60.00	79.60	92.80
0.3	0.00	20.00	40.00	59.96	78.96	90.16
0.4	0.00	20.00	40.00	59.86	78.18	87.92
0.5	0.00	20.00	39.98	59.71	77.32	85.97

24.

$T(x, t)$				x,cm		
t, s	0.0	0.1	0.2	0.3	0.4	0.5
0.0	0.00	20.00	40.00	60.00	80.00	100.00
0.5	0.00	19.94	39.78	59.17	76.91	88.45

35.

$T(x, t)$	x, cm					
t,s	0.0	0.1	0.2	0.3	0.4	0.5
0.0	0.00	20.00	40.00	60.00	80.00	100.00
0.5	0.00	20.00	40.00	60.00	80.00	80.00
1.0	0.00	20.00	40.00	60.00	70.00	80.00
1.5	0.00	20.00	40.00	55.00	70.00	70.00
2.0	0.00	20.00	37.50	55.00	62.50	70.00
2.5	0.00	18.75	37.50	50.00	62.50	62.50

Chapter 12 Hyperbolic Partial Differential Equations—The Convection Equation

6.

$T(x, t)$	x, cm												
t,s	0.0	0.1	0.2	0.3	0.4	0.5	0.6	0.7	0.8	0.9	1.0	1.1	1.2
0.0	0.00	20.00	40.00	60.00	80.00	100.00	80.00	60.00	40.00	20.00	0.00	0.00	0.00
1.0	−10.00	0.00	40.00	40.00	60.00	100.00	100.00	60.00	60.00	40.00	10.00	0.00	0.00
2.0	−10.00	−15.0	0.00	20.00	30.00	80.00	110.00	100.00	80.00	65.00	30.00	5.00	0.00

10.

$T(x, t)$	x, cm												
t,s	0.0	0.1	0.2	0.3	0.4	0.5	0.6	0.7	0.8	0.9	1.0	1.1	1.2
0.0	0.00	20.00	40.00	60.00	80.00	100.00	80.00	60.00	40.00	20.00	0.00	0.00	0.00
0.5	5.00	10.00	30.00	50.00	70.00	80.00	90.00	70.00	50.00	30.00	15.00	0.00	0.00
1.0	2.50	11.25	20.00	40.00	57.50	75.00	77.50	80.00	60.00	41.25	22.50	11.25	0.00

16.

$T(x, t)$	x, cm												
t,s	0.0	0.1	0.2	0.3	0.4	0.5	0.6	0.7	0.8	0.9	1.0	1.1	1.2
0.0	0.00	20.00	40.00	60.00	80.00	100.00	80.00	60.00	40.00	20.00	0.00	0.00	0.00
0.5	0.00	10.00	30.00	50.00	70.00	90.00	90.00	70.00	50.00	30.00	10.00	0.00	0.00
1.0	0.00	5.00	20.00	40.00	60.00	80.00	90.00	80.00	60.00	40.00	20.00	5.00	0.00

38.

$T(x, t)$	x, cm												
t,s	0.0	0.1	0.2	0.3	0.4	0.5	0.6	0.7	0.8	0.9	1.0	1.1	1.2
0.0	0.00	20.00	40.00	60.00	80.00	100.00	80.00	60.00	40.00	20.00	0.00	0.00	0.00
0.5	−2.50	10.00	30.00	50.00	70.00	95.00	90.00	70.00	50.00	30.00	7.50	0.00	0.00
1.0	−3.12	2.81	20.00	40.00	59.38	86.25	94.38	80.00	60.00	40.31	16.87	2.81	0.00

47.

$T(x, t)$				x, cm			
t,s	0.0	0.25	0.50	0.75	1.00	1.25	1.50
0.0	0.00	50.00	100.00	50.00	0.00	0.00	0.00
1.0	−5.83	30.26	92.85	66.03	12.70	2.54	0.00

52.

$T(x, t)$						x, cm							
t,s	0.0	0.1	0.2	0.3	0.4	0.5	0.6	0.7	0.8	0.9	1.0	1.1	1.2
0.0	0.00	20.00	40.00	60.00	80.00	100.00	80.00	60.00	40.00	20.00	0.00	0.00	0.00
0.5	0.00	−2.50	10.00	30.00	50.00	67.50	100.00	87.50	70.00	50.00	30.00	7.50	0.00
1.0	0.63	−2.81	1.87	20.31	40.62	53.91	95.00	79.38	59.69	40.62	17.19	1.87	0.47

Chapter 13 Coordinate Transformations and Grid Generation

8.

ξ	1	2	3	4	5	6	7	8	9	10	11
x	0.000	0.010	0.040	0.090	0.160	0.250	0.360	0.490	0.640	0.810	1.000

10.

$x(\xi, \eta)$					ξ				
η	1	2	3	4	5	6	7	8	9
5	0.000	0.500	1.000	1.500	2.000	2.500	3.000	3.500	4.000
4	0.000	0.500	1.000	1.500	2.000	2.500	3.000	3.500	4.000
3	0.000	0.500	1.000	1.500	2.000	2.500	3.000	3.500	4.000
2	0.000	0.500	1.000	1.500	2.000	2.500	3.000	3.500	4.000
1	0.000	0.500	1.000	1.500	2.000	2.500	3.000	3.500	4.000

$y(\xi, \eta)$					ξ				
η	1	2	3	4	5	6	7	8	9
5	1.000	1.354	1.500	1.612	1.707	1.791	1.866	1.935	2.000
4	0.750	1.015	1.125	1.209	1.280	1.343	1.400	1.452	1.500
3	0.500	0.677	0.750	0.806	0.854	0.895	0.933	0.968	1.000
2	0.250	0.338	0.375	0.403	0.427	0.448	0.467	0.484	0.500
1	0.000	0.000	0.000	0.000	0.000	0.000	0.000	0.000	0.000

17. The normalizing transformation is presented in Problem 13.10. The x coordinates for the Laplace grid generator are the same as for the normalizing transformation. The solution for the two passes through the Laplace grid generator are presented below. The Gauss-Seidel sweep logic proceeds from $j = 2$ to 4 in the outer loop and from $i = 2$ to 8 in the inner loop. The first pass results are identical for Parts (*a*) and (*b*).

$y(\xi, \eta)$				ξ					
η	1	2	3	4	5	6	7	8	9
5	1.000	1.354	1.500	1.612	1.707	1.791	1.866	1.935	2.000
4	0.750	0.973	1.107	1.200	1.274	1.338	1.396	1.448	1.500
3	0.500	0.650	0.738	0.800	0.850	0.892	0.931	0.966	1.000
2	0.250	0.327	0.370	0.401	0.425	0.446	0.466	0.483	0.500
1	0.000	0.000	0.000	0.000	0.000	0.000	0.000	0.000	0.000

$y(\xi, \eta)$				ξ					
η	1	2	3	4	5	6	7	8	9
5	1.000	1.354	1.500	1.612	1.707	1.791	1.866	1.935	2.000
4	0.750	0.964	1.100	1.195	1.271	1.336	1.394	1.448	1.500
3	0.500	0.631	0.726	0.793	0.845	0.889	0.928	0.964	1.000
2	0.250	0.317	0.364	0.397	0.423	0.445	0.464	0.482	0.500
1	0.000	0.000	0.000	0.000	0.000	0.000	0.000	0.000	0.000

$y(\xi, \eta)$				ξ					
η	1	2	3	4	5	6	7	8	9
5	1.000	1.354	1.500	1.612	1.707	1.791	1.866	1.935	2.000
4	0.750	0.963	1.099	1.195	1.271	1.336	1.394	1.448	1.500
3	0.500	0.632	0.726	0.793	0.845	0.889	0.928	0.964	1.000
2	0.250	0.317	0.364	0.397	0.423	0.445	0.464	0.482	0.500
1	0.000	0.000	0.000	0.000	0.000	0.000	0.000	0.000	0.000

25. (*a*) (0.0,0.0), (*b*) (0.813,0.0), (*c*) (0.188,0.5), (*d*) (0.5,0.813), (*e*) (0.5,0.188), (*f*) (0.813,0.813), (*g*) (0.188,0.188)

Chapter 14 Parabolic Partial Differential Equations—The Convection-Diffusion Equation

8.

$T(x, t)$						x, cm					
t,s	0.0	0.1	0.2	0.3	0.4	0.5	0.6	0.7	0.8	0.9	1.0
0.0	0.00	10.00	20.00	30.00	40.00	50.00	60.00	70.00	80.00	90.00	100.00
0.5	0.00	5.00	15.00	25.00	35.00	45.00	55.00	65.00	75.00	85.00	100.00
1.0	0.00	3.75	10.00	20.00	30.00	40.00	50.00	60.00	70.00	81.25	100.00

20.

$T(x, t)$						x, cm					
t,s	0.0	0.1	0.2	0.3	0.4	0.5	0.6	0.7	0.8	0.9	1.0
0.00	0.00	10.00	20.00	30.00	40.00	50.00	60.00	70.00	80.00	90.00	100.00
0.25	0.00	7.50	17.50	27.50	37.50	47.50	57.50	67.50	77.50	87.50	100.00
0.50	0.00	6.25	15.00	25.00	35.00	45.00	55.00	65.00	75.00	85.63	100.00
0.75	0.00	5.31	13.13	22.50	32.50	42.50	52.50	62.50	72.66	83.91	100.00
1.00	0.00	4.61	11.56	20.31	30.00	40.00	50.00	60.04	70.39	82.30	100.00

40.

$T(x, t)$						x, cm					
t,s	0.0	0.1	0.2	0.3	0.4	0.5	0.6	0.7	0.8	0.9	1.0
0.0	0.00	10.00	20.00	30.00	40.00	50.00	60.00	70.00	80.00	90.00	100.00
0.5	0.00	7.50	15.00	25.00	35.00	45.00	55.00	65.00	75.00	86.25	100.00
1.0	0.00	5.63	11.56	20.63	30.00	40.00	50.00	60.00	70.16	82.97	100.00

51.

$T(x, t)$						x, cm					
t,s	0.0	0.1	0.2	0.3	0.4	0.5	0.6	0.7	0.8	0.9	1.0
0.0	0.00	10.00	20.00	30.00	40.00	50.00	60.00	70.00	80.00	90.00	100.00
1.0	0.00	5.51	13.03	21.67	30.92	40.51	50.29	60.21	70.42	81.88	100.00

59.

$T(x, t)$						x, cm					
t,s	0.0	0.1	0.2	0.3	0.4	0.5	0.6	0.7	0.8	0.9	1.0
0.0	0.00	10.00	20.00	30.00	40.00	50.00	60.00	70.00	80.00	90.00	100.00
1.0	0.00	3.94	11.56	20.61	30.24	40.10	50.04	60.04	70.18	81.32	100.00

73.

$T(x, t)$						x, cm					
t,s	0.0	0.1	0.2	0.3	0.4	0.5	0.6	0.7	0.8	0.9	1.0
0.0	0.00	10.00	20.00	30.00	40.00	50.00	60.00	70.00	80.00	90.00	100.00
0.5	0.00	6.88	15.00	25.00	35.00	45.00	55.00	65.00	75.00	85.63	100.00
1.0	0.00	3.75	11.41	20.00	30.00	40.00	50.00	60.00	70.16	81.25	100.00

Chapter 15 Hyperbolic Partial Differential Equations—The Wave Equation

6.

P(x, t)				x, m				
t, ms	**0.8**	**0.9**	**1.0**	**1.1**	**1.2**	**1.3**	**1.4**	**1.5**
0.00	0.00	0.00	0.00	20.00	40.00	60.00	80.00	100.00
0.05	0.00	0.00	0.00	20.00	40.00	60.00	80.00	100.00
0.10	0.00	1.25	2.50	21.25	40.00	60.00	77.50	95.00
⋮	⋮	⋮	⋮	⋮	⋮	⋮	⋮	⋮
0.50	24.99	41.77	56.72	58.05	38.11	23.43	−1.74	−15.35

P(x, t)				x, m				
t, ms	**1.5**	**1.6**	**1.7**	**1.8**	**1.9**	**2.0**	**2.1**	**2.2**
0.00	100.00	80.00	60.00	40.00	20.00	0.00	0.00	0.00
0.05	100.00	80.00	60.00	40.00	20.00	0.00	0.00	0.00
0.10	95.00	77.50	60.00	40.00	21.25	2.50	1.25	0.00
⋮	⋮	⋮	⋮	⋮	⋮	⋮	⋮	⋮
0.50	−15.35	−1.74	23.43	38.11	58.05	56.72	41.77	24.99

10.

P(x, t)				x, m				
t, ms	**0.8**	**0.9**	**1.0**	**1.1**	**1.2**	**1.3**	**1.4**	**1.5**
0.00	0.00	0.00	0.00	20.00	40.00	60.00	80.00	100.00
0.05	0.00	0.00	10.00	20.00	40.00	60.00	80.00	80.00
0.10	0.00	6.25	12.50	26.25	40.00	60.00	67.50	75.00
⋮	⋮	⋮	⋮	⋮	⋮	⋮	⋮	⋮
0.50	24.98	29.52	28.41	29.04	24.60	23.66	19.47	20.64

P(x, t)				x, m				
t, ms	**1.5**	**1.6**	**1.7**	**1.8**	**1.9**	**2.0**	**2.1**	**2.2**
0.00	100.00	80.00	60.00	40.00	20.00	0.00	0.00	0.00
0.05	80.00	80.00	60.00	40.00	20.00	10.00	0.00	0.00
0.10	75.00	67.50	60.00	40.00	26.25	12.50	6.25	0.00
⋮	⋮	⋮	⋮	⋮	⋮	⋮	⋮	⋮
0.50	20.64	19.47	23.66	24.60	29.04	28.41	29.52	24.98

16.

P(x, t)	x, m							
t, ms	0.8	0.9	1.0	1.1	1.2	1.3	1.4	1.5
0.00	0.00	0.00	0.00	20.00	40.00	60.00	80.00	100.00
0.05	0.00	0.00	5.00	20.00	40.00	60.00	80.00	90.00
0.10	0.00	2.50	10.00	22.50	40.00	60.00	75.00	80.00
⋮	⋮	⋮	⋮	⋮	⋮	⋮	⋮	⋮
0.50	28.79	35.24	37.70	35.25	28.91	21.09	14.75	12.30

P(x, t)	x, m							
t, ms	1.5	1.6	1.7	1.8	1.9	2.0	2.1	2.2
0.00	100.00	80.00	60.00	40.00	20.00	0.00	0.00	0.00
0.05	90.00	80.00	60.00	40.00	20.00	5.00	0.00	0.00
0.10	80.00	75.00	60.00	40.00	22.50	10.00	2.50	0.00
⋮	⋮	⋮	⋮	⋮	⋮	⋮	⋮	⋮
0.50	12.30	14.75	21.09	28.91	35.25	37.70	35.24	28.79

36.

P(x, t)	x, m							
t, ms	0.8	0.9	1.0	1.1	1.2	1.3	1.4	1.5
0.00	0.00	0.00	0.00	20.00	40.00	60.00	80.00	100.00
0.05	0.00	0.00	2.50	20.00	40.00	60.00	80.00	95.00
0.10	0.00	1.56	6.88	21.56	40.00	60.00	76.88	86.25
⋮	⋮	⋮	⋮	⋮	⋮	⋮	⋮	⋮
0.50	29.22	38.95	44.58	43.71	33.84	19.01	8.28	5.01

P(x, t)	x, m							
t, ms	1.5	1.6	1.7	1.8	1.9	2.0	2.1	2.2
0.00	100.00	80.00	60.00	40.00	20.00	0.00	0.00	0.00
0.05	95.00	80.00	60.00	40.00	20.00	2.50	0.00	0.00
0.10	86.25	76.88	60.00	40.00	21.56	6.88	1.56	0.00
⋮	⋮	⋮	⋮	⋮	⋮	⋮	⋮	⋮
0.50	5.01	8.28	19.01	33.84	43.71	44.58	38.95	29.22

44.

$P(x, t)$				x, m				
t, ms	0.8	0.9	1.0	1.1	1.2	1.3	1.4	1.5
0.00	0.00	0.00	0.00	20.00	40.00	60.00	80.00	100.00
0.05	0.00	0.00	5.00	20.00	40.00	60.00	80.00	90.00
0.10	0.00	2.50	10.00	22.50	40.00	60.00	75.00	80.00
⋮	⋮	⋮	⋮	⋮	⋮	⋮	⋮	⋮
0.50	28.79	35.24	37.70	35.25	28.91	21.09	14.75	12.30

$P(x, t)$				x, m				
t, ms	1.5	1.6	1.7	1.8	1.9	2.0	2.1	2.2
0.00	100.00	80.00	60.00	40.00	20.00	0.00	0.00	0.00
0.05	90.00	80.00	60.00	40.00	20.00	5.00	0.00	0.00
0.10	80.00	75.00	60.00	40.00	22.50	10.00	2.50	0.00
⋮	⋮	⋮	⋮	⋮	⋮	⋮	⋮	⋮
0.50	12.30	14.75	21.09	28.91	35.25	37.70	35.24	28.79

50.

$P(x, t)$					x, m				
t, ms	0.50	0.75	1.00	1.25	1.50	1.75	2.00	2.25	2.50
0.00	0.00	0.00	0.00	50.00	100.00	50.00	0.00	0.00	0.00
0.25	0.00	8.33	11.76	41.67	70.59	41.67	11.76	8.33	0.00

61.

$P(x, t)$				x, m				
t, ms	0.8	0.9	1.0	1.1	1.2	1.3	1.4	1.5
0.00	0.00	0.00	0.00	20.00	40.00	60.00	80.00	100.00
0.05	0.00	0.00	2.50	20.00	40.00	60.00	77.50	100.00
0.10	0.00	2.50	5.00	22.50	40.00	60.00	75.00	90.00
⋮	⋮	⋮	⋮	⋮	⋮	⋮	⋮	⋮
0.50	28.73	39.12	43.95	46.79	33.22	19.66	6.68	4.69

$P(x, t)$				x, m				
t, ms	1.5	1.6	1.7	1.8	1.9	2.0	2.1	2.2
0.00	100.00	80.00	60.00	40.00	20.00	0.00	0.00	0.00
0.05	100.00	77.50	60.00	40.00	20.00	2.50	0.00	0.00
0.10	90.00	75.00	60.00	40.00	22.50	5.00	2.50	0.00
⋮	⋮	⋮	⋮	⋮	⋮	⋮	⋮	⋮
0.50	4.69	6.68	19.66	33.22	46.79	43.95	39.12	28.73

REFERENCES

Abramowitz, M. and Stegun, I. A. (1964), *Handbook of Mathematical Functions, Applied Mathematics Series No. 55*, National Bureau of Standards, Washington, DC.

Allen, J. S. and Cheng, S. I. (1970), "Numerical Solutions of the Compressible Navier–Stokes Equations for the Laminar Near Wake," *Physics of Fluids*, Vol. 13, pp. 37–52.

Ames, W. F. (1969), *Numerical Methods for Partial Differential Equations*, Barnes and Noble, New York.

Anderson, D. A., Tannehill, J. C., and Pletcher, R. H. (1984), *Computational Fluid Mechanics and Heat Transfer*, Hemisphere Publishing Corporation, New York, pp. 247–252.

Bashforth, F. and Adams, J. C. (1883), "An Attempt to Test the Theories of Capillary Action . . . with an Explanation of the Method of Integration Employed," Cambridge University Press, Cambridge.

Brailovskaya, I. (1965), "A Difference Scheme for Numerical Solution of the Two-Dimensional Nonstationary Navier–Stokes Equations for a Compressible Gas," *Soviet Physics Doklady*, Vol. 10, pp. 107–110.

Brandt, A. (1977), "Multi-Level Adaptive Solutions to Boundary-Value Problems," *Mathematics of Computation*, Vol. 31, No. 138, pp. 333–390.

Burstein, S. Z. (1967), "Finite-Difference Calculations for Hydrodynamic Flows Containing Discontinuities," *Journal of Computational Physics*, Vol. 2, pp. 198–222.

Colebrook, C. F. (1939), "Turbulent Flow in Pipes with Particular Reference to the Transition between Smooth and Rough Pipes," *Journal of the Institute of Civil Engineers*, London.

Courant, R., Friedrichs, K. O., and Lewy, H. (1928), "Uber die Partiellen Differenzengleichungen der Mathematischen Physik," *Mathematische Annalen*, Vol. 100, pp. 32–74. Translated as: "On the Partial Differential Equations of Mathematical Physics," *IBM J. Res. Dev.*, Vol. 11, pp. 215–234, 1967.

Crank, J. and Nicolson, P. (1947), "A Practical Method for Numerical Evaluation of Solutions of Partial Differential Equations of the Heat-Conduction Type," *Proceedings of the Cambridge Philosophical Society*, Vol. 43, No. 50, pp. 50–67.

Dennis, J. E. and Schnabel, R. B. (1983), *Numerical Methods for Unconstrained Optimization and Nonlinear Equations*, Prentice-Hall, Englewood Cliffs, New Jersey.

Douglas, J. (1962), "Alternating Direction Methods for Three Space Variables," *Numerische Mathematik*, Vol. 4, pp. 41–63.

Douglas, J. and Gunn, J. E. (1964), "A General Formulation of Alternating Direction Implicit Methods, Part I, Parabolic and Hyperbolic Problems," *Numerische Mathematik,* Vol. 6, pp 428–453.

DuFort, E. C. and Frankel, S. P. (1953), "Stability Conditions in the Numerical Treatment of Parabolic Differential Equations," *Mathematical Tables and Other Aids to Computation*, Vol. 7, pp. 135–152.

Fadeev, D. K. and Fadeeva, V. N. (1963), *Computational Methods of Linear Algebra*, Freeman, San Francisco.

Fehlberg, E. (1966), "New High-Order Runge–Kutta Formulas with an Arbitrary Small Truncation Error," *Zeitschrift fur Angewandte Mathematik und Mechanik*, Vol. 46, pp. 1–16.

Ferziger, J. H. (1981), *Numerical Methods for Engineering Application*, John Wiley & Sons, New York.

Fox, R. W. and McDonald, A. T. (1985), *Introduction to Fluid Mechanics, Third Edition*, John Wiley & Sons, New York.

Frankel, S. P. (1950), "Convergence Rates of Iterative Treatments of Partial Differential Equations," *Mathematical Tables and Other Aids to Computation*, Vol. 4, pp. 65–75.

Freudenstein, F. (1955), "Approximate Synthesis of Four-Bar Linkages," *Transactions of The American Society of Mechanical Engineers*, Vol. 77, pp. 853–861.

Gear, C. W. (1971), *Numerical Initial Value Problems in Ordinary Differential Equations*, Prentice-Hall, Englewood Cliffs, New Jersey.

Genereaux, R. P. (1939), "Fluid Flow Design Methods," *Industrial Engineering Chemistry*, Vol. 29, No. 4, pp. 385–388.

Gourlay, A. R. (1970), "Hopscotch: A Fast Second-Order Partial Differential Equation Solver," *Journal Inst. Maths. Applics.*, Vol. 6, pp. 375–390.

Hackbusch, W. (1980), *Multi-Grid Methods and Applications*, Springer-Verlag, Berlin, Heidelberg.

Hadamard, J. (1923), *Lectures on Cauchy's Problem in Linear Partial Differential Equations*, Yale University Press, New Haven, Connecticut.

Henrici, P. K. (1964), *Elements of Numerical Analysis*, John Wiley & Sons, New York.

Hildebrand, F. B. (1956), *Introduction to Numerical Analysis*, McGraw-Hill, New York.

Hilgenstock, A. (1988), "A Fast Method for the Elliptic Generation of Three-Dimensional Grids with Full Boundary Control," *Proceedings of the Numerical Grid Generation in Computational Fluid Dynamics Conference*, Edited by S. Sengupta et al., pp. 137–146.

Householder, A. S. (1964), *The Theory of Matrices in Numerical Analysis*, Blaisdell, New York.

IMSL (International Mathematical and Statistics Library), IMSL, Park West Tower One, 2500 City West Blvd., Houston, TX 77042.

Jeeves, T. A. (1958), "Secant Modification of Newton's Method," *Communications of the Association of Computing Machinery*, Vol. 1, No. 8, pp. 9–10.

Keller, H. B. (1970), "A New Difference Scheme for Parabolic Problems," *Numerical Solutions of Partial Differential Equations*, Vol. 2, Edited by J. Bramble, Academic Press, New York.

Lax, P. D. (1954), "Weak Solutions of Nonlinear Hyperbolic Equations and Their Numerical Computation," *Comm. Pure and Appl. Math.*, Vol. 2, pp. 159–193.

Lax, P. D. and Wendroff, B. (1960), "Systems of Conservation Laws," *Comm. Pure and Appl. Math.*, Vol. 13, pp. 217–237.

Leith, C. E. (1965), "Numerical Simulation of the Earth's Atmosphere," *Methods in Computational Physics*, Vol. 4, pp. 1–28.

Leonard, B. P. (1978), "Third-Order Finite-Difference Method for Steady Two-Dimensional Convection," *Num. Meth. In Laminar and Turbulent Flow*, pp. 807–819.

Lynch, R. E. and Rice, J. R. (1968), "Convergence Rates of ADI Methods with Smooth Initial Error," *Mathematics of Computation*, Vol. 22, No. 102, pp. 311–335.

MacCormack, R. W. (1969), "The Effect of Viscosity in Hypervelocity Impact Cratering," *American Institute of Aeronautics and Astronautics*, Paper 69–354.

Marcum, D. L. and Hoffman, J. D. (1988), "Calculation of Three-Dimensional Inviscid Flowfields in Propulsive Nozzles with Centerbodies," *American Institute of Aeronautics and Astronautics Journal of Propulsion and Power*, Vol. 4, No. 2, March–April, pp. 172–179.

Marcum, D. L. and Hoffman, J. D. (1985), "Calculation of Three-Dimensional Flowfields by the Unsteady Method of Characteristics," *Journal of the American Institute of Aeronautics and Astronautics*, Vol. 23, No. 10, pp. 1497–1505.

Milne, W. E. (1953), *Numerical Solution of Differential Equations*, John Wiley & Sons, New York.

Mitchell, T. M. (1969), *Computational Methods in Partial Differential Equations*, John Wiley & Sons, New York.

Muller, D. E. (1956), "A Method of Solving Algebraic Equations Using an Automatic Computer," *Mathematical Tables and Other Aids to Computation (MTAC)*, Vol. 10, pp. 208–215.

Noh, W. F. and Protter, M. H. (1963), "Difference Methods and the Equations of Hydrodynamics," *Journal of Mathematics and Mechanics*, Vol. 12, No. 2, pp. 149–191.

Peaceman, D. W. and Rachford, H. H. (1955), "The Numerical Solution of Parabolic and Elliptic Differential Equations," *Journal Soc. Ind. Appl. Math.*, Vol. 3, pp. 28–41.

Press, W. H., Flannery, B. P., Teukolsky, S. A., and Vetterling, W. T. (1986), *Numerical Recipes—The Art of Scientific Computing*, Cambridge University Press, Cambridge.

Ralston, A. and Rabinowitz, P. (1978), *A First-Course in Numerical Analysis*, 2nd Edition, McGraw-Hill, New York.

Rice, J. R. (1983), *Numerical Methods, Software and Analysis*, McGraw-Hill, New York.

Richardson, L. F. (1910), "The Approximate Arithmetical Solution by Finite Differences of Physical Problems Involving Differential Equations, with an Application to the Stresses in a Masonry Dam," *Phil. Trans. Roy. Soc. London*, Series A, Vol. 210, pp. 307–357.

Richtmyer, R. D. (1963), "A Survey of Difference Methods for Nonsteady Fluid Dynamics," *NCAR Technical Note 63-2*, National Center for Atmospheric Research, Boulder, Colorado.

Roberts, G. O. (1971), "Computational Meshes for Boundary Layer Problems," *Proceedings of the Second International Conference on Numerical Methods in Fluid Dynamics, Lecture Notes in Physics, Vol. 6*, Springer-Verlag, New York, pp. 171–177.

Smith, B. T., Boyle, J. M., Dongerra, J. J., Garbow, B. S., Ikebe, Y., Klema, V. C., and Moler, C. B. (1976), "Matrix Eigensystem Routines—EISPACK Guide," *Lecture Notes in Computer Science*, Vol. 6, Springer-Verlag, Heidelberg.

Southwell, R. V. (1940), *Relaxation Methods in Engineering Science*, Oxford University Press, London.

Steger, J. L., and Sorenson, R. L. (1979), "Automatic Mesh-Point Clustering in Grid Generation with Elliptic Partial Differential Equations," *Journal of Computational Physics*, Vol. 33, p. 405–410.

Steger, J. L. and Warming, R. F. (1981), "Flux Vector Splitting of the Inviscid Gas Dynamic Equations with Applications to Finite Difference Methods," *Journal of Computational Physics*, Vol. 4, No. 2, pp. 263–293

Stewart, G. W. (1973), *Introduction to Matrix Computation*, Academic Press, New York.

Thomas, L. H. (1949), "Elliptic Problems in Linear Difference Equations over a Network," *Watson Scientific Computing Laboratory Report*, Columbia University, New York.

Thomas, P. D., and Middlecoff, J. F. (1980), "Direct Control of the Grid Point Distribution in Meshes Generated by Elliptic Systems," *Journal of the American Institute of Aeronautics and Astronautics*, Vol. 18, No. 6, pp. 652–657.

Thompson, H. D., Webb, B. W., and Hoffman, J. D. (1985), "The Cell Reynolds Number Myth," *International Journal of Numerical Methods in Fluid Mechanics*, Vol. 5, pp. 305–310.

Thompson, J. F. (1982), Editor, *Numerical Grid Generation*, North-Holland, New York.

Thompson, J. F., Warsi, Z. U. A., and Mastin, C. W. (1982), "Boundary-Fitted Coordinate Systems for Numerical Solution of Partial Differential Equations—A Review," *Journal of Computational Physics*, Vol. 47, pp. 1–108.

Thompson, J. F., Warsi, Z. U. A., and Mastin, C. W. (1985), *Numerical Grid Generation, Foundations and Applications*, North-Holland, New York.

Vadyak, J., Hoffman, J. D., and Bishop, A. R. (1984), "Three-Dimensional Flow Simulations for Supersonic Mixed-Compression Inlets at Incidence," *Journal of the American Institute of Aeronautics and Astronautics*, Vol. 22, No. 7, pp. 873–881.

Wachpress, E. L. (1966), *Iterative Solution of Elliptic Systems*, Prentice-Hall, Englewood Cliffs, New Jersey.

Wang, B. N. and Hoffman, J. D. (1988), "Calculation of Annular Nozzle Trisonic Flowfields by the Method of Characteristics," *American Institute of Aeronautics and Astronautics Journal of Propulsion and Power*, Vol. 4, No. 3, pp. 228–235.

Wang, B. N. and Hoffman, J. D. (1986), "Algebraic Grid Generation for Annular Nozzle Flowfield Prediction," *Proceedings of the First International Conference on Numerical Grid Generation in Computational Fluid Dynamics*, Pineridge Press, Swansea, UK, pp. 399–409.

Warming, R. F. and Hyett, B. J. (1974), "The Modified Equation Approach to the Stability and Accuracy Analysis of Finite-Difference Methods," *Journal of Computational Physics*, Vol. 14, pp. 159–179.

Wilkinson, J. H. (1965), *The Algebraic Eigenvalue Problem*, Clarendon Press, Oxford.

Zucrow, M. J. and Hoffman, J. D. (1976), *Gas Dynamics, Vols. I and II*, John Wiley & Sons, New York.

INDEX